Science & Technology

"Give me a lever long enough," said
Archimedes, "and I will move the earth." We
now have that lever—the lever of enlightened
knowledge.
What is our modern mechanistic world all
about? How were the machines made, the
great inventions put into practical use? We live
in a world of bewildering complexity,
increasingly dominated by the all-pervading
influence of science and technology. Yet how
many of us really understand it?
This book attempts to provide some of the
answers in an informative yet stimulating
manner. The concise text has been written by
acknowledged experts. This approach,
combined with a series of striking
illustrations, gives the reader at least the
elements of that lever of knowledge so desired
by Archimedes.
Here is a straightforward account of the atom
and its nature and properties. Chemistry,
organic and inorganic, electricity and the
electron, the fundamental concept of energy
and all that flows from it. Everything is
covered—everything that an inquiring mind
would wish to know, from mathematics in
industry to harvesting the sea; from help for the
housewife to the plastics revolution.
The Encyclopedia of Science and Technology
both reveals and stimulates.

A
*Golden
Hands*
book

Marshall Cavendish, London

i

Published by Marshall Cavendish Publications Ltd,
58 Old Compton Street,
London, W1V 5PA.

© *Marshall Cavendish Ltd, 1968/69/70*
58 Old Compton Street,
London, W1V 5PA.

This material was first published by
Marshall Cavendish Ltd, in the partwork Mind Alive

This volume first printed 1973

Printed by Henri Proost, Turnhout, Belgium.

ISBN 0 85685 010 1

Picture Credits

Cambridge Scientific Instruments
Imperial Chemical Industries
Imperial College, London
Esso
Scotch Whisky Distillation
Pyrene
National Coal Board
Shell
Barnabys
Industrial Diamond Information Bureau
Picturepoint
Association of British Launderers
and Cleaners
British Rail
London Electricity Board
J. F. Skeljes
Diana Wyllie, Ltd
British Petroleum
General Motors
Cunard Line
John Kay
British Leyland
James Neill & Co, Sheffield
Jones Cranes
British Steel Corporation
Barratt's
Planet News
Courtaulds
Imperial War Museum
British Oxygen
Royal Institute of Chemistry
Meteorological Office
Dunlop
Du Pont
Albright & Wilson
Tony Last
Murphy Chemical Co
Goodyear
Pilkington Bros.
Blue Circle Group
St Mary's Hospital Medical School
Rio-Tinto Zinc Corporation
Copper Development Association
Zinc Development Association
Carlo Bevilacqua
Consolidated Gold Fields
Coll. Senor Gallo, Lima
Aluminium Foils
Michael Sharpin, Ltd
Times Newspapers
A. J. Huxley
Terry Mead
General Electric Co
John Watney
Steve Smith
National Physical Laboratory
Ford
Rank Precision Instruments
Bayeux, France
Rolf D. Schurch
Weinreb and Douwma
California Institute of Technology
Carnegie Institute, Washington
Ronan Picture Library
Ben Manchipp
Ayhan Peksen
Paola Martini
Thames TV
Elliott Automation
Eric Jewell Associates
IBM
ICL
Ferranti

Thames & Hudson
ICA
Cybernetic Serendipity
Terry Shaw
Musée Guimet
Pinacoteca Vaticana
Spectrum
Laszlo Acs
Hamleys of Regent Street
Rover Co
Decca Radar
US Navy
Ron Boardman
John A. Pierce
Ronald Thompson
Melody Maker
Eric Auerbach
Fluorescent Chrysanthemum
Institute of Contemporary Arts
Acoustical Investigation and
Research Organisation
Gordon Fraser Galleries
CBS Recording Studios, London
EMI Records
J. & E. Halls, Ltd
HM Postmaster-General
Standard Telephones & Cables
Chris Barker
British Publishing Corporation
W. M. Baxter
Tate & Lyle
Thomas A. Wilkie
G. A. Matthews
National Film Board of Ottawa
Metallurgical Services
W. H. Sansom
John Mayers
Nuclear Power Plant Co.
Institute of Geological Sciences
Vickers
Lilly Stunzi
International Wool Secretariat
Winterbottom Products
Royal Doulton Pottery
Ridgeway Potteries
National Steel Federation
Council of Industrial Design
King's Lynn Glass
British Aluminium
Alcan Industries
Stainless Steel Development
Association
Ministry of Defence, Navy
William Boby & Co
British Transport Films
H. C. Hunt
ZFA
E. I. du Nemours & Co
H. H. Wills
University of Bristol
Square One Studios
Dista Products
Edistudio
Pfizer Group
International Research and
Development Co
Kodak
Polaroid
Omega
Silicone Processing
Kenwood Group
Allied Ironfounders
Printing World
Museum of the History of Science

Church Missionary Society
Iris Hardwick
Product Knowledge
Sanderson's
Gas Council
Ster Magazine
W. Harstrick
Honeywell
Ministry of Transport
Anthony Price
H. M. Factory Inspectorate
Cavendish Laboratory, Cambridge
Science Museum
National Portrait Gallery
Manchester Corporation
Mary Evans Picture Library
Professor P. M. S. Blackett
Cambridge University Press
A. S. Eve
US Information Service
Barnaby's Picture Library
Popperfoto
Bob Cohen
Jan Brown
Tudor Art
Keystone
Sperry Gyroscope
Sotheby & Co
Barrie & Rockliff
Royal Astronomical Society
Eric Lessing
Magnum
Mr J. Wimshurst
Dr Joule, Manchester
Thorn Electrical Industries
Marconi
Sun Printers
COI
Tate Gallery
Axel Poignant
W. R. Hawes
Alan Clifton
Nature Conservancy
Ordnance Survey
Lick Observatory
G. W. Singer
National Gallery
Institute of Neurology, National
Hospital
Mt. Wilson and Palomar Observatories
Royal Astronomical Society
Philips Electrical
UK Atomic Energy Authority
Mondadoripress
NASA
Michael Holford
Mansell
Radio Times Hulton Picture Library
BBC
Camera Press
Novosti Press
United Press International
British Museum
J. Allan Cash
Transworld Features
Photo Researchers
Keystone
Syndication International
W. J. Garnett
Mullard
Daily Telegraph
Vu Picture Agency
Arcetri Astrophysics Observatory

Scala
Pirelli
Rex Features
South West Optical Instruments
Gene Cox

Contents

The atom that isn't.................................1
The atom answers back......................................5
Atoms by weight and number...........................9
The married life of atoms...............................13
A sun in the laboratory...............................17
Forces to hold the world together......................21
Equations for chemists..................................25
Acids and alkalis.......................................29
The helpful halogens..................................33
Elements of fire and brimstone.......................37
Black basis of wealth and beauty.....................41
Carbon's shapely compounds.........................45
Architects of the giant molecules.....................49
Begetters of giant molecules..........................53
The shapely world of crystals.........................57
Metals take shape.....................................61
Mixing metals..65
Odd men out in the chemical plan.....................69
The unsettled nature of gas...........................73
Hydrogen—the everywhere element..................77
The active element of oxygen.........................81
Nitrogen—the reluctant explosive.....................85
Mendeleef's missing elements.........................89
What is electricity?....................................93
Where electric current flows...........................97
The mysteries of the magnet.........................101
Putting electrons to work.............................105
Conductors and transistors...........................109
What is alternating current?..........................113
Power in a pin's head.................................117

The family life of electro-magnetic waves..............121
Open secrets in an X-ray's beam.......................125
The maser and laser....................................129
The silent echo...133
Electric messengers....................................137
The science of sound...................................141
The mechanics of music................................145
His master's voice?.....................................149
Dark energy and light..................................153
Heat and the agitated atom............................157
Energy rules the waves.................................161
Radiant energy's split personality.....................165
Max Planck and the quantum...........................169
Einstein and the speed of light........................173
Counting the cost of energy...........................177
Getting heat from here to there.......................181
The chemistry of fire...................................185
The quest for absolute zero............................189
Water—the prime liquid...............................193
In solution...197
When matter moves....................................201
On the edge of a turning circle........................205
The steadfast gyroscope...............................209
The moon is falling.....................................213
What happens on impact...............................217
Floating and flowing...................................221
Queen of the sciences.................................225
The world of number...................................229
Manipulating ideas....................................233
Shapes of mathematics................................237

Measuring with angles....................................241
Man must measure..245
The means of measurement...............................249
Two and two make why....................................253
Not and except or...257
Man-made brains..261
Mathematics and art......................................265
Mathematics in industry..................................269
Watchers of the sky.......................................273
Giant eyes on the sky.....................................277
Nine worlds in orbit.......................................281
The universe around us...................................285
The enigmatic cosmos.....................................289
The mystery of cosmic rays...............................293
Icarus and Apollo...297
What is engineering?......................................301
Bridging the world..305
The road-builders...309
The car makers...313
Power within the pile.....................................317
Atoms for peace..321
Down to the mines..325
Energy from underground..................................329
Inside the engine...333
The steam age..337
Age of automation..341
Refining natural products.................................345
Metals in the service of man..............................349
The steelmakers..353
Before the breaking point.................................357

Putting chemistry to work.................................361
Keeping in step with time.................................365
Plastics revolution..369
From fibre to fabric.......................................373
Fast and fugitive colours..................................377
Glass and ceramics.......................................381
Quinqueremes and queens................................385
Storehouse of the sea.....................................389
Mass-production test tubes................................393
Farming with machines....................................397
Farming with chemicals...................................401
The chemicals we eat.....................................405
The body's chemical crutches.............................409
A breath of fresh air......................................413
The cleaning revolution...................................417
Levers of power..421
Help for the housewife....................................425
Extensions of the human eye..............................429
The latent image...433
Putting ink on paper......................................437
Messages 'on the air'.....................................441
Science against crime.....................................445
Detective chemistry.......................................449
Technology and sport.....................................453
Exploding the myths......................................457
Damned lies and statistics................................461
Problems of waste..465
Instruments for death.....................................469
A better life or utter chaos?..............................473
Index..477

Science & Technology

The atom that isn't

Atom, from the Greek word *atomos*, means 'that which cannot be cut'. It has proved something of a misnomer. Yet the atom remains one of the most fruitful of scientific ideas. Where did it spring from?

SOME 2,400 YEARS ago, a young Greek philosopher, Zeno of Elea, insisted that it was impossible to shut a door. Say the door has to move three feet, he argued. Before it can shut it must cover half that distance. Before it can cover half it must cover a quarter. And so on *ad infinitum*. But how can a body possibly cross an infinite number of distances in a finite time? A closing door must obviously be an illusion and the same must apply to all motion and change. Reality must be one, immovable and continuous.

The point to notice is that the Eleatics, the school of philosophers to which Zeno belonged and gave his name, started from logical and mathematical ideas in their attempts to describe reality. Distrusting their senses they chose not to rely on observation, and their paradoxes lent intellectual weight to the 'common-sense' supposition that matter – a lump of lead for example – was perfectly solid and, in theory at any rate, infinitely divisible.

Only atoms and empty space

About 420 BC, another Greek philosopher, Democritus, who taught at Abdera in Thrace, tried to explain why various substances differed in density. His assertion that less dense substances had more 'open spaces' inside them, led him to conclude that matter was not continuous but made of 'pieces'. Moreover, though he too mistrusted the 'bastard evidence' of his senses, he found motion and change convincingly real and pointed out that there can be no movement without space to move in. Borrowing the Eleatic notion of the eternal oneness of reality, he described the 'pieces' making up the world of matter as invisible, indivisible, indestructible, impenetrable and eternal. Everything is merely an effect of the positions, sizes, shapes and motions of atoms. 'Only atoms and empty space exist,' he said, 'all else is superficial appearance.' (Democritus probably owed many of his ideas to Leucippus of Miletus, who is said to have lived *c.* 450 BC – though Leucippus' existence was

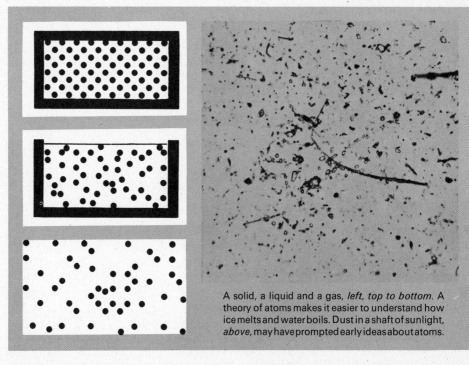

A solid, a liquid and a gas, *left, top to bottom*. A theory of atoms makes it easier to understand how ice melts and water boils. Dust in a shaft of sunlight, *above*, may have prompted early ideas about atoms.

denied by Epicurus, another Greek philosopher, who championed the atomism of Democritus *c.* 300 BC.)

But without experimental support, atomism was still little more than one bold idea among several. Unfortunately Aristotle (384–322 BC), the most influential of all Greek philosophers, rejected out of hand the notion that matter was discontinuous and lent his authority to the view of the philosopher Empedocles (*c.* 450 BC) that all material things were composed of four elements – earth (a solid), water (a liquid), air (a gas) and fire (an intangible element), combined in varying proportions. It was this speculative theory of matter that was to dominate thinking throughout the Middle Ages and give rise to the tradition of alchemy. Many alchemists – particularly the earlier ones – were dedicated investigators of the properties of matter, but for nearly 2,000 years they made virtually no progress in their efforts to under-

stand the ways in which various substances are related. The four-element theory was simply accepted as an article of faith. It did not rest on any basis of experimental proof and there was no obvious way of testing it. The alchemist's energies were dissipated by the need to explain the phenomena he observed in the philosophical language of Empedocles and Aristotle – a task requiring considerable ingenuity. Gradually investigators began to distinguish between the *general* problem of accounting for change in the world and the *concrete* problem of explaining actual changes in things.

Alchemy loses ground

The Englishman, Robert Boyle (1627–91), was the first to break away decisively from the four-element theory and fasten his allegiance on the experimental rather than the metaphysical. Although, like his younger contemporary, Isaac Newton, he

A blind alley. The alchemists' attempts to turn lead into gold and discover the 'elixir of life' were based on reasonings unaided by observation.

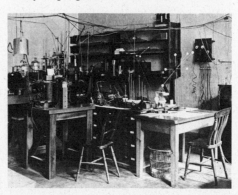

Order in apparent chaos. A corner of Lord Rutherford's laboratory at Cambridge where it was shown that the atom is not indivisible after all.

Less personal, more functional, the design of this tidy laboratory reflects the meticulous planning demanded by modern scientific research.

DEMOCRITUS

LUCRETIUS

NEWTON

DALTON

KELVIN

RUTHERFORD

Six great champions of the atom. Democritus, Lucretius and Newton span 2,000 years of speculation; Dalton, Kelvin and Rutherford could support their theories with experimental proof.

was never quite able to free himself from the fascination of alchemy, he sympathized with the atomism of Democritus (interest in which had been stimulated in 1649 by the French clergyman, Pierre Gassendi, in an appendix to a book on Epicurus' philosophy). Elements, in Boyle's view, were 'simple bodies of matter which cannot be resolved into other bodies of matter and of which all other bodies of matter are composed'. Unfortunately this definition was still unscientific, for Boyle – and he fully appreciated the difficulty – had no way of bearing it out experimentally. Isaac Newton (1642–1727), like Boyle, also knew where the future lay. 'First to enquire diligently into the properties of things, and of establishing these properties by experiment, and then to proceed more slowly to hypotheses for the explanation of them.' At last, the horse was being put before the cart.

A pair of scales argues for atoms

The path from metaphysical atomism to scientific atomic theory was paved by the French chemist Antoine Lavoisier (1743–94), beheaded during the French Revolution. In his hands, a simple but accurate weighing mechanism, the chemical balance, began to unlock the secrets of matter. For the first time, relationships between substances in chemical reactions began to be expressed in mathematical form. Lavoisier discovered that the weight of a new substance (tin oxide, a compound of tin and oxygen) formed when tin is strongly heated in air trapped in an inverted jar, invariably equalled the weight of the original tin plus the weight lost by the air (its oxygen content). This experiment became the foundation of the first

and most basic quantitative law in chemistry, the *Law of Conservation of Mass*[1] – that there is no loss of weight (or, rather, mass) during chemical change.

Carrying out similar experiments, chemists soon found themselves in a position to formulate a second law, the *Law of Definite Proportions*. This law states that when two pure substances combine to form a given compound, they do so in definite proportions by weight. The Law of Definite Proportions was to prove the first truly scientific clue to the existence of atoms, and it was seized upon by an English schoolmaster, John Dalton (1766–1844), the founder of atomic theory.

Dalton began his career of an amateur in chemistry by studying gases and was greatly struck by the way in which they can be converted first into liquids and then into solids by varying certain conditions – increasing pressure and decreasing temperature. Clearly a gas was somehow a dispersed solid, and the atomism of the ancients again strongly recommended itself as a possible explanatory model. Dalton brought this model to bear upon the Law of Definite Proportions and discovered that the law was suddenly illuminated. He saw that the law could have meaning only if each element were made up of separate particles all having the same weight. Take pure water, for example, a simple compound of the elements hydrogen and oxygen. No matter how many samples of whatever volume are analysed, the weight ratio of oxygen to hydrogen

---

[1] *Weight* unlike *mass* is dependent on variations in the pull of gravity. Mass is the measure of the inertia of matter. The weight of the two bodies under the same gravitational conditions are in the same ratio as their masses.

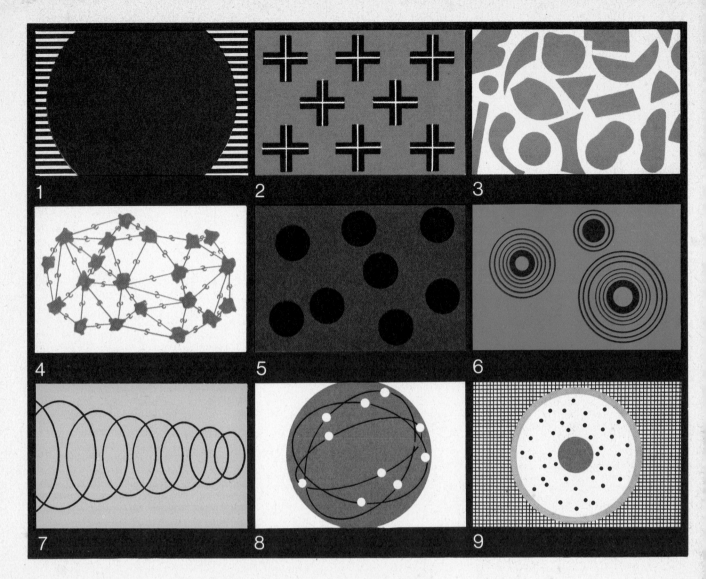

From atomism to atomic theory: the nine diagrams, *above,* show how key thinkers and investigators from Zeno of Elea to Rutherford may have pictured the structure of matter.

1 The common-sense view that matter is continuous and not composed of indivisible particles, was supported by the arguments of the Eleatic philosophers and approved by Aristotle.
2 The Pythagoreans thought that matter consisted of an infinite number of monads – geometrical points which in some way 'flowed' into line, surface and solid.
3 It was Leucippus and Democritus in the fifth century BC who first suggested that nothing exists except atoms in empty space.
4 Epicurus, whose philosophy is known through the work of the Latin poet, Lucretius, endorsed the new atomism. He suggested that atoms forming solids are hooked together mechanically.
5 The ancient atomism did not develop further until the seventeenth century. Sir Isaac Newton suggested that atoms are linked together by a force analogous to magnetism or gravity.
6 John Dalton pictured solid spherical atoms surrounded by atmospheres of 'caloric' or heat.
7 In the nineteenth century, Lord Kelvin visualized a ring of electricity whirling through space.
8 Sir Joseph Thomson's atom, defined early this century, was a ball of electricity studded with sub-atomic particles called electrons.
9 In 1911, Lord Rutherford stated that the atom has a heavy nucleus surrounded by electrons.

The man who propounded the first scientific theory of atoms, largely as a result of his study of gases, John Dalton stirs up the mud at the bottom of a pond while a young helper traps bubbles of marsh gas (methane) as they rise.

ELEMENTS

	W.t			W.t
⊙ Hydrogen	1	✛ Strontian	46
⊖ Azote	5	✳ Barytes	68
⬤ Carbon	54	Ⓘ Iron	50
◯ Oxygen	7	Ⓩ Zinc	56
⊘ Phosphorus	9	Ⓒ Copper	56
⊕ Sulphur	13	Ⓛ Lead	90
⊗ Magnesia	20	Ⓢ Silver	190
⊖ Lime	24	Ⓖ Gold	190
⊖ Soda	28	Ⓟ Platina	190
⊜ Potash	42	✽ Mercury	167

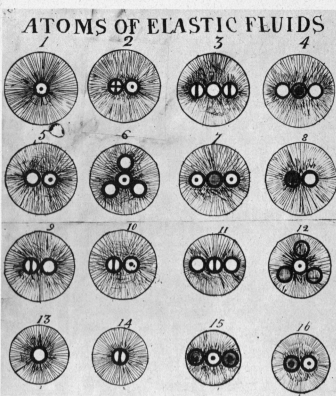

ATOMS OF ELASTIC FLUIDS

Dalton gave a special symbol to each element, *left*, in order to show more clearly how atoms combine to form molecules or 'compound atoms', *above*. These symbols were the forerunners of modern chemical symbols, and the diagrams of 'elastic fluids' (gases) closely resemble modern molecular diagrams. Notice that the hydrogen (1) and oxygen (13) molecules each have only one atom. Experimental evidence suggested two, but Dalton refused to reconsider.

always turns out to be the same – eight to one. Invariable ratios also occur in other compounds – even in cases where one element, combining with another, gives several different weight ratios. If, in these latter cases, the weight of one of the elements is standardized, that is, made the same in each case, the weights of the other element will be in simple ratios to each other. For example, under certain conditions, copper and oxygen will combine to form two different compounds. But analysis of these compounds shows that if the weight of copper is made the same in both cases, the weights of oxygen will stand in a ratio to each other of two to one. This and similar experiments led Dalton to formulate the *Law of Multiple Proportions* which states that a simple ratio must hold between the two weights of one element that can combine with a given weight of another.

If an element in a chemical compound were not present in the form of individual particles, and if each of these particles were not of the same weight, it is most highly improbable that water and the oxides of copper would analyse as they do. That the laws of definite and multiple proportions hold good is the strongest possible evidence for the existence of atoms. Accordingly, in 1808, Dalton published his famous atomic theory in which he made the following assertions: (1) Elements consist of tiny, indivisible, indestructible particles called atoms. (2) Atoms of any given element are identical in weight; while atoms of different elements invariably differ in weight. (3) Atoms combine with other atoms to form the 'compound atoms' (molecules) of chemical compounds, and always do so in fixed simple ratios. (4) Atoms of different elements may combine in more than one ratio. (5) If two elements form only one known compound, the compound must be made up of only one atom of each element. The fifth of these assertions, known as the 'rule of greatest simplicity' was the hardest to accept for, unlike the others, it took matters a step farther than the experimental evidence allowed. But Dalton clung to it obstinately and insisted that water molecules consisted of only two atoms – one atom of oxygen and one atom of hydrogen. As a result he ran his theory aground on a reef provided by the French chemist, Gay-Lussac (1778–1850).

Avogadro to the rescue

In experimenting with gases, Gay-Lussac had discovered that when two or more gases combine in a chemical reaction, the volumes of each of the combining gases are in the ratio of small, whole numbers. For example, he found that *two* unit volumes of hydrogen will combine with only *one* unit volume of oxygen to give *two* unit volumes of steam (gaseous water). If Dalton's view of the water molecule were correct, it would have taken *two* volumes of oxygen to produce the same result, and the painstaking Gay-Lussac, who could offer no explanation, found himself undeservedly accused of carelessness in his experiments. Others sided against Dalton and criticized his theory of atoms.

The controversy was to rage for nearly 50 years before it was finally resolved. Ironically the simple clue reconciling Dalton's theory with Gay-Lussac's observations had been published in a leading science journal in the early days of the controversy. An Italian physicist, Amadeo Avogadro (1776–1857), had seen at once that, if Gay-Lussac's observations were to support any atomic theory at all, equal volumes of gases under identical conditions of temperature and pressure must contain the *same* number of particles. And furthermore, each of these particles in the combining gases must consist of at least two atoms. Everything would fall into place if each two-atom particle of oxygen provides two pairs of hydrogen atoms with an oxygen atom apiece: (HH)+(HH)+ (OO) gives (HHO)+(HHO).

When this solution, known as Avogadro's Hypothesis, was resurrected in 1860 by another Italian chemist, Stanislao Cannizzaro, two of Dalton's assumptions were exploded: the unwary assumption that each of the particles composing a gas consisted of a *single* atom; and the 'simplicity rule' which had led him to insist (to the point of perversity) on his formula for water (HO).

Atomic theory had been badly shaken, but had emerged purified. Said one chemist at the time: 'It was as though scales fell from my eyes.' Avogadro had exposed Dalton's weaknesses, but at the same time resoundingly re-established the scientific relevance of the atom.

The atom answers back

Questioned by the ingenious experiments of Thomson, Millikan and Rutherford, the atom began to reveal its plan: one or more tiny particles orbiting round a central nucleus.

LESS THAN a century ago chemists still believed that elements consisted of atoms that were indivisible homogeneous balls of matter. Dalton and Avogadro had shown that atoms combine to form molecules, although they did not understand how the combination takes place. In the 1890's, the British physicist J. J. Thomson (1856–1940) began his study of cathode rays that led to the discovery of the electron.

It was already known that if two metal plates are sealed into the ends of a glass tube from which most of the air has been pumped out, an electric current can be made to flow between the two plates or electrodes. But to carry the current, something must move along the tube between the electrodes. A small sheet of glass coated with zinc sulphide and placed inside the tube glows when the current is turned on. The glow actually consists of tiny bursts of light. It is as if particles of

electricity are travelling along the tube and hitting the zinc sulphide.

By turning the zinc-sulphide screen around, Thomson showed that the stream of particles was coming out of the negatively charged electrode (cathode) and flowing to the positively charged electrode (anode). And by putting a piece of metal in the stream of particles, he got a shadow on the fluorescent zinc-sulphide screen, showing that the cathode rays travel in straight lines.

Electrons are discovered

When the rays fell on the vanes of a small paddle wheel inside the tube, the wheel turned, proving that the rays consist of particles. Thomson also found that the stream of particles was deflected by electric and magnetic fields. Since the stream was deflected towards the positive plate producing the electric field, the stream must

consist of negatively charged particles. He called these negatively charged particles of electricity *electrons*.

The deflection of the stream of electrons in an electric field depends on the charge on them and on the strength of the field. In a magnetic field, which has no effect on *stationary* charged particles, the deflection depends on the strength of the field, the charge on the electron, and its velocity. Thomson arranged a cathode-ray tube with external electric and magnetic fields and he adjusted the fields to work in opposite directions so that the stream of electrons remained undeflected. From a knowledge of the strengths of the fields, he was able to calculate the ratio of the charge on an electron to its mass, e/m.

But where do the electrons come from? When the current is flowing through the cathode-ray tube, they come out of the cathode and pass into the anode. But

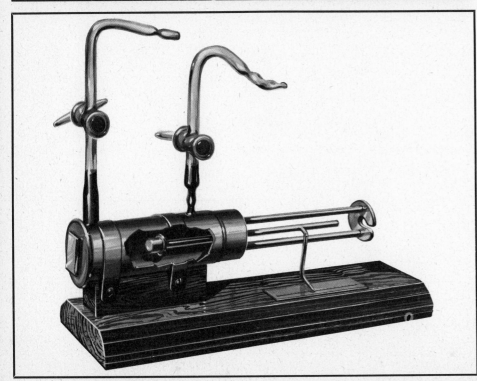

First man to break the nucleus of an atom, Lord Rutherford holds the apparatus of his 1919 experiment. In a nitrogen-gas-filled chamber, *left*, radioactive polonium emitted a stream of alpha particles. Sometimes, a nitrogen atom absorbed an alpha particle. When this happened, the atom shed a charged hydrogen nucleus which struck a fluorescent screen at the end of the tube, producing a flash of light. Later, the process was photographed in a device known as a cloud chamber. Cutting back across the stream of alpha-particle tracks, *above left*, is the path of an ejected hydrogen nucleus. As a result of this experiment, physicists worked towards the conclusion that the nuclei of all elements consist of hydrogen nuclei in greater or lesser quantities. They gave them the name *protons*.

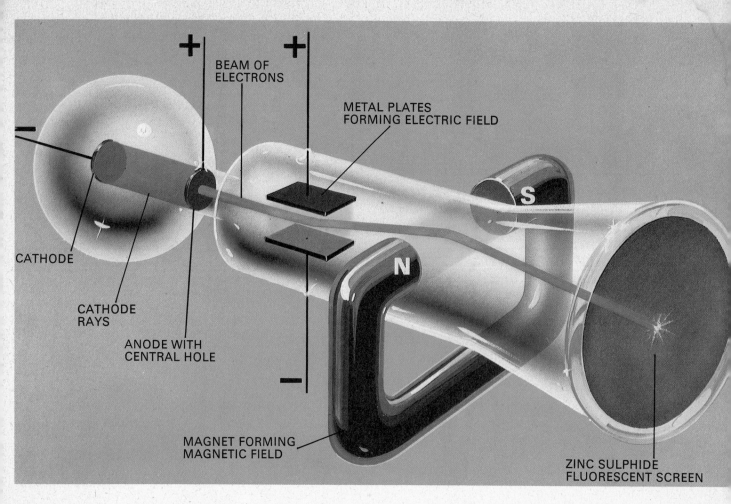

BEAM OF ELECTRONS

METAL PLATES FORMING ELECTRIC FIELD

S

N

CATHODE

CATHODE RAYS

ANODE WITH CENTRAL HOLE

MAGNET FORMING MAGNETIC FIELD

ZINC SULPHIDE FLUORESCENT SCREEN

Events in a vacuum tube enabled physicist J. J. Thomson to describe particles of electricity. He named them electrons. The particles flow from the negatively charged cathode to the anode, passing through a hole in its centre as a beam. Thomson found that the electric field (between plus and minus plates) and the magnetic field (between north and south poles) deflected the beam. Degree of deflection depends in part on the charge on the electron. By adjusting the fields, whose strength he knew, he could calculate the ratio of the charge on an electron to its mass.

where are they when no current is flowing? They must be in the metal that forms the electrodes and wires. But metals, and all elements, consist of atoms. Therefore electrons must come from inside atoms.

Electrons can be removed from atoms fairly easily. When a piece of amber is rubbed with fur, the amber becomes negatively charged. That is, it has a crowd of particles of negative electricity on it, a crowd of electrons. The electrons are removed from some of the atoms of the fur merely by rubbing and are deposited on the amber.

These facts suggest that all atoms contain electrons and that the electrons are probably near the surface of the atoms. But how heavy are electrons? Before Thomson discovered the electron, the lightest known particle was an atom of hydrogen with a mass of 1 on the atomic-weight scale. Since an atom of hydrogen contains at least one electron, the electron must weigh less than 1. How much less?

Thomson had measured e/m for an electron. An American physicist, Robert A. Millikan, reasoned that if he could measure the charge e, he could calculate its mass. To do this, he devised an ingenious experiment in which oil droplets were charged with an equivalent of one or two electronic charges and introduced between two horizontal metal plates connected to a source of electricity. Under the force of gravity, the droplets tended to fall towards the lower plate. By observing

the rate of fall and from a relationship known as Stokes' Law, Millikan calculated the weight of the droplets. And by arranging the plates so that the top one had an opposite charge to the charge on the droplets, he could use the electric field between the plates to overcome the force of gravity and attract the droplets upwards. By very careful control of the field, he could make the droplets remain stationary. When this happened, the upward electrical force on a droplet equalled the downward gravitational force on it and Millikan was able to calculate the charge. He found that the charge was always a small multiple of a certain quantity and this quantity is called the elementary electric charge, the charge on an electron, e.

Combining Thomson's value for e/m and Millikan's value for e gives the mass of the electron as about one two-thousandth of the mass of the hydrogen atom. The remainder of an atom, which includes nearly all of its mass, must have a positive charge to balance the negative charge on the electrons.

Chemists now had to revise their ideas of the atom. They knew it consisted of one or more tiny negatively charged electrons and a comparatively large positively charged part. But how were these various parts arranged? Thomson suggested that atoms consist mainly of a positively charged jelly-like mass with the tiny electrons embedded in it. This theory was abandoned as a result of experiments made

by Ernest Rutherford (1871–1937), who also used charged particles and a zinc-sulphide screen.

Rutherford used alpha particles which are given off spontaneously by the radio-active element radium. (Deflection experiments showed that alpha particles have a mass of 4 and carry two positive charges.) He directed a stream of alpha particles against a piece of thin gold foil and used the fluorescent zinc-sulphide screen to study what happened. He found that most of the alpha particles passed straight through the gold foil as if it were not there. Some particles were scattered as they passed through the foil, some through quite large angles even to the extent of bouncing almost directly back. Rutherford deduced that most of the gold atom must consist of empty space. An alpha particle that was scattered through a small angle was deflected as it passed not too near the positively charged part of the gold atom. And an occasional alpha particle must have passed very close to this part of the atom and as a result was deflected right back. Thus most of the mass of the gold atom and all the positive charge must be concentrated at the centre at what Rutherford called the *nucleus* of the atom.

The rest of the atom, and most of it in terms of volume, consists of a swarm of electrons. In order that the positive charge on the nucleus does not pull the negatively charged electrons into the centre of the atoms, the electrons must be moving rapidly round the nucleus, and the space containing the electrons was calculated at about ten thousand times the diameter of the nucleus.

Rutherford's model of the atom resembles the solar system. Electrons move in orbits in space a long way from the central nucleus in much the same way that the planets orbit round the sun. Hydrogen has one electron and a single positive charge on its nucleus. The hydrogen nucleus weighs very nearly 1 atomic weight unit, the weight of the whole atom. Other atoms have more electrons, with a similar number of positive charges on their nuclei. For example, carbon has six electrons and six positive charges on its nucleus. But the atomic weight of carbon is 12 – and the mass of the electrons is only six two-thousandths. In the hydrogen nucleus, *one* positive charge 'weighs' 1 unit but in the carbon nucleus, only *six* positive charges 'weigh' 12 units. In an attempt to resolve this anomaly, Rutherford in 1900, tried to break open atomic nuclei by bombarding them with streams of alpha particles.

He bombarded hydrogen atoms, and most of the alpha particles remained undeflected. But when a collision did take place, there also appeared a positively charged hydrogen nucleus. He then tried bombarding heavier elements such as nitrogen and sodium, but again he got only charged hydrogen nuclei. Rutherford had split the atomic nucleus and it began to appear that the nuclei of all elements were made up of hydrogen nuclei, which were given the name *protons*. A proton has a mass of 1 and a single positive charge. The carbon nucleus, with six positive charges, must contain six protons, which contribute 6 units to its mass. But what makes up the rest of the carbon nucleus (which has a mass of 12)? Also, since protons each weigh 1 unit, why are all atomic weights not whole numbers?

A new element

The answer to the second question was found first. The first clue came in 1906 with the discovery of a new element that was named ionium. It was found in the mineral pitchblende and its atomic weight was measured as 231·5. Another element found in pitchblende, thorium, has an atomic weight of 232·1. When chemists began to study the chemical properties of ionium, they found that they were the same as those of thorium. It appeared that there were two kinds of thorium, identical chemically but with different atomic weights. Then in 1910, Frederick Soddy suggested the complete answer. He said there *are* two kinds of thorium; both have the same number of electrons and protons (and therefore the same chemical properties) but one form has a nucleus of mass 230 and one a nucleus of mass 232. 'Ionium' and thorium are different mixtures of both forms. Soddy called the different weight-forms of a single element *isotopes*.

Further evidence for the existence of isotopes was obtained by J. J. Thomson. He again used an evacuated tube with an anode and this time a thick cathode having

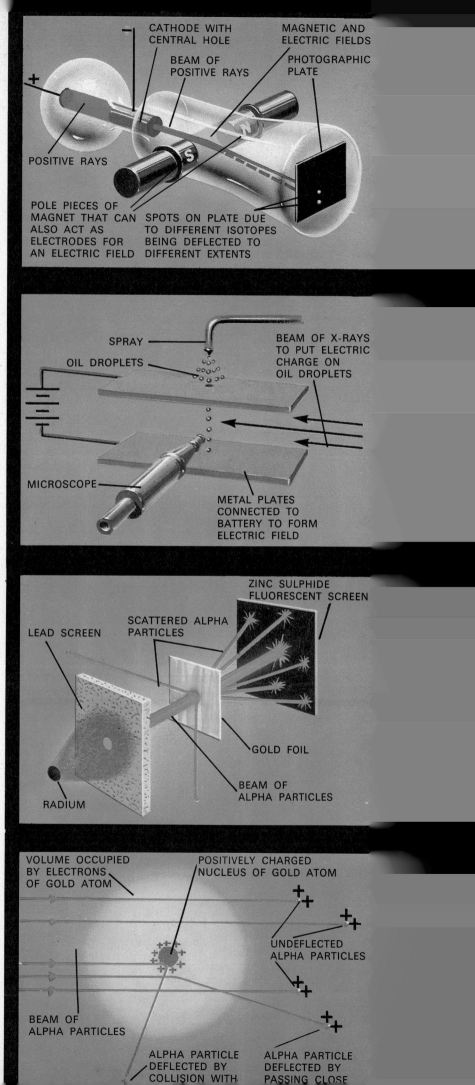

CATHODE WITH CENTRAL HOLE

MAGNETIC AND ELECTRIC FIELDS

BEAM OF POSITIVE RAYS

PHOTOGRAPHIC PLATE

POSITIVE RAYS

POLE PIECES OF MAGNET THAT CAN ALSO ACT AS ELECTRODES FOR AN ELECTRIC FIELD

SPOTS ON PLATE DUE TO DIFFERENT ISOTOPES BEING DEFLECTED TO DIFFERENT EXTENTS

SPRAY

OIL DROPLETS

BEAM OF X-RAYS TO PUT ELECTRIC CHARGE ON OIL DROPLETS

MICROSCOPE

METAL PLATES CONNECTED TO BATTERY TO FORM ELECTRIC FIELD

ZINC SULPHIDE FLUORESCENT SCREEN

SCATTERED ALPHA PARTICLES

LEAD SCREEN

GOLD FOIL

BEAM OF ALPHA PARTICLES

RADIUM

VOLUME OCCUPIED BY ELECTRONS OF GOLD ATOM

POSITIVELY CHARGED NUCLEUS OF GOLD ATOM

UNDEFLECTED ALPHA PARTICLES

BEAM OF ALPHA PARTICLES

ALPHA PARTICLE DEFLECTED BY COLLISION WITH

ALPHA PARTICLE DEFLECTED BY PASSING CLOSE

a hole drilled through it. If, when the current is switched on, negatively charged electrons are flowing from the cathode to the anode, Thomson reasoned that some form of positive rays should be flowing from the anode to the cathode. Some of these rays would pass through the hole in the cathode and emerge as a beam that could be detected by a photographic plate. He also reasoned that the rays would consist of gas atoms that had been stripped of electrons – that is, they would be positively charged particles, the nuclei of the gas atoms. And by using a magnet to deflect the beam of positive rays (in the same way as he had deflected electron beams), Thomson was able to calculate the mass of the charged particles. Heavy particles would be deflected less than light particles. For example, with a tube containing a trace of neon gas, he got a deflection corresponding to a particle of mass 20. Neon has an atomic weight of 20·18, and Thomson had detected positive neon ions. But when he examined the photographic plate more closely, he saw another faint spot corresponding to a particle of mass 22. There is no element of atomic weight 22 and so Thomson deduced that there are two kinds of neon, one of mass 20 and one of mass 22. Furthermore, ordinary neon is a mixture containing about 90 per cent of the lighter isotope and about 10 per cent of the heavier, giving the non-integral atomic weight of 20·18.

The neutron

The discovery of isotopes also provided evidence for the answer to our other question: what, in addition to protons, makes up the mass of the nucleus? The two isotopic forms of neon and thorium differ in mass by 2 units. It is as if there were yet a third atomic particle with unit mass but with no charge. Finally in 1932, James Chadwick also performed experiments with alpha particles. He bombarded beryllium and detected a powerful, penetrating radiation. The new rays are not deflected by thick sheets of metal nor by magnetic or electric fields, so they can have no electric charge. Occasionally, they do suffer collisions with atoms so they

must be particles. Chadwick showed that the new particle had the predicted mass of 1, the same as the proton, and he called it the *neutron*.

The main details of the atom and its nucleus were now complete. Every atom has a nucleus containing a certain number of protons, surrounded by an equal number of orbiting electrons. And where the mass of the atom is greater than that expected from the number of protons in its nucleus (which it is for all elements except hydrogen), the additional mass is supplied by neutrons. The nuclei of isotopes have the same number of protons but differ in the number of neutrons.

Consider again our previous examples, set out above in Table 1. The table shows that the element Hydrogen has one electron orbiting round one proton, giving a total mass of 1. Carbon has six electrons orbiting round a nucleus containing six protons and six neutrons, giving a total

Element	A	B	C	D	E
Hydrogen	1	1	0	1	1·00
Carbon	6	6	6	12	12·00
Neon 20	10	10	10	20	20·18
Neon 22	10	10	12	22	
(Ionium)	90	90	140	230	232·1
Thorium	90	90	142	232	

Table 1. Key: **A** No. of electrons. **B** No. of protons in nucleus. **C** No. of neutrons in nucleus. **D** Mass. **E** Atomic weight.

mass of 12. The two isotopes of neon have the same number of protons and electrons, but one contains two extra neutrons. Naturally occurring neon and thorium consist of mixtures of several isotopes.

Equipped with this picture of the atom and its structure, chemists can explain most of the common properties and reactions of the elements.

Two great Cambridge scientists of the early 1900s, Ernest Rutherford (right) and Joseph John Thomson (left). At the Cavendish laboratory both investigated the structure of atoms and the theory of electricity. Thomson was awarded the Nobel prize for physics in 1906; Rutherford the 1908 prize for chemistry. Rutherford developed the theory of the atom as a nucleus surrounded by electrons. His notes on his 'theory of structure of atoms' survive, *below*.

Atoms by weight and number

The atomic nucleus is surrounded by a whirling mass of electrons whose erratic orbits can never be plotted. Yet their configurations determine the chemical identity of all matter.

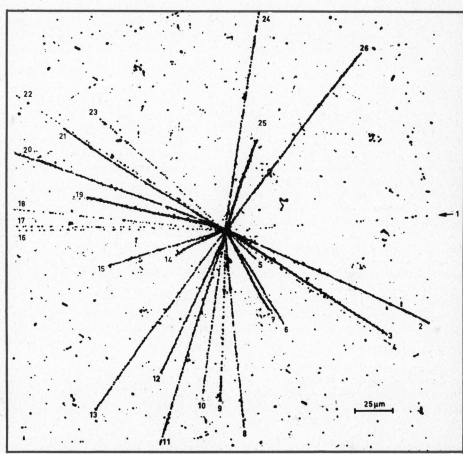

Left, Dmitri Mendeleeff, a foremost pioneer of modern chemistry. Through his detailed labour on the system of classifying elements by their chemical properties he was able to prophesy the discovery of new elements to fill gaps in his table. One of the most recently made transuranium elements was named Mendelevium (Md 101). Evidence for the most up-to-date theories of atomic structure derives from experiments in huge accelerators which bombarded atoms with high-speed sub-atomic particles. *Right,* an atom of a steel bar breaks up dramatically under the impact of a proton. Fragments of the broken atom fly off and are recorded on photographic emulsion (the darkest tracks are bits of nucleus).

FOR 2,000 YEARS, ever since the time of the Ancient Greeks, scientists held the belief that everything in the world is made from four fundamental elements – air, earth, fire and water. However, as seventeenth- and eighteenth-century experimentalists began renouncing armchair speculations in favour of stubborn laboratory facts, it became evident that air, earth, fire and water are neither fundamental nor are they elements.

The loss of this cherished belief, while a shattering blow in itself, soon palled before the realization that there was nothing to replace it. Instead of just four universal building blocks, there were now eight, ten, twelve, twenty, fifty. By the 1860s, the total number of known elements had passed three score, and there was no end in sight. Today there are 103. How were the chemists ever to make sense out of their burgeoning accumulation of reactions and compounds if each element differed from every other element, and if new elements were being discovered all the time?

Fortunately, just about the time the problem seemed to be getting out of hand, a partial solution appeared on the horizon in the form of an amazing classification scheme proposed by the Russian chemist Dmitri Mendeleeff in 1869. Not only was Mendeleeff able to show definite kinship relations between elements which apparently had little in common, he was even able to predict the existence of certain elements long before they were actually discovered. From the vantage point of twentieth-century knowledge, we now believe we know how Mendeleeff's remarkable periodic table is able to do the things that it does.

Numbers for atoms

The chemical properties of an element are determined by the number of its electrons or protons. This quantity is called the *atomic number.* The combined masses of the protons and neutrons in the nucleus is called the *mass number.* Some elements exist in several forms called isotopes. All the isotopes of a single element have the same number of protons (and electrons) but differ in their numbers of neutrons. So the isotopes of an element have the same atomic number but different mass numbers. It is the atomic number which gives an element its separate identity; two atoms of different mass numbers may both be the same element, but two atoms with different atomic numbers – that is, different numbers of protons – can never be the same.

The *atomic weight* is the weight of an element as it occurs in nature relative to the weight of carbon, arbitrarily fixed at 12.00 as a standard. If an element has more than one naturally occurring isotope, then the atomic weight is the average weight of the isotopes calculated with consideration given to their relative proportions. For this reason, the atomic weight of an element is seldom a whole number and seldom the same as the mass number.

One isotope of lithium has 3 protons and 3 neutrons in its nucleus, giving a mass number of 6. But the atomic weight of lithium is 6·940 because of a significant contribution by an isotope with 3 protons and 4 neutrons; that is, mass number of 7.

The average of these two isotopes is 6·940 rather than exactly 6·500 because there is much more naturally occurring lithium 7 than there is lithium 6.

According to Niels Bohr's original theory enunciated in 1913, the electrons of an atom occupy circular or elliptical orbits round the nucleus, something like the planets of the solar system going round the sun. The electrons described by the more sophisticated quantum theory are not quite so well-behaved. Though they tend to remain at predictable distances from the nucleus, they also tend to fly in all directions, rather than following a well-defined orbit. The result is a three-dimensional cloud, or shell, effect instead of the circles or ellipses.

Each one of these clouds, or shells, is given a particular quantum number and is further differentiated into various energy levels, or sub-groups, identified by appropriate letters. Each energy level in turn corresponds to a certain number of *orbitals,* each of which can hold a maximum of two electrons. So the number of electrons each shell can accommodate is limited by the number of orbitals in each sub-group. An *s* energy level corresponds to only 1 orbital and thus can hold only 2 electrons, a *p* energy level corresponds to 3 orbitals and can hold up to 6 electrons, a *d* energy level can hold 10 electrons, and an *f* energy level can hold 14 electrons.

Tidy electron shells

From the point of view of elementary chemistry, it is only the outermost electron cloud or shell which is of much interest, because it is the outermost shell which largely determines what kinds of chemical reactions an element will take part in.

Consider a simple example. Hydrogen, which has the distinction of being the only element one of whose isotopes has no neutrons in the nucleus, has only 1 electron circling its nucleus. Since the first shell of an element can hold a maximum of 2 electrons, this first shell of hydrogen is only partially filled, quite an unsatisfactory situation. There are two possible solutions: either the hydrogen atom can pick up an electron from some other element in order to complete its first shell, or it can throw off its electron and so have a completely empty first shell. The latter is the more common.

By contrast, fluorine has a total of 9 electrons – 2 in a completed first shell and 7 in its second shell. However, the second shell is capable of holding 8 electrons. So fluorine has an incomplete shell just like hydrogen, but in this case there is no question as to what it is going to do about it. It is much easier to pick up the 1 electron needed to complete the shell than it is to throw off 7 to empty the shell.

The act of either picking up electrons or throwing them off in order to complete or empty a partially filled shell is the fundamental process of a simple chemical reaction. Under the proper conditions, then, hydrogen will gladly throw off its solitary electron to empty its first shell and fluorine will happily accept it in order to complete its second shell. The result of

this swap is the gaseous compound hydrogen fluoride, HF. Since hydrogen has thrown off a negative electron, it now has a net positive electrical charge. Conversely, since fluorine has taken on an electron, it now has a net negative charge. So the two pieces of the compound, called ions, are held together by electrical attraction in an ionic bond.

If we look at an element such as oxygen, we find that it has 8 electrons – 2 in a completed first shell, and 6 in an incompleted second shell. Since the second shell can be satisfied with 8 electrons, oxygen gladly picks up 2 electrons whenever it can. If it is combining with hydrogen, it picks up one electron from each of two hydrogen atoms to give the familiar substance H_2O, or water. This process is slightly different from the formation of hydrogen fluoride, because the electrons are not actually transferred but shared. This is called co-valent bonding. Hydrogen fluoride shows some characteristics of this 'co-valent bonding', as well as simple ionic bonding in which the bonding electrons are quite separate.

The number of electrons an element is capable of accepting or giving away in a chemical reaction is called its valence number. If the element gives electrons away, the valence number is prefixed with a positive sign (because the resulting ion is electrically positive) and if it accepts electrons its valence number is prefixed with a negative (because the resulting ion is electrically negative). Thus, the valence number of hydrogen would be +1, fluorine −1, and oxygen −2. Some elements have more than one valence number, because they can throw off or accept different numbers of electrons under different conditions.

Since the chemical properties of an element depend largely on the number of electrons in the outermost shell, we would expect to find striking similarities among all elements whose outermost shells hold the same number of valence electrons. To a great extent, this is correct, though it is not necessary to know anything about atomic structure in order to observe such a pattern.

As far back as 1864, the British industrial chemist John Newlands noticed that when he arranged the elements in order of increasing atomic weight, elements with similar properties were situated at every eighth position along the series. These groups of eight Newlands called *octaves.* About six years later, a German physicist named Julius Lothar Meyer studied the physical properties of the elements and also correlated them with atomic weights. When he plotted a graph of an atomic parameter, based on a physical property such as density or specific heat, against atomic weight, he obtained a graph shaped rather like a chain of mountain peaks with valleys between them. Elements on similar parts of the curves were found to have similar chemical properties.

At almost exactly the same time, Dmitri Mendeleeff, a Russian chemist, published his now famous periodic table. He also arranged the elements in families, but left gaps where necessary to make ele-

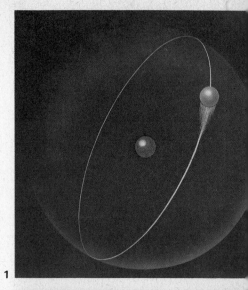

The building blocks of the atom – protons, neutrons and electrons – can be visualized so as to explain the properties of each element. 1 Hydrogen, simplest of the elements, has only one proton and one electron orbiting in the *s* subgroup of the first shell. Helium and lithium, **4,** the next two elements, are more complicated,

ments with similar properties fall into vertical columns called groups.

Mendeleeff made some remarkable predictions about the undiscovered elements to fill the gaps in his table. For example, he predicted the properties of a metallic element to fill the gap below aluminium and next to zinc. When gallium was discovered in 1875, it was found to confirm the almost uncanny accuracy of Mendeleeff's predictions. The 'missing' element below silicon in group IV was called 'eka-silicon' by Mendeleeff. He predicted it would be a greyish-white unreactive metal and have an atomic weight of about 73.

The missing element

Fifteen years later, the German chemist Clemens Winkler discovered an element called germanium. It turned out to be a greyish-white metal which does not dissolve in acids or alkalis and which has an atomic weight of 72·60. Germanium was the missing 'eka-silicon'.

The modern versions of the table (there are several) substantially differ from the original offered by Mendeleeff in 1869;

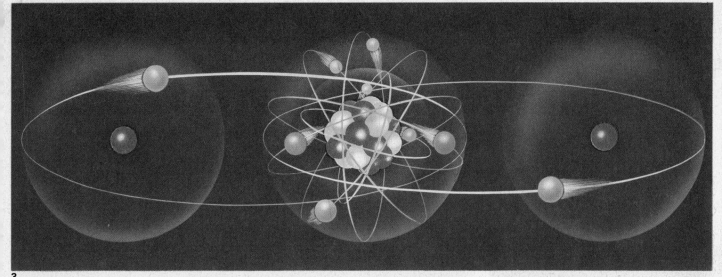

3

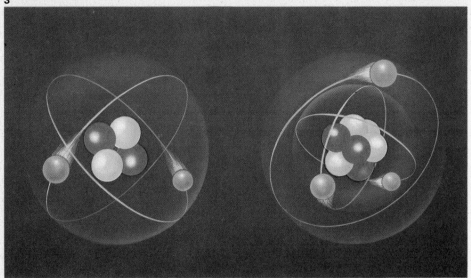

4

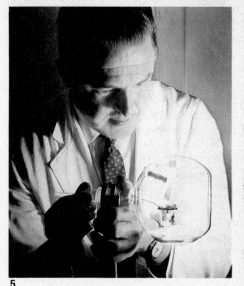

5

having more particles. In helium, *left,* two orbiting electrons fill the first shell, so the third electron which lithium possesses, *right,* has to orbit in the next shell, at a *2s* energy level. The nuclei of these atoms are made up of protons and neutrons; helium has two of each, but the lithium atom shown has three protons

however, the main features remain the same (see diagram, p. 12). The most obvious feature of the table is its arrangement into numbered columns and rows, plus the huge block without numbers, called transition elements, and the Lanthanide Series (called the 'rare earth' elements) and the Actinide Series. The transition elements and the rare earth elements represent an apparent disruption of our nice, orderly arrangement and will be dealt with in due course. The whole number under each element is its atomic number.

Each column, called a group, brings together those elements which have the same number of electrons in their outermost shell, i.e. they have the same valence. (The letter following each group number is a refinement which need not concern us, and will be omitted in what follows.) For example, hydrogen (H) in group I has only 1 electron, that in the first shell. Directly below it is lithium (Li), with 2 electrons in a completed first shell and 1 in an incompleted second shell. Sodium (Na) has 2 electrons in a completed first shell, 8

and four neutrons. This is an isotope of lithium known as lithium 7. Neon, **2,** is the first element to have a completely filled second shell with ten electrons orbiting in all the 1 and 2 energy sub-groups. *Co-valent* bonds between atoms form electrically stable compounds. Water, **3,** is formed in this way

electrons in its completed second shell, and 1 electron in its third. And so on down the line. Each succeeding element in the group also has only one electron in its outermost shell. At first glance they may not resemble each other too closely (hydrogen is a gas, sodium is a soft solid), but because they each have a solitary electron in the outermost shell, and consequently the same valence, they enter into similar chemical reactions. Because of special properties of lithium and the elements directly below lithium in the table, they are collectively called alkali metals.

Arranging the elements

The same thing applies to group II. Each element has 2 electrons in its outermost shell; and thus, despite marked physical differences, they all undergo similar chemical reactions. Likewise with groups III–VIII, also labelled with an 'O'.

If we look across the periodic table from left to right, we see the elements arranged into rows called periods. The original reason for arranging the elements in this way was so that each succeeding element

when two hydrogen atoms share electrons with a single oxygen atom in a tenacious atomic grip. For centuries Man has tried to understand and control chemical reactions, **5**; what was once largely a process of trial and error can now be predicted and explained by modern theories of atomic structure and interrelationships.

as one travels from left to right would have a higher atomic weight. This is important, because it led Mendeleeff to suspect that some of the atomic weights that had been calculated in his day were wrong. They just did not go into the table where he thought they should. In several instances, he was correct. These elements, with their revised atomic weights, now fit quite nicely where Mendeleeff said they should.

However, a few elements still refused to co-operate, such as tellurium (Te) and iodine (I). In period 5 near the right-hand side, iodine follows tellurium, but has an atomic weight of 126·92, while tellurium has an atomic weight of 127·61. Such discrepancies were quite a nettlesome problem to the early researchers, but today we can explain them quite easily in terms of isotopes, which were not known to exist in Mendeleeff's time. Every element was thought to have one form and one form only. Thus, the periods are no longer arranged in terms of ascending atomic weights, which are not completely regular, but ascending atomic numbers.

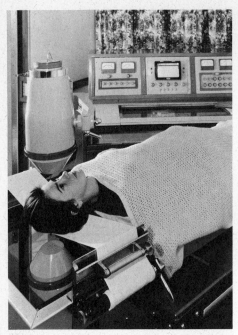

Radio-isotopes (unstable isotopes of ordinary elements made by artificially adding neutrons to nuclei in nuclear reactors or accelerators) give off characteristic radiation which can be easily detected by electronic instruments.

IA	IIA	IIIA	IVA	VA	VIA	VIIA	VIII			IB	IIB	IIIB	IVB	VB	VIB	VIIB	O
H 1																	He 2
Li 3	Be 4											B 5	C 6	N 7	O 8	F 9	Ne 10
Na 11	Mg 12											Al 13	Si 14	P 15	S 16	Cl 17	Ar 18
K 19	Ca 20	Sc 21	Ti 22	V 23	Cr 24	Mn 25	Fe 26	Co 27	Ni 28	Cu 29	Zn 30	Ga 31	Ge 32	As 33	Se 34	Br 35	Kr 36
Rb 37	Sr 38	Y 39	Zr 40	Nb 41	Mo 42	Tc 43	Ru 44	Rh 45	Pd 46	Ag 47	Cd 48	In 49	Sn 50	Sb 51	Te 52	I 53	Xe 54
Cs 55	Ba 56	∗ 57-71	Hf 72	Ta 73	W 74	Re 75	Os 76	Ir 77	Pt 78	Au 79	Hg 80	Tl 81	Pb 82	Bi 83	Po 84	At 85	Rn 86
Fr 87	Ra 88	★ 89·															

Lanthanides

∗

La 57	Ce 58	Pr 59	Nd 60	Pm 61	Sm 62	Eu 63	Gd 64	Tb 65	Dy 66	Ho 67	Er 68	Tm 69	Yb 70	Lu 71

Actinides

★

Ac 89	Th 90	Pa 91	U 92	Np 93	Pu 94	Am 95	Cm 96	Bk 97	Cf 98	Es 99	Fm 100	Mv 101	No 102	Lw 103

Left, a brain scan records the variations in concentration of a radio-isotope administered to help detect abnormalities. *Right,* table of the elements arranged to show resemblances. Solid blue indicates those elements built up by the regular addition of protons, neutrons and electrons on the appropriate energy levels. Further down the table the addition of electrons becomes much less regular, and lower energy levels are not always the first to be filled.

Each succeeding element has in its nucleus one more proton (and perhaps several more neutrons) than its predecessor, and so the atomic numbers are continuous from 1 to 103.

Now, what about those awkward transition elements and rare earths which play so much havoc with our orderly arrangement? The fact is, they don't really play any havoc at all; they behave precisely as Nature dictates they must. It is we who play havoc with Nature's arrangement by insisting that all the elements should fit into a pattern of columns and rows.

To find out just what arrangement Nature intends, we must again look at electron configurations and employ a bit of quantum mechanics.

Twentieth-century research has shown that the first electron shell can hold a maximum of 2 electrons, the second shell a maximum of 8 electrons, the third shell a maximum of 18 electrons, and the fourth and higher shells a maximum of 32 electrons. However, one of the fundamental conclusions of quantum mechanics is that no *outermost* shell can ever hold more than 8 electrons. The elements of group 'O' are known as the 'inert gases' and confirm this conclusion, because they enter into nearly no chemical combinations at all. They have 8 electrons in their outermost orbits and are quite satisfied with the situation.

Shells within shells

The first element with a potential of having more than 8 electrons in the outermost shell is potassium, with an atomic number of 19. Its first shell is completely filled with 2 electrons, its second shell is completely filled with 8 electrons, leaving only 9 electrons for the third shell, which we know can take up to 18. However, this third shell is the outermost shell, and from quantum mechanics we know that the outermost shell can never have more than 8 electrons in it. So the ninth electron begins a fourth shell. More succinctly, instead of the electron configuration 2, 8, 9 one might expect from non-quantum considerations, the actual configuration is 2, 8, 8, 1. Thus, potassium (K) has a lone electron in its outermost shell and is a member of group I.

Calcium, with an atomic number of 20, follows a similar pattern. Instead of the expected configuration of 2, 8, 10, two electrons from the third shell are shifted into the fourth, giving a configuration of 2, 8, 8, 2. So calcium has a pair of valence electrons and consequently falls into group II.

With the examples of potassium and calcium to guide us, we might expect the next element, scandium, to arrange its 21 electrons in a pattern 2, 8, 8, 3. This is another case of Man trying to impose an order on Nature which Nature never intended. The actual electron configuration is 2, 8, 9, 2. Again, quantum mechanics explain why this happens, but even without delving into complex mathematics, we should not be too surprised that it does. After all, the third shell is quite capable of holding up to 18 electrons, providing that it is not the outermost shell. With 2 electrons now in the fourth shell, the third shell is no longer the outermost and thus is quite ready to take on its full complement of electrons.

Each succeeding element after scandium adds at least one more electron to the third shell. (Chromium and copper add 2 by reclaiming 1 electron from the third shell, giving them configurations of 2, 8, 13, 1 and 2, 8, 18, 1 respectively.) It is only after the third shell finally has been completed that more electrons begin occupying the fourth shell again. So every element from scandium to zinc, with the exception of chromium and copper, has only two electrons in its outermost shell, and thus must belong to group II. Gallium, with an electronic configuration of 2, 8, 18, 3, finally gives us a new member of group III. Thus, all the elements from scandium to zinc may be thought of as a kind of bridge between group II and group III. This is one reason why they are called transition elements.

The fourth shell is now the outermost shell, and so must conform to the 'Rule of Eight'. Just as one would expect, when the fourth shell has acquired 8 electrons, a fifth shell is started. This happens with the element rubidium, which has an electronic configuration of 2, 8, 18, 8, 1, and so is a member of group I. The next element, strontium, also adds an electron to the fifth shell (2, 8, 18, 8, 2), and thus is a member of group II. But the next element, yttrium, in a manner very similar to that of scandium, adds a ninth electron to the fourth shell instead of a third electron to the fifth, giving the configuration 2, 8, 18, 9, 2. And so we have the beginning of another series of transition elements running from yttrium to cadmium.

'Rare earths'

Two more series of transition elements appear in the fifth and sixth periods. These series are often separated from the main body of the periodic table and grouped together under the name 'rare earths'.

The development of the periodic table and all the theory necessary to explain it has greatly enhanced the chemist's understanding of what happens in his test-tubes, and thus has given him greater control over what happens in his test-tubes. Though a bit arduous at first, all of this theoretical interpretation of chemical reactions is directly responsible for most of the plastics, synthetic vitamins, patent medicines, man-made fibres and other benefits of the chemical laboratory. It has even allowed for the creation of new elements which never existed until Man called them into being.

The married life of atoms

The union of humans into families requires certain adjustments by the members. The union of atoms into molecules also requires adjustments. Often, this means a complete loss of identity.

SODIUM is a soft, silvery metal which reacts with water with almost explosive violence. Chlorine is a green, choking gas, used during the First World War as a poison gas. Yet when atoms of the metal sodium react chemically with those of the gas chlorine, they combine to form molecules of the white crystalline substance we put on our food – common salt.

Sodium chloride (common salt) is not an exceptional substance. It is only one of the thousands of known chemical compounds, most of which consist of molecules which have properties completely different from those of the atoms which went to make them.

Chemical theory suggests that all molecules are combinations of individual atoms bound together by very powerful forces to

give them a stable structure. The binding forces for molecules are generally electrical attractions. These are the attractions between objects with opposite electric charges, such as the attraction of specks of dust or bits of paper to a comb which has been charged by drawing it through the hair.

One way of linking two atoms by these forces is called *ionic bonding*. Most atoms have either too many or too few electrons circling the nucleus in the outermost orbit for a 'stable configuration'. When two or more atoms combine in an ionic bond, the element with too many electrons 'donates' some of them to the element with too few electrons. So at the end of the exchange, each has the precise number of electrons that the quantum theory pre-

An atom may unite with only one partner or it may 'marry' into an enormous family. Some organic molecules (molecules in living organisms) may be composed of thousands of atomic members.

dicts they should for stability. The atom which has lost negative electrons now has a positive electric charge; the one which has 'accepted' electrons now has a negative charge. Since atoms by definition are electrically neutral, these charged atoms are called *ions*.

The attraction between ions of opposite charge produces energy as heat, and the resulting structure of closely bound ions is stable only if more energy is given up in the coming together of ions than was needed to form the ions in the first place. Because an ionic bond involves the electric charges, it is also known as an *electrostatic* or *polar* bond.

Evidence of the existence of ions and the validity of the ion-bonding theory can be seen in *electrolysis*. If an electric current is passed through a vessel containing molten sodium chloride (common salt), the molecules are steadily separated into their atoms, giving metallic sodium and gaseous chlorine. According to modern ionic theory, this process can be explained by saying that at the cathode (the negative electrode), the electric current is 'pumping' electrons into sodium ions and converting them to atoms of metallic sodium. At the anode (the positive electrode), electrons are being pulled out of the chloride ions, converting them back to atoms of chlorine gas. In this way, electricity supplies the energy to break up the stable salt formation, and to re-convert the ions to their atomic state.

X-raying salt crystals

The ionic theory satisfactorily explained the state of sodium and chloride ions in salt solutions and in molten salt. Later, experimental evidence was obtained which indicates that solid common salt crystals are also composed of ions. The method used was X-ray diffraction pioneered by Sir William and Sir Lawrence Bragg, and it has become extremely important since in the study of crystal structure. The method involves passing a beam of X-rays through a crystal, which deflects the beam in various directions.

A photograph of the pattern produced by the scattering enables calculations to be made of the number of electrons in orbitals around each type of atomic nucleus in the crystal. The original work on common salt estimated that there are ten electrons around the sodium nuclei (instead of 11, as in the ordinary sodium atom). This means that each atom has given up one electron to form an ion. Eighteen electrons were found around chlorine nuclei, corresponding to *chloride* ions which have one electron more than chlorine and so carry a negative charge.

Ionic bonding provides an explanation of the regularity of crystal structures. The ions of a solid are not bonded in such a way that each has a definite partner. For instance, in sodium chloride each positive sodium ion has several negative chloride ions as neighbours. Each chloride ion is equally attractive and each of them is an equal, and very short, distance away. Similarly each negative ion is separated from all its positive neighbours by the same short distance. As a result, the ions are arranged in a very regular pattern, in this case at the corners of a cubic lattice. As well as giving rise to this regularity, ionic bonding strongly opposes any large wanderings of the ions from their equilibrium positions.

Such motion of particles within a substance is the basis of the gaseous and liquid states – a liquid is liquid because its component particles are free to move about more than in a solid, and a gas is a gas because the particles are almost completely free to move. For this reason, 'rigid' ionic substances have a great

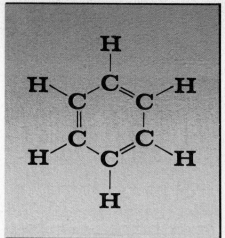

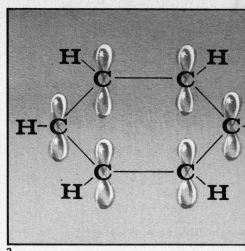

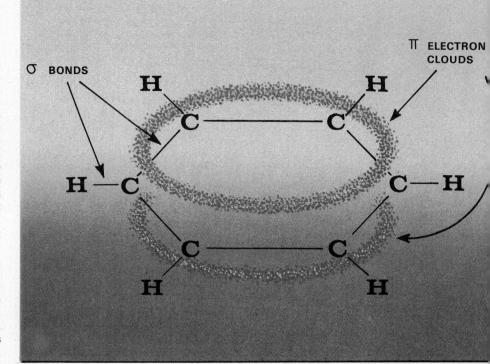

3
The mysterious behaviour of benzene yielded to research in two stages. First, it was suggested that the six carbon atoms must form a ring, with double bonds between each second atom, **1**, but benzene did not act as if it contained double bonds. This fact is now explained by assuming that each carbon atom has one electron travelling in a tear-drop shaped orbital at right angles to it, **2**. Because the carbon atoms are actually so close together, these orbitals overlap into two doughnut-shaped orbitals called π-orbitals above and below the ring, **3**. This accounts for benzene's peculiar behaviour. Benzene is the basis for a number of important products such as pain-relieving aspirin, **4**, aniline dyes, **5**, and certain common plastics, **6**.

resistance against becoming liquids or gases. In other words, they have high melting and boiling points.

In ionic bonding, one atomic partner gives up electrons and the other acquires them. But there is another kind of bond in which the partners share electrons. The shared electrons are, like all the electrons, continuously moving, but their average position is such that together they attract electrostatically both the nuclei at once. This attraction pulls the two nuclei together, and gives stability to the molecule which they make up.

A simple example is the hydrogen molecule, which is the basic particle of hydrogen gas. Each molecule consists of two atoms of hydrogen. Two electrons are shared and form a bond between the two hydrogen nuclei. Each electron spends half its time in an orbital around one nucleus, and half in an orbital around the other.

The mechanism of sharing electrons was first suggested in 1916 by G. N. Lewis and given the name *covalent bonding*. The theoretical basis for covalent bonding, derived from wave mechanics, came in 1927 in the work of Heitler and London.

Compared with the forces binding the molecule, there is very little attraction between neighbouring molecules of a covalent compound. Such molecules are quite 'self-contained' from the force point of view, and have a tendency towards independent motion. As a result, most covalent compounds melt and boil at low temperatures, and many of them are gases or liquids at room temperature. Examples of covalent compounds are methane gas

(Ch$_4$), water (H$_2$O), acetylene and petrol.

A further characteristic of covalently bonded substances is that they are resistant to electrolysis. By sharing electrons, the atoms within the covalent molecule have reached a stable electronic structure without having to acquire an electric charge. They therefore remain electrically neutral and are largely unaffected by electricity.

Molecules containing many atoms provide more complicated examples of covalent bonding. Whereas the atoms of nearly all non-metals have the ability of forming covalent bonds with themselves, carbon is exceptional in being able to form an apparently unlimited number of such bonds with itself. For instance, butane, which is the gas used as a fuel in some cigarette lighters, has a structure which can roughly be represented in a *structural* formula

$$\begin{array}{cccc} \text{H} & \text{H} & \text{H} & \text{H} \\ | & | & | & | \\ \text{H}-\text{C}-\text{C}-\text{C}-\text{C}-\text{H} \\ | & | & | & | \\ \text{H} & \text{H} & \text{H} & \text{H} \end{array}$$

Each letter C stands for a carbon atom and each letter H for hydrogen. Every short line represents a covalent bond formed by the sharing of two electrons.

The butane molecule is not perfectly flat, as the structural formula would suggest. The four bonds from each carbon atom are exactly equivalent, and to be so they point in space towards the corners of a regular tetrahedron (a pyramid on a triangular base). As a result, the chain of carbon atoms in butane is kinked.

A further complication in some large molecules is that atoms in a molecule may be joined by *double* or *triple* bonds, in which each bond involves the sharing of four or six electrons. An example of triple bonding occurs in the molecules of acetylene gas, used in high-temperature welding torches. This has the chemical formula C$_2$H$_2$ and can be represented by the structural formula H—C≡C—H. Two of the six carbon-carbon bonding electrons move in an orbital which resembles an ordinary covalent bond. This is called a σ (sigma) orbital. Each pair of the remaining four electrons moves in an orbital outside the line of the σ orbital and further away from the carbon nuclei. These special orbitals are called π (*pi*) orbitals. They are not very stable and can be thought of as being under 'strain', attracted by the carbon nuclei but repelled by the σ electrons.

Acetylene gas can produce temperatures in excess of 4000 °C. when burnt with oxygen in an oxy-acetylene torch. Part of the tremendous energy of burning acetylene comes from releasing the 'strain' on the π electrons.

The great benzene mystery

The theory of π orbital electrons has helped to solve a problem which puzzled chemists for more than a century: the structure of the molecules of the aromatic liquid benzene. Researchers knew that carbon has a covalence of four, and that each benzene molecule contains six carbon atoms and six hydrogen atoms (giving it the chemical formula C$_6$H$_6$). All the evidence seemed to point to a ring structure. The carbon atoms were found to have such a ring formation, but for each of them to have a stable electronic structure, three of the carbon-carbon bonds would have to be double and three single. But benzene lacks the reactivity characteristic of double-bonded compounds and all its carbon-carbon bonds are equivalent.

The true explanation is that the extra shared electrons, beyond those in normal σ orbitals, are travelling round the ring in special π orbitals. The π electrons can be pictured as forming two circular clouds, one above and one below the benzene ring.

Benzene is one of the most versatile of organic chemicals – its unusual structure allows it to form thousands of compounds. Whole industries are based on benzene chemicals – from drugs such as aspirin and sulphonamides, to explosives such as TNT.

There are some substances in which the bonds appear to be either ionic or covalent, according to the circumstances. An example is hydrogen chloride, which is a gas at room temperature – a fact which generally indicates covalency. But when hydrogen chloride is dissolved in water, it forms the substance hydrochloric acid. Like all acids, hydrochloric acid produces hydrogen ions, and it can be electrolysed to hydrogen and chlorine gas. These two facts indicate that in solution the substance has ionic bonding.

A possible explanation of this behaviour

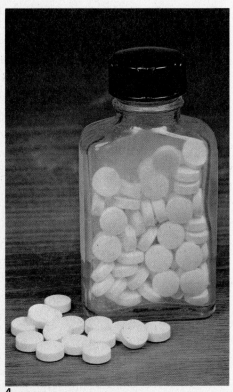

4

5

6

all covalent combinations of unlike molecules.

Some substances have very strong dipole effects which result in the positive end of each dipole being attracted to the negative end of a neighbouring one. This causes an additional weak form of electrostatic bond between adjacent molecules. Since the effect is found only with molecules containing hydrogen (in combination with oxygen, fluorine, nitrogen or chlorine), the bond is called a *hydrogen bond*.

Hydrogen bonds restrict the motion of individual molecules, causing the substances which they comprise to have a greater resistance to melting and boiling. That is, hydrogen-bonded compounds have higher melting and boiling points than expected. For example, if it were not for hydrogen bonds, water would be a gas at room temperature and would vaporize at about *minus* 100 °C., 200 degrees lower than its common boiling temperature.

A vibrating bond

We have already mentioned X-ray diffraction as a method of determining molecular structures. Another method, which can be used for gases, is electron diffraction. A beam of electrons is passed through a specimen of gas at very low pressure, and the nuclei of the gas molecules deflect the electrons to give a pattern of rings on a photographic plate. If a definite molecular structure for the gas is assumed, an expected pattern can be calculated and compared with the one actually found. (Trial and error continues like this until a structure is assumed which would produce the pattern found.) Neutron diffraction can be used in a similar way in order to determine molecular structure.

Another important method of determining molecular structure is *molecular spectroscopy*. Just as the wavelength (and hence colour) of the light emitted by an atom is characteristic of the atom's electronic structure, so is the spectrum of light emitted by a molecule characteristic of the molecule's structure. The light emitted from a molecule has parts which are due to the electronic structure of the individual atoms, and parts which are due to the characteristics of the bonds and the whole molecule.

A covalent bond between two atoms can be considered to be vibrating. The overall effect is like a dumb-bell with a rubber bar – the masses at the ends moving apart and together as the bond (bar) is stretched and compressed. A decrease in the amount of vibrational energy of a bond results in the emission of a quantum of light. The wavelength of this light is generally greater than that of light emitted by electrons changing orbitals, and can be used to calculate the structure of the bond. These calculations are complicated by the fact that changes in vibrational energy affect the electrons, and there may also be many bonds vibrating.

Chemistry is the science of how atoms and how various elements and compounds react with each other. The study of chemistry begins with a knowledge of how the chemist's basic materials – molecules – are formed, i.e. with the theory of bonding.

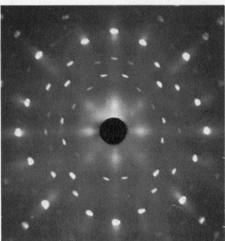

Top, the explosive power of dynamite, here being used to demolish a war-damaged building in Hanover, Germany, comes from the energy released when the chemical bonds holding together its complex molecules are broken. *Left,* a Laue X-ray photograph similar to the one used by Sir William Henry Bragg and his son, Sir Lawrence Bragg, to determine the bonding structure of common salt, *right.* Such basic work earned the father and son team the 1915 Nobel Physics Prize.

is that the bond of hydrogen chloride changes from covalent to ionic when the gas is dissolved in water. But how great is this change? Could it be that the molecules in the gas are *nearly* ionic to begin with? The chlorine nucleus is much bigger than the hydrogen nucleus, and so it should have a greater attraction for the bonding electrons. As a result, the electrons spend a greater part of their time near the chlorine atom, which gets more than its 'fair share' of the electrical charge.

This results in a small negative charge at the chlorine end of the molecule, and since the hydrogen molecule gets less than its fair share of electrons it becomes slightly positively charged. The charges are not completely separated as in true ionic bonding, but separation is sufficient to be noticeable. Such molecules are called *electrostatic dipoles*. There is strong evidence that such dipoles exist in almost

A sun in the laboratory

The sun's energy results from tremendously hot gases fusing to form new elements. Scientists are now attempting to control similar reactions on Earth to give Man an unlimited source of power.

The plasma space engine has been designed for stabilizing satellites in orbit. The engine operates on batteries recharged by solar cells and uses an inert gas, such as nitrogen, as fuel.

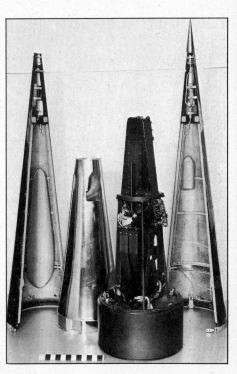

The nose cone of a rocket which is to be sent up to make measurements of the sun's corona. The cone assembly contains spectrographs and a pinhole camera to photograph soft X-ray emission.

PLASMA PHYSICS is the study of ionized gases. We say that a gas has become *ionized* when one (or more) of the electrons of the atoms of molecules comprising the gas are removed leaving the atom with a net positive charge. An ionized gas, then, is made up of an equal number of positively charged gas atoms, called *ions* and *free electrons,* and in this stage it is called a *plasma*. This has also been referred to as the fourth state of matter to distinguish it from solids, liquids and gases. Although plasma physics is relatively new, plasmas are, in fact, very common in nature – the sun and all the stars are entirely composed of plasma and since the advent of artificial satellites it has been found that the Earth is immersed in an extremely weak plasma which is streaming out from the sun. Other natural plasmas are the Aurora Borealis or Northern Lights and lightning flashes; plasmas also exist inside neon and fluorescent light tubes and electric sparks and arcs. As the upper regions of the atmosphere are ionized by radiation from the sun, it is possible to transmit radio waves for much greater distances than the line of sight distance because the plasma in the upper atmosphere reflects radio waves below a certain frequency back down to Earth.

As a plasma is composed of electrically charged particles which are free to move, it behaves as an extremely good conductor of heat and electricity; a fully ionized plasma, in which nearly all the atoms are ionized is a far better conductor than silver. Another important property of plasmas is that they are strongly affected by magnetic and electric fields which enable them to be contained in the laboratory. Because of the interactions between ions and ions, and between electrons and electrons, as well as between ions and electrons, the behaviour of a plasma is much more complicated and difficult to describe mathematically than the behaviour of an ordinary gas. If the effects of magnetic and electric fields (which do not affect ordinary gas atoms) are included, the overall behaviour can be very complicated indeed. For instance, the effect of a magnetic field is to severely restrict motion across the field lines, but has little effect on particle motion along the field and the plasma is then said to be *anisotropic* (its properties are not the same in all directions).

Predicting plasma behaviour

In order to describe the behaviour of plasmas, the effect of individual ions and electrons is often ignored and it is assumed that the plasma is simply a conducting fluid like, for example, mercury, but very much less dense. This approximation works well for some plasmas and can be used to describe and predict plasma behaviour under a variety of conditions. The study of such plasmas is called *magneto-hydrodynamics,* usually abbreviated to M.H.D.

A great deal of effort has gone into what is called the *M.H.D. generator*. This is a device which would convert the energy of a very hot gas – for example the flue gases from a conventional power station or the coolant gas used in a nuclear power station – directly into electricity. The general principle on which the generator works is quite simple: the hot gas is made into a plasma by adding a small quantity of material which can be ionized by the random motion of the hot gas atoms. This plasma is then allowed to flow between the poles of a powerful magnet; that is, across a magnetic field. In doing so, the negatively and positively charged particles are deflected in opposite directions so that the plasma develops an electric potential across itself which can be picked up on special electrodes and electric current can flow in an external circuit. As electrical energy is extracted from the moving plasma, it is slowed down and the thermal energy of the hot gas can be converted directly into electricity.

Although the M.H.D. generator would have many advantages if it can be shown to be practicable, a great many, if not the majority, of the world's plasma physicists are working on an even more revolutionary form of power generation – *thermonuclear fusion*. In the 1930s, physicists solved the mystery of how the sun and the stars produced their vast amounts of energy. Their studies showed that the process responsible was the fusion of light atoms into heavier atoms and, by a complicated cycle, four hydrogen atoms

were being fused together to create helium.

During this fusion reaction, a large amount of energy is released because the mass of the final helium nucleus is less than the mass of the four hydrogen nuclei which went into its manufacture and, although the mass difference is minute, the annihilation of matter produces a tremendous amount of energy. The process is the opposite of nuclear fission in which a very heavy nucleus, such as uranium, breaks up into two or more lighter nuclei, again with a large release of energy which comes from the difference in mass between the original nucleus and the sum of the masses of the final lighter nuclei.

Destructive power

It is the fission reaction which gives the atom bomb its tremendous destructive power. The even more powerful hydrogen bomb is due to a combination of fission and fusion reactions. The temperature at the heart of a fission bomb is so high that it triggers off fusion reactions between two isotopes of hydrogen, called *deuterium* and *tritium,* resulting in an even greater release of energy than fission.

Modern nuclear power stations rely on nuclear fission and physicists have succeeded in taming the atomic bomb. What plasma physicists would like to do is to tame the hydrogen bomb. If this is possible, it would give mankind an inexhaustible source of power since the basic fuel, which is heavy hydrogen or deuterium, can be obtained cheaply from sea-water. However, the problems involved in trying to obtain a fusion reaction are very formidable indeed – physicists are attempting to create a small sun in the laboratory.

In order to get fusion reactions to take

1 Zeta, the first major controlled fusion experiment in Britain. A current of 500,000 amps was passed through the plasma to heat it to 1,000,000 °C. in the toroidal chamber.
2 The thetatron experiment to measure the movement of plasma down a straight length of transparent silica tubing. Thetatron has now been dismantled and replaced by other experiments.
3 The plasma jet torch gives temperatures up to about 25,000 °C. by constricting an arc column in a flowing gas. In its laminar form a plasma jet can be extended up to three feet in length.

place, the nuclei must be brought very close together. This is extremely difficult since the nuclei are positively charged and therefore repel each other and try to stay apart. It is only by giving the nuclei a lot of energy and then making them collide that the electrical forces holding them apart can be overcome and fusion reactions take place.

It is possible to give energy to gas atoms by making them hot – the hotter they are the faster they travel and collisions between atoms become more energetic but, in order to obtain fusion reactions, the gas will have to be heated to the fantastically high temperature of 100 *million* degrees centigrade. How, then, can a gas at this temperature be contained when all known materials melt and

vaporize at temperatures of a few *thousand* degrees centigrade? The solution lies with plasmas. Because they are composed of charged particles they interact strongly with magnetic fields so it might be possible to make a magnetic bottle to hold the very hot plasma away from any solid material walls. Plasma physicists in Britain, the U.S.S.R. and the United States, together with colleagues from other nations, have been attempting to find a good 'leak-proof' magnetic bottle since the 1940s in order to obtain thermonuclear fusion reactions in the laboratory.

In October 1969, results of some work in the U.S.S.R., on what is called the TOKAMAK experiment, have shown that thermonuclear reactions are being observed. Some of the important measure-

ments of the plasma were made by a visiting team of British scientists, indicating the great deal of international co-operation existing in this field. Evidence of thermonuclear reactions has also been obtained in different experiments in the United States and Britain, but the significance of the Russian result is that the reactions lasted for a relatively long time, indicating that the type of magnetic bottle being used is a fairly good one. Whether or not it is good enough remains to be seen from future experiments because, although it is a very encouraging result, the plasma density, temperature and lifetime will all have to be increased by at least ten times before the fusion reaction will be self-sustaining and capable of supplying power.

The pinch effect

The TOKAMAK is one of several experiments which rely on the *pinch effect*. This can best be described as follows. If a current is passed in the same direction down a loose bundle of straight wires, they will all attract one another to form a tight bundle due to the magnetic forces set up by the electric current – they pinch together. If instead of using wires to carry the current, a large current is passed through a tenuous plasma in a tube, then the magnetic forces set up will, if they are strong enough, squeeze the plasma into a thin thread and hold it away from the tube walls. Some of the first pinch experiments were carried out in straight tubes because they are easier to make, but they suffer from the disadvantage that the plasma is cooled by conduction to the electrodes at the ends. The simplest way of avoiding

4 Using plasma torches to clean rail of contaminants such as a thin layer of grease, British Rail hope to increase the friction between the train wheels and the track.

5 Large banks of capacitors are needed to provide sudden sharp pulses of current to energize plasma reactions. Here they are being used in a magnetic trap stability experiment.

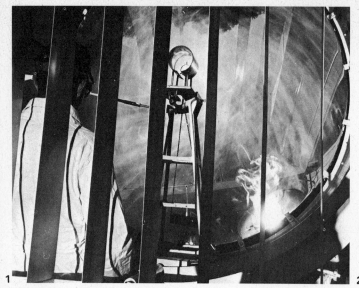

1 A technician makes tests in a solar furnace to study the effects of high temperatures on materials. Plasma gases provide temperatures that cannot, at present, be reached by other means.

2 Technicians at the Culham Laboratory in Britain fix insulated copper foil conductors to the torus of a stellarator magnetic trap. The trap is being used to study fusion.

3 The solar corona which consists of plasma extending far out into space from the sun is seen during a total eclipse. Using special equipment the corona can now be seen at other times.

this trouble is to bend the tube round until it closes on itself to make a doughnut shape or, as it is more properly called, a *torus*. The large current required to make the plasma pinch is induced in the torus by making it the single turn secondary of a transformer. The currents required are quite large – in the range of a few thousand up to one million ampères. These large currents are not applied continuously, but electrical energy is stored in large banks of condensers which can be charged over several tens of seconds and then all the accumulated energy is rapidly discharged in a few thousandths (or in some cases a few millionths) of a second to give a large pulse of energy. Apart from pulling the plasma away from the tube walls the electric current also heats the plasma to a very high temperature. The heating mechanism is essentially the same as that of an electric fire, only on a very different scale. The element in a fire becomes hot because of its electrical resistance. Similarly, although a plasma is a very good conductor, it still has some electrical resistance. By forcing current through the plasma against this resistance, it can be raised to a very high temperature. It was soon found, however, that the pinched discharge did not remain in the middle of the tube for very long but rapidly wriggled about until it struck the tube walls. The discharge is then said to be unstable. Some of the instabilities can be overcome, or at least their effects minimized, by putting conducting walls close to, but not in contact with, the plasma and also by the addition of a magnetic field round the torus.

Perhaps the most famous and most thoroughly studied toroidal pinch was the ZETA experiment at Harwell in Britain. The torus was roughly a yard in diameter and four yards across. The plasma was heated to a temperature of five million degrees centigrade and although fusion reactions were observed, they were found not to be of true thermonuclear origin but were due to further instabilities in the

3

plasma.

Another scheme for confining a hot plasma in an endless tube is the *stellarator concept* which relies, not on currents carried by the plasma, but on externally produced fields. In order to hold the plasma, simple coils wound round the torus will not do, and either more complicated fields are needed or the torus with its coils has to be twisted into a figure eight. Stellarators are being studied in laboratories throughout the world in order to see whether or not they can contain hot plasmas for times of the order of one second needed for controlled fusion.

Magnetic mirrors

Although a great deal of effort is being put into the study of toroidal systems, there is an alternative form of magnetic bottle called the *magnetic mirror*. This is basically a straight tube in which the magnetic field is stronger at the ends of the tube than in the central portion. The strong field at the ends reflects most of the ions and electrons back into the central region of the tube – hence the name magnetic mirror. The magnetic mirror was found to be a good bottle for containing very low-

density plasmas, but as the plasma density was increased, the plasma started to leak out across the magnetic field due to an instability.

The plasma instability and associated loss was basically due to the fact that although the magnetic field increased at the ends of the tube, it decreased outwards along a radius and the plasma escaped to where the magnetic field was weakest. By adding extra coils the simple mirror system could be converted into what is called a magnetic *well* in which the magnetic field increases outwards in all directions from the plasma and it is unable to escape. Since magnetic mirrors are such good bottles for holding hot plasmas, there is difficulty in filling them – if the bottle is so good that plasma cannot get out, then it cannot get in either. Sophisticated filling techniques have been developed but, as yet, they are not powerful enough to overcome some very slight leakages. Because the magnetic mirror is basically a straight tube, some plasma leakage is always bound to take place through the ends because the magnetic mirrors will not reflect ions which have too high a velocity along the magnetic field. This unavoidable end-loss puts magnetic mirrors at a disadvantage with respect to the endless or toroidal systems. However, mirror systems are much simpler to build and easier to treat theoretically than toroidal systems and, in spite of their end-losses, they still stand a chance of developing into a reactor in which the end-loss problem could be turned to an advantage by directly converting the energy of the escaping hot plasma into electricity.

There are many types of bottles being used in attempts to produce and contain the equivalent of a piece of sun in the laboratory, and many techniques used by plasma physicists to examine these plasmas. Although many problems have been overcome, many remain to be solved before the energy source of the sun and stars can be used for the good of mankind.

Forces to hold the world together

Scientists believe the world to be composed of microscopic particles moving around in a void, yet we see strong, solid objects around us everywhere. So why doesn't everything fly apart?

THE SO-CALLED ATOMIC AGE was born just a little more than 20 years ago. But the idea of the atom was conceived more than 2,000 years ago. Of course, the atomic theory proposed by the Greek, Democritus, and his followers was very different from the modern picture of the atom created by men such as Dalton, Thomson and Einstein. Nevertheless, many of the questions the Ancient Greeks asked themselves about these minute particles are still relevant today. For instance, how is it possible that a solid object such as an oak table is really nothing more than a collection of microscopic particles flying around in a void?

Before we can answer such questions, we must first understand the difference between *microscopic* and *macroscopic* phenomena. The prefix 'micro' means very small, usually too small to be seen with the unaided eye. 'Macro' means large, and in atomic theory it has the more precise meaning of large enough to be seen without the aid of some optical instrument.

Occurrences in the macroscopic world are often caused by microscopic events which are frequently quite different from the phenomena they produce. A television picture is the result of hundreds of thousands of electrons striking the screen. We never see these electrons, but we do see a coherent picture, which is nothing at all like the electrons that make it. With this idea in mind, we can now take a closer look at how atoms and molecules interact with one another.

Molecules are collections of positively charged atomic nuclei, associated with negatively charged electrons. If two molecules are brought extremely close together, there is a strong force of electrical repulsion between the parts of the two molecules which bear the same charge. This repulsion tends to push the molecules apart as if they were two rubber balls being pressed tightly together.

Atoms ignore gravity

If two molecules are not quite so close, the charges within each molecule take positions that produce an overall force of *attraction* between the molecules. This attraction tends to pull the molecules towards each other until they are so close that the force of repulsion is set up, and the molecules tend to fly apart again.

The two intermolecular forces just described are very important on the micro-

scopic scale, although we are not directly aware of them in the macroscopic world. But one universal force which we know well in the macroscopic world is the force of gravity. This is the attraction which every physical object has for all other objects (the force between any two objects depends on the masses of the two objects, and decreases the further they are apart). The most familiar example is the weight of an object on Earth, which is a measure of the force acting on it due to the gravitational attraction of the massive Earth.

Although gravity is a powerful force in the macroscopic world, it provides a force between two very close molecules which is many millions of times *smaller* than the molecular attractive force just described. Gravitational forces can normally be ignored on the microscopic scale.

Returning to our example of a solid oak table, we can now better understand how it holds together. Usually the best way of understanding the microscopic structure of any solid object is by means of a model.

The differences between solids, liquids and gases depend mainly on molecular interaction. We demonstrate with people. *Right,* molecules of a solid are closely packed together; they can vibrate, but they cannot change their relative positions. *Below left,* liquid molecules move about, but tend to remain with the group. *Below right,* gas molecules move with almost complete independence.

Imagine a pile of similar balls, regularly spaced in all directions, and each joined to its immediate neighbours by a rubber rod. These rubber rods are equivalent to the forces between the molecules. If two neighbouring balls were to move apart, they would stretch their rubber connecting rod. The stretched rod would spring back, pulling the balls together again. This springing back is equivalent to the attractive force between molecules. If two balls move closer together than normal, they will compress a rod and it will push them apart again with the equivalent of the repulsive force between molecules. In our model, we can consider all the balls to be moving individually and acted on by the forces provided by the rods.

A billion-to-one chance

Each ball will move about an average *equilibrium* position – going near one neighbour and being repulsed, going near another neighbour and being repulsed, and so on. Thus, the molecules of a solid substance are continually moving about an equilibrium position; in other words, they are vibrating. Because of the very powerful forces between the molecules, none of them is able to move far enough to change neighbours before being pushed back towards its equilibrium position. The directions in which the molecules move is completely general; some move one way, some move another, but the solid substance as a whole does not move.

However, since there are billions upon billions of molecules in an object such as a table, the chances that they will all move *in the same direction* at a given instance are extremely remote. But if one day this billion-to-one chance occurred and all the molecules moved at the same moment sideways, then the whole table would also move a tiny distance sideways of its own accord.

The energy of motion of molecules about their equilibrium position is what we know macroscopically as the heat within the solid object. If extra heat is supplied to a solid, its molecules vibrate more violently about their equilibrium positions, and take up more space with their vibrations. The average distance between molecules increases, and macroscopically the solid expands. This mechanism accounts for the expansion of solids when they are heated.

If more and more heat is supplied to a solid, the molecules vibrate more and more violently until they reach a state in which they have enough energy to overcome the attractions and repulsions of their immediate neighbours (in our model, they are moving fast enough to break the

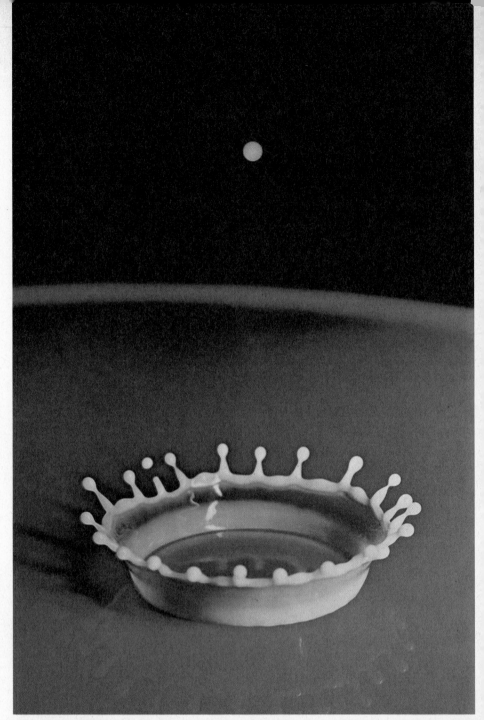

Top, the high-speed camera catches the spherical drops and the crown-like beauty of a milk splash before gravity and other forces have a chance to distort the pattern. The pool of milk is bathed in red light to aid the split-second photography. *Right,* a small drop of mercury on a smooth surface shows gravitational distortion and mercury's resistance to 'wetting' caused by surface tension. *Far right,* surface tension is also an explanation for the convex meniscus of mercury in a tube in comparison to the concave meniscus of water in an identical glass tube.

rubber connecting rods). The molecules are now able to move more freely among and between their neighbours. The solid has lost its rigidity, melted and become a liquid. In a liquid, each molecule is moving about between other molecules. It travels in a straight line until it happens to collide with one of the others. In a collision, the molecules come close enough for the force of repulsion to act and push them apart again. Each of the molecules involved in the collision then travels off among the other molecules in a straight line, hardly affected by repulsive forces until it happens to collide with another molecule or, possibly, the walls of a containing vessel.

One fact which is macroscopically obvious about liquids is that they have no definite shape; the shape is generally defined by the containing vessel at the bottom and sides, and by the surface at the top. But a liquid does have a definite volume. A pint of milk is still a pint of milk whether in its bottle or in a glass.

The attractive forces from other liquid

Below, evaporation is a slow form of vaporization. When a liquid is below its boiling point, some of the molecules escape from the surface, a majority bounce back off air molecules. But when the liquid boils, most of the molecules have enough energy to escape despite the air.

molecules pull any one molecule more or less equally in every direction, so the motion of a molecule in the body of a liquid is normally unaffected by them.

A molecule at the surface of a liquid has attractive forces towards all other liquid molecules, below and to the sides of it. Above it, however, there are only widely scattered air molecules, and the attractive forces from these are very small.

The attraction between molecules in the layer of liquid at the surface is equal in all directions, so that each surface molecule has an overall attraction towards the main body of the liquid. This is the microscopic explanation of *surface tension.* It helps us to understand why surface tension causes small drops of water to take a spherical shape – all the molecules on the outside are attracted towards the main body of the liquid inside.

A sphere is the shape which allows all the outside molecules to be as near the centre as possible. To understand this, think of a swarm of bees, with a queen bee in the middle. Each bee wants to be as near the queen as possible, and some struggle through to her, pushing others away. The continual pushing in of the bees makes the swarm have a spherical shape. Falling raindrops tend to assume a spherical shape, but may have a 'tail' caused by

friction as they move through the air. Small drops of liquid resting on a flat solid surface take up various shapes. These shapes depend on the effect of gravity; and the attraction which the surface has for liquid molecules. Water drops on a smooth polished surface retain an almost spherical shape. On an unpolished, rougher surface, water drops tend to spread to a pancake shape; in this case, the solid surface has a greater attraction for the water molecules.

The angle between the surface of the drop and the solid surface under the drop is called the *angle of contact.* This angle is a measure of the attraction between a liquid and a solid.

Angle of contact is useful in understanding the process of waterproofing light fabrics. The fibres of the cloth are coated with a waxy substance – not to block up the pores in the cloth but to increase the angle of contact of water. Rainwater falling on the fabric tends to gather as nearly spherical droplets and, as they have no great attraction to the cloth, they run off. By contrast, detergents are used to reduce the angle of contact, so that water can work its way under grease on dirty dishes and help to float it away.

The angle of contact between a liquid and a solid determines the shape of the surface of a large amount of liquid in a container. This surface shape is called the *meniscus.* If the angle is low, the meniscus is *concave,* curving back towards the liquid. Water has a concave meniscus in most containers, because there is some attraction between the molecules of the glass and the molecules of water. A high angle of contact causes a *convex* meniscus, which curves upwards, away from the liquid. Such a liquid is mercury, which forms a convex meniscus with the glass of a thermometer. There is no attraction between the molecules of the glass and the molecules of mercury.

Into the air

If the end of a very narrow tube is dipped into some water, the water rises up the tube. This phenomenon is called capillary action. The attraction of the glass inside the tube on the water molecules at the surface pulls the water up the tube. The capillary rise is opposed by the weight of the water, and the wider the tube, the greater the effect of gravity in comparison with the pull at the surface. So the wider the tube, the less is the capillary rise. Capillary action causes ink or water to soak up into blotting paper against the pull of gravity.

What happens at the surface of a liquid to molecules which happen to be travelling very fast towards the surface? They can pass straight *through* the surface (if they are travelling fast enough) and overcome the attraction of the other liquid molecules. In fact, there are always many molecules leaving the surface of a liquid in this way, and forming a *vapour.*

Vapours are microscopically the same as gases – their molecules are moving independently of each other, except when they collide. Their motion is limited only by container walls and collisions; they have no surface and no definite volume.

This process, by which faster-moving

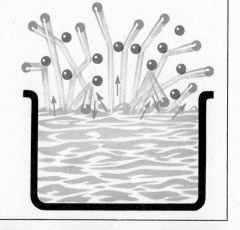

air molecules   liquid molecules

molecules leave a liquid, is called *evaporation* and explains the eventual disappearance of water or other liquids left in open vessels. As the faster-moving molecules leave a liquid, the average energy of the remaining molecules decreases and so the temperature of the liquid tends to fall. Heat must be supplied to the liquid to keep it at its original temperature, replacing the great amount of energy taken out by the evaporating molecules. This amount of heat is known as *latent heat*. Most of it comes from the surrounding air and from the container.

Earlier we discussed melting, the change from solid to liquid. The melting process also needs latent heat to provide the great energy required to free the molecules of the solid from their equilibrium positions so they can move among and between the other molecules.

Latent heat explains how sweating reduces body temperature. We sweat when we are too hot. The evaporation of the water in the sweat absorbs its latent heat from the body and so the body cools down.

The process of evaporation is reversed in a thundercloud, where the condensation of water vapour gives out latent heat which supplies a thundercloud with its enormous energy. If the condensation of a cloud takes place in about half an hour, the rate of energy production equals about 4 million horse power. It is strange to think that the vast energy of a thunderstorm depends for its power on the attractions between infinitesimally small molecules of water.

Cooking at 10,000 feet

There is a further limitation on evaporation besides latent heat. The motion of vapour molecules above the liquid causes some of them to move down and collide with the liquid surface. Some of the collisions result in vapour molecules rebounding away from the liquid, while others are caught up by the attraction of the liquid molecules and stay in the liquid. In this way, some of the vapour molecules are always returning to the liquid, and if the vapour concentration above the liquid reaches a certain level, an equal number of molecules return from the vapour as are evaporating from the liquid.

The level of this concentration is measured as the *saturated vapour pressure* of the liquid. At any given temperature, every liquid has a definite saturated vapour pressure; it will continue to evaporate until the pressure of its vapour reaches this value. This, of course, is true only if the container of liquid is closed. If vapour can escape, or if the space above the evaporating liquid continually increases, saturation will never be reached. For example, imagine liquid put into a cylinder behind a piston, and the piston continually withdrawn to keep the vapour slightly below saturated vapour pressure. If the liquid is kept at its original temperature it will continue evaporating until it is all vapour.

Saturated vapour pressure increases with rising temperature until it reaches a value equal to the total pressure (normally air pressure) acting on the surface of the

Top, the sun warms the oceans of the world and causes vast quantities of water to evaporate into the air. Later, massive clouds move through the sky, the vapour condenses and falls as life-giving rain on the Earth, *above.* This is the rain cycle – upon which all life on Earth depends.

liquid. Evaporation can then take place in the body of the liquid, in addition to that at the surface. Collections of high-energy molecules within the liquid can fly apart and push back the liquid, because they equal the pressure holding it down. Bubbles appear in the liquid and rise to the surface and we say the liquid is boiling.

The temperature at which a liquid boils depends entirely on the pressure at the surface of the liquid, provided the necessary latent heat is available. Climbers trying to boil water for cooking at the top of a high mountain, where the atmospheric pressure is low, find that the water boils at only 80–90 °C. and cooking takes much longer. On the other hand, if the pressure on water is raised above atmospheric pressure, the boiling point rises above 100 °C. This is the principle of the pressure cooker, in which the water boils at 110–120 °C. The food in the cooker is maintained at this temperature and cooks faster than it would kept at 100 °C. by water boiling at

atmospheric pressure. The conclusion from these facts is that the pressure on the surface of a liquid is essential to prevent it from all changing to a vapour.

In view of this, is it possible to convert all gases to liquids by subjecting them to enough pressure? No, for every gas there is a certain temperature, the *critical temperature,* above which no amount of compression can make it become a liquid. Above the critical temperature, the gas molecules have sufficient energy to move independently of each others' attractive forces, no matter what the pressure. The critical temperature of water is 365 °C., and that of air is −140 °C. (under atmospheric pressure, liquid air boils at −190 °C.).

Intermolecular forces and motions – all at the microscopic level – are responsible for all the macroscopic properties of objects we see around us. Whether an object is hot or cold, or solid, liquid or gas, depends on the arrangement and movement of its molecules.

Equations for chemists

No good cook would bake a cake without a recipe, for fear of the outcome. Likewise, no good chemist would produce compounds without equations and formulae. The results could be disastrous.

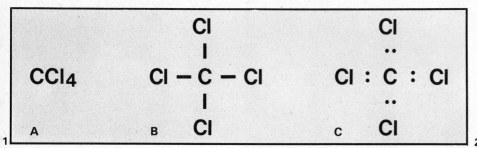

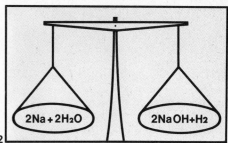

THROUGHOUT MOST OF ITS HISTORY, chemistry has been a hotch-potch of unexplained processes and suspicious formulae. The traditional picture of a chemist pottering around in his laboratory, mixing together foul-smelling substances in test-tubes to see what would happen, although exaggerated, was not too far wrong.

This is not to imply that pre-1900 researchers stumbled around blindly, with no real scientific basis for their efforts. On the contrary, they often knew precisely what they were about, and many important laws and ideas grew from their efforts long before such things as electrons, orbitals and nuclei were even thought of. The advent of quantum mechanics and twentieth-century atomic theory made their ideas more comprehensible and consequently more useful.

Two of the most important ideas to emerge from the eighteenth and nineteenth centuries were atomic weights and chemical formulae. When brought together in a coherent, logical structure, they form one of the modern chemist's most powerful tools.

Weighing atoms

The task of 'weighing' atoms is no mean assignment. Atoms are so exceedingly small that not even the most delicate balance could hope to weigh one. Early chemists found, too, that there was no use in weighing a large chunk of some element and then dividing the result by the number of atoms it contained, because at the time there was no way of counting atoms. There was, however, a way of determining relative atomic weights from gaseous compounds.

For instance, ammonia is a compound of three hydrogen atoms and one nitrogen atom. Appropriate experiments show that the nitrogen ion in this compound is slightly less than five times as heavy as the three hydrogen ions; therefore, the nitrogen atom turns out to be slightly more than 14 times as heavy as each hydrogen atom used to make the ammonia. Since hydrogen is the lightest of all elements, pre-1900 chemists gave it the *arbitrary* designation of 1. Accordingly, nitrogen was just over 14.

In this way, all elements could be compared to hydrogen as a standard. No

1 A molecular formula (A) shows the elements and their combining proportions. A structural formula (B) indicates how the elements attach themselves to one another. A dot formula (C) is

units are necessary, because atomic weights are ratios, not quantities, like pounds, ounces or grams. Because the process of determining relative weights could be more conveniently carried out using oxygen rather than hydrogen, oxygen was eventually chosen to replace hydrogen as the standard. To avoid having any atomic weights less than one, oxygen was given the arbitrary designation 16, which makes hydrogen 1·008. In 1961, the atomic weight scale was revised once more, and was this time based on carbon 12, an isotope of carbon.

Another useful idea to come from pre-1900 chemists – the *chemical formula* – is not just a shorthand method of writing long chemical names, but an accurate description of the chemical composition of chemical compounds.

For instance, the chemical formula for carbon dioxide (the gas which green plants use for raw materials in photosynthesis) is CO_2. This tells the chemist that the compound is made from one atom of carbon and two atoms of oxygen. Another

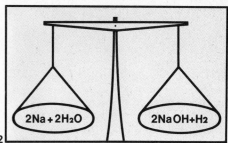

Jöns Jacob Berzelius (1779–1848), one of the founders of modern chemistry. His contributions to chemistry include his development of the modern system of chemical symbols and formulae.

another type of structural chemical formula.
2 Chemical equations must balance. For every element on the left (the reactants), there must be an equivalent on the right (the products).

extremely important compound is H_2O, or water. Water is a chemical combination of two atoms of hydrogen and one atom of oxygen. Other chemical formulae are more formidable, such as $CaSO_4$, H_2SO_4 and K_2CO_3, but they all serve the same function – that of easing the chemist's work by telling him exactly what he is handling.

It is possible to approach the idea of chemical formulae from precisely the opposite point of view: by starting with the elements and determining the ultimate compound, rather than looking at the compound to see what it is made of.

For instance, what compound is formed by the reaction of hydrogen and chlorine? From quantum theory, we know that most atoms have either too many or too few electrons whizzing round their nuclei for stability. So, when combining into compounds, they often swap electrons until each resulting ion has its most stable complement.

Predicting compounds

The *valence number* of an atom indicates the number of electrons it is capable of accepting or giving away when forming a compound. The resultant ions are held together by electrostatic forces. Hydrogen has a valence of +1 (that is, it has one electron in its outermost shell to give away). Chlorine has a valence of −1 (that is, it seeks one electron to complete its outermost shell). So, when conditions are right, hydrogen donates an electron to chlorine and the result is HCl, or hydrogen chloride.

The process works exactly the same way for slightly more complicated compounds. Suppose one did not already know that water is H_2O and asked the question: 'What compound is formed by the reaction of hydrogen and oxygen?' Again, hydrogen has a valence of +1, oxygen has a valence of −2. At first, we try the formula HO, but this won't do, because oxygen has gained only one electron and needs two. The obvious solution is to bring in another hydrogen

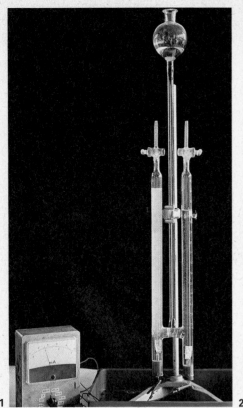

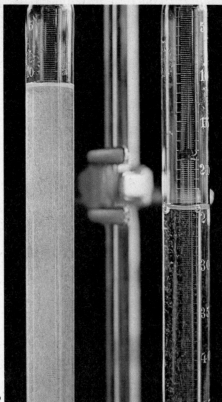

1 An electric current passed through water will break it apart into hydrogen and oxygen.
2 The volume of the hydrogen (right) is roughly twice the volume of the oxygen (left), as indicated by the chemical formula, H_2O. The clouding is caused by oxygen bubbles rising to the top.

atom, giving H_2O. Each of two hydrogen atoms now rids itself of an unwanted electron, and the oxygen atom takes up the two electrons it was lacking, one from each of the hydrogens.

The idea of valence works not only with simple elements, but with *radicals* as well. Radicals are clusters of elements which act as a unit. Some common radicals are hydroxide $(OH)^{-1}$, sulphate $(SO_4)^{-2}$ and carbonate $(CO_3)^{-2}$. The superscript is the valence of the radical.

What compound is formed by the reaction of calcium and sulphate? Calcium (a constituent of bones) has a valence of $+2$; sulphate has a valence of -2. So the two electrons from calcium are exactly enough to satisfy the sulphate, and the compound is calcium sulphate, $CaSO_4$.

Chemical equations

Now what happens when calcium combines with hydroxide? Calcium still has two electrons to dispose of, but hydroxide can only take one of them. So instead of just one hydroxide, calcium unites with two hydroxides, to give calcium hydroxide, $Ca(OH)_2$, commonly known as slaked lime.

This explanation of formulae and valency is rather oversimplified, for two reasons. First, not all elements unite with one another by swapping electrons (*ionic bonding*). Some merely share electrons (*co-valent bonding*), in which case the prediction of the formula can be much more complicated. In fact, water is a co-valent compound, but its correct formula, as we have seen, can be deduced from ionic considerations. Secondly, radicals, unlike elements, do not normally exist as independent entities, but are bound

up in compounds. In order to make a new compound containing a radical, it is usually necessary to prise the radical away from another compound.

As might be expected from this discussion, most chemical reactions can be somewhat involved, so a chemist would write out the whole procedure in the form of a *chemical equation*.

As an example, let us return to water: its chemical formula is already known to be H_2O, and investigation has shown that both hydrogen and oxygen are *diatomic* gases (each molecule contains two atoms). So one is tempted to write $H_2+O_2=H_2O$, where H_2 and O_2 indicate diatomic molecules of hydrogen and oxygen. However, a quick inspection of the equation suggests that something is wrong. If a chemical equation is an equation in the same sense as a mathematical equation (and to a large extent it is), then all the elements on the left must be equal to all the elements on the right. There are, indeed, two hydrogen atoms on the left and right; but there are two oxygen atoms on the left and one on the right.

One way out of this difficulty is to tack the excess oxygen on the right side:
$$H_2+O_2=H_2O+O.$$
However, oxygen never likes to stand alone like that. Another possible solution is to make two water molecules instead of just one:
$$H_2+O_2=2H_2O.$$
There are now two oxygens on either side; but now there are four hydrogens on the right (two in each water molecule) and only two on the left.

Suppose one starts with two hydrogen molecules:
$$2H_2+O_2=2H_2O.$$

Now it balances: four hydrogens on both sides and two oxygens on both sides.

The procedure we have just gone through is called *balancing* an equation. For more complicated reactions, the technique of hit and miss comparisons of left and right can be quite tedious. For this reason, more powerful techniques have been developed, such as the so-called Redox method. Redox is short for 'reduction-oxidation', a somewhat unfortunate choice of words, because oxygen need not appear in the balanced equation at all. 'Oxidation' refers to valence numbers. Redox relies mainly on the idea of valence and keeping track of swapped electrons. For fairly simple reactions, hit or miss techniques work just as well as Redox.

In order to clarify the idea of formulae and equations, let us follow through a typical reaction from start to finish.

When metallic sodium is dropped into water, it reacts violently, producing sodium hydroxide and hydrogen gas. First, to determine the formula for sodium hydroxide, one must know that sodium has a valence of $+1$ and that hydroxide has a valence of -1. So sodium hydroxide is NaOH. Hydrogen forms a diatomic gas, so it is reasonable to suspect that the equation will be:
$$Na+H_2O=NaOH+H_2.$$
This does not balance: there are two hydrogens on the left and three on the right. Since each water molecule always contains two hydrogens, it is impossible to have an uneven number of hydrogens on the left, so the only thing to do is to try to even the number of hydrogens on the right. There are now three hydrogens on the right, which can become four by using two sodium hydroxide molecules:
$$Na+H_2O=2NaOH+H_2.$$
But now there are four hydrogens on the right and only two on the left. So one tries:
$$Na+2H_2O=2NaOH+H_2.$$
Again, a problem. There are now two sodiums on the right and only one on the left, so the next step is to insert another sodium atom and get:
$$2Na+2H_2O=2NaOH+H_2.$$
Having balanced the equation, one has accomplished quite a good bit of chemistry. But with very little additional effort, more can be accomplished. For instance, consider the balanced equation $2H_2O+C=CO_2+2H_2$. A quick glance at a table of atomic weights shows that carbon has an atomic weight of 12 and oxygen has an atomic weight of approximately 16. So carbon dioxide (CO_2) has a *molecular weight* of $12+16+16=44$. If an actual weight unit, such as grams, is put on this number, it is found that carbon dioxide has a *gram molecular weight* of 44 gm.

Question: How much water (as steam) is required to make 44 gm of carbon dioxide? *Answer*: The atomic weight of hydrogen is 1 (approximately) and the atomic weight of oxygen is 16, so the gram molecular weight of water is 1 gm+1 gm+16 gm=18 gm. The balanced equation shows that for each gram molecular weight of carbon dioxide needed, *two* gram molecular weights of water are required. Thus, $2×18$ gm=36 gm. The answer is, in order

Element	Symbol	Atomic Number	Atomic Weight	Year Discovered	Element	Symbol	Atomic Number	Atomic Weight	Year Discovered
Actinium	Ac	89	(227)*	1899	Molybdenum	Mo	42	95·94	1782
Aluminium	Al	13	26·9815	1825	Neodymium	Nd	60	144·24	1885
Americium	Am	95	(243)	1944	Neon	Ne	10	20·183	1898
Antimony	Sb	51	121·75	B C	Neptunium	Np	93	(237)	1940
Argon	Ar	18	39·948	1894	Nickel	Ni	28	58·71	1751
Arsenic	As	33	74·9216	1649	Niobium	Nb	41	92·906	1801
Astatine	At	85	(210)	1940	Nitrogen	N	7	14·0067	1772
Barium	Ba	56	137·34	1808	Nobelium	No	102	—	1957
Berkelium	Bk	97	(247)	1949	Osmium	Os	76	190·2	1804
Beryllium	Be	4	9·0122	1797	Oxygen	O	8	15·9994	1772
Bismuth	Bi	83	208·980	1739 c.	Palladium	Pd	46	106·4	1803
Boron	B	5	10·811	1808	Phosphorus	P	15	30·9738	1669
Bromine	Br	35	79·909	1826	Platinum	Pt	78	195·09	1735 c.
Cadmium	Cd	48	112·40	1817	Plutonium	Pu	94	(244)	1940
Calcium	Ca	20	40·08	1808	Polonium	Po	84	(210)	1898
Californium	Cf	98	(251)	1950	Potassium	K	19	39·102	1807
Carbon	C	6	12·01115	B C	Praseodymium	Pr	59	140·907	1885
Cerium	Ce	58	140·12	1803	Promethium	Pm	61	(147)	1947
Cesium	Cs	55	132·905	1860	Protactinium	Pa	91	(231)	1917
Chlorine	Cl	17	35·453	1774	Radium	Ra	88	226	1898
Chromium	Cr	24	51·996	1798	Radon	Rn	86	(222)	1900
Cobalt	Co	27	58·9332	1742	Rhenium	Re	75	186·2	1925
Copper	Cu	29	63·54	B C	Rhodium	Rh	45	102·905	1803
Curium	Cm	96	(247)	1944	Rubidium	Rb	37	85·47	1861
Dyprosium	Dy	66	162·50	1886	Ruthenium	Ru	44	101·07	1844
Einsteinium	Es	99	(254)	1955	Samarium	Sm	62	150·35	1879
Erbium	Er	68	167·26	1843	Scandium	Sc	21	44·956	1879
Europium	Eu	63	151·96	1901	Selenium	Se	34	78·96	1818
Fermium	Fm	100	(253)	1955	Silicon	Si	14	28·086	1823
Fluorine	F	9	18·9984	1771	Silver	Ag	47	107·870	B C
Francium	Fr	87	(223)	1939	Sodium	Na	11	22·9898	1807
Gadolinium	Gd	64	157·25	1880	Strontium	Sr	38	87·62	1787
Gallium	Ga	31	69·72	1875	Sulphur	S	16	32·064	B C
Germanium	Ge	32	72·59	1886	Tantalum	Ta	73	180·948	1802
Gold	Au	79	196·967	B C	Technetium	Tc	43	(99)	1937
Hafnium	Hf	72	178·49	1922	Tellurium	Te	52	127·60	1798
Helium	He	2	4·0026	1895	Terbium	Tb	65	158·924	1843
Holmium	Ho	67	164·930	1878	Thallium	Tl	81	204·37	1861
Hydrogen	H	1	1·00797	1766	Thorium	Th	90	232·038	1828
Indium	In	49	114·82	1863	Thulium	Tm	69	168·934	1879
Iodine	I	53	126·9044	1811	Tin	Sn	50	118·69	B C
Iridium	Ir	77	192·2	1804	Titanium	Ti	22	47·90	1791
Iron	Fe	26	55·847	B C	Tungsten	W	74	183·85	1783
Krypton	Kr	36	83·80	1898	Uranium	U	92	238·03	1789
Lanthanum	La	57	138·91	1839	Vanadium	V	23	50·942	1830
Lawrencium	Lw	103	(257)	1961	Xenon	Xe	54	131·30	1898
Lead	Pb	82	207·19	B C	Ytterbium	Yb	70	173·04	1907
Lithium	Li	3	6·939	1817	Yttrium	Y	39	88·905	1794
Lutetium	Lu	71	174·97	1907	Zinc	Zn	30	65·37	1400 c.
Magnesium	Mg	12	24·312	1755	Zirconium	Zr	40	91·22	1789
Manganese	Mn	25	54·9380	1774					
Mendelevium	Md	101	(256)	1955					
Mercury	Hg	80	200·59	B C					

* Value in brackets denotes the mass number either of isotope with the longest-known half life or, for berkelium, californium, lawrencium, polonium, promethium and technetium a better known one.

27

1 Large-scale manufacture of chemicals depends on an accurate knowledge of the relationship between reactants and products, including chemical composition and quantity of product.

2 A knowledge of chemical formulae and reactions is a vital part of the pharmacist's stock-in-trade. Here, a compound is being prepared using the traditional pharmacist's measuring glass.

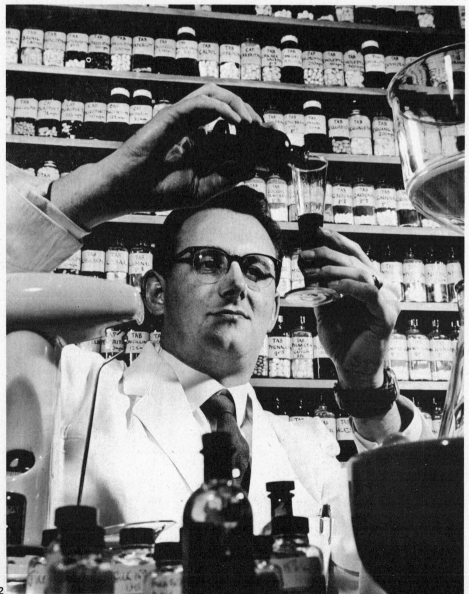

to produce 44 gm of carbon dioxide, one must start with 36 gm of water.

It is not always necessary to deal in even molecular weights. For instance, how much water is needed to produce 66 gm of carbon dioxide? One gram molecular weight of carbon dioxide is 44 gm, so 66 gm is $66 \div 44 = 1\cdot5$ gram molecular weights. Since one gram molecular weight of carbon dioxide requires 36 gm of water, then $1\cdot5$ gram molecular weights require $36 \times 1\cdot5 = 54$ gm of water.

To take another example, 11 gm of carbon dioxide is $11 \div 44 = 0\cdot25$ gram molecular weight. Therefore, in order to produce 11 gm of carbon dioxide, one requires $36 \times 0\cdot25 = 9$ gm of water.

For practice, try this problem (the answer to which is at the end of the article): How many grams of water are required to produce 110 gm of carbon dioxide?

It is apparent that equations tell the chemist quite a lot about chemical reactions. But there is still a lot they don't tell him. The mere writing of a chemical equation does not ensure that the reaction will take place; this must be checked by actual experiment. Nor does the equation tell him under what conditions – high temperature, low temperature, high pressure, low pressure – the reaction will take place, or how fast it will take place. But, if properly written, it does tell him in what 'direction' it takes place.

Equilibrium reactions

In numerous chemical reactions, the reactants (left side of the equation) combine into the products (right side of the equation) and the process is complete. Such reactions are said to be *irreversible,* and are said to 'go to completion'. The 'direction' of the reaction is indicated by replacing the equals sign with an arrow:

$$2Na + 2H_2O \rightarrow 2NaOH + H_2.$$

For many other reactions, however, there is a tendency for the products to decompose almost as soon as they are formed and to become reactants again. These reactions are *reversible*; the reactants and products are said to be in a state of *equilibrium*. These reactions do not go to completion, unless forced to do so by artificial means. Reversible reactions are indicated by double arrows, such as:

$$3H_2 + N_2 \rightleftharpoons 2NH_3.$$

(In actual fact, nearly all chemical reactions are reversible, even those marked with a single arrow, because the products can be forced to break up into reactants by changing the conditions under which the reaction takes place.)

The operation of chemical equations is most easily explained in terms of twentieth-century atomic theory. But most of the ideas underlying their uses, including techniques to prevent reversible reactions from reversing, were developed before 1900. Our debt to these pioneer chemists is still great.

Answer to the problem: 110 gm of carbon dioxide is 110 gm $\div$ 44 gm = $2\cdot5$ gram molecular weights. But 36 gm of water produce one gram molecular weight of carbon dioxide, so $36 \times 2\cdot5 = 90$ gm. The answer is: 90 gm of water are required to produce 110 gm of carbon dioxide.

Acids and alkalis

All liquids in the world are acid, alkali or neutral. Many of their chemical properties — and consequently many of their uses — intimately depend on the category to which they belong.

'TAKE VITRIOL OF CYPRUS, saltpetre, and alum of Yemen; extract the water, heating to redness.' This recipe — or chemical experiment as we should now call it – was written down by an Arabian alchemist in the thirteenth century. But it still works and the product, nitric acid, is still one of the most important acids today. It is used for etching metals, and for making explosives.

Alkalis were also known to the alchemists, who were early experimenters and theorists who established the science of chemistry. In fact the word *alkali* – like alchemy, alcohol, and many others – comes from Arabic (alkali means the ashes of a plant). Potash, an alkali known for hundreds of years, also reveals its origin in its name. It was made by mixing wood ash with water and evaporating the 'liquor' in pots. Today we call it potassium carbonate. Its stronger relative, caustic potash, is potassium hydroxide. It is called 'caustic' because it 'burns' – it can attack and dissolve skin and flesh. Even in weak solutions, alkalis have a characteristic 'soapy' feel to the skin.

Simple definition

Today most chemists use the following simple working definitions of acids and alkalis: an acid is a substance which generates hydrogen ions (H^+), and an alkali is a substance which generates hydroxyl ions (OH^-). To understand just what these definitions mean, we will follow the way in which chemists have arrived at them and, as we go, like chemists, find out some of the properties which make these compounds interesting to the scientist and important in technology and

Acids and alkalis have been studied almost from antiquity. Here, a medieval alchemist employs four different acids in a vain attempt to turn base metals into gold.

the industry of a modern economy.

Early chemists found that acids have the property of being able to dissolve metals. For instance they found that hydrochloric acid dissolves zinc. (They called this acid 'spirits of salt' because they made it from common salt by a distillation process similar to that used for nitric acid.) The resulting solution, called 'killed spirits of salt', we now know contains zinc chloride. In fact, acids were often named after their corrosive effects on metals. Nitric acid was called *aqua fortis* – 'strong water'. A mixture of nitric and hydrochloric acids was called *aqua regia* – 'royal water' – because it can dissolve the noble metal, gold. The origin of sulphuric acid was also reflected in its name: *oil of vitriol* (a 'vitriol' is what we now call a sulphate).

What these early chemists did not know was that the fizzing which takes place when a metal dissolves in acid is caused by

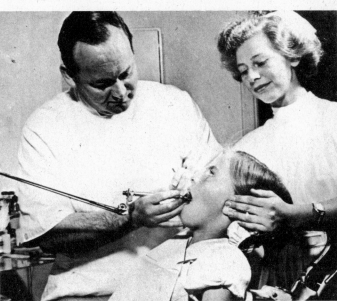

1 Acids and alkalis appear everywhere, sometimes in the most unlikely places. The painful irritation of a bee sting is caused from acid injected into the skin. By contrast, the sting of a wasp injects an alkali into the skin, but to the victim the result is painful, acid or alkali.

2 Acids formed in the mouth, usually from eating sugar, are believed to be a primary cause of cavities and other dental problems.

the evolution of a gas; the gas which is produced is hydrogen. Zinc dissolves in hydrochloric acid to give zinc chloride and hydrogen. Iron dissolves in sulphuric acid to give ferrous sulphate and hydrogen.

Already we have some information about what acids are. They dissolve metals to form salts, and they contain hydrogen. Now, let us see if we can get a similar simple definition of alkalis by considering some of their chemical reactions, and so get a clearer idea of the differences between these two types of compounds.

If caustic potash (potassium hydroxide) is added to hydrochloric acid, a salt is again formed. (Remember a salt is a substance formed when the hydrogen of an acid is replaced by a metal.) The salt is potassium chloride, and this time no hydrogen is evolved. We know the hydrochloric acid contains hydrogen and potassium chloride does not, so where has the hydrogen gone? Since we can find no other chemical substance in the salt solution, the hydrogen must have formed water itself.

This reaction can be written in the form of a chemical equation:

$$KOH + HCl \rightarrow KCl + H_2O.$$

It tempts us to define an alkali as a substance that reacts with an acid to form a salt and water. However, consider the following equation:

$$CuO + H_2SO_4 \rightarrow CuSO_4 + H_2O.$$

This tells us that copper oxide (CuO) dissolves in sulphuric acid to form copper sulphate (a salt) and water. So is copper oxide an alkali? The answer to this question must be 'no'. Copper oxide is a harmless insoluble black solid, not in the least bit caustic, as are the things we call alkalis.

Chemists have solved this apparent anomaly by introducing a new word: *base*. We can retain our tentative definition above, but say that a *base* is a substance which reacts with an acid to form a salt and water. Chemists reasoned that the base in the earlier reaction between potassium hydroxide and hydrochloric

1 Acids turn blue litmus paper red, but leave red litmus unchanged. Alkalis have the opposite effect. No changes occur in neutral solutions.

acid is potassium *oxide,* which should take part in a reaction given by the equation:

$$K_2O + 2HCl \rightarrow 2KCl + H_2O.$$

The difference between a base such as potassium oxide and one such as copper oxide is that potassium oxide dissolves in water (to give potassium hydroxide (KOH)) whereas copper oxide will not dissolve in water. An alkali, then, is a base which dissolves in water. We can also come full circle and re-define an acid as a substance with which a base reacts to form a salt and water.

These simple definitions of acids and bases worked fairly well until more intensive study revealed reactions which cast doubts upon them. For instance, in 1807 Sir Humphry Davy discovered that sodium dissolves in water to give hydrogen. Is then water an acid? Later experimenters found that some metals, such as zinc and aluminium, dissolve in alkalis to generate hydrogen. But was not the ability to dissolve metals with the liberation of hydrogen part of the definition of an *acid,* not of a base?

Obviously, our simple definitions need modifying in the light of modern knowledge. The first development after the simple ideas came from an attempt to define acids and bases in terms of what they are *before* they take part in a reaction. The ionic theory, which describes how inorganic chemical substances *dissociate* (split up) into ions on being dissolved in water, provided the first clue. For instance, consider the dissociations of several acids in aqueous solutions:

$$HCl \rightleftharpoons H^+ + Cl^- \quad \text{(hydrochloric)}$$
$$HNO_3 \rightleftharpoons H^+ + NO_3^- \quad \text{(nitric)}$$
$$H_2SO_4 \rightleftharpoons 2H^+ + SO_4^{--} \quad \text{(sulphuric)}$$

The common factor is the formation of hydrogen ions, and an acid is a substance which dissociates to give hydrogen ions in solution.

Similarly, the dissociation of a base such

2 Colour indicators give a good approximation of acid or alkali concentration by the colours they take on when dropped into a solution.

as sodium hydroxide (caustic soda):

$$NaOH \rightleftharpoons OH^- + Na^+$$

leads us to define a base as a substance which dissociates to give hydroxyl (OH$^-$) ions.

More recently this theory has been extended by J.N. Brønsted and T.M. Lowry who in 1923 independently proposed that an acid be defined as a substance which has a tendency to lose a hydrogen ion, and a base as one which has a tendency to gain a hydrogen ion. According to this theory, the base becomes the non-hydrogen part of the acid and is known as the acid's *conjugate* base. Thus when water dissociates according to the equation

$$H_2O \rightleftharpoons H^+ + OH^-$$

it is behaving as a sort of acid. And in the reaction between zinc and sodium hydroxide:

$$Zn + 2NaOH \rightarrow Na_2ZnO_2 + H_2,$$

the sodium hydroxide is also behaving in a similar way (the conjugate base being NaO$^-$, the non-hydrogen part).

Hydrogen ion concentration

For most practical purposes, however, we can distinguish between acids and bases by saying acids are hydrogen-ion (H$^+$) generators, and bases are hydroxyl-ion (OH$^-$) generators. This distinction also gives us a way of measuring the strength of acids in terms of the number of hydrogen ions produced in solution. Unfortunately, these concentrations, measured in grams of hydrogen ions per litre, are very small.

For example, dilute hydrochloric acid may have a hydrogen ion concentration of a thousandth or even a millionth of a gram ion per litre. Scientists often write small fractions such as these in index form, a thousandth being 10^{-3}, and a millionth 10^{-6}. In 1909, the chemist S.P.

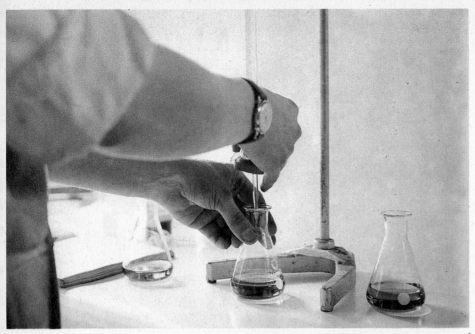

1 Acids are neutralized by introducing alkalis. Conversely, alkalis neutralize acids. A colour indicator shows when the process is completed. **2** Most solutions contain both acid and alkali ions. From pH 0 to 7, acid ions predominate; from pH 7 to 14, alkali ions predominate. A pH 7 solution is neutral. **3** A pH meter mechanically indicates the acid or alkali concentration of a solution.

Sørenson suggested that hydrogen ion concentrations be expressed in terms of the index, neglecting the minus sign. This quantity corresponds to the negative logarithm of the concentration and is given the symbol pH. For example, a hydrogen ion concentration of 10^{-3} gram ion per litre (a thousandth) corresponds to a pH of 3.

We said earlier that water dissociates into hydrogen ions and hydroxyl ions according to the equation:

$$H_2O \rightleftharpoons H^+ + OH^-.$$

The concentration of hydrogen ions produced is 10^{-7} gram ion per litre (and so is the concentration of hydroxyl ions), corresponding to a pH of 7. Since water on its own is neither acidic nor alkaline, because the concentrations of acidic (H^+) and alkaline (OH^-) ions are equal, a pH of 7 corresponds to a *neutral* solution. Acid solutions have a pH of *less* than 7, and alkaline solutions have a pH of more than 7. Strong acids have a low pH, strong alkalis have a high pH.

It is important to remember that the pH scale is a logarithmic one, so that a difference of one unit on the scale corresponds to a tenfold difference in concentration. For instance, an acid of pH 2 is ten times stronger than an acid of pH 3, and an alkali of pH 12 is a thousand times as strong as an alkali of pH 9.

One of the problems facing an analytical chemist given an unknown solution is to find out whether it is acid or alkaline and, more important, how concentrated an acid or how concentrated an alkali it is. The answer to this problem, like so many in chemistry, was found practically before the modern theory of acids and alkalis developed. It has long been known that the colours of certain vegetable dyes depend on whether they are an acid or alkali. For instance, green gooseberries become red when made into jam which is an acidic medium.

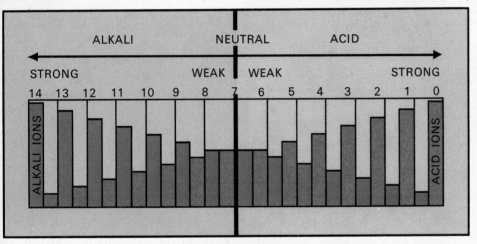

Use of indicators

A substance which changes colour in this way is called an *indicator*. Other examples found in the kitchen are the yellow substance turmeric, which changes red in alkalis, and purple cabbage, which changes red when pickled in the acid of vinegar. Vegetable dye indicators commonly used in chemistry laboratories include litmus and congo red. Neutral litmus is a purple colour: it changes bright red in acids and bright blue in alkalis. The colour changes of congo red are just the opposite (red in alkali, blue in acid).

Other important indicators consist of synthetic organic chemicals, such as methyl orange and phenolphthalein. Methyl orange is yellow in alkalis and red

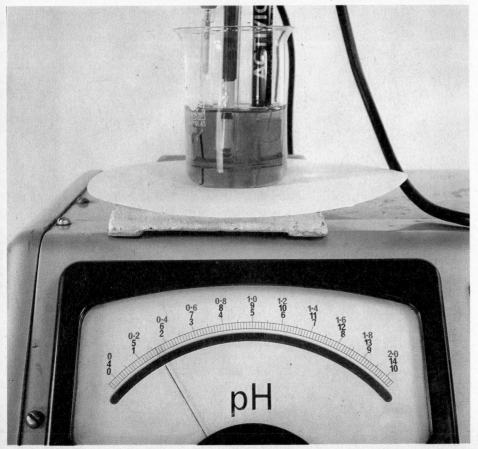

31

1 'Salt' is a general name for a compound which results from an acid-alkali neutralization. The most common salt is sodium chloride, often extracted from sea water by evaporation.

2 Acid soils are often 'sweetened' by spreading lime (calcium hydroxide) before planting. The lime reduces or completely neutralizes the acid properties of the ground.

replacing the hydrogen of an acid by a metal. For example, magnesium sulphate (Epsom salts) may be made by dissolving magnesium in sulphuric acid:

$$Mg + H_2SO_4 \rightarrow MgSO_4 + H_2.$$

A few salts may be made by direct combination of the component elements. For instance, ferric chloride may be made from iron filings and chlorine gas, and mercury iodide may be made by grinding iodine crystals in liquid mercury.

But by far the most important laboratory method of making salts is called *double decomposition*. This is an extension of the acid-base neutralization idea in which two compounds are mixed and the ions persuaded to 'change partners'. The method is useful in practice only when one of the salts formed is insoluble, otherwise the separation of the products is difficult and time-consuming. For example, if we mix solutions of lead nitrate and potassium iodide (both colourless and soluble salts), the soluble salt potassium nitrate and the bright-yellow insoluble salt lead iodide are formed. The equation for the reaction is:

$$Pb(NO_3)_2 + 2KI \rightarrow PbI_2 \downarrow + 2KNO_3.$$

lead   potassium   lead   potassium
nitrate   iodide   iodide   nitrate

The downward-pointing arrow alongside the formula for lead iodide indicates that this salt is insoluble and falls to the bottom of the solution as a precipitate.

These precipitation reactions are also useful in analytical chemistry for identifying metal salts. For instance, the reaction just described is a useful way of detecting any soluble lead salts. If a chemist takes a solution he suspects contains lead and adds potassium iodide to it, the formation of a yellow precipitate immediately confirms his suspicions. A similar set of reactions of silver salts is used to distinguish between solutions of chlorides, bromides, iodides – a knotty problem often facing the analytical chemist. Silver chloride, silver bromide and silver iodide are all insoluble and furthermore have different colours (the chloride is pure white, the bromide is a creamy colour, and the iodide is pale yellow).

The three classes of compounds described in this article, acids, alkalis and salts, are of immense industrial and biological importance. Acids are used to etch metals, make explosives and fertilizers, refine petroleum, and make paper, plastics, drugs and detergents. In fact, a useful yardstick for measuring a country's industrial capacity is merely to note how much sulphuric acid it uses in a year. Similarly alkalis are used for making rayon and soap. Salts are essential to living creatures – the sea is full of salts – and provide such diverse products as medicines and pigments. But by applying his theoretical knowledge, the chemist can devise new methods of making established compounds, and can provide the world with hundreds of new compounds from the subtle yellow-orange cadmium sulphide pigments now used by painters in oils to powerful rocket propellants and detonating explosives.

in acids, and phenolphthalein is red in alkalis and colourless in acids. For convenience, many indicators are available in the form of dyed paper strips. To test whether a liquid is acid or alkaline, the chemist merely dips in a strip of indicator paper and notes the colour change, if any. Other papers are available which are dyed with wide range indicators. These have a characteristic colour at a given pH so that it is possible to distinguish between pH of, say, 2 and 3.

Indicators are also important in neutralization reactions (acid+base→salt+water). To use this as a method of preparing the salt it is important to add just the right amount of acid exactly to neutralize the base. To do this, the chemist adds the acid gradually while testing the solution with an indicator. When the indicator just changes colour he knows the base has all been neutralized.

Indicators are also put to a similar use in analytical chemistry to find the strength of a solution of acid or alkali. For instance, to find the strength of a sample of alkali, a chemist can gradually add to it an acid of *known* strength and stop adding when exact neutralization is shown by an indicator. From a knowledge of the volumes of solutions used and the strength of the acid, he can easily calculate the strength of the alkali. Because it involves measuring volumes, this branch of chemistry is called *volumetric* analysis.

Neutralization of an acid by a base is not the only way of preparing salts. As we have seen, they can also be made by

The helpful halogens

The halogens are a family of Nature's most reactive elements. In their free state, they are all deadly poisons, yet their compounds comprise an enormous range of Man's most useful materials.

ON THE EVENING of 22 April 1915, the British and French troops who were dug in on the banks of the River Somme saw a large green cloud drifting towards them from the German trenches. Some ran. Many of those who did not died a horrible, choking death. Ironically, however, some of the very same chemical properties that make chlorine a deadly killer, at the same time make it vitally important to modern technology.

Chlorine is one of five elements showing similar chemical properties which make up the *halogen* family. The other members are fluorine, bromine, iodine and the man-made radioactive element astatine, first produced by nuclear bombardment in 1940.

Patterns for comparison

Astatine has been prepared only in very small quantities and rapidly decays into another element. Since astatine is still a chemical curiosity and of no commercial value at present, it is not normally considered in a discussion of the halogens.

Halogens are all group VII elements in the periodic table and thus lack only one electron in their outermost shell. By accepting an electron in a chemical reaction, they can achieve the extremely stable structure associated with a completely filled electron shell, so they tend to be chemically highly active. The lower the atomic weight of a halogen, the more active it is. Physically, the halogens show a gradation of properties: fluorine and chlorine are gases; bromine is one of only two elements which are liquids at room temperature (the other is mercury); and

Chlorine gas can be a choking killer to anyone who inhales it. These soldiers show the after-effects of a gas attack in the First World War.

iodine is a crystalline solid.

Even the naming of the elements follows a pattern. Their names are all derived from words which tell something of the source or properties of the element. Fluorine comes from the Latin *fluo* meaning to flow, from the use of the mineral fluor or fluor-spar (calcium fluoride) as a flux, to enable solder to flow more easily. Chlorine is named after the Greek word *chloros* meaning green, the colour of the gas. Anyone who has smelled bromine will approve of its derivation from the Greek *bromos* meaning stench. And finally iodine is named after the Greek for violet, the colour of iodine vapour.

The halogens are alike in other respects, too. They are all poisonous, though used in small quantities this property is turned to good effect. Chlorine is used for disinfecting drinking water and swimming baths; a solution of iodine in alcohol, called tincture of iodine, has long been used for disinfecting wounds.

The halogens are all non-metals which combine more or less vigorously with metals to form a series of salts called *halides* – fluorides, chlorides, bromides and iodides. In fact, the word *halogen* itself comes from the Greek word meaning *salt producer*. Aqueous solutions of halogen hydrides (compounds with hydrogen) are all strong acids, being hydrofluoric, hydrochloric, hydrobromic and hydriodic acids.

Fluorine is the most reactive of the halogens, if not the most reactive of all

elements. It was not finally extracted from one of its compounds until 1886, when the French chemist Henri Moissan (1852–1907) prepared it by the electrolysis of a freezing solution of the salt, potassium hydrogen fluoride (KHF_2) in hydrogen fluoride (HF). He used platinum vessels and electrodes, because fluorine attacks practically everything else, including the material from which chemists make most of their apparatus, glass.

At a temperature of -187.9 °C., fluorine condenses from a pale yellow gas to a liquid which, at -223 °C., freezes to a solid. Even at this low temperature, it reacts explosively with liquid hydrogen to form hydrogen fluoride (HF). Fluorine also combines with all the other elements, with the exception of oxygen, nitrogen and the rare gases (helium, neon, argon and family).

Facts about fluorine

Fluorine reacts with water to give a mixture of products including oxygen, ozone and hydrogen peroxide. As a result, a solution of fluorine and water is a powerful oxidizing agent.

The explosive reaction between hydrogen and fluorine is not used as a method of making hydrogen fluoride, which is generally prepared by the safer and more convenient action of hot concentrated sulphuric acid on calcium fluoride using lead or platinum vessels:

$$CaF_2 + H_2SO_4 \rightarrow CaSO_4 + H_2F_2\uparrow .$$

The product of this reaction is a *polymeric gas*, a mixture of various different forms of hydrogen fluoride. The formula for the gas

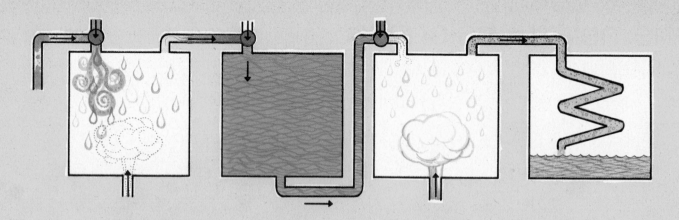

is generally written as H_2F_2. Below 19·5 °C. it condenses to a corrosive liquid (HF), which can produce painful and very dangerous wounds on the skin. It is used for etching glass and has recently found application in producing uranium hexafluoride, a gaseous compound from which the various forms (isotopes) of uranium are separated.

In water, hydrogen fluoride dissociates into hydrogen ions (H^+) and fluoride ions (F^-), giving a solution of hydrofluoric acid. Other ions such as F_2H^- are also present and important, because without them hydrofluoric acid would be a weak acid. As it is, hydrofluoric acid attacks glass and dissolves it, so the acid has to be kept in rubber or plastic bottles. Its salts, the fluorides, are also poisonous (about a tenth of a gram being a fatal dose), but about one part per million may be added to drinking water (fluoridation) where it is claimed that it promotes healthy teeth. Higher concentrations cause brown mottling and staining of teeth, which are characteristic of people who live in districts where the natural concentration of fluorides in the water is high.

Chemistry of chlorine

Organic fluorine compounds include the Freons, hydrocarbons with some or all of their hydrogen replaced by fluorine and chlorine. They are highly volatile liquids used as the fluids in refrigerators and as the 'propellants' in aerosol sprays. Long chains of fluorinated hydrocarbons form a series of heat-resistant plastics known as Fluon, Teflon and PTFE (polytetrafluoroethylene) used, among other purposes, for making gaskets and lining 'non-stick' frying pans.

Unlike inorganic fluorine compounds, all these substances are non-poisonous. This is even more remarkable because the analogous chlorine compounds are mostly toxic. For example, animals survive quite

1 Seaweed is an important commercial source of iodine, which is extracted from the ash of the seaweed after it has been dried and burned.
2 Plastics find uses everywhere. One of the most useful plastics is chlorine-based PVC, here fashioned into a colourful, light-weight raincoat.

happily breathing a mixture of 80 per cent fluoroform and 20 per cent oxygen, whereas a mixture containing less than one per cent of chloroform is generally lethal. However, in lower concentrations, chloroform once found use as an anaesthetic. It has long since been replaced by less dangerous anaesthetic compounds.

In terms of the number of years since its discovery, the oldest of the halogens is chlorine. It was discovered in 1774 by the Swedish chemist Karl Scheele (1742–86), the same year that Joseph Priestley in Britain discovered oxygen. Chlorine is the most abundant of the halogens, occurring (in the form of its compounds) as nearly 500 parts per million in the Earth's crust and as 15,000 parts per million in sea water. It is a choking greenish-yellow gas which condenses to a liquid at −34·1 °C. and becomes solid at −101 °C. As little as one part per million in the air can be harmful. More than 0·01 per cent (100 parts per million) in the air is lethal.

Preparing chlorine

The preparations of chlorine depend on releasing it from chlorides either by oxidizing agents or by electrolysis. The common laboratory preparation, and an early commercial method, used the oxidizing action of manganese dioxide on hot hydrochloric acid:

$$MnO_2 + 4HCl \rightarrow MnCl_2 + 2H_2O + Cl_2.$$

A more convenient oxidizing agent is potassium permanganate, which works with cold acid. But the common industrial process uses the electrolysis of sodium chloride (common salt) solution to form hydrogen, chloride and sodium hydroxide:

$$2NaCl + 2H_2O \rightarrow 2NaOH + H_2 + Cl_2.$$

This process is generally used to manufacture sodium hydroxide (caustic soda), and chlorine is a useful by-product. Unfortunately, chlorine reacts with sodium hydroxide and so the electrolytic cell used in the process has to be specially designed to prevent the products from mixing.

In the mercury-cathode cell, the sodium liberated by electrolysis (which normally reacts with water to form sodium

BLEACHING
pulp for paper, certain textiles

WATER PURIFICATION
swimming pools, drinking water

MANUFACTURING
dyes, drugs, cellulose, acetate

REFINING
oil, sugar

CHEMICAL WARFARE
poison gas, explosives

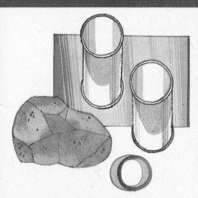

METALLURGY
extracting metals, tin, gold

FIRE EXTINGUISHERS

CLEANING FLUIDS

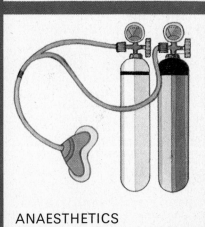

ANAESTHETICS

Chlorine is by far the most useful of the halogens. From purifying water for both drinking and swimming to bleaching paper and cloth, this element appears nearly everywhere in daily life.

hydroxide) dissolves in the mercury to form an alloy, called an *amalgam*. This is run off into a tank of water in which the sodium reacts to form sodium hydroxide and water, and the mercury is ready to be used again. Meanwhile chlorine is liberated at the carbon anodes.

In the porous diaphragm cell, the sodium chloride solution is contained in a porous pot. Again the anode is made of carbon, but this time the cathode takes the form of steel net covering the outside of the pot. Chlorine is produced at the anode, and sodium hydroxide formation accompanies the discharge of hydrogen ions on the steel cathode.

Although not quite as reactive as fluorine, chlorine is still a highly reactive element. It combines directly with all the elements except carbon, oxygen, nitrogen and the rare gases. It is an oxidizing agent and is used as a disinfectant and as a bleach for cotton and paper. Powdered antimony or thin copper foil bursts into flame when dropped into chlorine, and burning magnesium continues to burn in the gas, both metals forming their chlorides.

Chlorine compounds

Note that this 'burning' is not true combustion – which is generally defined as direct combination with oxygen – although it is chemically a form of oxidation because the term oxidation is used to refer to chemical reactions involving a loss of electrons whether oxygen is involved or not. Copper and antimony lose

electrons in their reactions with chlorine.

With water, chlorine reacts to give a mixture of hydrochloric (HCl) and hypochlorous (HOCl) acids:

$$H_2O + Cl_2 \rightleftharpoons HCl + HOCl.$$

Hypochlorous acid is a weak acid, but it is a powerful oxidizing agent and it is to this substance that chlorine owes its bleaching power.

If chlorine is passed into a cold dilute solution of a caustic alkali such as sodium or potassium hydroxide, the corresponding *hypochlorite*, a salt containing a hypochlorite ion (OCl⁻) is produced:

$$2NaOH + Cl_2 \rightarrow NaCl + H_2O + NaOCl.$$

Potassium hypochlorite was produced in this way by the French chemist Claude Berthollet (1748–1822), who called the solution 'Eau de Javelle' and sold it as bleach. Sodium hypochlorite is still sold as a bleach and as a disinfectant solution for drains and lavatories or, under another trade name, for sterilizing babies' bottles.

Several years after Berthollet's success with Eau de Javelle, other chemists discovered that chlorine reacts with lime – the cheapest of all alkalis – to produce a compound called *bleaching powder*. The composition of the powder is not fixed, but it is generally given the formula $CaOCl_2$ which corresponds to a mixture of calcium hypochlorite $Ca(OCl)_2$ and calcium chloride $(CaCl_2)$. A factory for making bleaching powder (or chloride of lime as it was sometimes called) was opened in 1799 near Glasgow by the British chemist Charles Tennant. In the presence of acid, the powder releases chlorine, which may be used for bleaching cloth and indeed made an essential contribution to Britain's textile trade in the nineteenth century.

With hot strong caustic alkalis, chlorine forms a *chlorate* (containing ClO_3^-) and a chloride:

$$6KOH + 3Cl_2 \rightarrow 5KCl + 3H_2O + KClO_3.$$

Chlorates are also oxidizing agents and are used in matches, rocket fuels and weed killer. Tablets of potassium chlorate may be sucked to oxidize bacteria in mouth ulcers or sore throats.

The reaction between chlorine and hydrogen is only slightly less violent than that between fluorine and hydrogen and takes place explosively in the presence of sunlight. The gas formed, hydrogen chloride, is made in this way commercially by 'burning' a stream of hydrogen in an atmosphere of chlorine. Remember that these two gases are by-products of the electrolytic preparation of sodium hydroxide from common salt, and the two processes are generally carried out at the same plant.

In the laboratory, hydrogen chloride is generally made by the action of hot concentrated sulphuric acid on sodium chloride:

$$NaCl + H_2SO_4 \rightarrow NaHSO_4 + HCl,$$

which was the process used by early alchemists to make the gas. The vapour or distillate was called a 'spirit' and the solution in water was called 'spirit of salts'. Today we call such a solution hydrochloric acid.

Bromine and iodine

Hydrochloric acid is used for 'pickling' steel to remove oxides prior to finishing processes such as tin plating and galvanizing. A solution of zinc in the acid (that is, zinc chloride) is used as a flux by plumbers who still call the liquid 'killed spirit of salt'. It is used, together with chlorine, for making chlorinated organic compounds from which are made plastics such as PVC (polyvinyl chloride) and artificial rubbers based on chloroprene (dichlorobutadiene). Other important organic compounds of chlorine include a host of solvents such as methylene chloride, carbon tetrachloride, chloroform and trichlorethylene, the last two of which are also used as anaesthetics.

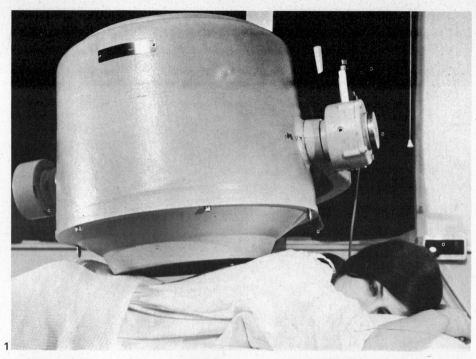

1 Radioactive fluorine-18 injected into the body concentrates in bone lesions more strongly than in normal bone. A photograph taken with a gamma-ray camera reveals the location of the lesion.
2 The human body requires only minute traces of iodine, but its absence becomes dramatically evident in a neck-bulging goitre.
3 Outside wall panels of PVC, a chlorine compound, provide a modern house with colour, a protective surface and improved heat insulation.

Insecticides such as gammexane and DDT also contain chlorine, as do antiseptics based on chlorinated phenols.

Bromine, the liquid halogen, was discovered by A.-J. Balard (1802–76) in 1826. It is produced commercially by pumping chlorine into solutions of bromides (obtained from sea water or salt mines):

$$2NaBr + Cl_2 \rightarrow 2NaCl + Br_2.$$

Every year, 200 million tons of sea water are treated in this way. Bromine is produced in the laboratory by treating a mixture of potassium bromide and manganese dioxide with hot concentrated sulphuric acid.

Most of the bromine manufactured is used as ethylene dibromide with tetraethyl lead to make an 'anti-knock' ingredient for petrol. The bromine compound is necessary to prevent metallic lead from being deposited in the engine. Bromides have been used as sedatives in medicine and to make light-sensitive emulsions in photography.

Last, and in many ways least, of the halogens is iodine. It is the least abundant (about 0·3 part per million of the Earth's crust), the least reactive, and probably the least useful. It was discovered in 1812 by B. Courtois (1777–1838). It was for a long time made from the ashes of kelp, a kind of seaweed, which contains up to one per cent iodine. But most is made commercially from Chile saltpetre, which contains the salt, sodium iodate, as an impurity. Solid iodine forms glistening black crystals which vaporize above 187°C. to form clouds of violet vapour.

Iodine is an essential trace element in the body for the correct functioning of the thyroid gland. Today iodine is generally added to table salt to ensure that everyone has sufficient in his diet.

As a family, then, the halogens, the 'salt producers', are the most reactive of the non-metals. They give rise to a host of compounds for practically every application, not forgetting the most common salt of all, sodium chloride.

Elements of fire and brimstone

Thrown up by long-dead volcanoes, phosphorus and sulphur are known for their inflammability. Their spectacular properties are only part of their role in modern chemistry and industry.

PHOSPHORUS AND SULPHUR are two elements that most young chemists find particularly exciting. Phosphorus may be seen as cream-coloured waxy sticks resting safely inside a bottle of water on the laboratory shelf. If a few chips are cut off with a pen-knife and exposed to the air, they start to smoke and soon catch fire. Sulphur is familiar as a bright yellow powder called 'flowers of sulphur'. When heated, the powder melts to a straw-coloured liquid and catches fire with a light blue flame, producing sulphur dioxide gas with its characteristic choking pungent smell.

Highly inflammable elements

It is probably these fiery properties that make most people familiar with phosphorus and sulphur, as these elements are both contained in matches. Early matches invented in about 1830, contained the 'yellow' phosphorus described above. They were not safe, however; yellow phosphorus is poisonous and people working in match factories contracted a disease of the jawbone called 'phossy-jaw'. As a result, the manufacture of these matches was stopped. Modern friction or 'strike-anywhere' matches contain a safe compound of phosphorus and sulphur called *phosphorus sesquisulphide,* with potassium chlorate to provide the oxygen for combustion. Safety matches contain sulphur and potassium chlorate in the heads and red phosphorus (a much less flammable and non-poisonous form of phosphorus) in the striking strip of the box or book.

Phosphorus and sulphur have in common far more than just being essential ingredients of matches. As chemical elements, they have great similarities in their properties, both forming similar kinds of chemical compounds. This is unusual because they occupy different groups in the Periodic Table – phosphorus is in group VB with nitrogen, arsenic, antimony and bismuth, and sulphur is in group VIB with oxygen, selenium, tellurium and polonium. The elements of a single group generally resemble each other in their reactions with other elements, and similarities between elements of different groups are less common. But phosphorus and sulphur do stand side by side in the Periodic Table – the atomic number of phosphorus is 15 and that of

1 Sulphuric acid is vital to many modern industries, including textiles and explosives. It is manufactured from sulphur in large, highly automated plants such as this one in West Africa.
2 Sulphur occurs as the natural element in many parts of the world. Mines such as this one in Sicily have been a prime source for hundreds of years.

sulphur is 16 – and the similarities between them are sufficient for them to be considered together.

Phosphorus is among the most active of the elements and consequently is never found free (as the element itself) in nature. It occurs mostly as calcium phosphate, both as a mineral and in the skeletons of all vertebrate animals. Large deposits of *apatite*, a mineral containing calcium phosphate and calcium fluoride, are found in the United States; these deposits were probably formed of animal remains many millions of years ago. Phosphorus also occurs in nature in cells, muscles and nerve tissues, and so is an important element in food. Cheese, milk, egg yolk, soya beans and wheat all contain comparatively large amounts of phosphorus. Phosphorus is also important in the metabolism of plants, and bone meal and superphosphate fertilizers are given to crops and flowers such as roses to provide them with essential phosphorus.

The phosphorus that we take in with our food is later excreted in urine as compounds with other elements. The element itself was first isolated by the reduction of the phosphorus compounds in urine by the German alchemist Henning Brandt in 1669. The element is now manufactured in large quantities by reducing phosphate minerals such as apatite with sand (silica) and coke (carbon) in electric furnaces. The overall chemical reaction that occurs is as follows:

$$2Ca_3(PO_4)_2 + 6SiO_2 + 10C \rightarrow$$
calcium   *silica*   *carbon*
phosphate

$$P_4 + 6CaSiO_3 + 10CO.$$
phos-   *calcium*   *carbon*
phorus   *silicate*   *monoxide*

The phosphorus is produced as a vapour and is condensed in water to form yellow phosphorus.

Allotropes of phosphorus

Solid phosphorus exists in three main forms or *allotropes*, a property it shares with sulphur, which has two allotropes. Phosphorus condenses from the vapour to a liquid at 280 °C. and this liquid solidifies at 44 °C. to a soft and waxy solid, called *yellow* phosphorus. The commercial phosphorus seen in chemistry laboratories is slightly impure and is a cream colour. Yellow phosphorus ignites spontaneously in air at about 40 °C. and so is always kept under water. It dissolves in solvents such as benzene and carbon disulphide. Yellow phosphorus is poisonous and can be seen to glow in the dark – it is phosphorescent.

If yellow phosphorus is heated (out of contact with the air of course) to about 250 °C., it changes into *red* phosphorus. This form of phosphorus does not catch fire in air unless heated to more than 240 °C. Red phosphorus is also non-poisonous and it is not phosphorescent; furthermore it does not dissolve in any known solvents. All these properties are

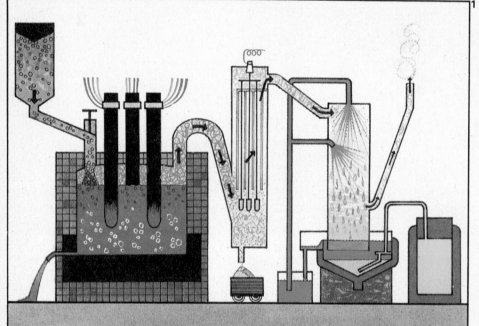

1 Yellow phosphorus is extracted electrolytically from calcium phosphate. Because it ignites in air, great care must be taken to exclude air from the equipment.

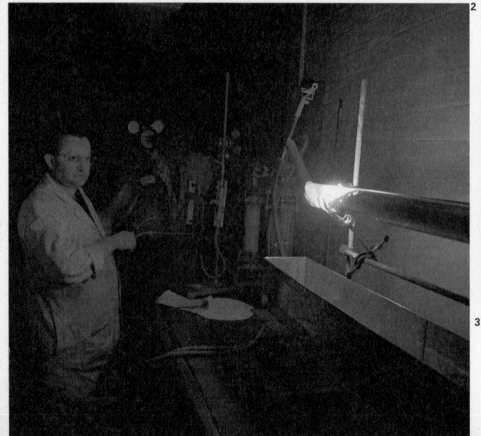

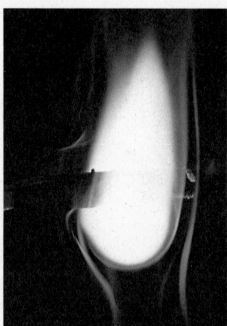

2 Both allotropes of phosphorus (red and yellow) burn readily in air to give phosphorus pentoxide. Under laboratory conditions the rate of combustion can be strictly controlled.
3 Red phosphorus is an ingredient of matches. At one time, yellow phosphorus was used, but it is highly poisonous and caused disease among workers in match factories.

to be expected as energy is liberated when yellow phosphorus changes to red phosphorus – red phosphorus is a 'less energetic', more stable form of the element and consequently its reactions are less vigorous than those of yellow phosphorus.

The third allotrope of phosphorus is black phosphorus. It is made by heating yellow phosphorus under high pressure in an inert atmosphere. Black phosphorus is the most stable form of the element and can be ignited in air only with difficulty.

Making crops grow

There are few uses for these various forms of phosphorus as free elements. As already mentioned, red phosphorus is used in safety matches. The main importance of phosphorus is as a plant food. The insoluble calcium phosphate in ground bones, or bone meal, is absorbed by the plants only very slowly. A more efficient fertilizer is superphosphate, which contains soluble phosphorus compounds called *acid phosphates*. Superphosphate fertilizers are made in large quantities by reacting phosphate rock or bone ash with dilute sulphuric acid:

$$Ca_3(PO_4)_2 + 2H_2SO_4 \rightarrow Ca(H_2PO_4)_2 + 2CaSO_4.$$

The calcium dihydrogen phosphate produced is soluble and therefore acts quickly as a fertilizer. Another phosphate fertilizer is calcium metaphosphate, $Ca(PO_3)_2$. This substance contains a greater proportion of phosphorus than does calcium dihydrogen phosphate and so is more economical to transport; it forms calcium dihydrogen phosphate when it reacts with water in the soil:

$$Ca(PO_3)_2 + 2H_2O \rightarrow Ca(H_2PO_4)_2.$$

Sulphur, unlike phosphorus, occurs in the free state wherever there is or has been volcanic activity. For this reason, it has been known since the beginnings of recorded history, when people held volcanoes in only slightly more awe than we do nowadays. Four thousand years ago, sulphur dioxide was used to bleach cloth. Sulphur was symbolic of fire to the

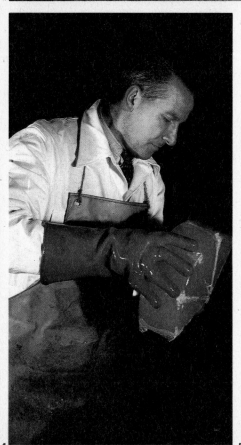

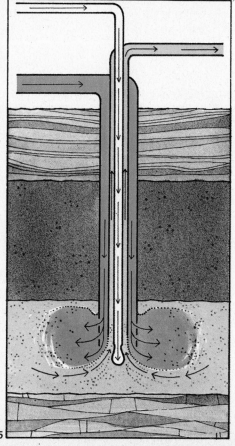

1 In plants, deficiency of phosphorus adversely affects the organism's ability to manufacture food by photosynthesis. This condition shows as discoloration of the leaves.
2 Cinnabar (mercury sulphide) occurs in many parts of the world, mainly in the United States, Italy, Canada and Spain. It is the chief source of mercury.
3 Packing material must be used to seal the gap around the electrodes in an electric arc phosphorus furnace. This prevents the escape of phosphorus in furnace gases.
4 Molten yellow phosphorus is cast into wedges or 'cheeses'. It must be stored under water as it ignites in contact with air.
5 In the United States, sulphur is extracted from underground beds by the Frasch process. Water and steam, at a temperature higher than the melting point of sulphur, are pumped down the outer pipe. The molten sulphur is then blown to the surface by hot compressed air forced down the central tube. The sulphur extracted in this way is so pure that for most purposes it needs no further refining.

alchemists and its common name 'brimstone' has long been associated with fire. Sulphur has also been affecting people's lives since the Middle Ages as an ingredient of gunpowder, together with saltpetre and carbon.

The largest deposits of free sulphur in the world are in Louisiana and Texas in the United States – they account for more than 80 per cent of the world's output. Rock-like deposits of sulphur also occur in Sicily near Mount Etna. Alternative sources of sulphur to this native sulphur are the various metallic sulphide ores, from which sulphur is obtained as a by-product in the production of the metal.

Pumping sulphur from the Earth

The free sulphur in the United States lies in soft beds underground and cannot be mined in the conventional way. Early attempts to do so failed, but in the 1890s an ingenious method for obtaining the sulphur was invented by Herman Frasch. In the Frasch process, wells are drilled down to the sulphur beds and superheated water and compressed air pumped down. The water, being under pressure, is heated above 115 °C. (the melting point of sulphur). The liquid sulphur is then forced to the surface by the pressure of the compressed air.

The liquid sulphur that is obtained is 99 per cent pure and solidifies to one of the two allotropic forms. This form is called *monoclinic* sulphur and consists of thin needle-like crystals. Monoclinic sulphur is stable only above a temperature of 95·5 °C. Below this temperature, it slowly changes to *rhombic* sulphur. The crystals of this allotrope are somewhat squarer in shape. Apart from slight differences in melting point, the two forms are otherwise much the same. They both have molecules containing eight sulphur atoms joined in a twisted ring.

If solid sulphur is melted, the viscosity of the liquid diminishes with increasing temperature up to 157 °C. As the temperature increases further, the viscosity starts to increase, reaching a maximum at 187 °C., and the liquid sulphur changes colour from yellow to red. Above this temperature, the viscosity again diminishes until the liquid boils at 444 °C. This behaviour is very unusual and is caused by variations in the number of atoms in the molecules. Up to 157 °C., the eight-membered rings break down into short chains. Then up to 187 °C., the chains get longer and longer until a molecule may contain more than 100 atoms. Such long chains get entangled and the liquid consequently becomes very sticky. Above this temperature, the chains break down again. If the vapour from boiling sulphur is allowed to condense on the walls of a cold chamber, it forms a powder which clings to the walls in flower-like patterns (flowers of sulphur), rather like ice crystals formed by frost on a window pane.

If the viscous liquid sulphur is poured into cold water, a rubbery brownish mass of *plastic* sulphur is formed. The long chains still exist, causing the plasticity, but they soon change into the eight-membered rings of rhombic sulphur, the

only stable form of sulphur at room temperature, and the solid becomes brittle.

The greatest single use of sulphuric acid is in the manufacture of fertilizers. The production of superphosphates has already been mentioned; it accounts for nearly half the world's production of sulphuric acid. The acid is also used in the manufacture of ammonium sulphate, which is used as a fertilizer to feed nitrogen to plants.

Sulphuric acid is manufactured from sulphur dioxide by two processes – the lead-chamber process and the contact process.

The lead-chamber process uses nitrogen dioxide to oxidize sulphur dioxide to sulphur trioxide which is then dissolved in water to form sulphuric acid. The reactions are complex but may be summarized as follows:

$$SO_2 + NO_2 \rightarrow SO_3 + NO,$$
$$SO_3 + H_2O \rightarrow H_2SO_4.$$

The nitric oxide is converted back to nitrogen dioxide by an excess of air:

$$2NO + O_2 \rightarrow 2NO_2.$$

In this way, the nitrogen oxides are used over and over again. The sulphur trioxide is not isolated as all the reactions take place simultaneously in large lead-lined chambers. Acid at a concentration of 60 per cent is produced.

For stronger and purer acid, the contact process is used. Sulphur dioxide is oxidized by oxygen directly to sulphur trioxide at a temperature of 800 °C.:

$$2SO_2 + O_2 \rightarrow 2SO_3.$$

1 Sulphur is conveniently stored by pouring it in liquid form into storage blocks, where it solidifies. The worker uses boots with climbing irons to give a foothold on the block.
2 Rubber is vulcanized by adding sulphur to the mix. This gives it its resilience, bounce and hard-wearing properties, which are absent in rubber in the natural state.

A catalyst such as platinum or vanadium pentoxide is essential for the reaction to proceed. The sulphur trioxide obtained is dissolved in 97 per cent sulphuric acid to give sulphuric acid at a concentration of almost 100 per cent.

A further important compound of sulphur is its hydride – hydrogen sulphide, H_2S. This is the evil-smelling gas whose odour of bad eggs is associated by many people with chemistry laboratories. It is a very poisonous gas – a concentration of one part in 50,000 parts of air is lethal. Fortunately its odour can be detected at much lower concentrations.

The smell of decay

Hydrogen sulphide is found in nature as a product of the decomposition of sulphur-containing organic matter, such as eggs and onions. It is usually prepared by reacting a dilute acid with a metal sulphide:

$$FeS + 2HCl \rightarrow FeCl_2 + H_2S.$$

The gas is a reducing agent, readily replacing its sulphur by oxygen:

$$2H_2S + O_2 \rightarrow 2H_2O + 2S.$$

A solution of hydrogen sulphide in water is initially colourless but gradually goes cloudy as it takes up oxygen from the air; the cloudiness is caused by fine particles of sulphur precipitating out of the solution. Hydrogen sulphide is used as a reducing agent, and in the preparation of insoluble metal sulphides from metal salt solutions.

As well as being essential constituents of many industrial products, phosphorus and sulphur play a vital part in the body's chemistry. As old as the Earth, they are still the mainstays of modern industrial society.

Black basis of wealth and beauty

Household soot and the gems in a king's crown are both forms of carbon. But let us not forget the other uses of this strange, versatile, yet unreactive middle-man of the periodic table.

A DIAMOND sparkling in an engagement ring, the charcoal used by an artist, soot clogging a chimney, and graphite used in pencil leads – all these things are forms of the element carbon. Biologists try to list the significant difference between plants and animals, and argue whether viruses are true living things or not. But all forms of life as we know them are based on carbon.

All living tissues consist mainly of carbon compounds. And coal, coke, oil, wood, peat – in fact all fuels except atomic 'fuel' – are carbon or its compounds. Man-made carbon compounds include plastics, drugs and explosives. Carbon dioxide is the gas breathed out by men and animals and used by plants in photosynthesis. Chalk, marble, limestone and sea-shells all consist of calcium carbonate. For these reasons carbon is one of the most important elements in the whole periodic table.

One element – many forms

The ability of an element to exist in several forms is called *allotropy*. Diamond, graphite and charcoal are all *allotropes* of carbon. Chemically they are identical – for instance, they all burn in air or oxygen to form the gas carbon dioxide. But the allotropes differ in their physical properties (such as density) because their atoms are arranged in different ways, although they contain only atoms of carbon. In addition, there are slight atomic differences within a given allotrope. Like many elements, carbon has several *isotopes*. The common isotope has a mass of 12, and all forms of carbon consist mainly of this isotope. It is now used as a standard for the calculation of the atomic masses of all the other elements. All forms of carbon also contain about 1 per cent of a natural isotope of mass 13, and carbon from living things contains minute traces of a radio-active isotope of mass 14. Carbon 14 slowly *decays* (changes into other atoms) and its formation in living things stops when they die. Half the carbon 14 in an object decays and disappears in about 5,500 years; thus, 5,500 years is the *half-life* of carbon 14. By measuring the amount of carbon 14 in, say, a piece of cloth from an Egyptian mummy, scientists can calculate the age of the cloth (or, strictly, how many years have elapsed since the death of the plant or animal from which the cloth was made). Other radioactive

1 Carbon dioxide crystals are used to 'seed' clouds in dry areas. These crystals cause the water vapour to condense and fall as rain.

2 Coal, which is largely carbon, has been the world's main fuel for many centuries. It was formed by the effect of heat and pressure on primeval forests.

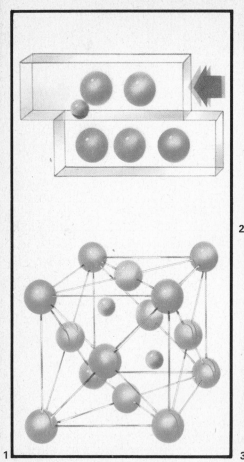

isotopes include carbon 10 (half-life about nine seconds) and carbon 11 (half-life about 20 minutes).

Diamonds are found in river gravels in Brazil and India, but most of the world's supply comes from mines in southern Africa. Diamond is the hardest known natural substance. In the diamond crystal lattice, each carbon atom is covalently bonded to four other carbon atoms. To split a crystal, one must break millions of these covalent bonds, hence the hardness. Although best known as sparkling gem stones, most diamonds are small coloured crystals used in industry for cutting and polishing. For instance, high-quality lenses are polished with diamond paste, and diamond-impregnated drills are used for boring rock and glass. Diamond saws cut stone and concrete and small diamonds are used in crystal pick-ups for gramophones.

Diamonds – artificial and natural

It is assumed that diamonds were formed in the Earth's crust when other forms of carbon were subjected to extreme pressure at very high temperatures. From time to time, several experimenters have tried to reproduce these conditions in the laboratory and make artificial diamonds. The first attempt was made by the French chemist Henri Moissan in 1894. He dropped small pieces of graphite into a ladle of molten iron and then plunged the ladle into cold water. After dissolving away all the iron in acid, he obtained some tiny hard crystals which he claimed were diamonds. Later scientists obtained similar results, but none of the products has been preserved for modern examination, such as X-ray crystallography, which would confirm whether or not the crystals were true diamond. Although calculations show that such a process is theoretically possible, the case for the early production of artificial diamonds must for the time being remain not proven.

High-temperature lubrication

Graphite is another crystalline form of carbon that is mined, mainly in Ceylon. Its crystal structure is quite different from that of diamond. It consists of layers of carbon atoms each joined in a plane to three neighbours, forming a hexagonal lattice resembling a honeycomb. Each layer is separated from the next by more than twice the normal carbon-to-carbon distance. As a result, the planes slide easily over each other, making graphite a good lubricant for use up to fairly high temperatures.

Graphite forms several compounds in which 'foreign' atoms enter the gaps (called *interstices*) between the layers of carbon atoms. These interstitial compounds are formed with the alkali metals potassium, rubidium and caesium giving definite compounds such as KC_8 and KC_{16}. Oxygen will also enter these spaces to give the so-called graphitic acids. The entry of foreign atoms prizes the hexagonal layers of carbon atoms farther apart, an action which accounts for the swelling or puffing up that takes place with certain forms of graphite.

1 Atoms of carbon will enter a metallic crystal to form an interstitial compound. They increase the strength of the metal by forming a 'stop' which prevents the crystal shearing along the 'glide planes'.

2 Marble, which is a form of calcium carbonate, occurs naturally in many parts of the world,

particularly in Italy.

3 The shells of crustaceans, like these oysters, consist largely of carbonates. Even the pearls, if any, are made of the same substance.

4 Diamonds are an attractive and very durable allotrope (alternative form) of carbon. Another common allotrope is graphite.

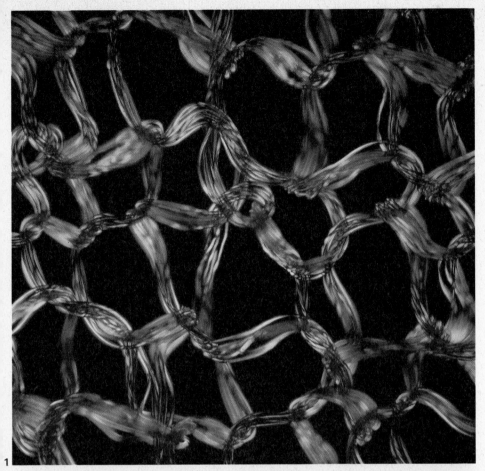

for making electrodes such as those in the centres of ordinary torch batteries. It is also used as a moderator in some nuclear reactors because it absorbs and slows down neutrons and so helps to control the chain reaction fission process.

Putting carbon to work

Charcoal, soot and coke are also forms of carbon of varying purity. Although generally described as amorphous, these allotropes consist of microscopic crystals similar to those of graphite. Wood charcoal is made by heating wood in the absence of air. The wood cannot burn, but chars. Charcoal is traditionally made by charring thin twigs and saplings on a fire banked over with earth or sods. Wood charcoal readily absorbs large amounts of various gases and is put to this use in gas masks and filters.

When bones are heated in the absence of air, bone or animal charcoal is formed. It absorbs the colour from chemical solutions and is used in the refining of sugar. If sugar itself is strongly heated in the absence of air, it chars to form the extremely pure sugar charcoal.

Soot is formed as fine particles whenever a carbon fuel is incompletely burnt. Soot from domestic chimneys contains ammonium salts and nitrates and is therefore used as a fertilizer. Very fine soot from burning oil is called lampblack. It is used as a black pigment in printer's ink and shoe polish and is mixed with rubber to make motor-car tyres wear less quickly.

When coal is heated in the absence of air, coal gas is produced and coke remains. Coke is the form of carbon used in heavy industry for smelting metals (as in the blast-furnace) and for making other fuel gases (such as *producer gas* and *water gas*). It is also used as a fuel in stoves and furnaces, though for domestic use it is being replaced by 'partially de-gassed coal' which is easier to light and requires a less complicated hearth.

Carbon has few chemical properties. It takes part directly in few chemical reactions and does not dissolve in any acids, alkalis or solvents. It does have an affinity for oxygen. It burns in a limited supply of air or oxygen to form carbon monoxide:

$$2C + O_2 \rightarrow 2CO,$$

and in enough air forms carbon dioxide:

$$C + O_2 \rightarrow CO_2.$$

Carbon will remove oxygen from many metal oxides, reducing them to the metal:

$$2CuO + C \rightarrow 2Cu + CO_2.$$

This type of reaction is the basis of the extraction of iron from its ores.

If coke is strongly heated with limestone (calcium oxide), the compound calcium carbide is formed:

$$CaO + 3C \rightarrow CaC_2 + CO.$$

With cold water, calcium carbide reacts to give the hydrocarbon gas acetylene:

$$CaC_2 + H_2O \rightarrow CaO + C_2H_2.$$

When acetylene is passed into solutions of metal salts, the metal carbide or acetylide

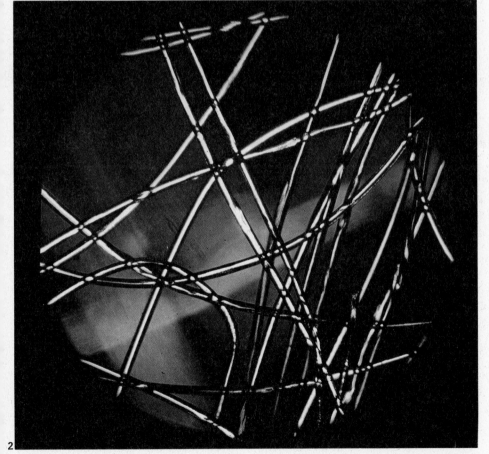

1 Nylon, one of the best known of the synthetic fibres, is a compound of carbon. The filaments can be knitted into garments such as these nylon stockings, shirts and underwear.
2 Replacement of natural textiles by synthetics has been one of the major achievements of the organic branch of chemistry.

Artificial graphite is made by the costly Acheson process in which coke is heated to high temperatures in an electric arc furnace. The process is operated near Niagara Falls where large quantities of cheap hydro-electricity are available.

Graphite conducts electricity and is used

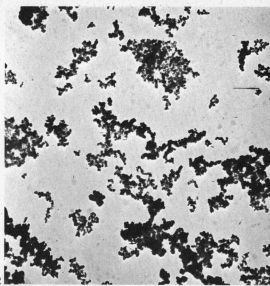

1 Carbon black is added to rubber to increase its conductivity and so reduce the accumulation of static electricity which can cause fires in certain circumstances.

2 Micrograph of the chain formation in carbon black which is used to make rubber conductive.

is precipitated. Many of these compounds explode on heating. Among the non-metals, important carbides include silicon carbide (carborundum) and boron carbide. With tungsten carbide, these compounds rival diamond in hardness and are used for making drills for cutting glass and stone, and for coating grinding wheels.

A lethal compound

Carbon monoxide is a colourless, odourless, poisonous gas. When breathed by men or animals, it competes with oxygen in the lungs and is preferentially absorbed by the haemoglobin in the blood to form bright pink carboxy-haemoglobin. A victim of carbon monoxide poisoning dies of oxygen starvation and the gas is responsible for the poisonous nature of motor-car exhaust fumes and coal gas. Occasionally people are poisoned by breathing the air in a room heated by a coke stove with an insufficient air supply. In a coke fire, the carbon dioxide first formed is reduced by hot carbon (coke) to carbon monoxide. Most of this burns to carbon dioxide with a blue flame, but some may escape into the air or fail to burn if there is not enough air passing through the fire.

In the laboratory, carbon monoxide may be made by the reduction of carbon dioxide, which is passed over red-hot charcoal. More conveniently it is made by the action of hot concentrated sulphuric acid on oxalic acid or formic acid. The former yields a mixture of carbon monoxide and dioxide, while the latter yields pure carbon monoxide.

With solutions of certain metal salts, carbon monoxide forms substances known as *carbonyls*. The best known of these is nickel carbonyl, $Ni(CO)_4$, which on heating yields pure carbon monoxide and metallic nickel.

Whenever carbon or fuels containing it are burnt in a plentiful supply of air, carbon dioxide is formed. It is also produced during respiration in men and animals, and is essential for photosynthesis in plants. It is formed when calcium carbonate is roasted to form lime:

$$CaCO_3 \rightarrow CaO + CO_2.$$

It is made in the laboratory by treating practically any carbonate or bicarbonate with any acid.

Carbon dioxide is a colourless, dense gas which dissolves slightly in water to form a weak acid solution called carbonic acid. Under high pressure, much more gas dissolves to form the soda water used in drinks.

At low temperatures carbon dioxide condenses to a solid known as 'dry ice' commonly used for keeping such things as ice-cream cold in the absence of a refrigerator. It is called 'dry' ice because it *sublimes* – that is, it changes directly from the solid to carbon dioxide gas without first melting to a liquid. Some rain-making experiments use powdered dry ice as 'seed' crystals to cause water vapour in clouds to condense and form rain.

Calcium carbonate, the calcium salt of carbonic acid, occurs in several forms such as marble, chalk and sea-shells. It is sometimes spread on cultivated land to lower the acidity of the soil.

Sodium carbonate is the familiar washing soda. It is a mild alkali and extremely important in the industrial preparation of glass and soap. It is made by the ammonia-soda (or Solvay) process. Salt solution is saturated with ammonia gas and trickled down a tower up which carbon dioxide is passed. The products of the reaction are ammonium chloride and sodium bicarbonate, which is then heated to form sodium carbonate. This latter heating regenerates carbon dioxide which is used again in the process. The ammonium chloride is heated with lime to regenerate the ammonia for re-use and leave the only waste product of the process, calcium chloride.

Sodium carbonate is used to soften tap water, from which it precipitates any soluble magnesium or calcium salts as their insoluble carbonates. At one time, it was used to make caustic soda (sodium hydroxide) by boiling it with slaked lime. This process has now been superseded by the electrolysis of brine. It is also used in soda-acid fire extinguishers, which consist of a cylinder full of sodium carbonate solution. At the top of the cylinder is a glass flask of concentrated sulphuric acid. When the knob on the top of the extinguisher is struck, the flask breaks releasing the acid which reacts with the sodium carbonate solution to form a large quantity of carbon dioxide gas. The pressure of the gas forces the liquid out of the nozzle of the extinguisher, which is therefore rather like a giant soda siphon.

Other important carbonates include ammonium carbonate, which is used in smelling salts because it readily decomposes to give ammonia:

$$(NH_4)_2CO_3 \rightarrow H_2O + CO_2 + 2NH_3.$$

Carbon dioxide is a by-product.

Compounds of carbon

Carbonic acid (H_2CO_3) is a *dibasic* acid – that is, it has two hydrogen atoms that can be replaced by a metallic atom or atoms to form salts. For instance, in calcium carbonate ($CaCO_3$) both the hydrogen atoms (in the form of hydrogen ions, H^+) are replaced by one calcium atom (in the form of its ion Ca^{2+}). In sodium carbonate (Na_2CO_3) the hydrogen ions are replaced by sodium ions. If only one hydrogen ion is replaced by sodium, we get the salt sodium bicarbonate, $NaHCO_3$. This is the familiar substance baking soda, used for making cakes rise and counteracting acidity in the stomach. It is made commercially by the Solvay process as described above. Sodium bicarbonate may be made in the laboratory by passing carbon dioxide into a concentrated solution of sodium hydroxide. It is not very soluble in this solution and is precipitated and may be filtered off. With acids, bicarbonates generate carbon dioxide and it is bubbles of this gas which make cakes rise.

Throughout the study of carbon and its compounds, their relation to living things becomes apparent. Carbon dioxide as a factor in respiration and photosynthesis; the production of carbon and carbon compounds from organic matter. But this field of study, covering almost a million known compounds, is now a separate discipline, organic chemistry, which shows, even more clearly, that carbon is the element of living things.

Carbon's shapely compounds

Plastics, penicillin and paints – all products of organic chemistry. This is the chemistry of a million compounds, complex, diverse, and holding the prospect of tomorrow's health and wealth.

IN 1828 a German chemist named Friedrich Wohler discovered by chance that a simple laboratory chemical, ammonium cyanate, could be converted into urea by evaporating a solution in water to dryness. Urea is an organic chemical present in the urine of many animals and is the form in which unwanted nitrogen is removed from their bodies. Before 1828 most scientists thought it would be impossible to prepare in the laboratory any substance made by a living organism because, they argued, there was a 'vital life force' that could be provided only by a living organism. Wohler's experiment was the beginning of organic chemistry as we know it today. Once the old idea of a vital life force had been discarded, scientists set about trying to prepare even more organic compounds in the laboratory.

On this planet, at any rate, living things are composed mainly of substances built up almost entirely from two chemical elements, carbon and hydrogen, although, of course, other elements such as oxygen, nitrogen and phosphorus are also present. Carbon is ideally suited to this 'building brick' role, as it has the property of being able to combine with itself to form either long chains or rings of atoms. This enables the very complicated types of molecules necessary for life processes to be formed. Silicon also possesses this property to some extent and it is possible that the life on a planet of some distant star might be based on silicon compounds (silanes) instead of carbon.

Oil as a source of chemicals

As our bodies are made of organic compounds they are naturally of great interest and importance to us and a lot of time and money is devoted to their study. Most of those which are used in the laboratory are derived from plants or from crude petroleum oils which are, of course, formed from the remains of prehistoric animals and plants. In a sense we have gone back to the days before the 'vital force' theory was exploded, in that we get most of our organic chemicals from what were originally living sources.

The starting materials for the chemical industry are obtained from crude oil by the process of *fractional distillation*. This separates the light substances, such as ether and petrol, from the heavy ones, such as motor oil and road tar, by boiling off increasingly heavy fractions as the temperature is raised. The fractionating columns in which the distillation is done are a familiar scene at any oil refinery. If the crude oil contains too many of the heavier chemicals they can be broken down into lighter ones by a process known as *catalytic cracking*. The newly formed light chemicals can then be redistilled. If,

Oil refineries reduce crude oil to its various components, which then form the basic 'building bricks' for the synthesis of many organic compounds, including plastics.

on the other hand, there are too many of the light chemicals present in the crude oil, then some heavy ones can be generated from these by a process known as *plat-forming* using a platinum catalyst. The light and heavy fractions from fractional distillation can be repurified until there are many fractions, each containing only one substance.

Then the real chemistry starts. Each of these simple substances can be converted into a variety of others, and these raw materials will be used to make the various products that we need. Practically every industry is dependent to some extent on these starting materials. The pharmaceutical, dyeing, fibre, plastics, engin-

eering and agricultural industries all need petroleum products at some time.

Nowadays, many clothes are made from artificial fibres such as nylon and terylene. These are both made from products of the petroleum industry. Nylon was the first of the two to be produced, although it was by no means the first artificial fibre to be developed. All fibres, whether artificial or natural, are made up from long, chain-like molecules which make it possible to spin the short filaments into strong, continuous threads. The long-chain molecules of artificial fibres are made up from many identical parts and are called *polymers*. They are often made in *autoclaves* which are large, heated pressure vessels rather similar to a domestic pressure cooker, but of course very much bigger. When these polymeric fibres were first being made, the small laboratory autoclaves sometimes used to burst, with

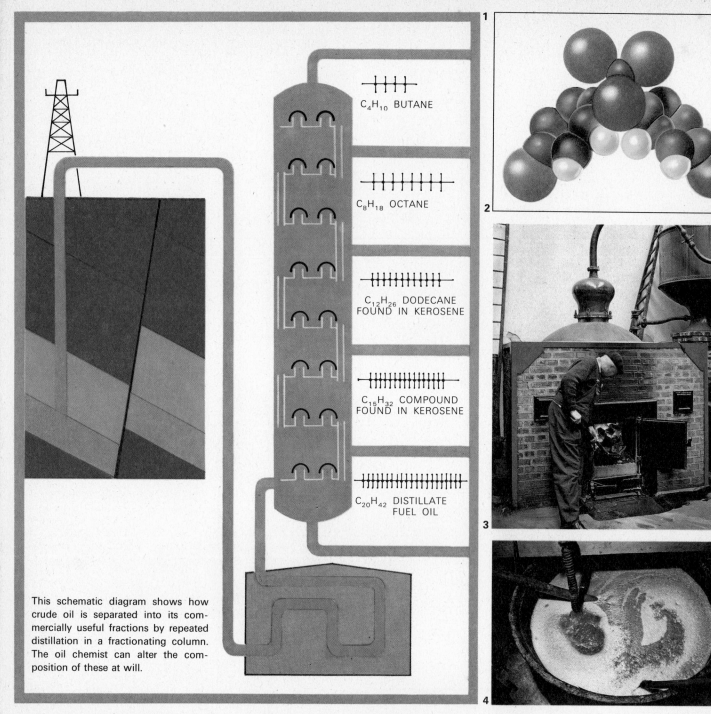

C₄H₁₀ BUTANE

C₈H₁₈ OCTANE

C₁₂H₂₆ DODECANE
FOUND IN KEROSENE

C₁₅H₃₂ COMPOUND
FOUND IN KEROSENE

C₂₀H₄₂ DISTILLATE
FUEL OIL

This schematic diagram shows how crude oil is separated into its commercially useful fractions by repeated distillation in a fractionating column. The oil chemist can alter the composition of these at will.

disastrous results. Great care is taken to ensure that this does not happen on the large scale.

Nylon is what is known as a *polyamide* fibre; that is, it is an amide polymer. An *amide* is a chemical compound formed when an amine combines with a carboxylic acid. An example of an amine is ammonia and an example of a carboxylic acid is acetic acid, which occurs in vinegar. The substance formed when these two compounds combine is an amide known as *acetamide*. In this process a molecule of water is eliminated.

To make a polyamide fibre, a substance with an *amino group* at each end of the molecule – a di-amine – is reacted with a di-acid, which has a carboxylic group at each end. In this way a very long chain in which the molecules alternate can be built up. In nylon the di-amine is a substance known as *hexamethylenediamine*, which is a chain of six carbon atoms with an amino group at each end. The di-acid

1 Light components of crude oil can be boiled off at comparatively low temperatures, while heavy fractions, including waxes and tars, require much higher temperatures.
2 The geometric distribution of the atoms in an organic molecule can be found by chemical techniques. 'Billiard ball' reconstructions are widely used in chemistry teaching.

used is known as *adipic acid* and also contains six carbon atoms.

A complete molecule of nylon is composed of a large number of both of these units, each alternating in the chain rather like a long line of boys and girls in which each boy holds hands with two girls and vice versa.

It is convenient that both the di-amine and the di-acid parts of nylon each contain six carbon atoms, as this means that they can both be made from *phenol* (popularly known as carbolic acid) which is available cheaply in large amounts from the petroleum industry. There is now another kind

3 Production of alcoholic beverages by fermentation is one of Man's most ancient skills. Stronger liquors are then produced by distillation, in this case of wine.
4 Grapes are fermented in vats. The action of yeast on the natural grape sugars produces alcohol. This reaction is self-regulating, production of alcohol ceasing automatically.

of nylon called *nylon-12* in which the di-amine part of the molecule contains 12 carbon atoms.

Terylene is another widely used artificial fibre. It is a polyester fibre, made from a chain composed of alternating di-alcohol and di-acid groups. In this case the di-acid is *terephthalic acid*; hence the name terylene. The di-alcohol used is *ethylene glycol*, another very common chemical which, by the way, is the main constituent of anti-freeze.

Once a fibre has been made there is the problem of developing a series of dyes which can be used on it. Modern dyes

1 Whisky, the traditional drink of Scotland, is a distillate of a barley mash. Malt whisky, favoured by connoisseurs, is made by double distillation in a traditional pot still.

2 Careful selection of the distillates produced is vital in the manufacture of whisky. This highly skilled process is controlled from the 'spirit safe'.

must be colour-fast and must not wash out. The artificial fibres were not problem-free at first because many of the dyes traditionally used for colouring wool and cotton did not suit the new fibres, which are chemically different from the natural fibres. Dyes stick to a fibre either by combining with it chemically or by means of parts of the molecule which are simply attracted to the fibre. Terylene is a very stable fibre and does not easily form chemical compounds with dyes.

This means that many of the older generations of 'combining' dyes do not stick to terylene very well. This sort of problem was overcome by synthesizing a whole new range of dyes and colouring specially for use with the new fibres.

Discovering dyes by accident

One of these new groups of dyes, the *phthalocyanines,* were discovered when some dye-workers were preparing a substance called *phthalimide.* They made it by heating *phthalic anhydride* with ammonia in an open vessel made of enamel-coated iron. On one occasion a dark blue pigment was formed as an impurity, and when this was examined it was found to contain iron. The enamel lining of the reaction vessel had become chipped, allowing some of the iron to dissolve and form this impurity. As this happened in a dye works there was naturally some interest in this new blue substance.

It was discovered that in the presence of copper a similar reaction took place which gave a beautiful greenish-blue pigment. This was found to have a rather complicated ring structure, composed of carbon and nitrogen atoms, which was wrapped round an atom of copper. The substance, named Monastral Blue, is extremely stable, but is almost completely insoluble in most solvents.

By making small changes in the struc-

ture of the molecule it is possible to alter the colour of these dyes. This can be done simply by putting a different metal atom into the middle; for example, lead phthalocyanine is a yellowish-green colour, while the phthalocyanines containing nickel and cobalt are a similar shade of blue. Other modifications to this type of dye include ones to make the dyes soluble in water so that they can be used as direct dyes. The very insoluble ones can be used only as pigments which are dispersed on to the fibre, or other surface, in the form of extremely fine particles.

Long-chain polymeric molecules similar to synthetic fibres, but more complicated, occur in our bodies, mainly as proteins and nucleic acids. Proteins comprise muscle fibres and, in the form of enzymes, are responsible for most of the chemical reactions which take place inside us. They are composed of long chains made up of amino acids. The links in the chains are amide bonds, the same as those which hold the molecules of nylon together. However, proteins are far more complicated than nylon for several reasons.

For one thing, the individual amino acids are sometimes quite complicated in themselves. Also there are about 20 different ones and they are not arranged in a regular fashion along the chains. Instead, they are in an apparently random order. However, this order is not really random, as it is always the same for a given protein. The absence of a regular order of amino acids allows an infinite number of variations in protein structure, and so any number of different proteins is possible.

In addition to the above complications, the protein chains can be coiled in many ways, but in only one particular spatial arrangement will the molecule possess all the properties of the true protein. The molecule is usually held in this shape by very weak attractive forces and also by

rather weak bonds known as *hydrogen bonds.* These are usually broken if the molecule is subjected to any kind of rough treatment such as being heated. When the hydrogen bonds are broken or disturbed, the protein loses its characteristic properties and becomes denatured. This is what happens to egg white as it gradually goes hard and opaque when the egg is boiled.

The nucleic acids are another important type of long-chain polymer which occurs in the cells of all living things. These substances contain one or two sugars, present as a phosphate. The sugar is either *ribose,* which is a molecule slightly smaller than *glucose,* or the related *desoxy-ribose.* It alternates along the chain of the nucleic acid with four different organic 'bases'. These are very weakly alkaline substances containing nitrogen. The usual bases which occur in nucleic acids are called *adenine, guanine, cytosine* and *uracil,* usually abbreviated to A, G, C, and U. Much of the work on the chemical nature of the nucleic acids was done at Cambridge by Sir Alexander Todd (now Lord Todd) and his collaborators.

The chemistry of inheritance

One of the two classes of nucleic acids, the desoxyribonucleic (DNA), are responsible for passing on the information about the make-up of the body from one generation to the next by means of the 'genetic code'. DNA is probably the factor responsible for all our inherited characteristics. In the past decade the fine structure of DNA has been worked out by James Watson and Francis Crick. Now this is known, it is possible to solve the genetic code to some extent. For example, it has been found that DNA is capable of specifying the order in which amino acid units are built into a protein molecule. The bases in the DNA chain are arranged in groups of three called *codons.* Each of these codons tells the cell which amino acid to attach next to the growing protein chain. The reaction is actually performed in cell components called *ribosomes* which move along a

1 Carbon tetrachloride, a simple organic chemical, is extremely useful in fighting petrol fires. Water would merely float the blazing petrol, so spreading the fire.

2 Insecticides and pesticides are a major industry based on petroleum products. Many of these are applied directly to the coats of infected animals.

molecule of 'messenger RNA', formed from the DNA. This messenger RNA is another nucleic acid, which contains ribose instead of desoxyribose, and it too contains the codons. The process is rather like an assembly line: the ribosomes move along the RNA adding another amino acid to the protein they are making as they come to each codon. It is similar to the way in which a car is made, a new bit being added at each step in the assembly line until the structure is complete.

As the groups of three bases forming codons can consist of any selection of the four bases in DNA there are 64 possible combinations (4×4×4). Each of these codons specifies an amino acid, although most of the amino acids correspond to

The efficacy of chloroform as an anaesthetic was first established by Sir James Young Simpson, who pioneered its use in surgery and childbirth.

more than one combination. There are also codons corresponding to 'start' and 'stop' so the sequence of bases along the length of a DNA molecule is a sort of computer programme for building up proteins. As proteins are responsible for the synthesis of all the other compounds present in the cells of living organisms the DNA is effectively the ultimate information store.

There is one more type of polymer which occurs in the body which should be mentioned. This is glycogen. It occurs mainly in the liver and is one of the body's ways of storing energy. It is a polymer made up of many thousands of glucose molecules. When these glucose molecules are required to supply energy to the body, they are split off and transported by the blood-stream to their site of action. This is why there is always some glucose in the blood. When the body is obtaining glucose faster than it is using it, more glycogen

is deposited. The structure of glycogen differs from the other substances described here in that it possesses many cross-links between the chains, and therefore occurs as more of a solid mass.

Not all long-chain chemicals are polymers. The soaps and synthetic detergents are also long, thin molecules; their backbone is composed simply of a chain of carbon atoms each carrying two hydrogen atoms. These substances also owe their typical properties to the shape of their molecules. One of the main functions of detergents is to remove greases which get on to clothes. Oily things are hydrophobic; that is, they tend to avoid water and stick to other surfaces. The principal action of a detergent is to render the greases water-soluble so that they can be rinsed away.

Carbon for cleanliness

The carbon and hydrogen (or hydrocarbon) end of the detergent molecule sticks to the grease because oily things are also made of hydrocarbon chains. However, the other end of the detergent molecule is a hydrophilic (water-liking) group which has an affinity for water. The result is that the detergent covers the surface of the grease particle with the hydrophobic groups on the inside and the hydrophilic ones sticking out. The grease-detergent complex, known as a *micelle,* is then free to float off into the water.

Soaps are really a special type of detergent which can be made by boiling natural fats with an alkali. In the soaps the hydrophilic group is the sodium salt of an organic acid. Soaps have the disadvantage that they do not work very well in hard water because the calcium and magnesium salts present in this water react to form the calcium and magnesium salts of the soaps. As these are not soluble in water, they form an unpleasant scum and use up much of the soap which is wanted for washing.

These are only a few of the many hundreds of kinds of organic compounds which have been manufactured by organic chemists. The skill of these chemists lies in making new substances, and determining compositions of new and unknown substances.

Architects of the giant molecules

Breaking down and rebuilding molecules to produce new and useful materials is the task of the organic chemist. How does he go about his work, and what are the tools of this exotic science?

WE ARE all made of organic chemicals; indeed the term implies an affinity with living things. It is this that has stimulated interest in the subject of organic chemistry, as Man has always been curious about those things which most directly concern him.

Organic chemistry is essentially the chemistry of substances containing atoms of both carbon and hydrogen. Carbon atoms are almost always tetravalent; that is, they can form bonds with four other atoms. If the atom of carbon is envisaged as a tetrahedron, the atom itself is at the centre and the four valencies reach out from this to the four corners. In the simplest of all organic compounds, methane (marsh gas or natural gas) all four bonds are to hydrogen atoms. However, not all the bonds need be to hydrogen atoms: they can be to oxygen, as in the alcohols and ethers; to nitrogen as in the amines and other organic bases; or they can be to almost any other atomic element. It is the oxygen and nitrogen atoms which are largely responsible for giving the compounds their characteristic chemical properties, as substances containing only carbon and hydrogen, like benzene, are usually rather unreactive. Oxygen is responsible for the properties of the alcohols, such as ethyl alcohol (ordinary alcohol), and acids like acetic acid, which is contained in vinegar. Nitrogen often makes substances slightly alkaline. These groups of atoms in the molecule which give substances their chemical properties, are known as *functional groups*.

What makes the chemistry of carbon so interesting is its ability to form bonds with itself. These bonds may be single, double or triple, and may be imagined as being the contact between the corners, edges or faces of adjacent carbon tetrahedra. This unusual property of self-combination allows carbon to form substances containing long chains, either straight or branched, or variously sized rings of atoms. Thus molecules of any size can be built up, rather in the way that a house is built of bricks, to form even the vast macromolecules that are found in the body.

It is important for the organic chemist to understand fully the molecular structures of the substances that he is working with. Without this information any attempt to make them artificially, to synthesize them, would be very 'hit or miss'. There is a variety of ways in which the structure of a chemical substance can be investigated, but first of all it is essential that the substance concerned is obtained in a pure state.

Many useful organic substances are found in animals or plants: they are natural products. Unfortunately, they do not often occur in a pure form, but are usually

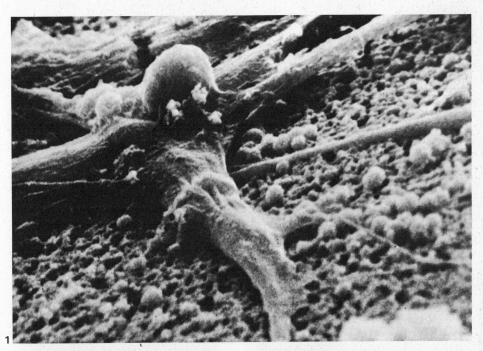

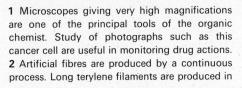

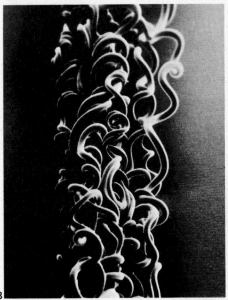

1 Microscopes giving very high magnifications are one of the principal tools of the organic chemist. Study of photographs such as this cancer cell are useful in monitoring drug actions.
2 Artificial fibres are produced by a continuous process. Long terylene filaments are produced in a spinneret, and their continuity contributes greatly to the strength of the finished article.
3 Apart from their other advantages, synthetic fibres can be treated during production to give them desirable 'feel'. They can be bulked or twisted depending on their intended use.

complicated mixtures. Sometimes there are hundreds of substances in the mixture although it is usual for only one or two to predominate. The first problem is to separate the components of the mixture and the next is to decide which of them are worth investigating in detail. Until the past few decades, almost the only methods which could be used to separate complex mixtures were crystallization, distillation and extraction with solvents.

Now we are much more fortunate. Probably the most useful technique is *chromatography*, a method first discovered early in this century but fully utilized only in the past couple of decades.

The essential principle of chromatography is that it makes use of the different affinities of the various compounds in a mixture for certain absorbing materials or solvents. The best way to explain this is to take an imaginary example. Suppose

that an open-ended vertical tube is filled with a powder, such as powdered chalk, which is held in the tube by a plug of cotton-wool at the bottom. The mixture to be separated is put on to the top of the chalk column and a solvent, such as water or alcohol, is allowed to trickle down through the column of powder. If all the substances are soluble in the solvent, then they will gradually move down the column of chalk as the solvent washes them through. However, if the substances have different affinities for the chalk – if they are 'absorbed' to different extents – then they will tend to be washed through the column at different rates.

Colourful analysis

The substance that is absorbed least strongly will reach the bottom of the column first; that which is absorbed most strongly will be last, and the intermediate substances will come off the column between these two. Each substance can then be collected separately as it drips from the bottom of the column. However, unless the conditions are just right, there is often some overlap.

In this example the chalk column is the *stationary phase* and the solvent is the *mobile phase*. In simple chromatography there is always a stationary phase and a mobile phase; however, these do not have to be, respectively, a solid and a liquid. The stationary phase can be solid, or a liquid absorbed on to a solid 'carrier', and the mobile phase can be a liquid or a gas. Gas chromatography, in which the mobile phase is a stream of gas, is exceptionally sensitive and can be used to detect the most minute quantities of a substance in a mixture. It is one way in which the alcohol content of a small sample of blood can be measured, so this method is used to check the results of the 'breathalyser'. In another type of chromatography, thin-layer chromatography, the stationary phase is a fine powder stuck to the surface of a glass plate. The solvent runs up this plate by

1 Electron microscopes are now common in organic chemistry laboratories. The latest models can distinguish surface characteristics and irregularities to provide a picture in depth.
2 Methane, the simplest hydrocarbon, can form compounds by single, double or triple bonds. It is this bonding ability of carbon which leads to the vast number of organic compounds.

capillary action, like water running up a sheet of blotting paper into it. With thin-layer techniques a mixture can be separated very quickly and the result can often be visualized by spraying the plates with a suitable reagent solution. This is often done with sulphuric acid, which chars the compounds to give dark areas.

With the advent of chromatographic methods the more traditional techniques have become even more useful. This is because many of them work best when the substance to be purified contains only small amounts of impurities; nowadays this is often the case as preliminary chromatography provides substances in an almost pure state.

Once the substance has been purified, the next task is to find out what it is. To do this the chemist used to have to rely solely on a series of chemical tests and also on his sense of smell. A good nose is a valuable possession, as it can often tell him quite a lot about the chemicals he is working with. The nose is really like a sensitive gas chromatograph and it will sometimes give most valuable information, not the least of which is likely to be that the substance sniffed could be rather dangerous.

There is a whole range of tests known as 'spot' tests because they can be done with tiny spots of material or single drops of solution. These usually rely on a definite colour change being produced if a particular type of substance is present. Some of these spot tests are incredibly sensitive: it is sometimes possible to detect traces of the test substance even after the tube it was in has been washed out a couple of

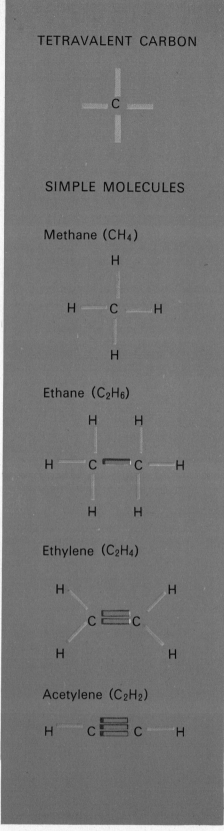

TETRAVALENT CARBON

C

SIMPLE MOLECULES

Methane (CH_4)

Ethane (C_2H_6)

Ethylene (C_2H_4)

Acetylene (C_2H_2)

times. Some spot tests are very complicated; however, there are quite a few that are simple, like one of the tests for an alcohol. Alcohols all contain a *hydroxyl* group, which consists of an oxygen atom joined to a hydrogen atom; when a liquid substance possessing a hydroxyl group is put into contact with a small piece of sodium metal, the sodium will fizz. This test, although not completely unambiguous, can be very useful. Another simple test is the Beilstein test, called after a famous chemist. In this test a spot

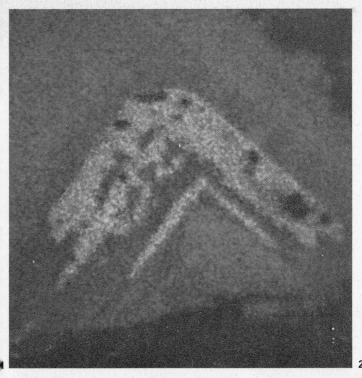

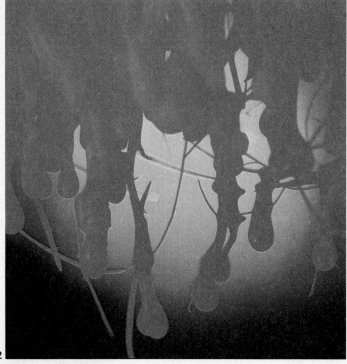

1 Micrographs of chemical compounds or naturally occurring minerals have greatly increased scientists' knowledge of the ways in which compounds are formed.
2 Wax is one of the heavier hydrocarbons contained in crude oil. After catalytic reduction, it forms the basis for many synthetic manufacturing processes.
3 This micrograph of wax shows that it has a crystalline form. Many crystalline organic compounds exhibit unusual characteristics, one of the best known being optical isomerism.

troscopic methods have largely superseded the spot test mentioned above; for example, infrared spectroscopy can detect the hydroxyl group in an alcohol. The infrared method can do this job on a much smaller sample of the substance than can the spot test, and so is almost always preferred.

Another useful thing to know when determining the molecular structure of a substance is its *empirical formula.* This tells the chemist the relative proportions of each element present in the molecule. For example, the empirical formula of ethyl alcohol is C_2H_6O: this means that the molecule contains carbon, hydrogen and oxygen atoms in the ratio $2:6:1$. Unfortunately, it does not indicate exactly how many there are of each; it could be $4:12:2$ or $6:18:3$. Neither does it indicate how the atoms are arranged. Even so, the empirical formula is very useful, especially if it is known which ratio is the correct one.

Automation in the laboratory

Where many analyses have to be done, automatic analyzing instruments are now often used. If a protein is hydrolysed – broken down into its constituent amino acids – and the mixture formed is put into the analyzer, the machine will separate and determine the concentration of each amino acid present. The machine can be set to do this while the chemist is at home asleep, and the results will be waiting for him when he comes to work the next

of the substance is put on to a clean copper wire and heated in a bunsen burner flame; a green flame means that the substance contains at least one of the halogen elements – fluorine, chlorine, bromine or iodine.

Spot tests are used much less now as there are several physical methods which can give valuable information about structure; nevertheless, spot tests are still useful. One of these physical methods, *spectroscopy,* is the study of the way in which electromagnetic radiations, such

as ultraviolet or infrared light, interact with substances. It is these interactions which give information about the structure of molecules. The functional groups in a molecule usually absorb the radiation in a characteristic pattern of wavelengths which can be seen when the spectrum of a substance is looked at, indicating that they are present in its molecule. As the groups often interact and alter each other's absorption in a predictable way, it is frequently possible to say how they are arranged in respect to one another. Spec-

thing of an art. Certainly it is possible to feel the thrill of creating some substance that no one else has made before. This is rather like the feeling experienced by the mountaineer as he reaches the top of a previously unclimbed peak. At the start of a synthetic project the chemist is like a motorist setting out on a long trip in a country he does not know with only an inaccurate map to guide him. In our case this map is known as a *flow sheet,* and is a complex diagram showing all the likely chemical routes that could be taken and all the possible starting points, which are usually decided by the availability of starting materials. The chemist then begins a game of 'snakes and ladders', with the difference that most mistakes, the snakes, almost always lead back to square one. The ladders, the strokes of luck, are often few and far between.

One of the big problems of synthetic work is that of the yield. This is usually expressed as a percentage; for example, a weight yield of 50 per cent means that if there was 100 gm of starting material there will be 50 gm of product. If two successive chemical steps each have this yield, the overall yield will be on 25 per cent. As some chemical syntheses contain many separate steps – some have as many as 20 – a good yield on each is necessary if there is to be any product at all when the end is reached.

Implications of organic chemistry

No one is perfect; neither is any chemical reaction. The aim of the chemist, however, is to get his synthesis as near to being perfect as possible. The way this is done is to go back to the analytical techniques, such as chromatography and spectroscopy, to try to find out what is going wrong. Often the culprit is a *by-product,* some unforseen substance which has been formed in the reaction. Once a by-product has been investigated fully it may be possible to devise a way to prevent it from forming. It is even possible that the by-product may have a use; the useful group of dyes called the phthalocyanines were originally discovered as by-products when a different type of material was being prepared. Sometimes a reaction does not go to completion. When this happens it is often possible to recover the unchanged starting material and use it again; this is frequently done automatically by a recycling process. Here there is a similarity to some of the chemical reactions in the body: they do not all go to completion the first time round, but can be repeated as many times as necessary so as to achieve a very high overall efficiency.

As we become more aware of how the natural processes of life work, we are learning to copy nature and adapt her methods to make them more directly useful to us. In the past we were completely dependent on our natural resources in their natural state; now we are finding out how to modify them so as to be able to produce an abundance of artificial fibres, colours, structural materials, drugs and even foods. All these advances have been dependent on the development of organic chemistry.

1 Scanning electron microscopes produce surface details which enable the chemist to examine chemical reactions while they are happening.
2 Chromatography is now accepted as one of the most exact analytical techniques. This vapour phase equipment employs electronic circuitry to make it easy and quick to use, as well as improving accuracy.

morning. Before the development of such instruments, the chemist would have to spend days, or even weeks, of hard work to achieve the same results.

Non-destructive analysis

One of the advantages of most of the physical methods for determining structure is that the small sample of precious substance which they need is not destroyed; a drawback of spot tests is that although only a minute sample has to be used it is almost always destroyed. With the spectroscopic methods it is possible to recover the sample and re-use it for something else. Unfortunately there are a few physical methods which do destroy the sample. One of these is *mass spectrometry.* In this case the destruction of the molecule is the object of the exercise: it is literally knocked to pieces by a stream of electrons. The pieces are then weighed, automatically and very accurately, and from a knowledge of the weights of the pieces the chemist can often build up an accurate picture of what the original molecule looked like. Fortunately, the destruction of a sample in the mass spectrometer does not usually matter, as only a minute amount of the substance under examination has to be used.

Once the full molecular structure of a substance has been worked out, the next task is to synthesize it from easily available starting materials. At one time this used to be necessary as a check on the structure, and with the more complicated substances this is still the case. Often, however, the synthesis is done because it is thought that it will be easier to obtain a lot of the material by making it artificially in the laboratory than by extracting it from its natural source. But many substances, like the new plastics and artificial fibres, have to be made in the laboratory as they simply do not occur in nature. Nevertheless, the idea which led to them often arose from an understanding of the chemistry of some natural product.

In a way, chemical synthesis is some-

Begetters of giant molecules

Free radicals are oddities in chemistry. More reactive than normal ions, they provide the means of making the giant molecules in plastics, and may be the key to many life processes.

WHEN A MIXTURE of hydrogen and chlorine is exposed to sunlight, the two gases react so vigorously that the explosion produced can easily shatter the glass vessel. Chemists have known for many years that these two gases have a strong affinity for each other, but the outstanding violence of their reaction was, for a long time, unexplained by the normal laws of chemical combination.

About the year 1900, however, a new chemical unit was identified which gave a reasonable explanation of this phenomenon – the free radical. Radicals themselves, groups of atoms which move intact through a chemical reaction, had been identified many years before, but this new unit was seen to be of a different kind.

The origin of free radicals lies in an abnormal breaking of the covalent bonds within a chemical compound.

Radical formation

In covalent bonding, for example between two chlorine atoms to form a chlorine molecule, each of the valence electrons of the atoms is shared by the other. When such a bond is broken, the normal result is that both electrons stay with one of the atoms, so forming charged ions. This process is known as *heterolytic fission*. Occasionally, however, under certain conditions, the bond may be broken in such a way that each fragment retains one of the bonding electrons. This process is known as *homolytic fission*, and the resulting fragments are known as *free radicals*.

Because these free radicals possess a single unpaired electron, they are generally extremely reactive, much more so than the corresponding ions, and two such radicals will readily combine to form a new covalent bond. In addition, a free radical will also unite with a chemically stable molecule to form another free radical. This new free radical will also be very reactive, and there is every possibility that it will combine yet again with another stable molecule.

Free radicals occur most frequently in organic chemistry. Knowledge about the formation of these radicals and the mechanism by which they combine has played an essential part in many manufacturing processes based on organic compounds. One of the most important of these is the formation of long chain molecules in the manufacture of plastics.

When writing a chemical equation to represent a reaction involving free radicals, chemists use a special notation to distinguish between free radicals and ions. Thus, for example, a hydroxyl free radical is written OH, while the equivalent ion is OH^-. Similarly, the reaction of a methyl free radical with a carbon tetrachloride molecule is written:

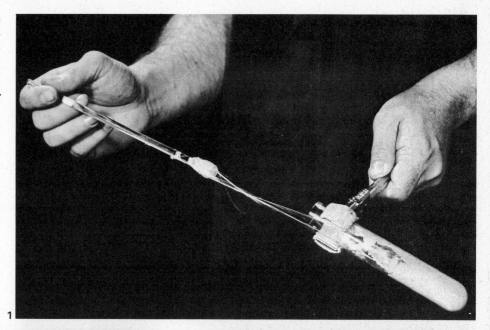

1 Nylon fibres drawn from a test-tube show that the material can be formed into narrow, immensely strong filaments which can then be spun and used in textiles.

2 Extremely thin plastic films can now be made at a very low price, and are used for many purposes. These rolls of mylar will form the base for magnetic recording tape.

$$CH_3^{\cdot} + CCl_4 \rightarrow CH_3Cl + {}^{\cdot}CCl_3.$$

This reaction gives methyl chloride and the trichloromethyl free radical.

But by far the most important reaction of free radicals, the basis of most commercial polymerization reactions for making plastics, occurs when they attack and add on to a carbon-carbon double bond. For instance, a methyl radical reacts with vinyl chloride at the double bond thus:

$$CH_3^{\cdot} + CH_2 = CHCl \rightarrow CH_3CH_2\, CHCl.$$

The chloropropyl free radical produced then reacts with more vinyl chloride, and so on along a chain reaction until the polymer *polyvinylchloride* (PVC) is formed. Almost any free radical will start off such a polymerization reaction. The material which gives rise to the free radicals is called the *initiator* of the polymerization. Regeneration of a free radical at the first step is common to all such chain reactions especially in plastics manufacture.

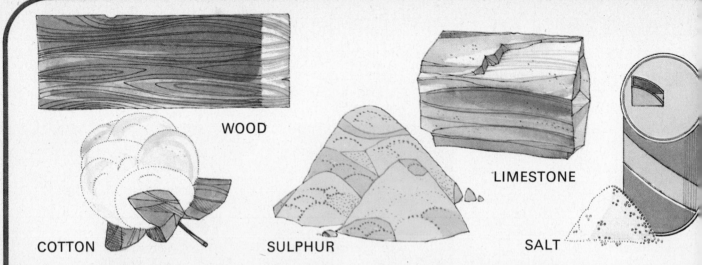

WOOD

LIMESTONE

COTTON

SULPHUR

SALT

Naturally occurring materials provide the starting point for the manufacture of plastics. The raw materials used are determined by the nature of the finished product, although very often alternative starting materials can be used. Oil and natural gas are the most widely used raw materials, and the industry which has been built up on these, and which manufactures many products other than plastics, is known as the petro-

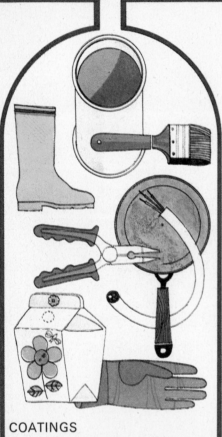

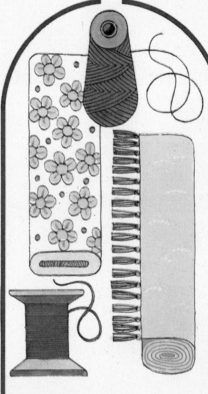

COATINGS
Various plastics are used to provide protective or non-stick coatings. They also provide the materials for tool handles. Many paints have a synthetic rubber base. Cartons can be given a waterproof plastic lining.

SYNTHETIC FIBRES
Clothes, furnishing fabrics and carpets are all end-products of the plastics industry. Synthetic fibres, although they do not look or feel like normal plastics, are made by the same methods.

FLEXIBLE PLASTICS AND FOAM
Bottles, brush handles, toys and artificial sponges are examples of the uses of flexible plastics. They are very resistant to accidental damage. Polyethylene is one of the most widely used of these materials.

The next stage is called *propagation*, in which the radical formed in the first step adds more vinyl chloride units successively to form a long chain, which is still a free radical:

$$RCH_2\overset{.}{C}HCl + CH_2 = CHCl \rightarrow$$
$$RCH_2CH\overset{.}{C}lCH_2CHCl$$

to give eventually

$$R(CH_2CHCl)_x CH_2\overset{.}{C}HCl,$$

where x may be 1000 or more.

If no other factors influenced the process, polymerization would continue in this way until all the vinyl chloride starting material was used up. In practice, however, there is a third and final stage called *termination*. In this step, two of the long-chain free radicals from the chain propagation stage meet end to end. They may react with each other by combination to form an even longer stable molecule:

$$-CH_2CHCl + Cl H\overset{.}{C}CH_2 - \rightarrow$$
$$CH_2CHClCHClCH_2 -$$

Or one radical may claim a hydrogen atom from the other in the process called *disproportionation*:

$$-CH_2\overset{.}{C}HCl + ClH\overset{.}{C}CH_2 - \rightarrow$$
$$-CH_2CH_2Cl + ClHC = CH -,$$

resulting in the formation of two separate stable molecules. The polymerization of styrene to form polystyrene terminates by combination and that of methyl methacrylate by disproportionation.

Free radical initiators may start chain

NATURAL GAS

COAL

OIL

WATER

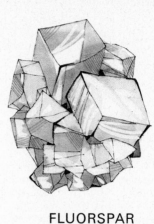

FLUORSPAR

chemical industry. Wood and cotton, composed of cellulose which is a naturally occurring polymer, are used to manufacture rayon, the oldest of all artificial fibres. It was comparison of the molecules of rayon and natural rubber, giving chemists their first clue to the relationship between molecular structure and physical properties, and gave them a lead towards the relationship between chemical formulae and physical properties.

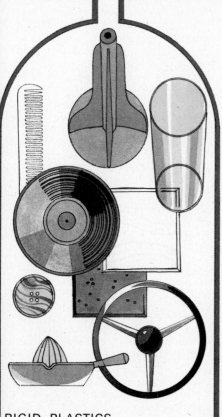

RIGID PLASTICS
Nylon, polyethylene and polyvinyl chloride are typical rigid plastics. The drinking glass shown is made from cellulose acetate, which has absolutely no taste. Rigid plastics are variants of other forms.

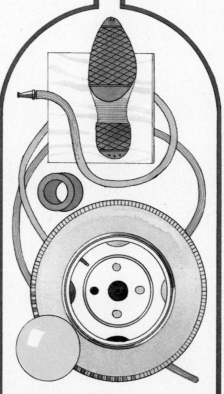

SYNTHETIC RUBBERS
Shortage of natural rubber during the Second World War accelerated the development of synthetic varieties. These are now more widely used than natural rubber, as their properties can be tailored to the application.

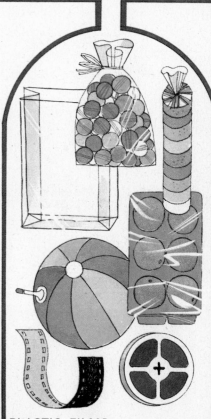

PLASTIC FILMS
Magnetic recording tape, photographic film and packaging are three major uses of plastic films. The thickness and strength of these can be very accurately controlled during the manufacturing stage.

reactions that do not involve polymerization. For example, the gases chlorine and ethane show no tendency to react with each other even when mixed and heated. But if a trace of tetraethyl lead is added to the hot mixture, the reaction rapidly goes to completion with the formation of ethyl chloride and hydrogen chloride. Ignoring the role of the free radicals, we would write the formal equation for the reaction as:

$$C_2H_6 + Cl_2 \rightarrow C_2H_5Cl + HCl.$$

However, the true mechanism is probably first a formation of a few ethyl radicals from the lead compound:

$$Pb(C_2H_5)_4 \rightarrow Pb + 4C_2H_5^{\cdot}.$$

These radicals then attack the chlorine molecules to form chlorine atoms (radicals) as the first step in a chain reaction:

$$C_2H_5^{\cdot} + Cl_2 \rightarrow C_2H_5Cl + Cl^{\cdot},$$

the second step being the rapid reaction between chlorine atoms and ethane:

$$C_2H_6 + Cl^{\cdot} \rightarrow HCl + C_2H_5^{\cdot}.$$

Ethyl radicals are regenerated by the second step to keep the chain going. The use of free radicals to form compounds of the halogens with the paraffin hydrocarbons has important commercial applications for making solvents and anaesthetics.

When a mixture of hydrogen and chlorine is exposed to light, some chlorine molecules decompose into atoms or radicals:

$$Cl_2 \rightarrow 2Cl^{\cdot}.$$

The following reaction then takes place extremely rapidly:

$$Cl^{\cdot}+H_2\rightarrow HCl+H^{\cdot},$$

and the hydrogen atoms immediately combine with chlorine to liberate more chlorine atoms:

$$H^{\cdot}+Cl_2\rightarrow HCl+Cl^{\cdot}.$$

The chain of reactions continues consecutively until all the reactants are used up. However, this takes only a fraction of a second and the result is a violent explosion. The recombination of pairs of atoms to form molecules of hydrogen and chlorine and the combination of a hydrogen atom and a chlorine atom to form a molecule of hydrogen chloride are termination reactions which use up free atoms and stop the chains. These reactions take place at the walls of the container. Introducing powdered silica or thousands of tiny glass beads into the container increases the effective surface and slows down the chain reaction.

In other reactions, the chains *start* at the walls of the vessel. For instance, if jets of hydrogen and oxygen are brought together in the centre of a large vessel, no reaction takes place. But if a quartz rod is placed at the mixing point, or if a smaller vessel is used, there is an explosion as the gases react violently. Probably hydrogen and oxygen molecules combine at the walls to give hydroxyl radicals:

$$H_2+O_2\rightarrow 2^{\cdot}OH.$$

These radicals then start two rapid chain reactions:

$$H_2+{}^{\cdot}OH\rightarrow H_2O+H^{\cdot},$$

and

$$H_2+O_2+H^{\cdot}\rightarrow H_2O+{}^{\cdot}OH.$$

The hydroxyl radical is thus regenerated and keeps the chains going.

In industry, free radicals obtained by the action of heat or light on organic or inorganic initiators are used to spark off polymerizations for making plastics. These may be carried out in bulk, in solution, in suspension, or with the ingredients combined with water to form an emulsion.

Bulk polymerization is not used when much heat is given out by the process, especially when the initiator generates its free radical by thermal decomposition. Small regions within the bulk of the ingredients may get much hotter than others, leading to a 'runaway' formation of solid products within the larger fluid mass. The method is usually reserved for making castings in acrylic plastics.

Polymerization in solution also presents practical problems because of the difficulty of removing *all* the solvent from the product. The method is used, however, when the polymer is normally supplied in solution form. For example, polyvinyl alcohol is generally sold in such a form for direct use as a lacquer, varnish, or adhesive.

In suspension polymerization, the free radical initiator is first dissolved in the starting material and the resulting solution suspended as droplets in water. For example, in the manufacture of polymethyl methacrylate (Perspex), a benzoyl peroxide initiator is dissolved in methyl methacrylate. The solution is then suspended in water containing an electrolyte, such as sodium sulphate, which encourages the formation of droplets.

Making hybrid plastics

In emulsion polymerization, the initiator is first dissolved in water and the starting materials emulsified in it with the aid of a wetting agent (a soap or detergent). The method is particularly useful in the manufacture of *copolymers* in which two different plastics are formed simultaneously. The synthetic rubber made on a large scale in the United States during the Second World War was a copolymer of styrene and butadiene called SBR (styrene-butadiene rubber) produced by emulsion polymerization. A mixture of three parts styrene to one part butadiene was emulsified in water, using ordinary soap.

During the last 50 years, free radicals, which started as chemical curiosities, have become essential tools to the synthetic chemical industry. Many solvents and practically all plastics and synthetic rubbers are made by chain reactions initiated by traces of free radicals. Now that the mechanism of polymerization is understood, chemists can design plastics for specific applications. By selecting the appropriate starting materials and the right free radical initiator, they can produce polymers with exactly the right strength, rigidity, flexibility, elasticity, or moulding properties or whatever combination of these properties is required.

1 Many of the components of motor vehicles including tyres, seats, and in some cases even the bodywork, are plastics made by free radicals.

2 Production of synthetic rubber is now a major international industry. Its output far exceeds that of natural rubber.

The shapely world of crystals

The practice of crystal-gazing is not confined solely to gipsies; scientists do it as well. But unlike gipsies, scientists do not foretell the future by looking at crystals; they make it.

THE WORD 'CRYSTAL' comes from the Greek *kryos,* meaning 'extremely cold', and possibly derived from the lacy crystalline structures of ice and snow. It is easy to see how an artist or designer might find interest in studying these delicately beautiful structures, but why should hard-headed, no-nonsense scientists have made crystallography (the study of crystals) a highly respected branch of their pursuits?

At first, scientists began studying crystals out of curiosity. But in modern times, they continue to study crystals because crystals are so useful. The word 'crystal' no longer refers exclusively to ice and snow, but to any substance, generally solid, 'whose atoms are arranged in a definite pattern, the crystal faces being the outward expression of the regular arrangement of the atoms'. And this includes an enormous variety of things, from common table salt to steel girders for skyscrapers and components for electronic computers. So a good theoretical knowledge of crystals can have important practical applications.

The most striking feature of the crystals comprising salt, for example, is their similarity; they all have exactly the same cubic shape. This is true of all crystalline substances – their crystals all have the same shape, though they are not necessarily cubic. The similarity of the shape of the crystals of a given substance was investigated in the seventeenth century by the Danish physicist Niels Stensen (1638–86). He studied the angles between the faces of quartz crystals (often found in sand), and found that the angles formed by the faces of a crystal have a definite mathematical relationship.

Lattices and symmetries

This discovery, announced in 1669, is nowadays sometimes referred to as the First Law of Crystallography, and is explained in terms of 'lattice' structures. A crystal lattice can be likened to the structure of steel girders for a large building. A lattice is a regular, three-dimensional pattern of points joined by some kind of connecting bonds. The girders correspond to the chemical bonds between the atoms and molecules of the lattice, and the atoms and molecules are the points of intersection of the girders.

An important concept in considering crystal forces and crystal lattices is symmetry. The most well-known form of symmetry is that in which a line down the middle of an object divides it into two halves, each a mirror-image of the other. For example, a capital 'A' has this kind of symmetry, which is called *bilateral.* Another symmetry operation is rotating an object about an axis. If, after a rotation less than a full turn, the object looks the

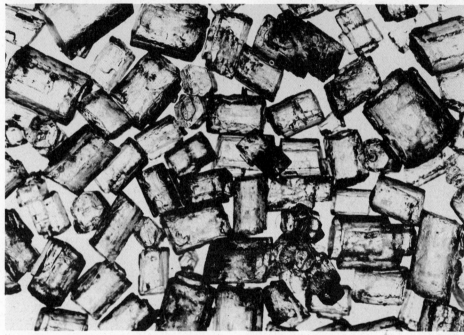

The delicate designs of snowflakes, *top left and right,* are of interest both to the artist and the scientist. The artist, of course, takes delight in their infinite variety; the scientist in their regular crystalline structure. All snow crystals are symmetrical and hexagonal (six-sided). Mineral crystals are more permanent than snowflakes, but also exhibit symmetry and definite geometrical structures. *Above,* 'hypo' crystals, in solution, are used in photography.

same as it did originally, the object is said to have rotational symmetry about the axis.

For instance, a rectangular sheet of paper rotated about a pin through the centre (the intersection of the diagonals) shows this kind of symmetry. If it is rotated through half a turn, it looks exactly as if it had not been moved. An axis through the centre of opposite faces of a cube would show the same kind of symmetry in three dimensions.

Applying the various types of symmetry to the crystal lattice, the French physicist Auguste Bravais (1811–63) showed that all lattices can be put in one of 14 possible classes, each having a different combina-

tion of symmetry operations. Bravais realized, however, that his 14 lattices did not explain all crystal shapes, and correctly credited the remaining variations to the particular arrangements within the crystals themselves. These usually come from one of the two main kinds of chemical bond, *ionic* and *covalent.*

Sodium chloride (common salt) is an example of ionic bonding, in which the sodium atoms each give up a negative electron and so acquire a positive charge. The chlorine atoms each take up an electron, and so acquire a negative charge. The charged atoms are called *ions.* There is an electrostatic attraction between each positively charged ion and all its

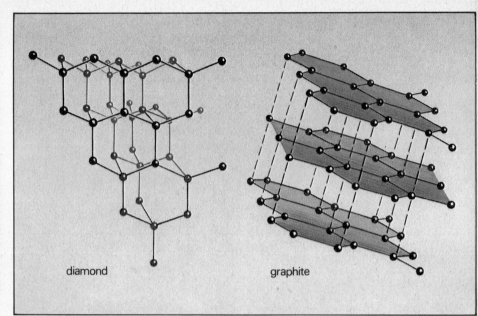

The internal structure of a crystal may be likened to the steel and rivet supports of a bridge, *top left*. The girders represent the inter-molecular forces holding the structure together, and the intersections of the girders locate the atoms and molecules of the crystal. Of course, in an actual crystal, the 'girders' are not solid chunks of matter, but invisible force fields. *Top right*, diamond and graphite are both forms of carbon; yet diamond is the hardest of all naturally occurring substances, and graphite is so soft that it is used for pencil 'lead'. The difference is that diamond forms a complex crystal which resists cleavage, but the layers of the graphite crystal easily slide over one another. *Bottom left*, crystals of zeolite take characteristic needle shapes, which help to identify the mineral. *Bottom right*, crystal-gazing is not reserved for the microscope alone. Many crystals, like these of tourmaline, together with quartz and apatite, are quite easy enough to see with the naked eye.

negatively charged neighbours. No ion has a special attraction for any particular oppositely charged neighbour; all are equally attractive, and are an equal distance away. For this reason, the atoms fit very well into a regular crystal lattice.

Covalent bonding involves the sharing of electrons with a particular neighbour or neighbours. In this case, the forces between bonded neighbours are much greater than the forces between neighbours which are not bonded to each other.

Diamond is a good example of covalently bonded crystal structure, and why crystal structures are so important. Diamonds, used industrially for cutting and drilling metals, are pure carbon. Graphite used in pencil 'leads' is also pure carbon. Graphite is extremely soft, and diamond is the hardest natural substance known. The difference is in the crystalline structure. Each atom of a diamond is covalently bonded to four neighbours in a rigid lattice, and each neighbour in turn is bonded to four more, and so on. In order to break a diamond, we must break millions of the strong covalent bonds between the carbon atoms in the lattice. Graphite has a crystalline structure which allows one 'plane' to slide over another, so it is not very rigid at all.

A sea of electrons

The atoms of metallic elements, when they are not chemically combined with other elements, show a special kind of bonding between themselves, which is rather like ionic bonding. Each of the atoms in the crystal lattice of a metal releases one or more electrons and so acquires a positive charge. The result can best be visualized as a sea of negatively charged electrons, dotted regularly with islands which are positively charged metal atoms or 'ions'. This sea of electrons, unattached to any particular atom, can 'flow' in an electric field. This is the explanation of the ability of metals to conduct electricity.

For the sake of discussion, atoms and ions of the same element can be considered as identical small spheres, and a crystal as thousands of spheres packed together. There are two ways of packing identical spheres as close as possible to leave the minimum volume unoccupied, and these are the basis of the structures of many unalloyed metals. One arrangement is the 'cubic-closest-packed', in which each sphere is in contact with 12 'nearest neighbours' – four above, four around it, and four below. The other arrangement, the 'hexagonal-closest-packed', also has each sphere in contact with 12 nearest neighbours – three above, six around it, and three below.

The cubic-closest-packed structure has vertical and diagonal planes of atoms in addition to horizontal planes, but the only planes in the hexagonal-closest-packed arrangements are horizontal. Deformation of metals by external forces, such as bending, is a result of planes of atoms within the metal crystal lattice sliding across other planes of atoms. Metals of the cubic-closest-packed structure, which has planes in many directions, are therefore easily deformed, are not resistant to ham-

mering and are easily drawn into wire. Examples are copper, silver, gold and nickel.

You can see this sliding action by experimenting with a simple model. Take a paperback book (in which the pages correspond to layers of atoms) and hold it with one hand gripping near the edges of the pages. If you hold the book lightly and bend it along the length of the pages, you will see how the pages slide over each other. But if you grip the book very tightly, you will not be able to bend it at all.

The hexagonal-closest-packed arrangement is the basis of metals with more resistance to deformation, and a greater resistance at right angles to the planes of atoms than along the planes. This is an example of *anisotropy,* in which properties of a crystal are not the same in every direction. Examples of metals with the hexagonal-closest-packed structure are zinc and magnesium.

These explanations of crystal shape were all suspected long before any definite proof of the atomic arrangement was found. An ordinary optical microscope was of no help: the smallest object it can detect is about 1,000 Ångström units (Å) across. The atoms in iron, for instance, are 2·3 Å apart (100 million Ångström units equal one centimetre). Detection of such distances requires a much shorter wavelength than that of the visible light used in the optical microscope.

Confirming the suspicions

The German crystallographer Max von Laue (1879–1960) was discussing this problem at Munich in 1912, when the idea occurred to him that planes of atoms in a crystal might act like a diffraction grating for X-rays. The effect would be rather like a reflection of X-rays by a plane of atoms. Following this suggestion two experimenters at Munich University shone a narrow beam of X-rays through a crystal of zinc sulphide, producing a pattern of dots which was photographed.

Since then, various methods of producing diffraction patterns have been tried. The most widely used technique involves rotating a crystal in a beam of X-rays which are all of the same wavelength, and photographing the diffraction pattern produced. It is possible, in most cases, to work out the structure which corresponds to the X-ray diffraction pattern produced by a crystal. The precision of the rotating-crystal method has allowed calculations not only of relative positions of atoms, but of actual sizes and interatomic distances.

Experiments of this type have proved certain crystal structures, but there is a further problem about crystals. If they have

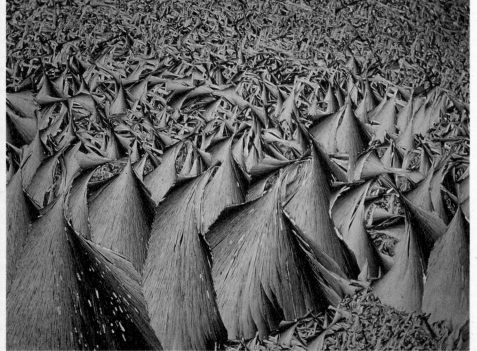

Nature seems to have anticipated modern art in the weird and wonderful designs of microscopic crystals. *Left,* the crystal structure of ammonium strontium platino-cyanide. *Below left,* the crystal of the mineral piperine. *Below right,* the crystal structure of sodium platino-cyanide.

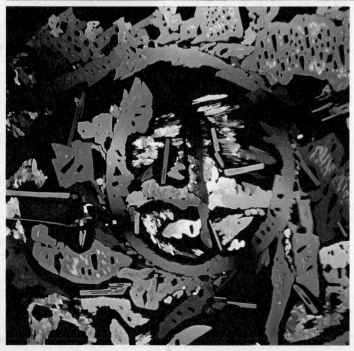

Diamonds serve mankind in two important ways. *Left,* an impregnated diamond wheel grinds the wear surface of an alumina ceramic cast. Only diamond, the hardest known natural substance in the world, can grind this ceramic, the hardest known synthetic substance. *Right,* diamonds as gem stones. Because of diamond's multi-faced crystalline structure, light can bounce round inside, producing the characteristic sparkle.

such regularity of structure, and there are strong forces between the atoms, why do they not display greater mechanical strength? Theoretical estimates of crystal strength give values a thousand times greater than those which are found experimentally. In fact, pure crystals of the metal tellurium have so little strength that they deform under their own weight at room temperature.

The type of force which breaks crystals and to which they have such surprisingly low resistance is a *shear* force. This can be visualized by thinking of a crystal anchored at the base being pushed from one side. When the pushing or shearing force becomes too great, the crystal deforms by the process of *slip*. This is a sliding of the planes of atoms across each other, and is the type of structural flaw which makes graphite so much softer than diamond, even though they are both a form of carbon. Similar shearing by slip along planes occurs when a short pile of books is pushed from one side. This slip deformation process is generally much easier to produce than expected due to the presence of small imperfections in the crystal lattice. These imperfections are *dislocations* in which one part of the crystal has slipped a short distance across the next, and set up a region of strain in the crystal.

When there is an external shear force on a crystal, slip starts from these dislocations, and the crystal deforms. There are two types of dislocation. When there is an *edge* dislocation, part of the crystal has slipped a short distance across the rest. The slipped region joins the unslipped remainder at the position of the edge dislocation. This situation is rather like a badly bound paperback book, in which the glue in the binding has allowed one page to slide forward a little. The dislocation is where the loose page meets the binding glue.

The other type of dislocation is the *screw* dislocation. This is like cutting part of the way into a crystal, and twisting the two halves of the cut in opposite directions. The number of dislocations crossing a square centimetre of a crystal is known as the *dislocation density*. Very well-formed crystals of germanium or silicon may have a density of between a hundred and a thousand dislocations per square centimetre. Heavily deformed metal crystals have densities of many millions of dislocations per square centimetre.

Whiskers and dislocations

Evidence for the existence of dislocations is provided in pictures produced by the electron microscope. Detection of dislocations involves etching the surface of the crystal with a chemical which dissolves it. This cleans the surface, and causes a pit in the surface where there is a dislocation. When the surface is viewed under an electron microscope, the pits show up. Dislocations can also be detected and counted by transmitting X-rays through a sample which has been etched. The dislocations show up as dark patches on an X-ray photograph.

One way of overcoming the weakening effect of dislocations is by stopping their movement through the crystal with small traces of foreign atoms. The presence of carbon in iron, for instance, 'pins' the dislocations and greatly increases the strength of the iron. Minute quantities of carbon alloyed with soft iron is the basis of steel, which is many times stronger because of the carbon 'pins'. Further effects which can arise from alloying metals are the increasing of irregularity within the metal. This increases the dislocation density to the point where the dislocations tangle and prevent each other from moving. Again the result is a strengthening of the metal.

The theory of dislocations throws some light on another problem: a crystal's rate of growth, which is much higher than theoretical predictions would suggest. Crystals of salts and sugars can be grown by dissolving as much as possible of the substance in water to give a *saturated* solution. A small well-formed crystal (the 'seed') is suspended on a piece of cotton into the solution, which is left uncovered and undisturbed. As the water in the solution evaporates, there will be an excess of the dissolved substance – the solution becomes *super-saturated*. Some of the excess is deposited on the suspended crystal, making it grow. Over a matter of days or weeks, large crystals can be grown by this method.

The theoretical prediction is that crystal growth from a super-saturated solution would be slow because of the difficulty of starting a new layer of atoms on the existing crystal surface. However, the presence of dislocations, which stop the crystal surface from being perfectly smooth, removes this difficulty. The presence of a screw dislocation can cause a rapid spiral growth of a crystal.

Another phenomenon of crystal growth is the development of hair-like *whiskers* in highly super-saturated solutions. These are very thin and can grow extremely quickly. They seem to be based on a single screw dislocation down their middle. This screw dislocation is immovable, so there is no starting point for the slip process and consequently these whiskers are very strong. For example, whiskers of tin are over a thousand times as strong as ordinary tin in bulk.

In many cases, the intense study of crystals has yielded information of direct benefit to industry and economic progress. In other cases, the information gleaned has remained the property of the theoretical physicists. But this does not mean that theoretical studies have been a waste of time. Just because no immediate applications have emerged, it does not mean that applications never will emerge. After all, when Niels Stensen began his investigations out of curiosity 300 years ago, he could not have begun to imagine how his labours would bear practical fruit in the twentieth century.

Metals take shape

Through a study of the structure of metals, their ores and alloys, metallurgists are paving the way for technological advances. The air and space industries constantly demand new alloys for new uses.

THERE IS little doubt that the first metals to be used by Man were those occurring in the native state – relatively pure ores in which the metal was combined with only a small proportion of other materials. Much of the iron used in early iron-work came from meteorites, while metals such as copper, gold and silver were found in surface quartz.

Craftsmanship in metals had reached a high standard as long ago as 1000 BC, when the Hittites, by careful control of carbon content during iron smelting, were able to make steel. In the third century A D metal workers in Damascus were making steel swords of a temper and quality that have hardly been surpassed. By the time of Paracelsus (1493–1541), metal workers had at their disposal more than 18 different metals, including zinc, mercury, antimony, iron, copper and lead, and had worked out methods of separating them from their ores.

Crystal structures of metals

Nevertheless, very little was known about the chemistry and physical structure of individual metals, and progress virtually depended upon empirical methods until the 1860s when Professor Henry Sorby of Sheffield laid the foundations on which was built the present science of metallurgy.

In 1861, Sorby invented the method of examining metals by treating their polished surfaces with etching materials and then observing them through a microscope. He also devised a technique for preparing thin slices of rock for microscopic examination. In this way he was able to prove that all metals are crystalline in structure, though this is not apparent from their surfaces. The crystal structure of a metal is one of its most important attributes, and anything done to a metal that alters its crystal structure affects its other physical properties: it may make it more or less liable to fracture, increase or decrease its temper or lengthen or shorten the time when it begins to suffer from fatigue. Crystal structure is equally important in the compounding of alloys designed for some specific purpose.

The modern technique for examining and establishing the crystalline structure of a specific metal is to melt some in a crucible and then allow it to solidify. Next, a piece of the metal is cut off and given a mirror-like polish with abrasives. The shiny surface is then dissolved away with a chemical reagent, so that crystals are attacked, resulting in the surface of the sample being no longer smooth. The crystal pattern can be seen quite distinctly through a microscope.

Liquid metal consists of a mass of atoms moving about independently of each other. When the metal starts to cool, small

1

2

3

groups of atoms, called *nuclei,* which are, in fact, tiny specks of solid metal, appear scattered throughout the liquid. As the metal cools, the groups of atoms build up into a lattice. When the metal solidifies, it consists of a matrix or mass of solid grains. The lattice consists of metal atoms arranged in a geometrical pattern. Each metal has its own specific pattern of crystals by which it can be identified.

While the metal is cooling, the lattice patterns formed simultaneously at several points grow as more solidifies. As the lattices form they extend out to meet each other in arrangements called *dendrites.* These are arranged rather like pine trees with long branches. As cooling continues, the dendrites continue extending until their branches interlock with more of their neighbours. The remainder of the molten metal then solidifies in the spaces between them until a solid metal structure is formed.

A lattice is a three-dimensional complex of atoms arranged in planes with all the atoms spaced at approximately equal distances from each other. They normally maintain these positions because there is a balance between the repulsive and attractive forces acting on them. Any outside influence that tends to disturb them and so distort the lattice meets with resistance. The strength or weakness of that resistance is the strength or weakness of the metal.

As the planes of the atoms in the crystals are not aligned with each other, the lattices are unable to react uniformly to any stress applied to the metal. If, for example, a strip of metal is bent backwards and forwards it will ultimately fracture. The reason for this is that the stress on the metal is being applied at right angles to the crystal lattice and so separating two of the planes of atoms.

On the other hand, if a shearing force is applied to the metal, one plane of atoms will slide over another. This sliding continues as long as the shearing force continues. Consequently, the lattices are deformed and the metal weakened. But if the application of the shearing force is stopped and deformation has not been applied too long, the atoms in the crystals

1 Found in the River Thames near London, this embossed bronze shield is a fine example of Iron-Age English metal-work. Bronze was gradually superseded by iron for most applications.
2 The internal structure of this lead water-pipe clearly demonstrates the crystals within the metal. The larger internal crystals are formed by the slower cooling of the inside of the pipe.
3 An electromagnet is used to test a steel shaft. Magnetic iron oxide particles sprayed on the surface adhere to lines of cracks on or just below the surface, revealing the faults.

return to their original planes and the metal's strength is restored. It is only when a shearing force is applied to its destructive limit that the metal fractures or fails.

The weakest point in any metal is the boundary between the grains, so that a metal's strength is to a great extent dependent upon the cohesion between grains. Where cohesion is good, the metal will have high strength, but where cohesion is poor, the metal will be liable to brittleness and fracture. In general, the finer the grains, the harder and stronger the metal. This fact provides metallurgists with one of the most important methods of controlling the properties of a metal.

It is difficult to give an exact definition of what constitutes a metal. Reference to the periodic table is not very helpful as there is no sharp distinction between those elements that are essentially metallic and those that are non-metallic. Elements such as carbon and arsenic seem to be borderline cases, as they have metallic and non-metallic features. However, metallic elements have some or all of the following characteristics in common: they have few electrons in the outer shells of their atoms, and have a tendency to lose electrons, either through chemical reaction or when some form of energy is applied to them. For example, the more sensitive and active metals lose electrons when light strikes them and they can be used in photo-electric devices. Metals also lose electrons when heated, making it possible to use them as the filaments in electronic tubes. The tendency of certain metals to lose electrons makes them good conductors of electricity. The greater the metal's tendency to electron loss, the better its conductivity. Metals are also good conductors of heat. When polished they assume a characteristic shiny surface and the close packing of the atoms in metals makes them much harder and stronger than other elements. Finally, metals have a greater tendency to combine chemically with non-metallic elements than with each other.

Metal groups

Once the characteristics of an element have been established to identify it as a metal, the metallurgist can classify the metals into four main groups; heavy metals; aluminium metals; alkali metals; and alkaline earth metals. The heavy metals can then be divided in sub-groups: for example, the iron group or the platinum group.

Heavy metals are very useful to Man. They usually occur in nature as silicates, carbonates, sulphides or oxides. These are insoluble compounds and form the bulk of the Earth's crust. With the exception of iron, the heavy metals are less common than the light ones, indeed, many are comparatively rare. Examples of the more rare and valuable heavy metals are nickel, tin, tungsten, chromium, copper, lead, zinc and gold.

Aluminium is virtually the only industrially important metal in the aluminium group. It is the most abundant and widely distributed of all metals – comprising

about eight per cent of the Earth's crust – because it is an active element, it is not easy to extract from the compounds in which it occurs in nature. Bauxite is the only natural aluminium ore from which the metal can be extracted profitably.

Best-known of the alkali metals are potassium and sodium. Practically all the salts formed from alkali metals are soluble in water, and in the course of millions of years this has caused them to dissolve in the rains and other waters that percolate through the Earth.

Amongst the best known of the alkaline earth metals are radium, strontium, beryllium, calcium, magnesium and barium. The salts of many of them are soluble and compounds of some, such as calcium and magnesium are relatively abundant in sea water. On the other hand, some of their compounds are insoluble, so that they are abundant on land. Although less active than alkali metals, alkaline earth metals have a strong affinity for other elements and it is usually difficult to separate them from their compounds.

1 Old-style forges like this are now uncommon, though there is still a demand for the metal-worker's skills. Here, an iron rod and its intricately worked head are about to be hammered together, after heating to white heat over a coke furnace.
2 Aluminium ingots in store at the Valco smelter, Tema, Ghana. The growing demand for this light and versatile metal has encouraged the expansion of mining of bauxite, the ore from which it is most easily extracted.
3 A section of an iron meteorite found in Agusta County, United States. The crystalline structure of the metal is brought out by polishing. The great heat to which meteorites are subjected falling through the Earth's atmosphere causes the formation of high-temperature crystal structures.
4 Taking a sample of steel from a furnace. The molten metal is spooned out of the furnace, poured into a small mould and left to solidify. The solid plug of metal formed in this way is then taken to the laboratory, where metallurgists examine and test the sample to find out whether the furnace is ready to be 'tapped'.
5 Welding involves joining together pieces of metal by melting a metal alloy into the gap between them. The heat to melt the alloy is provided by an intense electric arc.

4

5

Metals occur in minerals, rocks and ores. A true mineral is a natural chemical element or compound of elements. Quartz, marble, water and diamond are minerals. Not all minerals contain metals. Rocks, however, are mixtures of minerals which are so intermingled that only careful chemical analysis identifies their constituents. Ores are rocks or minerals from which the metals can be extracted economically. This is governed by the kind of metal that can be extracted from a given quantity of ore. For example, it is not economically feasible to process a ton of iron pyrites containing 40 per cent iron because of the low price of iron and the difficulty of extracting pure iron from that source. On the other hand, gold-bearing ore containing only an ounce of the precious metal to the ton is well worth working because of the scarcity and high price of gold.

Extraction and application

There are two main branches of metallurgy: the first is concerned with the extraction of metals from their ores or other sources, and the other deals with the application of the metals to industrial and other purposes. The vast majority of metals are found in combination with other elements from which they have to be separated.

The metal-bearing mineral is first separated from other minerals and from waste material, called *gangue*, in a succession of what are called *dressing operations*. After the ore has been broken up by crushers and mills into particles of roughly uniform size, it is concentrated in classifiers or flotation tanks. In many modern mines, the separation is done in these tanks which are continually agitated. By using a suitable liquid it is possible to arrange that one of the constituents is carried to the surface by the air bubbles while the others, being 'wetted', sink to the bottom.

In the next stage, the metal-bearing

mineral is treated chemically to separate the desired metal from the sulphur, oxygen or other elements with which it is combined. Different methods are adopted for treating each mineral.

Separation processes fall into three main groups. Firstly, smelting, whereby the concentrated ore is decomposed and the metal released by heat: the smelting of iron in a blast furnace is the best-known example. Next the desired metal is selected out by treating the ore with a solution of salts in water: an example of this is the cyanide treatment for extracting gold. Finally electrolytic techniques separate out the metals by electrolyzing a fused mixture of salts: the chief application of this is in the extraction of aluminium and magnesium.

Whatever the separation process, the crude metal obtained usually requires purifying, refining, before it can be put to any practical use. Some metals, such as nickel, copper, gold and silver, are refined by electrolysis, others, like zinc and cadmium, are refined by fractional distillation in special retorts. Fire-refining methods are used for lead and tin. Some of the rarer metals, beryllium and zirconium, for example, are refined by vacuum distillation.

When a metallurgist is evaluating a specific metal for some particular use, he looks for six main properties: strength, toughness, hardness, ductility, plasticity and brittleness. Special machines are used to measure these properties.

Strength is a measure of the weight or load which a specific metal will carry. Tension, compression and shear are the three chief ways of applying load to a metal, and any one of them may cause the metal to fail.

Fabrication

Strength is determined on a tensile-testing machine which applies a steadily increasing pull to the ends of a standard-shaped testpiece until it breaks. The amount the testpiece can be stretched in this test, before it breaks, indicates how ductile the material is and how suitable for shaping by various pressing operations. The size of the indentation produced when a pyramid or ball of very hard material, such as a diamond, is pressed into the surface of a piece of metal shows how hard the material is.

One of the unwanted properties of metal which has only comparatively recently been understood is fatigue. Fatigue depends upon several factors and, most frequently, occurs in the aluminium alloys, all of which will fail under fatigue stresses.

Contrary to what most people think, a metal is not stronger the more pure it is. In fact, the reverse is generally the case, and this is the chief reason for alloying metals. Alloying was one of the greatest single advances in metal working and has been understood to a limited extent since the Bronze Age. It is only comparatively recently, however, that alloying has advanced to a science.

Metal fabrication has also made tremendous advances since metallurgy became a science. Probably the most important

1 Steel is an alloy of iron and other metals, and its composition must be carefully regulated to ensure that it can easily be machined to a high degree of accuracy.
2 A modern silversmith at work. This ancient craft now makes use of such modern equipment as oxy-hydrogen burners and electric furnaces. But the basic principles of the art remain the same.
3 Radiation can be used to test for faults in metal castings. Here a worker in a Czech heavy engineering plant inserts a small piece of radio-cobalt to test for cracks in a large casting.

developments are in the cold-working of metals, as by spinning and stretch-forming. Powder metallurgy is increasingly used to make small components difficult to fabricate by the more traditional methods. Metal powders, mixed together in the correct proportions are compressed to the required shape and the resultant compacts heated to bind them together. Very hard materials, such as tungsten carbide cutting edges for tools, are often shaped in this way.

The joining of metals is an important province of physical metallurgy, from the familiar soldering or brazing processes to welding at high temperatures using oxy-acetylene or argon arcs or ultrasonic welders. In pressure welding, the metals to be joined are hammered or pressed together, without fusion, into a solid joint.

The coating of iron and steel with other metals, as a protection against rusting, for decorative purposes or to provide a hard surface is the basis of a number of specialized industries. Such coatings are applied by dipping, spraying, electroplating or cementation processes; galvanized hardware, tinned-food cans and chromium-plated cutlery are typical examples of their products.

Mixing metals

In their pure state, many metals are unsuitable for practical use. But by mixing two or more together, alloys can be produced with a huge range of special properties for particular applications.

APPROXIMATELY 75 per cent of the 92 natural elements found on Earth are classed as metals; of these only some two dozen are in common use as the basic materials from which are fabricated the countless everyday metal objects. The remaining metals are either too rare, too difficult to extract from their ores, or are too unstable for practical purposes. It is only by the process called alloying that Man has learned how to exploit to the full the wide range of metals at his disposal.

Even the commonest metals, such as iron, copper, aluminium, lead, have extremely limited applications in their pure state, because they are either too soft, too brittle, are too heavy, are too easily attacked by corrosion or are too liable to melt. However, most metals are capable of uniting with other metals to provide a composite mixture or alloy of metals possessing desired qualities that no component of the alloy possesses of itself in any marked degree.

Metallurgists define an alloy as an amalgam of two or more metals mixed together for such purposes as improving strength, hardness and heat-resistance. The properties of such an alloy are normally very different from those of its individual components. By varying the kinds and amounts of the metals incorporated in the mixture some 6,000 different alloys are now available and almost any desired qualities can be obtained.

Metals together

Nearly all alloys consist of mixtures or combinations of two or more of the following elements in various proportions: aluminium, antimony, arsenic, bismuth, cadmium, carbon, chromium, cobalt, copper, gold, iridum, iron, lead, magnesium, manganese, mercury, molybdenum, nickel, palladium, phosphorus, platinum, silicon, silver, thorium, tin, tungsten, vanadium, zinc. Most alloys are made by melting the metals together, but a few are compounded by electrochemical means or by pulverizing the component metals and then mixing and compressing them at a high temperature.

Sometimes when dissimilar metals are melted together to form an alloy they cool as a solid solution. In other words before solidifying, when the metals are still molten the atoms of each wander freely around in the solution. In an alloy of this nature, the metals remain in true solution even after they have cooled and solidified, and microscopic examination will reveal the same type of crystal throughout the alloy without trace of any crystals of either of the constituent metals. An alloy of this type is called a *one-phase* alloy.

There are two types of solid-solution alloys, dependent upon the relative sizes of the atoms of the metallic elements involved. These are called *substitutional* and *interstitial solid solutions*. In the former the two types of metal forming the alloy are of roughly the same size and an atom of one or other of the metals can take a place in a crystal-lattice structure without any great distortion of the lattice. With an interstitial solid solution the atoms of one of the metals are very much smaller and do not take up a place in the crystal-lattice structure. Instead, these atoms squeeze into interstices or gaps. Carbon with its small atoms can do this; steel, an alloy of iron and carbon, is an interstitial solid-solution alloy consisting of atoms of carbon filling in the gaps between the iron atoms.

In other types of alloys the constituent metals are only partially soluble in each other. The resultant alloy, of say two metals, consists of two different types of crystal. One consists largely of one metal with a little of the other metal dissolved in it, while the other type of crystal consists mainly of the second metal. This is what is called a *two-phase alloy* and most alloys are of this nature.

When two alloyed metals are insoluble in one another, crystals of one of the metals are embedded in a finely dispersed metallic mixture. Sometimes atoms of one metal in any alloy will creep into the crystals, stealing the place of atoms of another metal. Alloying two metals is relatively easy and the chemical or metallurgical structure of the alloy is comparatively simple. But when three or more metals are used to form an alloy the structure can become very complex. Despite the alloy looking like a single substance, microscope examination shows that it is made up of tiny crystals of one metal distributed in another.

Alloys that show minimum solubility often form what is technically called an *eutectic*. In such cases the two metals lower each other's melting points, although if the alloy contains specific portions of the two metals, the alloy solidifies as if it were a pure metal. This mutually instantaneous change from the liquid to the solid state is called the *eutectic point*. Another phenomenon of alloys is that

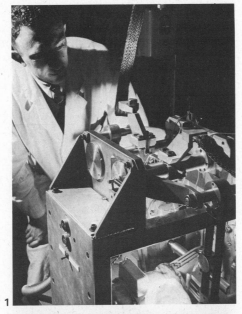

1 In a laboratory, nickel-chromium alloy is tested for resistance to heat fatigue. Specially developed alloys can resist the strain of rapid heating and cooling.
2 Copper alloys have been designed to have specific characteristics. The manganese-copper of this ship's propellor possesses special sound- and vibration-damping features.
3 Aluminium alloys have the great advantage of being exceptionally lightweight. These ridged sheets, produced on a roll-form corrugator, are used by the building industry.

sometimes two metals will combine to form an alloy only if the metals are melted together in certain proportions. Similarly some metals will only combine in certain proportions to form an alloy if they are melted together at a specific temperature; in such cases some of the metals may solidify separately when the alloy cools. In some alloys the metals may combine chemically to form a completely new substance or they may not dissolve into each other but separate into layers as the mixture cools. These layers do, however, solidify together to form a solid mass.

An alloy has different properties from its components because of the atomic structure of metals. Every natural metal is made up from layers of atoms arranged in a fixed pattern. Now imagine a metal with its atoms arranged in layers rather like a new pack of playing-cards. If you push the top cards of the pack, the cards slide over each other quite easily. But if the cards are old and sticky cards, you will have to push harder before the cards slip over each other. This is because the separate cards in the sticky pack are stuck together so that the grip between individual cards is greater and the combined strength of the pack has increased.

Slippery atoms

The layer of atoms in the metal are 'sticky' like the cards in the pack, the 'stickiness' being the electrical forces between the atoms. However, by pushing the atoms hard enough, they can be made to slip, just as the playing-cards were made to slip. That is what happens when an alloy is formed by melting together or otherwise combining two or more metals.

While the metals are molten, their atoms are all mixed up, but as the combined metals cool their various atoms start arranging themselves in layers. But the atoms are not in a regular pattern like those of an individual metal, because an alloy contains two or more metals, each of which has its own particular atomic pattern. Consequently when the metals in an alloy cool, the atom layers are rough and irregular, rather like the cutting edge of a file. Therefore it is much more difficult for mechanical or other conditions of stress to cause the layers of atomic patterns in an alloy to slip over each other. That is why an alloy is generally stronger and harder than the individual metals of which it is composed.

An alloy does not normally consist of equal parts of the metals forming it. The addition of a very small quantity of one metal can completely change the properties of the metal that is in the greater proportion; neither is it necessary that a hard metal be added to a soft metal to form a hard alloy. Aluminium and copper are both metals mechanically weak, but an alloy of 10 per cent aluminium and 90 per cent copper produces a metal three times stronger than pure copper and as strong as mild steel.

Another phenomenon of alloys is that increasing the amount of the strengthening metal does not produce a stronger alloy. Thus an alloy of 16 per cent aluminium and 84 per cent copper produces an

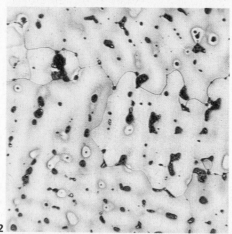

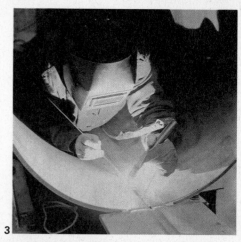

bronze some specially desired qualities. For example, plastic bronze, contains 73 per cent copper, 7 per cent tin, and 20 per cent lead; phosphor-bronze consists of 87·5 per cent copper, 7·5 per cent tin, 1 per cent of zinc, 3·5 per cent of lead, and 0·5 per cent of phosphorus; aluminium bronze contains in addition to tin and copper, 9·5 per cent of aluminium, 2·5 per cent of iron, and up to 2 per cent of nickel and manganese. Gunmetal, a bronze alloy which gets its name from having been first compounded for ship's cannons, consists of 86 per cent copper, 7 per cent tin, 5 per cent zinc and 2 per cent lead.

Bronze is only one of the thousands of different alloys now available to industry. Amongst the older alloys are: brass, a combination of copper and zinc; and pewter, an alloy of lead and tin. Another of the older alloys, and one of the first to take advantage of dissimilar melting and solidifying points of two metals, is the solder used by plumbers for making joints. The chief requirement of solder is that it must melt easily and remain molten long enough for the joint to be shaped by 'wiping' while it is still soft and malleable. This is achieved by alloying three parts of tin and seven parts of lead. Pure lead melts at 327 °C. and tin at 232 °C., but when the two metals are alloyed the solder-alloy stays malleable at 180 °C.

Changing properties

Some alloys are designed to have low re-melting points after solidification. One such is an alloy of tin (melting point 232 °C.), lead (melting point 327 °C.), bismuth (271 °C.) and cadmium (320 °C.). But when these metals are alloyed, the hardened alloy melts at only 66 °C. Because of this low melting point the alloy is used in safety devices such as plugs which melt at excessive rise in atmospheric temperature to set off automatic fire alarms and release fire extinguishers.

Calcium is a good example of a metal that has its natural properties radically changed by alloying. Pure calcium is little harder than wax. Yet an alloy of calcium and lead produces a metal as hard as mild steel. This is a particularly curious phenomenon as lead in its natural state is one of the soft metals.

Copper is one of the best electrical conductors, but power cables made of pure copper would break under their own weight when slung between pylons a reasonable distance apart. To make it strong but still possess high electrical conductivity copper is alloyed with aluminium, cadmium or with another good electrical conductor with poor mechanical strength. Many high-tension power cables are now made from aluminium-copper alloys.

Aluminium alloys are probably the most interesting of all metallurgical techniques. The great advantage of aluminium is its exceptionally light weight, but this is offset by its poor mechanical strength. Hence aluminium can for most purposes be used only when alloyed with a strengthening metal. All the various grades of aluminium used industrially and described as aluminium are, in fact alloys. Most of

1 Aluminium alloy is rolled at a mill. Aluminium can be alloyed with many other metals to increase its hardness and tensile strength.

2 A photograph taken through a microscope shows the structure of gunmetal. This alloy of copper, tin, zinc and lead, gets its name from having been first compounded for ships' cannons.

3 It was at one time impossible to weld copper or any copper alloy. Inert arc gas welding, which prevents the joint from being oxidized, has overcome this problem.

4 Aluminium alloys are used for aircraft because of their light weight and strength. Duralumin, alloy of aluminium, iron, copper, silicon, magnesium and manganese, is nearly as strong as mild steel but only one-third the weight.

5 Stainless steel, an alloy of steel, nickel and chromium, is widely used for household articles and in the chemical industry because of its resistance to corrosion and rust.

6 Aluminium brass is used in the condensing unit of a nuclear reactor. Two per cent aluminium and 98 per cent brass (itself an alloy), it does not corrode in water.

7 Extremely thin sections of an extruded copper alloy are used for window-frames in modern buildings. Strong and durable, they require no protective treatment against weathering.

alloy which is as brittle as a dry twig and quite useless for any mechanical application.

History does not tell us when the first alloy was formed, but it was most certainly a mixture of copper and tin to form bronze. The first bronzes varied greatly in quality and their composition was entirely empirical: the tin content was small and it was long before it reached 5 per cent. But from the primitive copper-tin alloy of nearly 6,000 years ago metallurgists have developed scores of bronze alloys containing other metals to impart to the

New steel alloys are being developed to meet competition from aluminium and plastics. Here they are being tested in a vacuum furnace which simulates atmospheric conditions of production.

them contain iron and silicon to increase aluminium's hardness and tensile strength. Aluminium can be alloyed with nearly all other metals, and many aluminium alloys gain strength by *annealing* (controlled re-heating and cooling) or *age hardening*.

Age hardening of aluminium alloys begins at normal temperatures and, unless the process is controlled, the alloy ingots harden so quickly that they cannot be machined or otherwise fabricated. The age hardening of some aluminium alloys is so rapid that ingots have to be held in refrigerators until required. Scores of aluminium alloys have been developed to combine in one metal the light weight of aluminium with the strength of steels. One of these is duralumin, an alloy of alumium, copper, silicon, iron, magnesium and manganese. Duralumin – extensively used in aircraft – is nearly as strong as mild steel but only one-third as heavy.

Aircraft travelling at supersonic speeds build up high temperatures due to friction with the atmosphere on their fuselage and wing surfaces. Such temperatures would cause serious distortion of ordinary metals and could lead to metal fatigue and failure. This problem was solved by using alloys based on stainless steel and titanium which maintain their strength and do not deform at high temperature.

Iron is a metal which has benefited most from alloying techniques. Adding nickel to cast iron increases appreciably its strength and makes it more resistant to shock, while the mechanical strength of steel (made basically from iron and carbon) is increased fourfold by alloying it with nickel. One of the greatest contributions made by alloys to industry and the household is stainless steel. A commonly used stainless steel consists of 8 per cent nickel, 18 per cent chromium and the remainder steel. Monel, another metal resistant to rust and corrosion, is an alloy of copper and nickel. A form of monel, called cupronickel, which consists of 75 per cent copper and 25 per cent nickel, is used for 'silver' coins because it resists tarnishing.

In its natural state beryllium is a very brittle metal with poor tensile strength. Yet its alloy with steel is exceptionally resilient. In fact steel-beryllium alloys are used for heavy-duty springs subject to constant expansion and contraction. Beryllium alloys are also highly resistant to heat, and for that reason are used for making the fuel-cases in nuclear reactors.

Nichrome, an alloy of nickel, iron and chromium combines great strength with a high melting point and is used for the wire heating elements in electric fires. Another nickel-iron alloy called invar shows mini-

'Silver' coins are minted at the Royal Mint in London. Most 'silver' coins are now made of copper and nickel alloy which is hard and resistant to tarnishing.

mal expansion and contraction with changes in temperature and was specially compounded for making surveyor's measuring tapes. It is also used for parts in watches demanding a high standard of accuracy.

Pure gold is far too soft to be used in its natural state and for most purposes is alloyed with some other metal. Yellow gold is gold alloyed with copper, and white gold is an alloy of gold and silver.

Occasionally, the properties of one or other of the alloyed metals can be worsened. For example, alloying copper with even a small amount of bismuth renders the copper brittle and useless. The bismuth in the alloy creates around each grain of copper a thin and weak envelope, so that when any stress is applied to an alloy, the copper breaks between the grains.

Alloying is now a fundamental and exact metallurgical science; the designer of a metal object, machine or component, merely has to tell the metallurgist what a metal is to be used for, and the required alloy will be produced. The alloy will always be the same if exactly the same materials and methods are used, but the slightest change in the proportions may radically alter the alloy's properties.

Odd men out in the chemical plan

Metals so light they float on water, so reactive they are never found as the element. What marks them off from their fellows and gives them their unusual and valuable chemical properties?

METALS ARE familiar substances to everyone – they are known as hard, durable and heavy substances, useful for making all sorts of things from the frameworks of buildings, huge aeroplanes and ships, down to jewellery and tiny components for watches. This is certainly true for metals such as iron and aluminium, but there are several metals which are so different from these that they cannot be used for any familiar purpose. One of them, lithium, is so light that it floats in water; another, rubidium, is so reactive that it virtually explodes on contact with water.

These metals are the alkali metals and alkaline-earth metals. They are extremely reactive and consequently are never found in nature as the free metals, but only as compounds with other elements. These compounds include two substances known to nearly everyone: common salt and chalk. In their reactions with other elements, the alkali metals and alkaline-earth metals resemble each other and that is why they are considered together.

Light and reactive

The alkali metals are so named because they all form strong alkalis when they react with water. There are six alkali metals: lithium, sodium, potassium, rubidium, caesium and francium, and they make up Group IA of the Periodic Table. Francium is a radioactive element and is rare, but sodium and potassium are common and their compounds are found in the sea and rocks throughout the world. The salt of the oceans and salt beds of many countries is sodium chloride (NaCl), and about 3 per cent of the Earth's crust consists of sodium. Potassium occurs in the minerals called feldspars as potassium aluminium silicate, and in sylvite and carnallite as potassium chloride (KCl). There are large deposits of sylvite and carnallite in Germany. Lithium, rubidium and caesium are much less common. Lithium occurs in some mineral waters and in rare minerals (composed of lithium aluminium silicates) analogous to feldspars of potassium.

All the alkali metals are tightly bound to other elements in these naturally occurring compounds and, as a result, were among the last common metals to be discovered.

In 1807, Sir Humphry Davy, the British chemist, discovered sodium and potassium by passing electricity through molten sodium hydroxide and potassium hydroxide. Nowadays, the metals are made mainly by electrolysis of the molten chloride. The alkali metal is produced as a liquid at the cathode and chlorine gas is liberated as a by-product at the anode. The sodium liberated floats on the top of the electrolyte and is run off.

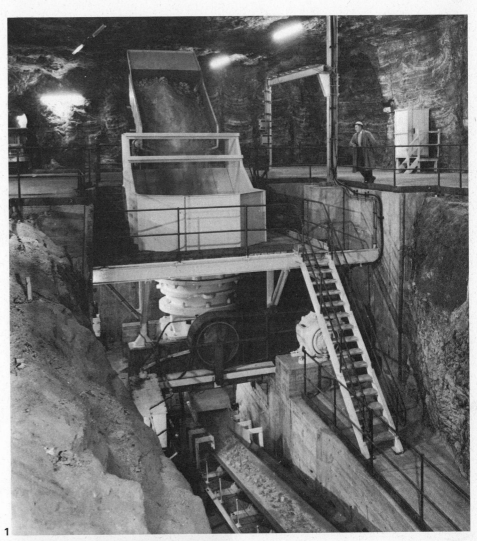

1 Common salt (sodium chloride) seen here being mechanically crushed in an underground mine, is one of the most abundant compounds of the alkali metals.
2 Sir Humphry Davy (1778–1829) was an English chemist who discovered sodium and potassium, two of the alkali metals.

The alkali metals have few uses as metals. They are so reactive that they must be stored in airtight containers, usually under liquids such as kerosene or naphtha. Sodium is the only one of the alkali metals that is of much use as a metal. Liquid sodium is used as a 'coolant' in atomic reactors called 'breeder' reactors; the coolant in an atomic reactor is used to transfer heat from the hot reactor core to a heat exchanger where steam is produced to power an electricity generator. Sodium metal is also used in organic chemistry in the synthesis and analysis of organic substances.

Most people are familiar with sodium in sodium lamps. These are the bright-yellow lamps that line main roads, and they contain sodium vapour. When an electric discharge is passed through sodium vapour, a yellow glow results. This colour is also produced in a gas flame when a sodium compound is held in the flame. The colour is so characteristic that this method is used to identify sodium compounds and many other metal compounds.

Sodium hydroxide is a very important

substance in the laboratory. Whenever a highly alkaline solution is required, sodium hydroxide is almost always used to produce the desired alkalinity. Caustic soda is used in industry in the manufacture of soap. Soap is made by heating caustic soda with fats or oils. Fats and oils consist of compounds of complex organic acids called fatty acids and, when heated with alkalis, they undergo a process called hydrolysis to yield soapy substances. Caustic soda is also used industrially in the manufacture of paper, dyes, bleaches and petroleum.

The most important sodium compound is sodium carbonate, Na_2CO_3. Sodium carbonate, or soda ash as it is sometimes called, is one of the most used chemicals in industry. It is prepared commercially by the Solvay process, which was invented by the Belgian chemist Ernest Solvay in 1864. In this process, a concentrated solution of common salt saturated with ammonia gas flows down a tower up which carbon dioxide is passed. A suspension of sodium carbonate in a solution of ammonium chloride is produced, and the solid sodium carbonate is removed at the foot of the tower:

$$2NaCl+CO_2+H_2O \rightarrow Na_2CO_3+2HCl,$$
$$HCl+NH_3 \rightarrow NH_4Cl.$$

Sodium carbonate is used as a water softener and it is sold for this purpose as large white crystals under the name of 'washing soda'. Sodium carbonate is cheaper to make than caustic soda and so it is used as a starting point for many other sodium compounds.

From fizz to fertilizer

There are two main reasons for the great use of sodium compounds. One is of course that sodium is an abundant element; the other is that the sodium ion present in the compounds does not adversely affect Man and, as a result, many drugs and medicines are sodium compounds. It is the other parts of the compounds that are actually useful. Simple medicines include Glauber's salt (sodium sulphate) and certain stomach powders, which consist of a mixture of sodium bicarbonate and a weak acid. When added to water, the acid dissolves and reacts with the bicarbonate, producing bubbles of carbon dioxide. Sherbet and baking-powders are similar mixtures, and some fire-extinguishers contain a solution of sodium bicarbonate and a glass phial of sulphuric acid. When the extinguisher is used, the phial is broken and the carbon dioxide gas suddenly released

1

2

3

4

1 The bright colours in fireworks are due to salts of metals such as strontium, beryllium, and magnesium.
2 The clay used by potters and sculptors contains large quantities of the oxides of metals such as aluminium.
3 The yellow light from modern high-intensity street lamps is caused by the element sodium. The colour is characteristic of the metal.
4 Calcium carbonate, in the form of chalk, occurs widely as outcrops. It is thus easily extracted. Calcium carbonate is also a major constituent of bones, sea shells, marble and limestone.

forces the solution in a jet out of the extinguisher.

Other useful sodium compounds include sodium thiosulphate, the photographer's 'hypo', which dissolves undeveloped silver salts from films and prints.

Sodium nitrate, or Chile saltpetre, is an important fertilizer acting as a source of nitrogen for plants, and sodium chlorate is used as a weed-killer. Sodium borate or 'borax' is used in the glazing of pottery, and sodium cyanide plays a part in the extraction of gold and silver from their ores.

Because potassium is chemically almost identical to sodium, potassium salts could be used in any of these processes in place of sodium salts. But potassium salts are more expensive. However potassium is different from sodium in one respect: it is an essential element for plant growth, and potassium chloride is an important fertilizer. Potassium nitrate, or saltpetre, is also used as a fertilizer as it is a source of nitrogen as well. Saltpetre is also used in explosives, such as gunpowder, as a source of oxygen for rapid combustion. Potassium bromide, on the other hand, is a well-known sedative.

There are few practical uses for the remaining alkali metals. An unusual compound of lithium, lithium aluminium hydride ($LiAlH_4$), is used as a strong reducing agent in organic chemistry.

The alkaline-earth metals are magnesium, calcium, strontium, barium and radium, and they make up Group IIA of the Periodic Table together with beryllium. The alkaline-earth metals resemble each other in their properties as do most elements of the same group in the Periodic Table. Beryllium, however, mostly resembles aluminium, which is in Group III.

Calcium is the most important of the alkaline-earth metals. Calcium carbonate occurs in the earth as chalk, calcite limestone and marble and in the shells of living creatures such as molluscs and corals as well as in egg shells. The mineral gypsum consists of calcium sulphate, and calcium occurs in many other minerals, such as apatite, which is composed of calcium phosphate and calcium fluoride. Magnesium occurs as the chloride in the mineral carnallite and also as the sulphate, which is used medicinally as Epsom salts. Dolomite is a mixture of calcium and magnesium carbonates, and magnesium makes up nearly 4 per cent of the salts present in sea water. Strontium and barium are less common, occurring mainly as sulphates in colestite and barite respectively. Radium is extremely rare; when Madame Curie isolated this element in 1898, she obtained only a few grains of radium from a ton of ore, pitchblende.

Down the reactive scale

The alkaline-earth metals are all obtained by electrolysis of molten compounds such as the chlorides, as are the alkali metals. Sir Humphry Davy was again responsible for the discovery of most of them; he isolated calcium, magnesium, strontium and barium by electrolysis in 1808.

Being less reactive than the alkali metals, the alkaline-earth metals do not need to be stored under inert liquids. But the metals tarnish on exposure to the air, becoming covered with a film of the oxide or hydroxide. Magnesium does not react with cold water, but with boiling water or steam it reacts slowly to form hydrogen:

$$Mg + 2H_2O \rightarrow H_2 + Mg(OH)_2.$$

Calcium is more reactive, forming hydrogen with cold water, and for this reason there are no practical uses for calcium and strontium metals. Barium is a constituent of some strong metal alloys. Magnesium metal burns with a very bright light and is used in flares, but its principal use is as a constituent of light strong alloys. But, as with the alkali metals, the main importance of these elements is as compounds with other elements.

The alkaline-earth metals all have two electrons in the outermost electron orbits

1 Coral – the skeletal remains of minute marine creatures – is mainly calcium carbonate.
2 Stalactites and stalagmites in underground caves are caused by rainwater, which is a dilute solution of carbonic acid, dissolving chalk from the ground above. This is then deposited in the characteristic icicle shapes within the cave.

of their atoms, and for this reason they show a valence of two in their reactions.

Magnesium hydroxide ($Mg(OH)_2$) is prepared by treating a solution of a magnesium salt with caustic soda. It is used to make milk of magnesia, a suspension of the hydroxide in water, which is taken to relieve acid indigestion. Magnesium carbonate is added to table salt to make it run freely. Both these compounds occur in nature, and if heated, magnesium oxide or magnesia is obtained. This substance is extremely resistant to heat and is used as a refractory material to line furnaces.

Calcium hydroxide ($Ca(OH)_2$) is formed when lime or quicklime (calcium oxide, CaO) is slaked with water; this reaction produces large amounts of heat. Lime is one of the most useful basic chemicals in industry; it is made by heating calcium carbonate, in the form of crushed limestone:

$$CaCO_3 \rightarrow CaO + CO_2.$$

Lime is the basis of the building industry. Cement is made by heating limestone and clay, producing a compound of lime, alumina and silica. Lime is also used in making mortar and concrete. Glass is basically made by heating a mixture of sand, soda ash and lime. Lime is also useful in agriculture; farmers dig slaked lime (calcium hydroxide) into soils that are too acid, to neutralize them. Lime has several other less important uses. It is used to make calcium carbide, which produces acetylene when mixed with water and is used in acetylene lamps. When lime is heated, it gives out a brilliant white light – this method was used in theatres to produce 'limelight'.

Calcium carbonate is known to everyone in the various forms mentioned above. An unusual feature of limestone deposits is the presence of caves, which owe their existence to a chemical reaction. As rainwater falls through the air, it dissolves carbon dioxide forming a very weak solution of carbonic acid, H_2CO_3. As the water seeps down through the limestone, it dissolves the mineral slightly to form a solution of calcium bicarbonate:

$$CaCO_3 + H_2CO_3 \rightarrow Ca(HCO_3)_2.$$

In this way caverns may be hollowed out by the dissolving action of the acidified water. When the solution drips down through the roof of a cavern on to the floor, the water evaporates, leaving deposits of calcium carbonate. These deposits hang from the ceiling as stalactites or grow up from the floor as stalagmites. A similar process occurs when hard water, which also contains calcium bicarbonate, is heated – a hard deposit of 'scale' or 'fur' is produced inside boilers, kettles and hot-water pipes. This causes a reduction in heating efficiency.

Colour tests for metals

Calcium carbonate in the form of limestone has two important uses in industry – it is used as a source of carbon dioxide, which it produces when heated, and as an ingredient of cement.

The other main calcium mineral, gypsum (hydrated calcium sulphate) is heated to produce plaster of Paris. This reaction is reversible and when water is added to plaster of Paris powder it sets hard, forming gypsum. In doing so, it does not expand or contract much, and so is valuable as a moulding material, particularly in surgery in the setting of broken bones and in the building industry.

Strontium compounds have few uses. In the flame test, strontium salts produce an

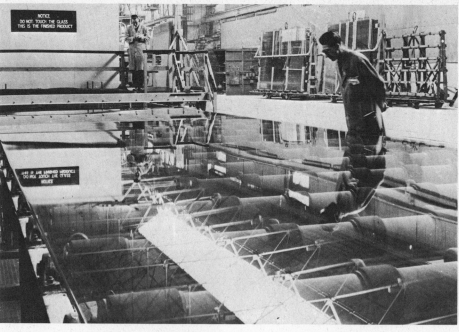

intense red colour, and strontium nitrate $(Sr(NO_3)_2)$ is an ingredient of fireworks. Strontium-90 is a radioactive form of strontium produced in nuclear explosions. It eventually falls to earth in the radioactive fallout from an explosion, and may be consumed by men and animals, by which it finds its way to the bones. This accumulation can be dangerous if large amounts are involved, as strontium-90 remains radioactive for a long time, losing only half of its radioactivity every 26 years.

Barium compounds are more useful to Man. As the barium atom does not easily pass X-rays, doctors give a liquid containing barium salts to patients whose digestive organs they wish to examine. The barium is opaque to X-rays and so the digestive tract shows up clearly on X-ray photographs of patients given barium. The

Small quantities of the oxides of the alkali and alkaline-earth metals are added to glass to give it particular characteristics.

salt they use is barium sulphate ($BaSO_4$), which is also used as a white paint pigment. Barium peroxide (BaO_2), made by heating barium oxide (BaO) in air, is used commercially to make hydrogen peroxide by adding sulphuric acid:

$$BaO_2 + H_2SO_4 \rightarrow H_2O_2 + BaSO_4.$$

Barium nitrate is used in fireworks to produce a green colour.

The last of the alkaline-earth elements, radium, is chemically similar to the others. But it is an intensely radioactive element, and is used as a source of radiation in the treatment of cancer.

The alkali metals and the alkaline-earth metals, being the most reactive metals, are never actually seen by most people. But because they have many important compounds, they do affect the lives of everyone in many ways every day.

1 The alkali metals are extracted from the ores by electrolysis. Before this can be done, the ore must be crushed and separated.

2 A mixture of barium sulphate (barium meal) is used to outline the alimentary tract for X-ray detection of ulcers.

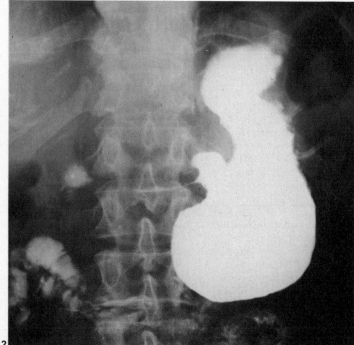

The unsettled nature of gas

Often invisible, always in motion, gas is the most unsettled form of matter. But out of the chaos have emerged predictable patterns of behaviour which allow Man to harness its energy.

The 'Horsehead Nebula', photographed by the Mt Wilson and Palomar Observatories in California, is a spectacular example of the gases in space from which stars and even galaxies are formed.

MOST PEOPLE have heard the expression, generally attributed to Aristotle, that 'Nature abhors a vacuum'. We now know that outer space consists of a vast vacuum, and the Universe consists largely of space. In fact nature, in the form of the physical Universe, is *mostly* a vacuum.

But up to the seventeenth century, before people understood the nature and properties of gases, scientists and philosophers held this 'abhorrent vacuum' fallacy as an important principle. It was thought to explain various phenomena, such as the rise of water in a pump. As the pump was operated, the water was supposed to rise to prevent the creation of a vacuum in the barrel.

In 1638, the Italian scientist and mathematician Galileo Galilei drew attention to the fact that water will not rise more than about 32 feet in the shaft of an ordinary pump. This led his fellow countryman Evangelista Torricelli to wonder to what height a denser liquid, such as mercury, might rise by nature's supposed abhorrence of a vacuum. A long tube was closed at one end and filled with mercury forcing all the air out. It was inverted and the open end put under the surface of a bath of mercury. The level of the mercury in the tube dropped until it was about 30 inches above the level in the bath.

Torricelli suspected the true explanation

– that is, that the height of the mercury column is due not to the behaviour of the mercury in trying to fill the vacuum above it, but to the pressure of the Earth's atmosphere acting on the surface of the mercury in the bath and forcing the mercury up the tube. The height of the mercury column is a measure of the atmospheric pressure – the higher the pressure, the further the mercury is pushed up the tube. With this experiment, Torricelli invented the first mercury barometer. The space in the tube above the mercury in such a barometer is called a Torricellean vacuum.

Air pressure and weather

It was not until 1659 that the air pressure explanation of the barometer was proved, by the British scientist Robert Boyle (1627–91). Boyle put a barometer in the receiver of his air-pump and found that as the air around the barometer was pumped away, the height of the column of mercury fell. When air was re-admitted, the mercury column rose again to its original height. This experiment proved that the air pressure was supporting the column of mercury.

Later, the German physicist Otto von Guericke (1602–86), who also invented an air-pump, found that variation in air pressure as measured by the barometer gives an indication of future weather con-

ditions. The barometer is still very important today in studying atmospheric behaviour for weather forecasting.

Von Guericke also provided a striking illustration of air pressure with his 'Magdeburg hemispheres', which fitted closely together to form a sphere. In one was a tap, through which air inside the sphere was pumped out. When the tap was closed, the two hemispheres were held together by the pressure of the atmosphere and could not be pulled apart by teams of eight horses harnessed to each.

Robert Boyle referred to gas pressure as the 'spring of the air' and carried out many experiments to try to understand it. In 1661 he announced an experimental relationship, now known as Boyle's Law, which is very important to an understanding of the nature of a gas; the volume of any sample of gas is inversely proportional to its pressure, provided it is kept at a constant temperature. In other words, if the pressure on a sample of gas is doubled, its volume will decrease to a half. Expressed mathematically, $V \propto 1/P$ where V is volume and P is pressure.

Boyle tried to explain his experimental

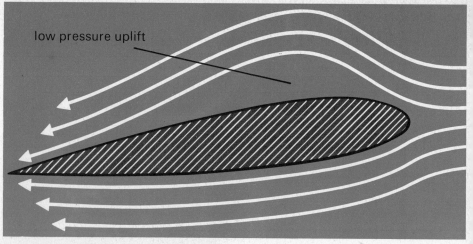

low pressure uplift

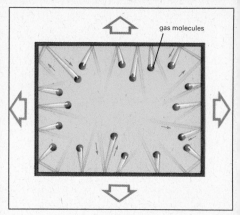

gas molecules

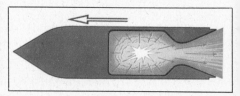

The operation of a modern jet aircraft such as the bat-like Vulcan, *top left,* depends on gases both within its engines and around its wings. Because the shape of the wings causes a slight hump in the streamlines of air flowing over the top, the pressure on the upper surface is less than the pressure underneath, so the aeroplane is literally pushed skyward, *top right.* Molecules of gas in a closed container strike the walls with the same force in all directions, so the net effect is nil, *centre right.* A force in one direction is balanced by a force in the opposite direction, as in a game of tug-of-war. If a hole is cut in one side of the container, the force opposite the hole has nothing to balance it. If the gas is under very high pressure, such as when volatile fuels explode inside a jet or rocket engine, *bottom right,* the tremen- dous force on the wall opposite the noz- zle propels the gas container forward. A jet en- gine scoops up the oxygen it needs for fuel com- bustion directly from the air it flies through, but a rocket engine carries oxygen with it, so it can fly in outer space where there is no air. The deep-sea diver, *above left,* also carries oxygen mixed with other gases in high-pressure tanks on his back in order to breathe under water.

law by picturing air as a collection of springy particles like little balls of curly wool piled together, but his explanation was not very convincing. Eighty years later, Daniel Bernoulli (1700–82) laid the basis of the modern view of the nature of gases with a theory that explained Boyle's Law. He pointed out that if gas particles were moving about, they would produce pressure by their action of bombarding the walls of the container. Reducing the volume of a portion of gas would push the molecules closer together, the rate of bombardment would increase, having the effect of increasing the pressure.

The modern view of gases is called the *kinetic theory (kinetic* comes from the Greek word *kinein* meaning *to move).* The molecules of a gas are continually moving, colliding with each other and bombarding any surface in contact with the gas.

An 'ideal' gas is a collection of molecules sufficiently separated so that their inter- molecular forces can be neglected. The volume of a molecule of 'ideal' gas is con- sidered to be zero, so that the gas can be compressed indefinitely and still obey Boyle's Law. Of course, there is no such thing as an 'ideal' gas, and the molecules of real gases do, of course, occupy some volume. But for most practical purposes this volume is negligible compared with that taken up by the gas as a whole, and so need not complicate ordinary calculations.

Smoke in motion

The independent motion of a gas mole- cule is restricted a little by the forces of attraction of other gas molecules. When a gas is compressed, its molecules are pushed closer together and their mutual attraction increased; so are their velocity and vibratory motion, which account for the consequent rise in temperature. The impact of molecules striking the container wall is slightly reduced by the attraction of the main body of gas molecules, so there is a slight reduction in the pressure of the gas below that predicted by Boyle's Law.

A useful piece of evidence in support of the kinetic theory came from the work of the Scottish botanist Robert Brown (1773– 1858). Brown was looking through his microscope at a suspension of pollen grains in water, when he noticed that the pollen grains were jigging about in a ran- dom fashion, never coming to rest. Brown- ian motion may also be observed in the random motion of smoke particles in the air.

The kinetic theory provides a simple explanation: each smoke particle is being continually bombarded by gas molecules in the air. At any instant, there may hap- pen to be more gas molecules bombarding one side than the other, so that there is a resultant force on the smoke particle. The particle moves for a short time, until it is given a push in a different direction by an excess of bombarding gas molecules.

In view of the uneven bombardment causing Brownian motion, why does not the pressure a gas exerts on its container fluctuate? The fact is that it does, but the area of any containing surface is many

Model aircraft, subjected to the torture of high winds in wind tunnels, give clues to the likely performance of the real thing before it is constructed. Here, a space capsule is tested for resistance to the stresses of re-entry velocity.

millions of times greater than the area of a smoke particle and there are so many collisions against the containing wall that the effects of local unevenness are smoothed out. No fluctuations in pressure are detectable under normal circumstances because they are averaged out.

Even when there are no smoke particles in the atmosphere, gas molecules in the air continually collide with each other. Each molecule is involved in about 10,000 million collisions every second. The average distance travelled by a molecule between collisions is called its *mean free path*. In air at room temperature, the mean free path is about 1,000 Ångstrom units (100 million Ångstrom units equal one centimetre). These molecules are moving at an average speed of about 500 metres per second. But the effective distance, i.e. the straight-line distance from a given starting point, moved during a second, is very small because of the millions of changes of direction caused by collisions. Because the mass of gas molecules is so small, we do not feel the effects of these collisions, despite their high speed.

In 1802, the French chemist Jacques Charles discovered that the changes in pressure of a sample of gas are related to the changes in temperature which caused the pressure change, provided the gas was kept at a constant volume. He found that if the temperature was raised from 0 °C. to 1 °C., there was an increase in pressure of 1/267 of the pressure at 0 °C. Later more exact work has shown that this fraction should be 1/273·15. The implication of this result is that if a gas is cooled to −273·15 °C., its pressure will become zero.

Absolute zero

In fact, every known gas becomes a liquid at a higher temperature than −273·15 °C. But all these gases behave as if they would have zero pressure at this special low temperature. The name *absolute zero* is now given to this temperature, and it is the zero of the *absolute temperature scale* denoted by the symbol A. (0 °C.=273·15 °A.). Lord Kelvin (1824–1907), working on purely theoretical grounds, calculated the lowest temperature it would be possible to reach, and his value agreed very closely with absolute zero. Consequently, the absolute temperature scale is often referred to as the Kelvin scale and denoted by the symbol K.

The gas thermometer based on Charles' Law is called the *constant-volume* thermometer. It consists of a large container of gas, which is kept at the temperature to be measured, connected to a mercury barometer. The barometer keeps the gas at constant volume and measures its pressure as an indication of its temperature. Helium is the gas generally used in the constant-volume thermometer, as its behaviour is the nearest to the ideal gas of the kinetic theory.

Theoretically equivalent to this thermometer is one which has a sample of gas kept at constant pressure. The function of this thermometer depends on the relation known as Charles' Law, which states that if the pressure on a gas remains constant, the volume of the gas is proportional to the change in temperature as measured on the absolute (Kelvin) temperature scale.

The *constant-pressure* gas thermometer is simply a glass tube closed at one end. A mercury bead inside the tube acts as a piston enclosing a sample of gas. The distance of the bead from the end of the tube indicates the volume of the gas and thus its temperature. The disadvantage of this type of thermometer is that the gas specimen is not really at constant pressure. One end of the tube is open to the atmosphere, and so the pressure on the gas varies according to atmospheric pressure.

Constant-volume gas thermometers are now taken as the standard of temperature measurement, because they minimize problems caused by glass in the apparatus (the expansion of glass becomes insignificant in comparison with that of the gas).

By a fortunate coincidence, the expan-

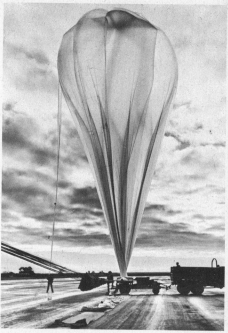

sion of mercury is uniform when measured on the standard gas-thermometer scale (other liquids show large deviations from uniform expansion on the gas-thermometer scale). The uniform expansion of mercury means that ordinary experiments can be easily related to the gas-thermometer scale by using an ordinary mercury-in-glass thermometer.

We described earlier how the pressure exerted by a gas depends on the motion of its molecules. From the relationship between pressure and temperature, we can see that gas temperature is related to the motion of gas molecules. This fact means that temperature is an indication of the average *kinetic energy* (energy of movement) of the molecules. The average kinetic energy is the same for all types of gas molecules at any given temperature.

If a moving body has a known kinetic energy, then the smaller its mass, the greater must be its velocity. Since all gas molecules have the same average kinetic energy at any given temperature, gases with the smallest molecular mass will have the highest average molecular velocity. So

During the seventeenth century, Otto Von Guericke dramatically demonstrated the existence of air pressure when two teams of strong horses could not prise apart two evacuated hemispheres,

we would expect molecules of a gas such as oxygen (molecular mass 32) to move faster than the molecules of a gas such as chlorine (molecular mass about 71).

Escape into space

The lightest gas molecule of all is hydrogen with a molecular mass of 2 and its average velocity is about four times that of oxygen molecules at the same temperature. The Maxwell-Boltzmann distribution curve for hydrogen shows a significant part at the right-hand end which is at a higher velocity than the Earth's escape velocity, about 7 miles a second. Since the Earth's gravity is not sufficient to hold a body travelling at this speed, this means that some of the molecules of hydrogen are allowed to escape into space. In this way, most of any hydrogen in the Earth's atmosphere is always leaking, so that the amount of hydrogen in the atmosphere

left. Human flight was first achieved in gas-filled balloons. Even in this age of jet aeroplanes, balloons are still important in weather prediction, *right,* and space-research projects.

remains exceedingly small.

In the same way, a proportion of helium is able to leak out into space, but the mass of all other gas molecules is great enough for only an insignificant proportion to reach escape velocity.

The fact that hydrogen escapes from the atmosphere is very important to life on Earth. If there were significant amounts of hydrogen in the air, lightning could start it burning or exploding and using up the atmosphere's oxygen. Similarly, if the Earth's escape velocity were much lower, oxygen would escape from the atmosphere (as it has from the atmosphere of Mars, for example).

Any object moving through a gas transfers some of its kinetic energy to the gas molecules as it collides with them. The property of a gas that makes it provide resistance or friction against a moving body is its *viscosity.* A peculiar fact about gas friction is that it does not vary with the pressure of the gas.

As an object moves through a gas, the gas flows across the sides of the object in *streamlines.* Some of the energy lost to the gas in collisions at the front of the object is transferred back from the gas in the streamlines on the sides and back of the object. If the gas pressure is reduced, there are fewer collisions at the front of the object. But since the mean free path of the gas molecules is now greater, the molecules colliding at the front move away more easily, and fewer of them stay in the streamlines to transfer energy back. The overall result is that the gas provides the same friction or *drag* on a moving object whatever the pressure of the gas.

This kind of drag, due to pressure differences at the front and back of the moving object, can be much reduced by *streamlining.* This means shaping the back so that the air flows evenly round the object – as in the back of an aeroplane or the 'tear-drop' back of some racing cars.

Evangelista Torricelli's research into the nature of gas led to the invention of the mercury barometer, *left.* Sir Robert Boyle, *right,* in-

vestigated the law relating the volume of a gas to the pressure on it. Boyle's research has applications in both chemistry and engineering.

Hydrogen - the everywhere element

Hydrogen is light, gaseous, invisible and nature's most abundant element. From the flaming stars of the galaxies to the cooling waters of the oceans, hydrogen is everywhere in the Universe.

THE MOST ABUNDANT ELEMENT in the Universe – making up more than 90 per cent of it – is hydrogen. The sun consists mainly of hydrogen and uses 550 million tons of it every second, converting four million tons directly into energy, a fraction of which the Earth receives mainly as heat and light. All the billions of other stars in the Universe are largely hydrogen, as well as much of the interstellar gas in 'empty' space.

But on Earth, hydrogen is not the most abundant element; it stands in ninth place (behind oxygen, silicon, aluminium, iron, calcium, sodium, potassium and magnesium). Free hydrogen is extremely rare because much of this gas is continually escaping from the Earth's atmosphere into space. So when it is found as free molecules, it is usually mixed with gases trapped underground, as it is under the North Sea off the coast of Great Britain. Most of it is found combined with other elements as a whole range of chemical compounds. Each molecule of water, for instance, consists of one atom of oxygen and two atoms of hydrogen – and two thirds of the world's surface is covered with water. Petroleum and coal consist mainly of hydrocarbons, compounds of hydrogen and carbon.

'Inflammable air'

Although hydrogen is very common, in the sense that it has many different types of compounds, it was not discovered as a distinct element until 1766, after much rarer elements such as cobalt and platinum. In that year the British chemist and physicist Henry Cavendish (1731–1810) delivered a paper to the London Royal Society on the properties of 'inflammable air'. Several years later he exploded a mixture of this 'inflammable air' and oxygen and showed that they combine to produce water. He then called this gas hydrogen (from the Greek words meaning *water producer*). Since hydrogen has no colour, taste or smell, it can be detected only by its physical and chemical properties. But some of these are unique.

Hydrogen is the lightest substance known. As a gas, it is about one fourteenth as heavy as the average weight of an equal volume of air. Like all gases, hydrogen can be liquefied if made cold enough, but to do so requires cooling to −253 °C., only 20 degrees above absolute zero. Liquid hydrogen is pale blue and is the lightest liquid known, having about one fourteenth of the density of water. If cooled a further seven or eight degrees, under pressure, liquid hydrogen becomes a solid.

The common hydrogen atom contains one proton and one electron. It therefore has an atomic number of 1 and stands at

the head of the periodic table of the elements. If a hydrogen atom is stripped of its single electron, it becomes a hydrogen ion (H^+) which, therefore, must be the same thing as a proton. The hydrogen in most *inorganic* hydrogen compounds exists to a greater or lesser extent as ions. And when such compounds are dissolved in water, they dissociate more or less completely into ions. For instance, the compound formed by hydrogen and chlorine is the choking colourless gas hydrogen chloride. When hydrogen chloride dissolves in water, it forms hydrochloric acid which dissociates almost 100 per cent into hydrogen ions (H^+) and chloride ions (Cl^-).

Hydrogen was used to lift the early gas-filled airships. But because it is highly explosive, it has long since been replaced by helium, which is slightly heavier but non-flammable.

Like many other elements, hydrogen has isotopes. The atoms of these must still contain only one proton and one electron (or they would cease to be hydrogen), but they contain also one or two neutrons in their nuclei. The isotope of mass 2 (whose atoms contain one electron, and a nucleus of one proton and one neutron) is called *deuterium,* sometimes given the symbol D. Deuterium oxide (D_2O) is called 'heavy water' because the extra two neutrons in each molecule (making ten, compared to ordinary water, H_2O, with eight) give a significant increase to the liquid's density. Other physical properties also differ: for instance, the density, freezing point and boiling point of pure heavy water are 1·107 gm per cubic centimetre, 3·8 °C. and 101·4 °C. (compared with 1 gm per c.c., 0 °C., and 100 °C. for ordinary water). Deuterium occurs naturally and ordinary water contains about one part in 6,000 of heavy water.

There is a third isotope of hydrogen called *tritium* which has two neutrons per atom and is given the symbol T. It probably does not occur naturally and is made by bombarding atoms of deuterium with ions of deuterium in a cyclotron. Any method of preparing hydrogen involves prising it out of one of its compounds. Water is the most common compound of hydrogen. Several metals react with water to form hydrogen and the metal oxide or hydroxide.

Hydrogen and metals

The ease with which a metal takes part in this reaction is a measure of the chemical reactivity of the metal. For instance, the highly reactive alkali metals such as sodium and potassium react vigorously with cold water:

$$2Na + 2H_2O \rightarrow 2NaOH + H_2.$$

The heat generated by the reaction is sufficient to melt the metals (which float in water) and in the case of potassium is enough to set fire to the hydrogen, which burns with a lilac-coloured flame. Less reactive than the alkali metals is calcium (which sinks in water and reacts fairly slowly to generate bubbles of hydrogen). This reaction is the reason why calcium, in other respects much like magnesium and more abundant, cannot be used for making everyday metal objects. An aircraft which dissolved the first time it rained would be of very little use.

The metals magnesium, zinc and iron do not react with cold water but do react with steam (which is to the chemist just

another form of water). Magnesium reacts sufficiently well to catch fire and burn when heated in a current of steam, even if there is no free oxygen present for normal combustion to take place:

$$Mg + H_2O \rightarrow MgO + H_2.$$

Under similar conditions, zinc oxidizes without catching fire, and this reaction can be used for making zinc oxide, a pigment used in white paint.

But by far the most important reaction in this group is that between iron and steam, which is the basis for an early commercial method for preparing hydrogen. If steam is passed over red-hot iron filings (or old nails or small pieces of scrap iron), hydrogen is generated and the iron is converted to its blue-black oxide:

$$3Fe + 4H_2O \rightarrow Fe_3O_4 + 4H_2.$$

This reaction is reversible, and in the commercial process, called the Bosch process, the iron oxide is changed back to iron by the reducing action of 'water gas' (carbon monoxide and hydrogen $CO + H_2O$). This reaction also heats the iron to red heat again. So by alternately passing steam and water gas over heated iron, a regular supply of hydrogen is obtained.

The only common non-metal which reacts with water in a similar way is carbon, and this reaction is the basis of the commercial preparation of water gas. Steam is passed up a tower of red-hot coke (a form of carbon) and a mixture of hydrogen and carbon monoxide is produced:

$$C + H_2O \rightarrow CO + H_2.$$

The water gas can then be used as a fuel or for the Bosch process just described.

Another way of getting the hydrogen out of water is to decompose it by electrolysis. If two metal electrodes are connected to a source of direct current and dipped into a container of water, hydrogen is evolved at the cathode (negative electrode). Generally, a little acid is added to the water to make it a better conductor of electricity. This is a costly way of making hydrogen, but it can be used where there

is a plentiful supply of cheap electricity. Hydrogen is a by-product of many other commercial electrolytic processes, such as the manufacture of caustic soda and of chlorine.

Acids are another class of compounds which contain hydrogen and which will fairly readily part with it. Such reactions are the basis of the laboratory preparations of hydrogen, which may be summarized by the general rule 'acid plus metal gives salt plus hydrogen'. Commonly zinc and dilute hydrochloric or sulphuric acid are used, and the hydrogen gas, because it is fairly insoluble, is collected over water.

Zinc will also dissolve in alkalis to produce hydrogen, as will aluminium and tin. The reaction is slow and not useful as a method of preparing hydrogen, although aluminium reacts fairly quickly with hot alkalis. For this reason, aluminium pans should not be used for heating solutions containing washing soda or they will dissolve.

Hydrogen will part with its single electron fairly easily (and accepts an electron less easily), so it will enter into chemical combination with other elements. It forms only a few compounds with metals. Of these calcium hydride, or hydrolith (CaH_2), is useful in the laboratory because it is decomposed by water to give hydrogen gas. Hydrogen reacts readily with non-metals, particularly oxygen and the halogens (fluorine, chlorine, bromine and iodine).

'Reducing' with hydrogen

When hydrogen burns in air, it combines with oxygen to form water. This reaction accounts for the steam and condensation formed where coal gas (which is about one half hydrogen) is used for heating or lighting in a room with insufficient ventilation. With pure oxygen, a flame as hot as 2,400 °C. can be obtained.

So great is the affinity of hydrogen for oxygen that it will take the oxygen out of certain compounds, such as metal oxides, to form water and leave the elemental

1 Sodium reacts violently with water to release hydrogen, which often flames from the heat generated by the reaction.
2 When the two 'heavy' forms of hydrogen, deuterium and tritium, fuse to form the heavier element helium, tremendous energy is released. But this fusion takes place only at very high temperatures. In an H-bomb, an ordinary A-bomb first explodes to give high temperatures; hydrogen then fuses to give the main explosion.

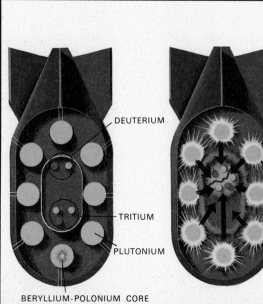

DEUTERIUM

TRITIUM

PLUTONIUM

BERYLLIUM-POLONIUM CORE

A-BOMB EXPLOSION

H-BOMB EXPLOSION

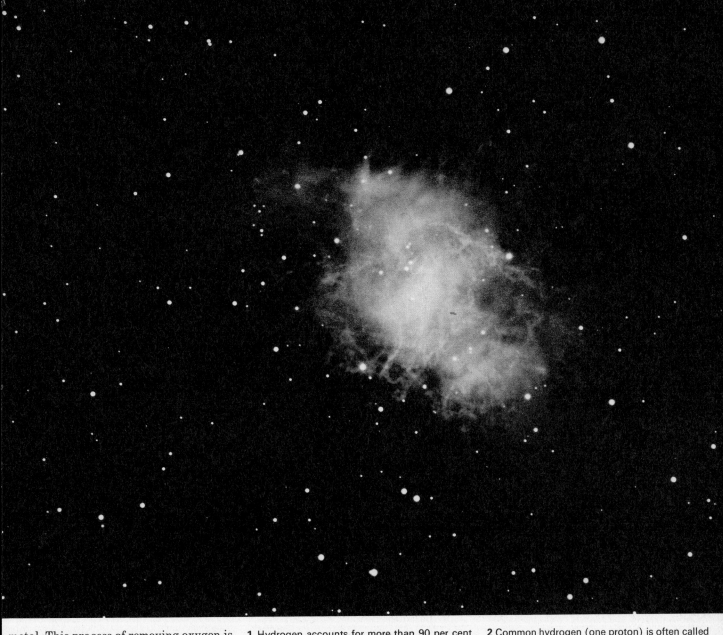

metal. This process of removing oxygen is called *reduction*. For example, if black copper oxide is heated in a stream of hydrogen, it is reduced to metallic copper:

$$CuO + H_2 \rightarrow Cu + H_2O.$$

The oxides of iron, tin and lead can be reduced in a similar way, but those of the alkali metals (lithium, sodium, potassium) are unaffected. These metals react with water to generate hydrogen.

Reducing metal oxides by free hydrogen is not commercially profitable. By far the largest percentage of free hydrogen is used as a fuel, either as pure hydrogen which burns in air or oxygen to give an extremely hot flame, or mixed with other gases in coal gas (50 per cent hydrogen, 30 per cent methane, 10 per cent carbon monoxide, 10 per cent other gases) and water gas (50 per cent hydrogen, 50 per cent carbon monoxide).

The reaction between hydrogen and fluorine is extremely violent, and the two gases combine explosively even in the dark at −253 °C. to form hydrogen fluoride:

$$H_2 + F_2 \rightarrow H_2F_2.$$

With chlorine, hydrogen combines only

1 Hydrogen accounts for more than 90 per cent of all the matter in the Universe. It is the main constituent of stars and huge inter-stellar gas clouds, such as the Crab Nebula.

2 Common hydrogen (one proton) is often called protium. Deuterium (one proton, one neutron) is so-called 'heavy hydrogen'. Tritium (one proton, two neutrons) is radioactive hydrogen.

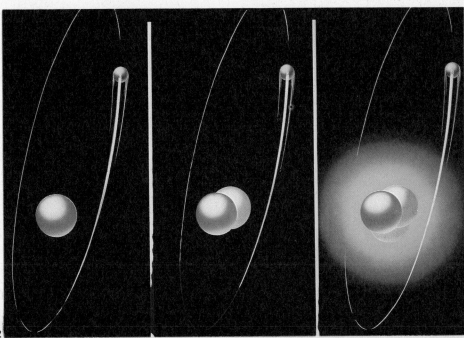

1 Combined with carbon in the form of solid coal, hydrogen is an important source of heat energy. When coal burns, the hydrogen combines with oxygen to form water vapour.

2 A more modern form of hydrogen-based fuels is natural gas. Once burnt off oil wells as waste, natural gas is now actively 'mined', as in the North Sea off Great Britain.

slightly less violently and this reaction also results in an explosion, but requires the presence of sunlight to make it start:

$$H_2 + Cl_2 \rightarrow 2HCl.$$

The general decrease in the reactivity of the halogen elements with increasing atomic weight (that is, as we go down group VII in the periodic table) is borne out by the reaction between hydrogen and bromine. The reaction does take place, but requires heat and will not give an explosion even in sunlight. Finally, the reaction between hydrogen and iodine, which also requires heat, is incomplete. Indeed, the hydrogen iodide formed decomposes back to hydrogen and iodine on further heating, so the process is reversible:

$$H_2 + I_2 \rightleftharpoons 2HI.$$

An important compound of hydrogen is ammonia, NH_3. Because it contains nitrogen, essential for plant growth, it is the basis of many artificial fertilizers, such as ammonium phosphate, ammonium sulphate and ammonium nitrate. More than a million tons of these fertilizers are produced every year in Britain. Ammonia is also the starting material for some explosives.

Haber and hostilities

Nitrogen is readily available from the air (it makes up about 78 per cent of it) and hydrogen can easily be made from water, as already noted. Air and water therefore appear to be attractively cheap starting materials for the synthesis of ammonia, but unfortunately hydrogen shows no particular keenness to take part in a reaction with nitrogen. Persuading it to do so was one of the early triumphs of industrial synthetic chemistry and was first accomplished in Germany by Fritz Haber immediately before the outbreak of the First World War. (In fact, without an independent supply of ammonia for fertilizers and explosives, Germany possibly would have had severe problems during a long war.) It was found in the laboratory that in the presence of a catalyst (a substance which speeds up or slows down

a chemical reaction without itself taking part in it) the two elements hydrogen and nitrogen combine. The reaction never goes to completion and there is always some hydrogen and nitrogen left. The reaction is also fairly slow. Increasing the pressure on the gases makes more of them combine, and increasing the temperature makes the reaction take place faster.

Hydrocarbons (compounds of hydrogen and carbon) are also difficult to synthesize from the elements. If an electric arc is struck between two carbon electrodes in an atmosphere of hydrogen, various hydrocarbons may be produced, depending on the conditions. These include acetylene (C_2H_2), ethane (C_2H_6) and benzene (C_6H_6), although the reactions never go to completion. They are the basis of hydrocarbon syntheses first performed by the French chemist Marcelin Berthelot (1827–1907), but hydrocarbons are generally now made

by other methods on an industrial scale.

This, then, is hydrogen, the lightest and most abundant element in the universe. Without it, life as we know it would be impossible, because many compounds necessary for life contain hydrogen. Its chemistry provides a useful yardstick for measuring the reactivity of other elements. For instance, the metals may be arranged in a series depending on the ease with which their oxides are reduced by hydrogen. This ordered list of metals, called the electrochemical series, is of fundamental importance in chemistry and crops up again and again.

Non-metals, too, can be classified in terms of their reactivity with hydrogen. As an element, hydrogen finds uses mainly as a fuel and for filling balloons. Its most important function is in its compounds – in ammonia, natural gas, petroleum and coal – and in vital substances such as fats, proteins and sugars. Its oxide (water) is taken for granted and seldom viewed as a chemical compound. And the nucleus of its atom, the proton, is the chief building brick for all the other elements.

British chemist Henry Cavendish first recognized hydrogen as an independent element in 1766. He also discovered that hydrogen and oxygen combine to produce water.

Ammonia, produced commercially by the synthesis of nitrogen and hydrogen, finds applications in products as wide-ranging as life-giving fertilizers and germ-killing disinfectants.

The active element of oxygen

Bread may be the staff of life, but oxygen is the stuff of it. Neither plant nor animal could survive for long without it. Yet most of it is not free in the air, but trapped in its compounds.

IF A PERSON is asked what element is most essential to life, he will probably reply 'oxygen'. Whereas a scientist could name another dozen which, in their own ways, are equally necessary, the answer 'oxygen' is hard to fault. It is the gas which men and animals breathe and which is essential to respiration in plants. In fact, almost without exception, no living thing can survive for long in the absence of oxygen.

Free oxygen is a colourless, odourless gas, and in this form it exists in the air (21 per cent by volume) where men breathe it, and dissolved in the water of oceans, rivers and lakes (up to four per cent by volume) where fish breathe it. The rest of the oxygen on Earth is combined with other elements as chemical compounds. About half the Earth's crust is composed of oxygen in compounds.

The most common compounds of oxygen are water and rocks. Water is a compound of hydrogen and oxygen (H_2O) which is eight-ninths oxygen by weight. Rocks vary in composition from simple oxides of silicon (such as quartz and sand) to complex silicates and carbonates. For instance, the White Cliffs of Dover are formed from chalk (calcium carbonate $CaCO_3$) which is 48 per cent oxygen by weight. Calcium carbonate is a chemical salt, one of the many which contain oxygen. The names of oxygen-containing salts generally end in '-ate' and include also chlorates, nitrates, phosphates and sulphates.

Oxygen from the air

When cooled to $-183\,°C.$, gaseous oxygen condenses to a liquid; below $-218.5\,°C.$, it is a solid. Both solid and liquid are pale blue. Each molecule of gas contains two atoms, and so chemists write its formula as O_2.

The commercial preparation of oxygen uses the cheapest possible starting material – air. Air consists mainly of a mixture of oxygen and nitrogen, so that liquid air is actually a mixture of liquid oxygen and liquid nitrogen. The boiling point of liquid nitrogen is $-196\,°C.$, 13 degrees below that of liquid oxygen at $-183\,°C.$ By taking liquid air at about $-200\,°C.$ and slowly allowing it to warm up, the nitrogen boils off first, leaving behind fairly pure liquid oxygen. The oxygen is then either kept as a liquid and transported in special insulated containers, or allowed to become a gas which is compressed and supplied ready to use in steel cylinders.

Oxygen was identified as a distinct chemical element in 1769 by the Swedish chemist Karl Wilhelm Scheele (1742–86) and quite independently five years later by the Englishman Joseph Priestley (1733–1804). Neither of these men realized the full significance of the discovery.

It remained for the French scientist

Credit for discovering oxygen belongs to a Swedish and a British chemist. But it remained for the great French chemist Antoine Lavoisier to recognize the significance of the discovery.

Oxygen is the element of combustion. Whether it is the slow oxidation of food in the body or the rapid burning of a flaming match-head, combustion requires oxygen.

Antoine Lavoisier (1743–94) to explain exactly what happened in their experiments. All these early scientists made oxygen by heating the bright red substance mercurous oxide:

$$2HgO \rightarrow 2Hg + O_2.$$

(Hg is the chemical symbol for mercury.) What Lavoisier did was to carry out the reverse process as well. He heated the liquid metal mercury in a closed retort for several days until nothing further happened. At the end of that time he found that scales of the oxide were floating on the mercury, and that about a fifth of the air in the retort had been used up. The remaining gas was nitrogen – although Lavoisier did not know this.

Lavoisier then removed the oxide, heated it on its own, and got back a volume of oxygen equal to the 'missing' volume of air. He had demonstrated that air is about one-fifth oxygen and, more important, that oxygen is essential for combustion. For the slow combination of mercury with oxygen, which in Lavoisier's experiment had taken 12 days, is chemically just the same as the rapid combination which takes place when a piece of wood or paper burns in air or oxygen. Today a chemist calls any such chemical combination with oxygen *oxidation* and the combining substance is said to be *oxidized*. Combustion is merely rapid oxidation accompanied by burning. The burning of all fuels such as coal, oil and gas and the respiratory processes in lungs and tissues – in which substances in a living creature combine with oxygen – are all examples of oxidation.

Lavoisier's experiment with mercury and its oxide had another important effect – it finally laid to rest that remarkable hangover from alchemy, the Phlogiston Theory of Combustibility. According to this theory, every substance contained an invisible fluid-like material called *phlogiston,* which was forced out when the material burned. Thus burning was caused by the loss of phlogiston.

Long before Lavoisier's time, it had been demonstrated that some materials are heavier after burning, rather than lighter, as the Phlogiston Theory would suggest. But this argument was countered by giving phlogiston the attribute of 'negative' weight – removal of phlogiston made things heavier. But when Lavoisier established that combustion requires the presence of oxygen, the Phlogiston Theory was finally toppled. (Phlogiston must not be confused with *caloric,* which was supposed to be responsible for heating, but not burning; see Vol. 2, page 777.)

If the salt potassium nitrate (common name saltpetre) is strongly heated it is changed into potassium nitrite and oxygen is evolved:

$$2KNO_3 \rightarrow 2KNO_2 + O_2.$$

The substances carbon (in the form of charcoal) and sulphur burn slowly in air. But when they are finely ground and mixed with saltpetre, they form the mixture called gunpowder which, as everybody knows, is extremely combustible. The potassium nitrate generates a supply of oxygen for the rapid and complete combustion of the carbon and sulphur needed for the gunpowder to explode. Chemists call a substance which readily makes oxygen available in this way an *oxidizing agent.*

Oxidizing agents

Another oxidizing agent which is used to prepare oxygen in the laboratory is potassium chlorate. If this substance is strongly heated on its own, a little oxygen is produced. This slow chemical reaction is one of those which can be accelerated using a *catalyst,* a substance which alters the speed of a reaction without itself taking part in it. In this case, the catalyst is manganese dioxide (the black substance found inside ordinary torch batteries). The potassium chlorate forms potassium chloride and oxygen:

$$2KClO_3 \rightarrow 2KCl + 3O_2.$$

The oxidizing properties of potassium chlorate have not been overlooked by inventors. A mixture of this substance with antimony sulphide and gum formed the heads of the first friction matches made in the 1820s. Later, some sulphur was also added (these matches were called Lucifers) and later still yellow phosphorus (giving matches called Congreves). Modern safety matches contain sulphur and potassium chlorate, and 'strike anywhere' matches contain red phosphorus and potassium chlorate. In both types the function of the chlorate is to supply oxygen for combustion.

The compound formed when an element combines with oxygen is generally called an oxide. One important exception to this naming is 'hydrogen oxide', or water, which is formed when hydrogen burns in air or pure oxygen:

$$2H_2 + O_2 \rightarrow 2H_2O.$$

Many other non-metals burn in oxygen to give oxides. For instance, sulphur forms the choking gas sulphur dioxide (SO_2), phosphorus forms the white solid phosphorus pentoxide (P_2O_5), carbon forms the gas carbon dioxide (CO_2), and

Iron readily combines with oxygen in the air to form the common nuisance, rust. Painting iron-based metals inhibits rust as well as making the metals look more attractive.

under certain circumstances nitrogen will form the colourless gas nitric oxide (NO). If these oxides are dissolved in water, an important fact emerges: in every case the solution formed is an *acid.* Sulphur dioxide gives sulphurous acid, phosphorus pentoxide gives phosphoric acid, carbon dioxide gives carbonic acid and nitric oxide gives a mixture of nitrous and nitric acids.

Cause of corrosion

What about metals which combine with oxygen? For instance, sodium, calcium and magnesium all burn vigorously in oxygen to form white solids which dissolve in water. In this case, the solutions of the soluble oxides are alkaline; for this reason they are called *basic* oxides. As a general rule, soluble oxides of metals give alkaline solutions.

The oxidation of iron does not produce a basic oxide because the oxide is insoluble in water, but it does produce a compound of tremendous commercial and economic importance: rust. The reddish-brown flakes of rust which form on iron and steel are iron oxide. They result from a reaction between iron and oxygen in the air, although water must also be present.

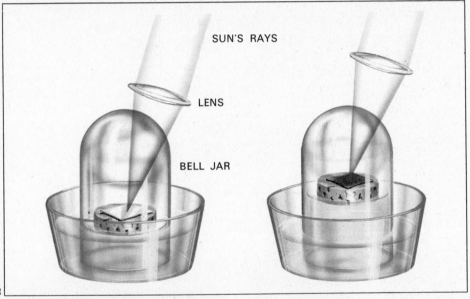

SUN'S RAYS

LENS

BELL JAR

1 About half the Earth's crust is composed of oxygen in its many compounds. The famous White Cliffs of Dover in England are impressive out-croppings of calcium carbonate (chalk), which is nearly half oxygen by weight.

2 High-pressure oxygen injected into newly formed steel forces out impurities which gather as the pile of waste shown here.

3 By a series of historical experiments carried out in the mid-eighteenth century, Antoine Lavoisier established the relationship between oxygen and burning. In one experiment, he focused the heat of the sun on tin floating inside a bell jar on a piece of cork. Slowly, the water level rose, evidence that the tin was combining with some-thing in the air – oxygen.

4 Hydrogen peroxide, a compound of hydrogen and oxygen, is a powerful oxidizing agent used for bleaching clothes – and other things.

5 Aluminium forms oxides which are either whitish or transparent and which may readily take on coloured dyes. These aluminium keys have been dyed different colours for easy identification. No more searching through an entire key-ring in order to open the front door.

Acidic gases in the atmosphere, such as carbon dioxide or sulphur dioxide, greatly accelerate rusting. For this reason, rust-ing takes place much more rapidly in polluted industrial atmospheres in towns than in the clean air of the countryside.

Other metals also oxidize in air. But in many cases, for instance with aluminium and zinc, the thin film of oxide first formed protects the metal from further oxidation. So good is the protection against cor-rosion afforded by such oxide films that for many applications aluminium is deliber-ately given an oxide coating in the electrolytic process called *anodizing*. Most anodic oxide films on aluminium are white; a few are transparent. The oxide o anodized aluminium can be dyed brig colours, and so the metal can be given attractive as well as a protective finis

Oxidation of metals is part of the

general phenomenon of *corrosion*. Some metals and alloys do not form oxides at all. Such metals include stainless steels, chromium and nickel. Of these, the last two are often used in the form of a thin electroplated film to protect easily oxidized metals such as iron and ordinary steel.

If certain metal oxides (such as barium or sodium peroxide) are treated with acid, the substance hydrogen peroxide is formed. It is made commercially by a complex electrolytic method. Hydrogen peroxide has the chemical formula H_2O_2 and most of its uses take advantage of the fact that it very readily splits up into water and oxygen:

$$2H_2O_2 \rightarrow 2H_2O + O_2.$$

The oxygen released by this decomposition is then ready for combination with other elements and chemical compounds.

Hydrogen peroxide is therefore a powerful oxidizing agent and is used as a bleach for cloth and hair, as a disinfectant and mouthwash, and as a rocket propellant. The German V-2 rocket used near the end of the Second World War had as its fuel alcohol and more than five tons of 83 per cent hydrogen peroxide – two-fifths of the take-off weight of the rocket. The Germans also developed rocket motors using hydrogen peroxide alone (which they called *T-stoff*); the decomposition reaction was hastened by a catalyst such as potassium permanganate, and the jet of steam and oxygen produced gave the rocket motor its thrust. A similar reaction was used in a turbine for powering German U-boats.

Oxygen allotropes

Pure hydrogen peroxide is an oily liquid with a much higher boiling point than that of water (H_2O_2 boils at 144 °C., water at 100 °C.). Because it is explosive, the pure liquid is dangerous to handle. It is sold as a bleach or disinfectant as a dilute solution in water. The strengths of hydrogen peroxide solutions are given in *volumes*, not per cent concentrations; the volumes referred to are the volumes of

In 1967 three American astronauts died when a fire swept through their space capsule filled with pure oxygen. Space capsules have since been redesigned to reduce this hazard.

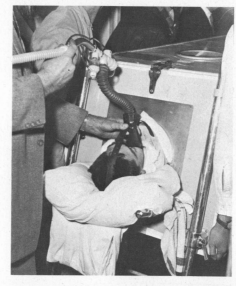

In an emergency, a ready supply of oxygen can be the difference between life and death. Hospitals and emergency rescue units store oxygen under high pressure in steel cylinders.

oxygen available from one volume of the liquid. For instance, one pint of a hydrogen peroxide solution of strength '20 volumes' will yield 20 pints of oxygen gas and so has a concentration of '20 volumes'. This corresponds to a concentration of six per cent hydrogen peroxide by weight.

The normal oxygen molecule contains two atoms and has the chemical formula O_2. But there also exists a compound with three oxygen atoms called ozone, O_3. Chemists call the phenomenon in which elements exist in several forms *allotropy*, and ozone is an allotrope of oxygen. Ozone is a gas with an acrid smell. It is formed when an electric spark jumps through air and can often be smelled near electrical machinery. It is made in the laboratory in an *ozonizer*, which is an apparatus in which a high-voltage electric spark is

made to pass through a stream of oxygen. Ozone also occurs in the atmosphere, especially at high altitudes where it is formed by the action of ultra-violet radiation from the sun on oxygen in the air.

Pure ozone is a blue gas which forms a dark blue liquid on cooling below about −112 °C. It has the remarkable property of almost completely absorbing ultra-violet light. Up to one part per million of ozone which exists in the Earth's atmosphere serves as a 'filter' for the sun's ultra-violet rays. According to one expert, if all the ozone were suddenly removed, everyone would die within a few minutes, killed by the sun's radiation. Ozone readily decomposes to oxygen, and in liquid form explodes spontaneously. It is a powerful oxidizing agent and its oxidizing properties are used in a germicide, being pumped at one time, for example, into the ventilation system of London's underground railway. In high concentrations, ozone is poisonous.

These then are the compounds of oxygen and their uses. But what of oxygen itself? Its uses all depend in some way on its oxidizing ability. Anything which burns in air burns much more vigorously and efficiently in oxygen. Fuel gases such as coal gas, hydrogen and acetylene give extremely hot flames when burnt in oxygen. An oxy-acetylene torch flame may reach a temperature of 3,000 °C. (twice the melting point of iron) and can be used for welding many metals. About a quarter of the oxygen produced commercially is used in this way.

Oxygen for astronauts

People suffering from lung diseases are given oxygen to breathe, and divers, firemen, pilots and astronauts breathe mixtures of oxygen and other gases.

Because this is the Space Age, this list of the uses of oxygen must include liquid-propellant rockets. Hydrogen peroxide was used in rockets in the 1940s as a source of oxygen. An even better source is liquid oxygen itself (often called *lox* by rocket engineers). Liquid oxygen was not used in the 1940s because of the technical difficulties of handling and storing a liquid which boils at −183 °C. Today, however, these difficulties have been overcome and liquid oxygen is used in rocket motors for ballistic missiles and moon rockets. Petrol is commonly used as a fuel (the other liquid component); America's Saturn V moon rocket will employ liquid oxygen and kerosene.

The ambition of contemporary rocket engineers is to design a motor using the chemical reaction discovered by Henry Cavendish more than 200 years ago: the combination of oxygen and hydrogen to produce water. A motor using liquid oxygen and liquid hydrogen would have a higher exhaust velocity than petrol and 'lox', shooting out exhaust gases at velocities up to 13,000 feet per second compared with about 7,000 feet per second from liquid oxygen and petrol or kerosene. So the earliest and simplest chemical reaction of oxygen known may still turn out to be one of the most important to twentieth-century technology.

Nitrogen – the reluctant explosive

Nitrogen is a rather odd element. Uncombined, it is docile and highly unreactive, but its compounds are often powerful explosives. Both characteristics make it a very useful substance.

NITROGEN GAS is one of Nature's most unreactive elements. It is colourless, tasteless, odourless, and very reluctant to take part in chemical reactions. Yet some of its compounds, notably TNT and nitroglycerine, explode violently. Another nitrogen compound, hydrazine, is used as a rocket fuel.

The story of nitrogen begins with its discovery as a distinct chemical element by the British physician Daniel Rutherford in 1772. Nitrogen comprises 78 per cent by volume of the gases in the air, and was first identified by removing it from the air. Today, commercial preparation of nitrogen still depends on extracting it from the Earth's atmosphere. It is made from liquid air. It boils off at −196 °C., leaving behind oxygen which boils at −183 °C. Or it can be made by using air to burn carbon in the form of coke. When the oxygen is used up in the combustion of carbon, nitrogen and a small percentage of other gases remain. The gaseous product of the combustion, carbon dioxide, is removed by dissolving it in water. If necessary, the other impurities may be removed as well, but since their presence is no real hindrance in the use of nitrogen, they are usually left.

One of the laboratory preparations of nitrogen uses the same principle of burning something in air, but this time the air is passed over heated iron filings because the resulting iron oxides are solid, so they do not contaminate the remaining nitrogen.

A few compounds of nitrogen decompose on heating to liberate the element.

Alfred Nobel (1833–96) tamed the shock-sensitive explosive nitroglycerine by combining it with an inert solid to form stable dynamite.

This decomposition reaction is the basis of other laboratory preparations. For instance, ammonium nitrite gives nitrogen and water on heating:

$$NH_4NO_2 \rightarrow N_2 + 2H_2O.$$

Ammonium nitrite tends to decompose explosively, so nitrogen is more often made by a 'double decomposition' reaction in solution. When ammonium chloride and sodium nitrite solutions are mixed, the various chemical radicals 'change partners' forming ammonium nitrite,

which immediately decomposes on heating.

The bright-orange salt ammonium dichromate also decomposes on heating, but not explosively, to give water and nitrogen, leaving a residue of a green oxide of chromium:

$$(NH_4)_2Cr_2O_7 \rightarrow Cr_2O_3 + 4H_2O + N_2.$$

Nitrogen itself is fairly unreactive, though it will combine with hydrogen under pressure (to form ammonia) and with oxygen at high temperatures (to form various oxides). Some metals which burn in air, such as magnesium, will also burn in nitrogen to form nitrides:

$$3Mg + N_2 \rightarrow Mg_3N_2,$$

which dissolves in water and decomposes to give the metal oxide and ammonia.

In the so-called Kalkstickstoff Process developed in Germany at the turn of the century, nitrogen is made to combine with calcium carbide (CaC_2) at high temperatures:

$$CaC_2 + N_2 \rightarrow CaCN_2 + C.$$

The compound formed, calcium cyanamide, may be used as a fertilizer, or as a source of other nitrogen compounds.

Making ammonia

Difficult though it is to persuade nitrogen to combine with other elements except at high temperatures or pressures, Nature has successfully solved the problem of how to use nitrogen from the air and make it available to plants. Certain members of the pea family, such as beans, clover and lucerne, have colonies of bacteria living in nodules on their roots. These bacteria 'fix' the nitrogen by the use of an enzyme catalyst and convert it into compounds which the plants can use as foodstuffs.

The calalytic combination of nitrogen with hydrogen to form ammonia (NH_3) is the basis of the Haber Process. A mixture of nitrogen and water gas (hydrogen and carbon monoxide) are heated to 500 °C. at 250 atmospheres pressure (one atmosphere pressure equals 14·7 pounds per square inch). The ammonia produced is liquefied or dissolved in water.

In the laboratory, ammonia is prepared by heating any ammonium salt with a base, for instance ammonium sulphate with slaked lime:

$$(NH_4)_2SO_4 + Ca(OH)_2 \rightarrow CaSO_4 + 2H_2O + 2NH_3.$$

Ammonia is a colourless gas with a characteristic pungent smell, familiar to

As an element, nitrogen is highly unreactive, but many of its compounds are explosive. Nitrogen compounds, therefore, are the bases of many kinds of ammunition important in wartime.

people who use ammoniated cleansers. Small amounts may be used as a stimulant. Smelling salts generally contain a salt such as ammonium carbonate which gives off ammonia at room temperature. This use also accounts for the old practice of burning feathers beneath the nose of someone who had fainted, because the burning protein generates ammonia.

Ammonia is extremely soluble in water (one volume of water dissolves about 800 volumes of ammonia) to form an alkaline solution called ammonium hydroxide (NH_4OH). The neutralization of this alkali with an acid gives rise to ammonium salts, for instance ammonium chloride:

$$NH_4OH + HCl \rightarrow NH_4Cl + H_2O.$$

Liquid ammonia behaves chemically in a very similar way to the behaviour of water. Although it boils at -33.4 °C., like water it is a good solvent for nearly all acids and salts. A whole field of chemistry has been developed in which reactions of compounds dissolved in liquid ammonia rather than in water are studied. Because of its low boiling point and the fact that it can be liquefied fairly easily under pressure, ammonia is used in some kinds of refrigerators.

Much of the ammonia produced commercially is converted into ammonium salts for use as nitrogenous fertilizers – more than ten million tons every year throughout the world. The most common of these are the ammonium sulphate, $(NH_4)_2SO_4$, made simply by passing ammonia into sulphuric acid, and ammonium nitrate, NH_4NO_3, which is doubly effective because it contains nitrogen in the 'ammonium' and in the 'nitrate'. Ammonium sulphate is also made from calcium sulphate (the mineral gypsum), ammonia and carbon dioxide. Some ammonia is used in the Solvay Process for manufacturing sodium carbonate (washing soda) from common salt, but most of this ammonia is recovered after the process is completed and can be used again and again.

Explosives and rocket fuels

Besides being used as a fertilizer, ammonium nitrate has also been used as the basis for many explosives; for instance 'Amatol' is a mixture of ammonium nitrate and TNT (another nitrogen compound). Ammonium chloride is used in ordinary torch batteries and as flux in soldering. The hydrochloric acid it releases when heated cleans the metal surfaces to be joined.

Another *hydride* (hydrogen compound) of nitrogen is hydrazine (N_2H_4) made from ammonia. It is a liquid, resembling water, boils at 113.5 °C., freezes at 1.8 °C., and like water and liquid ammonia is a good solvent. Hydrazine is fairly unstable, decomposing readily to ammonia and nitrogen, and can be very easily oxidized. It is used as a liquid rocket fuel.

With oxygen, nitrogen is capable of forming eight different oxides because it is capable of giving up one, two, three or four electrons to oxygen atoms. The most important oxides are nitrous oxide (N_2O), nitric oxide (NO) and nitrogen dioxide

(NO_2). Direct combination between oxygen and nitrogen is difficult. It takes place in the air to a very limited extent by the action of lightning in thunderstorms, and is the basis of the Birkland-Eyde Process for making nitric acid via the oxides. In this process, an extremely high voltage is used to strike a large electric arc between two electrodes in a magnetic field. The magnetic field pulls out the arc into a large disc, which at a temperature of 3,000 °C. makes the nitrogen and oxygen in

air passing through it combine to form nitric oxide:

$$N_2 + O_2 \rightarrow 2NO.$$

Nitrous oxide (N_2O) is the substance also known as 'laughing gas' and used for dental anaesthesia. Although Sir Humphry Davy had predicted such a use for gas as long ago as 1800, his suggestion was forgotten and it took the work of two dentists in the United States before nitrous oxide was generally accepted. In 1845,

1 Ammonia is one of the most important compounds of nitrogen, because it is the starting material for so many other useful things, from fertilizers for plants to plastics for Man.

2 Rayon is a man-made fibre made from cellulose. Here, high tenacity rayon is passing through a hot stretching process to prepare it for use in automobile tyres.

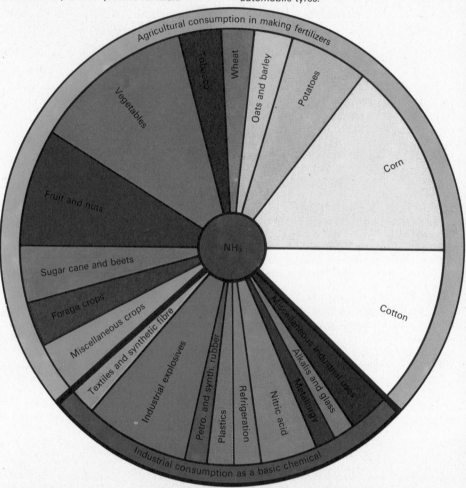

86

1 Nitrogen is essential to plant growth. When Nature does not provide enough of it, it may be added to the soil artificially by one of a wide variety of natural and synthetic fertilizers.

2 Flying high over desolate terrain, a helicopter rescue pilot could easily miss what he is looking for. An explosion sending up a brightly coloured cloud makes the task easier.

3 Nitro compounds – compounds containing nitrogen, oxygen, carbon and hydrogen – make good explosives as the products of their combustion are all gases, which exert high pressure.

Horace Wells and his colleague William Morton (who a year later helped to introduce ether anaesthesia) extracted a tooth painlessly while the patient was rendered unconscious by nitrous oxide.

Exhibitions of laughing gas followed in which people were encouraged to take the gas to 'laugh, sing, dance, speak or fight according to the leading trait in their character'. A contemporary poster adds, 'Probably no one will attempt to fight. The gas will be administered only to gentlemen of the first respectability. The object is to make the entertainment in every respect, a genteel affair.'

Nitrous oxide is made by cautiously heating ammonium nitrate:

$$NH_4NO_3 \rightarrow 2H_2O + N_2O.$$

The heating must be cautious because ammonium nitrate explodes at high temperatures.

The most important oxide of nitrogen is nitric oxide, used for making nitric acid. Apart from small quantities made by the Birkland-Eyde Process, most is made commercially by the high temperature catalytic oxidation of ammonia:

$$4NH_3 + 5O_2 \rightarrow 6H_2O + 4NO.$$

Oxides and acids

Air is used as the source of oxygen, and platinum gauze as a catalyst. In the presence of further oxygen, the nitric oxide dissolves in water to form nitric acid:

$$4NO + 3O_2 + 2H_2O \rightarrow 4HNO_3.$$

In the laboratory, nitric oxide is made by the reverse process, the reduction of fairly dilute nitric acid by copper turnings. It is a colourless gas which combines immediately with the oxygen in the air to form brown fumes of the oxide, nitrogen dioxide (NO_2). This oxide is more conveniently made by heating heavy metal

of toluene yields trinitrotoluene (TNT), nitration of glycerol gives nitroglycerine (more properly called glycerol trinitrate), and nitration of cellulose yields nitrocellulose. Since the cellulose for this process often takes the form of cotton fibres, the nitrogen compound is also known as gun cotton. This became the first 'smokeless' propellant to replace gunpowder for firearm cartridges and is made in a form called cordite in many countries.

Nitroglycerine is an oily liquid which is extremely sensitive to shock and dangerous to handle. The Swedish chemist Alfred Nobel (founder of the Nobel Prizes) had the idea of soaking up the nitroglycerine in an earthy substance called *kieselguhr* – which is much the same as china clay – to give the explosive called dynamite.

Many other nitro compounds are made from nitric acid and used as explosives. For instance, a mixture of ammonia and formalin yields a solid substance with the tongue-twisting name of hexamethylenetetramine. When this substance is nitrated, it gives the explosive called hexogen or RDX – which is easier to remember than its chemical name, cyclo-trimethylene-trinitramine. Mixed with TNT, this explosive is used for filling torpedo warheads. A complex alcohol called pentaerythritol can be nitrated to the explosive PETN (pentaerythritol tetranitrate).

All these nitro compounds consist of nitrogen, oxygen, carbon and hydrogen. One of the reasons why they are efficient explosives and propellants is because all the products of their combustion are gases and because they carry their own oxygen supply with them. On exploding, the nitrogen forms one or more of its many gaseous oxides, carbon forms carbon dioxide gas, and hydrogen forms water – or steam at the high temperatures involved.

Artificial fibres

Nitrocellulose also has another important use. If a sticky solution of this substance in a mixture of alcohol and ether is squirted through fine nozzles into air or water, very fine threads are produced. The nitrogen compounds are eliminated chemically to leave pure cellulose, which is spun to form rayon or artificial silk. Nitrocellulose is also used for making lacquers such as those for painting motor cars and for making 'patent' leather.

Nitric acid is also used for etching metals (artists' 'etchings' are printed from copper plates etched in nitric acid). Semiconductor materials such as silicon used in transistors are also etched with nitric acid.

Because nitrogen itself undergoes so few reactions, scientists study it through its compounds. However, it is the very inactivity of nitrogen which gives it its most important use of all – controlling combustion. Oxygen is explosively combustible. If nitrogen were not in the air (about 78 per cent by volume) to moderate the high combustibility of oxygen, the simple act of lighting a cigarette could set off a major explosion. As the poet John Milton observed, 'They also serve who only stand and wait.'

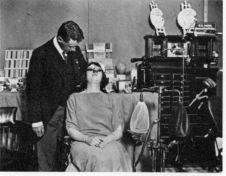

1 Producing ammonia and ammonia-derived compounds is big business, as indicated by this distillation column in an ammonia soda plant.
2 Nitrous oxide dissolved in cream under pressure liberates tiny bubbles when the pressure is released. The result – whipped cream.

3 Nitrous oxide, otherwise known as 'laughing gas', found use in bygone days as a dental anaesthetic. It was also used for entertainment, because people do strange things under its influence. Some other oxides of nitrogen are no laughing matter; they are deadly poisons.

nitrate such as lead nitrate:

$$2Pb(NO_3)_2 \rightarrow 2PbO + O_2 + 4NO_2.$$

Nitrogen dioxide is extremely poisonous because in the presence of oxygen it dissolves in the water of the lungs to form nitric acid. In the absence of oxygen, it dissolves in water to give a mixture of nitric and nitrous acids. At low temperatures, nitrogen dioxide changes from a brown gas to the colourless compound nitrogen tetroxide:

$$2NO_2 \rightleftharpoons N_2O_4.$$

This reaction is an *association* and the reversal which takes place at higher temperatures a *dissociation*.

The commercial importance of nitric oxide and nitrogen dioxide is their role in the manufacture of nitric acid, which is derived from the catalytic oxidation of ammonia. An earlier commercial pre-

paration and one known to the ancient alchemists uses the reaction between concentrated sulphuric acid and a nitrate such as potassium nitrate (saltpetre) or sodium nitrate (Chile saltpetre or *nitre*) – hence the names *nitric* acid and *nitrogen*. Four tons of ingredients are put into iron retorts heated over a furnace, and acid of 93–95 per cent strength distilled off.

Nitric acid is an oxidizing agent and is used to supply oxygen in liquid propellant rockets. With metals, metal oxides, hydroxides or carbonates, nitric acid forms an important series of salts called nitrates. Some of these are used as fertilizers and explosives.

Organic nitrogen compounds (complex compounds containing nitrogen and carbon) are made by *nitration,* a process in which an organic substance is treated with a mixture of concentrated nitric and sulphuric acids. For instance, nitration

Mendeleef's missing elements

Gases with full electron shells. Theoretically inert, they nevertheless play an important part in modern chemistry, and have provided vital clues in the development of chemical theory.

WHEN DMITRI MENDELEEF constructed his periodic table of the elements in 1869, he recognized only eight groups of elements. Twenty-five years later, the British physicist Lord Rayleigh and the chemist William Ramsay discovered a new gaseous element in the air. They could make it take part in no chemical reactions, so they christened it *argon* from a Greek word meaning inert.

Within four years, Ramsay had found four other similar gases and, to accommodate them in the periodic classification, he added a whole new group to the periodic table, labelling it 'group O', because they had zero valence. The other members of the group are helium, neon, krypton and xenon. Then in 1901 the German physicist Friedrich Dorn detected a highly radioactive gas which, because it was given off by radium, was known as 'radium emanation'. Ramsay again got to work and showed that the new element was the sixth member of his inert gas series, and he called it *radon*.

The element hunters

The story of the gases is therefore really the story of William Ramsay, the only man to have a hand in the discovery of a whole group of elements. He was born at Glasgow in 1852. He held various academic posts, becoming professor of chemistry at University College, London in 1887, where he worked until 1912. While at London he contacted Robert Strutt, better known as Lord Rayleigh, who was professor of physics at Cambridge and was studying the composition of air. Ramsay lived during the era of the element hunters – 24 new elements were discovered during his lifetime. He was probably the greatest chemist since Sir Humphry Davy a century earlier, and when he died in 1916 he had the satisfaction of knowing that he had equalled Davy's total of new elements discovered.

The inert gases have practically no chemical properties and are assigned a valence of zero. This behaviour is easy to understand in terms of the electronic structure of their atoms. Each of these gases has a completely filled outer shell or sub-group of electrons – that is why the group logically stands as the right-hand column of the Periodic Table. Since the outer shell or sub-group is full, there are no electrons *readily* available for taking part in a chemical reaction and bond-formation. As a result, the gases are monatomic – that is, their molecules each consists of one atom. Other gaseous elements, even highly unreactive ones such as nitrogen, are at least able to combine together into diatomic molecular units.

The lightest inert gas is helium, having

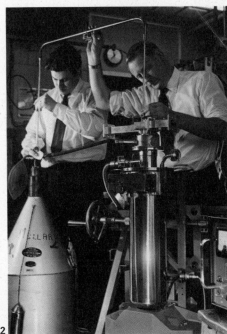

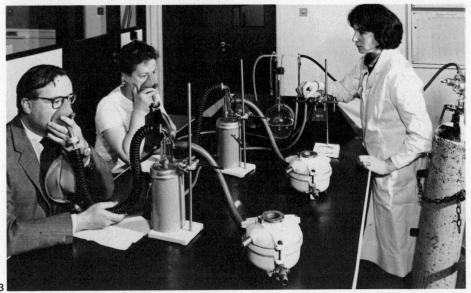

1 Sir William Ramsay (1852–1916) was a British chemist who had the unique distinction of having discovered a whole new family of elements – the inert gases.
2 Masers, devices used to detect signals from satellites, must operate at a very low temperature,

achieved by cooling with liquid helium. The maser being filled with helium is used in Telstar experiments at Goonhilly Down in Britain.
3 Radon, the radioactive inert gas, is used as a tracer element to measure the rate of excretion of waste gases from the lungs.

a density of 0·1784 gram per litre. This is twice that of hydrogen but still sufficiently low to make helium a better choice for filling balloons than highly inflammable hydrogen: helium does not burn. At −268·9 °C., helium condenses to a liquid which has some remarkable properties of superfluidity – it has an apparently zero viscosity. It tends to flow *out* of a vessel of its own accord by 'creeping' up the walls and spilling over. Liquid helium conducts heat about 200 times as well as does copper

at ordinary temperatures. Liquid helium is used in producing the lowest attainable temperatures, and under a pressure of 25 atmospheres (1 atmosphere=14·7 pounds per square inch) changes to a solid at about −272 °C. But by reducing its temperature, no matter how low, liquid helium will not be made to freeze (the only liquid for which this is true). It also requires pressure to make it solidify.

Because of its inertness, helium is also used mixed with oxygen to make synthetic 'air' for divers, pilots and astronauts to breathe under pressure. Natural air, containing four-fifths nitrogen, is unsuitable for this purpose because the nitrogen tends to dissolve in the blood and bubble out again on decompression to give the agonizing and sometimes fatal condition called 'the bends'. Unfortunately a man's vocal cords do not function properly in the less dense helium 'air' and his voice is distorted and takes on a 'Donald Duck' quality.

Spectrum of the sun

Helium was detected many years before it was finally identified by Ramsay. During the total eclipse of the sun in 1869, the English astronomer Norman Lockyer discovered a new line in the spectrum of the sun's chromosphere. He called the element causing the line helium, from the Greek word *helios* meaning sun. Later, in 1890, the American chemist and geologist William Hillebrand found a gas in uranium minerals which he thought was nitrogen. When Ramsay and William Crookes examined the spectrum of the gas in 1895, they found it to be the same as that in the sun, and helium had for the first time been identified on Earth.

It is now known that helium occurs in the atmosphere to the extent of 1 part in 200,000. It also occurs dissolved in many natural mineral waters and in natural gases associated with deposits of petroleum in North America. The gas from

some Texan oil wells is up to two per cent helium. It has also been found in the gases from coal mines and volcanoes.

On a small scale, helium is prepared by strongly heating a mineral containing it, such as clevite or thoriamite, or by dissolving such a mineral in sulphuric acid. Impure helium is separated from other inert gases by the action of active charcoal, which when cooled in liquid air has the property of absorbing all gases *except* helium.

It is interesting that helium turns up in nuclear fission reactions, such as in the decay of various radioactive elements, and in fusion (thermonuclear) reactions which take place in the hydrogen bomb and in the sun and other stars. The alpha rays emitted by radioactive substances and used to such good effect by Lord Ruther-

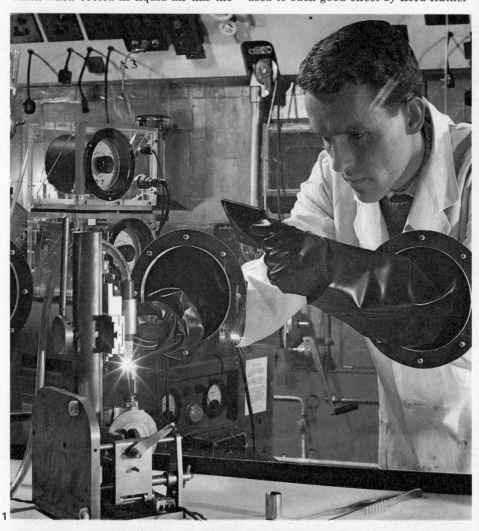

1 Argon is used in specialized welding to avoid oxidation of the metal. Its unreactivity ensures that the strength of the weld will not be affected by unwanted oxides.
2 Helium expansion turbines have been developed for extremely low temperature refrigerators used in nuclear research. The high polish on the casing minimizes heat absorption.
3 Lasers using inert bases give a continuous output of highly concentrated coherent light energy. Different gas mixtures are used according to the wavelength of light required.

ford and other experimenters for investigating the structure of atoms are in fact helium nuclei, He^{+2}. The fast moving helium ions (they travel at 18,000 miles a second, about one-tenth of the speed of light), consisting of two protons and two neutrons, possess tremendous amounts of energy and were used in early bombardment experiments to split other nuclei. If an evacuated glass vessel is put in a beam of alpha rays, after a while it is found to contain helium gas. This fact, as well as proving the composition of the rays, also shows that helium will undergo some sort of reaction, even if it is only the discharge of its own ions to neutral atoms.

The ion He_2^+ has been detected by the reaction between one atom of helium with the ion He^+. It has also been claimed that helium forms compounds with various metals, including mercury, platinum, tungsten and uranium. These 'helides' are said to be formed by striking an electric spark between electrodes of the metal concerned in an atmosphere of helium, but there is no definite evidence that true chemical compounds are formed.

Helium is formed in nuclear fusion from hydrogen. The series of reactions involved in the sun correspond to the combination of four hydrogen atoms to form two helium atoms and two positrons. However, if the masses of the atoms and particles involved are calculated, it is found that the products weigh less than the reactants. This 'lost' mass (0·0287 mass unit per reaction) appears as energy, and in the sun nearly 250 million tons of matter are converted into energy by this process every minute.

Neon in lighting

The second rare gas, *neon,* was one of three discovered by Ramsay and his assistant Morris Travers in 1898. Named after the Greek word for new, neon was found in air, revealed by its spectrum. It is nearly four times as abundant as helium in air (nearly 20 parts per million) and it, too, is sometimes found in mineral waters.

Neon is commonly used, generally mixed with helium, in the red-orange neon lamps used in advertising signs and for airport warning lights. In such lamps,

Mixtures of neon and helium at low pressure are used in lamps which give a high light output in relation to the power consumed. A wide range of different colours can be obtained.

which contain the gases at very low pressures, an electric current ionizes the neon which then carries the current between the electrodes in the lamp. Since a certain minimum voltage is required before neon will ionize, the gas is also used in devices to control voltages.

The next heavier inert gas, and the first to be discovered, is argon. When Lord Rayleigh prepared what he thought was nitrogen from air by removing all the oxygen, carbon dioxide and water, he found that the gas he obtained was denser than nitrogen made from its compounds by chemical methods. Like Henry Cavendish before him, he found that when he did remove all the nitrogen from his 'dense' gas (by forcing it to combine with burning magnesium), he was left with a trace of gas which refused to combine with anything. Ramsay repeated these experiments and studied the gas obtained with a spectroscope. He found lines corresponding to a new element. Because he could not make it take part in any chemical reaction he tried, he called it *argon* from a Greek word meaning inert.

Argon from air

Argon is the most abundant inert gas, making up nearly one per cent of the air by volume. It is generally prepared by repeated fractional distillation of liquid air. The air then contains the heavier rarer inert gases as impurities. It is used, often mixed with nitrogen, for filling ordinary incandescent electric lamps where its presence prevents the tungsten filament from evaporating and darkening the inside of the glass bulb (a common failure in earlier vacuum lamps). It is also used to form an inert atmosphere for the welding of reactive metals such as aluminium, which would oxidize or burn in air.

Argon forms a definite compound called a hydrate with water, in much the same way as do many salts. Argon hydrate melts at 8 °C. It has also been claimed that argon forms compounds with boron trifluoride, although more recent work has cast doubts on the existence of such compounds. A compound with quinol has been prepared and probably takes the form of a *clathrate* compound. In the molecules of this compound an argon atom is trapped in a 'cage' formed by the organic molecules. The gas in the hydrate is probably locked in a similar cage of ice crystals.

The last two inert gases discovered by Ramsay in the last century are krypton (from the Greek for hidden) and xenon (from the Greek for stranger). These, too, were discovered in air by means of their spectra. They are extremely rare, and occur as about one part per million in air. They dissolve in liquid air, and this fact is used as the basis for their preparation (Claude process), in which liquid air is used to wash them out of very cold air. They both form solid hydrates with water,

The rotor of this helium turbine cools compressed helium gas by expanding it. In this way, temperatures only a few degrees above absolute zero can be produced.

the krypton compound melting at 13 °C. and that of xenon at 24 °C. Krypton is used in discharge tubes for signs which produce a greenish light, and xenon is used in the tubes in photographers' electronic flash equipment, where its bluish-white light is similar to daylight.

As recently as 1962, chemists have prepared three compounds of xenon with fluorine, and an oxide, XeO_3, has been described. It seems that the least common of the atmospheric noble gases is also the least unreactive.

The sixth and last inert gas is radon. This element has had a chequered career,

High intensity floodlights, such as those shown here for use at Orly Airport in France, use a mixture of argon and nitrogen. This inert filling ensures that the filaments do not burn.

and even its name has been changed from time to time. Discovered by Dorn as a radioactive gas given off by radium, it was first called *radium emanation*. This was later shortened to emanation (symbol Em) when it was realized that similar gases are given off by other radioactive elements, particularly actinium and thorium. For a while radon was known as nitron, and the emanations from actinium and thorium were called *actinon* (mass 219) and *thoron* (mass 220). Finally, they were all identified as isotopes (different forms) of one element, radon. Since Rutherford discovered the isotope radon 220 (thorium emanation, thoron) in 1900, a year before the work of Dorn, he could be credited with the discovery of the new element. But this distinction is generally given to Dorn, although it was Ramsay who studied its spectrum and got the first tentative measurements of its physical properties.

Radium was discovered in pitchblende (a uranium ore) by M. and Mme Curie in 1898. If a solution of a radium salt is allowed to stand in a closed flask for several weeks, the radon formed dissolves in the solution (the solubility of radon is more than 50 per cent by volume).

It is now known that radium (mass 226) decays into radon (mass 222) by the emission of an alpha particle (a helium nucleus). Radium has a half-life of 1,622 years. This means that, every 1,622 years, half the radium in the world changes into radon. The radon then decays rapidly (half-life 3·83 days) by a series of changes which result ultimately in a stable isotope of lead (mass 206). These changes are accompanied by the emission of alpha particles, so that some helium is also produced.

Cornerstones of chemistry

Similarly, radon 220 (thoron) results from the decay of thorium, and rapidly changes into lead 208; and radon 219 (actinon) formed from actinium finishes up as lead 207. Incidentally, the existence of stable isotopes of lead of different masses finally explained why, over the years, various experimenters had got different values for the atomic weight of lead. Depending on how the lead weighed had been formed, it contained different mixtures of the various isotopes, lead resulting from the decay of thorium being heavier than that derived from radium.

Although the inert gases as a group have little or no chemical activity, they have, nevertheless, played a vital role in the development of modern chemistry. The existence of radon and its isotopes led to a complete understanding of radioactive decay and demonstrated a natural transmutation of the elements far more impressive than the alchemists' attempts to turn base metal into gold.

Helium and its thermonuclear formation by the fusion of hydrogen may ultimately provide the source of almost unlimited power. For, once men have learned to tame the hydrogen bomb, they will have as their 'fuel' hydrogen, a gas which makes up two-thirds of the atoms in all the water in the world.

What is electricity?

Elektron, Greek for amber, gave us our word for electricity. Today, we can explain electrical and magnetic phenomena in terms of tiny, negatively charged particles aptly called electrons.

THE MODERN theory of the atom has been developed over the last 60 years as a result of Sir Joseph Thomson's discovery of the electron in 1897. Scientists now know that atoms consist of numerous tiny particles, many of which carry an electric charge. The forces that hold the particles together in the atoms are also largely electrical. So that although electricity was discovered, most of the early experiments carried out, and fundamental laws formulated between 150 and 200 years ago, we can now interpret electrical phenomena in terms of our knowledge of the atom.

For example, early experimenters knew that a piece of amber which has been rubbed with fur has the capacity to attract light objects. This experiment is easy to repeat. A plastic comb pulled rapidly through the hair will pick up small pieces of paper. A nylon shirt or blouse pulled rapidly over the head crackles and makes the hair stand on end; in a darkened room tiny sparks may be seen. A similar charge will build up on a person who shuffles in rubber-soled shoes across a nylon carpet; he can make sparks jump from himself to another person or to something like a metal window frame. The cause of this behaviour is, as we know, electricity; the amber or the plastic comb becomes electrically charged.

Positive and negative charges

When a piece of plastic is rubbed with fur, some of the electrons, which lie near the surface of the atoms, are rubbed off. Electrons are charged particles whose charge is balanced in the atom by oppositely charged protons. When electrons are removed from atoms, they take their charge with them, leaving the atoms also charged. This removal of electrons by friction is the basis of all types of static electricity.

If the charged piece of plastic is brought up to the fur, it will attract the fur (in the same way, a charged plastic comb will make a person's hair stand on end). But if the charged plastic is brought up to another similar piece of charged plastic they repel each other. If, instead of using plastic, we rub a glass rod with silk, it also becomes charged, will pick up pieces of paper, and is repelled by a similarly charged glass rod. But if the charged glass is brought up to the charged plastic, the two attract each other.

The explanation for the difference in the behaviour of the two materials is that there are two sorts of static electricity. That on the plastic is called negative and that on the glass positive. The two sorts of charges attract each other, although two charges of similar type (both negative or both positive) repel each other. The situation may be summed up by the state-

A comb rapidly drawn through the hair attracts small pieces of paper, *below*. The comb has been charged with electricity by friction. The Wimshurst machine, *above*, builds up a charge of static electricity on the same principle, when the handle turns.

ment, 'like charges repel, unlike charges attract'. This conclusion was first stated in a scientific way by the English physician William Gilbert (1544–1603). Through the work of Sir Joseph Thomson, the American physicist Robert A. Millikan, and others, the exact value of the charge on an electron has been measured. The charge turns out to be the fundamental unit of electricity, the smallest particle of electricity that can exist on its own.

As long ago as 1789, the French physicist Charles de Coulomb studied electric charges, and reasoned that for them to attract or repel each other there must be a force acting between them. He constructed a kind of balance with electrically charged spheres and measured the force between them and a third sphere. He formulated his famous inverse square law which states that the force between two electrical charges is proportional to the product of the charges and inversely proportional

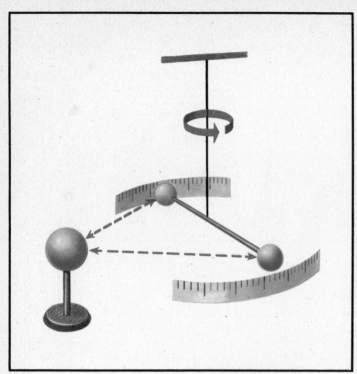

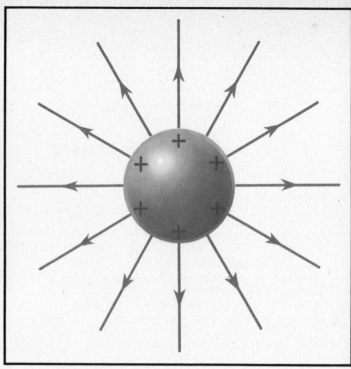

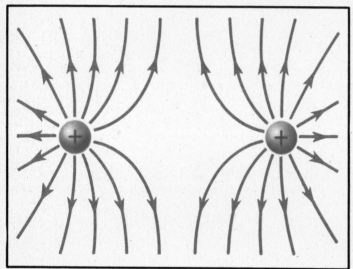

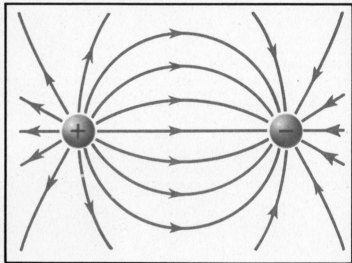

The charged comb can pick up small pieces of paper without having to touch them: an attractive force extends into the region round the comb. The area in which the force acts is called the electric field. In Coulomb's torsion balance, *top left,* the force between a charged sphere and two smaller counter-balanced charged spheres causes the suspension to twist. The force can be measured by noting the angle of twist. *Top right,* near a charged sphere, the electric field extends outwards radially. *Above left,* electric fields near two similarly charged spheres oppose each other; the spheres repel each other. *Above right,* electric fields near two oppositely charged spheres combine; the spheres attract each other.

to their distance apart. In mathematical terms, the law may be stated as $F \propto q_1 q_2/d^2$, where q_1 and q_2 are the charges and d is the distance between them. Coulomb's law is extremely important in physics and has been confirmed by several other experimenters, notably by Henry Cavendish (c. 1800), James Clerk Maxwell (1870), and S. J. Plimpton and W. E. Lawton (1936).

Returning to the experiment with the electrically charged piece of plastic (for example, a comb) which attracts small pieces of paper, we see that the plastic attracts and lifts the pieces of paper without having actually to touch them. This fact suggests that the attractive force extends into the region around the charged plastic. The area in which the force acts is called an electric field. The intensity of the field at any point near a small electrically charged sphere is proportional to the strength of the charge and inversely proportional to the square of the distance

between the point and the sphere. In mathematical terms, the intensity of the electric field, E, at a distance d from a charge q is given by the expression $E \propto q/d^2$.

As a result of the existence of the electric field, any charge situated in it is acted on by a force. Therefore, to move the charge to any other place in the electric field requires the expenditure of work. The situation is rather like that in which an object in a room is moved from one place to another at a different level. The object is always under the influence of the force of gravity (because it is in the gravitational field of the Earth).

How electricity 'flows'

To raise the object requires the expenditure of work and results in a change in the potential energy of the object. In the case of the electric charge, the work done is equal to the electric potential. It is pro-portional to the charge and inversely proportional to the distance it is moved ($V \propto q/d$).

Between two places of different potential, there is available to do work a quantity of energy called *the potential difference.* If the charges at two points of different potential are free to move, they will do so. Such a flow of charges is an electric current. We may re-state this fact by saying that for an electric current to flow (say along a wire) there must be a potential difference (between the ends of the wire). Potential differences are measured in *volts,* and the voltage between two points in an electric circuit is a measure of the amount of work that the circuit is capable of doing.

The whole question of potential and voltage can be considered in a slightly different way. Suppose we want to move electric charges, electrons, from one place to another in a circuit – that is, suppose we wish to make an electric current flow in

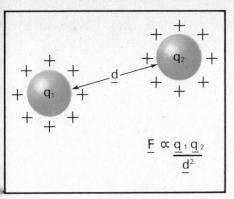

$$\underline{F} \propto \frac{q_1 q_2}{d^2}$$

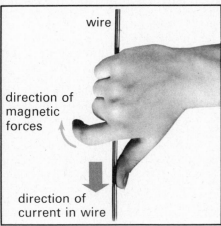

direction of magnetic forces

wire

direction of current in wire

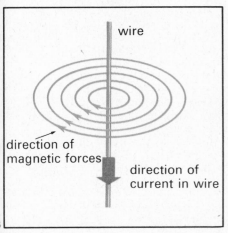

wire

direction of magnetic forces

direction of current in wire

1 Coulomb's law states that the force between two charges is proportional to the product of the charges and inversely proportional to the square of the distance between them. The law is known as the Inverse Square Law and is extremely important in physics. In its mathematical expression, *left*, q_1 and q_2 are the charges, *d* the distance between. 2 The direction of the magnetic forces round a wire is given by the right-hand grip rule. 3 The magnetic field associated with an electric current flowing in a wire is concentric with the wire in a plane at right angles to it.

a wire. To do this requires the application of a force, and the force that will cause electrons to move is called an *electromotive force* (e.m.f.). An e.m.f. is also measured in volts, and a voltage from, say, a battery applied across a circuit is the driving force that moves the electrons.

We have now mentioned electrons, the unit charges of electricity, in two ways: a crowd of electrons on a piece of glass or fur, causing it to be charged; and a stream of electrons flowing in a wire and forming an electric current. There is, of course, no difference between these two kinds of electrons. The difference lies in the way electrons behave in a piece of glass, which is an insulator, and in a piece of metal, which is a conductor.

Although the electrons in the atoms of glass can be rubbed off fairly easily, they are sufficiently well bound within their own atoms not to move along the piece of glass rod, even when there is a potential difference between the ends of the rod (or when an e.m.f. is applied between the ends). But in a metal, the electrons can move fairly easily among the atoms, so that if there is a potential difference between the ends of a wire (or an e.m.f. is applied), the electrons flow as an electric current along the wire.

The rate at which the electrons flow in a conductor is a measure of the current, usually expressed in *amperes* or *amps* – named after French physicist A. M. Ampère (1775–1836). Unfortunately, when scientists first discovered current electricity

they knew nothing of electrons. They wanted to assign a direction to current flow and quite arbitrarily they said that electric current flows from a region of positive charge to a region of negative charge. Or in a short phrase, 'current flows from positive to negative'. We now know that the carrier of the electricity, the electron, is itself negatively charged. For electricity to flow in a wire 'from positive to negative', the electrons must actually move in the opposite direction (from negative to positive). By the time the electron had been discovered, it was too late to change the convention about the direction of current flow, and the old idea has certain advantages when we are considering electric currents which are not in wires. For example, a stream of moving electrons such as that which flows between the electrodes of a cathode-ray tube constitutes an electric current. The electrons actually flow out of the negatively charged electrode (cathode) into the positively charged electrode (anode). But we still say that the electric current flows from positive (anode) to negative (cathode).

Good and bad conductors

Not all materials, even among metals, conduct electricity equally well. For a given potential difference, more electrons flow in some materials, which are good conductors, than in others, which are poorer conductors. When considering this situation in terms of current flow (before the discovery of the electron), scientists considered that some materials impeded current flow more than others.

The property of a material that opposes the flow of current is called its electrical *resistance*. Even with a single material, such as a copper wire, the resistance will vary, depending on its length and thickness. A thick piece of wire will conduct more current (have a lower resistance) than will a thin piece of wire. And a given potential difference will cause more electrons to flow along a short piece of wire

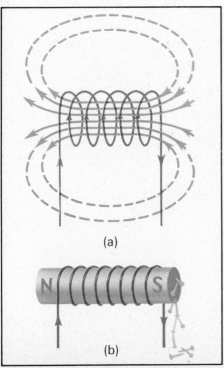

(a)

(b)

Left (a) The magnetic fields associated with the turns of wire in a coil carrying current combine to give a single concentrated magnetic field. *(b)* A simple electromagnet consists of a coil of insulated wire wrapped round a soft iron core.

The electromagnet, *above*, belonged to the English physicist James Prescott Joule. The discovery of electromagnetism was achieved by a Danish physicist, Hans Christian Oersted, in 1820. A whole branch of technology sprang from this.

than along a long piece; the resistance increases with increasing length. For this reason, when it is important that resistance be kept as low as possible, we use thick wires or short wires or, better still, wires that are both thick and short.

The best conductors (that is, those having the lowest resistance) are silver, copper, gold and aluminium in that order. Copper and aluminium also have the advantage of being relatively cheap, and for normal everyday use these are the metals employed – copper where flexibility is important, as in house wiring, aluminium where structural rigidity is needed too.

The high-voltage wires strung between the pylons of the National Grid are made of aluminium. Nearly all domestic house wiring is made of copper. Other metals, such as alloys of iron, nickel and chromium, have a high resistance and are poor conductors. They are used in the elements of electric fires, where their high resistance and high melting-point allows them to become red-hot.

The electrical resistances of various materials were studied by the German physicist Georg Ohm (1787–1854), and the unit of resistance, the *ohm*, is named after him. All three electrical units we have mentioned, the volt, the amp and the ohm, are chosen in such a way that a potential difference of one volt across a resistance of one ohm will cause a current of one amp to flow. Georg Ohm discovered the way in which these three quantities are interrelated. The relationship, called Ohm's Law, is that voltage is equal to the product of current and resistance. In mathematical terms, if V is voltage, I is current, and R is resistance, Ohm's Law may be written as $V = IR$. This equation is of fundamental importance in electricity.

In 1820, the Danish physicist Hans Christian Oersted (1777–1851) discovered that a pivoted magnetic needle near a wire is deflected when an electric current flows in the wire. He had discovered electro-

Georg Simon Ohm (1787–1854) was a German physicist who studied electrical resistance. The *ohm*, the unit of resistance, is named after him.

magnetism: that a magnetic field exists near a wire carrying a current. By using a small pivoted magnetic needle, such as a small compass, it is possible to plot the magnetic field near a conductor. When this is done for a straight wire, the magnetic field is found to be circular round the wire and in a plane at right angles to it. There is an easy way of remembering the direction of magnetic forces in the field around a wire. Imagine gripping the wire with the right hand, with the thumb pointing in the direction of the current. Then the fingers will curl round in the direction of the magnetic forces. This is called the *right-hand grip rule*.

What is magnetism?

We now regard magnetic force not as something different from electric force,

but simply as its necessary modification which we observe when we move relative to an electric charge. We notice a magnetic force whether an electric charge flies past us or we fly past an electric charge. It is then clear that an electric current, consisting as it does of a flow of electric charges, must produce a magnetic force. The curious thing is, then, not the magnetic effect of electric currents, but the existence of certain bodies which always exert a magnetic force, even when no observable current is flowing through them. Such permanent magnets (the needle of a compass is an example) have been known for much longer than the magnetic effects of electric currents, but are a complex and almost freakish phenomenon. They occur because in a few materials the atoms themselves are magnetic (through the motions of the electrons in them or through the elementary magnetism possessed by each electron owing to its 'spin') and can be aligned.

A whole branch of modern electrical technology is based on the application of the magnetic effects of currents. Only a year after Oersted's discovery, the British scientist William Sturgeon (1783–1850) made the first electromagnet. Better electromagnets were made by the American Joseph Henry in 1828. To understand how such magnets work, we must consider the magnetic field in the region of a coil of wire carrying a current. The magnetic fields round the wires making up each turn of the coil will join up to give a concentration of field inside the coil. The more turns there are on the coil, the stronger the magnetic field will be. A piece of magnetic material, such as soft iron, placed inside the coil will become magnetized and attract other magnetic objects. The electromagnetism disappears as soon as the current ceases to flow. A simple electromagnet can be made by winding a few dozen turns of insulated wire round an iron nail and connecting the ends of the wire to a battery.

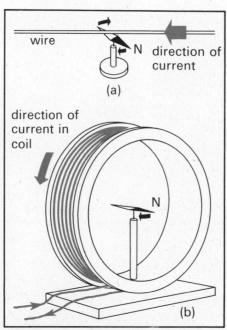

Left, Hans Christian Oersted (1777–1851), a Danish physicist, demonstrated to his friends that an electric current flowing in a wire deflects

a magnetized needle. The way the needle moves, in relation to the direction of the current, is shown at *(a), centre.* This principle is used in

the galvanometer *(b), centre* and *right.* It detects the presence of a current in the coil by the deflection of the central magnetized needle.

Where electric current flows

Why are some substances good conductors of electricity and others good insulators? Why is it that pure water is a good insulator, while salty or acidified water will conduct electricity?

SUBSTANCES WHICH ALLOW electricity to flow through them are called conductors, and substances which do not are called insulators. Copper is an example of a good conductor and glass an example of a good insulator. Normally pure water is also an insulator, but if a small quantity of an acid or a salt is dissolved in the water, it will conduct electricity. What happens to the water to change it from an insulator to a conductor?

The answer to this question can be found by considering an experiment. Imagine we take a beaker containing water to which a little sulphuric acid has been added. We can place in the acid solution two pieces of metal, say platinum (because this metal does not dissolve in sulphuric acid). We can then connect the pieces of metal to a battery, when they are called *electrodes*. The electrode connected to the negative terminal of the battery is called the cathode, and the positive electrode is called the anode. The acidified water will conduct the electricity from the battery and, after a short while, we will see bubbles of gas being formed on the electrodes. If we place a glass tube full of water upside-down over each electrode, we can collect the bubbles of gas as they rise to the surface. Chemical tests will show that the gas given off at the cathode (negative electrode) is hydrogen and the gas evolved at the anode is oxygen. We also notice that there is twice as much hydrogen as oxygen.

Splitting the molecule

From the results of this experiment, it is not difficult to guess what has happened. We know that water consists of molecules, chemical formula H_2O, each made up of two atoms of hydrogen combined with one atom of oxygen. It is as if the electric current has split up the molecules of water into their component atoms, which have formed molecules of hydrogen gas at the cathode and molecules of oxygen at the anode. The ability of electricity to split up liquids and substances in solution is called *electrolysis,* and the electrolysis of acidified water was first observed in 1800 by W. Nicholson and A. Carlisle.

Electrolysis was also studied by the English physicist Michael Faraday (1791–1867), who suggested that electricity is carried through a conducting solution (called an electrolyte) by charged particles which he named *ions.* In solution, an acid or a salt splits up into ions, some of which carry positive charges and some of which carry negative charges. This splitting-up of an acid or salt is called *dissociation,* and was first fully explained by the Swedish physicist Svante Arrhenius in 1887. The positive ions move towards the negatively charged cathode, where their

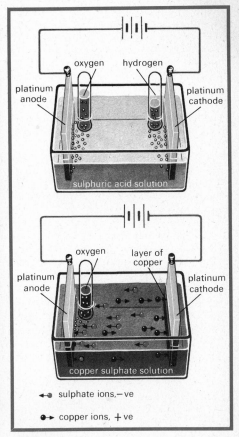

→● sulphate ions,−ve

●→ copper ions, +ve

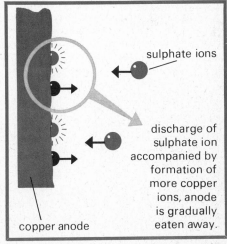

sulphate ions

discharge of sulphate ion accompanied by formation of more copper ions, anode is gradually eaten away.

copper anode

Man-made lightning, *left,* tests the conditions faced by insulators and transmission lines in thunder-storms. Conductors are substances that allow electricity to flow through them, and insulators are substances that do not. The experiment, *top right,* shows that acidified water acts as a conductor. Trapped in upturned jars, the bubbles that rise from each electrode are oxygen (from the anode) and hydrogen (from the cathode). The electric current splits up the molecules of water into their component atoms. Electricity's ability to do this is called electrolysis. Charged particles called ions carry the electricity through the conducting solution. If current is passed through a solution of copper sulphate, it dissociates into copper and sulphate ions, *above.* If the anode is copper, it will be eaten away.

charge is neutralized, and the negative ions move towards the anode.

If we consider our experiment with sulphuric acid, the complete explanation of what happens is as follows: in solution, sulphuric acid (H_2SO_4) dissociates into two hydrogen ions (H^+) and one sulphate ion (SO_4^{--}). (Notice that in the undissociated sulphuric molecule, the two positive charges on the hydrogen ions are exactly balanced by the two negative charges on the sulphate ion.) When electricity passes through the sulphuric acid solution, the hydrogen ions move towards the cathode, the sulphate ions move towards the anode. At the cathode, the hydrogen ions have their positive charge neutralized and become uncharged hydrogen atoms. Pairs of hydrogen atoms link to form molecules of hydrogen gas (H_2) which bubbles out of the solution and may be collected.

The situation at the anode is a little more complicated. Sulphate ions are neutralized and then react with water molecules to re-form sulphuric acid and to liberate oxygen gas ($2SO_4 + 2H_2O \rightarrow 2H_2SO_4 + O_2$). The overall result is that electricity is conducted through the solution by the ions, and the component elements of water are liberated as gases at the electrodes.

Consider now the case of a salt in solution, for example an electrolyte consisting of a solution of copper sulphate ($CuSO_4$). As soon as copper sulphate dissolves, it dissociates into copper ions (Cu^{++}) and sulphate ions (SO_4^{--}). If we now introduce platinum electrodes and pass an electric current through the solution, copper ions move to the cathode and sulphate ions move to the anode. At the cathode, copper ions are discharged to form atoms of copper metal which cover the platinum. This process is the basis of electroplating, and a solution of copper sulphate (with a little added sulphuric acid to improve conductivity) is used commercially for copper-plating metal objects.

The laws of electrolysis

At the anode sulphate ions are discharged, in the same way as in the electrolysis of sulphuric acid, with the formation of oxygen gas from the water. But if instead of a platinum anode we use a copper anode, the discharge of the sulphate ions is accompanied by the formation of more copper ions from the metal of the anode and the anode is gradually eaten away. The number of copper ions formed in this way is exactly equal to the number discharged at the cathode. For this reason, commercial copper electroplating baths have copper anodes which, by 'dissolving' during the plating process, exactly maintain the concentration of copper ions in the electrolyte. Many other metals can be electroplated from acid solutions of their simple salts, including iron, nickel and tin.

When Faraday studied electrolysis of salt solutions, he found that doubling the electric current doubled the weight of metal deposited in a given time. He also found that twice as much metal is deposited in, say, ten minutes as in five minutes. From these observations he for-

The English physicist Faraday, detail *above*, established the laws that govern electrolysis. Electroplating now plays important roles in many industries. *Right*, electroplating cylinders are widely used in printing. An impression of the plate required – a bank-note or book illustration, for example – is made in wax. The wax is thinly coated with a conductor material, then placed in a solution of copper sulphate. By electrolysis, copper is deposited to form an engraved copper plate. *Below*, National Grid pylons use aluminium conductors, glass and ceramic insulators.

mulated his first Law of Electrolysis which states that the amount of material deposited during electrolysis is proportional to the quantity of electricity passed through the electrolyte (the quantity of electricity is the product of the current and the time for which it flows).

Faraday also made another important observation concerning the amounts of material deposited at the cathode. By taking three different electrolytes – acidified water, silver nitrate solution and copper sulphate solution – and placing them in electrolytic cells connected together in series, he was able to pass the same current through all three. He then compared the weights of hydrogen, silver and copper appearing at the cathode in each cell. Faraday found that, for every gramme of hydrogen evolved, 107·88 grammes of silver were deposited and 31·77 grammes of copper. Now the atomic weight of hydrogen is 1·00 and that of silver 107·88 – that is, the metals were deposited in the ratio of their atomic weights. In other words, a certain quantity of electricity had deposited exactly the same number of atoms of hydrogen and copper, and so a hydrogen ion must carry the same electric charge as a silver ion.

The atomic weight of copper is 63·55. So the quantity of electricity that deposits an atomic weight of hydrogen and silver will deposit only half an atomic weight of copper. From this fact, Faraday concluded that a copper ion must carry twice the charge carried by a hydrogen ion or a silver ion. In modern terms, we should say that an *equivalent* weight of copper had been deposited (the equivalent weight of an element is its atomic weight divided by its chemical valence: the number of charges carried by an ion is equal to the valence of the element).

A faraday of electricity

Faraday summed up all this information in his second Law of Electrolysis, which states that the same quantity of electricity will deposit different substances in amounts that are proportional to their equivalent weights. The amount of electricity required to deposit one gramme equivalent weight of an element is called a faraday (symbol F).

Consider two electroplating baths, one containing monovalent silver ions (Ag^+, atomic weight 107·88, equivalent weight 107·88) and one containing divalent copper ions (Cu^{++}, atomic weight 63·55, equivalent weight 31·77). Then Faraday's second Law tells us that one faraday of electricity will deposit 107·88 grammes of silver or 31·77 grammes of copper. In other words, it will take nearly three and a half times as much electricity to deposit a given weight of copper as it would to deposit the same weight of silver.

So we see that by the late 1800s, the mechanism by which electricity passes through solutions was fairly well understood. In solution, the electrolyte dis-

Faraday's second Law of Electrolysis states that the same quantity of electricity deposits different substances in amounts proportional to their equivalent weights. *Right,* amounts deposited by one faraday of electricity (F).

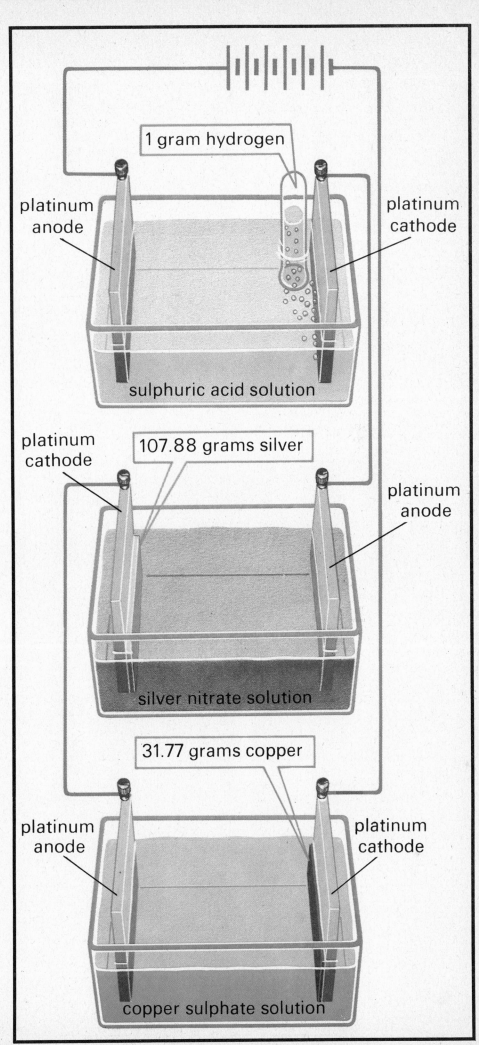

1 gram hydrogen

platinum anode

platinum cathode

sulphuric acid solution

platinum cathode

107.88 grams silver

platinum anode

silver nitrate solution

31.77 grams copper

platinum anode

platinum cathode

copper sulphate solution

sociates into charged particles (ions) which carry electricity between the electrodes. No formal proof of the existence of ions was needed because they demonstrated their presence by becoming neutral atoms of gas or metal at the cathode. But scientists understood only imperfectly how electricity passes through solid materials (such as metals) and could not account for the fact that some materials are conductors and some materials are insulators.

Thomson's explanation

Then, in 1897, J.J. Thomson made his famous discovery, which was to revolutionize men's ideas of the structure of atoms. With a knowledge of atomic structure came a truer understanding of the nature of electricity. He showed that the electron is the basic unit of electricity and that all atoms contain electrons. In other words, an electric current consists of a flow of electrons. A conductor, such as a piece of copper wire, has available from its atoms a sufficient number of electrons to carry an electric current through it. And an insulator has no such electrons available. Today we know that, in fact, the electrical properties of a solid material depend on the number of electrons

it possesses and the ease with which they can be persuaded to make themselves available for conduction.

One way of understanding the difference between conductors and insulators is to imagine an electric current presented with the choice of two possible paths: one along a conductor and one through an insulator. It will always 'prefer' to flow along the conductor which has the necessary free electrons available.

A good practical example of this sort of choice is the lightning conductor. Towers, church spires and other tall buildings are quite likely to be struck by lightning during a thunder-storm. Lightning, which is an extremely high-voltage electrical discharge, can do great damage to stonework or brickwork, set fire to wooden parts of buildings, and even electrocute people inside them. A lightning conductor consists of a steel or copper rod attached to the highest part of a building. Leading from the rod is a thick copper conductor which runs down the outside of the building with its lower end buried deep in the earth.

Lightning striking a building equipped with a lightning conductor has the choice of travelling through the building or

along the lightning conductor. It invariably 'chooses' the conductor and the electricity flows harmlessly to earth. Tall buildings such as the Empire State Building in New York City are struck by lightning many times a year but get complete protection from their lightning conductors.

All good conductors are metals. Some like gold, platinum and rhodium, are comparatively unreactive chemically and – though rare and expensive – are extensively used for such applications as switch points, where corrosion resistance is important. Aluminium and copper have less resistance to corrosion, but are even better conductors – and of course are much cheaper. For most industrial and domestic purposes, these are the metals used. For example, the high-voltage conductors strung between the pylons of the National Grid are made of aluminium. The wires that carry electricity from power stations to homes and factories, telephone wires, and all electric wiring inside houses, are generally made of copper.

Conductors and semiconductors

Conversely, good insulators are non-metals. The best insulators for high voltages are glass and porcelain, and insulators of these substances may be seen between high-voltage grid wires and the steel arms of pylons. Insulation for wires and cables must, of course, be flexible, and the best materials for this use are rubber and plastics. But these materials will not withstand high temperatures, and in such applications (for example, in the wiring to the elements of an electric fire), cloth or string made from asbestos or glass is generally used. In electric ovens and furnaces, glass or ceramic beads may be threaded on wires to insulate them.

Not all non-metals are good insulators. For example, carbon, in the form of graphite, finds many applications in the electrical industry. It is used for electrodes in batteries and arc lamps, and may be the conductive element in variable resistors used as volume controls on radio and television sets. The first electric lamps had carbon filaments.

But perhaps the most interesting materials are those which have electrical properties intermediate between conductors and insulators. These are the semiconductors used in transistors, without which tiny transistor radios and giant computers would not have been possible. In atomic structure, semiconductors more closely resemble insulators than conductors. Their atoms have few or no 'free' electrons available for conduction, but in the presence of an electric field a sufficient number of conductive elements are formed. Some of the materials used in semiconductors, for example arsenic and germanium, may also be considered to be intermediate chemically between metals and non-metals. With our present knowledge of atomic structure, we can explain chemical phenomena such as electrolysis, as well as physical properties such as electrical conductivity, in terms of the tiny molecules, atoms, ions and electrons too small ever to be seen by Man.

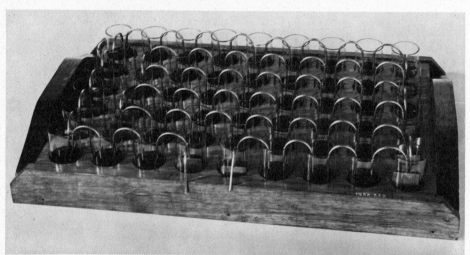

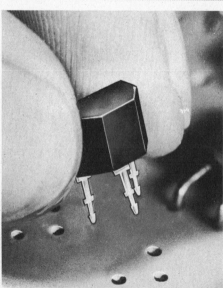

Volta described the experiment, *top,* to the Royal Society in 1800. When the crown of cups is connected to a circuit, a current flows through the salt solution and the intervening copper and zinc rods. The arrangement forms a battery. *Above left,* transistor radios and computors are made possible by the use of semiconductors. A Mullard 'lock-fit' transistor slots into place. *Above right,* a post-office engineer puts the final ties on a 'joint'. Each of the many wires is carefully insulated first. Flexible plastics and rubber are the most widely used wire insulators.

The mysteries of the magnet

Ancient Man believed magnets to be the resting place of invisible spirits. Today we explain their unusual behaviour in terms of 'flux' and 'lines of force'. But the fascination remains.

ONCE MANY PEOPLE BELIEVED that the stars were gods in their celestial home, that heat was a kind of mysterious fluid and that magnets worked by magic. Put yourself in their place. A magnet does pick up small pieces of metal as if an invisible hand were grabbing them. Magnets do attract and repel as if they 'like' and 'dislike' each other. And when suspended from a string or mounted on a pin (such as in a compass), a magnet always swings towards the north as if it had a will of its own.

No wonder, then, that people used to put so much faith in invisible spirits! Today scientists explain these strange phenomena in terms of 'magnetic fields', 'lines of force', 'magnetic flux' and other such expressions. But even these would require an inordinate degree of faith, were it not possible to 'see' these invisible magnetic fields.

'Seeing' the field

If a piece of paper is laid over an ordinary bar magnet and iron filings sprinkled on the paper, a definite pattern of curved lines appears radiating out from the bar. These lines are the *magnetic lines of force* or *magnetic flux,* and together they form a *magnetic field.* This pattern of lines is characteristic of the magnetic field round a single bar magnet. However, if two bar magnets are placed end to end near one another so that they are attracting, a new pattern appears. In the gap between the two magnets, finely spaced lines seem to connect them to one another. If one magnet is now turned round so they are now repelling one another, the pattern changes again. Now the lines between the gap seem to be pushing each other away.

With these pictures in mind, it is not difficult to 'see' how magnets attract and repel, though we still don't know why. Nevertheless, we can begin to predict some of the things magnets do. One of the earliest things discovered about magnets is that if they are suspended on a piece of string, one end will point north and the other end will always point south. Since the same end always points north, it was called the *north-seeking pole,* or north pole for short. Likewise, the end pointing south was called the *south-seeking pole.*

If the poles on two different magnets

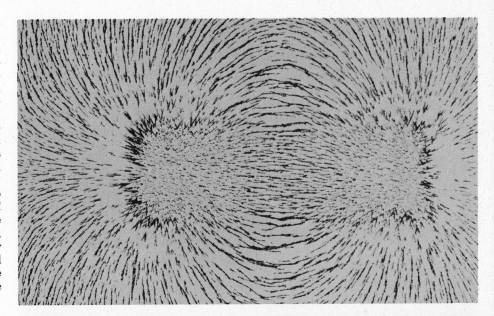

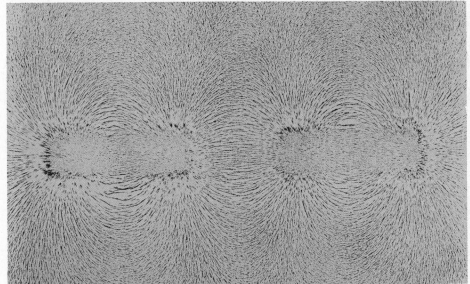

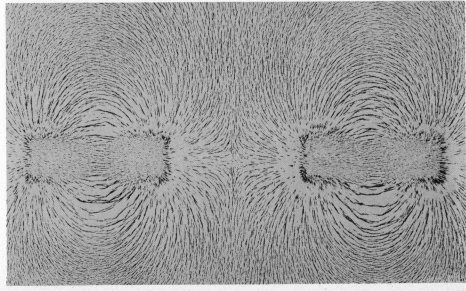

Top, magnets are enveloped in an invisible magnetic field, which can be made 'visible' with the aid of iron filings. *Centre,* the field between two attracting magnets comprises numerous 'lines of force' across the gap. This pattern strongly resembles the field round a single bar magnet, suggesting that a single magnet may be composed of smaller magnets or magnetic domains. *Bottom,* in the case of repulsion, the lines of force 'collide', pushing the two magnets apart.

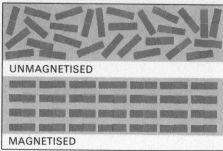

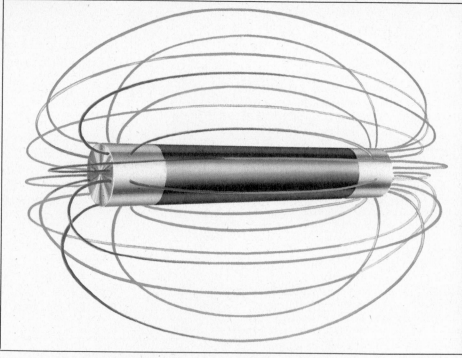

Top left, magnets find numerous uses in industry. During manufacture, steel plates tend to stick together. Here, two powerful magnets induce like poles in the plates, prising them apart by magnetic repulsion. *Top right,* a more common use of magnets is transporting heavy metal from one place to another. *Above,* the Domain Theory offers a convenient way of thinking about magnetism. In unmagnetized materials, the domains lie about in random fashion, cancelling each other's effect. But when aligned, the domains reinforce one another, producing a large magnet. *Right,* a magnetic field radiates in all directions, the lines of force surrounding the magnet like the atmosphere surrounding the Earth.

are marked, and then the two north poles brought together, it is found that they repel. Likewise, if the two south poles approach one another, they repel. However, if a south pole approaches a north pole, they attract. This leads us to the Law of Magnetic Attraction and Repulsion: opposite poles (north+south) attract and like poles (north+north or south+south) repel.

A close look at the fields round the single magnet and the two attracting magnets reveals another useful bit of information – they are remarkably similar. In fact, if you focus attention on just the central part of the single bar magnet, you would be hard put to decide if there is really only one magnet under the paper, or two different magnets attracting each other. This suggests that a bar magnet is perhaps two magnets put together. This

suspicion is confirmed by cutting the magnet in half; two new magnets result. These two new magnets could also be cut in half, giving four new magnets. This procedure could continue, producing more and more magnets, right down to the very molecules of the metal. This demonstration is the basis of the *Domain* or *Molecular Theory of Magnetism,* which states: Every large magnet is composed of thousands upon thousands of smaller magnets, or *domains.*

Making a magnet

This useful discovery will allow us to predict many new things about how magnets behave in various circumstances.

For instance, why is it that one piece of a certain metal, say iron, is a magnet, but another piece of the same metal is not a magnet? After all, if one piece of iron has

thousands upon thousands of little magnetic domains in it, so should any other piece of iron.

The Domain Theory and the Law of Magnetic Attraction and Repulsion combine to give a quick answer. The domains of unmagnetized iron are scattered haphazardly throughout the metal, so that the forces of attraction and repulsion among neighbouring domains are effectively cancelled out by one another. But in the magnetized iron, the domains are *aligned* in a regular pattern, so part of the magnetic field can escape to the outside of the bar.

This immediately suggests a way of making a magnet. All we need do is take an easily magnetized substance such as iron and align the domains. This can be accomplished by stroking the iron from one end to the other several times with a strong magnet, being careful to use the

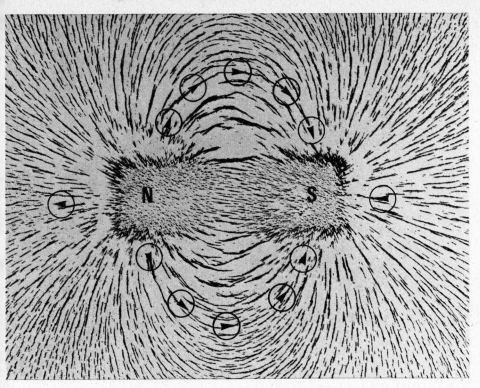

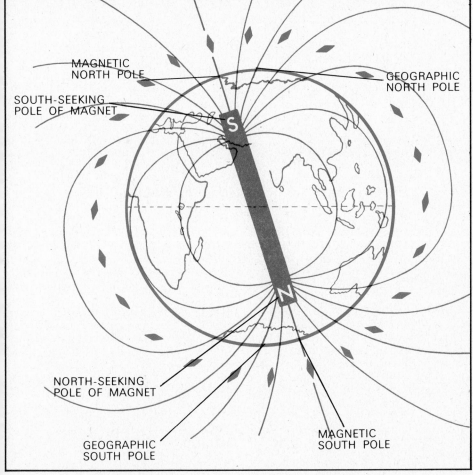

MAGNETIC
NORTH POLE

GEOGRAPHIC
NORTH POLE

SOUTH-SEEKING
POLE OF MAGNET

S

N

NORTH-SEEKING
POLE OF MAGNET

GEOGRAPHIC
SOUTH POLE

MAGNETIC
SOUTH POLE

you are warned not to drop magnets; a little bit of this treatment and they will no longer *be* magnets. Another method of de-magnetizing a magnet is to heat it to a very high temperature. The increased agitation of the molecules caused by the heat deranges the domains quite nicely.

With very slight alterations, experiment with magnetizing and de-magnetizing can be done at home. All one needs is a strong magnet, a few straight pins and a small toy compass. Pick up a pin with the south pole of the magnet. The fact that the pin is attracted to the magnet suggests that their domains have become aligned by the power of the strong magnetic field and that the pin is now magnetized. This is called *induced magnetism*. In addition, since north attracts south, we would expect that the end of the pin touching the magnet must be a north pole.

Remove the pin from the magnet and bring its north pole near the north pole of the compass needle (the end which is pointing north). The compass needle will swing away (north+north=repulsion), confirming the prediction of an induced north pole. To de-magnetize the pin, throw it on the floor a few times. Then bring it close to the compass needle. Nothing will happen.

The attracting Earth

The mention of a compass now raises the most baffling question of all about magnetism. Why does a suspended magnet (a compass needle, for example) always point north and south? Based on what we now know, one possible answer is that the magnet is *attracted* towards the north and the south. In other words, the Earth itself must be a magnet.

As expected, when Sir William Gilbert proposed this idea in 1600, most people scoffed at the suggestion. 'The Earth a magnet, indeed! Then why doesn't a suspended magnet point down, instead of north and south?' This was a valid objection, but a rather easy one to counter. If a small compass is placed next to a strong magnet, the compass needle does not point directly towards the magnet, but follows the lines of force. So one would not expect a suspended magnet to point directly down towards the Earth except in the frozen, icy wastes of the Arctic and Antarctic, where the lines of force of the Earth's magnet re-enter the Earth.

In Gilbert's day, of course, people could not make the hazardous journey necessary to check the theory in this manner, so direct confirmation of terrestrial (Earth) magnetism by travelling to the Arctic was impossible. But it was possible to predict that if a compass is laid on its side, rather than flat, the compass needle will not only point north and south, but will dip towards the Earth at an angle dependent on where one is doing the experiments. In other words, the compass needle will not lie parallel to the ground, but will follow the Earth's lines of force, just as the toy compass follows the bar magnet's lines of force. The angle measured between the compass needle and a horizontal line is called the *inclination* or the *angle of dip*.

Unfortunately, when cartographers first

Top, the needle of a small compass placed near a powerful magnet will follow the lines of force of the magnetic field. *Above*, in the same way, a magnet suspended so that it is free to swing

vertically will dip towards the ground, following the lines of force of the Earth's magnetic field. The diagram indicates the angle of dip at different locations on the Earth's surface.

same pole of the magnet on each stroke. Suppose we use the north pole of the magnet. Then on each stroke over the iron, the south pole of each domain will be attracted in the direction of the stroke, and will eventually all swing round until they are aligned north pole to south pole

all along the piece of metal, which has now been magnetized. Should we want to de-magnetize a substance, the Domain Theory tells us how – derange the domains. One obvious way of deranging the domains is to bounce the magnet a few times off something hard. This is the reason why

Tie a piece of thread to a metal pin and let the pin be attracted by a magnet. Now, carefully pull the thread. The pin will now hang suspended under the magnet like a 'magnetic balloon'. The more powerful the magnet, the further away the 'balloon' can be made to float.

began making world maps, they did not know that the Earth is a magnet; but they did know that it rotates on its axis. So in order to distinguish directions, they chose to call the North Pole the point where this imaginary axis emerges from the Earth pointing towards Polaris, the North Star. But a compass needle does not point towards this *geographic* North Pole; it points to another place several hundred miles (and 15 degrees of arc) away near Hudson Bay, Alaska, called the *magnetic* North Pole. So when talking about the North Pole, it is important to specify which one, because there are two of them. Likewise with the South Pole.

Electromagnetism

To be completely accurate, there are actually *three* North Poles: the geographic North Pole, the magnetic North Pole, and the north-seeking pole of a magnet. A freely suspended magnet swings its north-seeking pole towards the magnetic North Pole of the Earth. The Law of Magnetic Attraction and Repulsion tells us that a north-seeking pole is attracted by a south-seeking pole, so the end of the Earth's magnet at the magnetic North Pole must be a south-seeking pole, and the end of the Earth's magnet at the magnetic South Pole must be a north-seeking pole.

This may seem like a rather strange result, but this is only because of the words we use, not the physics involved. It would have been far better had the ends of a magnet simply been labelled + and −, instead of north and south. Then such strange-sounding statements as, 'The North Pole is really a south pole and the South Pole is really a north pole', would become, 'The North Pole is a + pole and the South Pole is a − pole'. Some day scientists may adopt a plus-minus system. But as long as we keep in mind which poles we are talking about – geographic North Pole, magnetic North Pole, north-seeking pole – there should be little need for puzzlement while we wait.

The source of terrestrial magnetism is still somewhat of a mystery, though a highly promising theory has evolved from a discovery made by Hans Oersted in 1820. A physics master of a school in Denmark, Oersted noticed that a compass needle in the vicinity of an electric current is deflected. That is, an electric current produces a magnetic field around it.

The great French physicist André Marie Ampère almost immediately suspected that perhaps electrical currents are the basis for all magnetic phenomena. Today it is theorized that countless electrically charged particles swirl round in the Earth's liquid core and produce a magnetic field in very much the same way as an electric current passing through a wire. This explanation of terrestrial magnetism is not completely satisfactory, however. Geological evidence shows that what is today magnetic North was once magnetic South, and what is today magnetic South was once magnetic North. It is as if the imaginary magnet in the Earth at some time in the distant past spun through a half turn, reversing its poles, or that the postulated current in the Earth's core has changed directions. This reversal of polarity has happened more than once. The simplified electrical origin of the Earth's magnetism theory described above fails to account for this fact, but it offers a convenient jumping-off place for further investigation.

Oersted's discovery, exploited and updated by William Sturgeon (1783–1850) and Joseph Henry (1797–1878), is of tremendous economic and technological importance in the form of *electromagnets*. Fundamentally, an electromagnet is nothing more than a current-carrying wire wrapped round a piece of iron or some other metal. As the electric current passes through the wire, a magnetic field is created. The metal core of the electromagnet itself becomes magnetized (its domains are aligned), thus increasing the magnet's strength.

Today, the applications of electromagnets include lifting magnets in industry, the electric bell, electric generators, radios, gramophones, and many, many others. Joseph Henry produced a lifting electromagnet as far back as 1832 which weighed only 60 pounds but could lift nearly a ton of metal. A very simple electromagnet can be made at home by wrapping a piece of copper wire round a nail and connecting the wire to a dry cell. Polarity may be determined by attracting and repelling a compass needle.

Electromagnetism is also the commercial way of producing permanent magnets. The metal to be magnetized is placed in a coil of wire and a current is passed. The larger the current, the stronger the magnetic field, so even hard-to-magnetize substances such as steel, cobalt, nickel, and alloys of these metals, can be magnetized, producing so-called *permanent* magnets, because they are hard to de-magnetize. When magnetization is complete, the current is cut and the metals removed from the coil ready for any task they may be called upon to perform.

The idea of domains to explain magnetism is a conceptual device. It allows us to picture what is going on, but it really doesn't tell us the source of magnetism. The modern idea is that all magnetism is caused by the motion of electrical charges.

Molecular magnets

In the Earth's core or in an electric conductor, the charges actually move from place to place. But even when no electric current is flowing, electrons are still whizzing round the nuclei of atoms. In addition, electrons spin on their axes, which also produces a magnetic field. When these multitudes of microscopic magnetic fields interact with one another, they tend to cancel each other out. But in some materials, such as iron, nickel, gadolinium and liquid oxygen, this cancellation effect is often far from complete, and so the material is strongly magnetic. Such strongly magnetic materials are classed as *ferromagnetic* materials. For other materials, the magnetic effect is so small as to be non-existent. These materials are said to be *paramagnetic*. Still other materials seem to shun magnetism, and when placed in a magnetic field will align themselves at right angles to the lines of force, rather than along the lines of force. These materials are said to be *diamagnetic*.

It should be recognized that explaining all magnetism in terms of the motion of electrons, rather than the alignment of little magnets called domains, really does not carry us much further than we were before. We still don't know what magnetism is, why it manifests itself in attraction and repulsion, and how the motion of electrons creates it. For this, we must delve into the space-time continuum and the Theory of Relativity. But at least we have eliminated the need for invisible spirits and moved a step or two away from the useful but dizzying Domain Theory argument that 'magnets are magnets because they are made of magnets'. And these seem to be steps in the right direction.

Putting electrons to work

Is it possible to harness an unseen power? This article explains how electric motors, heaters, lamps and radio valves are designed to exploit typical effects of an electric current.

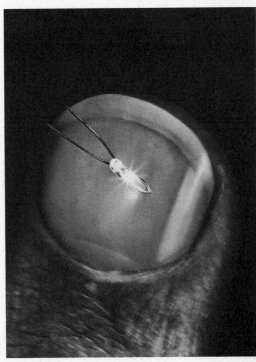

The compass points south as an electric current in the wire above it deflects the needle. Michael Faraday, an English scientist, reasoned that there was a turning force acting on the magnet. His line of thought made possible today's complex electrical industries. *Right*, a miniature lamp.

IN 1820, the Danish physicist Hans Christian Oersted discovered that an electric current flowing in a wire has associated with it a magnetic field. A pivoted magnetic needle placed near a straight wire is deflected when a current flows in the wire. If the wire is wound into a coil, each turn of wire contributes to a strong magnetic field at the centre of the coil.

This principle is used in the galvanometer, in which a magnetic needle is pivoted at the centre of a coil. Any current flowing in the wires of the coil produces a field which deflects the magnet, and the instrument may be used as a sensitive way of detecting even tiny electric currents.

If a piece of magnetic metal, such as soft iron, is placed inside a cylindrical coil of wire (called a solenoid), the magnetic field due to a current flowing in the coil magnetizes the metal. The metal behaves as a magnet as long as the current is flowing. The first electromagnets were made by an English physician, William Sturgeon (1783–1850). He bent a piece of iron into the shape of a horseshoe, insulated it, and wound a coil of copper wire round it. Such a magnet 12 inches long would lift a weight of 10 lb.

Meanwhile, in the United States, Joseph Henry (1797–1878) was also making electromagnets. He used straight pieces of iron and insulated the copper wire with strips of cotton or silk so that each magnet could have many turns of wire on top of each other. In 1832, Henry made an electromagnet weighing 60 lb that could lift a weight of nearly a ton.

But the most important applications of Oersted's discovery of electromagnetism were made by the English scientist Michael Faraday (1791–1867), who found the relation between electromagnetism and mechanical rotation, which led to the invention of the electric motor and the dynamo. Faraday reasoned that if a magnetic needle is deflected by the field near a conductor, there must be a mechanical force acting on the needle. And, more important, he also reasoned that if a mechanical force is used to move a magnet near a wire, an electric current will be generated in the wire. In other words,

was a turning force acting on the magnet. His line of thought made possible today's complex electrical industries. *Right*, a miniature lamp.

Faraday discovered that an electric current can be used to cause rotation, and that rotation can be used to generate current.

In 1821, only a year after Oersted discovered electromagnetism, Faraday performed two crucial experiments. In the first he arranged a magnet vertically in a dish of mercury with the magnet sticking through the surface. A piece of straight wire, free to pivot at its upper end, was hung with its lower end just dipping into the mercury. When Faraday applied the voltage from a cell between the wire and the mercury in the dish, the wire moved in

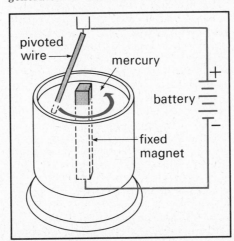

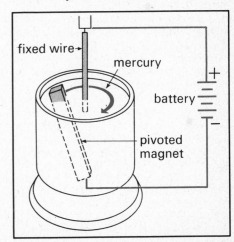

Faraday's discovery that electromagnetism could create a rotating movement led to the development of electric motors. *Above*, two forms of his experiment. *Left*, a pivoted wire rotates around a fixed magnet. *Right*, a pivoted magnet rotates around a fixed wire carrying a current in mercury.

a circle around the magnet. That is, Faraday had made an electric current produce rotation of the wire carrying the current.

In the other experiment, Faraday arranged that the magnet was free to pivot at its lower end. The wire, dipping into the surface of the mercury, was fixed. This time, when current passed, the magnet rotated around the wire; Faraday had made an electric current produce rotation of a magnet in the field associated with the current.

Each of these devices was a crude form of electric motor. Several inventors used these principles to make motors. Some had magnets rotating in electric fields, but the best results were obtained with arrangements in which wires rotated in magnetic fields.

Electric motors and dynamos

The principle of the electric motor as it finally evolved can be understood by considering a coil of wire carrying a current and free to rotate between the poles of a magnet. As the current is switched on, the coil will rotate through half a turn and stop. But if the direction of the current in the coil is then reversed, it will rotate through a further half a turn before stopping again. If the direction of the current is again changed, the coil will move again. And so if the coil is provided with an arrangement that reverses the direction of the current every half a turn, the coil will rotate continuously.

The arrangement for automatically reversing the direction of current in the coil is called a commutator. If the coil consists of a single turn of wire, the commutator has two segments of metal on the same shaft as the coil. The segments are insulated from each other; one is connected to one end of the coil and the other segment is connected to the other end of the coil. Current is passed from a battery to the metal segments and hence to the coil through two pieces of carbon, called *brushes*. Every time the coil moves through half a turn, the direction of the current in it is automatically reversed. Large electric motors have many coils wound on the same former, and the ends of each coil are connected to a pair of segments on a multi-segment commutator.

The principle of the dynamo is exactly opposite to that of the electric motor. If the coil in the motor just described is rotated by hand, an electric current is generated in the coil. In this way, the power from any rotating machine, such as a water-wheel, a wind-driven wheel, a steam engine, a petrol engine or a turbine, can be used to turn a dynamo and generate electricity. The same machine can act as a motor or a dynamo, depending on whether it is supplied with current or with mechanical power. For example, in electric locomotives current is supplied to turn the motors which drive the wheels. But when the driver wants to stop the locomotive he switches off the current; the forward motion of the locomotive as it slows down keeps the coils in the motors turning; they act as dynamos and generate

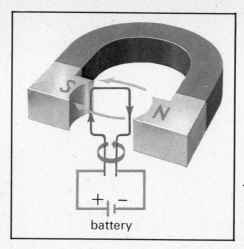

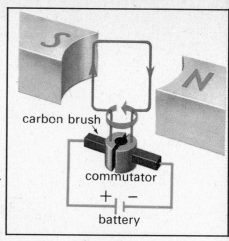

carbon brush

commutator

battery

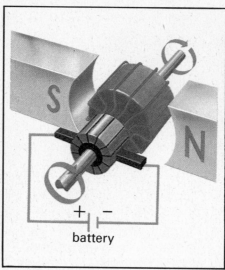

battery

driving wheel

Top left, a coil carrying current placed in a magnetic field tries to turn, but stops when in line with the magnetic field. *Top right,* by arranging a commutator to reverse the direction of the current in the coil every half turn, the

coil will turn continuously. *Above left,* most electric motors have many sets of coils, each connected to a pair of segments on the commutator. *Above right,* in a dynamo, mechanical power turns the coils to generate electricity.

electricity.

The principle of the dynamo was discovered by Faraday in 1831. At first he generated short pulses of current by moving a magnet in and out of a coil. Many early dynamos made use of this idea, with moving magnets and stationary coils. Faraday also generated electricity by moving a coil in a strong magnetic field, and this is the method used in most modern dynamos which have moving coils and stationary magnets.

We now know that when an electric current flows in a metal, it is the electrons from atoms of the metal which actually carry the electricity. The movement of the electrons is accompanied by a rise in temperature of the metal. The amount of heat produced depends on the current flowing and the electrical resistance of the metal (heat equals the product of the resistance and the square of the current).

There are many practical applications of the heating effect of an electric current. Metals with a high melting-point and a high resistance, such as alloys of nickel and chromium, can be used to make the heating elements of electric fires and irons. The heat generated by the passage of the current can make these metals glow red-hot. A metal of very high melting-point, such as tungsten, can be made to glow white-hot and become *incandescent*. This

is the principle of the electric-light bulb, in which a tungsten filament is surrounded by an inert gas to prevent its oxidizing.

The first commercially successful incandescent lamp was made by the American inventor Thomas Edison (1847–1931) in 1879. His early lamps had carbon filaments, made from charred thread or paper, surrounded by a vacuum. At about the same time, Joseph Swan (1828–1914) in England also made incandescent lamps with carbon filaments, produced by charring threads of cellulose. There was for a long time a controversy about which of these men, Edison or Swan, was the first to invent the electric lamp. Their differences were settled when the two inventors combined their interests in one firm, the Edison and Swan Electric Light Company.

Fuses and arc lamps

In some applications, we make use of the heating effect of an electric current on metals of low melting-point. Most electric fuses contain a fine strand of copper wire. The wire will pass only a limited amount of current, say 5 amps. If this current is exceeded, the copper wire gets so hot it melts and the electric circuit containing it is broken. Fuses with wires that will melt at known values of current are used to protect electric circuits and appliances from overloading.

The life force of urban civilization, electric current supplies conductor rails beneath the London tube train, *top left,* and overhead wires for the British Rail locomotive at Manchester, *centre left.* In London's Piccadilly Circus, *above,* as in city centres the world over, the lights of advertising gain their characteristic glow from traces of gas left between electrodes in a tube. *Left,* the windings of a huge stator in a turbine-generator undergo inspection in Ireland.

If electricity at a sufficiently high voltage is forced through a poor conductor, the conductor will get very hot indeed. For example, a high voltage applied across a pair of carbon rods a fraction of an inch apart produces an *arc* between the rods. An arc is a continuous spark produced when air, which is a poor conductor, is forced to conduct electricity. This principle is used in arc lamps, such as those used in cinema projectors and theatre spot-lights. On a much larger scale, the same principle is used in electric arc furnaces in which the tremendous heat produced will melt iron for steelmaking or melt rock for extracting phosphorus.

If a pair of wires or plates connected to a high-voltage source of electricity are fused into a glass bulb from which most of the air has been removed, an electric current will flow between the plates (or electrodes). The electrode connected to the source of negative electricity is called the *cathode,* and the positive plate is the *anode.* An elongated bulb, with a cathode at one end and an anode at the other, is called a cathode-ray tube. When electricity is passing between the electrodes

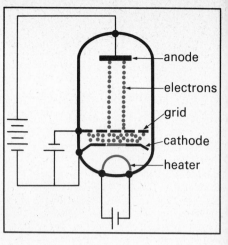

Diagram of a modern indirectly heated thermionic triode valve, *above*, shows the heater inside the cylindrical cathode. *Left,* a valve used in 1915. *Centre,* a contemporary design.

the tube may light up, the colour of the light depending on traces of gas left in the tube. For example, traces of neon gas give an orange-red light which is used in neon advertising signs. Traces of sodium in discharge tubes, as these glass tubes are called, give the characteristic yellow light that is commonly used for street lighting.

The electric current is carried along a cathode-ray tube by invisible cathode rays. In 1897, the English physicist J. J. Thomson showed that cathode rays consist of electrons. In other words, electrons move completely out of the atoms in the metal of the cathode, cross the space between the electrodes (carrying with them the electric current) and enter the atoms in the metal of the anode. The passage of the stream of electrons from cathode to anode is accompanied by a complementary passage of positive ions from anode to cathode. In the discharge tubes we described, these ions are neon ions or sodium ions.

Radio valves

Cathode-ray tubes require high voltages and pass only tiny currents. But if the metal of the cathode is heated, electrons escape from its atoms more easily; much lower voltages may be used and higher currents passed. The generation of electrons from a heated cathode is called *thermionic emission,* and it finds important application in radio valves. The number of electrons emitted depends on the material of the cathode and its temperature. Tungsten is one of the best emitters, but it needs a temperature of nearly 2,000 °C. A mixture of barium oxide and strontium oxide will emit well at about half this temperature.

The cathodes of thermionic valves may be heated in one of two ways: directly or indirectly. A directly heated cathode generally takes the form of a loop of thin tungsten wire. The cathode current passing through the loop heats it (in much the same way as an electric-fire element is heated), and clouds of electrons are emitted. An indirectly heated cathode has a separate tungsten wire filament, with its own current supply, which heats the cathode material. This is the method

which must be used when the emitter is a non-conductor of electricity, such as a mixture of strontium and barium oxides. The oxides are coated on to a metal cylinder which is connected to the source of negative electricity and heated by a filament mounted inside the cylinder. The first thermionic valve, made by Sir John Ambrose Fleming in 1904, had a directly heated cathode. It resembled an electric lamp with the filament as the cathode, and an extra plate (the anode) fused into the glass. Most modern valves have indirectly heated cathodes.

The simplest form of thermionic valve is the diode, which has only two electrodes (cathode and anode). The cathode is heated, to give thermionic emission, and the anode remains cold. When the cathode is connected to a source of negative electricity and the anode is connected to a positive source, electrons pour out of

Sir Charles Wheatstone (1802–75), English physicist and inventor, designed the 'self-exciting dynamo', *below*, to generate electricity.

the heated cathode and pass into the anode in much the same way as do the electrons in a cathode-ray tube. The diode passes electric current just like a conductor such as a piece of wire.

But if the polarities of the two electrodes in a diode are changed – that is, the cathode is connected to positive and the anode to negative – current ceases to flow through the valve. A diode will not conduct in the opposite sense because the cold anode will not emit electrons. In other words, a diode valve has the property of conducting electricity in one direction only. Most of the practical uses which have been evolved for diodes depend on this 'one-way switch' action.

Anodes and triodes

As we have just seen, a diode is like a switch: it is either 'off' or 'on', More subtle control of the electric current flowing through a valve can be obtained by introducing a third electrode between the cathode and the anode. This electrode has holes in it through which electrons can pass to the anode and is for this reason called a *grid*. Such a three-electrode valve is called a triode. If the grid of a triode is made negative with respect to the anode (though not as negative as the cathode), it will repel some of the electrons trying to pass through it. By varying the negative voltage on the grid, we can control the current passed by a triode. For this reason, the third electrode in a triode valve is also called the *control* grid.

If the voltage between the grid and the cathode varies, the current from the anode will vary in step with it. But quite small variations in the grid voltage can produce large changes in the anode current. In this way, a triode may be used to amplify small signals. And by feeding the output from the anode of one triode into the grid of another, two *stages* of amplification are achieved. In practice, circuits in radio sets and television receivers use several stages of amplification. The triode valve was invented by an American, sometimes called 'the father of radio', Lee de Forest, in 1907, who made possible its use in radio detectors, radio and telephone amplifiers, and as an oscillator.

Conductors and transistors

At temperatures near absolute zero the electrical resistance of certain metals and alloys becomes vanishingly small. In certain other substances, however, it decreases as temperature *rises*.

HIGH-SPEED ELECTRIC LOCOMOTIVES pick up their electricity from a third rail, called a conductor-rail, or from overhead wire conductors. Electricity is distributed over the country by high-level wires strung between pylons of the National Grid. And in homes, wires from the electric meter carry the supply into every room and to every appliance. The whole of the electrical industry and all applications of electricity employ metal conductors to carry current. In this article, we will look at various types of conductors and explain how they work. We shall also discuss semiconductors – substances that gave birth to transistors and all the complex electronic apparatus which employs them.

An electric current is a stream of electrons flowing in a conductor. A conductor, therefore, is any material which has a supply of 'free' electrons available to make up the current. In practice, metals are the only substances which have a plentiful supply of electrons, and most metals are good conductors. Other materials, such as wood, paper, rubber, plastics and glass, have no 'free' electrons and these materials are therefore used as electrical insulators.

Like birds in a forest

To understand why some materials have conduction electrons and some have not, and why some metals are better conductors than others, we need to know something of the structure of metals. Metals are composed of atoms, as are all other materials. And the atoms are made up of even smaller particles, such as nuclei and electrons. The atoms of a metal are held in a regular array called a *lattice*, just like the atoms in a crystal. But one or more of the electrons in each atom is less firmly bound than the others and, in an electric field, makes itself available for conduction. Remember that atoms are made up largely of empty space, and electrons are the smallest known particles. So that, although the atoms of a metal are fixed in the lattice, the electrons can easily move between them in much the same way as a bird easily flies between the trees in a forest.

Not all electrons in a metal are bound to the atoms to the same extent. The energy of an electron is a measure of how firmly it is bound to the atom. A high-energy electron can be persuaded fairly easily to leave the atom entirely. For example, heat energy supplied to the atoms of some metals in a vacuum will give them enough additional energy to 'boil' off from the surface of the metal and give rise to the phenomenon called thermionic emission.

The range of energies possessed by

Transistors the size of pencil stubs do the work of much larger valves in controlling or amplifying electric currents. But the circuit being planned above will be reproduced in even more miniature form as an 'integrated circuit' in a silicon chip less than two millimetres square.

electrons is not continuous, but consists of definite separate energy 'levels' (this is one consequence of the quantum theory of matter). For this reason, the electrons may be thought of as existing in separate energy *bands,* and two conditions are necessary for an electron to move from one band to another nearby higher band and be available for conduction. Firstly, it must be supplied with the required extra energy, which may come from light radiation, heat or electricity. And secondly, there must be room for the electron in the higher band – that is, the higher band must already be partly

An electric current is made up of electrons on the move. Metals make good conductors because they have a plentiful supply of 'free' electrons available to move along the lattice of atoms.

empty. If the higher band is full, as it is in all materials that are electrical insulators, supplying extra energy will not promote an electron to a higher band and the material will be incapable of conducting electricity. Of course, if really enormous amounts of extra energy are applied, electrons may be forced to jump all the way into the completely empty band and made available for conduction. This is what happens at extremely high voltages and an insulator 'breaks down'.

It is interesting to notice in passing that materials which are good conductors of electricity are also good conductors of heat. On the other hand, materials which are good electrical insulators are also good thermal insulators. These facts are not surprising if we assume that a material conducts heat by means of its free electrons. Thus a metal, such as copper, conducts heat well and for the same reason that it conducts electricity. But a material such as sulphur or glass, in which all the energy bands are full, and which has no free electrons, is a bad conductor of heat and of electricity.

In all solids, the atoms are rapidly vibrating due to their thermal (heat) energy. As a metal is heated, although at first more electrons are made available

109

for conduction, the atoms also begin to vibrate more. If we return to our analogy comparing a conducting electron moving between atoms in a metal lattice with a bird flying between trees, it is as if a high wind springs up and starts blowing the trees around. There will come a point at which the trees (atoms) are vibrating so much that the birds (electrons) begin to find it more difficult to get through the gaps. But now consider the opposite situation in which the metal is cooled down. The atoms will vibrate less and less until, at extremely low temperatures approaching absolute zero (temperatures of between about −260 and −272 °C.), the atoms will hardly vibrate at all. Under these conditions, some metals become extremely good conductors indeed and are called *superconductors*.

The temperature at which a metal becomes superconducting varies with the strength of the magnetic field in which it is placed; the stronger the magnetic field, the more the metal must be cooled before it becomes a superconductor. This fact is used in making memory elements for digital computers. Such elements, consisting of tiny coils of superconducting wire immersed in liquid helium, occupy very little space. This system has the advantage that a great number of digits can be stored in such memories and yet occupy only a small volume.

Semiconductors

One of the most useful developments of recent years, and one which incidentally helps to justify the band theory of electronic conduction, has been the discovery and exploitation of semiconductors. Some materials, such as silicon and germanium, have a band structure similar to that of an insulator with one band completely full of electrons and the next band completely empty. But the presence of small amounts of an impurity makes these basically insulating materials into good conductors, which are called *impurity semiconductors*.

There are two types of impurity semiconductors, characterized by the kind of impurity and the mechanism by which their band structure is changed into that of a conductor. Consider the element germanium. When absolutely pure, it has a completely full conduction band and so behaves as an insulator. Germanium has a chemical *valence* of four – that is, each atom has four electrons available for forming chemical bonds with other elements. For this reason, the full conduction band of germanium contains four electrons. Now imagine the effect of adding to the germanium a few 'foreign' atoms (an impurity) which each have five electrons. For example, we could add a small amount of the element arsenic, which has five valence electrons. Four of the arsenic electrons take the place of four of the germanium electrons in the conduction band. But the fifth electron cannot be accommodated (because the band is full) and must go into the next empty band. The band structure of the germanium is now changed into that typical of a conductor, with a partly filled

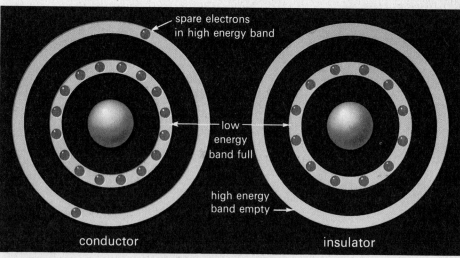

spare electrons in high energy band
low energy band full
high energy band empty
conductor
insulator

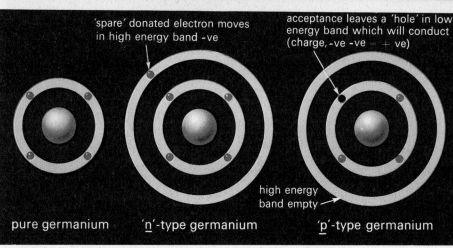

'spare' donated electron moves in high energy band -ve
acceptance leaves a 'hole' in low energy band which will conduct (charge, -ve -ve = + ve)
high energy band empty
pure germanium
'n'-type germanium
'p'-type germanium

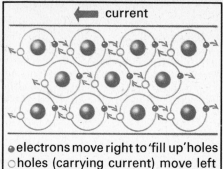

← current
● electrons move right to 'fill up' holes
○ holes (carrying current) move left

Top, in insulators, electrons completely fill the low energy bands. Conductors carry 'spares' which must move in higher energy bands. *Centre,* pure germanium insulates (it has no 'spares'). Impurities give it 'spares' or 'holes' which will conduct. *Right,* rectifiers use this principle and allow one-way flow of current only. *Above,* as on a pegboard, electrons and holes interchange.

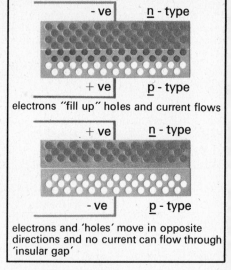

− ve   n - type
+ ve   p - type
electrons "fill up" holes and current flows

+ ve   n - type
− ve   p - type
electrons and 'holes' move in opposite directions and no current can flow through 'insular gap'

band containing electrons that are available for carrying electric current.

The arsenic in this example is called a *donor,* because it gives or donates its extra electron to the conduction band, and the semiconductor formed is called donor or *n-type* (n stands for negative, the charge on the donated electron). Other five-valent donor atoms include phosphorus and antimony. They may be added to silicon or germanium, giving technologists a choice of several combinations of elements for making n-type semiconductors.

The second type of impurity semiconductor is a little more difficult to explain. In this case, the impurity is an element with only three valence electrons (such

as boron, aluminium, gallium or indium). When an atom of, say, aluminium takes the place of an atom of germanium, it contributes only three electrons to the conduction band instead of the four formerly supplied by the germanium atom. As a result, there is a deficiency of electrons, which physicists call *holes*. A hole is an absence of an electron and, because it is mathematically a minus negative charge, can be considered as a positive charge. For this reason, semiconductors with trivalent impurity atoms are called *p-type*. The impurity is called an *acceptor* because it takes or accepts one of the germanium electrons to leave a hole in the lattice.

But how do *p*-type semiconductors con-

part of arsenic in 10,000,000 parts of germanium.

It is interesting to note that germanium and silicon have chemical properties in between those of metals and non-metals. For this reason, some chemists call such elements *metalloids*. With a knowledge of how semiconductors work, chemists have produced compounds which behave in the same way as do silicon and germanium. By taking a three-valent element (gallium or indium) and alloying it with exactly the correct amount of a five-valent element (arsenic or antimony), they have made compounds such as gallium arsenide and indium antimonide.

The rectifier

For example, in gallium arsenide, the gallium contributes three electrons to the conduction band and arsenic contributes five. The total contribution from both atoms, eight electrons, is exactly the same as that from two atoms of germanium. But since gallium or arsenic can also be used as the impurity atoms, a slight excess of gallium makes gallium arsenide into a *p*-type semiconductor and a slight excess of arsenic makes it into an *n*-type semiconductor.

One of the earliest applications of semiconductors was in making a *rectifier*,

duct electricity? They do so by what amounts to a movement of the holes through the lattice in much the same way as electrons move through the lattice of normal conductors. One way of picturing how such a hole can move is to imagine a regular array of holes in a board, all but one of which are occupied by pegs. If we move one of the pegs next to the hole (say on the right of it) into it, the original hole will be filled and a new one left. If we move the peg on the right of the new hole into it, another new hole will appear one step further to the right. By continuing this process, moving pegs (which represent electrons) only one space at a time, the hole can be made to move across the board. In a similar way, electrons in the

lattice of a *p*-type semiconductor move into the holes in one direction, causing the holes to move through the lattice in the other direction. While the conduction of electricity is still a movement of electrons, it is convenient to consider conduction in this case as being movement of the holes.

Very little of an impurity is required to change the conducting properties of silicon or germanium. One of the reasons why semiconductors have been developed only fairly recently (semiconductor action was first discovered about 30 years ago) is that techniques for producing the extremely pure materials required are themselves only recent developments. A typical impurity concentration is one a device that allows electric current to pass in one direction only. In alternating current, the direction of current flow changes rapidly many times a second, flowing for a fraction of the time one way and for a fraction of the time the other way. In direct current, the direction of current flow remains always the same, from positive to negative. Batteries and accumulators produce direct current (d.c.). But generators in power stations, which supply the current for the mains electricity supply to homes and factories, produce alternating current (a.c.). Any electrical apparatus that requires d.c., such as parts of a radio or television set, a computer, or many electric locomotives, must have a rectifier if it is to work off an a.c. mains supply. The rectifier passes current flowing in one direction but blocks current flowing the opposite way, so converting a.c. into d.c.

One of the most compact modern types of rectifier has a sandwich consisting of a slice of p-type semiconductor next to a slice of n-type. This arrangement is called a *p-n junction*. At the join, some of the electrons from the n-type will diffuse into the p-type and some of the holes from the p-type will diffuse into the n-type. In the middle, electrons and holes will 'cancel out' each other. Now consider connecting a battery across the junction. If the n-type is connected to the negative terminal of the battery and the p-type is connected to the positive terminal, current will flow through the semiconductor sandwich. Current flows because the battery pumps more electrons into the n-type which combine with more holes from the p-type, the current crosses the junction and emerges from the p-type side of the sandwich.

The transistor

But if we connect the battery the other way round (n-type to the positive terminal, p-type to the negative), no current will flow. At the junction, the electrons and holes will move in opposite directions leaving a region containing neither electrons nor holes – that is, leaving the material as an insulator.

So that when an alternating current is applied across such a p-n junction, the semiconductor sandwich will allow current to flow across it in one direction only. For the fraction of the a.c. cycle when the n-type is made electrically negative, current flows. But for the part of the a.c. cycle when the n-type is made positive, the current is blocked. In this way, the p-n junction acts as a rectifier and converts a.c. to d.c.

Perhaps the most important outcome of research into semiconductors is the *transistor,* which was invented in 1949 by two American scientists, W. Shockley and J. Bardeen. A typical transistor consists of a three-layer sandwich with a slice of p-type semiconductor between two slices of n-type. Two p-n junctions are formed, and the arrangement is called a junction transistor. A transistor can be made to control or amplify electric currents in much the same way as can a triode

The ability of the electrical parts in a colour television tube to conduct heavy currents without failure is tested for up to 8,000 hours on this overhead conveyor. A process known as 'spot-knocking' removes sharp points where exceptional currents may 'flash-over' causing a short-circuit.

Although the miniature dimensions of transistors have made possible the complex electronic devices and computers that now serve Man, they also make more everyday aids both cheaper and easier to use. *Above,* a tiny transistorized hearing-aid contrasts with its much larger predecessor.

valve. A triode has three electrodes: a negatively charged cathode (which must be heated to cause thermionic emission of electrons from it), a grid on to which the control current is fed, and a positively charged anode. In the transistor, the p-type material corresponds to the triode grid, and the n-types correspond to the anode and cathode.

The transistor has two great advantages over the triode. Firstly, it requires extremely little electric power to operate it. This is an important consideration both in small applications, such as a portable radio set, and in large applications, such as a radar set or a computer. Formerly, portable radios had to have batteries to supply power to heat the cathodes of its valves (the actual current consumption of the rest of a radio circuit is extremely small). Such sets had to be large

enough to accommodate a battery power supply. A transistorized portable radio needs no power supply for heating, and will run for a long time on the current from a small battery which supplies the rest of the circuit. A large apparatus, such as a computer, may contain thousands of valves which consume many watts of power.

Secondly, transistors are many times smaller than valves. A modern triode is a cylinder one inch across and about two inches long. Several thousands of these in a computer would occupy a whole room. An average-sized transistor is no longer than quarter of an inch off the end of a pencil – some are as small as a grain of rice – and thousands of them can be fitted into the space occupied by a desk. In fact, without transistors, with their small size and modest power requirements, really large computers would not be possible.

What is alternating current?

If engineers were unable to generate alternating current, it would be extremely difficult to transport electric power over great distances, and radio communications would be impossible.

FLICK ON the electric switch as you come through the door, and what happens? The lights in the room go on. And off . . . and on . . . and off again, so fast that you can't see the flicker. Indeed, turn on just about any electrical appliance and it will go on and off, on and off, because this is the nature of the current coming in through the mains. Electric current which continually turns itself on and off, or more precisely reverses direction, is said to 'alternate'.

Alternating current electricity plays a vital part in modern life. It supplies heat, light and mechanical power for homes and industry. It is also useful for most types of electronic equipment, from telephones, record players and transistor radios to complicated communications systems, radar sets and computers.

For an electric current of any sort to flow there must be a voltage, a source of *electromotive force* (emf), to drive the current round the circuit. For example, in an electric torch the emf is provided by a battery. When the torch is switched on, a steady or *direct* current (d.c.) flows through the lamp. The strength of this current depends on the strength of the battery emf and on the opposition to current flow, which is the *resistance* of the lamp. An electric lamp plugged into the mains supply in most countries in the world is connected to an emf which varies regularly in strength and direction. The a.c. causes the lamp to light but, because the current is varying, the lamp pulses up and down slightly in brightness, although much too fast for the eye to follow.

Changing current

Alternating current, unlike the d.c. of the torch, is produced mechanically by *electromagnetic induction*. Any type of electric current sets up a magnetic field around the wire carrying it, as in the familiar electromagnet. Conversely, a magnetic field may be used to produce an electric current by simply moving a wire through it, or by moving the magnetic field around a wire. In the first instance, the strength of the induced emf depends on how fast the wire, wound into a coil called a solenoid, rotates in the magnetic field. In the second case, it depends on how fast the magnetic field moves through the coil, i.e. how fast the field is increasing or decreasing in strength. In either case, the emf and the consequent current will continually change strength and reverse direction.

Now consider the case in which the *current* in the coil is changing. Both of the effects just described will be present. For example, should the current be increasing, its associated magnetic field will also be increasing. And since this field surrounds the coil itself, an emf will be 'self-induced' in the coil. This emf

Top left, a household electric-light bulb, probably the most familiar electrical appliance utilizing a.c. *Top right,* a gallery of giant alternators – the hydroelectric power terminal at McNary Dam, in the United States. These squat

always opposes the change producing it, and so tries to stop the current in the coil from increasing. If the original current is decreasing, the self-induced emf is in such a direction that it tries to keep the current steady. The strength of the emf is equal to the product of the rate of change of current and the *self-inductance* of the coil. Inductances are measured in units called henries, named after the American physicist Joseph Henry who did pioneer work in this field of study.

An important use of the effects of electromagnetic induction is in the design of machines for producing electrical power, such as dynamos generating d.c. and alternators for generating a.c. A

monsters instantly convert mechanical energy supplied by water-driven turbines into alternating current. A.c. is more versatile than d.c. because a.c. voltages can easily be stepped up or down by transformers like those *above.*

simple alternator consists of a coil rotating at a constant speed in a magnetic field between the poles of a magnet. As the coil turns, it moves alternately parallel to and then perpendicular to the magnetic field. As a result, the change in field it experiences is alternately zero and then a maximum.

If one plots a graph of current strength and direction against time, he gets a picture which very nearly reproduces the familiar sine curve from trigonometry. This is quite fortunate, because the mathematics of sine curves is already worked out and easy to apply.

If one plots changes in emf against time, another sine curve is produced. But if the

Above left, part of the output stage of one of the most powerful radio transmitters in the world, the valve in the foreground can produce some 250 kilowatts of power. The intercon-tinental communications satellite Early Bird, *top right,* receives radio waves, converts them into alternating currents, amplifies and relays them. Here it undergoes tests before launching in 1965. *Above right,* a 'trip switch' on a gargantuan scale – a safety device which protects power lines in Arkansas, United States, whenever a sudden surge of electric current is generated.

emf curve is laid over the current curve, they do not fit exactly, causing what is known as a *phase difference.* The greater the phase difference, the greater the influence on the operation of the circuit. By comparing the emf and current curves with the standard sine curve, the phase difference may be measured in angles, and the effect on the circuit calculated by trigonometric equations.

Each repeated section or *cycle* of the sine wave is produced by one revolution of the alternator coil. The number of cycles completed in one second is called the *frequency* of the alternating emf, and the maximum value of the emf reached in either direction is called the *amplitude* or peak value. For example, the mains emf in Britain follows a sinusoidally alternating form with a frequency of 50 cycles a second. The mains emf is generally quoted as about 230 volts. This is not the peak value but an average voltage called the *root mean square* (RMS) value. It is equal to the peak emf divided by $\sqrt{2}$. RMS values are more useful than peak values for indicating the strength of an alternating emf or current. For instance, the RMS value of an a.c. produces the same heating effect in a resistance as does an equal number of amps of d.c. The actual peak value of the 230-volt RMS mains supply is about 322 volts.

The frequency of an alternating emf produced by a rotating coil depends on the speed of rotation. For this reason, alternator frequencies are generally limited to a few hundred cycles a second. But radio uses alternating current of up to many millions of cycles a second. To produce these frequencies, an inductance is linked with a condenser (generally called a capacitor). A simple capacitor is made by sandwiching a type of insulating material, called a dielectric, between two conducting metal plates. When a capacitor is connected to a steady emf, the current flowing through it builds up an electrical charge on the plates.

High-frequency currents

As the charge increases, a voltage develops across the plates which opposes the applied emf. The current eventually falls to zero when the capacitor voltage is equal to the applied emf. In this way, the charge built up on the plates is stored in the capacitor, and the voltage appearing across the plates is equal to the charge divided by the capacitance measured in farads.

When a charged capacitor is connected across a coil of wire called an inductance, it creates an electrical system very similar to an extended coil spring with a weight on one end. If the weight is pulled down and released, it bobs up and down on the spring. In much the same way the current in the circuit flows backwards and forwards between the two components, setting up an a.c. whose frequency depends mainly on the value of the inductance and the capacitance present. Just as the oscillating spring eventually comes to rest, the oscillating current in such a circuit gradually dies away as the energy originally stored in the capacitor is used up in heating the resistance of the coil.

The form of the a.c., while it lasts, is a sine wave. In a practical device for producing high-frequency a.c., called an oscillator, the losses in the circuit are made up regularly and a continuous a.c. output is produced, in the same way as the weight on a spring can be kept moving by giving it an extra pull at the right moment.

If an alternating emf of any frequency is connected across a resistance, the a.c. produced keeps in step with the rise and fall of the emf, and the current and emf are said to be *in phase.*

When the circuit contains self-inductance, however, a rise in the applied emf does not produce an immediate rise in current. There is a constant time lag or *phase difference* between the rise and fall of the emf and of the current. The actual amount, expressed as an angle, by which the current lags behind the applied emf depends on the resistance of the circuit. If the resistance is negligible, the phase angle is 90 degrees. This angle is reduced if a significant amount of resistance is present. The opposition to the flow of a.c. by self-inductance is called inductive *reactance,* and it increases as the frequency of the a.c. increases.

In a circuit containing capacitance, the conditions are reversed and the current actually rises and falls before the applied emf. The phase angle is again 90 degrees, or less if a significant quantity of resistance is present. The opposition to the flow of a.c. through a capacitance is called capacitive reactance.

When a resistance is present in a circuit containing inductive or capacitive reactance, it makes the total opposition to current flow rather more complicated as well as reducing the phase angle between current and voltage. Resistance and reactance cannot be added together directly, but have to be dealt with in a special way to give what is called the *impedance* of the circuit, which is the total opposition to a.c. flow. The impedance Z, is measured in ohms and equals $\sqrt{(R^2+X^2)}$, where R is the resistance and X the reactance. The actual phase angle ϕ, by which the current and voltage differ, is found by $\tan \phi = X/R$. By Ohm's Law in an a.c. circuit, $I=E/Z$, using either peak or RMS values of I and E.

The resonance effect

In a circuit containing inductive and capacitive reactance together, the total reactance is the difference between the two reactances, since their effects on current flow are exactly opposite. Since inductive reactance increases and capacitive reactance decreases as frequency increases, at some frequency the reactances will be exactly equal and opposite with no net reactance left in the circuit. The total opposition to current flow will then be the resistance only, so the current will be at a maximum and in phase with the applied emf at this frequency. This effect is called *resonance.* It is an important condition in a.c. circuits, because it occurs at this one predetermined frequency of the applied emf.

Since a high current flows through a circuit at resonance, the voltages developed across the inductance and capacitance, although in opposition, become very high. They can be made as much as a hundred times the applied emf if the resistance in the circuit is small. This mechanism, by which a resonant circuit 'magnifies' the applied emf, is a useful way of selecting one frequency from a number of frequencies. In a radio receiver, the tuning control is a variable capacitor which is adjusted so that the resonant frequency of the aerial circuit coincides with the frequency of the desired station. An inductance and a capacitance in parallel also resonate at a very similar frequency to their natural frequency. But in this case, the supply current at reso-

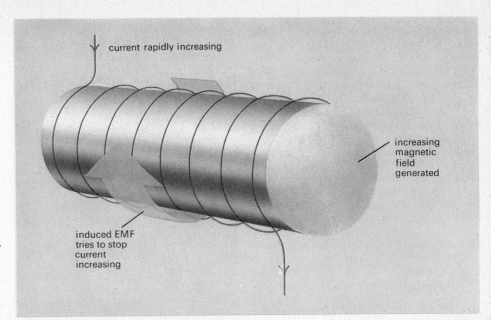

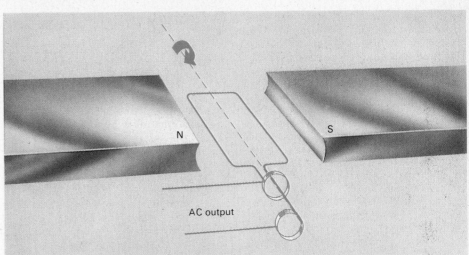

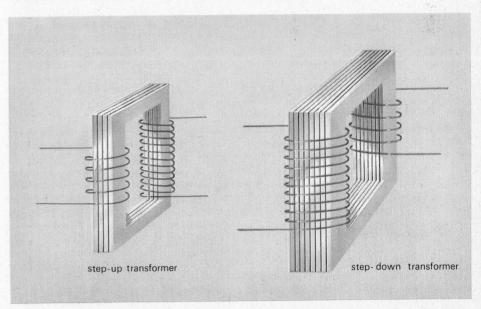

step-up transformer   step-down transformer

nance falls almost to zero.

Another important a.c. device is based on an extension of the magnetic effects of self-inductance in a coil. If a second coil is placed in the varying magnetic field of the first, a varying emf will be induced in the second coil. Two such magnetically linked coils form the basis of the *transformer.*

In practice, the coils of a transformer are generally wound on a closed metal

Top, a rapidly increasing electric current in a coil creates a magnetic field which in turn induces an electromotive force opposing the change producing it. *Centre,* schematic diagram of an alternating-current generator. As the coil is rotated in the magnetic field, current passes from the slip rings to the carbon brushes first in one direction and then in the other. *Above,* simple diagrams of, left, a step-up and, right, a step-down transformer. Any change in the current in one coil induces a voltage in the other proportional to the ratio of turns per coil.

core which concentrates virtually all the magnetic field from the first coil (called the *primary*) into the second coil (or *secondary*). Under these conditions, the emf induced in the secondary is equal to the primary emf multiplied by the ratio of turns in the secondary and primary. A step-up transformer, which gives out more volts than are fed in, has more turns in the secondary than in the primary. A step-down transformer, which changes a voltage to a smaller value, has more turns in the primary than in the secondary. The product of volts and amps in primary and secondary circuits must be the same. So that if the secondary induced emf is higher than the primary, the secondary current must be lower than the primary current, and vice versa.

Transformers are very efficient devices and usually about 95 per cent of the power supplied to a transformer is transferred to the secondary circuit. The remaining 5 per cent is lost as heat developed in the resistances of the two coils, and small magnetic losses in the core. In power transformers, large amounts of heat may be produced in this way necessitating cooling arrangements such as circulating oil.

Transformer operation relies on a changing magnetic field, and a transformer supplied from a d.c. source will give no secondary emf. For this reason, electricity supplies are generally a.c. and are much more versatile than d.c. They can be converted to any required voltage by a suitable transformer.

The mains electricity supply is a good example of how transformers make possible the distribution of very large quantities of electric power over long distances. In many areas, early domestic mains were d.c. Power stations operated only locally, because the transfer of power by d.c. over long distances is very costly and inefficient. The emf from the power station had to drive all the current required by the consumer along the whole length of the cable connecting the two. The cable had to be very thick to minimize losses due to its resistance, making it both expensive and heavy. In case of a breakdown at the power station, there had to be huge banks of storage batteries to maintain the supply.

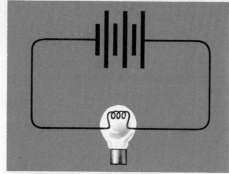

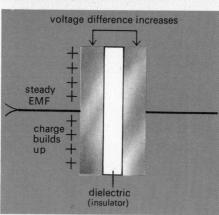

voltage difference increases

steady EMF

charge builds up

dielectric (insulator)

By changing to an a.c. system, it became possible to transform the power-station voltage to a very high voltage indeed. This high voltage involves only a small current and can be passed along cables over long distances. Since the current is small, the losses due to the cable resistance are low. The cables can be much smaller, cheaper and lighter than for a d.c. supply. The British National Grid operates on this system, which interconnects all the power stations in the country and so does away with the need for standby supplies. The power-station output is generally about 6,600 volts, which is transformed up to about 132,000 volts for transmission across the country on the familiar cables strung between pylons. The reduction in current at the transformer is the same as the increase in voltage – that is, 20:1. At suitable points close to large cities, transformer-fed branch cables tap off power from the trunk lines at a lower voltage, such as 66,000 or 33,000 volts. At substations in

Top left, a constant emf is applied to the circuit of a battery-powered electric torch. *Left,* a simple capacitor made by sandwiching a dielectric between two conducting metal plates. In a capacitor connected to a steady emf, a voltage which opposes the applied emf develops across the plates. *Above,* an application of the step-up transformer at Harwell, England, which has resulted in momentary temperatures of 5,000,000°C.

the city outskirts, the supply voltage is further reduced by transformers to 6,600 volts, for distribution by underground cable to small local substations where the domestic 230 volts is produced.

The circuits and devices we have described so far all operate with sinusoidally varying a.c. currents and emfs. The a.c. in some electronic circuits may, however, follow very different and more complex waveforms, such as a square wave or a saw-tooth wave. But as long as they repeat regularly, they are nevertheless alternating currents whether they work an electric lamp or a space satellite.

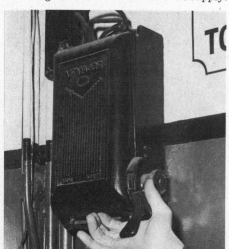

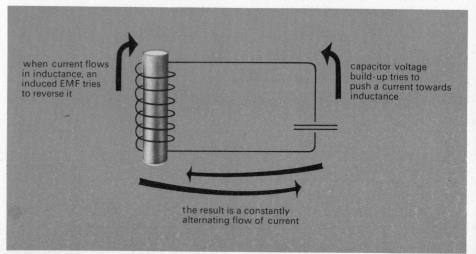

when current flows in inductance, an induced EMF tries to reverse it

capacitor voltage build-up tries to push a current towards inductance

the result is a constantly alternating flow of current

The fuse-box, *left,* traditional fail-safe in the home. If an unexpectedly high current from a faulty appliance is rammed through the fuse wire's resistance, the resulting heat melts the wire, breaking the circuit. *Right,* two forces of reactance constantly pitted against each other will cancel out at the frequency where resonance occurs. This effect is used in tuners which resonate with desired radio broadcasts.

Power in a pin's head

Electronics — based on a deep understanding of the structure of matter — enables us to make circuits no bigger than a pin's head and to derive power from components smaller than the eye can see.

OF ALL the technological advances of the twentieth century the development of electronics is perhaps the most important. Not only do devices employing electronic techniques play a large part in daily life, but fundamental scientific discoveries are involved in their operation.

Radio, television, electronic computers and automatically controlled equipment are possible only through an understanding of the basic structure of matter.

Nineteenth-century physicists had begun to examine a number of phenomena related to electricity and to see the connections between them. When a voltage was applied to electrodes at either end of a tube containing gas at low pressure, a glow was observed and an electric current passed along the tube.

In 1897, J. J. Thomson was led by his experiment to put forward the view that electrical charge was transferred by the movement of *electrons*. These were tiny particles, each charged with negative electricity, and, as Rutherford showed a little later, every atom of matter was made up of a central positively charged nucleus, with electrons revolving around it. It was the passage of electrons that constituted

electric current, and caused the glow in the vacuum tube.

Electrons also were identified with the 'β-rays', found to be emitted from radioactive substances.

In 1883, in the course of his work on the electric lamp, Edison had noticed that if an electrode was placed inside one of his vacuum bulbs an electric current passed across the vacuum from the hot filament. By 1904, understanding of the nature of electricity had developed to the point where Fleming could make use of this 'Edison effect' in making the first *thermionic valve.*

Electrons did not merely remain attached to the atom. In conduction they moved from atom to atom. Under certain conditions, they were detached altogether, as in radioactive emission. A high temperature, as in Edison's filament, allowed them to be pulled away more easily.

In Fleming's 'diode', negative electrical charge, in the form of a stream of electrons moved from the 'cathode', the hot filament, to the 'anode', a metal plate when this was at a positive potential in relation to the cathode but not otherwise. This was therefore a method of 'rectifying' an alternating current, allowing the current to flow in one direction only.

The application to the development of radio was clear. Electromagnetic radiation could be made to induce an alternating current in a radio aerial. In order to allow this current to move a telegraph

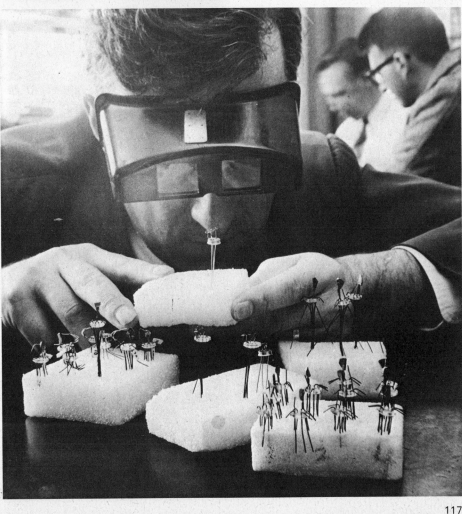

1 Automatic telephone exchanges, like this prototype undergoing tests before installation, rely heavily on electronic devices to overcome the limitations of manual and mechanical switches.
2 One of Sir Ambrose Fleming's experimental diodes. Fleming's invention, closely followed by De Forest's invention of the triode, paved the way for modern electronics.
3 An American research scientist tests different types of semi-conductors made of new heat-resistant materials. Electronics companies spend a great deal on research into new materials.

mechanism, it had to be rectified. This was already possible by means of a crystal touched by a fine wire. Owing to a peculiar property of certain crystals electrons could move out of the crystal, but not into it.

But the Fleming valve was a far more efficient rectifier than the 'cat's whisker'. Once the technique of manufacturing valves was improved, a huge industry was developed, as the radio set spread into the lives of millions of people. Filaments were made of tungsten or of barium or strontium oxide.

Another big advance was to take place in 1907. De Forest placed a metal grid between the filament and anode, producing the triode valve. A negative charge on this grid inhibited the flow of electrons to the anode. If a varying potential was applied to the grid, the degree of variation was magnified in its effect on the current flowing between the other electrodes. The triode valve was an amplifier as well as a rectifier.

By incorporating valves in circuits with resistances, electromagnetic coils, (inductances) and condensers (capacitors), devices were obtained which would resonate to oscillating currents of definite frequencies, amplify variation in their amplitudes and turn these variations into direct currents.

Later development of the valve introduced further grids, the most familiar form being the pentode, with three grids. These were usually arranged in concentric cylinders, with the cathode running along the central axis. Gas-filled tubes were also developed, in addition to the vacuum tube.

In the Fleming valve, a direct current had to be used to heat the filament. In order to run a radio set from alternating current mains valves were made in which the cathode was not itself the filament, but was heated by one, the heat being produced by alternating current.

Frequency modulation

Still more sophisticated circuits are used when the radio signal is conveyed, not by varying the amplitude of the carrier wave, but by modulating its frequency. Frequency modulation (FM) gives a far more accurate reproduction of the transmitted signal, and one less affected by 'noise'.

Since the 1950s, an entirely different type of method of constructing electronic circuits has displaced the valve. This employs the transfer resistor – for short, transistor. This uses the same principle as the cat's whisker of crystal-set days.

If certain crystalline substances have an electrical potential difference applied over a very small distance, electrons may be emitted from the crystal. This produces a semi-conductor, which will allow electricity to pass in one direction only.

Moreover, the volume of such a current is radically dependent on the potential at which the crystal is held. We thus have an analogy with the triode valve. High-frequency current will be rectified by the semi-conductor and variations in a base potential will be amplified.

Once the engineering problems of manufacturing such devices were solved, tran-

sistor circuits, far smaller, lighter and cheaper than the corresponding valve circuits, and needing less electrical power to operate, became possible.

The latest developments are integrated circuits, which are actually formed by 'growing' crystals in various chemical solutions. Tiny crystals may then embody not only the transistors, but all the necessary connections between them.

Before the discovery of the electron, the emission in a vacuum tube from a hot filament was known as a 'cathode ray'. In a *cathode ray tube,* a beam of electrons is deflected by electrostatic or electromagnetic forces. By suitably coating one end of

1

2

the tube it is used as the anode and also made to glow at the point where the electrons hit it.

Varying the currents in electromagnetic coils deflecting the beam causes this spot to trace out corresponding shapes. The television receiver contains the most familiar form of this device, but it has many other applications in industry and in medicine, for example in radar and in electrocardiography.

We have not yet mentioned all the conditions under which electrons are emitted from matter. Television cameras are made possible by the *photo-electric effect*. When light hits certain conducting material, electrons are also thrown out.

In one of his three famous papers of 1905 (the others were on the so-called Brownian motion and on the theory of relativity) Einstein showed that whether an electron was emitted, and, if so, its speed depended only on the *frequency* of the light ray, that is its colour, and not on its intensity. Only the *number* of emitted electrons varied with the intensity of light.

A television camera employs this principle by using a photo-electric cell. A ray of light is made to give rise to an electric current. This is amplified and modulates a radio wave.

In a television receiver, the signal is turned back into light on a cathode ray tube. But this is still a long way from transmitting a picture. For this, the scene must be scanned. At each instant, light is received by the photo-electric cell from one direction, one point of the scene.

This point moves across from left to right in a series of lines which cover the scene from top to bottom, as a typewriter does with letters.

At the receiver, the spot at the end of the tube is moved in a similar and synchronized manner. In this way, an entire picture is transmitted many times a second. In colour television, several such pictures must be reproduced at once, each corresponding to a different colour.

So far, we have mainly concentrated on the radio applications of electronics. In terms of the number of devices manufactured in the last 50 years, these are certainly the most important uses. But,

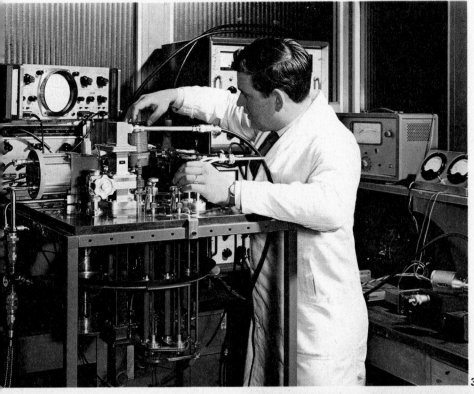

1 A special cold suit is required for testing this electronic tracking device for a space satellite. The temperature of the surface of the device is −454 °F.

2 Assembling an electron 'gun' at an electrical components factory. The 'gun' is used to provide a source of electrons for a number of electrical engineering applications.

3 An electronics development engineer tests a satellite component at a factory producing electronic devices. Stringent testing is essential for today's exacting requirements.

4 Automatic doors open as visitors to the building approach. These electronic devices are often just status symbols for large firms, but are useful in hospitals and homes for the handicapped.

5 An electron beam − the purple beam in the photograph − assists the welding of a metal workpiece in this experimental set-up in a United States aircraft company.

on the basis of the radio industry, electronics advanced in the 1920s and 1930s to a stage where other applications were possible, with still greater significance.

In transmitting messages, sounds and pictures by radio what is really happening is the transformation of information from one form to another, and the combination of different pieces of it. The variation in amplitude of a radio wave, corresponds to the kind of sound hitting the microphone in the transmitting studio. A radio receiver decodes it, transforming it back into sound.

Suppose numbers could be coded into electrical form. Could an electronic circuit be devised to combine numbers in accordance with mathematical rules? The electronic computer does just that.

Over a century ago, Charles Babbage constructed his Automatic Computing Engine. Driven by steam and clockwork, it performed addition and multiplication under instructions coded as holes in cards. The techniques then available made it impossible to take his ideas any further, and Babbage's 'engine' remained a curiosity. (It may be seen in London's Science Museum today.)

But by the Second World War, electronics made it possible to embody and develop the conceptions of Babbage. To carry out the calculations needed for the atomic bomb, John von Neumann had constructed a Mathematical Analyser, Integrator and Calculator, pronounced MANIAC.

This coded not only numbers but the 'programme' of instructions of what to do with them, in the form of electrical impulses. Since instructions were held in the same form as numbers, they could themselves be altered by other instructions, making the electronic computer a device of tremendous versatility and speed.

While they were first thought of as powerful calculators, or 'number crackers,' computers were soon seen to have wider application. Information could be sorted, analysed and combined which went beyond mere numerical data. The electronic office and the automatic factory had arrived on the scene.

In an industrial process, objects are moved from place to place, their shape changed by machining, for example, components assembled into more complex objects. Apart from the application of energy in machining, human beings are needed to decide where and when each mechanical operation should take place, correcting and halting machines when necessary.

Automatic decisions

Electronics, and in particular the computer, makes it possible for these decisions to be made automatically. For example, objects may have to be packed in boxes, 12 per box. An electronic counter, using a photo-electric cell to find out when an object passes by on the conveyor, can send a 'message' when the required number have arrived. Receiving the 'message', the packaging machine can move to the next stage of its work.

Entire plants can be run in an integrated way by such means. This is the way in which space vehicles are controlled, computers translating the requirements of the controller into the appropriate 'instructions' to the rocket apparatus.

It is in this field of automatic control, that electronics is already having its greatest effect on our lives. In the transformation of information the application of mechanical power is automatically directed.

More than one writer has asked the question, 'Can such machines take over'? After all, computers are already widely employed in the design and construction of other computers, more complex than themselves. Someone made the obvious reply to this question: 'We could always pull the plug out.'

To which a more pessimistic thinker retorted: 'Perhaps we shall find it already cemented to the wall.'

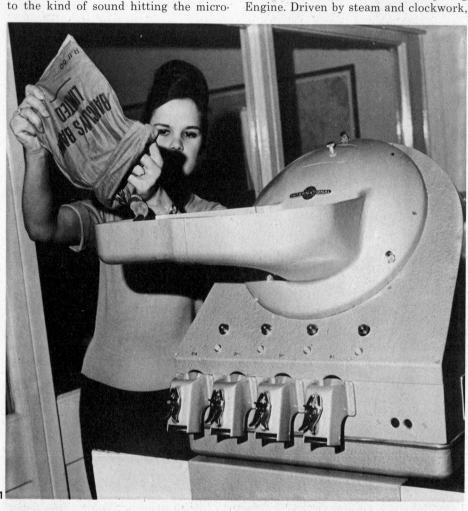

1

2

1 The bank clerk's job is greatly facilitated by this electronic coin counter, which sorts and counts miscellaneous British coinage at the Bank of England.

2 An accuracy of better than a thousandth of an inch can be obtained easily and quickly by reading off the thickness of this skin panel on an electronic thickness guage.

The family life of electro-magnetic waves

Ordinary light and exotic X-rays are kith and kin in the family of electro-magnetic waves. The study and application of electro-magnetic waves has significantly altered everyday life.

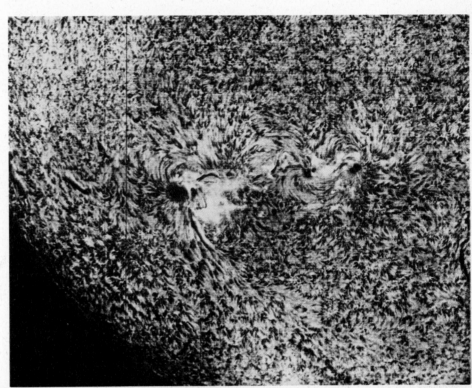

The fundamental research of the German Heinrich Hertz, *above left,* established basic properties of the electro-magnetic spectrum and led to modern radio communications. Spectroheliographs of the sun show vast pulsating hydrogen clouds surrounding sunspots, *right.* Such pictures are made by recording only hydrogen-associated wavelengths. Absorption spectra of thallium, *bottom,* show identifiable characteristic lines.

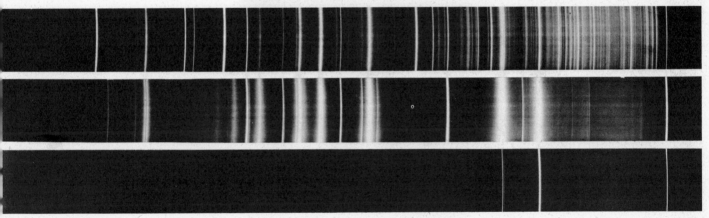

WHEN IN 1690 Christiaan Huygens first put forward the idea that light is not particle-like in nature but travels in the form of waves, he could hardly have foreseen how far-reaching his theory would be. Of course he had no means of telling whether or not there were other forms of waves having similar properties to light. But we now know that light waves are just a small part of a whole family of radiant energy called electro-magnetic waves, which range from radio waves to X-rays and gamma rays. Light is the part of the spectrum we can see. Other parts, such as infra-red, ultra-violet, X-rays, and gamma rays, can be 'seen' by photographic plates. Radio waves can be detected using an aerial and suitable amplifying equipment.

Sir Isaac Newton and other early investigators had shown that white light can be split up by a prism into a range of colours from red to violet which form the visible spectrum. Later, the wave properties of each colour – its speed, wavelength, and frequency – were examined. It was found that in a given medium, such as air, the speed of each colour was the same (nearly 30 thousand million centimetres per second). But their frequencies and wavelengths differ, ranging from about 0·00004 cm and 750 billion cycles per second for violet light to 0·000075 cm and 400 billion cycles per second for red light.

Heat and colour

In 1800, Sir William Herschel investigated the amount of heat associated with each colour in the spectrum. He detected more heat at the red end of the visible spectrum than at the violet end, and surprisingly he measured even more heat at a position past the visible end of the spectrum beyond the red. He had discovered the first invisible light-like waves, now known as infra-red radiation. It was soon realized that heat waves occupy a region in the electro-magnetic spectrum next to light waves.

As their name suggests, electro-magnetic waves can also be produced electrically (over a certain range). An electric current flowing in a wire produces electric and magnetic fields around the wire. If the current alternates (a.c.), so do the fields.

When the frequency of the alternating current is small, the magnetic field around a wire carrying it is very much stronger than is the electric field, and no significant electro-magnetic wave is produced. As the frequency of the current increases, the electric field increases until, at frequencies of 10 to 15 kilocycles per second, an electro-magnetic wave is radiated, having the same frequency as the frequency of the alternating current in the wire. These forms of waves were first investigated by the German physicist Heinrich Hertz (1857–94) and were known as Hertzian waves; we now call them radio waves.

As a belated recognition of the pioneering work done by Hertz, in 1966 radio stations around the world began giving their frequencies in 'kilohertz' or 'megahertz' instead of the standard 'kilocycle' or 'megacycles'. There is, of course, no difference between a 'hertz' and a 'cycle'. A frequency of 200 kilohertz and 200 kilocycles are exactly the same.

Using radio wavelengths of 150 metres (frequencies of 2 megacycles per second) and less, it is possible to communicate across the Atlantic Ocean. This is because the radio waves zig-zag around the Earth by bouncing backwards and forwards between the surface and ionized layers in the upper atmosphere (called the ionosphere). The ionosphere can act as a kind of mirror to radio waves down to about 7 or 8 metres wavelength. Shorter wavelengths, such as those used for VHF (very high frequency) radio and television, pass through it. Radio waves originating from distant stars and galaxies also have short wavelengths; they penetrate the ionosphere and can be received at the Earth's surface. These very short wavelengths are used for radar and for communicating with orbiting satellites and space vehicles.

Hertz showed the physical similarity between radio waves and light waves. At high frequencies, about 1,500 megacycles per second and above, micro-waves, the electro-magnetic radio waves, be-

have in many respects as do light waves. For this reason, micro-wave aerials are constructed on similar basic principles as are reflecting light telescopes, with large reflecting concave 'bowls' to 'focus' the waves. Radio telescopes such as that at Jodrell Bank in Cheshire, are used to 'listen' to radio waves from distant stars. Satellite communications aerials such as that at Goonhilly also use these principles.

Another property of micro-waves is that they can be passed along closed pipes called *waveguides*. The radio wave can be thought of as bouncing down the waveguide. This is the way in which micro-wave signals are conducted in radar sets and communications equipment.

Cooking by micro-wave

At very short wavelengths, micro-waves exhibit some of the properties of infra-red radiation, their near neighbours in the electro-magnetic spectrum. For example, they produce heat when passed through a substance and are used in micro-wave 'cookers' for food. The micro-waves pass right through the food and heat it all over at once, unlike the situation in a conventional cooker which heats the food from the outside surfaces only. For this reason, micro-wave cooking is extremely rapid.

The shorter wavelength infra-red region of the electro-magnetic spectrum was known 150 years ago, but the existence of longer wavelength infra-red waves was not proved until sometime later. During the early part of this century, experiments into the reflecting and refracting pro-

perties of certain crystals revealed the existence of infra-red wavelengths of up to a tenth of a millimetre. Since the upper wavelength limit of micro-waves is also in this range, the continuity of the electro-magnetic spectrum at this point was established.

Infra-red waves are given out by all hot bodies, even those that are not sufficiently hot to produce visible light waves as well. In fact, black surfaces are the most efficient radiators of infra-red waves. Photographs may be taken using infra-red 'light' and suitable films, and infra-red viewing devices are used to 'see' at night when there is no illumination from visible light. Infra-red sights may be fitted to guns and rifles, and infra-red detectors often form the basis of the guidance system in ground-to-air and air-to-air missiles which seek out the hot gases from the exhaust of an aircraft's jet engines. But perhaps the most important infra-red radiation to Man is the heat waves arriving on Earth from the sun.

The continuity of the electro-magnetic spectrum from infra-red to visible light was known early in the days of the wave theory. We can demonstrate this continuity by heating an object such as a metal bar. At first the metal becomes hot without glowing, and we can feel the heat coming from it in the form of infra-red waves. As more heat is supplied to the bar, it begins to glow a dull red (corresponding to longest wavelength light waves), gradually changes to a yellowish colour (shorter wavelength), before glowing white hot

1

2

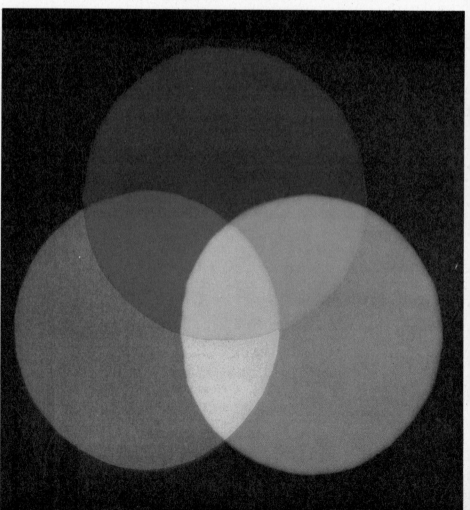

3

when many infra-red and visible wavelengths are emitted together.

The visible spectrum is familiar to most people as a rainbow produced by the diffraction of light by small droplets of water in the air. When mixed together, the colours we see make up white light. We can also observe parts of the spectrum as the atomic spectra produced by individual elements, such as in sodium (yellow) and neon (orange) lighting. We can also produce any colour of light by simply using a source of white light masked by the appropriate colour filter, which allows only waves of certain wavelengths to pass through.

Infra-red and visible light wavelengths can be measured using the important wave property of diffraction. By projecting the waves on to a specially-made diffraction 'grating', a pattern of light and dark bands is produced. From the arrangement and spacing of the bands, the wavelength of the radiation can be found.

Why a sunset is red

Light waves are easily scattered by small particles such as dust, and the amount of scattering depends on the wavelength of the light. Long wavelengths (red light) are scattered very little, but short wavelengths (blue) are easily scattered. We can observe this effect on a cloudless day when the sun sets. The sun and surrounding sky are red, because all the blue from the sun's white light has been scattered away by the dust particles in the atmosphere. The eastern sky, opposite the sunset, is blue because all we see is blue light scattered back from the dust; the red light passes out into space and is not scattered backwards at all. Infra-red photographs are unaffected by mist and haze because infra-red is not scattered by particles in the air.

Immediately next to the blue end of the visible spectrum is the ultra-violet region of the electro-magnetic spectrum. The sun emits ultra-violet waves (as well as infra-red and light waves), so the existence of ultra-violet was also established relatively early. We now know that ultra-violet light is important to animal physiology because it plays a part in the formation of vitamin D in the body – and it causes sun tan.

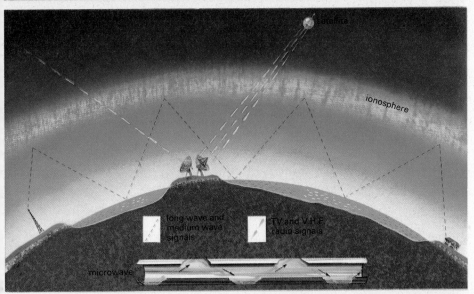

A micro-wave oven, **1,** can heat food better and faster than standard models, because it is able to heat it right through. Dropping low on the horizon, the setting sun appears gloriously red as the intervening air scatters most other colours away from our eyes, **2.** The blue of the sky is also caused by scattering. **3,** With the exception of the three primary colours – red, green and blue – all other shades are mixtures, including white. Red and blue are also primary *paint* colours, but green is then a mixture of yellow and blue. When hot enough, even dull metal becomes incandescent and gives off light, the colour of which gives a clue to the temperature, **4.** Different types of electro-magnetic waves are transmitted in different ways, depending on their properties. Long and medium waves may be bounced off satellites. Micro-waves are transmitted through underground pipes or waveguides, **5.** Giant radio telescopes, **6,** are used to detect radio signals emanating from outer space.

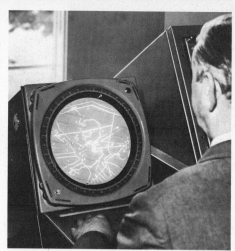

Modern radar equipment, *top left,* makes airline flights both smoother and safer. A panel of mirrors, *top right,* gathers in infra-red rays from the sun to heat water in this French solar energy central-heating system. A British 'ray gun', *below left,* splits rocks by using micro-wave energy to boil moisture content, causing violent expansion. This apparatus may some-day have important applications in quarrying and tunnelling, and even replace the noisy pneu-matic drill. An advanced radar, *below right,* spots aircraft as far away as France and Holland.

People such as miners who spend much of their time away from the sun may need ultra-violet lamp treatment to replace the natural sunlight they miss. Ultra-violet waves can also be detected photographic-ally, as can visible light and infra-red. But ultra-violet has different penetrating pro-perties and will not pass through ordinary glass. Materials such as nylon are trans-parent to ultra-violet, which will also pass through a thin foil of silver. Under ultra-violet 'light', white clothing washed in so-called 'whiter-than-white' detergents, which contain special additives, gives off visible light. This property gives the whitening effect to clothes when viewed in sunlight – they really are brighter! Ultra-violet wavelengths may be as short as a ten-millionth of a centimetre.

The discovery of X-rays

The electro-magnetic waves which lie beyond the ultra-violet were first investi-gated nearly 70 years ago by another German physicist, Wilhelm Konrad Rönt-gen (1845–1923). Röntgen was experiment-ing with high voltages applied across metal plates in a tube containing gas at low pres-sure. He called the new waves *X-rays,* and found that they had strong penetrating properties and also that they fogged photo-graphic plates. (It was their effect on some of his stored plates near the experimental tube that first caused Röntgen to investi-gate the new waves.) It was later found that X-rays are emitted whenever a high-speed stream of electrons strikes a metal target enclosed in a tube similar to Rönt-gen's. When produced this way, X-rays span a broad spectrum as does visible light. Some X-rays also have certain special wavelengths, which can be com-pared to the single-wavelength light pro-

duced, for example, by sodium light. The special or *characteristic* X-ray wavelengths depend on the material from which the target in the tube is made. X-rays of extremely short wavelength, called gamma rays, are emitted by certain radio-active substances such as radium.

Following Huygens's theory on the wave properties of light, which in the opinion of most scientists satisfactorily explained diffraction, refraction and inter-ference, the corpuscle versus wave battle died down. But when the photoelectric effect was discovered and investigated, the wave theory could not explain it and the long-forgotten particle or corpus-cular theory, championed by Newton, seemed to fit. Max Planck then proposed, initially in connection with heat carried by electro-magnetic waves, that radiant energy can exist only as multiples of certain fixed quantities of energy, called quanta. According to the quantum theory, the energy of each quantum increases with increasing frequency.

This theory was then extended by Albert Einstein, who proposed that light radiation is composed of short bursts of waves, each burst or *photon* being a quantum of energy. In this way, the quan-tum theory effectively combines the cor-puscular and wave theories and provides a convenient explanation of the photo-electric effect without abandoning the wave theory's convincing explanation of diffraction and so on. The quantum theory also explains why, say, sodium emits

yellow light, and accounts for characteris-tic X-ray wavelengths in terms of electron 'jumps' between orbitals of different ener-gies, which result in the emission or absorption of quanta of radiant energy. In the late 1920s G. P. Thomson showed which X-rays are diffracted by a crystal. The wavelengths concerned are found to depend on the velocity of the electrons, and are in the range 1·0 to 0·1 Ångstrom units. (A hundred million Ångstrom units equal one centimetre.)

Seeing without light

Use is made of this property in the elec-tron microscope; instead of using light, the microscope uses a beam of electrons 'fired' into the object to be studied. The power of any microscope to form a separate image of two close objects depends on the wavelength of the waves used. An electron microscope (using an electron 'wave-length' of 1 Ångstrom unit) is far more powerful than an optical microscope (using light wavelengths of about 5,000 Ångstrom units), and can resolve down to almost the size of a single atom.

In 1932, experiments showed that beams of atoms or molecules are also diffracted by crystals and exhibit wave properties. This was experimental proof that matter may behave either as particles or waves, the nature of the experiment determining which of these two facets is the more prominent. The new science of wave mechanics could now confidently be ap-plied to the study of atoms and molecules.

Open secrets in an X-ray's beam

A mysteriously fogged photographic plate was among Wilhelm Röntgen's first clues to the strange rays loose in his laboratory. Today, art, science and medicine use the name he gave them.

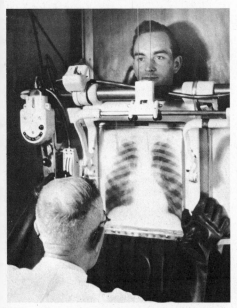

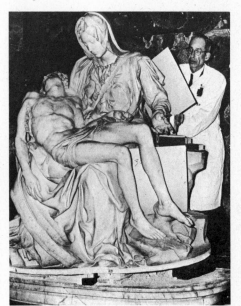

Left, perhaps the best known use of X-rays is viewing the interior of the human body. However, when X-rays were first announced, people feared their use for seeing through clothing as

well. Hucksters made a fortune selling 'X-ray proof' undergarments. A lesser known use for X-rays, *right,* is checking important sculptures for tiny cracks and other dangerous flaws. The

work shown here is Michelangelo's 'Pietà'. X-rays were discovered by the German physicist Wilhelm Röntgen, *centre,* in 1895. Some people still call them Röntgen rays in honour of his work.

MANY PEOPLE have at some time been X-rayed, either in hospital or at a mass X-ray unit. From X-ray pictures taken of a part of the body, doctors can detect and diagnose illness, examine bone structures, and even determine whether an unborn baby can be born naturally or requires a Caesarean birth.

But X-rays have many other important uses both in and out of medicine. For instance, hidden defects in metal structures can be detected by X-ray techniques, and the effects of crystal structures on X-rays is used to examine the forms of crystals and the arrangements of their atoms.

The discovery of X-rays in 1895 by the German physicist Wilhelm Röntgen was the result of investigations into quite different effects. Like many of his contemporaries, Röntgen was studying the newly observed cathode rays which were found to stream from the cathode of a low-pressure discharge tube when a high voltage was applied across its electrodes.

Cathode rays produce a bluish glow from the small amounts of gas or air left in the tube, and Röntgen had covered a tube with black paper to contain this light. He noticed, however, that a nearby zinc sulphide screen glowed or fluoresced when the voltage between the tube electrodes was about 10,000 volts. Also some of his photographic plates near the tube, although unexposed to light, became fogged during the experiments. Since both the tube and the plates were covered in black paper, light had certainly not caused this fogging. To trace the source of the effect, Röntgen set up near the tube a lead screen

(he had found that this prevented the new 'rays' from passing) with four holes in it. Behind the screen he put a photographic plate, and then adjusted the tube to the correct conditions.

When the photographic plate was developed, it had four spots where rays passing through the holes in the lead screen had fallen on to it. By replacing the plate in its original position and tracing lines back from the spots through the holes in the screen, Röntgen showed that the new rays came from the end of the discharge tube where the cathode rays fell. Cathode rays, when given sufficient energy by a high electric potential across the tube, had caused certain rays to be given off on striking a 'target'. Röntgen called the new rays X-rays. Today, cathode rays are known to be a stream of electrons, and, in general, any high-energy electron beam striking a metal target causes X-rays to be emitted.

Waves that could penetrate

X-rays were carefully studied to discover their nature. It was concluded that since they were unaffected by magnetic or electric fields (which a stream of charged particles such as electrons would be) and also travelled in straight lines, they must be similar in nature to light. By 1900, more evidence to support this idea had been found from diffraction patterns produced by X-rays. The form of the patterns suggested that if X-rays are waves like light, they have a much shorter wavelength. In 1912, the British physicist Sir William Henry Bragg succeeded in measuring the wavelengths of X-rays, using diffraction

patterns produced by crystals, and, as expected, the wavelengths were very short. In this way, the relationship between light and X-rays was confirmed, and X-rays were recognized as a form of electromagnetic waves, as are visible light, radio and infra-red waves.

Early X-ray tubes used cathode rays in a similar way to Röntgen's discharge tube. But they were unreliable because the low pressure in the tube was difficult to maintain at a constant level and the quality of the X-rays was unpredictable. When techniques for maintaining low pressure improved, these early tubes were replaced by the Coolidge tube. In this, the stream of electrons previously provided by the cathode rays comes from a heated tungsten filament in rather the same way as in a thermionic valve or a television tube. The electrons are then 'fired' on to a metal target, the high voltage between the filament and the target giving the electrons sufficient energy to cause X-radiation as before.

The basic properties of X-rays were observed by Röntgen: their penetrating power, their ability to cause fluorescence, and their effect on photographic plates. Later wave properties were demonstrated, including diffraction, refraction, interference, an X-ray 'photoelectric' effect, and even polarization. This confirmed the kinship of X-rays and light.

Some of these properties of X-rays are used in the X-ray spectrometer, an important instrument developed by W. H. Bragg and his son W. L. (Sir Lawrence) Bragg to measure X-ray wavelengths accurately. It is basically similar to an optical spectrometer used for measuring light wavelengths. A narrow 'beam' of X-rays is directed at an acute angle on to a crystal mounted on a turntable. The crystal diffracts the X-rays in much the same way as a diffraction grating diffracts light, and the diffracted X-rays pass towards a detecting device. This consists of a tube filled with a gas such as methyl iodide, which absorbs X-rays strongly and which becomes ionized when X-rays pass through it. The electrical charge of the gas ions is then measured using an electrometer, giving an indication of the strength of the X-rays falling on to the tube. The energy associated with a particular wavelength can be studied by moving the crystal and the detecting device to the correct positions for that wavelength.

The wavelength itself is found by calculation, using a knowledge of the crystal structure (its dimensions, atomic weight, and so on) and the angles of alignment between the crystal and the detecting device. The relationship giving the wavelength is called Bragg's Law. For this work the Braggs were awarded a Nobel prize in 1915, when W. L. Bragg was only 25.

New metal, new wavelength

Interference of X-rays can be produced by passing them through very narrow slits, and techniques using special mechanically produced diffraction gratings have been developed. By projecting the X-rays at a small angle of incidence, the grating lines appear very close together and diffraction occurs even at the very short wavelengths of X-rays. This method has given values of X-ray wavelengths which confirm Bragg's Law based on the calculated dimensions of the crystal.

Using the X-ray spectrometer, the Braggs investigated X-ray wavelengths from a tube whose target could be changed from one metal to another, and in which the voltage across the plates could be varied. For relatively low tube voltages, they found that a range or spectrum of X-ray wavelengths is produced which ends abruptly at the short wavelength end. Increasing the tube voltage moves this cut-off point to a shorter wavelength. At a certain high value of voltage, in addition to the broad X-ray spectrum the tube produces strong X-rays at definite wavelengths.

They found that changing the metal of the target from, say, copper to nickel and repeating the experiment produces another broad spectrum and again at high voltages a set of strong X-ray lines. But the lines for nickel have different wavelengths from those for copper. These strong X-ray lines are called *characteristic X-rays* because they are characteristic of the target metal.

Shortly after W. H. Bragg's observations, the origin of characteristic X-rays was linked with the production of characteristic light wavelengths by certain elements. (For example, sodium produces yellow light, neon produces red light, and so on.) From a knowledge of quantum theory these can be explained. The high-speed electrons falling on to the target have a certain energy. While this energy

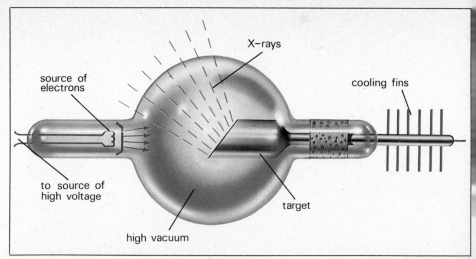

A stream of electrons 'fired' from a source of high voltage, thus carrying a large quantity of energy, strikes a metal target, *top*, and X-rays are given off. The vacuum is to prevent dissipation of the electrons' energy through collision with air molecules. This X-ray photo of a rattlesnake digesting a prairie dog, *above*, offers invaluable information to the biologist.

is relatively low (that is, at low tube voltages), the electrons collide with the heavy target atoms and are scattered about. At each collision they lose energy which is radiated in the form of X-rays.

Since they lose various amounts of energy at each collision, the X-ray wavelengths produced are many, and a broad X-ray spectrum is formed. But at a certain tube voltage, the electrons have sufficient energy to eject other electrons from the innermost orbits of the target atoms. The spaces left by the ejected electrons are filled by electrons falling from higher orbits, each releasing a definite quantum of energy in doing so. According to quantum theory, the quantum of energy is related to the frequency of the energy released. So for a particular target atom, X-rays of definite wavelength are emitted. A different target atom has a different arrangement of orbits, and so the quanta

X-rays can probe behind the painted surface of a masterpiece to reveal important secrets. The painting of St Michael, *left,* by Piero della Francesca, now hanging in the National Gallery in London, was suspected to be part of a lost five-panel altarpiece prepared for the Church of St Agostino in Italy in the mid-1400s. An X-ray revealed a tell-tale piece of drapery in the lower right-hand corner, as in the cleaned painting, *right.* Four of the five panels have now been located, and the art world is now on the lookout for the fifth to complete the work.

of energy involved are also different, leading to characteristic X-rays of definite wavelengths.

The important investigations into the structures of crystals using X-rays were begun by M. von Laue (who in 1912 first predicted diffraction of X-rays by crystals) and continued by the Braggs. The way in which a simple crystal such as that of common salt diffracts X-rays was explained by W. H. Bragg in connection with his X-ray spectrometer. He considered that X-rays are scattered by each of the crystal atoms. In any direction, the scattered X-rays will add together only if their waves are in phase (in step). If we consider one crystal plane (in a cubic crystal there will be three sets of such planes at right angles), the scattered X-rays from that plane will be in phase for one direction only. This direction has the same relationship to the angle of incidence as do the incident and reflected light rays at a mirror. If the same effect occurs for the many crystal planes lying beneath the one considered, and if all the reflected rays are in phase, there will be a strong overall reflection in one direction only. This direction depends on the wavelength of the X-rays, the angle of incidence, and the spacing between the crystal planes, and is predicted by Bragg's Law.

If the crystal is rotated and other crystal

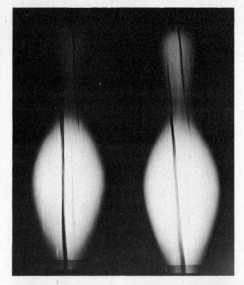

A man came to a doctor complaining of stomach pains. An X-ray, *top left,* revealed the cause. He had swallowed a fork. Bowling pins, *top right,* are regularly X-rayed to detect flaws. Brain tumours, a more serious kind of flaw, are also revealed by X-ray, with the aid of radio-isotopes, *above left.* Numerous lives have been saved in this way. Study of X-rays and other such phenomena led to the need for protection. This make-shift lead mask, *above right,* is an example of the primitive protective devices the early researchers had to fashion for themselves. It is an exhibit at the Röntgen Museum in Remscheid, West Germany, where Röntgen was born.

planes used, the shape and volume of the crystal can be found and the number of atoms in the crystal determined. With extremely simple crystals, the numbers of atoms can be found by calculation without using the spectrometer; but for complex crystals, this method is the basis of the most useful way of analysing them. Techniques developed by W.L. Bragg have enabled scientists to measure even the structures of organic crystals. Other important X-ray crystal studies include those of the structures of metals and new alloys, and of organic fibres.

Shadow pictures

The more familiar applications of X-rays use their penetrating properties. Unlike light, which is stopped by even a flimsy material such as paper, X-rays can penetrate quite dense materials. In passing through a material, the intensity or 'brightness' of the X-rays is progressively reduced (like light passing through cloudy water). Since different materials reduce the intensity at a different rate, X-rays passed through, say, the human body will be more strongly absorbed by bone than by the surrounding flesh. By placing a photographic plate behind the body, a 'shadow' X-ray picture may be produced. Tissues which are or have been diseased, for instance the scar tissue left in the lungs after tuberculosis, show up darker than the surrounding tissues because they

absorb slightly more X-rays. Additional techniques, such as the barium sulphate meal used for X-raying the stomach, are used to make soft tissues show up on X-ray photographs. In this example, an ulcer would absorb some of the barium sulphate and would show up strongly on the X-ray plate.

X-rays are also used in industry; for example, to examine metal objects encapsulated in plastic, or to 'see' through an opaque substance as in the locating of grids in thermionic valves. Important too are X-ray techniques for detecting flaws in metals. Although a metal casting or a machined component may appear sound, it can contain an internal flaw which seriously affects its strength. If X-ray photographs could not be used, the only other ways of easily detecting the flaw would involve destroying the component. For example, hitting a small casting with a big hammer detects flaws, but it smashes the casting.

The dangers of X-irradiation to the body are now recognized, and people who work with X-ray machines are well protected by lead shielding. Until about 15 years ago, it was common to see X-ray machines in shops to aid in fitting shoes, especially for children. These machines projected X-rays up through the foot and on to a fluorescent screen. If they were used frequently, there may have been some danger, so most of them have now been withdrawn. The

effects of small doses of X-rays on tissues are negligible. But prolonged exposure can have serious consequences and ultimately destroys the tissues. Important too is the effect of X-rays on genes and chromosomes. Mutated genes can have disastrous effects if they are passed on in reproduction. For this reason, X-rays are rarely used on women in early pregnancy, although in some cases the slight risk may be justified by the essential information an X-ray examination can provide.

Medical science has turned the damaging effects of X-irradiation to good use. X-ray therapy is an important part of the treatment for malignant diseases such as cancer. Using a very carefully directed and controlled X-ray source, the affected tissues can be destroyed, and the cell-multiplying effects caused by certain kinds of cancer arrested.

The quantum explanation of the energy associated with X-rays showed that, as the wavelength of the radiation becomes shorter, so the energy becomes greater. Short wavelength X-rays therefore have more penetrating power than do longer wavelengths. Very short wavelength X-rays are very penetrating, and closely resemble their near neighbours in the electro-magnetic spectrum, gamma rays.

Gamma radiation

Gamma rays have many of the properties of X-rays (they can be diffracted by crystals, they affect photographic plates and cause feeble fluorescence, they pass through metals, and so on); their origin is different. Characteristic emission of light and X-rays is due to electrons jumping between energy levels. Gamma radiation is produced by activity originating in the nucleus of the atom. It occurs when the nucleus adjusts itself from one 'excited' state to another. It is interesting that the quantum theory again satisfactorily explains the mechanism: the nucleus can settle in only certain energy states and in moving from one state to another of lower energy, a quantum of gamma radiation is emitted. The nucleus gets into a position from which it must change in this way after the emission of a beta particle (an electron).

Gamma rays can also be responsible for the emission of X-rays. As a gamma ray leaves the nucleus, it passes through the electron orbits of the atom and may eject an electron from one of them. The conditions are then similar to those in an X-ray tube, and another electron falls into the vacant space, emitting a characteristic X-ray quantum. In this way, a radioactive material emitting gamma radiation may also produce X-rays. This phenomenon can be used for analysing mixtures of elements. If the mixture is made radioactive, its X-ray spectrum can be examined and, from the characteristic lines present, the elements in the mixture can be identified.

When X-rays were first discovered, many people were quite apprehensive. However, research has stripped them of their mystery and technology has put them to useful work. X-rays have become an important part of our daily life.

The maser and laser

Pure single frequencies of light and of radio waves beamed coherently out from a special source are the basis of the laser. This powerful tool has given rise to a new and useful technology.

WHEN THE AMERICAN ASTRONAUTS, Neil Armstrong and Buzz Aldrin, blasted off from the moon in 1969 on the start of their return journey, one of the pieces of hardware they left behind on the moon's surface was a laser reflector. Within hours of the blast-off, this reflector was used in conjunction with a powerful laser on Earth to confirm the exact spot where the moon landing was made and to measure more accurately than had hitherto been possible the distance separating Earth and moon.

And yet, ten years earlier the laser had not been invented. What, then, is a laser? How does it work? What can it do?

The word laser is an acronym made up of the initial letters of Light Amplification by Stimulated Emission of Radiation. The laser was developed directly from an earlier device, which operated on similar principles, but which amplified radiation in the lower *microwave* frequency part of the electromagnetic spectrum. This was called the maser – standing for Microwave Amplification by Stimulated Emission of Radiation.

The maser was born out of military research efforts to produce and amplify super high frequency radio signals for a superior radar.

As it turned out, the maser principle appears to have been discovered independently by American and Russian physicists in 1951. But this was only the principle. No working device then existed.

The first practical maser was conceived by a United States physicist, C. H. Townes,

in the laboratories of Columbia University, who managed to get a maser working towards the end of 1953.

The culmination of the research was a device which would produce an intense beam of microwaves (radio waves of a few centimetres wavelength) with each wave almost exactly the same size and in step with every other wave. The maser could also be used to amplify very weak radio signals and one of its first uses was as an amplifier in radio telescopes. The lasers, which soon overshadowed maser developments, produced similarly intense beams of much shorter, visible waves, all travelling parallel and in step. Thus was born a completely new type of light-producing device.

From Einstein

What was this new way of producing radiation that set research on optics humming in a way that has not occurred for 50 years? First of all, the basis of the new technology – stimulated emission of radiation – was not at all new, and had been considered by Einstein in 1917. There were also quite familiar lamps available, such as gas discharge tubes which operated on the principle. This was the production of radiation by exciting molecules of certain materials to well defined, high energy states, so that they then returned to a low energy, or ground state, giving up the energy as precise 'packets' of radiation with precise frequencies. The key to the maser and laser was to get a majority of molecules in a system into an excited state, and then to trigger off their return to the ground state together so that all the radiation produced was in step and reinforced itself to produce an intense, amplified beam of radiation.

It was possible to conceive of a device that would operate like this, because molecules of certain materials can be excited to a high energy level by absorbing the same or similar wavelength radiation that is produced in decaying to the ground state. In the case of the first maser, the material in question was ammonia gas, which would absorb microwave energy until most of the molecules were in an excited energy state and then emit a burst of microwaves at an exact frequency of approximately 1·25 cm.

Designing a set-up that would produce bursts of microwave energy called for a great deal of ingenuity, and Townes realized that just pumping radiation into ammonia gas was not good enough, as there was just as much chance that the radiation pumped in would be absorbed, as that it would trigger a molecule to return to a ground state and produce more radiation. There would be no build-up of excited molecules and sudden release of their energy radiation. The solution was to concentrate ammonia molecules into a stream, to excite them, and pass them into a small cavity with end walls that reflected microwaves. Most of the radiation emitted was reflected back and forth between the walls of the cavity, which were one half a wavelength apart, so that the waves were all in step and reinforced one another. In this way, the ammonia gas was pumped to a state where more of the molecules were in a higher energy state than in the lower one and the maser action could take place.

Townes's first maser was not used to

Lasers are proving very useful in certain types of microsurgery. One such use is to spot weld the retina of the eye back in place after it has accidentally come away.

The argon ion gas laser generates a beam of light that is extremely bright and narrow. The gas laser is being developed for deep-space communication, for television and for computers.

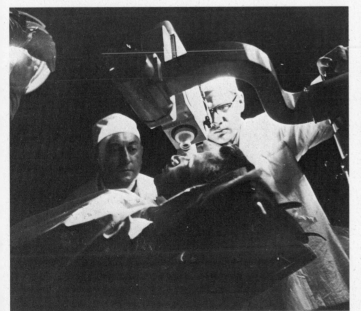

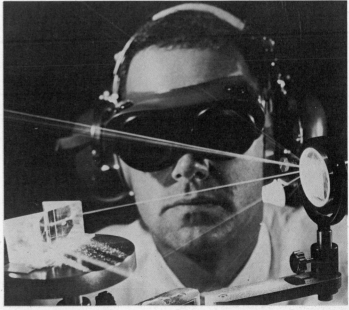

produce beams of microwave energy for very little radiation was leaking out of the end walls of the cavity. Instead it was used as an oscillator. The oscillations produced in the cavity of the ammonia-beam maser could not be tuned but had amazing stability. At its working frequency of 24,000 MHz the maser could be used as a highly accurate time-measuring device – in fact as a clock. The ammonia atomic clock, it was calculated, had an accumulated error rate of about one second in every 10,000 years which was an enormous advance on previous clocks.

When the news broke that a working maser had been achieved, interest increased to fever pitch and physicists in other laboratories started looking seriously at how to exploit the device.

Nicolaas Bloembergen, a Dutch physicist working at Harvard University, solved the problem of tuning a maser to produce different frequencies in 1956, and went on to devise a maser that would produce continuous beams of radiation rather than short bursts. The principle of this was a 'three-level' stimulation of molecules in which the radiation used for pumping would raise the molecule through the energy levels, while the energy lost by the stimulated emission would drop it through just one smaller level. This meant that pumping radiation and emitted radiation were of different wavelengths, and pumping and emission could go on simultaneously and continuously.

Working on Bloembergen's theories, a team of physicists at Bell Telephone Laboratories in America produced the first solid-state maser, an oscillator. At the Massachusetts Institute of Technology another team went one step further and produced a true amplifier of microwave signals. The maser had arrived.

The two characteristics which put the

maser in a class of its own as an amplifier were its superior sensitivity and exceptionally low noise. In practice this means that if a maser is used as the first amplifying stage in a radar receiver, the radar's sensitivity, and therefore, its range, is enormously improved. As a first stage in a radio-astronomy telescope it will improve the performance at least 100 times over

other forms of amplification.

Even with the active communication satellites of the 1960s which carry their own receivers and transmitters for relaying signals, the maser amplifier is still a valuable adjunct at the ground terminal and the quality of intercontinental television transmissions would be the worse without it.

By the mid-twentieth century the physicists were already working on the possibility of applying the maser principle to even higher frequencies. Why not an optical maser? One that worked at or near the frequency of visible light?

'Mechanical men'

Again, Townes was to the fore and, together with Arthur L. Schawlow, suggested a way of achieving an optical maser, or laser as it was later to be called. Their hypothesis called for molecules that could be excited to produce visible wavelength radiations to be placed between two parallel mirrors. The material would be pumped by a flash of light, and the radiation produced by the decay of molecules to the ground state would be reflected back and forth between the mirrors, stimulating further emissions. Schawlow described the stimulated emission going on between the two mirrors in a laser cavity – 'It is as if tiny mechanical men, all wound up to a certain energy and facing along the axis of the laser were set in motion by other marchers and fell into step until they became an immense army marching in unison row upon row (the plane wave fronts) back and forth in the enclosure.' One of the mirrors in the laser would be semi-transparent so that some of the light could escape as a beam, all of it at practically the same wavelength, with all waves in step, travelling parallel, to the laser axis. This was the coherent beam of light unique to the laser.

In July 1960 at Hughes Research Laboratories in southern California, a young physicist, Theodore H. Maiman, produced the first working laser. It consisted of a ruby crystal irradiated by a xenon flash lamp. It produced a coherent light beam of deep red light such as had never been produced before.

Maiman's achievement triggered off an even greater wave of research activity. Men of vision saw the laser as the key not only to new forms of offensive and defensive weapons but also as a powerful tool which had a vast potential in peaceful applications in communications, industry, medicine and science.

Maiman's ruby laser emitted short pulses of light of exceptional brilliance, brighter than the sun, and of extreme spectral purity. It was true coherent light.

When we look around us, what we see is illuminated by incoherent light. Sunlight covers a broad frequency spectrum. It is a jumble of many frequencies of electromagnetic radiation as can be shown by passing light through a prism and seeing the individual colours (frequencies) separated out which, mixed together, make what we call 'white' light. The waves are also all out of step – they are not coordinated in phase.

1 Using lasers as death-rays has not really proved a viable proposition. However, because of their power they can be destructive, as seen when one is aimed at an ordinary light lamp.
2 The American astronauts left a laser reflector behind on the moon's surface. By aiming a laser on Earth at this reflector scientists have confirmed the position of the landing.

3 Laser beams used at the Royal Institute, London, to investigate how certain substances, such as rubber, change their molecular structure under the influence of light.
4 The coherent light from a ruby laser is so bright and piercing that it will cut through a diamond – the hardest natural material known – in a 200-millionth of a second.

Laser beams make excellent signals for transmitting television and voice. In this experiment the lower television set is laser-operated and the other conventionally.

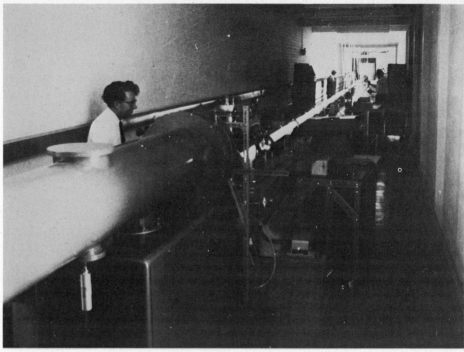

Physicists hope to use this powerful carbon-dioxide laser at the University of Essex to raise plasma to such high temperatures so as ultimately to lead to the fusion of atoms.

Laser light, on the other hand, is both coherent in frequency and in phase. Because it is coherent, it does not waste its energy by fanning out. With a suitable optical system using a 12–in. mirror, a laser beam from Earth may be only one mile wide by the time it reaches the surface of the moon. At short range the energy in the beam is so concentrated and intense that it can burn holes in steel plate. Moreover, because the laser beam is coherent, it can be modulated in a similar manner to the more familiar radio waves to carry voice, music or television signals. It has the added advantage that a single laser beam used as a communications link can carry tens of thousands of simultaneous telephone conversations or several television channels.

Maiman's ruby laser was indeed a breakthrough but it was followed by other types soon afterwards. In 1961 the gas laser was developed at Bell Laboratories by a team headed by Ali Javan. This laser used a radio frequency to excite an electrical discharge in a tube containing a helium neon gas mixture. The radio frequency excited the helium atoms, which, in turn, passed energy to the neon atoms to produce higher and lower energy levels, thus achieving the conditions for 'lasing'. Javan's gas laser was of even greater spectral purity than the ruby laser and it worked continuously, unlike the ruby laser which worked only in short pulses with an interval between each burst of energy. The radiation from Javan's gas laser was in the invisible infra-red regions.

The next development, towards the end of 1962, was the injection laser developed almost simultaneously by a number of research groups. This laser uses gallium arsenide, a semi-conductor element, which had long been observed to give an infra-red radiation when an electric current was passed through it. By increasing the current to a critical level it was discovered that laser action occurred.

Since 1962 all three types of laser have been under intensive development, and many applications have been found, but there are few of great practical significance or which promise a mass market for the laser, although one American company recently proposed a colour television system using lasers. One reason for this is that the laser is moderately expensive, but in specialized applications it is well worth the expense.

For communications on Earth the big disadvantage is our own atmosphere which, even in clear weather, can cause 'noise' on a point-to-point system through random atmospheric variations. In outer space, however, there is no such limitation and it has been theoretically calculated that with lasers of today's power a communications link over a distance of ten light years would be possible. The snag, even in space, is that the laser beam is so narrow that it is extremely difficult to aim the beam accurately at the receiving station. So far as is known every attempt by American astronauts to aim a beam from an orbiting satellite on to an Earth receiving point has failed.

No death ray

One area of development which has been under investigation is to protect the laser beam from our atmosphere by sending it along pipelines either directly or through the medium of fibre-optic paths. Although basically an expensive system it could be economically viable for very high density traffic in the tele-communication service.

In the military sphere the laser brought a great wave of optimism as a counter-measure to the intercontinental ballistic missile. Here, at last, was the death ray so popular in science-fiction. Batteries of lasers could be used to vaporize missiles before they hit the ground and enemy tanks and troops could be made to disappear in a puff of smoke. This is an extremely unlikely development.

But the laser is already in military use. Laser rangefinders are superior to either optical or radar rangefinders. A good optical rangefinder with a one metre base length is typically accurate to within ten metres at a range of 1·5 kilometres. The laser rangefinder has an accuracy of ten metres at a range of ten kilometres.

Using optical interference methods engineers can achieve a great improvement in accuracy for measuring length by using the coherent light from a laser rather than a conventional lamp. The National Physical Laboratory was among the first to use a laser in this way and using a helium neon laser achieved checking accuracies over a distance of one metre of 0·0000005 in.

The 'death-ray' concept has already found many applications in engineering where high-powered pulsed lasers can be used for microwelding or for piercing tiny holes or for cutting intricate shapes in metal up to $\frac{1}{8}$ in. thick. Another application is in surgery where the very fine laser beam can be used most effectively on the eye. Among the most successful surgical uses has been the correction of a detached retina which can be spot welded back in place with a laser beam. Other methods have been used but treatment time, for example, using an optical photo-coagulator, takes as long as a second, during which time the patient's eye might move. The laser flash lasts only about one thousandth of a second and the chances of getting the shot spot on at the first attempt are very much better.

The laser, hailed as the wonder of the age, perhaps had too much publicity at the beginning but after ten years of life it is steadily gaining acceptance as new and practical uses are found for it in the fields of communications and medicine. Clearly, it is not going to solve every problem but in suitable applications it has more than proved itself as one of the most brilliant developments of the mid-twentieth century.

The silent echo

Once a weapon of war, radar is now used for many civil purposes as well. Fighting the locust, safer navigation, satellite tracking and even electronic walking-sticks for the blind depend on radar.

IN THE AUTUMN of 1968 a Land-Rover field car trekked across the Sahara Desert. Mounted on its roof was a small radar scanner. Inside was the radar display unit. This was not, as might be supposed, a highly secret military operation – an outpost collecting intelligence on aircraft movements. But it had a war-like intent – the war against the dreaded locust.

The expedition, led by Dr Glen Schaefer of Loughborough University, England, was undertaken on behalf of the Locust Research Centre in London. After his practical work in the desert he was able to report the feasibility of tracking locusts by radar. Large swarms of locusts, some covering an area of 20 square miles and containing possibly 100 tons in weight of insects were located and tracked at ranges of 30 miles. At night, individual migrating locusts could be detected at ranges of two miles.

The value of the experiments lay not only in being able to get early warning of large swarms of locusts and to initiate defensive action, but also to check on smaller migrations in order to control breeding. The expedition was so successful that it may result in a radar chain across locust-infected areas. This would be expensive but could prevent the loss of valuable food crops.

1 This wartime German photograph shows soldiers operating an early type of mobile radar installation. Such radars were used together with anti-aircraft batteries.
2 Radar installations frequently pick up the traces of flocks of birds. Here a radar scanner has traced a large flock of birds migrating over East Anglia.
3 The three giant 'radomes' of the Ballistic Missile Early Warning Station at Fylingdales, Yorkshire, contain powerful radar scanners to give advance warning of approaching rockets.

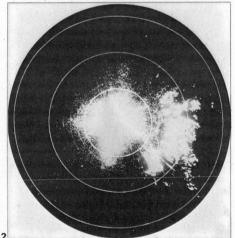

Radar has an interesting history. In the pre-war years of the 1930s, the only detecting devices against hostile aircraft were sound amplifiers. The most impressive of these was a 200 ft long by 25 ft high curved wall on Romney Marshes facing the Straits of Dover. The wall was shaped like a giant concave mirror to reflect sounds into microphones located at the focal point. Its object was to hear aircraft engines at great distance. But even under the most favourable conditions of wind and weather the range of detection was only 24 miles and in average conditions only half that.

Radar's birth certificate

About the same time, the techniques of generating high-powered radio waves had developed to a point at which some interest was being displayed in the possibilities of a 'death-ray' which could be directed at an aircraft to disable or destroy it. A young British Government scientist, Robert Watson-Watt, was consulted by Air Ministry officials but he declared that the idea was not feasible. But as a result of discussions he put forward to the Committee for the Scientific Survey of Air Defence, a notable memorandum, entitled 'Detection and Location of Aircraft by Radio Methods'. The date was 27 February 1935 and the memorandum was the birth certificate of radar.

If an enemy aircraft could be located in good time there was a fair possibility of destroying it by conventional ground-to-air or air-to-air gunnery. Robert Watson-Watt's thesis was that if an all-metal aircraft were to be irradiated with radio energy it would re-radiate a small amount

of the energy and this could be detected. If the radio energy were transmitted in short high-powered bursts with a listening period between each burst (or pulse as it is called) then, by measuring the time interval between the outgoing pulse and the reflected signal, and knowing the speed of radio waves, it would be possible to determine the distance away, or range, of the aircraft. A further refinement would be to make the radiation highly directional so that the aircraft could be detected not only in range but also in bearing from the radar station.

Watson-Watt had been studying atmospherics – lightning discharges and their origins – and he had much practical experience in radio methods in general and in particular the use of cathode-ray tubes for visual display and for measuring devices. It was common knowledge that radio waves could be reflected. Hulsmeyer of Düsseldorf was experimenting with reflected radio waves in 1903. In 1922 Marconi noticed reflections from metallic objects some miles away when using short wavelengths. A Post Office report in 1932 referred to interference by aircraft with transmissions of very high frequency radio waves. There were surges of intensity of the signals of high nuisance value when an aircraft flew over – an effect which causes interference to television pictures.

The multi-cavity magnetron

By 1939 the approaches to Britain were already guarded by radiolocation stations, as they were then called, and a crash-programme of construction resulted in a complete chain of stations in operation by the time of the Battle of Britain.

The early stations had very large aerials quite unsuitable for mounting on aircraft and the second phase of development was to use a much shorter wavelength with small aerials. If such equipment could be built and mounted in a night fighter it could be used to close in to within gun range of an enemy bomber.

To achieve this it was necessary to develop a small but extremely powerful radio valve capable of operating on very much shorter wavelengths than hitherto. Two British physicists, J.T. Randall and H.A.H. Boot, had been working on such a device at Birmingham University. It was called the multi-cavity magnetron and had been made to work in 1939. In 1940 the British magnetron was taken to America and tested by Bell Telephone Laboratories. The Americans were duly impressed and intensive work on both sides of the Atlantic put the Allies firmly in the lead over the Germans. The term Radar was coined by the American Navy from RAdio Detection And Ranging and came into general use as a shorter and more convenient term than radiolocation.

The magnetron made the lightweight radar possible but it also did more. Because it worked at centimetric wavelengths the reflections from radar targets were much more sharply defined than when using metre wavelengths and the returned signals were also reflected from other than metal objects. By pointing the aerial systems towards the ground and using a

radar display called the Plan Position Indicator (PPI) it became possible to see a map of the ground from an aircraft even at night through heavy cloud. This type of installation was used in the pathfinder aircraft which directed heavy bombers to their targets.

The enormous development effort put into radar during the war years led directly to the electronic revolution after the war. Since the war there has been continuous development of radar for military use. The huge chains of giant radars such as the Distant Early Warning Line across the northern parts of North America and the Ballistic Missile Early Warning System with stations in Alaska, Greenland and Yorkshire are examples. Radar techniques are also used for missile guidance.

During the past 20 years radar has moved into general use in civil aviation,

1 Bats make use of the radar principle to avoid obstacles when flying in darkness. Their regular high-pitched squeaks echo from obstacles and are picked up by their sensitive ears.
2 The flight deck of the British aircraft carrier H.M.S. *Eagle* with the control tower in the background. Aircraft carriers are well equipped with powerful and versatile radar installations.

shipping, meteorology, and, to the dismay of motorists, has even evolved into a scientific method of catching offenders exceeding speed limits.

Nowadays no large civil airport is without radar for control purposes. Major airports may need several sets of equipment: for general surveillance of the skies around and another system for surveillance of the situation on the ground giving indication of aircraft positions on the runways. Yet another, known as secondary surveillance radar (SSR), detects aircraft and causes their equipment to transmit automatically the aircraft identification number, its altitude and destination or other useful information.

The aircraft itself, if it is a large passenger transport, will normally have a radar display on the flight deck with a radar scanner concealed in the nose which can scan the area ahead for bad weather conditions or be tilted downwards to show on the display tube a map of the terrain over which the aircraft is flying. Two other types of radar equipment may also be fitted. One is a radar altimeter which by directing a radar beam vertically towards the ground gives the correct altitude above ground – a superior instrument to the ordinary altimeter which shows only height above sea level – and a Doppler radar which gives true ground speed and indicates any drift from side winds. These are all valuable aids to flight safety and reduce the navigational load on the flight crew.

The *Doppler effect,* from which Doppler radar gets its name, is the change in pitch of a wave from a moving body as it passes the observer. If you stand in a railway station as an express train approaches, the sound of the train is high-pitched but as it rushes past and recedes into the distance the pitch of the sound appears to drop. Radio waves show the same effect, and by measuring the change of wavelength of the directly transmitted and reflected wavelengths it is possible to determine the velocity of the object causing the reflection. This is the principle on which police radar speed traps are based.

As with airports and aircraft so it is with shipping. There are several large harbour radar installations from which harbour masters can give advice by radiotelephone to captains on the position of their own ships in relation to others. Some ships carry as many as three separate radar installations. On ferries, for example, there could be a long-distance radar, a short-range high definition radar for inshore work and another, of similar type, fitted at the stern for use when berthing backwards.

1 The radar screens at the heart of London Airport's control tower give the flight controllers detailed information about incoming and outgoing aircraft.
2 This huge reflector at the satellite tracking station in Woomera desert, Australia, provides scientists with a means of following rockets from the moment they are launched.

A recent development in marine radar is the racon beacon. A number of these have been installed on lightships and lighthouses round the British coast. The racon is a radio transmitter/receiver working on radar wavelengths. Any ship within radar range with its radar switched on will be emitting pulses of energy. When the racon receiver detects the pulses it automatically causes the racon transmitter to send out a coded series of pulses which are picked up on the ship's radar screen giving the location and identification of the racon in relation to the ship.

Racon buoys

Because the racon sends out its own signal in reply to the ship's radar the range of the detection is much greater than would be possible with the weak radar reflection upon which the ship would normally have to rely. A coastal racon can be 'seen' on a ship's radar screen long before the outline of the coast appears. Tiny microminiature low-power racons have also been designed for mounting on navigational buoys. They can operate unattended for periods up to a

Packed with electronic equipment, the R.A.F.'s famous Shackleton aircraft is really a flying radar station. Its chief use is to track down submarines and undertake naval searches.

H.M.S. *Boxer,* heavily equipped with sensitive radar installations, searches the English Channel for the submarine H.M.S. *Affray,* lost on a diving exercise in 1951.

year and are far more effective than the common diamond-shaped radar reflectors used to help intensify an otherwise unaided radar reflection from a small bobbing object such as a buoy.

Radar principles are also used underwater but in this case ultrasonic sound waves are used instead of radio waves. The transmitter/receiver units are mounted in the hull of the vessel, the two principal uses being for measuring the depth of water below the hull and for locating fish. By directing a beam of ultrasonic waves down vertically through the water and measuring the time interval for the returned echo from the sea-bed it is possible to check the depth of water. Giant supertankers have as many as four echo-sounders mounted fore and aft and on the beams to assist navigation in shallow channels. Fish-finding equipment works in the same way, some of the more advanced installations being capable of distinguishing the echo from a single fish only a foot or two from the sea-bed. Underwater radar or, to use its correct title, sonar, is not as accurate as radar because the velocity of the ultrasonic

sound waves through the water is dependent on a number of factors such as salinity and temperature which vary from place to place.

In meteorology one of radar's most extensive uses is in wind finding. A small balloon is released and as it floats higher and higher its movements are tracked by a small radar on the ground. The balloon frequently carries a package of instruments measuring temperature, humidity and height and this information is sent back to the ground by a small radio transmitter. By using radar and an instrument package a 'picture' of the atmosphere can be obtained. Before the advent of radar it was necessary to check the flight of the balloon by optical means which meant that complete information depended on perfect visibility.

Gunn diode

The future of radar in really wide-scale use now lies in the development of low-cost solid-state semiconductor electronic devices which can generate pulses of very short wavelength. The most promising of these is the Gunn diode made from gallium arsenide, doped with impurities and excited in a strong electric field. That such a device could generate oscillations at microwave frequencies was first observed in 1963 by John Gunn, a young British physicist working at the IBM Research Centre, New York State.

Complete radar sets using the Gunn diode have been built small enough to be held in the hand. One model is held like a pistol and merely pointed at a moving object to detect its speed which is read from a calibrated scale. Weight can be as little as a couple of pounds and operation is from ordinary torch batteries.

Mini-radars of this type, if produced in sufficient quantity, could be sold for a few pounds and would have wide application as burglar alarms, for instant speed indication of moving objects, for navigation of small vessels and, with suitable audible alarms generated by the radar, as 'seeing' aids for the blind.

On the bridge of a modern trawler. Small ships are now generally equipped with compact and efficient radar and other electronic navigation equipment.

Electric messengers

We are so accustomed to telephones, television, radio and other means of telecommunication that we often overlook the vast changes these devices have brought about in their short history.

THE TRANSMISSION of information over long distances is one of the aspects of technology which has transformed life in the twentieth century. Telephones and television sets have rapidly become everyday objects for millions of people. As media of communication they now almost rival direct speech and written language.

When human beings communicate in speech or writing, the information must first be transformed into sounds or written words. The recipient of the transformed message or *signal* must then 'de-code' it, turning it back into its original form.

With the discovery of electricity, it occurred to many people that an electric current could be so varied so as to convey a message. As early as 1800, such a *telegraph* system was devised.

In 1838, the American Samuel Morse invented his code of long and short pulses, 'dashes' and 'dots', to represent the alphabet in electrical currents. He later constructed machines which automatically coded and decoded such messages but it was soon found that this could be done faster and more accurately by hand. Nowadays, of course, the job is done automatically, but using perforated paper tape. The tape is punched on a *teletypewriter* and fed into the transmitter which converts it to electric pulses. At the receiving end another paper tape is produced, and a second teletypewriter turns this into printed form.

A world-wide telegraph system of cables was laid in the last century, the first transatlantic cable being begun in 1858.

The telephone

A still greater advance in communication was made in 1876. This was the invention by Alexander Graham Bell of a device to turn speech into variations in electrical currents and vice versa. Bell's *telephone*, both transmitter and receiver, consisted of a magnetic diaphragm in front of an electro-magnet. When the diaphragm was moved by sound waves, electricity was generated in the coils of the electromagnet. Sent through the coils of a similar device, current caused the receiver's diaphragm to be attracted and repelled and thus to produce sounds imitating the transmitted message.

Later, the transmitting mechanism consisted of carbon granules, compressed more or less by a diaphragm. The resulting electrical resistance was thus altered in time with the sound waves hitting the diaphragm. A current passed through the carbon was therefore increased and decreased in a way which reproduced the sound at the receiver.

With the spread of the telephone system, *switchboards* were needed, to connect one telephone with another. These were opera-ted by hand in accordance with verbal instructions to the operator. So fast did the system grow, that it was calculated in 1914 that several million telephone operators would soon be required in the United States.

In practice, however, this did not happen, because of the invention of automatic switching apparatus. A dialling system had already been invented in 1889. The dial produces a series of electrical impulses which operate an automatic device to connect the caller with the desired number.

Michael Faraday began his experiments with electro-magnetic radiation early in the last century, but it was not until 1888 that Hertz was able to transmit radio waves and detect them at a distance.

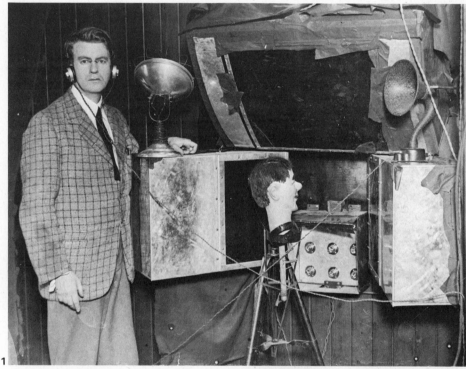

1 The world's first television 'studio'. Inventor John Logie Baird stands beside his transmitting machine, the forerunner of present-day television cameras.
2 The Croydon telephone exchange in 1884. One operator and a small amount of equipment was all that was required to service a town of more than 100,000 people.
3 Wiring up equipment for a modern telephone exchange. Large numbers of skilled workers are required to build and maintain the intricate wire mazes that form the 'guts' of the exchange.

Radio waves are produced by rapidly alternating electric currents. If they are to be received, they must be made to induce a similar, though naturally weaker, current, some distance away and cause it to actuate some mechanical movement. But to turn radio waves into mechanical (sound) energy more effectively, the alternating current in the receiving apparatus must be converted to direct, one-way, current, or *rectified* as was done in the early 'crystal sets' with a silicon crystal and a fine 'cat's whisker'.

By 1896, Marconi was able to use such means to send 'wireless' messages, and in 1901 the first radio telegraph message was sent across the Atlantic. The potential of the new medium was brought home vividly when the ship *Republic* sank in 1909, and rescue of survivors was only made possible by the wireless calls for help.

In 1904, the next big step was made towards the modern radio: Fleming invented the *thermionic valve*. By passing currents between a heated filament to a metal plate through a vacuum, Fleming obtained a method of turning high-frequency alternating current into direct current, and also of *modulating* the amplitude of alternating currents. This is because only the hot filament will emit electrons.

A microphone could thus be incorporated in the radio transmitter and a telephone receiver could be operated at the receiving end. *Radio telephony* had arrived.

The basic radio wave, at whose frequency the receiver is tuned to resonate, is called the *carrier wave*. Its amplitude varies with the sound waves hitting the microphone, waves of *audio-frequency*. More modern forms of radio transmission

employ *frequency modulation,* instead of this *amplitude* modulation. The transmitter converts sound waves into changes in the frequency of the carrier wave above and below its average level. This enables the message to be reproduced much more accurately than by the older method.

During the Second World War, the use of *semi-conductors* was developed, chemical devices which only allow electricity to pass in one direction. These were used as

rectifiers and made possible radio circuits which were smaller and eventually cheaper than those using valves.

In the early days of radio, the distance a message could be sent was thought to be limited by the curvature of the Earth. Later, however, it was discovered that this limitation could be overcome. Surrounding the Earth a layer of electrically charged particles was discovered, the Heavyside Layer. Short radio waves (i.e.,

1

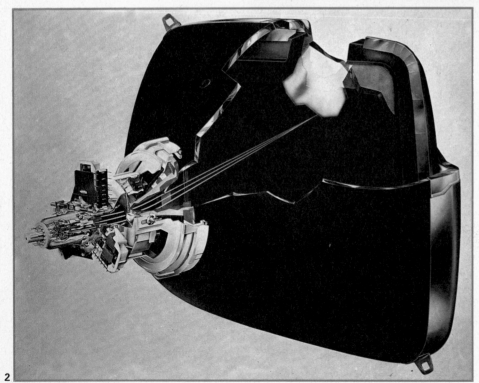

2

3

1 Inside the BBC's video-tape library. On the left is a video recorder with large reels of tape, while the operator at the console is watching taped images in colour and black and white.

2 Cutaway diagram of the interior of a colour television tube shows how the screen is struck by three electron beams which activate the three primary colours on the screen.

3 Testing the U.S. Navy's Sealab II submarine in shallow water off the coast of California. The diver in the background is using a television camera to monitor his colleagues' work.

those of higher frequency) were found to bounce off this layer back towards the Earth's surface. It was thus possible to receive radio transmissions 'round the corners' of the globe.

The rapid development of the radio industry in the 1920s and 1930s made possible a still more astonishing application. For some time, radio had been used to transmit pictures for newspapers. The picture is broken into small squares and the radio signal indicates how dark each square is.

Television applied this idea to 'live' pictures. A television camera 'scans' the scene to be transmitted in a series of horizontal lines. At each instant, the light from the particular point being viewed is converted into an electrical current whose level is proportional to the intensity of light, by means of a photo-electric cell. This 'message' is transmitted by radio and must be converted into a spot of light simultaneously 'scanning' the receiver's screen.

Television tubes

In the modern television tube a beam of electrons strikes the screen and produces a luminous spot. The direction of the beam is controlled electro-magnetically with great precision and moves in a way which is exactly synchronized with the camera.

Speech, music and pictures are not the only 'messages' which are nowadays transmitted by radio waves or telephonic lines. Instructions to automatic equipment, data for computers and information from remote industrial processes are all sent and received by such means.

The best known examples of these today are perhaps to be found in space vehicles. Rockets are fired far away from the Earth

1 A launch, carrying two television cameras and transmitting equipment, follows the annual Oxford and Cambridge Boat Race on the River Thames in England.

2 An early table telephone shows the ornate decoration the Edwardians considered necessary for household objects. The box underneath holds a hand-cranked generator.

3 The television aerials at Emley Moor, Yorkshire carry the television broadcasts over the top of surrounding natural and man-made obstacles and increases the station's range.

1 Alexander Graham Bell built his first telephone in 1871. The wooden framework supports an electromagnet over a drumskin with a metal vibrator attached to it.
2 On this modern telephone, by contrast, numbers in frequent use can be pre-recorded on punched cards, which are then merely inserted into a slot to give the required number automatically.
3 A picture transmitter, a regular item of equipment in newspaper offices, makes it possible to send and receive photographs instantaneously over the public telephone system.

other applications, may one day revolutionize telecommunications.

What do we mean here by 'quantity of information'? it may be asked. In the course of the expansion of the American telephone system, this question became very important. Hartley, Shannon and later Norbert Wiener, investigated mathematically the nature of messages in general.

Essentially, the signal conveying a message is the variation of some quantity, for example, the level of an electric current, or the amplitude of a radio wave. The amount of information conveyed in a signal was related to how far this variation was from what might be predicted. For example, a message from the North Pole: 'It is cold here!' would not appreciably increase our knowledge, while the news of a heat wave might.

Information theory

The *theory of information* enabled scientists to consider the problem of *'noise'*. When a signal is transmitted, it inevitably gets distorted, mixed up with random variations which interfere with it. The decoded message at the receiver will thus be more or less different from the message originally sent off. The *capacity* of a channel of communication could be measured and the best means of sending information decided in terms of the 'signal to noise ratio'.

For example, it can be proved that frequency modulation is less affected by noise than amplitude modulation. Modern telephone systems also employ *pulse-modulation,* in which the signal consists of a series of pulses, the intervals between which may be slightly varied. This can give very small amounts of distortion even when the same channel is conveying many different messages simultaneously.

And so we see that the rise of telecommunications has given rise to entire new industries and sciences. Vast resources are devoted to improving the ways in which men can communicate ideas to each other, all over the world.

However, *what* they communicate is quite another matter.

as a result of instructions coded and sent out by radio. Not only can television pictures be received from the moon, but also information about temperature and radiation levels. Highly sophisticated equipment is needed, to convey such 'messages' with the required degree of precision and freedom from error.

On a more mundane level typesetting of newspapers is frequently carried out by machines controlled by tapes, whose instructions may be conveyed over radio and telephone links.

A completely new development in recent years has been the application of the laser beam to communication. Since the laser makes it possible to produce light waves covering extremely narrow bands of frequency, these may be used to convey messages similar to the use of radio waves. Because the frequency of light is so much greater than radio, large quantities of information may be transmitted using a single beam. The laser, as in so many

The science of sound

The rising volume of noise in our cities is one of the undesirable by-products of civilization. But sound itself is finding many startling uses in applications from fishing to testing metal parts.

PHILOSOPHERS AND THEOLOGIANS used to argue over some rather odd questions. For instance, how many angels can dance on the head of a pin? Or, if a tree falls in a forest and there is no one there to hear it, is there a sound? Modern science has very little to say about angels dancing on the head of a pin, but it has a great deal to say about sound.

First, what is meant by sound? This question is not quite as simple as it may first appear. The common definition 'sound is what we hear' has a number of serious deficiencies.

How would one convey the idea of sound to a deaf person? After all, he cannot hear. Thus, defining sound as 'what we hear' restricts its understanding only to those persons fortunate enough to have good ears. This violates the precept that a good definition should be something to which *everyone* can agree.

Secondly, to define sound as 'what we hear' deals with the symptom, not the cause. It tells how sound is experienced, but says nothing about what sound *is*. This violates the precept that a good scientific definition should facilitate investigation of the thing being defined.

Defining sound

In order to concoct a really useful definition of sound, it is first necessary to do a simple experiment. Take a heavy metal fork and strike the tines (the prongs of a fork) sharply against a hard surface. Quickly touch the tines to your ear and see if you notice anything. Alternatively, press your ear hard against the speaker of a radio with the volume turned up loud. Most simply of all, press your fingers against the front of your throat while speaking.

In each case, especially the third, you should notice that the sound is accompanied by a slight movement, or *vibration*. Experiments such as these have shown that *every* sound is accompanied by vibrations. Thus we are led to the following definition of sound: 'sound is a vibration that travels through suitable materials and to which human beings and animals may be sensitive'.

Though somewhat abstract, this definition has several virtues. First, it characterizes sound by noting its cause. Thus, even a deaf person is capable of discussing it, even if he has never heard a sound in his entire life. Second, it retains the common notion of sound by adding that it may be experienced by humans and animals, that is it may be heard. Thirdly, it does not overlook the fact that many things one would like to call sound cannot be heard by human ears; for example, the 'ultrasonic' whistles used to train dogs. Finally, by defining sound in terms

of travelling vibrations, it charts a course for further investigation.

Most people are aware that in order to be heard, a sound must normally cause the tympanic membrane (ear-drum) to vibrate within the ear. This in turn, by a rather complex process, stimulates nerve-endings which send messages to the brain.

The workings of the human ear is a fascinating story of physiology and evolution. But no less fascinating is the story of how a sound *propagates* (moves) from where it is produced to reach the ear, where hearing takes place.

Tie one end of a rope to a door knob and shake the other end up and down

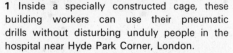

1 Inside a specially constructed cage, these building workers can use their pneumatic drills without disturbing unduly people in the hospital near Hyde Park Corner, London.
2 Ultrasound now finds many technical uses, particularly in the detection of faults in metal parts. Here an ultrasonic hand-held 'gun' is used to check power cables for leaks.
3 Cleaning and degreasing are now carried out by ultrasound in many factories. A glass block is here being cleaned of paint by the action of ultrasound in a waterbath.

several times. The result is a wave pattern which apparently moves from the hand holding the rope, down the rope and back to the hand again. Of course, nothing physical is really moving down the rope; after all, the rope is moving up and down, not back and forth. Only the *pattern* moves down the rope. This type of wave, in which the direction of the wave pattern and the *direction* of vibration causing it are different is called a *transverse* wave.

Now imagine a person at the end of a long queue. He pushes the person in front of him, who in turn bumps into the person in front of him, and so on down the line until everyone has been bumped. This is an example of a *longitudinal* wave. As with the rope, nothing physical moves down the queue; only the wave pattern. At the end of the process, everyone is precisely where he started. But unlike the example with the rope, this time the vibration or movement causing the wave is in the *same* direction as the wave pattern.

Sound waves are longitudinal. At first, this statement may not seem to say very much, but it has significant ramifications. As any practical joker knows who has tried the trick of shoving the last person in a queue, the results are usually much more gratifying if the people are standing fairly close together, because it is easier for the wave pattern to travel from one end of the queue to the other.

Testing for oil deposits under the sea. A small explosive charge has just been detonated on the sea-bed, and delicate instruments on board record the echoes from rock strata.

Since sound is the same kind of longitudinal wave motion it should travel more easily through substances whose molecules are fairly close together than through substances whose molecules are widely separated. More specifically, it should be easier for sound to travel through a solid than through a liquid, and through a liquid than through a gas.

Even though transverse and longitudinal waves have important differences, they also have important similarities. For instance, transverse waves propagate, or move, from place to place with measurable speeds. Light – which is a transverse wave – travels at 186,000 miles per sec.

Speed of sound

Longitudinal waves, such as sound, also propagate at measurable speeds, but nowhere near as fast as light. Still, the speed of sound is sufficiently fast (1,090 ft per sec in air at 0 °C.) that measuring it requires a certain degree of scientific sophistication. But anyone who has witnessed a thunderstorm knows that sound travels much more slowly than light. First he sees a lightning flash, but he may have to wait several seconds to hear the thunder. Similarly, watching from a distance a woodman chopping down a tree gives rise to the strange effect of hearing the clang of the axe long after seeing the blade bite into the wood.

In each of these cases, the event is seen before it is heard, showing that light travels faster than sound.

Note that when the speed of sound in air was given, the temperature is also specified. This is because the speed of

sound depends on the temperature. As the temperature increases, so does the speed of sound. At 0 °C. the speed is 1,090 ft per sec, but at 10 °C. it is 1,110 ft per sec, and at 20 °C. 1,130 ft per sec.

Does sound travel through every substance – wood, water, steel, mercury vapour – with the same speed as through air? Since sound travels better through solids and liquids than through gases, one would guess not. Experiments prove this guess to be correct. At 0 °C., the speed of sound in hydrogen is 4,220 ft per sec, in oxygen 1,041 ft per sec, in aluminium 16,700 ft per sec and in iron 16,800 ft per sec. In vulcanized rubber, the velocity of sound is a scant 177 ft per sec, much less than in air. This is one of the exceptions to the rule about how sound travels in solids, liquids and gases.

Modern fishing boats are equipped with *sonar,* which is a simple electronic device for sending sound waves through water. Suppose a boat is over a shoal of fish, but the captain does not know precisely where they are. To find out, he sends out a sonar beam through the water in different directions. When one of these beams strikes the shoal of fish, it reflects or echoes back. By timing how long it takes to hear the echo and knowing the speed of sound in sea water, the captain can easily calculate precisely where the fish are, and so he knows where to cast his nets.

Geologists searching for petroleum use

The connection between sound and vibration is clearly shown when a tuning-fork is immersed in a tumbler of water. The vibrating fork throws water out of the tumbler.

1 One of the big problems posed by supersonic aircraft like the Concorde is the sonic boom. This is known to be able to cause damage to buildings in built-up areas and may affect health.
2 The vowel 'o' produces this pattern when it is spoken into a tonoscope, an instrument which displays speech patterns on a screen. The tonoscope is particularly useful in speech studies.

dynamite to create sound waves in the earth. Through special listening devices they can hear the echoes. By knowing how fast sound travels through certain types of rock, they can get a fairly clear picture of what is under the surface, hundreds of feet deep. If the echo soundings indicate a petroleum deposit, they go ahead and drill. If not, they continue the search elsewhere.

Few people other than geologists, fishermen and other specialists care about how fast sound is, but most people are concerned with how loud it is. But measuring loudness presents a rather sticky problem. Everyone perceives sound differently. A sound which may seem extremely loud to one person may be only mildly irritating to another. Conversely, a sound which may be so soft as to be inaudible to one person may be quite audible to another.

One way to get around this difficulty is to measure *power* rather than loudness. Power is a technical concept related to the way energy is transmitted by a wave. Because it is so technical, it is used **2**

mainly by technicians. For ordinary purposes, loudness is expressed in terms of *intensity levels,* measured in units called *bels* or *decibels* (a decibel being one-tenth bel). Intensity is also a rather technical concept; in fact, it is really a variant of the idea of power. However, it has the advantage of being a fairly close mathematical representation of how the human ear hears.

The concept of intensity levels can most easily be understood by examples. An intensity level of 0 decibel is called the 'threshold' level, because this is about the softest sound a person can ordinarily hear. An average home has an intensity level of 32 decibels; when the television is switched on, this rises to about 40 decibels. A restaurant has an intensity level of about 50 decibels, while a business office may run to about 57 decibels. A boiler factory has a noise intensity level as high as 100 decibels, which is about as much noise as a person can tolerate without pain. Above 100 decibels the noise level is decidedly too high.

Today intensity levels have become the concern of national and local politicians as well as sound engineers. As man invents more and more mechanical gadgets and crowds himself tighter and tighter together in his cities, noise levels inevitably rise. Doctors have expressed the fear that unless noise levels in cities are kept under control, they will soon reach a stage which could affect people's health.

The concept of frequency

Sound, it has been established, is caused by vibrations. The number of vibrations per second producing a given sound is called its *frequency.* For example, if the reed of a clarinet should vibrate 440 times in one second, it would have a frequency of 440 cycles per second, written 440 cps. This is the note A on the Diatonic C Major Scale. A vibration rate of 297 cps is the note D, while the note C has a frequency of 396 cps. In fact, all musical notes have a definite and calculable relationship to the frequency of the vibrations producing them, a discovery made by the great Greek mathematician Pythagoras in about 530 B C.

The physics of music is an interesting but rather complex story in its own right. For the present, it suffices to recognize that frequency is intimately related to the characteristic sound called *pitch.* Pitch, of course, refers to the 'highness' or 'lowness' of a sound. In speech people generally begin a sentence at a relatively high pitch and complete it at a lower pitch. In fact, pitch is one of the major distinguishing characteristics of British English and American English. British speech is highly inflected; that is, a sentence begins relatively high and the pitch varies markedly from the beginning of a sentence to the end. American speech is more monotone. Americans start a sentence on a lower note than do Britons and tend not to inflect, remaining relatively constant from beginning to end.

To a large extent, reactions to sound levels are psychological. But they do have a physical basis. The average person

1 Ultrasonic whistles (which produce a note outside the range of the human ear, but audible to dogs) are now widely used, particularly to control 'working' dogs.

2 This 'sonic brain gauge', developed in the United States, sends an inaudible sound wave through the head. The time for the sound to pass through the head gives a measure of temperature.

can hear sounds with frequencies between 20 and 20,000 cps, though many people are deaf to sounds above 18,000 cps or below 40 cps. Sounds below 20 cps are called *infra-sonic,* meaning 'below the level of hearing'. Sounds above 20,000 cps are *ultrasonic,* meaning 'above the level of hearing'.

While the terms ultrasonic and infrasonic may be unfamiliar to many people certainly the term *supersonic* is not. Supersonic means 'faster than sound'. Until the 1940s, exceeding the speed of sound or 'breaking the sound barrier' was believed to be unattainable for man-made aircraft. Today, military aircraft do it quite regularly, and 'breaking the sound

barrier' will soon be quite commonplace for civilian aircraft as well.

Supersonic flight was a tremendous technological advancement and promises to be a great boon to mankind. But it is also the cause of a great nuisance, the *sonic boom.*

When an aeroplane flies at less than the velocity of sound, we hear a continuous noise in the same sequence as the noise emitted by the aircraft. Thus, if the plane is two miles up and four miles distant, the sound made then is heard before the sound made when the plane is two miles distant. But if it is flying faster than the speed of sound, the sound from later parts of the flight can reach the observer before the sound from earlier parts. This is because the noise made by the plane 'lags behind' the plane itself.

The plane is some distance above the ground, and the noise travels along a line between the plane and the observer. Because of this, the sound from whole sections of the flight can arrive more or less simultaneously at the observation point. It is this concentrated sound, derived from a considerable portion of the flight and arriving with a thunderous clap at the observer's ear-drum that creates the annoying, sometimes dangerous 'boom'.

An important idea associated with supersonic flight is *Mach numbers.* To say that an aircraft is flying faster than the speed of sound really does not say very much, because the speed of sound is not constant. It is different at different altitudes, generally becoming less and less at very high altitudes because of the drop in temperature. Near the Earth's surface, the speed of sound is between 600 and 700 miles per hour, but this can become substantially less at extreme heights. For this reason, speed is often indicated in terms of Mach numbers, which are ratios between the local speed of sound and the speed of the aircraft.

For instance, an aircraft moving at Mach 0·5 is travelling at one-half the speed of sound at the particular altitude it is flying. Mach 1·0 means the same as the speed of sound; Mach 2·0 is twice the speed of sound, and so on.

Sound and light

Despite the many similarities, there is one outstanding difference between sound and light. Light can travel through a vacuum; sound cannot. This fact is usually demonstrated in the laboratory by placing a ringing buzzer inside a special bell jar and removing the air. As the air is pumped out, the sound from the buzzer becomes softer and softer, until it finally disappears. But it is still easy to see the buzzer working. When air is allowed to return to the inside of the jar, the sound is heard again.

There is really no need for special laboratory equipment to demonstrate the ability of light to pass through a vacuum and the inability of sound to do the same. All one need do is look at the sky. The sun is a huge ball of fiercely glowing gases. It is easy enough to *see* through the 93,000,000 miles of vacuous space which separates it from the Earth, but who has ever *heard* the sun's fiery roar?

The mechanics of music

The design of musical instruments involves some basic sciences, from acoustics to electronics. The relationship of science and music has always been close, and may now involve the ubiquitous computer.

THE SOUND OF MUSIC is almost inescapable in modern living. The electronics industry has seen to that by developing new means of recording, sound reproduction, and broadcasting. The transistor and miniaturization in general have made radios and record players fully transportable, so that whether your taste is for the Beatles or Beethoven, it can be satisfied almost any time by the flick of a switch.

Most people are aware that this modern gadgetry owes its existence to the application of scientific principles, even though they may not understand them. What is less generally perceived – or even thought about – is the fact that the primary means of musical production, the instruments, can only be understood in terms of scientific principles. The disciplines involved are many and include acoustics, mechanical engineering and electronics. Basic to the whole proposition, of course, is acoustics. We are able to hear sounds because sound waves beat upon the tympanic membrane or drum of our ear. But something has to set up these sound waves in the first place. In almost all cases, then, the process begins with a vibrating source, which, moving in one direction, pushes the surrounding molecules of air before it. These molecules crowd and therefore energize the molecules of air next to them before returning to their original position, and thus a process of alternate crowding and thinning is passed through the air. These are sound waves, and this is the basic mechanism of sound production. But in the various branches of the family of instruments – percussion, wind and strings – the manner in which the sound production is carried out varies considerably.

It is useful to take percussion instruments, in particular the drums, first since certainly these were the first musical instruments. Since in most cases they are only capable of one note, they are also the easiest to comprehend. The first drums probably consisted simply of a piece of wood placed over a hole in the ground. When beaten with the hand, a stick, or stamped with the feet, vibration was set up in the wood and this was in turn imparted to the air in the hole and the air above the wood.

A page from a medieval manuscript shows two ways of producing a musical scale. The man in the background is striking bells of graded sizes, while in the foreground water-filled glasses are struck.

The actual note produced in this way depended upon a number of variables – the size and thickness of the wood, the depth and diameter of the hole and so on. In other words the sound depended upon the frequency, that is the number of oscillations per second, of the vibrating surface. Generally speaking, the smaller the area of drum head the greater will be the frequency of vibration and hence the higher the note. Likewise the smaller the volume of air trapped inside the drum, the higher the note.

Drum design

Modern drums, seen in any beat group or dance band (snare, tom-tom, and bass) are designed to combine these factors in different proportions to make a whole range of sounds available to the drummer. The snare drum and the tom-tom, for example, may have the same area of skin (which has long since replaced wood as a vibration surface) but the snare drum is also much more shallow. It therefore has the higher pitch of the two. Incidentally it gets its distinctive sound and also its name from snares, or thongs, which are stretched across the inside diameter of the drum just below the skin. When the surface above is beaten, these rattle against it with a sound like the impact of tiny stones.

The bass drum has the largest skin surface and the largest volume of enclosed air; it therefore emits the lowest note of the three, and since it has no snares, the note is 'clean'.

There is one other factor which affects the note produced in a drum. This is the relative slackness or tightness of the skin. Once again, the tighter the skin the more rapid will be the vibrations when struck. The sound waves therefore reach the ear

Glass-harp virtuoso Bruno Hoffmann, of Stuttgart, made his harp himself. Fifty glasses were specially blown to give a four-octave range. The harp is played by rubbing the rims with damp fingers.

Jazz musician Jesse Fuller's one-man band. Apart from guitar and cymbals, he has a mouth-organ and kazoo on a harness round his neck, while his right foot operates a bass-like 'fodella'.

Two members of a steel band from Trinidad tune one of the oil-cans which serve as drums. The drums are tuned by denting the lid of the can, thus rendering it more or less taut.

in quicker succession and the received sound is higher in pitch. It was mentioned above, that most drums are capable of only one note, but it would be more accurate to say that the note *can* be changed by slackening or tightening the skin – but only with some trouble. In other words it cannot be varied at will during the performance of a piece.

However, there is one drum on which this is possible. It is called the timpani, and the player is easily able to tighten or slacken the skin by turning 'taps' around the circumference of the bowl-shaped shell.

This by no means exhausts the list of percussion instruments, but all the rest employ the same basic principle, in that surfaces – brass in the case of cymbals, wood in xylophones and maraccas – are struck directly or indirectly and therefore caused to vibrate.

Vibration is also the key to the effectiveness of the next major group of musical instruments, the strings. But these musical machines are generally much more sophisticated in a number of ways.

The guitar is probably the most widespread stringed instrument and it embodies most of the technical qualities of the stringed instruments in general. The strings are made of nylon (sometimes gut) or steel and they are stretched between two fixed points, one on the sound box and the other at the extreme end of the finger board.

When plucked with the fingers or struck with a plectrum the oscillations of the strings are transmitted to the wooden upper surface (belly) of the sound box which itself vibrates as does the air inside

1 Tunisian musicians play their plaintive, minor-key melodies on pipes and drums. These relatively primitive instruments are found in different forms all over the world.

2 Village bands, frequently with a variety of brass instruments, have long been a feature of the development of European music. Here a military band plays outside the town hall.

3 Victoria de los Angeles is one of the world's most famous operatic sopranos. The quality of a singer's voice is largely inherited, though training can improve it.

146

the box. The original sound of the string is therefore amplified.

Most guitars have six strings, all the same length. However, they are of different thicknesses, the thickest at the bottom, the thinnest at the top. The frequency of vibration in the thick ones is lower than in the thin; therefore the note produced is lower.

The guitar has as many notes as it has strings and even further variation is achieved by a process called stopping. This depends upon the principle that the shorter the length of a vibrating surface, the higher the note. As pointed out already, the guitar string when in its natural state is fixed at either end. If, however, a finger is pressed against the string bringing it into hard contact with the neck of the instrument, a significantly shorter length is free and the sound emitted will be raised in pitch. It is therefore possible for the instrumentalist to play complicated tunes by stopping the strings in this manner. Chords can be played by stopping two or more strings at the same time and strumming them together.

The violin family

These same principles also apply to the instruments of the violin family, except here the initial vibration of the strings is caused by friction with the strings of a bow. Stopping is again employed for melody and chord playing. But with other stringed instruments, like the piano and harp, things are done differently. Here there is a string for each note, and the range is achieved by variation in length and thickness only.

We can appreciate then that the stringed instruments are heavily dependent on applications of science other than acoustics. There is, for example, the selection of materials, wood for the main structure, nylon and metal for the strings themselves. Experiments have shown that straight-grained pine is an excellent material in which to construct the bellies of guitars, violins and so on, since it allows the transmitted vibrations to spread easily and rapidly both along and across the grain.

Again, engineering is used in the devices for tensioning the string, in the internal structure of the instruments, and in the keyboard and hammer mechanisms where there are any. The internal structure is particularly important. It must be arranged so that the relatively flimsy belly is supported against pressure of the strings, bow or hand, yet the sound is in no way muffled. In most cases the job is done by a series of transverse bars glued to the underside of the belly. They provide support but do not inhibit flexibility; on the contrary they aid the spread of the vibrations across the grain.

The wind instruments can be divided into two categories: brass, which includes trumpet, trombone, tuba and so on; and the woodwind, which includes reed instruments like clarinet, oboe and saxophone, and pipe instruments like flute and piccolo.

Without doubt the most spectacular sounding brass instrument is the trumpet. Again all depends on vibration but here it

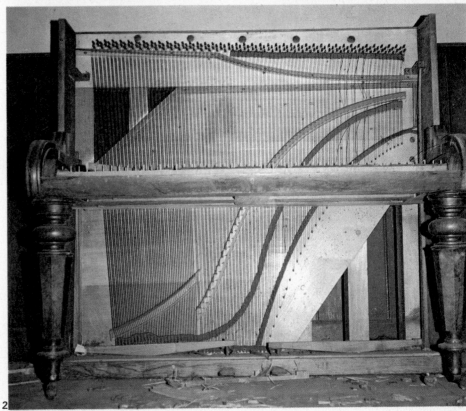

1 Jazz immortal Dizzy Gillespie plays a bent trumpet. The horn of his instrument was swung round so that the sound would be directed into the hall rather than into the footlights.

2 A piano, showing how the strings are attached. The note given by a stretched string depends on its length and tension. Strings are short and tight for high notes, longer and looser for low notes.

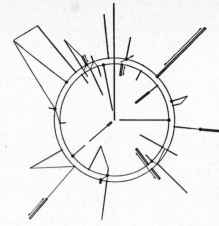

Prelude No. 7 from part II of Johann Sebastian Bach's 'Well-Tempered Clavier'. This was one of many pieces written by Bach to promote a new and more versatile system of tuning.

A modern piano composition by the Japanese composer Toru Takemitsu. The composition, generated by computer, can be played as three different variations by moving the inner ring.

is the lips of the player which do the job. Very simply, he tenses them across the cup-shaped mouthpiece of his horn and blows what can only be described as a 'raspberry'. This sets a vibrating column of air echoing through the instrument to the bell, and on its journey the original noise is both modified and amplified until it emerges with the typical bright hard sound of the instrument.

Brass instruments

Just as the violinist or guitarist is able to get a wider variety of notes by shortening or lengthening his strings, the brass player can do the same by altering the length of his column of air. There are two ways in which he can do this – by means of valves as in the trumpet, French horn and tuba, or by a slide as in the trombone.

In all cases, the mechanics involved are relatively simple. In the trumpet there are three valves and attached to each is a loop of tubing. When the valve is pressed the column of air is deflected through this loop; it is therefore lengthened and the note produced is lowered. In the case of trombones it is even more simple. The slide is actually a looped sleeve which, when extended, also adds to the length of the vibrating air column. (Incidentally, similar but smaller slide mechanisms are also fitted to many brass instruments for tuning.)

The earliest form of woodwind instrument was probably the flute, which, as previously explained, has no reed. In this case the flautist produces his sound by blowing across the opening of the instrument. The air hits the far edge of this hole and forms eddies both above and below it. The result is a rapid pressure oscillation which causes the air inside to vibrate. In the simplest kinds of flute, variation of note is then achieved by opening and closing holes with the fingers, for where a hole is uncovered the column of air is allowed to escape and so is shortened. In the modern concert flute, the holes are opened and closed by a complicated system of keys.

Finally, we come to one branch of music making in which physics is most truly at home. This is, of course, electronic music, and it is a far cry from the conventional kind. The instruments involved produce vibrations which are electrical and not acoustic. They therefore cannot be heard unless passed, like radio signals, through an amplifier and loudspeaker or headphones.

The vibrations themselves can be of any desired frequency and of any harmonic content. It is possible, therefore, to imitate the sounds of most, if not all, the conventional instruments and also to produce sounds which have never been heard before. These advances in electronic music have been mostly applied to the organ. In the future it is likely that they will be used to build completely revolutionary instruments which will greatly broaden the range of tone colours and harmonies available to the composer.

Some composers have experimented using tape recorders to modify the sounds produced by instrumentalists. Karlheinz Stockhausen has written music in which the notes produced by a group of per-

Testing the thickness of a violin's sound-box. Violin-making demands exceptional skill, blending art with science to produce a full-bodied tone and an aesthetically pleasing shape.

formers are recorded, and played back a short time later but in a greatly changed form. One performer has to 'play' the tape recorder; by moving the controls on his electronic equipment he can decide just *how* the notes are modified. As he plays the changed notes back the performers have moved on to new notes, and startling effects are produced by the combinations which arise. As the players of all the instruments (including the tape recorder) are, to a certain extent, free to choose what they will play, such pieces will never sound the same at two separate performances.

Music, of course, existed long before the Greeks attempted to explain it in terms of scientific principles. And famous violinmakers produced beautiful-sounding instruments without knowing exactly why they sounded so good. We can still enjoy music today without understanding how it works. But the alliance between physics and music is just beginning to open up a whole new world of sound which is revolutionizing the art of music.

His master's voice?

One of the early commercial record companies used a label showing a dog listening to 'His Master's Voice' – recorded on wax. The problem of reproducing 'live' sound accurately is still being solved.

ENRICO CARUSO, the famous Italian tenor, was able to break a wine glass merely by singing a particular note. Violinists, too, have broken glasses by playing high notes. This phenomenon, which has been demonstrated many times, shows that sound has at least some of the attributes of a physical force. What we hear and understand as sound or noise in some way transfers energy, and thus must have required energy to initiate it.

If one plucks the string of a guitar, or bows the string of a violin, the string can be seen to vibrate. Plucking harder or softer produces a louder or a quieter note, and it can be seen that the distance that the string moves from its stationary position, the amplitude, is also related to the loudness or softness of the sound. In wind instruments, like the organ, the air in the pipes vibrates while a note is being produced, and the loudness of the sound is again related to the extent of the vibration.

Vibration

When an organ pipe vibrates, it sets the air molecules nearby vibrating at the same frequency. This can readily be observed by watching the motion of specks of dust near a bass organ pipe. This vibration is passed on to neighbouring molecules, so that the sound is transmitted to the listener. When these vibrations strike the ear-drums, they set them vibrating too and the listener gets the impression of sound.

The frequency of a note, played, say, on a flute, sets up in the human brain a response which indicates to the hearer the sound of a flute. The average adult can hear notes with a frequency up to about 20,000 cycles per second. At the other end of the scale, sounds with a frequency of about 20 cycles per second separate into

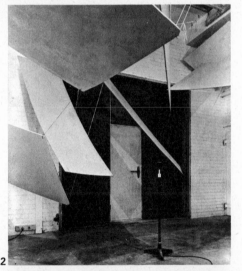

individual impulses rather than a continuous note. Thus the effective frequency range of the human ear is approximately from 20 cycles per second to 20,000 cycles per second. Measurements on the instruments of the orchestra show that the frequencies of the pure tones produced range from about 16 cycles per second to about 4,000 cycles per second.

But the pure tone produced by an instrument is only part of the story, otherwise middle C played on a trumpet would be identical with middle C played on a piano. A pure tone is normally accompanied by overtones, vibrations having a frequency which is a multiple (that is, two, three or four times) of the frequency of the fundamental tone. It is this which extends the frequency of the orchestra to the upper part of the range of the human ear.

If a guitar string is plucked, it can be found, by positioning small pieces of paper on the string, that at certain points the string does not vibrate. These stationary points are called *nodes,* and the distance between two nodes is, in fact,

1 Thomas Alva Edison invented his 'phonograph or speaking machine' in 1877. The original model recorded sound on a cylinder covered with tin foil and turned with a hand crank.
2 A reverberation chamber for testing the sound insulation of a door. The hanging baffle boards cut out echoes from the walls, enabling the sound transmitted through the door to be measured.
3 This Czech musical box, built in 1825, operates on the principle of a player piano. It has 137 organ pipes, and is equipped with 29 cylinders playing dance and opera music.
4 An early type of mechanically operated gramophone. The large horn is necessary to amplify sound produced by the motion of the needle on the disc which carries the recording.

equal to the wavelength of the sound. When a string is sounding its fundamental note, these nodes are at the ends only, but when it is producing overtones, nodes will be found in other places.

Apart from frequency and loudness, other factors also influence the sound as one hears it. Everyone has heard the echo reflected off a cliff or hillside. What happens in this case is that the sound leaves the source, spreads out in all directions, and is generally heard by anyone who happens to be in the vicinity. But when the sound reaches a solid object, preferably large, hard and smooth, the sound is echoed or reflected, in roughly the same way that a ray of light is reflected by a mirror, or a ball is bounced from a wall.

Acoustic differences

Echoes also account for the difference in sound between a violin played in a cathedral and in an ordinary domestic living room. Identical notes sound entirely different, and this cannot be accounted for by frequency or overtones. In a cathedral there are a large number of hard, smooth surfaces which serve to bounce the sound back to the listener. In most buildings of this type, there is a multiple echo, which makes a single struck or plucked note appear to persist and will give a blown note from a wind instrument a fullness and swelling quality which it would lack in the open. When the echo is strong, and when the interval between sound and echo is large, however, the result is confusion between one note and its successor, so that much of the music is indistinct.

In a normal domestic lounge, reflecting surfaces which are present are usually quite close to the source, and the echo interval is so short as to be virtually unnoticeable. In addition, there are a number of objects such as carpets, curtains, cushions and people, which absorb rather than reflect the sound. There will still be a certain amount of echo, or the music would lack its lifelike quality. In concert halls, the designers aim to get the best compromise between acoustic 'deadness' – that is, no echo – and troublesome long-lasting echoes. Despite advances in acoustic design, this is still to a great degree an art as well as a science.

Loudness is another attribute of sound which must be taken into account when evaluating its quality. For scientific or engineering purposes, sound loudness is measured in terms of the amount of power which is put out by the source, or which reaches the listener. In this context, it should be remembered that the ratio of powers between a very quiet and a fortissimo passage in music may be 1,000,000, so that the scale of loudness is very large indeed. Loudness is always measured in ratios, and the standard used is a very quiet room. Everything is measured in relation to this. To avoid the use of very large ratios, and also for a number of scientific reasons, it is the logarithm of this ratio which is used. Now the logarithm of 1,000,000 is 6, and the logarithm of the ratio is a unit called a bel, and so one is able to say that the loud passage in a symphony is 6 bels louder than a

quiet passage. For many purposes, the bel is inconveniently large, and so it is subdivided into tenths, or decibels. The ratio now becomes 60 decibels or 60dB. By simple calculation, it can be shown that if one sound is twice as loud as another, then it is almost exactly 3dB louder.

It is in the light of these complex and interrelated factors, frequency, overtones, loudness and resonance, that the work of sound-recording scientists and engineers must be viewed. Sound recording is a means of holding up a mirror to the music and din of the world, in a similar manner to the recording of visual phenomena with a camera.

Sound exerts a force, or a pressure, on objects falling in its path, and it is on this note that the recording of sound depends. In the earliest mechanical recorders, a diaphragm or thin plate was placed near the source of the sound. The vibrations of the air made this diaphragm vibrate at the same frequency, and this movement was linked mechanically to a cutter which carved a groove in a moving cylinder or disc of some suitable material, usually wax. If the procedure was reversed, with a

London's Royal Festival Hall has a series of baffles in the roof to prevent too great an echo, and the position of the boxes along the side of the hall can be varied to change the acoustics.

needle moving in the precut groove and driving a diaphragm, an approximation to the original sound could be heard. Thomas Alva Edison was the first man to demonstrate that sound could be recorded in this way. But while Edison's 1877 phonograph represented a major step forward, it suffered from some appalling drawbacks. Not least of these was that the singer virtually had to stick his or her head within the recording horn, while on the other hand the volume of sound produced on playback was pitifully small. These early machines could only record a limited range of frequency, so that the high notes in a piece of music were eliminated. Because of the friction between the playing needle and the disc or cylinder, there was also a high degree of surface scratch and hiss, or noise. Add to this the fact that it was virtually impossible with hand-driven machines to record and play back at the same speed and it is obvious that while the early machines were fascinating toys, they were less than satisfactory from the musical point of view.

While scientists and engineers held to mechanical methods of recording and reproducing, there was a limit to the degree of improvement which could be attained. But the invention of the thermionic valve by Fleming placed a new component in the hands of sound engineers.

The triode valve allowed electric currents to be amplified, or increased in power without introducing distortion. The microphone, which converted sound waves into electrical signals, was already in use in the telephone. Then signals taken from a microphone, and representing the sounds falling on that microphone, could be amplified by a series of valves until they were powerful enough to drive a record cutting stylus. On playback, the oscillations of a needle produced by that groove in a disc could be made to produce electrical signals, which were again amplified to activate a loudspeaker and give high volume reproduction with what was then comparatively low distortion.

The same basic principle is used today. Music is still generally recorded on flat discs, a groove being cut on the surface of the disc in accordance with the sound received by the microphone. Modern records use a new material – vinyl – which is much more durable than its predecessors, wax or shellac; emits very little scratch or hiss; will take much more detailed impressions and is virtually unbreakable, unless treated very harshly indeed.

As in so many fields, the introduction of vinyl was only one of a parallel set of improvements, each of which depended on others. To produce high-quality records it was necessary to have a cutter which

1 Echo-less rooms in which the walls are studded with baffles to absorb sound and prevent echoes are used by sound engineers to obtain special recording effects and to test equipment.
2 The acoustics of a large church like St Paul's Cathedral are mainly determined by the hard, smooth surfaces which bounce sound back at the listener, giving rise to reverberations.
3 The sound engineer's instrument panel at a recording studio enables him to control the quality of the sound recorded, to add special effects and to mix different sounds together.

Women inspectors at a modern record factory test records taken at random from the production line. They are listening for scratches and other production faults in the records.

The master mould from which records are pressed is produced by growing nickel electrochemically on a silvered lacquer original. The nickel plate formed is an exact replica of the original disc.

would respond faithfully to the musical sounds, and on playback it was necessary to have a record player which would read out exactly the information contained on the disc, and reproduce it faithfully. If any one of these fell short, the whole effort would be wasted.

In the early days of recording it was enough to make one copy of any sound or piece of music, because the recorder was merely a toy. But with the improvement of equipment a demand was created for recorded music, and so a means had to be found of mass-producing these recordings.

Disc-cutting

The first step in making a recording is to record the relevant piece, generally on a tape recorder. This tape is then edited to remove any blemishes or accidental noises which may have strayed on to it. The next stage is disc-cutting. The disc-cutter is essentially an electronic amplifier which drives a sharp, fine-pointed cutter. This cutter is mounted above a turntable which rotates at a precisely controlled speed. The cutter itself is mounted on a threaded drive, and can be moved gradually at a predetermined rate towards the centre of the disc as the recording proceeds.

The electrical signal from the tape, is fed into the amplifier, which drives the cutter, and the combination of turntable and cutter drive produce a spiral groove running towards the centre of the disc and bearing undulations corresponding to the music. A soft material is used for this master, so that the groove can follow the sound exactly. Wax was the original material used, but it has been superseded by lacquer or plastics.

A copy of the master, a negative copy or mould, is then made. This in turn, after processing and reinforcing, is used to produce other moulds, by a two-stage

moulding process. The commercial records are made from these mould-copies. The first and second moulds, sometimes called the father and the mother, can then be stored in safety in case one of the working pressing masters is accidentally damaged.

Absolute cleanliness is essential at all stages in the making of the matrices, as a small speck of dust which sticks to a matrix will make its presence heard as an unwanted noise on the finished records. Similarly, the grinding and compounding of the vinyl material must be done with the greatest precision as a grainy material gives an unacceptable background noise. In fact the major advantage of vinyl over the acetate which was used for the older 78 r.p.m. records is this absence of surface noise.

But although records are a source of musical pleasure for many homes, it is out of the question for most people to record a family occasion on disc. In the 1940s, tape recorders became available for ordinary domestic use. These use an entirely different principle from the disc, and are almost wholly electronic apart from the driving motors. At the heart of a tape recorder are the recording and playback heads, sometimes, on less expensive machines, combined into one unit. When an electrical signal is passed from the microphone, it is amplified electronically and passed to the recording head, which is rather like a small electromagnet with a minute air gap between the poles. The fluctuating signal, or oscillations, produce a strong fluctuating magnetic field in the gap. Recording tape is a continuous narrow strip of a base material – polyvinyl acetate, polyester, or some other suitable plastic – coated on one side with a thin layer of finely-divided magnetic iron oxide. When the tape is carried at a steady speed past the recording head, the magnetic field in the vicinity of the gap magnetizes the iron oxide particles in patterns which correspond to the electrical signals.

On playback, the tape is again transported past the playback head which

'reads' these patterns from the tape. The impulses pass the amplifier and a loudspeaker, and an image of the original sound is heard. Miniaturized tape recorders developed over recent years, have made recording even more versatile than it originally was. This type of tape recorder frequently uses a cassette of tape, which can be loaded and unloaded without complications. These developments make tape recorders usable in almost every situation.

An outstanding advantage of tape recording is that the original recording can be erased at any time by subjecting the tape to a high-frequency erasing signal, and the tape can be re-used. This process can be repeated time and time again with little deterioration in the quality of the tape. In addition, the quality of sound reproduction from a well-made tape is generally considerably higher than from a gramophone record, as there is little friction to cause unwanted noise or distortion.

Permanent record

Apart from its applications in entertainment, tape recording has eased the task of people in many walks of life. The tape recorder is used by teachers for preparing lessons, businessmen for dictating letters or reports, and by journalists for recording interviews. It is used throughout science and industry for recording research data, in automatic checking procedures, and has even been used in burglar alarms.

So many of the things which we take for granted in the twentieth century depend on sound recording. It has been said that Edison did for sound what Kodak did for sight. Between them they have enabled men to put a large part of their physical world on permanent and reproducible record.

Dark energy and light

Between the longest radio waves and gamma rays of the shortest wavelength is a broad spectrum of radiant energy. At one point it is punctuated by a narrow 'rainbow' of light waves.

TO MOST PEOPLE, light is what happens when the sun comes up at dawn, when we strike a match or set fire to a candle-wick or when we turn on an electric lamp. In the sun, the light comes from a nuclear reaction similar to the one which takes place when a hydrogen bomb explodes. In a candle, light comes from a chemical reaction as the wax of the candle burns. And in an electric lamp, light comes from a metal filament that is heated by the electric current until it becomes incandescent.

All these sources of light are hot. So we would expect light to be closely related to heat; and like heat, light is a kind of energy. In fact, if we take a piece of metal and make it hotter and hotter, it begins by emitting heat. Then it becomes red-, yellow- and finally white-hot, dazzling to the eye because it is emitting light.

Radiation and the hot mouse

To the scientist, light is a form of *electromagnetic radiation*. There are many such forms of radiation ranging from radio waves, microwaves used in radar and heat rays through to light and X-rays and cosmic rays. They all take the form of waves (radio waves have the longest wavelength and cosmic rays the shortest). They make up a continuous spectrum of electromagnetic radiation with visible light forming just a small part of the spectrum in the middle. Or put another way, light is the part of the electromagnetic spectrum to which our eyes are sensitive.

Human beings cannot see other types of electromagnetic radiation, although they can be detected. For example, we can 'feel' heat rays and we can take photographs using X-rays. The kind of radiation with a wavelength slightly longer than red light is called *infra-red*. We can take photographs using infra-red radiation and obtain aerial and satellite photographs of great clarity, because infra-red rays easily penetrate thin cloud and haze.

Although we cannot 'see' infra-red rays, there is evidence that some animals can. Some rattle-snakes (or pit vipers) have pit-shaped organs on the sides of their heads. By means of these organs, the snakes seem to be able in pitch darkness to detect any object or animal that is a few degrees warmer than its surroundings. For example, a mouse sitting absolutely still in the blackness of the desert night emits feeble infra-red radiation because of the warmth of its body. A rattle-snake seems to be able to detect this radiation, use it to estimate the range and direction of the mouse and unerringly strike at it.

Other animals have their range of light sensitivity shifted towards shorter wavelengths, beyond blue light into the *ultra-*

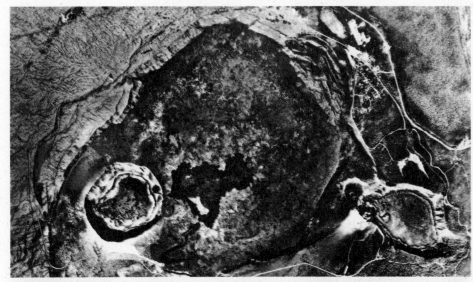

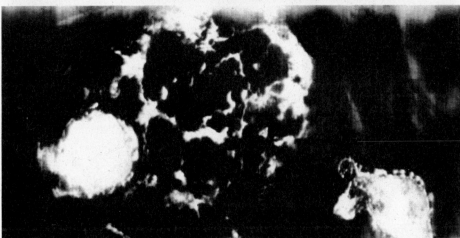

Heat rays invisible to the eye pour up from two volcanoes in Hawaii. These are the infra-red rays, lower in frequency than red rays in the visible spectrum, longer in wavelength than *violet*. For example, bees and ants are completely blind in red light but can see perfectly well by ultra-violet light. We can also take photographs by such light and our bodies are slightly sensitive to the ultra-violet rays in sunlight – they cause sun tan.

The part of the electromagnetic spectrum which human beings can see is called visible light. There is nothing mysterious about infra-red and ultra-violet radiations, which are invisible to us. It is just that they are outside the range of sensitivity of the receptors in the human eye. They may be 'visible' to animals and to photographic emulsions.

Light is a type of wave motion characterized by such quantities as wavelength, frequency and amplitude. Wavelength is the distance between successive crests of waves and, since this is very small for visible light, is generally measured in angstrom units (Å) or millimicrons (mμ).

visible light. Specially sensitive photographic film records this radiation in the lower picture. Penetrating mist and darkness, the infra-red photographer can find enemy transport by night.

An angstrom unit equals a hundred-millionth of a centimetre, and a milli-micron equals a ten-millionth of a centimetre. Visible light has wavelengths between about 390 mμ (violet) and 700 mμ (red).

Frequency is the number of wave impulses emitted in one second. Since light travels through space at a constant velocity of 300,000 kilometers per sec (symbol c), frequency equals c divided by wavelength. Amplitude is half the vertical distance from a crest to a trough. Large amplitude means bright light, small amplitude means dull light.

In 1666, the British mathematician and physicist Sir Isaac Newton (1642–1727) discovered that when a beam of sunlight is passed through a prism, the light is split up into bands of coloured lights called a *spectrum*. If the coloured lights are mixed in the correct proportions, white light again results. Lights of different colours

If the clouds in the sky are sailing from right to left, they will move from left to right in the mirror image of the glass wall, *above*. Reflection reverses the picture of the real world.

When you, raindrops and the sun are in line, a rainbow appears, *top right*. Light bends as it enters a raindrop, is reflected inside, and bends again as it leaves — splitting into colours.

Fluorescent substances, such as the crystals *above,* emit visible long-wave light when invisible short-wave ultra-violet light falls on them. This quality forms the basis of flourescent lighting.

differ in wavelength, red light having a longer wavelength than blue light.

How does a prism separate white light, which consists of a mixture of many wavelengths, into the various components of the spectrum? To answer this question we need to understand *refraction* of light. As we have seen, light always travels at the same velocity in a single medium, such as air. But in different media, light travels at different velocities. If the second medium is optically more dense than the first (as in the case of a ray entering a piece of glass), the speed of the light is decreased and the ray changes direction slightly. The light ray is effectively and abruptly bent from its original path, and this bending is called refraction.

The effect of refraction can easily be seen by looking at a stick dipping into a pool of water or a straw in a glass of water. That part of the stick under the water appears to be bent; this is because light rays reflected from the immersed part of the stick are refracted as they leave the

water, making our eyes 'see' the stick in a different position.

Bending the beam

Different materials refract light to different extents, and the property of a transparent material which determines the extent of refraction is called its *refractive index*. Refractive index is the ratio of the velocity of light in air to the velocity of light in the transparent material. Since light always travels slower in the denser medium, the refractive index is always greater than 1. For example, light travels through water at about three-quarters of its velocity in air, and the refractive index of water is about 1·3.

Glass lenses work by refraction. Rays of light passing through the curved surface of a lens are refracted and, depending on the shape of the lens, emerge travelling in a new direction. For example, with a simple *convex* lens (which has both its curved faces bulging outwards), a parallel bundle of light rays passing through the

lens converge and are brought to a focus. The bending of the rays as they pass through the lens is due to refraction.

Returning now to the glass prism, we can see how a beam of white light is split into a spectrum. The beam of white light consists of a mixture of wavelengths, and each wavelength is refracted to a slightly different extent as it passes through the prism.

Spectra are studied by means of an instrument called a spectroscope. It has a system of lenses to produce a narrow, parallel beam of light; a turntable on which a prism is mounted; and a telescope for viewing the spectrum. The telescope may be replaced by a camera for photographing the spectrum, and the instrument is then known as a spectrograph.

Like other waves, light can exhibit the phenomenon of *interference*. When two light waves of the same wavelength overlap, they may interfere. If the waves are *in phase* (in step), the crests of one wave coincide with the crests of the other. As a

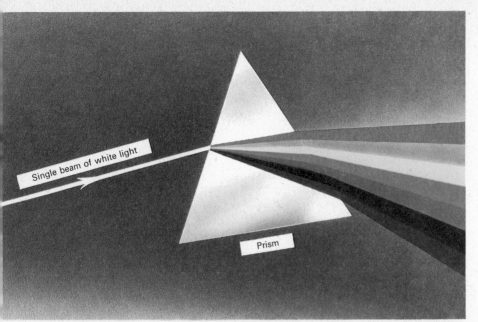

Single beam of white light

Prism

result, the amplitude of the combined wave is increased and with it the intensity of the light. But if the waves are out of phase, the crests of one coincide with the troughs of the other, the waves cancel, and the amplitude and intensity are decreased. If the interfering light waves fall on to a screen, waves in phase produce bright bands of light on the screen and waves out of phase produce dark bands.

The rainbow on the bubble

Interference bands may be seen when light is reflected from an extremely thin film of transparent material or from a thin film of air trapped between two pieces of glass. In the case of a thin film of material, such as the skin of a soap bubble or a thin film of oil or petrol on water, interference produces brilliant colours of the rainbow. Some light is reflected from the front surface of the film, and some passes through the front surface and is reflected inside the thickness of the film from the back surface. Since the film is so thin, rays reflected from the back surface have to travel just a small distance farther, and some of them may emerge out of phase with the rays reflected from the front surface. The interference bands are coloured because only light of a certain wavelength, and hence of a certain colour, will be exactly out of phase for a particular thickness of film. This colour is therefore missing from the reflected light and we see only the remaining spectral colours.

Thin films of air between two pieces of glass give interference bands known as Newton's rings. In white light the rings are coloured, and may be seen when photographic transparencies are mounted between two sheets of glass for projection. If monochromatic light is used – that is, light of a single colour (and hence a single wavelength) – Newton's rings appear merely as alternate light and dark bands with no coloured fringes.

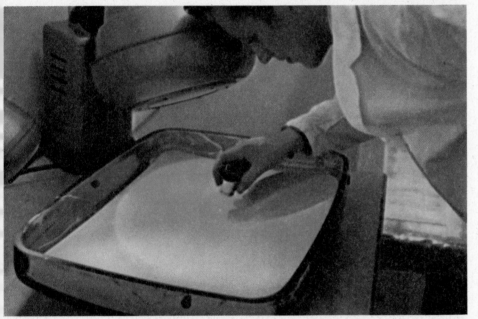

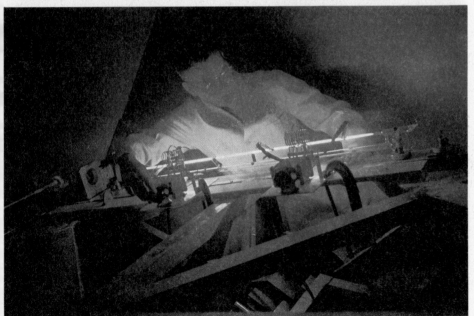

Top, white light is a mixture of many wavelengths. It moves faster in air than in glass. The effect of slowing it is to *refract,* or bend it. The glass prism refracts each wavelength by different amounts, and so splits the light.

Centre, ultra-violet reveals imperfections on the screen of a colour television set. *Bottom,* a light beam that can drill holes in diamonds is created in the device called a laser (light amplification by stimulated emission of radiation).

Why is the colour of molten metal yellow, not green or blue? The explanation is that heat and light are both made up of wavelengths on the same electromagnetic spectrum. Yellow light, red light and heat rays are close neighbours.

Coloured interference fringes can also be produced by using a point source of white light to cast shadows of an object on to a screen. These fringes are due to a slight bending of the light rays as they pass the obstacle casting the shadow; this bending is called *diffraction*. Some rays are bent more than others – that is, some travel a little farther. If the waves become out of phase, interference occurs and fringes are formed.

Diffraction is easier to understand if we consider a coherent source of monochromatic light passing through a very narrow slit (monochromatic light consists of waves of the same wavelength; coherent waves are perfectly in step). Light passing through the slit on to a screen produces a series of light and dark interference bands. With two narrow slits close together instead of one, the interference bands are brighter and sharper. With several slits, the bands become even finer.

A diffraction grating consists of a piece of glass with thousands of very fine lines scribed on it close together. The unscribed parts of the glass act as very narrow slits and diffract light passing through them. The first diffraction gratings were made by Joseph von Fraunhofer (1820) and Henry Rowland (1882).

Light through a grating

As we have seen, different wavelengths of light are diffracted to different extents. So that if white light is passed through a diffraction grating, it is split up into a spectrum in the same way as is light passed through a prism. A diffraction grating can be used instead of a prism in a spectroscope.

Ruling fine lines close together on the surface of a glass or metal mirror produces a *reflection* grating. This grating behaves in much the same way as does a normal diffraction grating and produces spectra. But if the ruled mirror is also correctly curved, it will focus its own spectral lines without the need for glass lenses. This technique is used in spectrometers for studying ultra-violet light, which is absorbed by glass. Coloured interference fringes may be seen when white light is reflected from a finely ruled or grooved surface, such as a long-playing gramophone record, which acts as a reflection grating.

All the properties of light described in this article can be explained by regarding light as existing as waves. But physicists have not always thought that this is so, and since the 1900s new ideas have been put forward about the nature of light.

Originally, physicists thought that light consists of tiny particles called *corpuscles*. Newton was a champion of the corpuscular theory, and he developed explanations for all common phenomena of light in terms of it. Light sources were supposed to shoot out corpuscles in all directions at great speeds. In reflection, the corpuscles were assumed to bounce off an object such as a mirror rather as a ball bounces off a wall – or, rather, as a bullet richochets off a tank. But Newton had great difficulty in accounting for the refraction of light as it

passes from a less dense to a more dense medium. To do so, he assumed that the speed of the corpuscles *increased* inside the denser medium. Experimental measurements, the first of which were made by Foucault in 1853, showed that the opposite was true: light travels more slowly in a denser medium.

Energy in packets

Even while Newton was elaborating the corpuscular theory, other scientists such as Robert Hooke (1635–1703) and Christian Huygens (1629–95) were suggesting that light is a form of wave motion. One of the convincing arguments for the alternative theory was its satisfactory explanation of refraction.

Then at the end of the last century, the German physicist Max Planck introduced his famous *quantum theory,* which postulates that there is a fundamental unit of energy, called a quantum. According to this theory, radiant energy such as light does not consist of continuous waves but of separate 'packets' of energy, called

photons in the case of light. In certain circumstances, photons behave as if they were particles, in agreement with Louis de Broglie's hypothesis (1924) that all forms of radiant energy can be considered to be made up of particles, and that all fundamental particles can be considered to exist as waves. The amount of energy 'carried' by a photon depends on the wavelength (or frequency) of light.

The theories about light seem to have turned full circle. Neither Newton nor Huygens was completely right – but, according to modern views, neither was completely wrong.

In the future, it may well be that the intensely powerful beams of lasers, which show up one million times brighter than the brilliance of our sun, could well be used to transmit interstellar messages. But light-borne conversations across space will always be lengthy affairs. Even at the speed of light, a reply from Alpha Centauri, our nearest star, could not be received until eight and a half years after a question reached it from Earth.

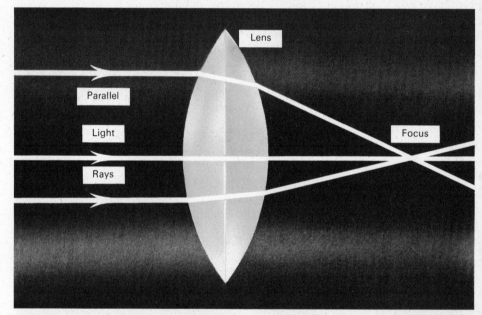

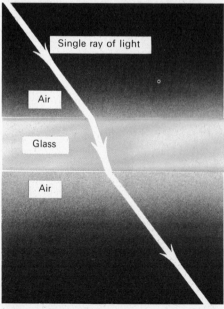

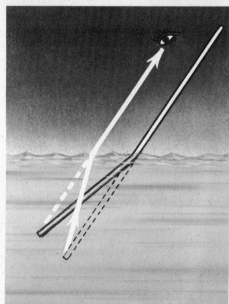

Top, parallel rays of light bend towards a single point – the focus – after passing through a double convex lens. *Above left,* the velocity of light changes when it passes from one optical medium to another. The decrease in speed changes the direction of the ray. *Above right,* the effect of refraction, or bending of light can be seen by looking at a stick in water. The stick seems bent.

Heat and the agitated atom

Out of control, a terrifying and destructive natural force – under control, it has helped mankind since a caveman first rubbed two sticks together. What is heat, and how can we measure it?

HEAT IS a form of energy. This fact can be confirmed by making heat do work. For example, if we heat a metal bar, the bar expands and increases in length. Think of the amount of work which would be required to stretch the bar if it were suspended vertically and pulled, say by attaching heavy weights to the lower end. Many machines convert the heat energy from burning fuels into mechanical energy: a steam engine, a turbine and a petrol engine all give mechanical energy derived from heat.

Heat, like light, can travel in the form of radiant energy. It is a radiation which makes up the part of the *electromagnetic spectrum* called the infra-red and lies between the red end of the visible light spectrum and short-wave radio waves. There is much evidence that confirms this statement. If a beam of sunlight is passed through a prism to form a spectrum, a thermometer placed just past the red end will detect the invisible infra-red heat rays arriving there. If we place our hands near a hot electric iron or a water-heated radiator, we can feel the heat rays hitting our skin.

At the other end of the heat spectrum, short-wave radio waves (which correspond to the longest wavelength heat waves) and long-wave infra-red rays can be used to heat meat and cook it extremely quickly. Physiotherapists use such waves for deep heat treatment on patients with muscular disorders; the waves pass into the patient's flesh and heat his tissues.

So we see that radiant heat is a form of wave motion, similar to light. But what form does heat take when it is 'in' an object such as a hot piece of metal? To answer this question, as with so many questions in physical science, we must consider the atoms and molecules that make up the metal. If it were possible to see the atoms in a piece of metal, we should find that they are not at rest but are all vibrating slightly, rather in the same way that ears of corn vibrate slightly in a gentle breeze. When the piece of metal is heated, the atoms vibrate more vigorously and each one jostles its neighbour.

The jumping molecules

If more and more heat is supplied to a solid, its atoms vibrate more and more violently, until they have enough energy to start moving about among themselves. At this point, the solid becomes a liquid, and its atoms are able to 'flow' (this is the mechanism of fusion or melting). That is why a liquid will not hold its own shape and takes up the shape of its container. If we supply more heat to the liquid, the molecules vibrate more and more. Some jump right out of the surface of the liquid to form vapour (this is the mechanism of evaporation). And given sufficient heat, the molecules move so fast that they fly apart and the liquid boils, turning completely to a gas or vapour.

In the opposite situation when a solid is cooled down, its molecules vibrate less and less. Theoretically at a certain very low temperature, which we shall discuss in more detail later, the molecules would

The destructive power of flame shows what can happen when heat is out of control. Most substances have a temperature at which they begin to oxidize rapidly – their combustion temperature.

cease to vibrate at all. This accounts for certain metallic properties at low temperatures, such as *superconductivity* in which the near-stationary atoms provide no obstruction to the flow of electrons carrying an electric current among them.

If a metal bar is heated red hot at one end, the heat gradually passes along the bar towards the cooler end. How does the heat move? The hotter molecules vibrate more vigorously and jostle their neighbouring molecules. These, in turn, nudge their neighbours, and the vibration, and hence the heat, passes along the bar. To return to the analogy of the cornfield, if a car passes along the side of a field of corn it creates a draught. The wind from the car blows hard on the ears of corn at the edge of the field, making them vibrate vigorously. They pass the vibration on to their neighbours, and the effect of the wind on the edge of the field can be seen as a wave of bending corn passing inwards across the field.

The ability of a material to conduct heat depends on the way in which its molecules are combined and arranged. For example, if one end of an iron poker is heated red hot, the other end may be too hot to hold. But a small length of glass rod may be heated until molten at one end and the other end held comfortably with the fingers. Notice the correlation between

157

good conductors of heat and of electricity (for example, metals) and poor conductors of heat and of electricity (for example, glass and plastics). In fact, poor conductors of either are both called insulators (electrical or thermal). This correlation suggests that the mechanisms of both kinds of conduction may be similar and that, in fact, it is the vibration of the electrons in the atoms of a material that is important.

Taking a temperature

It is essential at this stage to make a clear distinction between heat and temperature. They are not the same. We can quite easily convince ourselves of this fact by a simple experiment. Take two kettles, one with much water in it and one with little water in it, and place each on separate burners. A few minutes later, use a thermometer to read their temperatures. You will see that the one with little water in it has a higher temperature than the one with much water in it. But they have both taken in the same amount of heat, because they have both been on the burners for the same length of time.

Though heat and temperature are not identical they are nevertheless related. The more heat something has, the hotter it is; the less heat, the cooler it is. Can we say then that temperature is a way of measuring heat? Not quite, because if the boiling kettle with little water is removed from the burner, its temperature will begin to drop, while the temperature of the kettle on the fire will continue to rise. At some point, the two temperatures will be equal. That is, the two kettles will have the same temperature, but different amounts of heat!

Temperature, then, does not measure the amount of heat an object contains. At best, it indicates *change* in the amount of heat an object contains; it tells us if heat is going in or coming out, but does not say how much. What the temperature in fact *does* measure is the average vibrational state of the atoms and molecules of which the object is composed, i.e. how hot it is.

Any calibrated device for measuring temperature is called a thermometer. All types of thermometers make use of the effect of heat on the physical properties of a substance. For example, in an ordinary glass thermometer, temperatures are recorded by the expansion on heating of a thin column of mercury or alcohol (which is generally dyed red or blue to make it easier to see). A platinum resistance thermometer makes use of the effect of temperature on the electrical resistance of a coil of platinum wire.

All thermometers must be calibrated with a scale of temperatures. The three most usual scales are named after the men who devised them: Celsius (also commonly called centigrade), symbol C.; Fahrenheit, symbol F.; and Réaumur, symbol R. Each scale is based on *fixed points,* which are known temperatures which are easy to reproduce. Two important fixed points are the melting-point of ice (0 °C. on the centigrade scale, 32 °F. on the Fahrenheit scale and 0 °R. on the Réaumur scale) and the boiling-point of water at normal atmospheric pressure

1

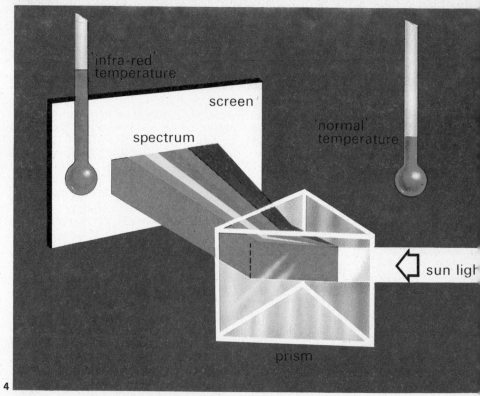

4

(100 °C., 212 °F. and 80 °R.). (Higher temperatures are generally standardized in terms of the boiling-point of sulphur and the melting-point of gold.)

Between these two fixed points, each temperature scale is subdivided into degrees – 100 degrees on the centigrade scale, 180 on the Fahrenheit scale and 80 on the Réaumur scale. The centigrade scale of temperature is commonly used in science, and the Fahrenheit scale in medicine and engineering, although there is a trend to go over to centigrade for all these purposes. The Réaumur scale is used in continental Europe for everyday domes-

tic temperature measurements. The rather strange figure of 32° for the freezing-point of water on the Fahrenheit scale comes from the fact that Daniel Fahrenheit used for his lower fixed point the temperature of a mixture of ammonium chloride and ice. This mixture freezes at 0 °F. For his upper fixed point he used the temperature of the human body, which he seems to have called 100 °F. (giving a scale of 100 degrees between the two fixed points), although doctors now regard this temperature as being just less than 99 °F. (It is interesting to note that the average human body temperature, long quoted as 98·4 °F., has

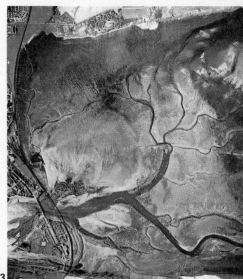

The distorted world of red, magenta and blue. Infra-red radiation, 'invisible heat' to human senses, can also be 'seen' by certain types of colour film. As green plants reflect infra-red they show up in different shades of red. **1** Langstone Harbour, Hampshire, in normal light. **2** Infra-red picture shows all vegetation clearly. Purple areas on the mudflats indicate certain grasses. **3** Seaweed in Montrose basin at low tide shows up as bright red and magenta.

4 There is more in sunlight than meets the eye. A ray of sunlight broken up by a prism seems to cast no radiation on the screen beyond the red light, but a thermometer can detect heat. The colours are shown solid for clarity, but in fact they merge into one another. When heat experiments are carried out, great care must be taken to minimize heat loss, so the calorimeter, **5**, is highly polished and placed in a lagged container. Atoms are constantly vibrating, **6**; in cool objects the amount of vibration is small, but as the temperature rises it increases greatly.

thermometer

hot metal

stirrer

water

polished calorimeter

lagging

6

COOL

HOT

water is 373 °A. A similar scale was devised by the British scientist William Thomson (1824–1907), later Lord Kelvin, and absolute temperatures are sometimes quoted in degrees Kelvin (for example, 273 °K.).

At the upper end of the temperature scales there is theoretically no limit, for there is no theoretical limit to the amount by which atoms can vibrate. Temperatures at the centre of stars such as the sun and in man-made thermonuclear reactions such as a hydrogen bomb explosion are estimated to be about 100,000,000 °C.

No single thermometer could span the whole range of temperatures from absolute zero to 100,000,000 °C. Each type has its own usable range. For example, an ordinary mercury-in-glass thermometer can be made to work from the freezing-point of mercury (−38·5 °C.) to a temperature approaching its boiling-point (356·7 °C.), although filling the space above the mercury with carbon dioxide or nitrogen gas extends the upper limit to about 550 °C. Alcohol is liquid between −80 °C. and 79 °C., and can be used in thermometers over this temperature range. A liquid-filled thermometer consists of a narrow-bore glass tube sealed at one end and with a bulb or reservoir at the other. When the liquid in the bulb is heated, it expands

recently been officially changed to 98·6 °F. so that it is equivalent to an exactly whole number of centigrade degrees, 37 °C.)

Of course, temperatures do not 'stop' at the fixed points of the various scales. Temperatures below 0° are written with a minus sign. For example, the freezing-point of the anti-freeze mixture commonly used in motor-car radiators is about −12 °C. In Polar regions, temperatures down to −100 °F. have been recorded. But is there a lower limit to a temperature scale, is there a limit to how cold an object can become?

We can predict the answer to this ques-

tion by again considering heat as a random vibration of the atoms and molecules in a solid. As the solid is made colder and colder, its atoms vibrate less and less. Theoretically, there will be a temperature at which the atoms are stationary. The material will then have no heat at all and cannot be any colder. Scientists call this lower limit of temperature *absolute zero*, and it is equal to about −273 °C. They have also devised another temperature scale for stating the temperature of an object in centigrade degrees above absolute zero. It is called the absolute scale, symbol A.; for example, the temperature of boiling along the tube, and temperature is indicated by the position of the end of the column of liquid relative to a scale inscribed on the stem of the thermometer.

Why do liquids and solids expand when they are heated? Consider again the atoms and molecules in, say, a solid material all vibrating at a given temperature. If the temperature of the material is increased, the atoms vibrate more vigorously and, as a result, each atom takes up a very little more room – in effect, the 'size' of the atom is increased. All the millions of extra bits of space add up to increase the overall volume of the material and each of its dimensions is slightly increased. Engineers must allow for the expansion of materials with increasing temperature when they design bridges or lay railway lines. Expansion joints are included to allow for changes in length that take place between winter and summer.

For measuring temperatures outside the range of liquid-filled thermometers, scientists use the platinum resistance thermometer. The electrical resistance of platinum (and of most other metals) increases with increasing temperature. From a precise knowledge of the resistance of a coil of platinum wire at all temperatures, we can measure an unknown temperature merely by measuring the resistance of the platinum coil. A platinum resistance thermometer is generally accurate to a hundredth of a degree up to 500 °C., and to a tenth of a degree up to 1,000 °C. or more.

Measurement by colour

Extremely high temperatures are measured with an instrument called a *pyrometer* in which the colour of a hot metal wire (heated by electricity) is compared with the colour of an object at the temperature to be measured. The amount of electric current needed to heat the wire until its colour exactly matches that of the hot object gives an indication of the object's temperature. For this reason, the instrument is called a *disappearing filament pyrometer*. This type of pyrometer may be used for temperatures of 600 °C. and upwards.

Heat is measured in various units, the common ones being the *calorie* and the *British thermal unit* (Btu). A calorie is the amount of heat required to raise the temperature of one gramme of water through one centigrade degree. For large heat measurements, scientists use as units *kilocalories*; a kilocalorie is 1,000 calories, and is sometimes written as the *Calorie* (with a capital *C*). A British thermal unit is the amount of heat required to raise the temperature of one pound of water through one Fahrenheit degree; 1 British thermal unit equals 252 calories.

The amount of heat needed to raise the temperature of one gramme of *any* substance through one centigrade degree is called its *specific heat*. The specific heat of water is 1·0 calorie per gramme and that of, for example, copper, is only 0·1 calorie per gramme. That is, it takes ten times as much heat to raise the temperature of a mass of water by a given amount as to heat the same mass of copper by the same amount.

The welder heats two touching pieces of metal to the melting-point. The two liquid surfaces mix and on cooling he has a single piece of metal.

Conversely, water gives off ten times more heat when it cools than does a similar mass of copper cooling by the same amount.

The amount of heat required to raise the temperature of the whole mass of a substance through one centigrade degree is called its *thermal capacity*. The thermal capacity of a given mass of water is ten times that of a similar mass of copper – in other words, water will 'hold' ten times as much heat as will a similar mass of copper. Specific heat may also be defined in terms of thermal capacity; it is the ratio of the thermal capacity of a certain mass of a substance to the thermal capacity of a similar mass of water.

The specific heat of a substance is generally determined by measuring the amount of heat required to raise its temperature by a certain amount. In practice, advantage is taken of the fact that the heat is given out again when the substance cools. For example, a piece of metal of unknown specific heat is heated to a certain temperature. It is then immediately plunged into a liquid of known mass, temperature and specific heat (generally water). As the metal cools, it gives its heat to the liquid, which becomes warmer. We measure the increase in the temperature of the liquid, and can then calculate the amount of heat lost from the metal and, knowing its mass, work out its specific heat. This way of measuring specific heats is called the method of mixtures.

Various precautions must be taken so that all the heat is accounted for in the experiment just described. The liquid is placed in a vessel called a *calorimeter* whose mass and specific heat must be known and included in the calculations because it too is heated during the experiment. The calorimeter is polished to reduce heat losses by radiation and supported in a lagged outer container to prevent losses by convection and conduction. The liquid in the calorimeter is generally stirred during the experiment to ensure rapid and efficient mixing of the hot and cool parts of the liquid. A lid may be fitted to reduce losses by evaporation.

The same type of experiment can also be used to measure the temperature of a flame or some other extremely hot region. A piece of metal of known specific heat is used and heated as hot as possible in the flame – that is, until it is at the temperature of the flame. The rest of the experiment is carried out in exactly the same way as before, and the only unknown quantity is the temperature of the hot piece of metal. From the rest of the data obtained during the experiment, this temperature may easily be calculated.

Metals flow like water when they are so heated that their atoms can no longer be held in the metallic grid. The blast furnace is tapped by using this principle – the gate is opened and the dramatic flood of liquid iron and slag begins. The iron is then processed directly into steel.

Energy rules the waves

Early seafarers were well aware of the phenomenon of wave-motion and its effect on their lives. But they had yet to learn that the sight and sound of the swells are also wave-borne.

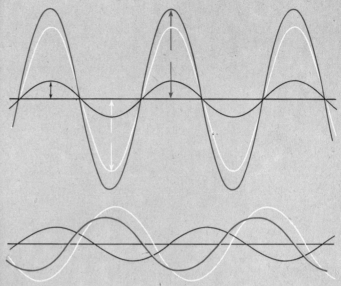

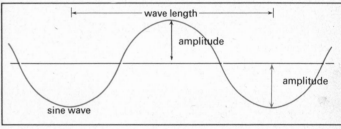

EVERYONE HAS SEEN waves on water, from small ripples on a pond to great ocean breakers. Water waves may be caused by something dropped into the water, by wind, by tides, or even by a passing ship. They represent energy given to the water – a large sea wave may have enough energy to smash a sea wall. In physics, many other kinds of energy take the form of waves, including light, sound, radio and heat radiation. And an important theory of modern physics considers that tiny atomic particles such as electrons may also exist as waves. All kinds of waves have certain features in common, and although we shall describe these features for one type of wave at a time, the same facts apply also to the other types.

Consider a wave moving across the surface of a stretch of water. The first question to be answered is: What actually moves? At first sight we might think that the water is moving along, but a simple experiment will show that this is not so. Consider floating a cork (or any other small light object) on the water in a large bath or pond. We can cause ripples, small waves, by dropping a stone into the water. As the ripples spread out they pass the floating cork. But the cork merely bobs up and down in the same place, it does not move along with the waves. In other words, as waves pass along, the surface of the water only moves *up* and *down*, not sideways in the direction of the wave.

Another simple experiment demonstrates that a material carrying a wave does not move sideways. Consider a long piece of thin rope or thick string laid out in a straight line on the ground. By holding one end of the rope and giving it a quick flick up and down, we can make waves or ripples pass down the rope. Obviously the rope itself cannot move along, because we have hold of one end. The material of the rope merely moves up and down as the wave passes.

What is a wave

There are certain fundamental quantities that characterize wave motion, and these must be understood before we can go any further with the discussion. They can be thought of in terms of the waves on water or in a piece of rope. The speed at which the wave moves along is called its *velocity*. The distance between successive crests (or troughs) is called the *wavelength*, and represents the length of one complete wave. The time taken for one wave to pass a given point is called the *period* of the wave motion and is equal to the wavelength divided by the velocity.

We can describe a wave in terms of its wavelength or its period. But since for many types of waves the period is extremely small (in the case of radio waves it may be as little as a millionth of a

The movement of water in a wave is up and down, not across: the oarsmen's ripples persist despite the boat's wake. *Top,* two waves – one black, one white – will produce the higher peaks and troughs (coloured line) if they are in step with each other. Out of phase, *centre,* the waves tend to cancel each other out. *Bottom,* two terms of measurement of a sine wave are its amplitude and its wavelength.

second), physicists use another quantity called the *frequency,* which is the number of waves passing a given point in a second. Frequency equals wave velocity divided by wavelength. Since one wave may be considered to be a complete cycle of movement, frequencies are generally measured in cycles per second. For example, the frequency of the alternating current in Britain's mains electricity supply is 50 cycles per second. The frequencies of the sounds in normal speech generally lie between 1,000 and 3,000 cycles per second.

Two other quantities are needed for a complete description of wave motion. One, called *amplitude*, is the height or depth of a wave measured from its equilibrium position (the distance our floating cork would bob above or below the surface of calm water). The other quality, called *phase*, is best understood from an example. If two waves of the same wavelength start from the same point together, they will always remain perfectly in step with each other and they are said to be *in phase.*

If they were to start at different times, they would be out of step because the crests of one wave would no longer coincide with the crests of the other. The two waves are then said to be *out of phase*.

What do these various quantities, such as wavelength, frequency and amplitude, mean to an observer studying wave motion? Let us consider again the case of waves in water and, for the sake of argument, let us make the water the sea and put our observer in a small boat. Wavelength is the distance between successive wave crests, and we can readily see how it is related to frequency. If the wavelength is long, say 20 yards, the boat will move up and down fairly slowly – the frequency will be low. But if the waves are close together, the wavelength is small and the boat will bob up and down at a higher frequency. But more important to the comfort of the observer is the amplitude of the waves, the height between crest and troughs.

If the amplitude is only small, corresponding to a gentle swell, the boat will move up and down only slightly. But if it is large, the sea will be rough and the boat will be flung up on the crest of each wave and then sink rapidly into the following trough.

Wind and water

The worst situation for our observer is when the wavelength is short (so the frequency is high) and the amplitude is large. This combination will give big waves close together. In the open sea, wave height (in feet) is generally about half the wind speed (in miles an hour) causing the waves. So that if our observer gets caught out in a 60-mile-an-hour gale, he may meet waves nearly 30 feet high. If the wavelength is at the same time short, his boat might not be able to rise up and down fast enough and the boat could be swamped – ending the experiment for that particular observer.

Frequency (or wavelength) and amplitude have analogous meanings in other forms of wave motion. For example, with sound waves, frequency determines the pitch of a note. Notes of high frequency are also high in pitch. The highest note audible to a human being has a frequency of about 20,000 cycles per second. The lowest note we can hear has a frequency of about only 16 cycles per second. The amplitude of a sound wave determines its intensity or loudness, a large amplitude corresponding to a loud noise. This is easy to confirm by plucking a guitar string or twanging a ruler clamped to the edge of a table. The greater the displacement of the string or ruler, the greater is the amplitude of the sound wave and the louder is the sound produced.

In the case of a sea wave, we have demonstrated that the water moves up and down. But what is the corresponding movement with a sound wave? It is the air or other medium in which the sound is travelling which responds to the passage of a wave. This fact can be proved by an experiment in which a sound source, such as an electric bell, is placed in a glass jar and from which the air is pumped out.

Top, why does a wave break? Near shore, the shallow bottom slows the front of the wave. Its back, still travelling faster than the front, topples over. Gently sloping seabeds give incoming waves a long and intact run, ideal for surfers. Steeply sloping shores may be hammered by breakers which can shatter sea walls or fling huge boulders high into the air.

On watch night and day, the Distant Early Warning Line – known as the Dewline – is a radar system which stretches along the northernmost frontiers of the North American continent. Caught as if in a net, *above,* the electromagnetic waves reflected by any incoming aircraft or missile are made visible on radar screens to warn the defence systems of the West of attack.

As the air pressure in the jar becomes lower and lower, the sound gets quieter until, when all the air has gone, the bell cannot be heard at all. In other words, sound will not travel through a vacuum.

The passage of a sound wave through air causes fluctuations in the air pressure. For example, the vibrating skin of a drum can be thought of as a kind of piston alternately pushing and pulling against the air, and generating sound waves. In a similar way, the cone of a loudspeaker is moved in and out by an electromagnet, so converting electrical energy into sound waves.

Sound detectors work by picking up the vibrating air pressure which accompanies a sound wave. In the human ear the membrane of the ear-drum vibrates at the same frequency as the sound wave and passes the vibrations to the inner-ear, where they are converted into nerve impulses (tiny electric currents) and transmitted to the brain. The ear-drum gets its name from the fact that this mechanism is the exact reverse of the way in which a drum generates sound. In a simple microphone, the sound waves vibrate a diaphragm which moves carbon granules or a crystal and by this means is able to generate a varying electric current.

The 'echo' in the mirror

Another property of waves is that they can be reflected. Ripples in a pond may be reflected by the bank, and sound waves may be reflected by a large building or a cliff to create an echo. But perhaps the most important example of reflection occurs with light waves. We are only able to see objects at all because light waves from the sun or some other light source are reflected off them into our eyes. If there is no light to be reflected, we cannot see. Light waves striking a mirror are also reflected and may reach our eyes, which see a light 'echo' of the light striking the mirror.

Light waves also exhibit all the other wave properties we have mentioned. Wavelength (or frequency) of light determines its colour; light near the red end of the spectrum has a longer wavelength than light near the violet end. The amplitude of light waves determines their intensity. A bright light source gives off waves of large amplitude and a feeble light source gives waves of small amplitude.

An important phenomenon of light waves is related to phase, which we mentioned earlier. If two light waves are exactly in phase (in step), the crests and troughs of the waves coincide, reinforcing each other, giving a single wave of larger amplitude and so greater light intensity. But if the two waves are exactly out of phase, they tend to cancel each other and give light of lower intensity. If the waves initially have the same amplitude, they cancel each other completely if they are out of phase, resulting in darkness.

This overlap or cancellation of light waves is called *interference*. If we take two points of light (for example, by making two pin-holes close together in a piece of card and placing it in front of a *coherent*

Top, the dish of the radio telescope of Jodrell Bank in Cheshire catches radio waves from space. Such radiation can derive from a range of sources. Colliding galaxies, sunspots, clouds of interstellar gas, all produce distinctive radio information. Jodrell Bank can also track the artificial satellites launched from Earth: the dish tilts in pursuit of objects of interest in the sky.

Sound waves guide the bat, *above,* in flight. Emitting up to 60 ultrasonic signals every second while on the wing, the bat gauges (from the time his squeaks take to bounce back to him from objects in his path) the route he must take to steer clear. Not unlike Man's radar systems, the bat's warning system – a larynx powerfully equipped with muscles – is unique in the animal kingdom.

source of light – another piece of card with a single hole in it placed in front of a bright lamp), we can see the effect of interference on a screen placed in front of the point sources. Where light waves arrive at the screen in phase, they reinforce each other and produce a bright area on the screen. Where they arrive out of phase, they cancel and no light reaches the screen. As a result, the screen shows a pattern of alternate light and dark areas with faintly lit gaps between them. In the gaps, the waves are arriving neither in phase nor out of phase. The light and dark bands are called *fringes*.

Sound waves can also exhibit interference. Two notes close together in pitch (but not exactly the same) consist of waves of slightly different wavelength. Imagine the waves overlapping each other. Then every so often along the wave train, the crests of two waves will coincide and the amplitude and hence the intensity of the sound momentarily is increased. Similarly, at other places the waves will be exactly out of phase and will cancel. A listener, instead of hearing two steady notes of slightly different pitch, hears regularly varying sound intensities – that is, the notes sound alternately loud and soft.

The orchestra tunes up

These variations in intensity are called *beats*, and musicians use them in tuning musical instruments. Generally the note to be tuned is compared with a standard note of known pitch. A piano-tuner may compare the note of a piano string with that of a tuning fork, and a violinist in an orchestra may compare the pitch of one of his instrument's strings with a note played on an oboe, which is used as a standard by the whole orchestra. The musician varies the pitch of the note to be tuned (in the case of a stringed instrument by varying the tension of the string). He listens for beats, which tell him that the note he is tuning is getting close in pitch to the standard note. The closer the notes are in pitch, the fewer beats he can hear.

Beats are actually a third note, whose frequency is the difference between those of the two notes producing it. For example, two notes of frequencies 3,000 and 3,050 cycles per second produce beats corresponding to a note of 50 cycles per second. This fact is used in an electronic apparatus for generating notes of a given frequency. The apparatus consists of two *oscillators* (note generators). One oscillator generates a note of fixed frequency, and the frequency of the second oscillator is varied until the required note appears as the difference between the two oscillator frequencies. This principle is used in a superheterodyne (or superhet) radio receiver.

We stated right at the beginning of this article that even atomic particles may be thought of as waves. When J. J. Thomson discovered the electron in 1897, he found it to be the smallest known particle of matter. Later, physicists accurately measured the electron's charge, mass, and even the speed at which it moves. Then electrons were found to exhibit certain

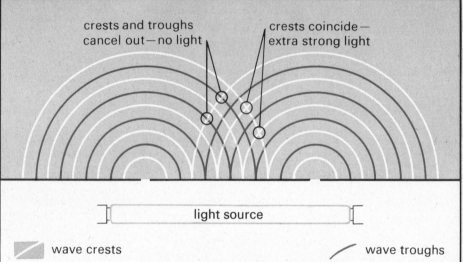

crests and troughs cancel out—no light

crests coincide— extra strong light

light source

wave crests   wave troughs

Top left, demonstrating that light comes in waves, the pattern of stripes is formed as two pin-points of light fall on a screen. Darkness results where waves arrive out of phase.

Top right, the overlap of light waves is known as interference. 'Newton's Rings' are a result of such interference fringes. *Above,* the pin-hole experiment produces crossing crests and troughs.

properties that are generally associated only with waves. For example, several scientists have succeeded in obtaining interference patterns from beams of electrons by projecting them through a thin piece of gold foil.

But there are some waves, such as light waves, which behave at times as if they consist of particles. For instance, if a small, delicately balanced paddle-wheel is mounted inside an evacuated glass bulb, light falling on the vanes of the paddle-wheel causes it to rotate. This fact indicates that light can be considered to consist of tiny particles (called *photons*).

To explain these and other experimental results, in 1924 the physicist L. de Broglie proposed a hypothesis which states that all forms of radiant energy can be considered to be waves *or* particles and that all fundamental particles can also be

considered to be waves. Of course, the dual wave-particle characteristics are never both exhibited in the same experiment – electrons behave either as waves or as particles. So that in an optical microscope, light behaves as waves that are focused by the microscope lenses.

In the paddle-wheel experiments just described, it behaves as a collection of particles. A beam of electrons in a cathode-ray tube can also be made to turn a miniature paddle-wheel, an experiment which confirms that electrons are the fundamental particles of atomic physics. But as they are used in an electron microscope, beams of electrons behave as waves and can be focused by magnetic 'lenses'. The electron microscope gets its high resolving power from the fact that the wavelengths of electron waves are extremely small – much smaller than the wavelengths of visible light.

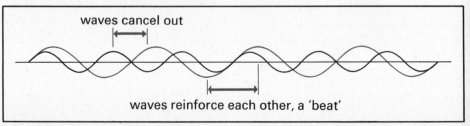

waves cancel out

waves reinforce each other, a 'beat'

Sound waves also can interfere with each other. *Above,* two notes close together in pitch produce crests and troughs of sound which result in a note

with a beat, alternately loud and soft. Musicians listen to such beats in tuning their instruments. The closer two notes are in pitch, the fewer beats.

Radiant energy's split personality

Radiant energy has been one of the most baffling, yet most useful, concepts of physics for centuries. Advances since 1900 have greatly enriched fundamental ideas about its nature.

ENERGY CAN TRAVEL vast distances across space by the process of radiation. Heat and light are two forms of energy which can travel in this way. They are 'neighbours' in the electromagnetic spectrum and they overlap in the region occupied by infra-red radiation, which can be considered as an invisible form of light of extremely long wavelength, or as a penetrating form of heat radiation of short wavelength. Infra-red radiation is invisible to human beings. Some insects can see objects illuminated by infra-red radiation and photographic emulsions are sensitive to infra-red; photographs may be taken using infra-red 'light'. There are also other forms of radiation that can be detected using photographic films, including ultra-violet, X-rays and gamma-rays. They all share the fundamental properties of light waves, for example diffraction, refraction and interference. They consist of waves, and therefore differ from light and heat in their wavelengths only.

For an object to give off heat, it must be hotter than its surroundings. The higher the temperature of an object, the more heat it radiates. But the rate at which an object radiates depends on the nature of its surface. A bright, polished surface, which reflects well, radiates poorly; a dull black surface, which reflects poorly, radiates well. Scientists call an object that radiates heat at the greatest possible rate a black body. Radiation from any other object, called its *emissivity,* is expressed in terms of how well it compares to that of a black body. For example, an object which gives out 80 per cent as much radiation as a black body has an emissivity of 0·8.

Radiation from a black body

The law connecting radiation and temperature was found experimentally by the Austrian physicist Josef Stefan (1835–93) in 1879, and later confirmed theoretically by fellow Austrian Ludwig Boltzmann (1844–1906). Stefan's law states that the total radiation emitted from a black body in unit time (say 1 second) is proportional to the fourth power of its temperature measured on the absolute scale (absolute temperature approximately equals Centigrade temperature plus 273). This law enables scientists to compare the emissivity of various surfaces by taking their temperatures.

Polished metals or objects coated with aluminium paint have an emissivity of less than a third of that of a black body. Central heating radiators in public buildings and offices are commonly painted silver; as a result, they radiate heat poorly and would be far more effective as radiators if painted matt black. But if we want to trap heat and keep radiation loss to a minimum, it is sensible to use polished

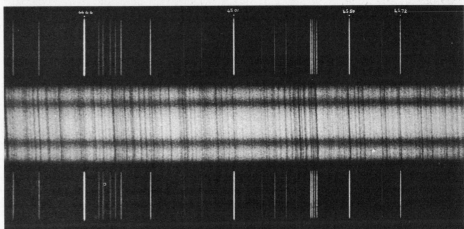

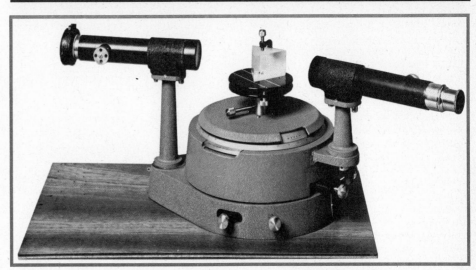

Although millions of miles away, Saturn, *top,* and the other planets of the solar system have yielded up their secrets to spectral analysis. By passing the light coming from celestial bodies through a spectroscope, *bottom,* astronomers can use the resulting spectrum, *centre,* to determine chemical composition. As a matter of fact, the gaseous element helium, today used for inflating high-altitude weather-research balloons, was discovered in the sun before it was known to exist on the Earth. The usefulness of spectral analysis depends on the fact that every known element produces a distinct combination of spectral lines, so that by examining the lines, one can identify the element. Spectral analysis requires a good understanding of radiant energy.

2

surfaces. For this reason, hot-water pipes, tea-pots and calorimeters used in physics heat experiments should be brightly polished. Strangely enough, some of the worst sunburns happen to people at the North Pole, due to reflection off the highly polished ice.

An interesting property concerning heat and surfaces is that good radiators of heat are also good absorbers. A dull black surface absorbs heat much more readily than does a bright, white surface. People in tropical climates wear white or light-coloured clothing that does not absorb much heat from the sun. Astronauts and cosmonauts wear silvery, metallized space-suits for their walks in space so that their bodies will not be 'cooked' by the rapid absorption of heat radiation from the sun. The shiny surface also bounces back radiation of heat from inside the suits, thus helping to keep them from freezing to death.

If an object is made sufficiently hot, it radiates light, which can be used to learn things about the nature of the emitter. The light is passed into an instrument called a *spectroscope,* in which a prism splits the light into its component colours or wavelengths. A solid object heated to incandescence gives a continuous spectrum in which all the colours merge into each other. But the spectrum from a gas or vapour consists of separate bands of coloured light with regions of darkness between the bands; this is called a *band spectrum.* Under high magnification, these spectral bands can be seen to consist of closely spaced fine lines. The spectra from heated atoms consist only of lines, and these are called line spectra or atomic spectra.

How are atomic spectra produced? If a metal salt is heated in the flame of a Bunsen burner, the flame often becomes brightly coloured; the colour produced is characteristic of the metal in the salt. For example, sodium salts produce a bright yellow flame, strontium salts produce a bright red flame (this property

is used in making signal flares and fire-works), and copper salts produce a green flame. If such a coloured flame is studied with a spectroscope, the atomic spectrum of the metal is obtained.

Atomic spectra can also be produced by means of a high-voltage spark or arc. The element being studied can be incorporated into the electrodes producing the arc, or an electric spark can be formed in a gas or vapour containing the element. Atomic spectra may be seen by viewing such sparks with a spectroscope.

Lines in the spectrum

The lines in an atomic spectrum each correspond to light of a certain wavelength. For example, the hydrogen spectrum consists of a series of lines, ranging from the ultra-violet through the visible and into the infra-red, which may be produced by passing an electric spark through hydrogen gas. In 1885, the physicist J. J. Balmer worked out an equation for calculating the wavelength of the hydrogen lines in the visible spectrum. A similar equation enabled later workers to discover series of hydrogen lines in the ultra-violet and in the infra-red regions of the spectrum.

To find out where the light that makes up the atomic spectrum comes from, we can look at the 1913 theory of the Danish physicist Niels Bohr (1885–1962), which, though now superseded by a more complicated model, is still useful for thinking about atomic physics.

Bohr believed that electrons move around the atomic nucleus in orbits, in much the same way that the planets of our solar system move around the sun. Each electron had more than one possible orbit and could be made to jump from one to another by changing its energy. If energy were added, the electron would jump to a higher orbit; if some energy were removed, the electron would fall into a lower orbit. In the second case, the excess energy would escape from the atom in the form of light. Since there were only a

limited number of orbits possible, the light associated with each downward electron jump had to correspond to a certain known quantity of energy – that is, had to have a certain colour and wavelength.

Light is not the only type of radiation believed to result from electron jumps. High-energy emissions, often in the form of X-rays, form a spectrum of lines similar to an atomic spectrum; but since X-rays are invisible, the spectrum can be studied only by taking a photograph of it.

Scientists are still quite indebted to Bohr's theory which, though now outdated, led them to many useful applications of spectra. A line spectrum produced from a mixture of several elements is made up of the spectra of each individual element present. Since each of the elements has its own special spectrum, which can be used as a sort of 'finger-print', the elements in the mixture can be easily identified. In addition, the brightness of the lines in the spectrum gives an indication of the relative amounts of the elements producing them. A trace of a particular element in a mixture gives only dim lines, an abundance of an element gives bright lines.

Another extremely important consequence comes from this explanation of how atoms emit radiation. It had been believed for more than 100 years that light is continuous, that is, a wave. But according to Bohr, an electron could give off energy (and hence light) only when it jumped from one distinct orbit to another, but not while it was actually in an orbit. Therefore, the light had to be emitted in packets or quanta, and what appears to our eyes as continuous light radiation is really made up of millions of these quanta. By logical extension of this idea, all forms of radiation, including heat and light, can be considered to consist of quanta. A quantum of light is given the special name, *photon.*

These ideas concerning the quantum nature of radiation were first put forward in 1900 by the German physicist Max

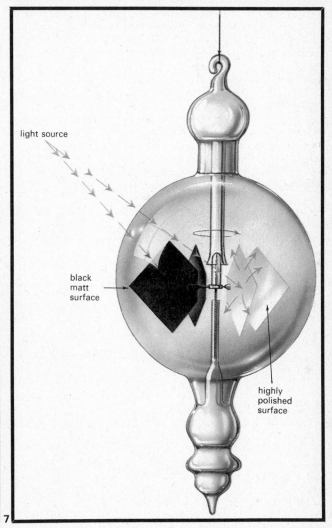

light source

black matt surface

highly polished surface

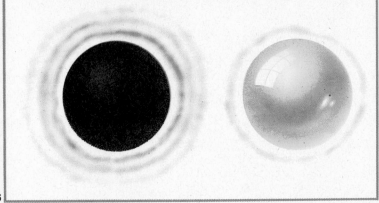

The same radiant energy which colours the skies for holiday celebrations (1) and gives such an eerie cast to public monuments (2) may also be used to turn winter into summer (3) and to alter the structure of metals (4). The success of the greenhouse in (3) depends upon the fact that heat and light are both forms of energy. Visible light from the sun, radiation having short wavelengths, passes readily through the glass windows of the greenhouse and is absorbed by the plants and soil inside. It is then re-emitted as long-wave infra-red radiation, which does not pass easily through the glass windows to the outside. The trapped infra-red radiation is the cause of the heat. The bedouin's white cloak (5) is another application derived from radiation physics. Materials and objects having bright colours or highly polished surfaces strongly reflect radiation such as light. Conversely, dark colours and dull surfaces absorb radiation quite strongly (6). The white cloak reflects away the desert sun in the daytime, keeping the wearer cool, and holds body heat inside at night, keeping him warm when the sun goes down. Crooke's radiometer (7) works on the same principle. The black side of the paddles absorbs light faster than the polished side and re-emits it faster. This gives the paddles a 'kick' and causes the radiometer's centre piece to rotate.

Planck (1858–1947), and were strongly supported by Bohr's theory 13 years later. Light, then, which had largely been accepted as being a wave phenomenon, was shown to be explicable in terms of stream of particles, as had been argued in previous centuries. Scientists again began choosing sides, some insisting light was a wave, others that it was a stream of particles.

It was then, with the controversy at its height, that a young French prince began to take an interest in theoretical physics. Louis Victor Pierre Raymond, prince de Broglie, was born into a distinguished family of statesmen and scientists in the year 1892. The family, founded in France by a Piedmontese nobleman in 1643, had included an ambassador to London, and a revolutionary who had gone to the guillotine during the Terror. De Broglie was 32 when, in 1924, he reached a dramatic new conclusion about the nature of light (four years later he was professor of physics in Paris, and in 1929 the winner of a Nobel prize in physics for his achievement).

What de Broglie did in 1924 was to lay the whole wave-particle controversy to rest by advancing a concept that combined the two ideas in a sort of 'wavicle'. According to de Broglie, all waves can also be thought of as particles, and all particles can be thought of as waves. De Broglie's hypothesis may be applied to any particles – even whole atoms – which is just what was done by the Austrian Erwin Schrödinger (1887–1961). In 1926 Schrödinger worked out the complete wave equation for hydrogen and made a major contribution to wave mechanics, which is the theory generally accepted today in place of the one offered by Bohr.

De Broglie's 'wavicle' resolves many paradoxes in physics. For example, in 1923 the American A.H. Compton discovered that the wavelengths of X-rays scattered on passing through a block of material such as paraffin wax were longer than expected. He produced a satisfactory explanation of the phenomenon, which is now called the *Compton effect,* by assuming that the X-rays consist of quanta (high-energy photons) which collide with electrons in the scattering material. The electrons pick up some of the energy of the incident X-rays.

Electrons and the burglar

With some semi-metallic materials, photons striking them completely disappear and the energized electrons produced flow in the materials as an electric current. This phenomenon is called the *photoelectric effect* and is the basis of photoelectric cells and instruments employing them (such as photographers' light meters and some kinds of burglar alarms). A photoelectric cell contains a material such as selenium. When light strikes the selenium, an electric current is produced which may be detected by a sensitive ammeter. The amount of current produced is proportional to the intensity of the light (that is, to the rate at which photons are striking the selenium), and the strength of the electric current is used as a measure of the strength of the light.

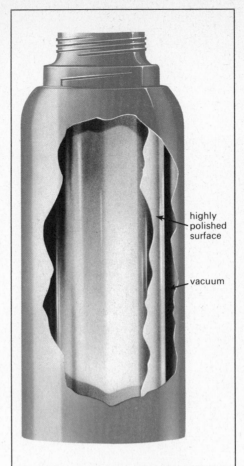

highly polished surface

vacuum

The highly polished wall of the Thermos flask reflects heat trying to enter from the outside and traps heat trying to radiate away from the inside, thus keeping the contents at a constant temperature. In the same way, the astronaut's space-suit prevents both freezing and scorching.

Radiant heat also consists of quanta. When these quanta strike an object, they give up their energy to the atoms and molecules that make up the material of which the object is composed. The energy increases the rate of vibration of the atoms, and the temperature of the object rises. When the object cools, it re-emits quanta of heat as radiation of a longer wavelength. A greenhouse functions on this principle. Light radiation from the sun passes through the glass of the greenhouse and is absorbed by materials inside it. The materials re-emit this solar energy as heat radiation, which is trapped inside by the glass walls.

Heat also travels by conduction in which the vibration of molecules is passed on to neighbouring molecules and hence along a material. If there is no material present, heat cannot travel by conduction; for this reason, heat cannot conduct through a vacuum – although it can travel by radiation.

These principles are all embodied in the vacuum (or Dewar) flask used for storing liquids and 'isolating' them from heat changes. The flask consists of a double-walled bottle, silvered on the internal surfaces and evacuated. The silver surfaces are poor radiators, thus heat cannot travel into or out of the flask by radiation. The vacuum prevents heat movements by conduction. Notice that the construction of the flask prevents heat movements in either direction, in or out. As a result, a vacuum flask may be used for keeping hot liquids (such as tea or coffee) hot, or with equal effectiveness for keeping cold liquids (such as liquid air) cold.

Max Planck and the quantum

Waves which are particles, particles which are waves, and a form of mathematics which makes sense out of the paradox — this is the story of a startling revolution in twentieth-century physics.

Nuclear radiation has an enormous potential for both good and evil. The tomato-plant stem covered with clusters of abnormal tumours, *left,* was exposed to 300 röntgens a day for several weeks. By contrast, the potatoes, *right,* were exposed to different amounts of radiation over a period of 16 months. One which received the largest dose remains firm and ready to eat. The other five show very noticeable deterioration.

THE STORY of the quantum theory spans the first 30 years of this century. It evolved as a result of scientists' attempts to explain theoretically certain physical phenomena, most of them concerned with radiant energy such as light and heat. At about the same time, other scientists were trying to learn more about the composition of the atom. Their theories were based on experimental studies of the properties of materials also involving radiation and radioactivity.

As more and more information emerged from the concerted efforts in these two fields of study, it became evident that the explanation of the properties of atoms and the particles of which they are composed

and the explanation of the properties of radiant energy were not entirely dissimilar. It was found that one all-embracing theory could account for most of the observed facts; matter, particles, waves and radiation were all related and interconnected by the quantum theory and the branch of mathematics developed to handle it, called wave mechanics.

The impetus to theories on atomic structure – indeed the first real evidence that the atom *has* a structure ('atom' derives from Greek, meaning 'indivisible') – came with J. J. Thomson's discovery of the electron in 1897. Later, scientists discovered the proton and the neutron, and a picture of the way in which these particles

are arranged within the atom began to emerge. The neutrons and protons were found to form the relatively massive central nucleus, and to be surrounded largely by empty space through which move the atom's electrons.

Then in 1913, Niels Bohr suggested that the electrons do not move about just anywhere, but are restricted to certain specific orbits. Different orbits correspond to electrons of different energy. From this description emerged the concept of energy 'levels' for electrons in the atoms of a material. This was the beginning of the idea that the energy distribution among the electrons in an atom is not continuous but is characterized by separate (*discrete*)

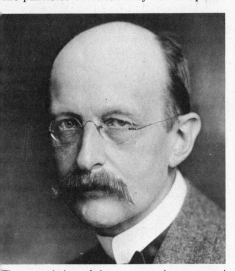

The enunciation of the quantum theory around the turn of the century by Max Planck, *left,* created a revolution in scientific thought. Niels

Bohr, *centre,* furthered acceptance of the theory when he applied it to his model of the structure of the hydrogen atom. However, persistent diffi-

culties led to the belief that energy has both a wave and a particle nature. Erwin Schrödinger, *right,* fashioned this idea into wave mechanics.

energy levels. For an electron to change orbits, there has to be a change in its energy. For example, an electric field or heat can supply the necessary energy for an electron to move to an orbit of higher energy – that is, to move to a higher energy level.

Meanwhile, other workers were trying to understand what happens to the atoms of a material when it conducts electricity or gives off energy such as heat and light. They discovered that these phenomena were also concerned with the movement of electrons. When an electron changes orbits or 'falls' from one energy level to a level of lower energy, it emits the excess energy as radiation, which may take the form of X-rays, light or heat. It therefore follows that the energy emitted is not continuous, but composed of discrete levels just as is the energy absorbed by an atom.

Various unsuccessful attempts to explain the distribution of heat energy in a black body (a perfect radiator of heat) on the basis of 'classical' thermodynamics and electrodynamics were made by Wein and by Rayleigh and Jeans. Then in 1900, Max Planck (1858–1947) proposed his famous theory that all radiant energy – whether being absorbed by an atom or emitted by a black body – is composed of *quanta*. Each quantum of energy has a characteristic frequency given by the equation $E=h\nu$. where E is energy, ν is the frequency of the radiation concerned, and h is a constant called Planck's constant. Using this equation, Planck was able to account for the distribution of energy in a black body. The heat energy, formerly considered as continuous waves of radiation, was shown to consist of discrete quanta.

Where light strikes

Another phenomenon inexplicable by earlier wave theories of radiation is called the photoelectric effect. It occurs when light strikes certain metals to produce an electric current (as in the photocell of a photographer's light meter). In 1905, Albert Einstein (1879–1955) applied Planck's quantum theory to this problem and produced an entirely satisfactory explanation. Light energy is also composed of quanta, called *photons,* and when these strike the atoms of a metal they transfer enough of their energy to electrons to make them flow as an electric current.

A similar situation was discovered by A. H. Compton in 1923. Beams of X-rays are scattered by a slab of carbon, and their scattering is accompanied by a movement of electrons. This effect, called the Compton effect, is also explicable in terms of the quantum theory.

Heat quanta and photons are therefore 'packets' or particles of energy, and radiant energy is not continuous. A beam of light consists of millions of photons moving at a velocity of 186,000 miles a second. Experimenters were also studying beams of other known particles, particularly beams of electrons. The old name of 'cathode rays' has fallen into disuse, and a stream of millions of electrons produced by making a metal cathode *emit* at high voltages is called an electron beam.

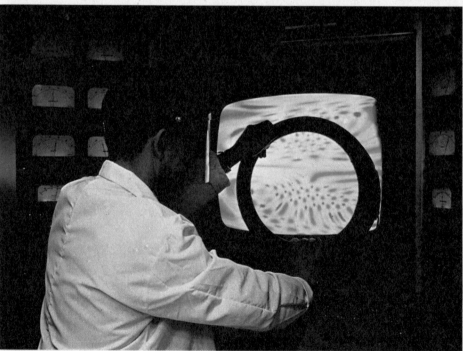

When the same particles are emitted from a radioactive substance, they are called beta-rays, but they also consist of electrons.

In 1927, two American physicists called Davisson and Germer succeeded in diffracting, or bending, beams of electrons by 'bouncing' them off metallic crystals. A year later, G. P. Thomson obtained diffraction patterns by passing an electron beam through a thin gold foil. Later workers produced diffraction patterns with atoms of hydrogen and helium. Now

Fundamental to research in atomic physics is the geiger counter, *top,* an instrument for measuring radioactive emissions. The counter shown in the photograph is being lowered into a nuclear fission training reactor in the U.S.A. A British technician, *above,* demonstrates a practical application of fundamental research – colour television. The picture on the screen is produced by a stream of electrons fired from an electron gun inside. Nuclear fission and television are both the progeny of theoretical and practical research into the nature of matter carried out largely, but not entirely, in the twentieth century.

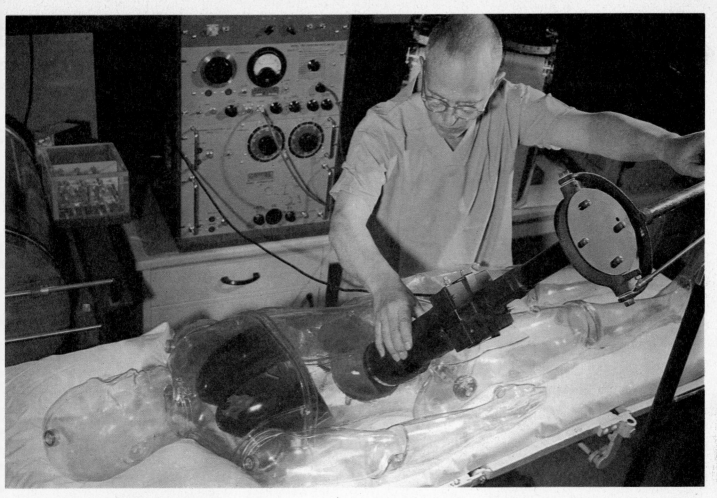

The mannequin, *top,* is not being prepared for burial. It has been exposed to atomic radiation and is being prepared for insertion into a type of machine which will measure absorption of radiation by the plastic-encased skeleton. Experiments such as this one are essential in readying Man to go into space and in evolving new medical techniques here on the Earth. The botanist, *above,* checks the results of a similar experiment carried out on snapdragons in order to detect genetic changes caused by radiation. Knowledge of how radiation affects plant growth could be a key weapon in the war against hunger.

diffraction is one of the characteristic properties of wave motion, and in these experiments particles (electrons or atoms) were behaving as if they were waves. However, this behaviour is consistent with a hypothesis proposed by Louis de Broglie in 1924 – originally formulated to account for the Compton effect and the photoelectric effect – which states that all waves can be considered to consist of particles and that all particles can behave as if they are waves.

If electrons knocked out of atoms behave as if they were waves, why should not electrons *inside* an atom behave in a similar way? The answer to a question of this sort was supplied by E. Schrödinger in 1926 when he formulated his wave equation for the hydrogen atom. Schrödinger approached the problem mathematically and replaced Bohr's idea of electrons in orbits with an equation that describes only where an electron is *likely* to be in space in terms of its energy. The highly complex mathematics involved is called *wave mechanics,* in recognition of the dual wave-particle nature of the electron.

An alternative name for the special mathematics involved is *quantum statistics.* This name gives an insight into the physical interpretation of Schrödinger's wave equation. Further physical evidence was provided in 1927 by the physicist Heisenberg who proposed his uncertainty principle. This states, in effect, that it is impossible to see an electron anyway (even given a sufficiently powerful microscope). For us to be able to 'see' anything, it has to be illuminated. Even if we could capture a stationary electron and put it

under some sort of super-microscope, we would have to shine a light on it to see it. As soon as a photon (a particle of light similar in size to an electron) came along to illuminate our electron, it would collide with it and knock it out of the way. Heisenberg's principle states that there is always an uncertainty about simultaneously knowing the velocity and position of a particle: if we know how fast it is moving we do not know where it is, and vice versa.

A good guess

This situation can be coped with mathematically by considering not an electron in a given position or orbit, but by considering the *probability* that an electron will be in a given region in space at a given time. That is, even though we cannot say precisely where an electron is or how fast it is moving at any point in time, we can make a pretty good guess. This involves a form of statistical analysis and applied to atomic physics is called quantum statistics. The Schrödinger wave equation may be interpreted using these techniques, and its physical significance is that it gives the probability distribution of the electrons in an atom – that is, the likelihood that an electron will be in a given energy level. The actual parameter used to describe the position of an electron is the square of the probability as it appears in the wave equation. This is analogous to the situation in ordinary waves where the square of the amplitude of a wave is proportional to the intensity of the wave concerned.

To solve the wave equation for actual atoms requires even more specialized

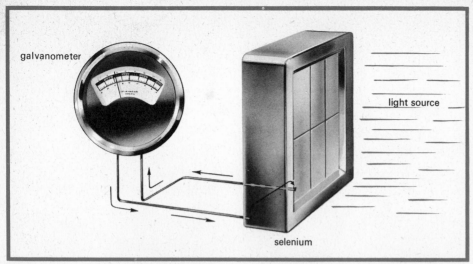

galvanometer

light source

selenium

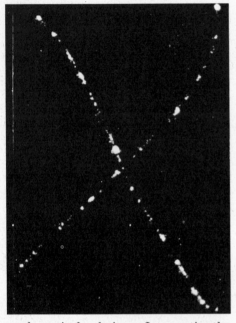

Light quanta, or photons, striking certain sensitive substances such as selenium can dislodge electrons, thus causing an electric current to flow. This is called the photoelectric effect, *top left,* and this explanation based on quantum theory won Albert Einstein the 1921 Nobel Prize for physics. Other applications of the quantum theory are found in the cathode-ray tube, *top right,* and in the Wilson Cloud Chamber, *bottom left,* a device for studying atomic particles in flight. The photograph of the leaf, *bottom right,* was taken after it had absorbed some radioactive phosphorus, to study plant growth.

mathematical techniques. Interpreting the overall *macroscopic* effects, i.e. those which we can easily observe by conventional means, of *microscopic* particles is one of the functions of statistical mechanics. Three approaches are commonly used, each based on a different set of assumptions, and they are named after the men who developed them. They are called Bose-Einstein statistics, Fermi-Dirac statistics, and Maxwell-Boltzmann statistics and use special mathematical functions such as those associated with their inventors Legendre, Bessel, Hermite and Laguerre.

Using these mathematical techniques, it is possible to derive theoretically many of the fundamental relationships of the quantum theory and of other aspects of physical sciences. For example, by applying Bose-Einstein statistics to solve the wave equation relating to electron jumps generating quanta of heat energy, it is possible to obtain exactly the same equation as that originally postulated by Planck for the energy distribution in black-body radiation.

The energy possessed by an electron in an atom is made up of various forms, such as vibrational energy, rotational energy and so on. An electron spins on its axis, vibrates, carries an electric charge, and has an associated magnetic field. Accord-

ing to the quantum theory, each of these forms of energy is quantized, and each is assigned a quantum number that characterizes it. The regions in space around the nucleus occupied by electrons are now called *orbitals* (not orbits as in the Bohr model), and there is a limit to the number of electrons that can be accommodated in each orbital. That is, there is a limit to the number of electrons with the same energy.

Explaining the conundrums

However, if one orbital contained two electrons of the same energy which also had the same spin and so on, the two electrons would be indistinguishable. They could have no separate identity. This problem was recognized in 1925 by W. Pauli, who solved it by proposing his *exclusion principle,* which states that no two electrons in an atom can have all their quantum numbers the same. For example, if one electron is spinning, say, clockwise on its axis (corresponding to a spin quantum number of $\frac{1}{2}$), the other electron must be spinning anti-clockwise (and have a spin quantum number of $-\frac{1}{2}$). Another way of interpreting Pauli's exclusion principle is to consider that it excludes the possibility that two electrons may both be at the same place at the same time.

Wolfgang Pauli was only 25 when, in 1925, he published the scientific paper

setting out his exclusion principle. In 1945 he was awarded a Nobel Prize for this major achievement. By then he was one of the world's most noted physicists.

The development of quantum theory and wave mechanics has led to many interesting and useful applications. In the practical field, these two views of nature serve as the theoretical underpinning for research in preserving food by radiation, for treating cancer by radiation, for studying growth by radio-isotopes, and for protecting astronauts and cosmonauts from the hazards of space travel. Also, many conundrums of theoretical physics have given way under quantum and wave interpretations. The photoelectric effect is now understood, and new insights have been gained into the mysteries of chemical reactions and sub-atomic structures.

But perhaps the most unappreciated derivative of wave mechanics and quantum theory has been their influence on philosophy. Some prominent scientist-philosophers (scientists often take an interest in philosophy) have contended that the Heisenberg uncertainty principle re-establishes the Christian doctrine of free will, which came under such severe questioning in the wake of the theories of physics developed by Sir Isaac Newton and others in the seventeenth and early eighteenth centuries. Physical theories and laws which apparently predicted precisely future happenings led to a common acceptance of fatalism. Whether or not the philosophical interpretation of the uncertainty principle has any justification or will bear up under the test of time is yet to be determined, but the fact that science will continue to play an important role in influencing Man's view of himself stands without question.

Albert Einstein and the speed of light

What would happen to a space-ship approaching the speed of light? According to Einstein's *Special Theory*, it would shrink, yet its mass would increase, and its time would slow down.

EIGHTEENTH- AND NINETEENTH-CENTURY physicists knew that sound travels in waves. They also knew that sound-waves can pass through air, water and solids – but not through a vacuum. Wave motion, they therefore assumed, could only arise in a supporting medium.

When they discovered that light also travels in waves whose length and frequency they could measure, they not unnaturally reasoned that light waves must also have a supporting medium. This medium, however, could not be a form of matter in the ordinary sense – like air or water – because light *could* pass through a vacuum. This strange medium, present even in a vacuum, they called the *ether*. Many people spent a great deal of effort trying to detect the presence of the ether – with no success.

Another problem that puzzled physicists was the fact that, whenever they measured the velocity of light, no matter how fast the source of the light was moving and no matter how fast the person who did the measurement was moving, they always got the same answer – 186,000 miles per sec. To understand why this was puzzling, we must know something about relative velocity.

Where is the observer?

Ordinarily, velocities are measured by an observer who is stationary. If a man is standing by the side of a road and he sees two cars going past in the same direction but travelling at different speeds, by timing them he can correctly conclude that one car is travelling at, say, 30 mph and the other is travelling at 50 mph. In scientific language we say that the two cars move at 30 and 50 mph *relative* to the stationary observer. But what if a passenger in the slower car times the faster car and measures its velocity? He will find that the other car is travelling at 20 mph *relative* to him. And to a passenger in the faster car, the slower car is apparently moving backwards with a relative velocity of 20 mph.

Applying this idea of relative velocity to the speed of light, scientists reasoned that the value obtained for the speed of light should depend on the velocity of the observer. If the observer is stationary, he will measure the speed of light as 186,000 miles per sec. But if the observer is himself moving, say in a space-ship at 86,000 miles per sec, and he is 'overtaken' by a beam of light, we might expect him to measure the speed of light relative to himself as only 100,000 miles per sec.

These two problems, whether or not the ether exists and whether or not the velocity of light is dependent on the velocity of the observer, were solved in 1905 by Albert Einstein, when he proposed

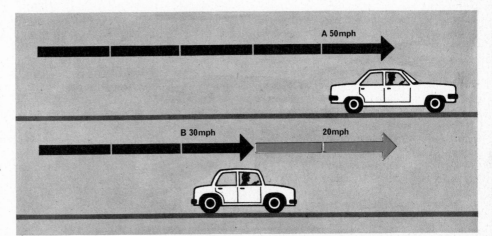

A bystander sees one car going by at 50 mph, and another at 30 mph. But from the point of view of the driver in car *B*, the faster car is travelling past him at 20 mph. We say that car *A* has a *relative velocity* of 20 mph. The concept is a key one in understanding the Relativity theory.

his famous *Special Theory of Relativity*. (The name *relativity* comes from the reference to *relative* velocities.) The Special Theory is based on two main assumptions, called *axioms*: that ether cannot be detected and the velocity of light is the same for all observers; and that all motion is relative so that no observer is absolutely at rest.

The justification for the first axiom, that the velocity of light is constant, stems from the fact that each observer uses his own standards of time and distance, standards which cannot be universal for moving observers. We will discuss these changes later. But immediate confirmation of the constancy of the velocity of light came from a study of stars. Certain stars which appear as single points of light to the naked eye are seen through a telescope to be actually double. They consist of a pair of stars, held relatively close together by their attractive forces of gravity and orbiting round their common centre of gravity – rather like a pair of skaters holding hands and circling a spot on the ice between them.

In such pairs, at one instant, one star is moving towards the Earth, the other away. Some time later the situation is reversed: the first star is receding, the

other advancing. But the astronomer, by examining the spectra of the stars and detecting the effects of the motion on them, finds that the light from each star takes exactly the same time to reach the Earth, no matter which way each star is moving, and the velocity of light from each is the same. This fact confirms the theory that the velocity of light is completely independent of the speed of the light source.

Additional confirmation came from an experiment performed by two American physicists, Albert Michelson and Edward Morley. In 1887, they attempted to detect the presence of the ether by measuring the velocity of light in two directions at once. They reasoned that if one of these directions were the same as the Earth's in its orbit (the Earth orbits round the sun at an average speed of 19 miles per sec) and one was at right angles to this direction, the two values for the velocity of light would differ if the ether were present. But they obtained identical values.

The second axiom, that no observer is absolutely at rest, is easier to accept. Consider again our example of the two cars travelling at 30 and 50 mph. Imagine that the passengers could not see the roadside or the sky or any other point of reference

1908 July 21 1915 September 22 1920 July 10

Two stars orbit round each other. But no matter whether the star is advancing or retreating, seen from a viewpoint on Earth, the velocity of light from each is the same. Such observations confirm a basic assumption of the Special Relativity Theory – that the speed of light is invariable.

outside, but could see only the other car. If the observer in the slower car assumed he was stationary, he would think the faster car was moving at 20 mph. If the observer in the faster car assumed that *he* was stationary, he would think the slower car was moving backwards at 20 mph.

Or consider the pilot of a space-ship travelling away from the Earth along the Earth's orbit. To an observer on Earth, the space-ship would appear to be moving away at, say, 100 miles per sec. To the pilot of the space-ship, who could assume he was stationary, the Earth would appear to be moving away from him at 100 miles per sec. In fact, the Earth moves in its orbit round the sun at a speed of 19 miles per sec. So that to a third observer out in space, the Earth would appear to be moving at 19 miles per sec and the space-ship at 119 miles per sec, relative to the sun. Velocities, therefore, can only be calculated relative to the observer, and the Special Theory of Relativity says that no observer may assume that he is at rest.

Coming back to the first axiom, we must now look at what happens when an observer studies quantities such as length, mass and time, in a system that is moving relative to him. The complicated mathematics involved had already been worked out by a Dutch mathematician called H. A. Lorentz, to account for the constant velocity of light through the ether, and so similar equations concerning relativity still bear his name. One of the predictions of the Special Theory is that the length of a fast-moving object will appear to an outside observer to have contracted or shrunk to a value smaller than that when the object was at rest (relative to the

same observer). In mathematical terms, the new length is given by the equation $l_{new} = l_{old}/\sqrt{1-v^2/c^2}$, where v is the velocity of the moving object and c is the velocity of light.

To take an actual example, if a space-ship 50 feet long is travelling at higher and higher speeds relative to an observer, the observer will 'see' the space-ship travels faster and faster, its length will appear to get shorter and shorter until, when it is travelling at nearly the speed of light, it will become infinitely small.

Shrinkage of length with increasing velocity is one of the reasons why the velocity of light remains constant. From considerations of relative velocity, we might expect that light emitted from a body approaching an observer at 100,000 miles per sec would appear to have a velocity of $186,000 + 100,000 = 286,000$ miles per sec. But the Special Theory tells us that the 'mile' on a body moving at 100,000 miles per sec is shorter than a 'stationary' mile. So that the light does not travel as 'far' in one second from the moving body and its velocity again works out at 186,000 miles per sec.

When time slows down

A second prediction of the Special Theory is that to an outside 'stationary' observer the mass of a moving body is increased. In this case, the equation is $m_{new} = m_{old}/\sqrt{1-v^2/c^2}$. Notice the term $1-v^2/c^2$ turns up again.

As an example based on this equation, suppose our 100,000 mile-per-sec space-ship has a mass of five tons when it is at rest. To an outside observer, its mass

would increase by nearly a ton when it was travelling at speed. And as its speed approached the velocity of light, it would get more and more massive until at the speed of light its mass would be infinite. The increase of mass with velocity has been confirmed by several experiments.

In the early 1900s, two physicists, Kaufmann and Bucherer, were independently studying the fast-moving electrons, called beta rays, given off by certain radioactive elements. In 1909, Bucherer determined the ratio of the charge to the mass of the electrons by deflecting them in electric and magnetic fields, in much the same way as J. J. Thomson had done when he discovered the electron 16 years earlier. He found that the mass of the electrons varied with their velocity, as predicted by the Special Theory. Similar experiments were performed in 1939 by M. M. Rogers, A. W. McReynolds and F. T. Rogers, who found that at three-quarters of the speed of light, the mass of an electron increases by half as much again as its rest mass. Finally in 1952, scientists at the California Institute of Technology accelerated electrons in a *betatron* (a type of cyclotron) to very nearly the speed of light. They found the mass of the electron moving at such speeds was more than 200 times the rest mass.

The Special Theory also predicts that time will be affected by velocity and will pass more slowly on a fast-moving object. The extent of slowing, the so-called *time-dilation,* is given by a similar equation to that for length contraction: $T_{new} = T_{old}/\sqrt{1-v^2/c^2}$.

On our hypothetical space-ship, already shrunk by about eight feet and more

Stationary and on Earth, a space rocket may be 50 feet long and weigh five tons. In space and moving with a velocity of 100,000 miles per sec,

the same rocket appears to be only 42 feet long and to have a mass of nearly six tons. The faster it moves, the shorter it will appear to the

observer. The special Theory of Relativity enables us to predict what happens to length, mass and time in a system moving relative to an observer.

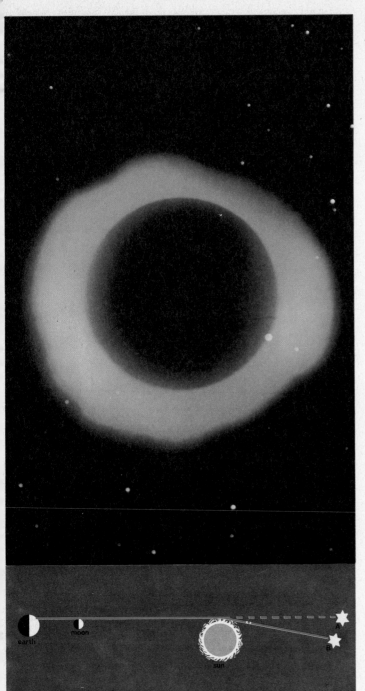

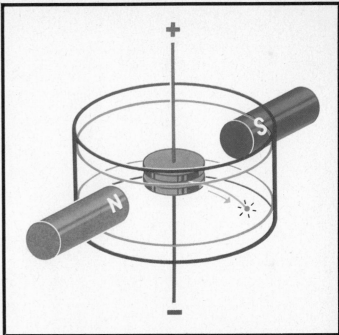

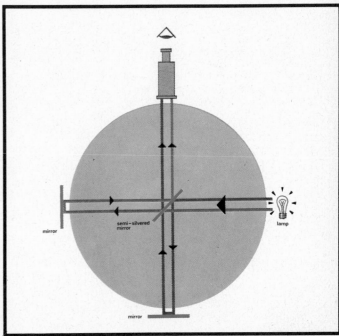

Light from a star is bent by the sun's gravitational field. An eclipse makes it possible to see the effect. *Above*, the star then appears to be at *A*, instead of its real position, at *B*.

Two key experiments endorsed some basic assumptions of the Relativity Theory. Bucherer's experiment, *top*, found that the masses of electrons varied according to their velocity. The Michelson-

Morley experiment, *above*, determined the velocity of one light beam travelling in the same direction as the Earth in its orbit, and one at right angles to it. The velocities were identical in each case.

massive by about a ton because it is moving at 100,000 miles per sec, time will pass at about four-fifths of the rate at which it passes for an outside stationary observer. One of the consequences of this fact, popular with science-fiction writers, is that a man who leaves the Earth at speeds approaching the velocity of light, on a space journey that takes (according to clocks on Earth) 50 years, will not have aged by that amount when he returns. In fact, at a speed of 100,000 miles per sec, only about 42 years will elapse on the space-ship during 50 years on Earth.

As with other predictions of the Special Theory, experiments have confirmed the existence of time dilation. We might devise a hypothetical experiment with two clocks: they are initially synchronized, and one clock is kept on the Earth while the other is sent off into space at a velocity

approaching that of light. We would expect to find the fast-moving clock running slow, compared with the time kept by the Earth-bound clock.

Some of the most accurate clocks ever made rely on the internal oscillations of atoms to keep good time. For example, an atomic clock based on the vibrations of atoms of caesium is accurate to within one second in several thousand years. In 1938 a physicist named Ives accelerated atoms of hydrogen to a velocity of 1,100 miles per sec. He measured the rate of vibration of electrons in the moving hydrogen atoms and compared it with the rate for stationary hydrogen atoms. He found, as predicted, the rate for the moving atoms – that is, the rate of a moving hydrogen 'clock' – is slower than that for stationary atoms.

One of the most important results

derived from the Special Theory is the equivalence of mass and energy. The increase of the mass of an object with velocity is ascribed to the kinetic energy. That is, every mass m has an associated energy E. The exact equivalence is given by Einstein's famous equation $E=mc^2$, where c is again the velocity of light. This equation allows us to calculate the total amount of energy available in a given mass. For example, one gramme of mass is equivalent to about one thousand million billion ergs of energy, which in the form of electricity equals no less than 20 billion watts – enough to serve a large city for several months.

Soon after Einstein made his startling announcement, physicists began to devise experiments to measure the energy release accompanying a change in mass. To do this, they studied the atoms of elements. In 1932

Albert Einstein proposed his famous Special Theory of Relativity in 1905. He predicted the conditions spacemen are now meeting. Outside the Earth's gravitational field, the astronaut is weightless, unless the craft is steadily accelerating. Then, said Einstein, he will not know (without looking) whether acceleration or a planet's gravity is giving him weight again.

Sir John Cockcroft and Ernest Walton, two British scientists, bombarded atoms of lithium with protons. Occasionally a proton collided with a lithium nucleus, smashed it in two, and released much energy. Cockcroft and Walton knew the mass of the original nucleus and the masses of the two pieces. They found that the two pieces together weighed less than the original nucleus. Some mass had disappeared and was converted into radiant energy. They measured the amount of energy released and found it was exactly the same as that predicted by substituting the 'missing' mass into Einstein's equation $E=mc^2$.

Once the structures of atoms and their nuclei were understood, scientists were able to calculate the mass of an atom by adding up the masses of its component particles (protons, neutrons and electrons). But when they did this, they found that the total did not agree exactly with the measured mass. Using the equation $E=mc^2$, the difference in mass is equivalent to a quantity of energy called the binding energy (the energy used in binding the nucleus together). With heavy elements, the actual mass of the nucleus is *greater* than the sum of the masses of its components. If the nuclei of such atoms are split, energy is released. In the cases of uranium and plutonium, the sudden release of this energy, called nuclear *fission,* makes an atomic bomb. The controlled release of the energy is used in

nuclear reactors, for peaceful purposes.

With very light elements, however, the actual mass of the nucleus is *less* than that of its component parts. This fact suggests that if the parts could be made to combine to form a heavier atom, energy would be released. This process, called *fusion,* is the basis of the hydrogen bomb. It is also the process by which the sun and other stars get their vast quantities of energy. In the sun, the fusion process involves the combination of four hydrogen atoms to form one atom of helium. The mass 'lost' during this reaction is converted to energy in accordance with Einstein's equation.

Gravity deflects light

All the consequences of the Special Theory of Relativity apply only to systems in the absence of gravitation or when, as for fast particles of the Earth, gravitation has a negligible influence. In 1916, Einstein introduced his *General Theory,* which deals with gravitation. An important concept needed to understand the General Theory is the principle of *equivalence,* which concerns gravitation and acceleration.

Consider what happens to objects (and people) in a descending lift. As the lift accelerates downwards, people and objects feel lighter. If the lift were to accelerate fast enough, people and objects would be weightless – as, at times, are astronauts.

In a freely falling lift, all its contents

move together (since all bodies fall equally fast) and so no gravity can be detected inside the lift. But now imagine placing the stationary lift and its contents in outer space, away from the Earth's gravity. The people and objects in the lift would be weightless. Now suppose that a rocket pushed the lift, accelerating it steadily to higher and higher speeds. The occupants will be accelerated too, and so a force must be acting on them. If they are standing up, this force will be exerted by the floor of the lift on their feet. If an occupant releases a pen, it will have no force acting upon it, will therefore not be accelerated and will *appear* to the accelerating passenger to be accelerated towards the floor. Uniform acceleration produces inside the lift a situation *equivalent* to gravitation.

One of the predictions of the General Theory is that light should be affected by a gravitational field. To confirm this prediction, astronomers began to try to detect any deflection in the path of light from a star when the light path passed close to the sun. According to Einstein, a ray of light passing in this way through the sun's gravitational field should be deflected by about 1·7 seconds of arc. Unfortunately a star close to the sun's disc cannot be seen because of the glare. But during a total eclipse the positions of nearby stars can be measured. During an eclipse in 1919, astronomers found that the positions of stars near the sun were in fact shifted through about 2 seconds of arc.

Counting the cost of energy

For more than a century, thermodynamics has been a faithful ally in Man's quest to build perfect machines. But at the same time, thermodynamics insists mechanical perfection is impossible.

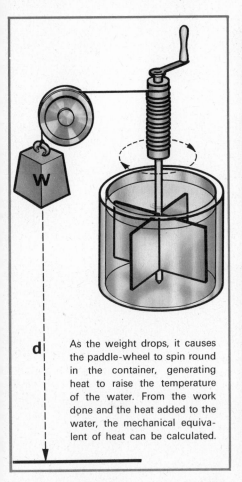

As the weight drops, it causes the paddle-wheel to spin round in the container, generating heat to raise the temperature of the water. From the work done and the heat added to the water, the mechanical equivalent of heat can be calculated.

WHEN MAN first tamed fire eons ago, little could he imagine that someday nearly every aspect of his life would be governed by the control of heat. Yet today whenever we ride in a car or a bus, we are dependent on heat energy inside the engine; whenever we turn on an electric light, we are dependent on the heat energy produced by the current; whenever we sit down to a meal, we are dependent on the heat energy which cooked it; whenever we do anything at all, we are dependent on the heat energy within our bodies which allows us to move. Heat, then, is one of the most pervasive of nature's phenomena. The science which attempts to fathom the laws which govern it is called *thermodynamics*.

The term thermodynamics derives from the Greek *therme,* meaning 'heat', and *dynamis,* meaning 'power'. Thermodynamics deals not only with the movement or transfer of heat from one place to another, but also with the conversion of the heat energy into other forms of energy, and vice versa.

For a proper understanding of thermodynamics it is important to remember that the terms 'heat' and 'temperature' are quite distinct, although it is a common error to consider them as meaning one and the same thing. Heat is a form of energy, whereas temperature is a measure of 'hot-ness' in relation to some fixed point on a temperature scale.

Benjamin Thompson, better known as Count Rumford, is largely responsible for this modern energy idea of heat. When Minister of War for Bavaria in the late 1800s, he drilled metals under water. The temperature of the water rose, even when only a few chips of metal had been drilled out. This convinced him that the caloric theory, which conceived of heat as a sort of fluid, must be incorrect. The heat could only be related to the mechanical action of boring and not to any caloric matter in the metal being bored.

Nothing for nothing

Rumford was further convinced that heat is a form of energy and that heat and mechanical work are interchangeable, because heat can be converted into work and work can be converted into heat. Using steam in an engine is an example of heat being converted into work, while primitive man rubbing two sticks together to induce fire illustrates work producing heat. But always there must be strict equivalence between the mechanical or other work performed and the heat produced; a certain quantity of heat can produce only a certain amount of work, and vice versa.

James Prescott Joule established the exact relationship between mechanical work and heat by experiments such as that in the diagram, *left,* and heating water by use of electric currents.

This relationship between heat and other forms of energy is known as the First Law of Thermodynamics. The outstanding experimental evidence in support of this law was provided by James Prescott Joule in the mid-nineteenth century.

To that purpose he generated an electric current at a constant voltage and passed it through a resistance immersed in water. He found that the electrical energy was converted into heat which raised the temperature of the water. By measuring the amount of work put into the dynamo to generate the current and measuring the heat produced when the current passed through the immersed resistance, Joule was able to establish the relationship between heat and mechanical work.

Another of Joule's experiments was to arrange falling weights rotating a tightly fitting paddle in a cylinder of water. This created friction which induced heat to raise the temperature. Thermometer readings of the water then enabled Joule to compare the heat needed to raise the temperature of the water with the work done by the falling weight.

Top, in a static system (**A**), gas molecules hit the container wall and rebound with the same velocity and temperature. But during compression (**B**), the molecules pick up some energy from the moving piston, and so rebound faster and hotter. During expansion (**C**), the retreating piston absorbs some energy from the molecules, so they rebound slower and cooler. Thus, barring outside sources of energy, gases heat when compressed and cool when expanded. *Above left,* modern electric fires are an example of heat energy under Man's control. *Above right,* Nature still rules the energy stored in the sky, but continuing research into basic thermodynamics holds out the promise of weather control.

Joule gave his name to a unit of energy, the joule. Using this unit, the value for the *mechanical equivalent of heat* is 4·18 joules per calorie. That is, 4·18 joules of mechanical energy are the same as one calorie of heat energy. This idea can best be understood by an example. Suppose that a certain mechanical operation, such as raising a weight by a pulley, requires 25 joules of mechanical energy. How much heat energy in calories would be required to perform the same work by a heat engine (assuming 100 per cent efficiency)? Answer: 1 calorie is equivalent to 4·18 joules, 25 joules are equivalent to 25÷4·18, or approximately 6 calories.

Since both units, joule and calorie, measure energy, it is presently being considered to abandon calories and use joules exclusively. So, someday, the calorie may become an historic relic, but it is still quite useful today.

In essence, then, the First Law of Thermodynamics states that during a transformation of heat into any other form of energy, energy is neither created nor destroyed; it only changes its form. The total amount of energy remains the same. In plain language, you can't get something for nothing.

Perfection impossible

An example of this idea is the internal-combustion engine, which must produce mechanical energy to move the vehicle driven by it. To do this, the engine must be given at least as much energy of another kind – the chemical energy released by the combustion of the petrol or other fuel. Conversely, when the fuel vapour is ignited in the engine cylinders, some energy must come out of the engine.

Not all the energy released by the engine is mechanical energy: some of it is lost in the form of heat. But irrespective of the heat loss or the useful mechanical energy produced, the total energy released is exactly the same as that put into the engine to begin with.

In addition to stating that energy can be neither created nor destroyed, the First Law also defines 'heat energy' and 'mechanical energy'. Mechanical energy is work energy, the energy of motion of whole, large bodies (or the potential energy of such a body at rest), while heat energy is the energy of motion at the atomic level.

The distinction between these two kinds of energy is not always easy to determine. Continuing with the example of the petrol

Natural gas is a storehouse of energy waiting to be tapped, but sometimes it runs wild. Here, a gas leak under the North Sea off Britain burns away its energy into the atmosphere. The gas was purposely ignited as a safety precaution.

engine, the gases within the cylinder are alternately compressed and expanded as the pistons move up and down. At the instant the gases ignite, energy is released as heat. Because heated gas expands and its molecules try to push apart, pressure is exerted against the piston. In other words, the gas 'works' against the piston and as it 'works' part of the heat energy is converted into mechanical energy.

However, the gases are hotter than they were before ignition and they retain some of the energy which is called 'internal heat energy'. The First Law states that the internal energy plus the mechanical energy equals the energy initially supplied to the gases.

In 1824, Nicolas Carnot, a young engineer officer in the French army, published a paper, 'The Motive Power of Heat', in which he pointed out that some heat must always be dissipated and lost. From this he was able to show that no one could ever construct a steam engine, or any other kind of engine, which would have 100 per cent efficiency in turning heat energy into mechanical energy.

Heating by compression

Carnot's work on thermodynamics was done early in the nineteenth century when the rapid development of the steam engine and its application to the Industrial Revolution made it very important to discover the conditions under which the maximum efficiency is obtained when all the operations of a steam engine are carried out in a 'reversible' manner.

The reversible process plays an important role in applied thermodynamics. To return to the example of the petrol engine, to compress the gas the piston has to be forced in, to overcome the forces due to

the pressure of the gas. The mechanical energy of the moving piston becomes heat energy in the gas, the temperature of which rises, as shown by thermometer reading.

When compression is carried out very slowly, the piston may at any time be considered as in equilibrium under the forces of the load and those of the gas – they are almost exactly balancing the other. In other words, the gas can be considered as going through a series of equilibrium states as the compression proceeds. Such a process is termed 'reversible' because only infinitesimal alteration in the existing condition is required to make it work in the other direction.

At this point, we should be careful to distinguish between two apparently contradictory ideas. It has previously been stated that when a gas is compressed, it becomes hotter; yet it is common knowledge that when a gas is heated, it expands. This difference is that in the first case, no heat is supplied from an external source. The gas heats up because it is being forcibly compressed: mechanical energy becomes heat energy. But in the second case, heat is supplied from an external source, such as a flame or spark-plug. So just as one would expect, lighting a fire under molecules causes them to fly further apart, and the gas to expand. In a very similar manner, we may resolve the apparent contradiction between saying that when gas is allowed to expand it cools, and that when gas is cooled it contracts.

Sir William Thomson (later Lord Kelvin) and Rudolph Clausius, a German physicist, both made careful re-examination of Carnot's work and eventually drew the conclusion: heat cannot of itself, without the performance of work by some external agency, pass from a colder to a warmer body. This is the basis of the Second Law of Thermodynamics.

In other words, under normal conditions, the balance of the heat flow is always 'downhill' to the object of a lower tem-

perature. Heat cannot go 'uphill' of its own accord. In refrigeration, the Second Law appears to be reversed. Heat flows 'uphill' out of the refrigerator – that is, from the cooling compartment to the warmer air outside – but this requires the work of an electric motor and expanding gas. Left to itself, heat would remain in the refrigerator to keep its temperature the same as the surrounding air.

Inherent in the Second Law of Thermodynamics is the theory of *entropy*. Since only temperature differences lead to the possibility of turning heat energy into other forms of energy, and since heat flows on its own only from hot to cold, there is a tendency for temperature differences to diminish. A perfect machine would be able to transfer all its heat energy into mechanical energy or work, but there is no perfect machine even in theory (because efficiency depends on temperature differences). The measure of unavailability of a system's heat energy for conversion into mechanical work is known as *entropy*. The Second Law indicates that every natural process leads to an increase in the entropy of the Universe as a whole.

Unwinding the clock

This concept has a number of interesting implications. Some physicists for this reason regard the Universe as a sort of clock which is always running down. The movement of heat energy is continual and on this basis the Universe will one day come to a standstill, because the available store of energy will be exhausted. Neither thermodynamics nor physics as a whole can explain how the Universe came to be wound up in the first place, nor how this natural process can be reversed.

Broadly speaking, we can say that the heat tends to spread itself out like water until it finds a level or state of equilibrium where all things are at the same temperature. Lord Kelvin's postulations on the 'waste' and dissipation of useful energy led him to make the gloomy philosophical

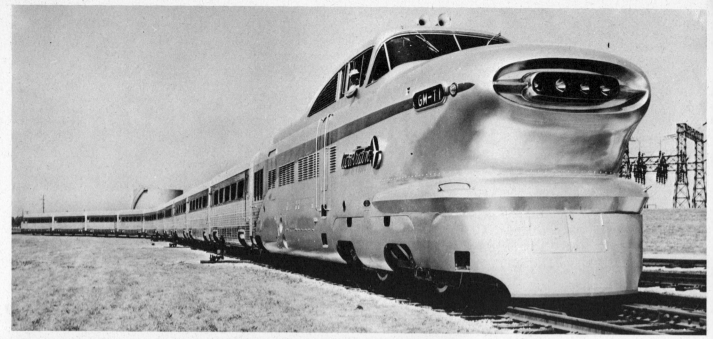

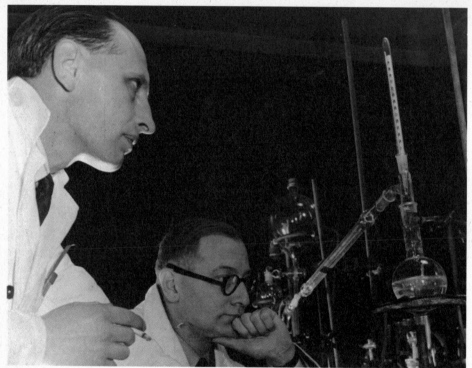

speculation that the total energy in the Universe would eventually be so evenly spread out that the flow of heat energy from one place to another, such as the Sun to the Earth, would cease. Thus, he subscribed to the idea of the Universe as constantly running down its useful energy supply like a clock-spring that can never be wound up again.

Scientists who shared Kelvin's belief even worked out the rate at which the solar 'spring' is unwinding and from this fixed a period in time when the 'spring' would be completely unwound and the world at an end. But the clock-spring theory has been badly shaken by modern physics, which indicates that solar energy is constantly being released by the process of nuclear fusion.

Thermodynamics has important applications in chemical reactions, because it allows for a better understanding of what reactions are possible. The First Law of

Thermodynamics can be applied to calculations proving that hydrogen and oxygen will react almost completely to form water if sparked off by a flame, but that the reverse reaction is not possible without supplying large quantities of heat or other energy.

The limits of theory

The laws of thermodynamics thus enable reactions to be predicted, and then tested in practice. In this way, complex formulations of different chemical substances can be worked out and the interaction of different types of substances can be calculated.

Despite its usefulness, thermodynamics has certain definite limitations in its application to chemistry. It cannot tell us anything about the properties or nature of a substance, its size, nor can it explain why a substance will react or behave in a certain way. It can show that hydrogen

and oxygen may react to form water; but thermodynamics cannot give any indication of the rate at which the water will be actually produced and only a limited knowledge of how it is produced.

Thermodynamics is concerned with 'equilibrium states' as well as movement of energy. A system is said to be in equilibrium if it is not likely to undergo any further change of its own accord, and any further change can only be produced by external means. In fact, strict equilibrium conditions do not exist in nature, but they sometimes so nearly exist that thermodynamical theories can be applied with sufficient accuracy for all practical purposes.

To take once again our example of hydrogen and oxygen. When these two gases are simply left together at room temperature they do not react at all – or, more accurately, the reaction under these conditions is so slow that the reaction can be safely regarded as being in equilibrium. We would not expect to see the two gases suddenly combine into water, though a few water molecules are being formed and coming apart all the time. On the other hand, they explode to give water in a fraction of a second if the reaction is initiated by a spark. The spark has destroyed the equilibrium. The water formed re-establishes equilibrium but in a different form.

Equilibrium is the end-product of all physical processes, and is possibly the key idea of thermodynamics. If one keeps in mind that everything is tending towards a state of energy balance – every action is countered by an opposing action – the flow of energy and the processes of the physical world are more easy to comprehend.

Getting heat from here to there

In an industrial society, control of heat means health, wealth and comfort. But one scientific theory says that heat is never really under control, and someday may destroy all the Universe.

HEAT IS one of Man's oldest servants. The story of its domestication goes back to prehistoric times when some caveman rubbed two sticks together and made a fire to keep himself warm. However, a clear understanding of what heat is had to wait thousands of years until the late eighteenth and early nineteenth centuries. Appropriately, the illuminating spark that brought about the modern theory of heat was also struck by a man rubbing two objects together, but this time instead of two sticks, the objects were a cannon barrel and the spinning drill used to hollow it out.

The man was Benjamin Thompson, an American who found refuge in Europe because of the American Revolution and eventually became Minister of War for the German state of Bavaria. While in this post, Count Rumford, as he is better known, became interested in the fact that when a cannon is bored, a seemingly endless supply of heat is produced. This continual flow of heat could not be explained with the then current 'caloric' theory of heat.

According to this theory, 'heat is an invisible self-repulsive weightless substance called caloric that can be added to or subtracted from a body whose temperature depends on the amount of free caloric present'. Although he accepted the possibility that friction could drive the caloric out of the cannon barrel, Rumford could not believe that the cannon contained unlimited caloric. After a series of experiments, including one in which he boiled kettles of water on the hot cannon barrel, he became convinced that the caloric theory was wrong.

A challenge to caloric

The caloric theory is probably the finest example of a scientific theory being able to account for most of the observable facts, while at the same time being totally wrong. And as so often happens, people were reluctant to give up a familiar idea which had served them so well. However, after nearly 50 years and many more brilliant experiments by other researchers, the world of science grudgingly had to admit that the new idea of 'heat is a vibratory motion' (which is another way of saying *kinetic energy*, the energy of motion) clearly explained several phenomena which the old caloric theory left in doubt.

Consider, for instance, the important matter of how heat gets from one place to another, a branch of physics called thermodynamics. There are three separate processes by which heat travels: conduction (heat transfer through a solid); convection (heat transfer through a fluid, i.e. a liquid or a gas); and radiation (heat transfer through a vacuum). Applying the old

Methods of producing heat and fire by friction have been known for thousands of years. But it is only within the last 200 years that the physics of friction heat has been understood.

Count Rumford, who took refuge in Europe from the American Revolution, made a major contribution to the modern understanding of heat by studying cannon-boring techniques in Bavaria.

caloric theory, one would explain conduction by saying that if you put the tip of a metal rod into a flame, the caloric from the flame flows through the metal until your hand feels hot at the other end. This would be quite a satisfactory explanation, except for the fact that in many instances heat flows rapidly through substances whose molecules are very close together. How does the heat pass through so quickly?

The 'vibratory motion' idea gives a cogent answer. For heat to travel through a solid, adjacent molecules must strike one another, increasing their vibration. The more closely packed they are, the more easily they can strike each other, so one would expect heat to travel through quickly. Exceptions to this rule can be accounted for by crystalline structure, intermolecular forces and other explanations at the atomic level.

Convection, the transfer of heat through a fluid (liquid or gas), looks very different from heat transfer through a solid, but also lends itself to Rumford's explanation.

If you drop tiny pieces of paper into an open pan of water, and then place the pan so that only one edge of it is on the fire, you will observe that as the water comes near the boil, the pieces of paper over the flame will rise, travel across the pan, sink, move towards the fire, and then rise again. The circular motion of the pieces of paper indicates the motion of the water molecules pushing them.

According to modern interpretation, the water molecules directly over the source of heat increase their vibration, kicking neighbouring molecules aside. As a result the water over the flame expands, the density at that particular point is decreased, and this slightly heated water rises, pushed up by more dense cool water coming in at the bottom to take its place. The same thing happens to this new portion of water; it expands, the density is reduced and it is pushed up by cooler water moving towards the source of heat. The result is a circular convection current, with each molecule continually returning to the fire to pick up more heat.

Radiation, the transfer of heat through a void or vacuum, does not lend itself to a vibratory motion analysis, because there are no molecules to vibrate. The modern solution to the puzzle of how heat can pass through empty space had to wait until the 1870s and involves a complex interaction between electric and magnetic fields combined in electro-magnetic waves.

Expansion at work

It was pointed out that a fundamental aspect of convection is the expansion of that portion of the fluid taking on heat. In solids, expansion is only an incidental by-product. Nevertheless, it happens and for precisely the same reason – heated molecules kicking their neighbours farther away. This is the reason why (before modern continuous-welded rails were developed) small spaces were left between sections of railway line. If they were not there, on hot days the metal rails would expand, press against one another and force the track to warp or buckle. The same thing applies to bridges, including those made from concrete or other non-metallic materials, because nearly all solids expand when heated.

A thermostat, a device for automatically regulating the temperature, puts metal expansion to good use. The thermostat is basically a bar of two different metals riveted together, called a bimetallic strip. As the temperature rises, the bimetallic strip begins to expand; but since one metal expands more than the other, the strip bends. When the temperature rises above that set for it, the strip bends so far that it cuts off the electric circuit controlling the heating appliance. When the temperature drops slightly below that set for it, the bimetallic strip contracts and bends back again, completing the electric circuit and turning on the heater again.

A caloric theorist would have explained this expansion in solids by saying that the caloric shoulders aside the molecules as it passes through (though it is somewhat difficult to imagine a 'weightless' substance doing such a thing). A modern

Above, most people associate ice with cold, but the Eskimos of North America build igloo homes from it. The close-fitting ice blocks shield them from the winds outside and insulate the igloo against loss of heat from inside. *Right,* liquid refrigerant pumped through cooling coils at the top of a refrigerator vaporizes, drawing heat from anything inside. The vapour returns to the bottom where it is compressed and liquefied again, ready for re-cycling. Insulation round the cooling compartment prevents outside heat from entering to warm the foods inside.

theorist, of course, credits the whole thing to the vibratory motion of the molecules of the two metals.

An interesting outcome of the idea of heat being the energy associated with molecular motion is 'absolute zero'. If adding heat increases molecular motion, and removing heat decreases molecular motion, then at some point it should be possible to remove all the heat from a body, so that the molecules come to an almost complete standstill. Lord Kelvin in the nineteenth century accepted this idea and tried to calculate theoretically at what temperature this should happen for several different substances. The surprising result was that the temperature at which molecular motion should cease turned out to be precisely the same for *all* substances, −273·16 °C. Gold, silver, zinc, sulphur, water, petrol – all would come devoid of heat energy at the same temperature. For this reason, −273·16 °C. is called 'absolute zero'; it is theoretically impossible for anything to become colder.

The discovery of absolute zero by Lord Kelvin was a happy one, because it gave theoretical support to a previously known, but little understood, phenomenon associated with gas. When gas is heated, it expands by approximately 1/273 of its volume at 0 °C. for each 1 °C. increase in temperature. To make calculations easier, scientists had devised a new temperature scale called the absolute scale, on which every temperature reading is the same as the centigrade temperature plus

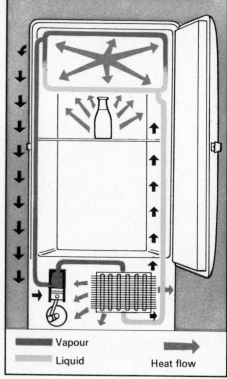

Vapour
Liquid
Heat flow

273. For example, 100 °C. would become 100+273=373 °A. But more significantly −273 °C. becomes 0 °A., or absolute zero. Kelvin's theoretical calculations coincided almost exactly with experimental facts. In honour of Kelvin, the absolute temperature scale is also known as the Kelvin temperature scale, and temperatures on it are designated by the symbol 'K'.

Heat, then, has a direct and calculable relationship to temperature. It is the amount of vibratory (kinetic) energy a body contains; temperature indicates the average energy of the atoms and molecules. Temperature can indicate the intake or outflow of heat from a body by a thermometer column rising and falling, but it cannot measure the amount of heat itself. Heat must have measuring units of its own.

but before seeing in what way, let's take a closer look at an insulator at work.

It is a puzzling fact that the same woollen blanket people in cold climates wrap themselves in to keep out the winter chill can be used in warmer countries to keep ice from melting under a hot tropical sun. But this is puzzling only because of the mistaken idea that the warmth we feel when wrapped in a blanket comes from the blanket itself. In fact, the heat we feel comes from our own bodies. Because wool is a good insulator, it traps the heat and prevents it from escaping through the blanket; so the heat stays near our bodies and we feel warm. But when wrapped round ice, it acts as a heat shield, preventing the warming rays of the sun from melting the ice inside.

In a similar way, houses are kept warm in the winter and cool in the summer by insulation (often glass wool) in the walls and ceiling. In winter the insulation keeps out the cold and prevents the heat generated inside from escaping. Conversely, in the summer, the same insulation wards off heat from outside.

How to harness hidden heat

If we again place a pan of water on a fire, we can learn something else important about the nature of heat. As already mentioned, temperature does not measure heat, but the rise and fall of the thermometer indicates the flow of heat. However, as the water in the pan comes to the boil, the thermometer stops rising and remains steady, usually at about 100 °C. Heat is still flowing into the water, but the thermometer is no longer able to detect it; this heat is hidden or 'latent'. Actually, it is not really hidden at all. The clouds of steam billowing up from the pan strongly suggest that this unaccounted-for heat energy is being used to break the bonds which hold the molecules together as a liquid, so that they may race apart as a vapour. This suspicion is confirmed by measuring the temperature of the steam, which turns out to be exactly the same as the boiling water.

The 'latent' energy going into a boiling liquid is called the *heat of vaporization,* and is defined as the quantity of heat required to change 1 gm of the liquid at its boiling temperature to 1 gm of vapour at the same temperature. Since heat may also be removed from a vapour, which then condenses into a liquid, the heat of vaporization is sometimes called the *heat of condensation.* For water, this quantity of heat is enormous, 540 calories per gm.

At the other end of the temperature scale, the heat of fusion is defined as the quantity of heat required to melt 1 gm of a solid into 1 gm of liquid. Again, since heat may be removed from a liquid in order to change it into a solid, we also have the term *heat of solidification.* The heat of fusion for water is 80 calories per gm.

This information may be put to use. If 1 gm of boiling water turns into steam, the fire heating the pan must supply 540 calories of heat. Conversely, if 1 gm of steam condenses into 1 gm of water, it must give out 540 calories of heat. This

Top, water in its vapour state, steam, has many uses. Here a blast of steam is used for cleaning and pressing garments in a professional cleaning plant. Steam irons are common in many homes.

Above, high-temperature oxy-acetylene torches can be used to weld metals by melting them and allowing them to cool and set. Many metals conduct heat well, and melt at high temperatures.

In the metric system, the unit of heat is the calorie, defined as the amount of heat required to raise the temperature of 1 gm of water by 1 °C. Thus, if you have 1 gm of water and change its temperature from 5 °C. to 6 °C., you would require 1 calorie of heat. One gram of water changed from 5 °C. to 7 °C. would require 2 calories of heat, and so on.

However, if you were to heat another substance, such as aluminium, you would find that aluminium requires only 0·2 calorie to change the temperature of 1 gm of it by 1 °C. In other words, aluminium heats five times more easily than water.

The heat required to change the temperature of 1 gm of a substance by 1 °C. is called its specific heat. In general, the lower the specific heat of a substance, the less heat is required to change its temperature, and the more readily it will conduct heat.

Every substance will absorb heat and allow it to travel through it to some extent. But some materials do this so poorly that for most practical purposes, we may consider that they transfer little or no heat at all. Such materials are called heat *insulators.* Insulators play a very important role in our day-to-day existence,

to make use of them. The Wasukuma, a pastoral tribe of East Africa, have had refrigerators for hundreds of years, but not the slightest knowledge of theoretical physics. The Wasukuma refrigerator (which has a cousin in the British butter cooler and similar devices round the world) consists of a large, unglazed pot used for storing water. Because the pot is porous, droplets of water can work their way through the walls to the outside surface, from which they evaporate. Evaporation is simply a very slow form of vaporization, carried out at a much lower temperature than boiling. Nevertheless, each gram of water that evaporates must absorb 540 calories of heat energy from somewhere. A good portion of it comes from the water remaining inside, so the temperature drops. Of course, the Wasukuma refrigerator is not as efficient as modern ones; for instance, it can't make ice. But it does provide an interesting way to get a cold drink in the heat of the East African sun.

In almost exactly the same way, Nature helps cool the human body on hot days or after strenuous exercise by evaporating water from the surface of the skin. This water is excreted from inside the body in the form of sweat.

Heat – slave or master

Likewise, a spinning fan is cooling, not because it passes cool air over the skin. Probably the moving air is slightly warmer than the still air in the rest of the room because of its motion. However, moving air aids evaporation of water from the pores of the skin by sweeping away water vapour so more can come out, and for each gm that vaporizes the body loses 540 calories of heat.

Even though the domestication of heat and flame began before recorded history, the search for more and better ways of putting it to work for the benefit of human society continues in laboratories throughout the world. But however many shackles we put on it, heat may yet prove to be the master. The Second Law of Thermodynamics asserts that the natural flow of heat is from regions of high temperature to regions of low temperature, unless some work is done to make it go the other way. In other words, hot things tend to cool to the temperature of their surroundings, just as cold things tend to warm to the temperature of their surroundings. This is a relatively obvious statement, and seems harmless enough – until we carry it to its logical conclusion.

If everything is trying to reach the same temperature as everything else, it seems reasonable to assume that some day they may succeed. But if they do, scientists predict that the Universe will become a homogenous blob. Everything will be the same as everything else, nothing will have separate identity, and the world as we know it will cease to exist. This is the so-called 'Heat-Death of the Universe' theory. It doesn't present a very promising future, but there is no need for alarm; the Universe is still good for many more millions of years. Besides, like all other scientific theories, this one has its critics, and may yet prove to be wrong.

Top, heat generated by hollowing out a cannon can boil a kettle of water on it. Count Rumford used experiments such as this to bolster his criticism of the caloric theory of heat. *Above,* railway tracks expand when hot, causing them to warp and buckle, as in this demonstration. If engineers did not allow for this when laying track, serious accidents would result. *Right,* blankets are good insulators. When wrapped round a person, they trap body heat and prevent its escape. Wrapped round ice, blankets exclude heat and prevent the ice from melting.

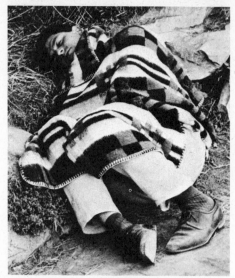

fact is commonly applied in steam central-heating systems. A central boiler turns water into steam, which is then allowed to circulate through the building in pipes and radiators. Inside the radiators, the steam condenses back into water, giving out 540 calories for each gram. Since 1,000 gm of water occupies a volume of just over two pints, it doesn't take very much steam to supply a great deal of heat. Steam heat is today giving way to more modern forced-air and gravity-water methods.

Perhaps the most intriguing application of 'latent heat' is the electric refrigerator. In a typical electric refrigerator, a liquid of very low boiling point such as Freon is pumped into the cooling coils which surround the refrigeration compartment. The pressure in these coils is reduced to help the liquid vaporize. Much of the heat of vaporization is drawn out of the cooling compartment, so the temperature inside drops. The vapour is then pumped out of the cooling coils into a second set of coils outside the refrigerator, where it is compressed and liquefied, ready to do its work again. When the gas liquefies, it gives up its latent heat. This is why the coils often found outside the back of a refrigerator are hot.

The main purpose of an electric motor is to move the refrigerant liquid round the cooling coils and to compress it back into a liquid after vaporization. In some refrigerators, the electric motor is replaced by a gas or paraffin flame and a clever arrangement of pipes and coils which does the same thing.

Of course, it is not always necessary to understand physical principles in order

Chemistry of fire

Fire is one of the basic elements of human civilization and its use marks one of the dividing lines between Man and the animals. But what is fire and what happens when a substance burns?

FIRE IS the visible effect of combustion, and combustion is induced by the chemical combination of oxygen with one or more other elements or with one or more constituents of a substance. Man has been using fire for thousands of years, and his ability to create and to use it for his own benefit marks a dividing line between himself and all other animals; not even the most intelligent ape in nature has ever learned to light a fire.

We do not know how Man discovered fire or the manner of making it serve him. Perhaps he first became aware of it when lightning struck dried vegetation and set it ablaze, or when he saw flaming lava belching from a volcano. No doubt he discovered that such natural fire could be collected and preserved by adding wood and leaves to protect him from wild beasts or for use in elementary cooking. The next step was the invention of some method of creating fire at will, either by friction of wood against wood, or by the percussion of minerals, or with flint and pyrites.

Although Man learned to use fire he did not understand the strange phenomenon he had learned to control. Throughout the ages he must have wondered, 'What is fire?' and 'Why do some materials burn while others do not?'

A material element?

Greek philosophers, who were no mean scientists, believed that the world was composed of four distinct elements: fire, water, earth and air. Even Robert Boyle (1627–91), who first realized that air is essential to combustion, believed that fire was a material element. What he and his immediate successors in chemical study failed to appreciate was the fact that fire was the product of combustion and that combustion was in turn the product of oxidation. Moreover, they equally failed to appreciate that combustion was not a phenomenon limited to the traditional inflammable substances.

When oxygen combines with another element, the process is called *oxidation*. If the reaction goes on slowly, as when iron rusts or wood decays, it is known as slow oxidation. If it is sufficiently rapid for appreciable light and heat to be produced it is called burning or comt ustion: fire is simply the visible manifestation of combustion. In other words, oxidation is a *chemical change* – a chemical change is one in which some new chemical is formed. The more simple chemical combustions are those where two atoms join together to form a molecule of a compound; the compound so formed differs in behaviour and appearance from its constituent elements. Among the more common examples of chemical change are those brought about by the burning of substances.

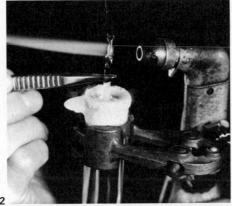

1 Firemen use an experimental mixture of carbon dioxide foam and white powder to extinguish an aircraft fire. Firefighters need an all-round understanding of combustion chemistry.
2 An experiment to analyse the chemicals produced during combustion. Combustion products are frozen in the glass tube and removed for analysis before they have time to react together.
3 A number of laboratories devote attention to the problems of preventing undue noise from flames. Here, a scientist is testing the resonance of a flame with controlled characteristics.

When a piece of wood, which is mainly carbon, burns in air, oxidation takes place and results in combustion; each atom of carbon has combined with two atoms (one molecule) of oxygen. Reaction between the two elements has released heat. At the same time, a colourless gas called carbon dioxide is formed which is something quite different from the wood. In the same way, the burning of coal, another substance of high carbon content, produces heat and the resulting carbon dioxide escapes to the atmosphere.

Although it is not visible in the form of fire, combustion is always taking place in the cells of the human and other animal bodies. The food we eat is slowly and flamelessly burned in the body to provide us with energy and to keep us warm. The resultant carbon-dioxide waste is breathed out of the lungs during normal respiration.

Just how important an adequate supply of oxygen is to combustion is indicated by the fact that air blown from bellows on to a fire increases the heat from combustion. This was soon discovered by the old-time blacksmiths, who blew air across the fires in which they heated and melted their metals. Iron-smelting depends upon extra oxygen being blown through to the furnace, and the same method is used in converters for making steel. The early designers of the steam-engine realized that if air was blown across the fuel burning in the boiler, the heat needed to raise and maintain the head of steam could be increased. The explosive force (another form of combustion) in a petrol engine depends upon mixing air and petrol in a carburettor for feeding to the cylinders.

An important point about combustion is that it is *self-sustaining:* that is, the heat it produces is responsible for igniting further material. That is why a coal fire keeps alight so long as coal is added to it and why a forest fire spreads.

There are innumerable examples of oxidation which normally do not reach the stage of combustion. Rust is simply oxidation which does not develop into combustion. Sodium, magnesium, copper powder and iron filings take up oxygen from the atmosphere or burn in oxygen to become oxides. Similarly non-metals such as phosphorus, sulphur and hydrogen will burn in oxygen to produce the appropriate oxides.

The more pure the oxygen, the more rapidly combustion takes place and the greater the heat generated, particularly when certain metals have to be burned. An example of this is the photographer's photoflash lamp. The lamp consists of a glass bulb containing pure oxygen and strips or filaments of either magnesium or aluminium. When an electric current is passed through the lamp, combustion of the metal is almost instantaneous and it burns with great brilliance.

Blowtorches

The high temperatures induced by combustion in pure oxygen makes possible the oxy-hydrogen blowtorch used for cutting metals. The torch has two tubes, one inside the other; oxygen flows through the inner and hydrogen through the outer tube. The two gases combine chemically at the top of the torch and their consequent combustion produces a flame with a temperature of about 2,000 °C. Even higher temperatures are produced by the combustion of acetylene and oxygen in the oxy-acetylene torch. This also has two tubes, one carrying acetylene and the other pure oxygen. The metal is first heated by the flame from the acetylene tube after which a stream of oxygen is released from the oxygen tube against red-hot metal. The combustion of the two gases creates combustion producing temperatures of over 3,000 °C.

Wood, leaves and other vegetable substances decay, that is, oxidize, very slowly, and combustion does not normally take place until heat is applied to them, when they will oxidize rapidly and burst into flame. The temperature to which any specific substance must be heated before combustion occurs is called its *kindling temperature* or *flash point.* A substance with a high kindling temperature needs a great deal of heat to cause it to burn.

The greater the area of a combustible substance in contact with oxygen, the better it burns. A cubic foot of wood, for example, burns much more slowly than the same amount of wood split into sticks. Similarly, sheets of crumpled newspaper burn much more quickly than a small book thrown on a fire.

It has already been stated that rust is caused by oxidation and that rapid oxidation induces combustion or burning. Why then, does not rusting iron become combustible, particularly when it is known that heat is produced when iron rusts?

1 Fireworks were one of the early products of combustion chemistry and were known in China and India in very early times. Brilliant pyrotechnic effects are achieved by the combination of various chemicals.
2 Testing a powerful new torch at a combustion laboratory. The torch, which burns a mixture of propane and air, achieves a large steady flame with a high temperature.
3 Modern rocketry is directly descended from the early rockets of the Chinese and Greeks. Burning must be carefully controlled to ensure that the rocket stays on course.
4 Primitive Man may have discovered fire through the effects of lightning. This bush fire at Ayers Rock in central Australia was caused by lightning hitting dry spinifex plants.
5 A fire-eater in a Cairo street. Exact timing and concentration are needed to control the flame and avoid being badly burned.

The answer is that iron is a good conductor of heat and the heat generated by oxidation when it rusts is quickly dissipated to the atmosphere. Conversely, there are certain substances which are such poor conductors of heat that once they start to oxidize the heat accumulates on them to a degree that the kindling temperature builds up so rapidly that combustion takes place and they burst into flames. This process is called *spontaneous combustion*.

Spontaneous combustion

Leaves decaying close to a shed often build up a degree of combustion that causes them to burst into flames and the same thing sometimes happens when damp hay is stored in a barn. Because mineral oils oxidize very slowly, they are not liable to spontaneous combustion, but rags containing vegetable oils, or paints containing such oils, oxidize very rapidly, and are liable to burst into flames through spontaneous combustion. Some floor and furniture polishes contain ingredients which oxidize so rapidly that they are liable to spontaneous combustion. Explosions can be the result of spontaneous combustion, as happens when dust from substances such as coal, flour or cotton becomes scattered throughout the air and oxidation rapidly builds up.

Liquids such as petrol, ether and benzene are liable to combustion at relatively

low temperatures because they emit vapours which a spark can ignite. In these instances, the liquids are converted into explosive gases. The temperature at which a liquid emits enough vapour to form a combustible mixture with atmospheric oxygen is called the flash point of that liquid.

At the other end of the combustion scale, there are substances which do not readily take oxygen from the air, but do take it when it is transferred to them through substances containing oxygen. Substances containing oxygen are called *oxidizing agents*. Hydrogen peroxide, saltpetre, nitric acid and potassium chlorate are examples of oxidizing agents; they are rich in combined oxygen which they release as a gas when heated.

Non-safety 'strike anywhere' matches are an example of an oxidizing agent put to practical use. The match heads consist of a mixture of chemicals which includes an oxidizing agent. When the match is rubbed against a surface, friction creates a rise in temperature in the chemical mixture and the oxidizing agent is split up to give a concentrated supply of oxygen. As a result, the other materials in the match head oxidize so rapidly that combustion is created and the consequent heat is sufficient to set the match stick alight. Of course, the oxygen in the air surrounding the match stick helps to accelerate its combustion and so induce the required flame.

Smothering fire

Just as oxygen encourages combustion, so lack of it prevents, or limits, combustion. A small fire can be extinguished by smothering it with a coat or blanket, because the fire has been shielded from the oxygen-containing air essential to combustion. In the same way, aircraft fires can be extinguished by smothering them with a blanket of foam that forms a barrier between the fire and the atmosphere.

Atmospheric oxygen is the most common oxidizing agent, but oxidation with consequent combustion can be induced by substances such as hydrogen peroxide. This phenomenon makes possible the combustion of rocket fuels in space craft, which have to burn in the absence of atmospheric oxygen. Hydrogen peroxide is also used as the oxidizing agent to induce combustion of the diesel fuels for

1

1 The flame of an oxy-acetylene torch can reach temperatures of over 3,000 °C. Here junior firemen are being trained to use a portable torch by cutting a hole in a metal tank.
2 Antoine Lavoisier, the French chemist, with his wife. In 1774, after a series of experiments, he made the first accurate and scientific explanation of fire.

2

submarine engines, so conserving the limited amount of atmospheric oxygen in a submerged submarine.

George Stahl (1660–1734) was the first chemist to make a serious study of oxidation and combustion. Stahl had, as a young man, earned a precarious and not particular honest living as an astrologer. Later he repudiated his dubious practices and studied chemistry so successfully that in 1694 he became professor of chemistry at Halle University. It was there that he propounded his phlogiston theory to explain the phenomenon of combustion.

According to Stahl, all the then known combustible materials, such as wood, coal and oil, contained a substance called phlogiston which was released into the air during burning. The only function of the air or atmosphere – its oxygen constituent had not then been discovered – was to absorb the phlogiston. Stahl knew that air was essential to combustion, but he propounded that the sole reason for this was that air was the only substance that could absorb phlogiston, and unless phlogiston could be absorbed from a burning material combustion was impossible. Substances that burned quickly contained a lot of phlogiston and things that burned slowly were deficient in phlogiston. Stahl elaborated his theory by explaining that the spluttering of burning wood was caused by the phlogiston in it having difficulty in escaping. Ashes left over from burning coal or wood were simply wood or coal that had lost their phlogiston.

Priestley and Lavoisier

Joseph Priestley (1733–1804) was the next chemist to investigate the causes of combustion and, by his discovery of oxygen, took the first step that was to explode the phlogiston theory. Priestley was a firm believer in the phlogiston theory and was convinced that his new gas was the one in the atmosphere with which phlogiston combined when released from a substance by combustion. He was equally emphatic that the new gas had of itself no phlogiston content; therefore he always referred to it as 'dephlogisticated' air.

Soon after his discovery of dephlogisticated air. Priestley visited Paris and discussed his work with the French chemist Antoine Lavoisier (1743–94). Lavoisier was particularly interested in Priestley's new gas as his own experiments had proved to him that it was impossible for any substance to burn unless air was present. He found, for example, that when a lighted candle was covered with a jar to exclude the air, the flame was immediately extinguished. He then concluded that something in the air was essential to combustion and that during combustion the candle did not lose phlogiston to the atmosphere. Instead it was the presence of 'dephlogisticated air' in the atmosphere that was responsible for combustion. Lavoisier decided that the combustion-inducing gas in the atmosphere could only be Priestley's 'dephlogisticated air'.

Lavoisier called the gas oxygen, meaning acid-forming, because he was under the impression that the element was present in all acids. This was later proved to be incorrect. Nevertheless, Lavoisier finally solved the problem of combustion and dismissed the phlogiston theory which for over a century had plagued all efforts to explain combustion.

Lavoisier's correct theory of combustion laid the basis for the scientific research into this important phenomenon. Combustion chemists now study not only the gross products of burning, but are able to isolate almost all the stages of the combustion process.

Quest for absolute zero

There is a point, it is calculated, beyond which substances cannot be cooled any further. As this temperature – absolute zero – is approached, electrical resistance vanishes and liquids flow uphill.

THE COLDEST natural places known to Man – the freezing wastes of the polar regions, and soon, probably, the dark side of the moon – are torrid compared with the coldest temperatures now produced in the laboratory. It is nearly a century since samples of the air were turned into a transparent liquid by repeatedly removing heat from the gas until its temperature fell hundreds of degrees below the melting point of ice. In more recent years, scientists have come within a few thousandths of a degree of the lowest temperature attainable in the Universe, while the common gases, oxygen, nitrogen and hydrogen, once considered to be 'permanent', are now used as liquids by the ton, in processes as mundane as food preservation and as exotic as space-flight.

This progress into the world of very low temperatures – known as *cryogenics* – had its origins in nineteenth-century attempts to liquefy the 'permanent' gases. But by the turn of the century it had turned into a more basic quest for the absolute zero of temperatures.

Lowest possible temperature

That there was a temperature below which it was impossible to go had been realized since the end of the seventeenth century. The idea followed naturally from the proposition that it would eventually be possible to remove all the energy from any material to reduce it to a state of absolute rest, or 'zero temperature'. There was also the experimental evidence that the pressure of a fixed volume of a gas like air decreased by an equal amount for every degree centigrade that its temperature was reduced. If these results were extended on paper to cover the case when the pressure had fallen to zero, it was clear that the lowest conceivable temperature was approximately 273 °C. below the melting point of ice.

What exactly is meant by the absolute zero of temperature in terms of the state of matter is still not fully explained, as it has proved impossible to remove all the energy – down to the motions of electrons and nuclear particles – from atoms or molecules. The picture so far achieved is the result of 50 years' work by some of the greatest physicists, including Albert Einstein and Max Planck. They have grappled with the strange, contradictory world that was revealed as Dutch, British, Russian, American and German experimenters probed the behaviour of materials at temperatures near to absolute zero – a world where electrical resistance vanishes and currents continue to travel in closed circuits for ever; where liquids flow uphill and lose all viscosity.

What is certain is that as heat is removed from materials they lose their internal

1 This superconducting motor runs on minimal electric current without any loss in power. To achieve this, the field coil is cooled to temperatures approaching absolute zero.
2 Testing different electric cables at a temperature of liquid hydrogen shows they are 500 to 1,000 times less resistant to the flow of an electric current.

motions and become progressively more rigid, ordered structures, the most ordered of which is a crystalline solid. But crystalline solids are commonplace at room temperatures, and even further ordering is possible beyond the packing of atoms tightly together like apples in a box. This is because the particles inside the atoms themselves may also start to fall into a more rigid pattern as the temperature nears absolute zero and interact together in a manner never experienced at room temperatures to produce the strange properties of the super-cold.

Any understanding of extreme cold is inseparable from a clear visualization of what is meant by heat. The most useful simple model of heat energy is the motions of atoms or molecules in the gas, liquid, or solid state in question. This picture readily explains the way in which matter changes from a solid to liquid to gas. Heat energy entering a solid causes the molecules or atoms, which are closely packed, to vibrate until they overcome the forces holding them together sufficiently to move freely and become liquid. Further heating will enable them to attain sufficient speeds to escape from their neighbours completely and boil off to shoot about in space as gas molecules or atoms. Further heating causes the speeds of the particles to increase. Collisions between molecules in a molecular gas, and between the molecules and the walls of a container are responsible for pressure. This example explains the way in which gas pressure increases with temperature and volume. This so-called *kinetic* theory gives a good idea of the way in which the great experimenters in cryogenics managed to liquefy the gases we breathe and establish the technology of refrigeration.

Squashing gas molecules together rapidly increases the number of collisions and also the speed of collision so that both the pressure and the temperature of the gas go up. This is why a bicycle pump heats up on the compression stroke. Expanding a gas rapidly – against a moving piston or into the atmosphere – will similarly slow down the molecules as they lose speed in collisions with the receding piston or slower air molecules. The reduced speed – and thus lower temperature – will swiftly be spread through the rest of the gas by collisions. This is the reason why the valve in a tyre cools down as the air is let out through it. It is also the principle of the air liquefiers developed in the early years of the century to liquefy nitrogen, oxygen, hydrogen and, with greatest difficulty, helium. This last gas brings us nearest to absolute zero with a condensation temperature only 4·1 °C. above absolute zero, or 4·1 °K. on the more convenient Kelvin scale of temperature.

The liquefiers consisted of a number of stages in which gases were compressed, the heat of compression removed from them, and the gas expanded against a piston or turbine, or in later machines through a specially shaped nozzle, before being recycled through a heat exchanger back to the compressor. As the gas worked against the pistons and turbines, or against its own internal forces in the nozzle, it cooled and eventually liquefied. It was in a vessel, rather like a vacuum flask, attached to a liquefier of this sort that the Dutch physicist Heike Kamerlingh Onnes first saw helium liquefy in 1908, and first observed the strange properties of materials near to absolute zero.

What is so special about super-cold to interest so many of the century's greatest

scientists? It is clear that the physical behaviour of most materials at the temperatures with which we are familiar can be roughly explained in terms of the motions of individual atoms and molecules. But how does a gas, such as hydrogen, behave when these motions are stilled which is what happens to materials as their temperatures approach absolute zero? As the thermal motion of the molecules ceases it no longer masks their intrinsic mechanical properties – properties which are the result of the fundamental structure of the molecule and are governed by principles known as *quantum mechanics*.

This is the reason why the scientists who first approached absolute zero in their laboratories stumbled unexpectedly on a world where the rules of conductivity, specific heat and other physical properties no longer applied. When, for example,

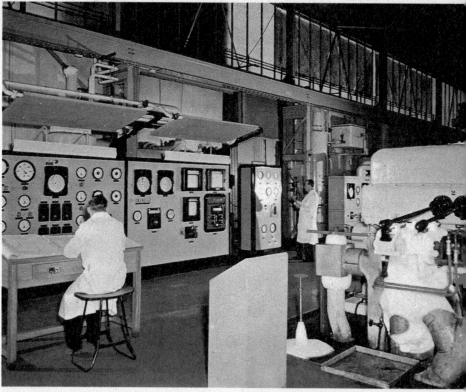

1 The control room of a modern air separation plant. The increasing demand for liquefied gases, such as nitrogen and oxygen, has made their separation an important industry.
2 At the temperature of liquid helium, amplifiers become far more efficient. Here one is tested; in time it is hoped to incorporate such amplifiers into satellite communication systems.
3 With an increase in work in the cold regions of the world, engines are needed to run satisfactorily under these conditions. Here a diesel has been modified to run under 'constant cold'.

Kamerlingh Onnes submerged a coil of lead in liquid helium in 1910, he found that it had no measurable electrical resistance. He connected a battery to the coil and then disconnected it and found that the coil still produced a magnetic field, indicating that the current continued to circulate without the battery. In an even more impressive experiment, he lowered a lead sphere over two lead rings kept at liquid helium temperatures, and previously maintained in a strong magnetic field. The sphere floated above the lead rings by magnetic repulsion due to induced currents in the sphere, which flowed without loss.

The phenomenon of zero resistance became known as *superconductivity* and was followed by another strange low-temperature effect – *superfluidity*. Liquid helium, it appeared, would defy gravity, and flow in a thin layer up the walls of a beaker that contained it and over the lip and down the outside. The helium would also flow through extremely narrow slits, and in some experiments appeared to have no viscosity – a measure of its ability to flow. The liquid would flow without friction and it was even possible to cause a jet of it to spurt up into the air without applying any pressure.

Clues to the cause of these strange phenomena, which are still not fully understood, lie with the removal of thermal motions in the material at very low temperatures and with a more regular arrangement of the constituents of the atoms – a far more subtle ordering than just the packing of atoms in the crystal lattice. Superconductivity in metals, for example, is thought to be due to the way in which the electrons which carry current may arrange themselves to travel with more ordered motions at low temperatures.

Superconductivity

Superfluidity remains a fascinating phenomenon for the pure scientist to explore, but superconductivity has obvious practical applications. Power lines could carry electricity from power stations to the users without the present costly losses due to resistive heating of the cables, if a superconductor were used. Also huge magnets, of far greater power than was previously possible, can be built using superconducting coils to form electromagnets. Magnetic fields of this intensity are strong enough to contain nuclear fusion reactions of the type responsible for the hydrogen bomb and make the energy usable for electric power production.

The application of superconductivity has been slowed down, however, by the difficulties in producing superconductors that engineers can use and which remain superconducting to higher temperatures than liquid helium – to the 20 °K. of liquid hydrogen, if possible. Promising alloys have been developed in Europe, Russia and the United States. Coils which will withstand huge magnetic fields without losing superconductivity have been built, and large helium-cooled magnets are used in research into fundamental particles. These magnets are energized by connecting them to a simple 12-volt car battery, which is

4 Diminishing fish stocks in the sea have forced trawlers to go further afield. These long voyages have been made possible through the use of liquid nitrogen to preserve the catches.

5 These insulated columns are used to separate oxygen and nitrogen. The columns are built to withstand extreme conditions of cold that result in the purification process.

then removed and not needed again for a long time.

In Britain, the world's first superconducting electric motor has been built and will soon be followed by a generator. The machine produces high torque at low speeds from direct current. The use of superconducting stator windings, bathed in liquid helium, makes it possible to reduce considerably the size of this type of machine. The zero-resistance power cable is, however, still some way in the future, as an alloy capable of conducting without resistance losses at the temperature of liquid hydrogen must be freely available, if the cost of liquid helium is to be avoided.

Superconductivity may yet have a vital part to play in the development of that other twentieth-century phenomenon, the digital computer. Individual digits of information can easily be stored as currents circulating perpetually in tiny pieces of superconductor, and the magnetic field produced makes it easy to read out the digit. A memory of this type would be extremely fast and highly compact, and the voracious appetite of the computer industry for faster, smaller machines may make superconductivity a key technology.

There are many other uses for zero resistance conductors, including the extension of the famous experiment of Kamerlingh Onnes in which he suspended a lead ball over a coil. This can be used directly to provide a frictionless bearing for a gyroscope, making gyroscopic compasses

This refrigerator produces temperatures as low as a tenth of a degree above absolute zero. It is used in conjunction with superconducting magnets to study the properties of solids.

still more accurate.

The exploration of absolute zero grew out of efforts to liquefy the common gases, and this original root of research has borne a more obvious fruit in the shape of the liquefied gas industry. The cheapest way of producing oxygen, nitrogen, and argon to fairly high purity has proved to be liquefaction of the air followed by distillation of the component gases. This is the basis of a huge industry which supplies oxygen, mainly to the steel mills, nitrogen for a growing list of refrigeration processes and liquid argon to the electronics industry. Air is liquefied by huge compression and expansion machines which have developed directly out of the liquefiers of Kamerlingh Onnes and his contemporaries. It is now no longer a unique experience to have held shimmering liquid air gingerly in one's hand for a few seconds as it boiled away and disappeared.

A useful refrigerant

The last property makes liquid nitrogen an almost ideal refrigerant as it cannot contaminate food in any way. In the food industry, liquid nitrogen is finding increasing use as a means of freezing fish, meat and vegetables so quickly and so hard that ice crystals do not have time to form inside the material and rupture the cells. The result is a method of preserving food that does not alter flavour or texture.

Swift freezing to low temperatures also makes it possible to preserve such fluids as blood, plasma and semen so that no physiological damage is caused and the liquid may be stored indefinitely. Blood transfusions and cow inseminations can be performed with liquids that have been

stored and transported in liquid nitrogen. This has reduced wastage in blood banks and makes rare types of blood more readily available. Freezing techniques have also been developed to preserve skin required for grafting.

The surgeon has other uses for cryogenics, as the new technique of cryosurgery gains ground in hospitals. Here bloodless surgery is possible as the surgeon uses a hollow probe filled with liquid hydrogen instead of a knife. The cold probe can be used to destroy diseased tissue, and this technique has already proved successful in many brain operations. On a cruder scale, ultra-cold brands are now in use as a means of marking cattle – the skin darkening caused by a liquid-nitrogen-cooled probe is not likely to fester and the animal suffers less pain during the branding.

Cryogenics covers a wide range of activities from the most fundamental research into the nature of matter, to the most basic technologies of industrialized society such as power production. The rocket engines which power the Saturn rockets on moon flights are fuelled with liquid oxygen and liquid hydrogen, while bottles of liquefied oxygen are a familiar sight in hospitals and industry. The physics of very low temperatures has been studied for only half a century, but already low temperatures, far surpassing anything found naturally on Earth, are part of our way of life.

The behaviour of matter alters fundamentally at temperatures approaching absolute zero. Studies are in progress to decipher what happens to electrons during superconductivity.

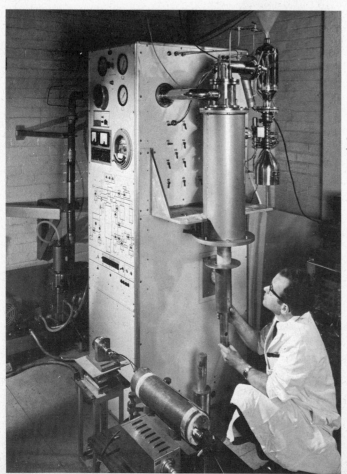

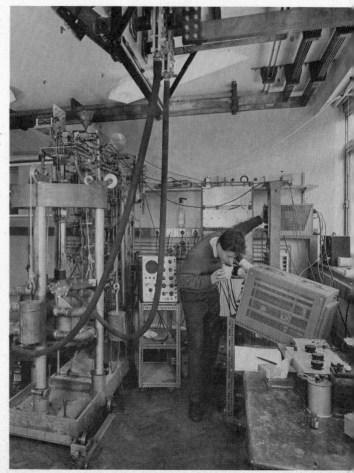

Water: the prime liquid

If ice did not float, if steam was generated with less heat, life probably could not exist on Earth. What are the physical and chemical properties of water which make it so remarkable?

WATER IS the most plentiful and widely distributed of chemical compounds and the most important to Man, for without water no form of life could exist. Over the entire surface of the Earth there is not a cubic inch of air nor an ounce of soil in which water is not present. It penetrates deep into the Earth's crust and enters into the composition of rocks and crystals. The bodies of living things consist mainly of water, which makes up as much as 90 per cent of the weight of some plants and animals.

Because water is liquid, it was thought to be an element or distinct substance until 1781, when Henry Cavendish demonstrated that it was a compond of two gases by burning hydrogen in oxygen and producing water. In 1806 Sir Humphry Davy confirmed this by passing an electric current through water and obtaining hydrogen and oxygen. The chemical formula for water is H_2O, showing that each molecule of the liquid is a combination of two atoms of hydrogen and one of oxygen.

Since 1931, however, it became known that water may be a compound of oxygen with either ordinary or heavy hydrogen – called deuterium – so giving the heavy water now associated with the release of nuclear energy. One part of heavy water with its double-weight hydrogen exists in 5,000 parts of water. It can be separated by evaporation or electrolysis, and its density, boiling and freezing points are higher than those of ordinary water.

Water is so plentiful and its presence is so widespread that the layman seldom thinks of it as a chemical substance. But to the chemist water is one of the most remarkable of all substances. It is extremely stable so that it can be subjected to extremes of pressure and temperature without breaking up; it can change its state, from solid to liquid and then to vapour and back again within narrow and ordinary temperature ranges and with the absorption and release of vast amounts of energy.

Water is also one of the prime promoters of chemical activity. Besides causing metals to rust and corrode, and rocks to decay into soil, it has tremendous and widespread effects on climate through ocean currents which act as distributors of the Earth's heat. Through its remarkable ability to change its state, water continually rises as a vapour from the sea and then condenses to fall on the land as rain. Water levels the hills and mountains as it flows to the sea, and through its capacity for dissolving other substances carries with it mineral materials from the land and is responsible for the saltiness of the sea.

As with any other substance, the properties of water can be divided into two

1 Life depends on water and Man has had to use his ingenuity to obtain water for arid regions. This aqueduct built by the Romans carried water to Acre in the Near East from the Kabri springs.
2 This limpid drop of dew on a garden leaf retains its shape because of the physical force of surface tension. This tension causes the outer molecules to form a surface skin.
3 An 1845 engraving of refining sugar; the basic process is still in use. By boiling the solution in a vacuum pan the boiling point of water is reduced and the sugar is not burnt.

main classes: *physical* and *chemical*. Physical properties are those that can be observed without a substance undergoing chemical changes, whereas chemical properties are those that manifest themselves in chemical activities.

At ambient temperatures, water is a tasteless, colourless and odourless liquid. These are its physical properties which are common to several other liquids and do not enable water to be specifically identified. Therefore, for the scientific identification of water its properties must be measured and expressed in precise values. The principal of these are: *density, specific heat* and freezing and boiling points. Density of a substance is the weight of a definite volume of that substance under any given conditions, while its specific heat is the amount of heat a definite weight of the substance must absorb to raise its temperature a given amount.

As the volume of a given weight of water varies with temperature changes, it is essential to state the temperature at which the density is measured. Water has its maximum density of 1 kg. per litre (62·4 lb per cubic ft) at a temperature of 4 °C. Water is the only compound that has this maximum density at 4 °C.

Knowledge of the density of water enables its pressure to be calculated for different depths. Thus the pressure at the bottom of a body of water 100 ft deep is 100 × 62·4 or 6,240 lb to the square in. A knowledge of the pressure of water at various depths is essential in the design of diving equipment, submarines and the construction of dams. All these must be able to withstand the force exerted on them by water pressure.

The boiling point of pure water under atmospheric pressure at sea level is 100 °C. or 212 °F., but with increasing altitude the boiling point is lowered. This is because air pressure is less at high altitudes. Lowering of the boiling point of water at high altitudes can be avoided by the use

of an autoclave or other pressure vessel to hold the water. Such a device holds in the steam, thereby increasing pressure on the liquid and raising its boiling point. Pressure also affects the freezing point of water; increased pressure lowers the freezing point.

Certain industries, notably those refining sugar and evaporating milk, exploit the phenomenon that reduced pressure lowers boiling point. Part of the air in which the sugar syrup or milk is being evaporated is evacuated by means of vacuum pumps. It is then possible to boil off the water content of the syrup or milk at a temperature low enough to obviate scorching the sugar or scalding the milk.

Profound effect on climate

Water also has an exceptional capacity to retain heat. It heats up very slowly. This is proved by the fact that the amount of heat necessary to warm one gram of water by 1 °C. is nine times as much as is needed to warm one gram of iron by 1 °C. and 30 times as much as is necessary to warm one gram of mercury by 1 °C.

Water's capacity to retain large amounts of heat is one of the reasons why it has such an effect on climate. Heat from the sun over tropical regions is absorbed by the sea and then carried by ocean currents to colder regions where it is released by the gradual cooling of the water. The Gulf Stream is a striking example of this phenomenon. The British Isles are as far north as Labrador, but they have a much more temperate climate because they are warmed by the Gulf Stream.

Water is the standard used when comparing the specific heats and densities of liquids and solids. Water has a specific density, in grams per c.c. of 1·000, whereas a liquid such as glycerin has a density, in grams per c.c. of 1·258 by the same standard. Water's maximum density at 4 °C. has an important bearing on the freezing of ponds and lakes in winter,

since the resultant ice is lighter than the water from which it is derived. That explains why an iceberg floats with a proportion of its bulk above the sea.

Pure water is a poor conductor of electricity; in fact no current at all can pass through distilled water. The reason why badly insulated electrical fittings in, for example, a bathroom are a source of danger is that the water in common use contains traces of dissolved minerals which are good electrical conductors. On the other hand, water is an excellent conductor of sound, and the greater its mineral content the greater its conductivity. At 0 °C. sound velocity in air at

1 Water can induce iron to rust by making it react with the oxygen of the atmosphere. The brownish-red substance that forms consists mainly of an oxide of iron combined with water.
2 Cumulus clouds tend to form in the warmth of a summer day. Like all clouds they consist of condensed water vapour, in the form of tiny drops of water, or of ice crystals. A great number of heavy cumulus clouds is a sign of rain.
3 When water freezes to ice, it expands instead of contracting, like other frozen liquids. This expansion has forced the cap off the top of a milk bottle.
4 Stalactites and stalagmites, like these in Gough's Cave at Cheddar, are formed by dripping water. As the water evaporates, it leaves a deposit of the minerals dissolved in it.
5 Because ice is less dense than the water from which it is derived, it floats with a proportion of its bulk above the surface. If ice sank, lakes, rivers and even seas would freeze solid in winter, killing fish and underwater life.
6 Because his weight is concentrated on the fine metal edges of his skates, the skater exerts such pressure on the ice that a thin layer melts wherever he moves. This film of water acts as an excellent lubricant for him to skate over.

4

5

6

sea level is 1,087 ft per second; in fresh water sound travels at a speed of 4,714 ft per second and in sea water the speed of sound increases to 4,990 ft per second.

Water can make an excellent lubricant under certain conditions. When, for example, a sledge is pushed over ice, the pressure under the runners melts the ice so that the sledge actually lubricates itself with a thin film of water as it slides along. Similarly, a skater can achieve high speeds on ice because he is skating over a thin film of lubricating water. In fact water would have many applications as a lubricant were it not so liable to evaporate and to induce the chemical reactions leading to corrosion.

If a needle is placed on a cigarette paper and the paper laid on the surface of water in a bowl, the paper will become saturated and sink; but the needle will be left floating on the surface of the water. Close inspection will show that the needle is actually lying in a hollow formed on the surface of the water. This is a striking demonstration of water's *surface tension*.

A state of tension

Surface tension is the phenomenon whereby the free surface of a liquid tends to contract to a minimum area. In water, as in other liquids, every molecule of which it is composed is surrounded by other molecules. All exert attractive forces on each other but as all molecules are pulling on each other, their pulls are cancelled out. On the surface of the liquid, however, molecules have neighbouring molecules underneath, and at the sides, but none above. As there is no upward pull to balance the downward pull, the surface molecules are pulled downwards to put them in a state of tension. It is this that enables the needle to float in a little hollow on the surface of the water without penetrating it. The pond-skater insect's ability to 'run' across water is a natural example of surface tension. The insect's feet stretch and depress the surface skin, which does not break but supports the pond-skater.

One manifestation of surface tension disproves the old adage that water cannot move upwards without being pumped. This manifestation is called *capillarity* and is due to the attraction of the molecules of the liquid for each other or for the solid surface with which the water is in contact. If water is enclosed in a narrow glass tube, the attraction between the glass walls of the tube is greater than that between the molecules of water. Consequently, when a glass tube is dipped into water, the water

rises some distance up the tube. A common example is when a lump of sugar soaks up a drop of water in which it is laid.

One of the most important physical properties of water is its ability to dissolve other substances and mix with them to form solutions. In this respect water is supreme and produces some of its outstanding effects. A solution of a substance in water is called an aqueous solution, and such solutions have countless applications in industry, the home and the laboratory. Amongst the many substances which mix easily with water to form solutions are solids such as salt and sugar; gases such as carbon dioxide and ammonia; and liquids such as alcohol and sulphuric acid. The quantity of any substance that will form a solution in a given quantity of water is governed mainly by temperature and pressure. When the limit to which a substance will dissolve in water is reached, the solution is said to be saturated.

Anti-freeze solutions

An aqueous solution has a lower freezing point than the water component of the solution. This is put to practical use in the anti-freeze solutions that protect the cooling systems of internal-combustion engines in cold weather. By adding substances, such as ethylene glycol or methanol, to the water in the radiator a solution is formed that has a lower freezing point than water by itself. It is the salt held in solution in the oceans that prevents sea water freezing as quickly as the fresh water in ponds and lakes.

Although water is a stable compound in that it does not decompose readily, it can take part in a variety of chemical reactions as a catalyst. Many reactions which occur readily in the presence of water, even in just traces of it, will not occur in its complete absence. Examples of the catalytic action of water are the combination of phosphorus with oxygen, the union of carbon monoxide with oxygen, the dissociation of ammonium chloride and of mercurous oxide.

Without water's catalytic properties, many chemical reactions between solids would be very difficult and the chemist could achieve his desired results only by the use of furnaces and other high-temperature devices. Water reacts by addition with most inorganic oxides to form acids or bases. Probably the most important reaction of water is that called *hydrolysis*, in which the water reacts with a salt to form an acid and a base. Hydrolysis of carbohydrates, fats and proteins is an essential step in the digestion and

1 Heavy water is now being used for the release of nuclear energy. Up to 500 tons a year are extracted from ordinary water at this plant on the Savannah River by dual temperature chemical exchange and vacuum distillation.
2 High-speed photography catches the ripples and disturbances as a droplet strikes the water.
3 The desalination plant at Canvey Island on the Thames Estuary produces 55,000 gallons each day of fresh water from sea water. The sea water has to pass through a ten-stage flash evaporator before the process is complete.

assimilation of food in the animal body.

Water exists in nature as a liquid, a solid (ice) and as a gas (steam), and each of these states can be changed from one to any of the other simply by raising or lowering temperature. Although each of the three states of water behaves the same way chemically, they are physically different. Water is a liquid because the molecules are attracted together quite strongly. When, however, water is heated, the attraction between the molecules is loosened and their motion increases. The higher the temperature of the applied heat, the faster the movement of the molecules. Eventually a temperature is reached when the molecules overcome the forces holding them together and exert enough pressure to push the liquid aside and form vapour bubbles. The bubbles then rise to the surface of the liquid and their contents escape as the gas called steam.

Boiling point of water is that point in its heating when large numbers of the molecules acquire enough motion to break entirely free of their neighbours, overcome the pressure of the atmosphere, and go free. When water boils into steam, it expands approximately 1,600 times, and further heating increases the molecular action still more, so causing even greater expansion. It is the expanding properties of steam that made possible the invention and development of the steam engine.

Contrary to a popular idea, the vapour seen issuing from the spout of a boiling kettle is not steam. Steam is a colourless and odourless gas, and the visible vapour is simply a cloud of minute droplets of water cooling and condensing on contact with the lower temperature of the atmosphere. The steam from a kettle is the minute and invisible gap between the spout tip and the visible vapour.

When the temperature of water is lowered beyond a certain point, it begins to freeze, and at and below 0 °C, it becomes ice. Consequent upon this process its atomic structure is different from that of steam. Whereas steam is composed of separate molecules, ice has an ordered structure, called a crystal, which can be considered as one large molecule consisting of several water molecules held together by hydrogen bonds. The molecules in ice are so arranged that each oxygen atom has four hydrogen atoms linked fairly closely: two of them are attached by strong covalent bonds; that is, by shared electrons; the other two are held to their oxygen atom by weaker hydrogen bonds and at a greater distance. The crystalline nature of frozen water is well illustrated by the beautiful and geometrical pattern of snow flakes, which are, of course, frozen water.

Every year increasing amounts of water are needed by industry, agriculture and for human consumption. And every year the available supplies of water become less, not only in the arid regions of the world but even in temperate zones. The fact that three-quarters of the Earth's surface is covered with water does little to meet the shortage; for mankind's need is for fresh water and the available supplies of that are limited.

In solution

When a substance – liquid, gas or solid – is dissolved and thoroughly mixed into another substance, a solution is formed. Such solutions are vital in the home, in industry and to life itself.

WHEN SUGAR is thoroughly stirred in a cup of tea, the sugar appears to disappear without trace. It is still there, of course, but it has dissolved in the tea and its particles are so minute and evenly distributed throughout the tea that they cannot be seen. In other words, by stirring the sugar in the tea, a *solution* has been made. A chemist would say that a solution of sugar has been made, or that sugar is in solution in the tea.

In chemical language, a solution is an extremely intimate mixture, of variable composition, of two or more substances, one of which is usually a liquid. A true solution is formed when two or more substances are so thoroughly mixed together that the mixture is *homogeneous*; that is, identical throughout its bulk. The more common solutions consist of a solid or a liquid dissolved in a liquid; but there are others. Gas may be dissolved in a liquid, as in fizzy drinks; water, in the form of vapour, may be dissolved in air; and one solid may be dissolved in another, as with certain metal alloys.

Solutions are used every day in the home and in industry, and without solutions life itself would be impossible. The air we breathe is a solution of different gases, such as oxygen and nitrogen. The bulk of our food is broken down by digestive processes into a solution so that it can be carried in the blood to the cells and tissues of the body. Nearly everything we drink, be it water or beverages, is some kind of solution.

The seas and oceans are solutions formed by the salts and other substances dissolved in water. The petrol in a car's

fuel tank is a solution, as is glass and many medicaments such as tincture of iodine. Mineral salts occur as solutions in the water in the ground and are drawn through the roots of plants as solutions to reach the topmost branches and leaves.

Every solution must have a *solute* or dissolved substance, and a *solvent* or dissolving substance. If the constituents of a solution are not in the same physical state, that is if one is a solid and the other a liquid, the solvent is generally the substance that exists in the same state as

the resulting solution. Thus the sugar dissolved in the tea is the solute and the tea is the solvent. Similarly, when water, in the form of water vapour, evaporates in the air, the air is the solvent and the water is the solute.

Constituents of a solution may be in the same physical state: liquid, solid or gaseous. In that event, the substance present in greatest quantity in the solution is the solvent. Water and alcohol can be mixed to constitute a solution in any desired proportion, but in any particular solution the water is not necessarily the solvent nor is the alcohol always the solute, or vice versa. If, for example, 20 parts of water are mixed with 80 parts of alcohol, alcohol is the solvent and water is the solute. If the proportions are reversed, alcohol is the solute and the water is the solvent.

When a solute, such as sugar, goes into solution in a solvent, such as tea, individual particles of the sugar break loose and move about freely in the solvent as individual sugar molecules. In the case of a solution of water and table salt, the action of the solute is rather different. The particles of table salt separate into negatively charged chlorine atoms, called chlorine ions, and positively charged sodium atoms, called sodium ions.

Sugar and water provide one of the best examples of an interaction between a solid and a liquid to produce a simple solution. When a lump of sugar is placed in a glass of water, the water is initially all water and the sugar all sugar. Almost at once, however, the water starts to dissolve the sugar and the sugar molecules

1 Salt is sprinkled on icy roads in Britain in winter. The salt forms a solution with the surface water, lowering the freezing temperature, and the ice melts.

2 A fishing boat steers clear of icebergs off Greenland. When seawater freezes, the salt is left behind in the water and the ice can be melted for use as drinking water.

3 Automatic coin-operated petrol pumps are tested at Essen, Germany. Petrol is an effective organic solvent and is useful for forming solutions with organic compounds.

begin to leave the solid lump and form a solution. Initially, there are only a few sugar molecules in solution in the water, and the sugar will be very weak: a *dilute solution*. Occasionally one of the sugar molecules in solution will strike against the solid sugar and may remain attached to it. This occurs more frequently as the solution becomes more concentrated; that is, as the solvent takes up more of the solute. This is because the more sugar molecules there are in solution, the greater chance that some of them will collide with the solid solute.

If the temperature of the solution does not change, the number of sugar molecules that leave the solid solute and go into solution in each second per square inch of surface remains constant. On the other hand, the number of sugar molecules that leave the solution and are deposited on the solid solute in each second will increase as the number of sugar molecules in a given volume of solution increases: that is, as the concentration of the solution increases towards saturation.

Eventually, the number of sugar molecules going into solution in each second will be just equal to the number of sugar molecules leaving the solution. At that point – the *point of saturation* – the sugar in solution will be in equilibrium. When the solution is completely saturated, the solute that cannot dissolve in the solvent remains at the bottom of the dish.

The influence of heat

Because the forces of cohesion existing between the molecules in a solid solute have been overcome in the solution process, the process entails a change of energy. This may manifest itself in the absorption or the generation of heat. In the former case, an increase in temperature supplies the heat deficiency and so increases the solubility of the solute. That is why sugar and salt are more soluble in hot water than they are in cold.

The solubility of solid solutes depends upon the nature of the solvent in which they are being dissolved. Thus salt and sugar readily form solutions with water,

but many important organic compounds, such as the nitrocellulose lacquers, are not soluble in water, although they are in organic liquids such as benzene.

When dealing with solutions, it is essential to remember the difference between solutions and *suspensions*. Certain solids mixed with a liquid do not break down into individual molecules. Instead, they make the liquid cloudy, as when chalk powder is shaken up with water. This liquid is a suspension. Although the particles of chalk are spread throughout the liquid they are not dissolved in it, for if the mixture is left standing for a time the particles will settle on the bottom of the container.

If a suspension of chalky water is poured through a fine filter, the water passes through the pores of the filter, but the chalk particles remain behind. Many medicine mixtures are suspension, which is why the bottles have instructions to shake before a dose.

In some solutions, dissolving the solutes results in their particles being mixtures of molecules and ions. White vinegar, a solution of acetic acid in water, is an example. There are three kinds of solute particles in vinegar: positively charged hydrogen ions, negatively charged acetate ions and acetic-acid molecules.

When the particles of a solute moving about in a solution are positively and negatively charged ions, the solution can conduct an electric current. In that case the solute is called an electrolyte. A conductive solution is the basis of the electric cell.

The concentration of a solute in a given solvent that will produce saturation at a given temperature is called the *solubility* of the solute. Solubility of a solution is defined as the number of grams of solute that will dissolve in 100 gm of solvent at a specified temperature. Thus a saturated solution of calcium hydroxide, better known as lime, in water contains 0·165 gm of lime in 100 gm of water at 20 °C. Consequently even a concentrated solution of lime and water is relatively dilute. Conversely, when sugar is dissolved in water,

1 A drop of ink is slowly dispersed in a glass of water to form a solution. Because of the proportions of ink to water, water is the solvent and ink the solute.
2 The sea contains huge amounts of salt in solution. At Swakopmund, Southwest Africa, seawater is pumped into pans. It then evaporates, leaving deposits of salt.
3 As well as salt, the sea also contains other minerals, such as uranium, in very low concentrations. Methods have now been devised to extract uranium from the seawater solution.
4 A turbulent river is brown with mud. The solid particles of earth do not dissolve in the water but remain in suspension to form a cloudy liquid. When the river reaches flat land, the mud settles on to the bed.
5 At an oil research laboratory in the Netherlands, a solution of lubricating oil is tested to determine its alkalinity.

the solution will not be saturated until 200 gm of sugar have been dissolved for every 100 gm of water.

Temperature has an important effect upon the solubility of substances. In general, the higher the temperature, the greater the solubility of a solid or liquid. In the case of gases, however, the higher the temperature the less soluble the gas. This is because fewer gas molecules occupy a given volume of solvent.

A glass of tap water left standing in a warm room gives visual indication of the effects of temperature on a gas-water solution. Cold water drawn from a tap contains dissolved gases in the form of air. Gases are more soluble in cold water than in warm water. Consequently, if the cold water from the tap is saturated or nearly saturated with dissolved air, some of the dissolved air must leave the solution when the glass stands in a room and the temperature of the gas-water solution rises. This causes the air to separate from the water as small bubbles on the inner surface of the glass. The higher the temperature, the greater the amount of gas released from the gas-water solution. When tap water is heated towards its boiling-point, bubbles of gas (the air in the water) rise to the surface. At boiling-point, the gas can be completely driven out of the water.

Density and pressure

Pressure is another very important factor in solutions. If a quantity of water is put into a closed container, water molecules escape from the liquid into the confined space above it by a process called evaporation. At the same time, molecules of the gaseous water-vapour strike the surface of the water and are held to it to become molecules of liquid water by condensation. As evaporation continues, the density, and therefore the pressure, of the gas above the water increases until a state of equilibrium is reached between the rate of evaporation and the rate of condensation.

Adjustment of equilibrium between condensation and evaporation of a solution of gas and water explains what happens when a bottle of soda water or other fizzy drink is opened. Soda water consists of carbon dioxide dissolved in water. When the bottle is tightly sealed, the carbon dioxide in the space above the liquid in the neck of the bottle is under pressure. The carbon dioxide dissolved in the water is in equilibrium with the gas under pressure, and no bubbles are visible. But when the cap is removed, the pressure is reduced and the superfluous gas rises to the surface as fizzing bubbles.

Water is the most common of all solvents and has been called the 'universal solvent' because so many substances dissolve in it. Even what are normally considered to be insoluble substances, such as sand, chalk or glass, will form extremely weak solutions with water, but the amount of solute in such solutions is so minute that it can be detected only with the most sensitive of instruments and analytical techniques. When water is the solvent, the solution is called an *aqueous solution*.

To dissolve organic compounds a solvent

which is itself organic is often required to form a solution. Effective organic solvents are petrol and carbon tetrachloride. Benzene solvents will form solutions with rubber, and alcohol will dissolve substances such as iodine and shellac. Similarly lacquers and nail varnishes are based on solutions of amyl acetate and cellulose. Turpentine forms a solution with most oil-bound paints, and is used as a thinner or for removing paint stains.

Not all liquids mix with each other to form solutions, and for that reason they are classed as either *totally miscible*, *partially miscible* or *immiscible,* according to whether or not they mix together completely to form a solution. Alcohol and water are totally miscible because these two liquids will dissolve completely in one another as a single solution, irrespective of the amounts of alcohol and water. Partially miscible liquids are those which will mix only to a certain extent in solution, examples being alcohol and petrol. Oil and water are immiscible.

Crystalloids and colloids

While studying the diffusion of liquids, the Scottish chemist Thomas Graham (1805–69) defined substances as *crystalloids* which in solution could pass freely through a porous membrane. Those substances which also formed apparently homogeneous solutions, but which were unable to pass through a parchment membrane, he called *colloids*.

On the basis of his experiments, Graham divided all substances which form solutions into crystalloids and colloids. Later investigations have shown that Graham's arbitrary divisions are no longer acceptable. The difference between crystalloids and colloids is not so much a matter of

kind as it is of degree, and these terms cannot be accepted as indicating different kinds of matter, but merely different states of matter.

There is, however, a distinction between a true solution and a colloidal solution. When the particles of a substance are very much larger than those of the solvent in which they are dissolved, the mixture is in colloidal solution. If the particles of the solute and the solvent are of approximately the same size, the mixture is a true solution and behaves as such. Colloidal solutions of metals, such as gold, silver and platinum, are made by striking a direct-current arc between two electrodes of the particular metals beneath the surface of cooled water.

Under some circumstances solutions can become *supersaturated*. Normally, the maximum amount of a solid solute that will dissolve in a solvent is the quantity necessary to yield a saturated solution. However, it is possible to have a solution which contains more solute than is necessary to saturate it. The solution is then said to be supersaturated.

Supersaturation normally occurs when a hot solution, containing neither crystals of the solute nor dust, is left to cool. The excess of solid will remain in solution as long as the solution is undisturbed. But if a tiny crystal of the solid solute is dropped into the solution, or even if dust enters, crystallization is immediately initiated and then continues until only sufficient

of the solid solute remains in the solvent to saturate it.

One of the practical uses of solutions is that the boiling-point of a solution is higher than that of its solvent, while the freezing-point of a solution is lower than that of the solvent. Thus when an antifreeze, such as ethylene glycol, is added to water in car radiators, it lowers the freezing-point of the water.

Similarly, the ice on snowbound roads can be melted by sprinkling salt on it. The salt is dissolved in the small amount of liquid water present on the surface of the ice or snow and so forms a salt solution. As the freezing-point of the salt solution is lower than that of the water solvent, the ice melts and goes into solution. If, however, the temperature is below the temperature at which the salt solution freezes, the ice will not melt when the salt is added.

Chemists can separate and identify constituents of solutions by analytical methods including filtration, distillation and the passage of an electric current. Sometimes separation can be done by simple application of heat. Nature can separate the constituents of salt water by the formation of ice. When a salt solution such as seawater freezes, ice crystals separate leaving the dissolved salt behind in the unfrozen water. In the Arctic, Eskimos living where natural fresh water is unobtainable get their drinking water by melting the ice formed from seawater.

1 Complex apparatus in the distillation department of a research laboratory is used for the more difficult separation of liquid solutions.
2 Champagne is bottled and corked at a vineyard in France. The gas, produced by secondary fermentation, dissolves in the wine under pressure. When the cork is removed the pressure is reduced and the superfluous gas rises as bubbles.

When matter moves

Why do rifles kick and rockets lift off? How can we predict where a cricket ball or intercontinental ballistic missile will land? This article introduces the basic laws of motion.

TO UNDERSTAND what is happening when an object moves, it is necessary to be clear about the difference between speed and velocity, velocity and acceleration, mass and momentum. But first we must be able to describe a particle's position and the way it changes its position.

A particle's position can only be described clearly by referring to a previously fixed position. We may say that a particle is at a position X units along a line from position O, the *origin* or point where the line begins. Or we can give the position of a particle by measuring its distance from two fixed lines at right angles. It could be X units from one line and Y from the other. A pair of such lines at right angles are called rectilinear axes or co-ordinates. In each case, we need to know a distance (a number and its units) and a direction to define the position of a particle by its distance from the origin and its direction from the origin in terms of the angles the direction makes with one of the rectilinear axes. A measurement, such as that just described, which has magnitude and an associated direction is called a *vector*.

For example, if we describe a place as being four miles to the east, we are defining its position in terms of distance and direction. In this example, 'four miles to the east' is a vector quantity.

Plotting a course

The rate at which a particle moves in a given direction is its velocity. Velocity has the units of distance per unit time (such as feet per second or miles an hour) and is also a vector quantity. Speed also has such units, but direction need not be specified. Thus a train may have a speed of 60 miles an hour, but its velocity will be, say, 60 miles an hour in a northerly direction. Since we have seen that position requires a vector to define it, we may say that velocity is the rate of change of position. If this rate remains constant and a particle is displaced a distance S in a time t, then its velocity $V = S/t$. If a moving particle changes direction but always covers the same distance in the same time, it is moving at a constant *speed* but not with a

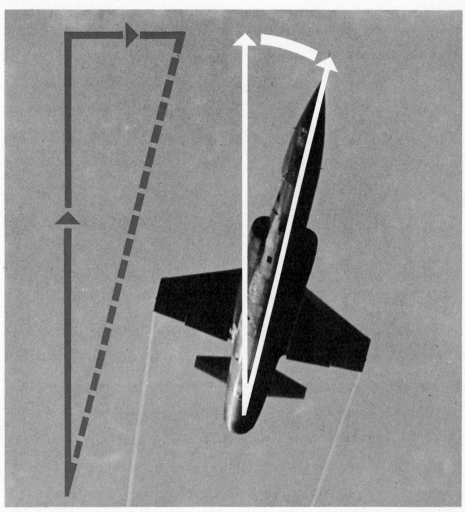

What happens when a wind shifts a jet off course? We use vectors to find the new speed and direction. This plane was moving north at 200 m.p.h.

Draw a vector 20 units long. The wind was easterly at 50 m.p.h. – a vector 5 units long. The dotted line measures 20·6 units – a speed of 206 m.p.h.

constant velocity.

If the velocity of a moving particle increases while it is still moving, then the particle is said to accelerate. Since it involves velocity, acceleration is also a vector quantity. It is the rate of change of velocity and has the units of distance per unit time per unit time (such as feet per second per second, generally written as feet per sec²). For example, if a train takes

1 minute to increase its velocity in a given direction from 20 feet per second to 80 feet per second, its acceleration is $(80-20) \div 60$ $= 1$ foot per sec².

The quantity of matter in a particle is its *mass* measured in such units as grams, pounds, tons, and so on. It is the measure of the property that makes it resist a change in its motion that is, its inertia. If a particle of mass m is moving with a

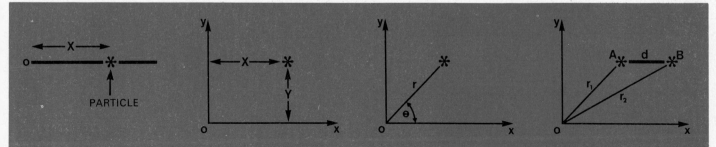

How to plot the position of a particle and a change in its position. (1) We may define the position of a particle as being X units along a line from the origin O, or (2) as being X units from the y-axis and Y units from the x-axis of a set of rectilinear co-ordinates. (3) Position may also be defined in terms of a distance and direction, in this case as a distance r from the origin along a line making an angle θ with the x-axis. (4) A change in position from A (defined by the vector r_1) to B (defined by the vector r_2) is given by the new vector $\mathbf{d}$.

velocity v, the product of the mass and velocity is called its momentum, p. Momentum is also a vector quantity and has units such as gm-cm per sec or lb-ft per sec. A 12-stone man running at 15 miles an hour (equal to 22 feet per second) has a momentum of 3,696 lb-ft per sec. A rifle bullet weighing half an ounce and moving at 3,200 feet per second has a momentum of 100 lb-ft per sec.

To change the momentum of a moving particle requires the application of a force. And to start a stationary particle moving also requires a force. The effect of a force will depend on its magnitude and direction (so that force is also a vector quantity). For example, a force applied to a moving particle in the same direction as that in which it is already moving will tend to make it move faster. A force applied at right angles to this direction will tend to make it change its course and move off in a different direction.

Force has special units. The force that will give an acceleration of 1 cm per sec^2 to a mass of 1 gram is called 1 dyne, and 1 poundal is the force that will accelerate 1 lb at 1 ft per sec^2. In mathematical terms, the force F required to give an acceleration a to a mass m is given by: $F=ma$.

In drag-motor-car racing, the object is to make the car cover a measured distance (usually a quarter of a mile) from a standing start in the shortest possible time – that is, to achieve the greatest possible acceleration. The force involved is that generated by the engine. Since $F=ma$, for a given power of engine the most acceleration will be achieved by the car of smallest mass. For this reason, drag-racing cars weigh as little as is possible, and consist of lightweight frames with just wheels, engine, and steering wheel. (Some car designers sacrifice a little weight in order to carry a parachute for stopping the car at the end of its headlong dash.)

Newton's First Law

Isaac Newton studied the motion of particles and the quantities we have just defined. He formulated three Laws of Motion. The first law states that a particle at rest will remain at rest or a particle moving in a straight line with uniform velocity will continue to move in this manner unless acted on by an outside force. The first part of the law may seem obvious; an observer watching a book on a table would be very surprised indeed if the book suddenly, of its own accord, moved across the table or up into the air. But the second part of the law is less obvious and not confirmed by common experience unless we think about it.

Imagine rolling a marble across a large floor or pushing a small wheeled vehicle such as a trolley across a large, flat, open space. We observe that, sooner or later, the marble or the trolley comes to rest. According to Newton's first law, they should go on moving indefinitely *unless* there is an outside retarding force. In our examples, the outside force is friction; friction between the marble and the surface on which it is rolling and friction between the wheels of the trolley and its axles.

Confirmation of the first law may be ob-

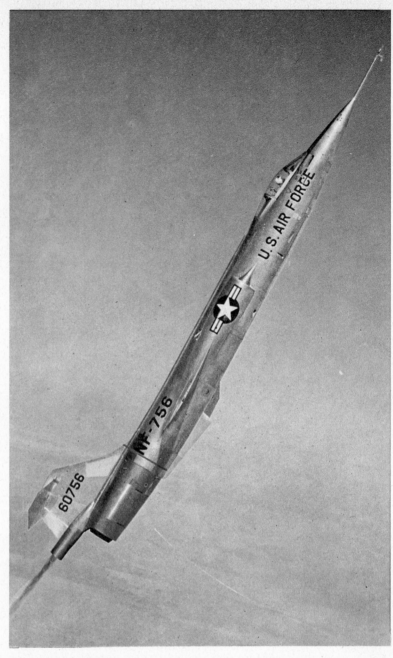

tained by studying particles moving with uniform velocities in straight lines with little or no friction or air resistance to impede their motion. Such conditions exist when atomic particles, such as protons and mesons, are fired through an apparatus called a cloud chamber. Droplets of water condensing on the track of the invisible particle after it has passed mark its progress (rather in the way that a vapour trail in the sky reveals the presence of a high-flying aircraft).

Only when an outside force acts, such as an electric or magnetic field on charged particles or a collision with another particle, do the tracks deviate from straight lines. Using the equation connecting force, mass, and acceleration, we see that the gravitational force acting on any falling body is given by $F=mg$, where m is the mass of the body and g is the acceleration due to gravity (equal to 981 cm per sec^2 or 32·2 ft per sec^2). But the quantity mg is also the weight of the body. Thus we see that weighing a series of objects merely compares the force of gravity acting on each of them. Strictly speaking, these comparisons should be made in units of

force (dynes or poundals); but since the acceleration g is a constant factor in all weighings, we use similar units to those of mass (grams and pounds) and distinguish them by calling them grams-weight and pounds-weight.

According to Newton's first law, force is required to stop a falling body. Any cricketer who has got under and caught a falling cricket ball will confirm the truth of the law. And if he misses the ball, the required arresting force is supplied by the reaction from the ground where the ball lands.

Why rockets lift off

Newton's second Law of Motion states that, as force is required to change the momentum of a moving particle (the first law), the rate of change of momentum is proportional to the applied force and takes place in the same direction as that in which the force is applied. We saw that momentum equals mass multiplied by velocity, $p=mv$. If the force F takes a time t to change the velocity of a moving particle from v to u (changing the momentum from mv to mu), the second law may be

stated mathematically as $F=(mv-mu)/t$.

This equation looks like another way of defining force. We may re-write it as $F=m(v-u)/t$. But the quantity $(v-u)\div t$ is the acceleration a. So the equation becomes $F=ma$, exactly as before.

Confirmation of the second law is easiest to obtain by studying particles that are initially at rest. When a billiards player hits a stationary ball, the force from the cue is transmitted to the ball and the ball moves off in the same direction as the cue was moved. It then obeys the first law and continues to move in a straight line until acted on by another force. In this case, that will mean a collision with another ball or a cushion.

Newton's third Law of Motion states simply that for every action there is an equal and opposite reaction. If the action is a force, then there must somewhere exist an equal force acting in the opposite direction. A book resting on a table is acting downwards due to the force of gravity. At the same time, there is an equal and opposite force (a reaction) in the table acting upwards.

Or consider the case of a cartridge

Velocity, acceleration, momentum and force – the vector quantities that measure space travel. The Starfighter, *left*, can fly to the edge of space – and rockets in nose and wing-tips change direction and momentum. In airless space, the Delta rocket, *centre*, fires four gas jets and

exploding in the breech of a rifle. The force of the explosion (action) pushes the bullet forwards. Reaction causes the rifle to recoil and move backwards into the shoulder of the firer. If we know the weight of the bullet and rifle, and know the speed of the bullet, we can calculate just how hard is the 'kick' felt by the firer. If the bullet weighs half an ounce and the muzzle velocity of the rifle is 3,200 feet per second, the force of the explosion gives the bullet a forward momentum of 100 lb-ft per sec. And if the rifle weighs 10 pounds, it moves backwards with the same momentum – that is, at a velocity of 10 feet per second. So we can see why a heavier rifle, firing the same type of cartridge, does not recoil as fast and gives less 'kick'.

Consider now an automatic firearm producing a stream of bullets. Newton's third law requires that there must be a reaction for every exploding cartridge and

moves by reacting against their force, just as a gun recoils when fired. Rockets demonstrate Newton's third Law of Motion: 'for every action there is an equal and opposite reaction'. To lift the rocket, *right*, a force greater than the force of gravity is released in the roar of the blast-off.

indeed there would be a sharp kick backwards each time a bullet is accelerated. Special recoil springs are fitted to machine guns which turn these frequent sharp kicks into a gentle constant push. This same principle applies to a rocket. Instead of bullets, a rocket 'fires' a stream of hot gases. Reaction to the force of the gas stream causes the case or body of the rocket to move in the opposite direction. For this reason, rockets will work in outer space in the total absence of air – they do not work by 'pushing against' air but purely by reaction.

Walking in space

Another demonstration of reaction has come within the first years of the 1960s, from Man's ventures into space. Imagine an astronaut, having climbed out of his space capsule, 'walking' in space and tethered to his capsule by a life-line. When he pulls on the line, instead of the capsule moving closer to the astronaut, the astronaut moves towards the capsule. The force along the rope tending to pull the capsule is balanced by a reaction tending to pull the man. And since the capsule is much more massive than the man, he moves towards it. Similarly, an astronaut outside his capsule might try to tighten a nut with an ordinary spanner. But since he has nothing to 'hang on' to, the reaction to the force he applies to the spanner causes the astronaut himself to turn round, and not the nut.

Newton's Laws of Motion enable us to predict what will happen when forces are applied to stationary or moving particles. The quantities we have been using, such as velocity, acceleration, momentum, and force, are all vector quantities. We require one final technique in order to manipulate them: we must be able to add vectors.

Bullets and drag-racers

The following problem is a simple one involving the addition of vectors: an aircraft is flying northwards at a steady speed of 200 miles an hour. Suddenly it is struck by an easterly gale blowing at 50 miles an hour. What is the final speed and course of the aircraft? Let us go through the method of working.

The initial speed and direction of the aircraft (its velocity) is a vector quantity and may be represented by a vertical line drawn, say, 20 units long. One unit of length stands for 10 miles an hour. The 50-mile-an-hour wind may then be represented by a horizontal line 5 units long.

By drawing the second arrow at right angles to the head of the first arrow, a new line joining the end of the first to the head of the second shows the final course of the aircraft. Furthermore, the length of this line, about 20·62 units, represents the speed of the aircraft – that is, on our scale, 206·2 miles an hour.

In this example, the angle of the new

course is about 14° east of the original course. We can determine the new velocity and direction of the aircraft by measuring the length of the line and its angle. Or, if we know trigonometry, we can calculate them. This method of completing the triangle of vectors can be applied to all such problems of this type. It is used to calculate the speeds and courses of ships, aircraft and rockets, and obviously has great practical uses.

The explosion that pushes the bullet forwards also drives the gun backwards. One way to find the kick of the rifle is to fire it. But if we know the speed of the bullet, and the weight of bullet and rifle, a simple calculation yields the force of the recoil against the shoulder.

Because $F=ma$, drag-car racers strip their cars to minimum weight – an engine, four wheels and a steering column. F is the force supplied by the engine. It equals m, the mass or weight, multiplied by a, the acceleration. The lower the mass, the greater the acceleration of the vehicle.

On the edge of a turning circle

When objects follow a circular path, odd and alarming events may occur: men may walk up walls, satellites maintain their orbits, and motor cars overturn. What forces are involved?

EVER SINCE ANTIQUITY, the circle has been considered a very special geometric figure. Aristotle thought it to be the most perfect figure, and so postulated that the heavenly bodies must move in perfect circles. It was the 'natural' thing for them to do. Two thousand years later, Johannes Kepler (1571–1630) showed that the planets do not move in circles but ellipses, and Isaac Newton (1642–1727) showed that circular motion is anything but natural.

For most practical purposes, however, it is still useful to conceive of the planets and other orbiting bodies as moving round in perfect circles, although the explanation of why they go round as they do is more properly based on Newton's Laws of Motion, not Aristotle's respect for the perfection of heavenly orbits.

Importance of inertia

All three laws of motion play a part in circular movement, but perhaps the key is the first one, which states: a body at rest will tend to remain at rest, and a body in motion along a straight line will continue to move in a straight line, unless acted upon by some outside force. More simply, physical objects will not do anything – move or change their straight-line motion – unless forced to do so.

This property of physical objects is generally referred to as *inertia*, and may be easily demonstrated. Place a square of stiff cardboard over the mouth of a glass and put a heavy coin in the centre. Now,

Right, a huge cylinder begins to turn, slowly at first, then faster and faster. People find themselves pressed against the wall. The floor drops away, but they stay 'pinned' in place, held there by the reaction of their bodies to centripetal force and the friction of their clothes against the wall. *Below,* on a flat surface, only tyre friction provides centripetal force. Banking a turn allows part of the car's weight to be used to keep it on the road.

with a sharp snap of the fingers, strike the edge and the cardboard will go flying off, but the coin, because of its inertia, will tend to remain behind and will fall into the glass. Competent magicians do this very same trick in a more dramatic manner using a full dinner setting. By a skilful jerk of the arms, the table cloth can be pulled out from under the dishes and silverware, which will end up sitting on the table undisturbed. To aid their skill, the magicians often weight the dishes and silverware to increase their inertia.

The fact that moving bodies tend to remain in motion along a straight line (the second part of the definition of inertia) is the reason for the familiar sensation of 'flying forward' when an automobile comes to a sudden stop. The car stops, but your body doesn't, unless you are restrained by a safety belt or have the misfortune to crash against the windscreen.

Since inertia keeps physical bodies moving in a straight line in the absence of an outside force, it is apparent that to cause a body to move in a circle, there must be an outside force. In the case of a sling-

shot or a 'hammer' thrown in athletics, the force is supplied by someone's arm. In the case of a satellite circling the Earth or the Earth circling the sun, the necessary force is supplied by gravity – the Earth's gravity in the first case, the sun's gravity in the second. This force is directed towards the centre of the circle, so it is often called the *centripetal force,* the word 'centripetal' meaning 'towards the centre'.

Anyone who has swung a hammer or a slingshot will have felt another force apparently causing the swinging weight to pull away from the centre. This is often called the *centrifugal force.*

A great deal of confusion exists concerning this force: some people say it is real, others say it is a figment of the imagination, and still others say it is a mathematical fiction invented to make calculations about objects moving in circles easier. Each one of these points of view has only part of the truth.

As has already been pointed out, circular motion is not 'natural', so a force must be supplied to cause it. At the same time, because of the property of inertia, a mass resists a change of motion from a straight line. The force felt at the hand of the hammer thrower is caused by the reluctance of the swinging mass to be pulled out of straight-line motion. The centrifugal force, then, is real insofar as it acts on the hand, but fictitious if conceived to act on the hammer. In fact, centrifugal force is caused *by* a swinging object, it is *not* a second force acting *on* a swinging object.

Origin of acceleration

This interpretation of centrifugal force is quite in accord with Newton's oft-quoted Third Law of Motion: for every action, there is an equal and opposite reaction. In this case, the action is the force from the hand acting on the object; the reaction is the force of the object acting on the hand. *There is no outward, or centrifugal, force acting on the object,* though for mathematical purposes it is often convenient to think so.

There is another way of thinking about circular motion which is particularly useful in understanding planetary movements and satellites orbiting the Earth. Newton's Second Law of Motion states: the force applied to a body is directly proportional to its mass and acceleration. In simple language, this means that whenever a force is applied to a physical body and not countered by an opposing force, the body will accelerate. This law is expressed mathematically by the equation:

$$F = ma$$

where F is the force, m is the mass and a is the acceleration. Since a swinging mass

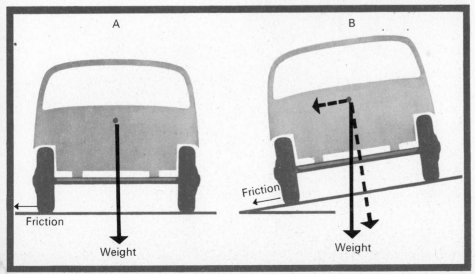

A

B

Friction

Friction

Weight

Weight

has a centripetal force acting towards the centre of the circle, but no counter force on it acting away from the centre of the circle, it must be accelerating, i.e. changing velocity.

This conclusion may seem a bit strange, because a heavy object swung round on a string often appears to have a constant velocity. Physicists, however, have a special meaning for the term 'velocity' which is different from the common meaning. To a physicist, velocity is a *vector* quantity, meaning that it has both magnitude and direction. In physics, then, speed and velocity are two different things. Speed is how fast something moves (in feet per second, miles per hour or other such units). Velocity is speed (magnitude) in a definite straight-line direction.

A change in either speed or direction, or both, constitutes an acceleration. A heavy object, or an Earth satellite, moving round in a circular orbit may show no change in magnitude (speed), but it is constantly changing direction, because it is constantly being pulled out of a straight-line path.

Forever falling

If one throws a ball horizontally very hard, it starts out parallel to the ground, but rather quickly curves down until it hits the ground. Inertia would tend to keep it parallel to the ground, so the fact that it curves means a force must be acting on it. This force, of course, is the force of gravity. Now imagine throwing the ball so hard that gravity causes its path to curve exactly the same amount that the Earth itself curves. That is, as the ball curves towards the Earth, the Earth curves away from the ball by exactly the same amount, so the ball never hits the ground. This happens all the way round the globe.

With this analysis in mind, the answer to the rather puzzling question asked when people see a satellite passing overhead becomes obvious, if hard to believe. What keeps it up there? The answer is, nothing keeps it up there! It is constantly falling,

A racing motor-cycle corners a banked track at high speed. Banking the machine increases the centripetal force acting to hold the vehicle on the road and makes high-speed cornering possible.

but the ground 'falls away' just as fast as the satellite falls towards it. The result is an orbit right round the world. The satellite will remain in that orbit circling round the Earth forever, so long as no extra forces such as air friction, radiation pressure, or solar winds cause it to deviate from its circular path.

This is the main reason why satellites are put into orbit so high up where the atmosphere is thin or absent. It is quite possible to orbit a satellite at 100 feet, rather than 100 miles. But this would be most impractical. If the satellite were fortunate enough not to hit anything, it would very quickly come down due to friction with the air, if it did not melt from the friction first.

Research has shown that the amount of force required to keep a body moving in a circular orbit is given by the equation:

$$F = \frac{mV^2}{r}$$

where F is the force, m is the mass, r is the radius of the circle and V is the *tangential velocity*, that is, the straight-line velocity the object would have were it not being accelerated into a circle. For all practical purposes, the tangential velocity is identical with what most people mean by the word 'speed', so these two terms will be used interchangeably. However, it is important to remember that they are not exactly identical, because in some circumstances the difference becomes quite important. More precisely, 'speed' is the magnitude of the tangential velocity.

An analysis of the force equation shows several interesting things about circular motion. First, the greater the tangential velocity V, the more centripetal force required to keep a body moving in a circle. In the case of an automobile whizzing round a curve, the centripetal force comes from the friction of the tyres against the surface of the road.

Banking for safety

The greater the speed, the more friction needed to keep the automobile going round the curve. This is the reason why it is dangerous to speed round a corner on a wet road. The water reduces the friction, so the car skids off the road.

Second, the smaller the radius r, the more force required to maintain circular motion. This is the reason why it is so hard to 'take a sharp curve' at high speed. Unless the tyres and the road create enough friction to produce the proper amount of centripetal force, the car's inertia will tend to carry it in a straight line off the road.

There are two obvious ways to counter the danger of curved roads: (1) reduce speed (which is the highway patrol's solution), (2) increase the radius of the curve (which is the road engineer's solution). There is a third useful solution, however.

When a car is travelling on a perfectly horizontal surface, all the force of its weight acts vertically, straight up and down. But if the road is banked so that the

Left, an athlete whirls his 'hammer' round and round, faster and faster. The muscles of his powerful arms strain to keep the heavy metal ball in its circular path. This is a dramatic example of centripetal force. *Right,* at just the proper moment, the athlete lets go, and the hammer is sent hurtling on its way, going 'off on the tengant'. Though complicated by the pull of gravity, the motion of the hammer is a clear example of Newton's First Law of Motion. Objects must be forced into circular motion; otherwise they go off in a straight line.

outer side of the curve is higher than the other, part of the force of the car's weight acts horizontally in a direction away from the high side. In other words, part of the car's weight now acts to push it inwards as it rounds the curve and so adds to the centripetal force F caused by the tyres.

As an automobile travels faster and faster round a curve, the road must be banked more and more to prevent it from going off the road. This is the reason why the curves round very small automobile race tracks are banked so much. If they weren't, there would be far more tragic deaths in this daredevil sport than there already are.

A much more useful application of inertia and rotary motion is the medical centrifuge. The various solid constituents of blood have different mass densities and

Experiences such as rapidly whirling round in a fairground 'octopus' led to the idea of centrifugal force. To a physicist, this 'force away from the centre' is imaginary.

consequently different degrees of inertia. (In fact, *mass* is defined as a measure of inertia; the greater the inertia of an object, the greater its mass.) A test-tube of blood is placed into the centrifuge and rapidly swung round. The denser con-

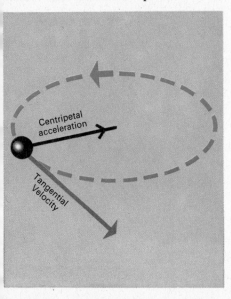

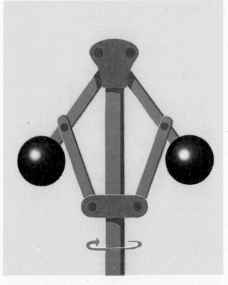

Left, a body moving in a circle constantly accelerates, even though it may not be changing speed. To a physicist, 'acceleration' means a change in speed *or* direction, or both. In this case, there is a constant change of direction towards the centre of the circular orbit. *Centre*, a whirling body pivoted at the top moves up and out in order to increase the centripetal force available to maintain the circular path. *Right*, use can be made of this motion. For instance, a speed governor for steam engines uses this kind of motion to open and close valves.

stituents, because of their greater inertia, resist circular motion more than the lighter ones. As they continually try to move off in a straight line, they are 'thrown' to the bottom of the test-tube, separating them from the lighter constituents, which remain nearer the top of the test-tube.

In the same way, a chemist can use a centrifuge to 'throw' precipitates (solids) to the bottom of a test-tube for later separation and analysis. Closer to home, the spin cycle of an automatic clothes washer 'throws' the water out of wet garments in preparation for drying.

Of course, precipitates are not really 'thrown' to the bottom of a test-tube nor is water really 'thrown' out of wet clothes. Likewise, regardless of how real it may seem, your body is not 'thrown' against the side of the car when it makes a sharp turn.

Off on a tangent

The car turns, but you tend to continue in a straight line, so you and the side of the car collide. There may seem to be a centrifugal force pushing you against the car door, but this force is fictitious. It would be far more correct to say that the car is thrown against you, because of the very real centripetal force applied to make it turn.

Amusement parks and fair grounds abound with examples of circular motion in such rides as the 'chairoplane' and others which swing the joy-seekers rapidly round in a circle. The physical laws which govern these amusements are the same as those which govern the simple conical pendulum. Suspend a heavy bob from a piece of string and swing the string so that the bob goes round in a circle at the end of the string. As the bob is rotated faster and faster, the circle becomes bigger and bigger. At the same time the bob begins to rise.

What causes it to move upwards as well as outwards? The answer is again inertia,

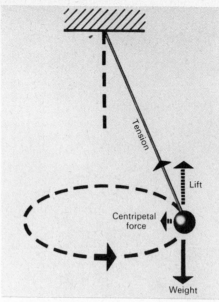

Left, the faster a conical pendulum revolves, the more centripetal force needed to keep it going round in a circle. The pendulum moves up and out; this allows some of the tension

and the process is somewhat similar to banking a curve in a road. As the pendulum bob swings round the circle, its inertia continually tries to carry it off in a straight line, or 'off on the tangent' as a physicist would say. So a force must be supplied to keep it in its circular path. This force comes from the hand pulling on the string, but so long as the string is vertical, it can only supply a force straight up and down, not horizontally towards the centre of the circle as required. The string, therefore, begins moving out at an angle, or is 'banked', so to speak.

Because the string must now supply a centripetal force to keep the bob moving in a circle as well as a vertical force to keep the bob from falling, it is necessary to increase the tension in the string. In other words, the wider the circle and the higher the bob rises, the more force the person

of the string to pull inwards, thus increasing the centripetal force. *Right,* as this potter's wheel shows, circular motion was harnessed long before its laws were understood.

swinging the pendulum must provide. If enough force is supplied, it is possible to raise the pendulum bob so high that the string is almost straight out, parallel to the ground.

As stated at the outset, circular motion at one time held a special place in the world of science, because Aristotle believed the heavenly bodies to move in perfect circles. The fact that Kepler showed that celestial motion is really in ellipses removed the special aura which once surrounded circles, but did not significantly diminish their importance. Within the limits of acceptable error, many motions which are really ellipses may be treated as circular. The physical laws governing motion in a circle and motion in an ellipse are precisely the same, but the mathematics for circles is very much easier.

Centrifuge. Interior of the human centrifuge building at the Naval Air Development Centre, Pennsylvania, America, being inspected by two astronauts who will use the centrifuge in their training. At the end of the arm is the gondola in which an astronaut sits at the controls. It is whirled around to simulate the high-gravity effects of acceleration and deceleration which they will feel in a rocket-powered flight into space.

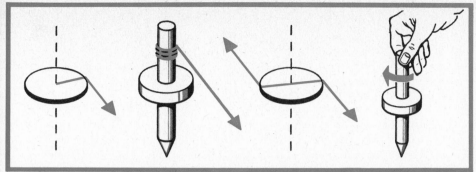

Two ways to spin a top demonstrate two key terms: *couple* and *torque*. A couple, *near left*, is a pair of equal and opposite forces acting parallel to each other (the top is spun between the fingers). A torque, *far left*, is exerted when a force is applied at a tangent and at a distance from the axis (top is spun by pulling a piece of wound string).

The three tops *below* show why a leaning top is able to right itself. While the top is upright, gravity is exactly balanced by an upward reaction in the supporting surface. When the top leans, gravity and the reaction form a couple and the top begins to precess. Then the action of the gyroscopic reaction moment moves it upright again.

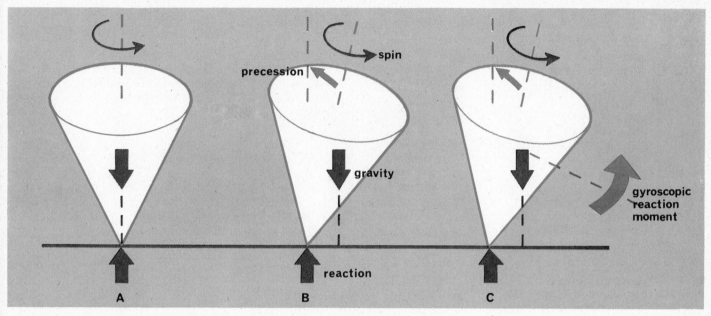

version is a single-frame (or single-axis) gyroscope, sometimes called a gyro top. It has an axle and rotor mounted in a circular frame, generally with fixed balls attached to the frame at the ends of the axle. The rotor is spun by pulling a string wound round the axle. Once the rotor is spinning, the single-frame gyroscope behaves much like a top and may be used to try all the experiments described previously. It precesses if subjected to an outside force, and it tends to move upright if started at an angle.

Independent of external forces

The most useful form of gyroscope in technology is the two-frame (or two-axis) type. It resembles a gyro top mounted and pivoted inside yet another circular frame. Put another way, it is an axle with a rotor mounted inside a set of *gimbals*. When the rotor is spun, the gyroscope seems to behave as if it were completely independent of its surroundings. For example, if the rotor is spun with its axle horizontal, it will remain horizontal no matter what position is taken up by the outer gimbal. Not only that, the axle will remain pointing in the same direction.

It is this independence of outside influences which makes the gyroscope useful for steering and stabilizing mechanisms on ships, aircraft and rockets. For no matter which way the craft moves, left or right, up or down, the axis of a spinning gyroscope on the craft remains pointing in the same direction and can be used as a reference for manually or automatically adjusting the course of the craft.

The use of a gyroscope for stabilizing a ship depends on gyroscopic inertia. If a gyroscope is made with a vertical axle and a heavy rotor (weighing several tons) and the outer gimbal is clamped to the ship, any rolling motion of the ship that tends to tip the gyroscope out of the vertical will be resisted. Gyroscopic inertia will tend to hold the ship upright and defy the effect of swell trying to make it roll.

The first successful gyro-stabilizer was made by a German, Otto Schlick, in 1906. An improved version was tested by an American, E. A. Sperry, in 1913. A similar device is used in automatic pilots on aircraft and in monorail trains to keep them upright. Vertically mounted gyroscopes are also used to stabilize the aim of guns in bucking tanks and pitching ships.

Guided missiles

Gyroscopes used for navigation and steering are generally mounted with their axles horizontal. In 1898, in one of the first applications of a horizontal gyroscope, Ludwig Obry mounted a small gyroscope in the nose of a torpedo. The outer gimbal was clamped to the torpedo and the axle pointed directly forward on the required course. If the torpedo began to veer off course, the inner gimbal moved relative

Once the axis of a horizontal gyroscope on a ship has been adjusted so that it points to the north, it will continue to point north, however often the ship changes its course.

A gyroscope can be put to work to reduce the rolling movement of a ship. As the ship rolls the gyroscope stays steady and operates the stabilizing vanes that project from the ship.

to the axle (which continued to point in the required course direction) and worked a control valve. This in turn worked the steering mechanism of the torpedo to bring it back on course.

A rocket can be fitted with two gyroscopes, one with its axle vertical, and the other with its axle horizontal. The horizontal gyroscope prevents the rocket from spinning, like a bullet, along its longitudinal axis. The vertical gyroscope keeps the nose of the rocket pointed in the required direction.

The gyrocompass

In rockets and aircraft, stabilization does not require huge vertical gyroscopes with heavy rotors in which gyroscopic inertia keeps the craft on an even keel. Instead, the effect of any roll or rotation on a small gyroscope is used to work *servo-mechanisms* that operate the control surfaces of the craft, in much the same way that Obry's gyroscope guided the torpedo.

If a sensitive gyroscope is constrained to be horizontal, but left free to turn about the vertical, it will be affected by the rotation of the Earth. For this rotation steadily twists the horizontal plane. The resulting precession will make the gyroscope oscillate across the north-south direction, and, with a little friction, align along it. This is the gyrocompass which is very widely used in ships and aircraft.

At sea, by fixing the outer gimbal to the ship, any required or unknown course can be found by comparing the ship's bearing with north as indicated by the gyroscope. The gyrocompass was invented in Germany in about 1906 by Auschütz-Kaempfe.

A similar device is used in aircraft. A

The gyrocompass is superior to the magnetic compass because it has no error due to variation — the difference in direction between the true north and the magnetic north. Nor is it affected by magnetic fields in its vicinity. But a gyro-

gyrocompass of the type just described will not work close to the Earth's poles. (Since near the pole the Earth's rotation hardly twists the horizontal plane.) But a gyrocompass is more accurate and convenient than a magnetic compass. It has no error due to *variation* (the difference in direction between true north and magnetic north, which varies from place to place on the Earth). And it has no error due to *deviation* (the effect on a magnetic compass of magnetic materials near it – an extreme nuisance on steel ships, against which special corrective measures have to be taken).

It was on 24 September 1929 that an

Two gyroscopic devices form the basis of the 'automatic pilot' that will keep the aircraft on a predetermined course. The device with a

compass set to point true north will not function as the aeroplane bearing it passes over the north pole: its axis will attempt to point vertically. In the Arctic summer, the lowest position of the midnight sun gives the Pole's direction.

American pilot, 'Jimmy' Doolittle, first lifted an aeroplane from the ground using gyroscopic devices alone to guide his course – a hood over the cockpit, and a thick fog, cut off the view a pilot normally relies on.

In recent years, stabilizing and navigational systems containing gyroscopes have become an essential part of the space age. Missiles and rockets are automatically guided by them. A magnetic compass, after all, which was pointing vaguely in the direction of the Earth's magnetic north pole, would not be of much use to astronauts in a space capsule on a trip to Mars. But a gyroscope certainly would.

vertical axis controls the elevators and ailerons in the wings, and the gyroscope with the horizontal axis controls the aircraft's rudder.

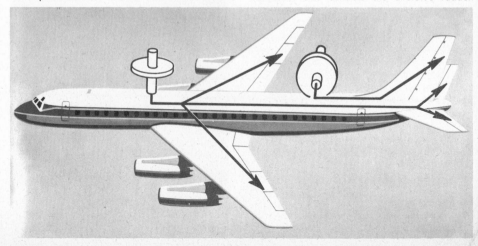

The moon is falling

It is only the moon's speed that keeps it aloft. It follows a curved path through space because the force of gravity is constantly causing it to fall towards the Earth. How do we measure this force?

WHAT HAPPENED to Newton's apple is common knowledge. Space-age Man knows too that an apple released near the surface of other large bodies in the solar system would also fall. In 1959, Russia placed a space probe near the moon and it crashed into the surface, pulled by the moon's gravity. A similar demonstration was obtained of the gravitational attraction of Mars and, in 1967, of gravity on Venus. Yet if the first Russian cosmonaut, Yuri Gagarin, had tried dropping an apple, during his orbital flight in 1961, the apple would have appeared to stay where it was and not fall.

We know that massive bodies like the moon and planets exert a gravitational pull on objects near them. We also know that the effects of gravity get less as the distance from the massive body increases. But it required the pioneer experimental work of Galileo Galilei (1564–1642) and Isaac Newton (1642–1727) to systematize

and clearly demonstrate the facts.

Before the work of Galileo, most people thought that heavy objects fall faster than light ones. One of the difficulties of proving or disproving this belief was that they had no way of measuring short intervals of time and their eyes were not quick enough to watch the points of impact of two stones of different weights dropped from arm's length. Galileo had the idea of slowing down the effect of gravity by tying the stone to the end of a piece of string and then letting it 'fall'. He made a pendulum from the arrangement and pulled the stone sideways and let it go.

Galileo's simple experiments

Instead of falling straight down, of course the stone swung in an arc of a circle. But Galileo reasoned that it was still being affected only by gravity. He found that, as long as he kept the string the same length, it did not matter how heavy the

stone was, the pendulum always took the same time to make one swing. It also took the same time to swing no matter how far he pulled the stone sideways. If he pulled it through a large angle, it had to move faster to complete a swing in the same time as when pulled through small angles, but it always took the same time as long as he did not change the length of the string.

Galileo tested the effect of gravity on falling objects by dropping a very heavy one and a lighter one from a great height. As he predicted, they appeared to hit the ground at the same time. (In fact, one hit slightly before the other due to air resistance and other factors. In a perfect vacuum, two objects hit the ground at *exactly* the same time.)

Galileo had noticed that the pendulum bob speeded up as it approached the bottom of its swing, and he wanted to study how it did so. Since he could not mark off in the air, as it were, the position of the bob

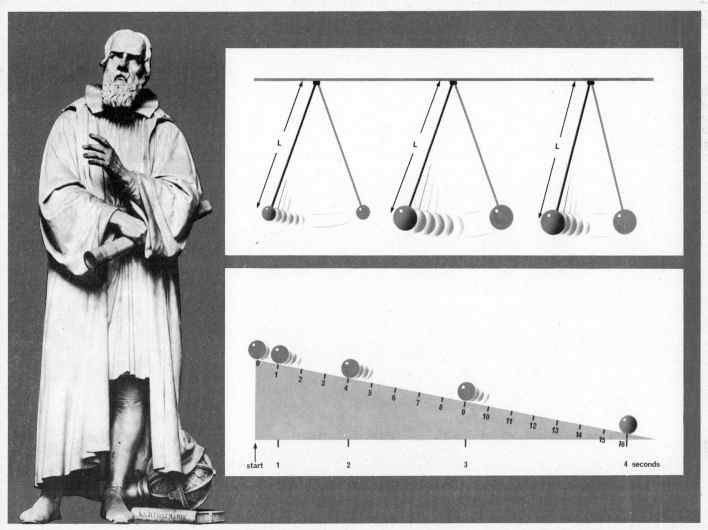

In a famous series of experiments, the Italian scientist Galileo Galilei (1564–1642) pioneered modern understanding of the effects of gravity. First, by means of a pendulum, he demonstrated that for a given length of string, the time of a pendulum's swing is always the same — whatever its weight, and whatever the size of the swing. Then, using a ball rolling down an inclined plane, Galileo measured acceleration under gravity. He found that the total distance travelled increases as the square of the time taken. In one second the ball travels one unit; after three seconds, nine.

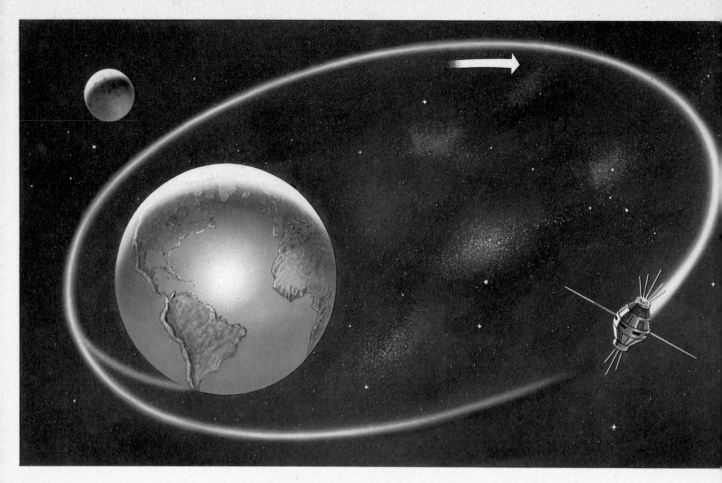

after successive intervals of time, he studied instead balls rolling down an inclined plane.

This experiment was similar to that with the pendulums, except that the inclined plane and not the string caused a sideways movement. And he could mark off on the board the position reached by a ball after one, two, and three seconds, and so on. He found that if he called the distance moved by the ball in the first second one unit-distance, the ball moved through four unit-distances by the end of the second second, nine unit-distances at the end of the third second, and 16 at the end of the fourth second. He also found this to be true for any weight of ball. In other words, the distance travelled increased as the square of the time of travel. Galileo found the acceleration due to gravity at the surface of the Earth to be 981 centimetres per second^2.

The falling moon

But how does the force of gravity vary as the distance from the Earth's surface grows? The answer to this question was first given by Newton. Although traditionally Newton got his first clue from watching an apple fall, he says in his writings that his real inspiration was the moon. Newton argued that if the Earth's gravitational pull extends outwards towards the moon, even if it decreases with distance, why does the moon not fall down to earth?

If Galileo, instead of *dropping* a weight from a height had thrown it horizontally, it would still have fallen to earth but some distance from the tower. But the Earth is round and the surface curves and drops away towards the horizon. So if we could

throw a stone hard and fast enough, it would begin to fall but its curving path would match the curvature of the Earth and it would never hit the ground but go on circling the Earth.

Newton realized that the same arguments apply to the moon, which is moving along in its orbit with just sufficient speed to overcome the Earth's gravity. He was able to calculate the acceleration due to the moon's motion, situated 38,440,000,000 cm from the centre of the Earth, as 0·27 cm per sec^2. The acceleration due to gravity at the Earth's surface (637,000,000 cm from the centre of the Earth) is 981 cm per sec^2. The ratio of the acceleration is 981:0·27, about 3,640:1. The ratio of the distances is 38,440:637, about 60·4:1. Like Galileo, Newton spotted the square relationship

A stone thrown fast enough from a tower would follow a curved trajectory but keep missing the Earth and so circle it. The moon behaves similarly. Its speed in orbit overcomes the Earth's gravity.

An artificial satellite travels round the Earth in an elliptical orbit. Its speed varies: the closer it is to the Earth, the faster it moves. Planets around the sun follow similar paths.

$(60·4)^2$ is about 3,648. He had discovered that the force of gravity decreases as the inverse square of the distance. Furthermore, Newton deduced that the magnitude of the force must depend on the masses of the bodies concerned (since, at a given distance, the acceleration is constant). He therefore proposed his Law of Universal Gravity: the force of attraction between any two objects is proportional to the product of their masses and inversely proportional to the square of the distance between them.

Several scientists tried to prove this law experimentally. Their experiments all involved bringing a large, massive body up to a small, light body. If Newton's theory is correct, the smaller body should be attracted towards the larger by a force proportional to the product of their masses. In the method devised by an English physicist, Sir Charles Vernon Boys (1855–1944), two small gold spheres are hung at different levels from a glass rod which is, in turn, suspended by a long quartz fibre. The whole arrangement is supported in a glass tube to avoid the effect of draughts. Two large lead spheres, one level with each gold sphere, are brought up to the glass tube.

Gravitational attraction causes the gold spheres to move towards the lead spheres. As long as the lead spheres are not in line with the glass rod, the effect of this attraction is to make the quartz fibre suspension twist. By carefully measuring the angle of twist and the distances between the spheres, Boys was able to calculate the gravitational constant.

In another method, a German physicist, Karl Braun in the 1890s and improved by Heyl in the 1930s and 1940s, all the metal spheres are at the same level. This time the small spheres are suspended by a metal wire, which will twist and untwist, a process called torsion suspension, and the small spheres are allowed to oscillate in the gravitational field of the large spheres. By timing the swings for different weights of small spheres, Heyl calculated the gravitational constant.

Gravity varies with mass

A third method uses torsion suspension for both pairs of spheres. Both are twisted and released and the two systems adjusted until they are oscillating at the same rate. From the masses of the spheres and their distances apart, the gravitational constant can be calculated.

All three of the experiments just described suffer from the disadvantage that a third, large massive sphere is exerting a gravitational pull on the experimental spheres. This third sphere is the Earth itself and its gravitational pull, while useful for making everything hang downwards, limits the accuracy of the results.

Tradition credits the Leaning Tower of Pisa as the site of an experiment by Galileo. To prove that light and heavy objects fall at the same speed, he dropped two stones from the tower.

In the method devised by John Henry Poynting (1852–1914), the gravitational field of the experimental spheres is arranged in the same direction as the Earth's gravitational pull. Two spheres of lead alloy are counterpoised on a balance, and another large sphere is placed below one of the smaller ones. The gravitational attraction of the large sphere on the smaller one tilts the balance, and from the angle of tilt, the masses of the spheres, and their distance apart, G can be found.

Thus when we let go of a stone, there is a force of attraction between the stone and the Earth. The force decreases with the height of the stone above the Earth, and if we take the stone out far enough into space, the gravitational pull of the Earth becomes so feeble that the stone stays where we put it. Similarly, when we 'let go' of a space probe near the surface of the moon, there is a force of attraction between the probe and the moon. The moon has approximately one-eightieth of the mass of the Earth and is only about a quarter of the size, and as a result the moon's force of gravity at its surface is only about one-sixth of that of the Earth at its surface.

If we weighed our object on a spring balance on Earth and on the moon, it would appear to weigh six times as much

Man's efforts to overcome the pull of gravity have a long history. It was in 1716 that the Swedish philosopher-scientist, Emanuel Swedenborg, first proposed the idea of riding on a

on Earth. On the moon, the mass of the object (that is, its material content) would be exactly the same as on the Earth. But the force of gravity pulling the object, and thus stretching the spring balance, would be only one-sixth as strong as on the Earth, so the weight would be one-sixth. Mass, then, is constant throughout the universe; weight depends on the force of gravity.

Planets and satellites

The motion of a body orbiting round a central mass in a gravitational field (such as the motion of a small artificial satellite round the Earth) is analogous to the motion of an object tethered to a central point, such as a stone at the end of a piece of string. About 50 years before Newton had formulated his Law of Gravitation, a German astronomer, Johannes Kepler, had found that the orbits of the planets round the sun are ellipses, not circles. Kepler's first Law of Planetary Motion states that planets travel round the sun in elliptical orbits with the sun at one focus. Newton applied his Law to the problem, allowing for the gravitational pull of the sun on the planet and obtained a proof of Kepler's first Law.

The planet actually orbits, not round the

cushion of compressed air. Today, skimming from sea to land, hovercrafts speed ferry services in many countries. They ride on just such an air cushion, kept in place by the craft's skirts.

Ballooning, *right*, first lifted Man from the ground in the late 1760s. Two hundred years later, an American astronaut, 120 miles from Earth, learns to manoeuvre, weightless in space.

centre of the sun, but round the common centre of gravity of the planet-sun systems. Since the sun is so massive, for most planet-sun systems the centre of gravity lies within the sun's volume and, to a first approximation, may be considered to be at the centre of the sun. Newton also proved Kepler's second Law: the line joining the planet to the sun (the radius vector) sweeps out equal areas in equal times.

As a result of Kepler's second Law, we see that the velocity of an orbiting planet must vary. When it is near the sun, it must be moving quite fast for the radius vector to sweep out the same area as when it is far from the sun, when the planet must be moving much slower.

Elliptical orbits

Kepler's first Law should also hold for objects orbiting the Earth. We normally assume that the trajectory of a shell or rocket fired from one point on the Earth to another is a parabola. It is as if the trajectory were really an ellipse with the centre of the Earth as one focus. But the trajectory is only a small part of this huge ellipse far from the focus, and is thus very close to a parabola – a simple curve for calculators. But when we come to calculate the orbits of artificial satellites, we must remember that they are ellipses. Sometimes, they are made very eccentric so that the height of the satellite above the surface of the Earth varies considerably during a single orbit. They obey Kepler's second Law and their speed varies accordingly.

Launching such satellites is a matter of carrying out our hypothetical experiment of throwing a stone from the top of a tower. The rocket is sent upwards to a great altitude and then turned more or less parallel with the surface of the Earth. It is given just sufficient speed to fall on a trajectory (elliptical) that does not curve quite as much as does the Earth's surface.

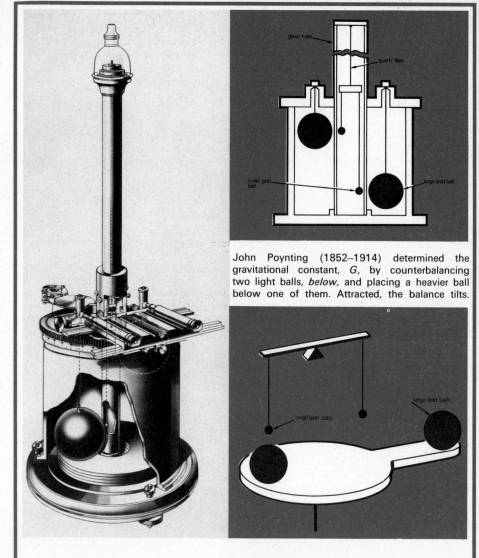

John Poynting (1852–1914) determined the gravitational constant, G, by counterbalancing two light balls, below, and placing a heavier ball below one of them. Attracted, the balance tilts.

Sir Charles Vernon Boys devised the apparatus, *left, top right,* to determine the gravitational constant. Two small gold spheres hang at different levels from a glass rod which is suspended from a quartz fibre. Two large lead spheres, one level with each gold ball, are brought close to them, but not in line. Gravitational attraction pulls the gold spheres towards the lead, twisting the fibre.

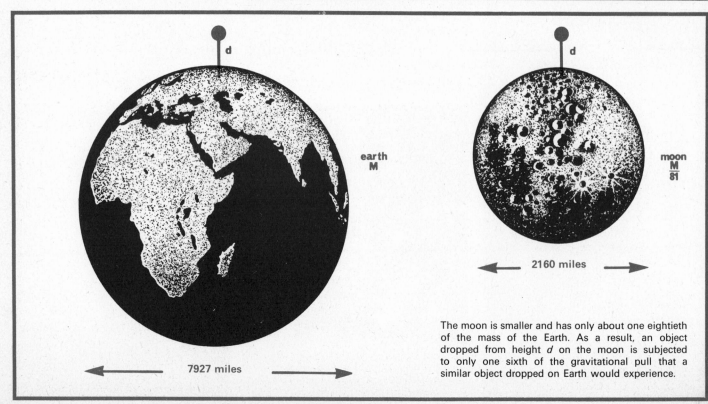

The moon is smaller and has only about one eightieth of the mass of the Earth. As a result, an object dropped from height *d* on the moon is subjected to only one sixth of the gravitational pull that a similar object dropped on Earth would experience.

What happens on impact

Behind the wall of a large dam lie enormous reserves of energy. Should the wall burst, the ensuing flood could flatten a town. How is energy stored; what happens when it is released?

ANY MOVING object can do work. A motor car does work in towing a caravan; the wind does work in turning a windmill. The capacity to do work is called *energy,* and the energy associated with the movement of an object called *kinetic* energy.

A stationary object also has a capacity for work. A five-pound weight resting on a table might be pushed over the edge. Were this to happen, it would fall; and in striking the floor it would give up the kinetic energy it had acquired during the fall by virtue of its original position. This kind of energy is called *potential* energy.

A stretched or compressed spring and a taut piece of elastic also possess potential energy. The energy 'locked in' a spring can be made to do work driving a clock or a clockwork motor. A stretched piece of elastic can be made to do the work of propelling a stone from a catapult. But once

The energy of a moving object is called kinetic energy. The *square* of the speed is involved in calculating it. That is why a crash at 20 mph can be four times worse than a crash at 10 mph.

the stone is released, it has kinetic energy.

The kinetic energy of a particle of mass m moving with a velocity of V is $\frac{1}{2}mV^2$ expressed in *ergs*. To change the kinetic energy of a moving particle requires work to be done, and the work done is equal to the change in kinetic energy. For example, a billiard ball of mass 200 gm moving with a velocity of 100 cm per sec has a kinetic energy of 1,000,000 ergs. The work done in making the ball move from rest – that is in changing its kinetic energy from zero to one million ergs – is also equal to 1,000,000 ergs. The units of kinetic energy are the same as the units of work.

The potential energy of a stationary particle is the work forces acting on it would have to do to bring it to its position. Work done equals force multiplied by distance; therefore the work necessary to lift a particle of mass m through a height h against the force of gravity equals mgh ergs, where g is the acceleration due to gravity (981 cm per sec^2). This quantity is the potential energy of the particle at its new position.

Crashing at speed

If we now allow the particle to fall back through the same height h, it loses its potential energy but gains kinetic energy because it is moving. The total energy of the particle remains constant during the descent, so that at any instant the sum of the kinetic and potential energies is also

constant. This is in agreement with the principle of conservation of energy. That is, the kinetic and potential energy of an object may be continually interchanged, but the sum of the two types of energy remains constant.

Notice that kinetic energy depends on the square of the velocity of a moving object (kinetic energy $=\frac{1}{2}mV^2$). So that doubling the speed of, say, a motor-cycle increases its kinetic energy four times. A motor-cycle weighing 400 lb moving at 60 ft per sec (about 40 mph) has a kinetic energy of $\frac{1}{2}\times400\times60^2=720,000$ ft-poundals. At 120 ft per sec (about 80 mph), the same machine has a kinetic energy of $\frac{1}{2}\times400\times120^2=2,880,000$ ft-poundals. This is one of the reasons why a crash at 80 mph is much more than twice as serious as a crash at 40 mph.

Men frequently make use of potential

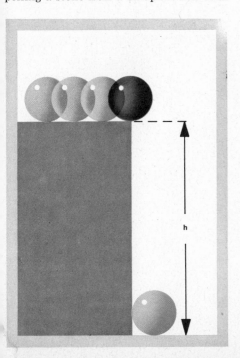

The ball, *left*, expends kinetic energy as it rolls to the edge of the block. But it also has a 'store' of *potential* energy, related to its height. When the ball drops over the edge of the block, and as the weights in the clock mechanism, *right*, descend, potential energy is transformed into kinetic energy. To determine potential energy multiply together the object's mass, height, and the force of gravity.

Behind the dam lies an immense reserve of potential energy, readily convertible into kinetic energy as the water is released to drive turbines and generate electricity. In a 100-foot-deep reservoir, the weight of water is measurable in millions of tons, the foot-poundals of energy in billions. The catastrophic effects of a large dam-burst illustrate dramatically what can happen when potential energy is converted into kinetic energy.

energy as a means of 'storing' energy. For example the weights of a large tower clock may be wound up to the top of the tower once a week. As they are allowed to fall slowly down again over the following seven days, their potential energy is given up to drive the clock. Of course, the man or electric motor puts as much energy into winding the weights up to the top of the tower in, say, five minutes as the falling weights give up in a week.

Mathematically, the potential energy required to raise a weight of 200 kg a height of 20 metres (potential energy=mgh) is $200,000 \times 981 \times 2,000 = 392,400,000,000$ ergs. And theoretically all this energy is available to drive a clock; it may be sufficient to work the clock for several days.

A bouncing ball

The weight of water stored in a reservoir behind a dam may exceed millions of tons. This mass situated at an average height of, say, 100 ft possesses billions upon billions of ft-poundals of potential energy. When the water is released, its potential energy is converted into kinetic energy that drives a turbine to generate enough electricity to supply the needs of a whole town.

A bouncing ball is an example of an object in which kinetic and potential energy are continually being interchanged. At the top of the bounce, the ball is stationary – it has no kinetic energy, but its potential energy, due to its position, is at a maximum. As the ball falls, it loses potential energy and gains kinetic energy until it hits the ground, when its potential energy is zero and its kinetic energy is at a maximum. As the ball rises again, the opposite conversion takes place and kinetic energy is converted back into potential energy.

Using the formulae for the two forms of energy, we can calculate how fast the ball is travelling as it hits the ground. The potential energy at the highest position mgh, equals the kinetic energy at the lowest position, $\frac{1}{2}mV^2$. So that $mgh = \frac{1}{2}mV^2$. If the ball weighs 100 gm and falls 100 cm, the above equation becomes $100 \times 981 \times 100 = \frac{1}{2} \times 100 \times V^2$, from which $V^2 = 196,200$ or $V = 442 \cdot 9$ cm per sec.

Notice that the final velocity of the ball is the same, no matter what its weight, and depends only on the height from which it is dropped. That is, objects of different weights all fall at the same speed. This observation was first made by the Italian mathematician and astronomer Galileo Galilei (1564–1642) who studied falling weights and so was able to calculate the acceleration due to gravity, g.

The potential energy required to raise a weight a given height is the same no matter how fast it is raised. A 12-stone man climbing a staircase ten feet high gains the same amount of potential energy (1,680 ft-pounds force) whether he walks up or runs up. But he is more out of breath when he runs up; he feels as though he has worked 'harder'. What varies in this example is the *rate* of doing work, which is defined as *power*. A lift that carries the same man up ten floors of an office building in 15 seconds is more powerful than the man because it achieves in 15 seconds what would take him three or four minutes were he to walk up.

When James Watt was building his steam engines in the 1700s, he had to devise a way of measuring their power. He set a horse to work pulling a 100-lb weight up a mine-shaft. He found that the horse could do such work while walking at a speed of $3\frac{2}{3}$ ft per sec. This rate of doing

To turn the water wheel, force acts at right angles to the radius. Application of force in this way is called a *torque*, the size of which is the product of the force and its distance from the wheel's axis.

Two factors determine the power of the capstan winches, here shown raising a heavy object — the length of the spokes and the strength of the men and horses pushing them round. Equal and opposite parallel forces tending to cause rotation about an axis are called a *couple*.

work, 367 ft-pounds force per sec, was increased by Watt when he defined one horsepower (hp) as a rate of working of 550 ft-pounds force per sec.

If the man in our earlier example took ten seconds to run up the ten-foot flight of steps (remember he weighed 12 stone), he was working at a rate of $(168 \times 10)/10 = 168$ ft-pounds force per sec. His horsepower is $168/550 = 0.305$ hp.

A difference in momentum

Imagine a tennis ball thrown into the air and caught by a boy when it comes down. If the boy instead catches a cricket ball under the same circumstances, he will find it more difficult to stop and hold than the tennis ball. As long as the two balls were travelling at the same speed when the boy caught them, the only difference between the two cases is the mass of the balls. The property of the balls that varies is the *momentum*. Momentum of a moving object is defined as the product of its mass and its velocity.

A particle of mass m moving with a velocity V has a momentum of mV. Thus a bullet weighing 30 gm moving at a speed of 50,000 cm per sec has a momentum of 1,500,000 gm-cm per sec. A man weighing 80 kg walking at 2 metres per sec has a momentum of 16,000,000 gm-cm per sec.

An important principle states that, if no external forces act on a system, the total momentum in a given direction remains unchanged. Thus if a model railway wagon having a mass of 50 gm and moving with a velocity of 10 cm per sec collides with a similar stationary wagon, and they both move on together, what is the new velocity of the wagons? The momentum of the first wagon before the collision is $50 \times 10 = 500$ gm-cm per sec. The momentum of the second wagon before the collision is zero (because its velocity is zero). After the collision, the two wagons of combined weight 100 gm move off with a velocity of, say, V. Their momentum is $100V$ gm-cm per sec. The law of conservation of momentum tells us that the total momentum before impact equals the total momentum after impact. That is, $500 + 0 = 100V$, from which $V = 5$ cm per sec.

A gun to stop a car

We might have guessed that doubling the moving mass by attaching the second wagon would have the effect of halving the velocity. But when the mass of the objects in collision are not the same, and both are moving to start with, the final velocities are not easily predictable and the law of conservation of momentum is very useful.

For example, some years ago a police authority wanted to develop a gun with sufficient 'stopping power' to stop a moving car. For this to happen, the momentum of the bullet must be equal to or greater than the momentum of the car. Three of the quantities were known: the weight of the bullet (say 100 gm), the weight of the car (say 800 kg), and the speed of the car (say 14 metres per sec, about 30 mph). The only unknown quantity, needed to calculate the quantity of explosive to be used in the specially designed cartridge, was the velocity of the bullet, V.

Applying the law of conservation of momentum to this problem, the momentum before impact is the sum of the momenta of the bullet and the car: $(100 \times V) - (800,000 \times 1,400)$. (The second term, the momentum of the car, is negative because the car's velocity is opposite in direction to that of the bullet.) For the bullet to stop the car dead, the momentum after impact is zero. That is $(100 \times V) - (800,000 \times 1,400) = 0$, or $100V = 1,120,000,000$. From which we have that $V = 11,200,000$ cm per sec.

Similar reasoning can be applied to problems in which both of the colliding objects are moving before and after impact. For example, a ball-bearing weighing 50 gm is rolling along a smooth surface with a velocity of 100 cm per sec and it catches up with and hits a glass marble of mass 10 gm moving with a velocity of 40 cm per sec in the same direction as the ball-bearing. If the velocity of the ball-bearing is reduced to 80 cm per sec by the impact, what is the increase in velocity of the marble?

Orbital velocities

If the final velocity of the marble is V, the momenta before and after impact are as follows: ball bearing before impact, $50 \times 100 = 5,000$ gm-cm per sec; marble before impact, $10 \times 40 = 400$ gm-cm per sec; ball bearing after impact, $50 \times 80 = 4,000$ gm-cm per sec; marble after impact, $10 \times V$. Equating the total momenta before and after impact: $5,000 + 400 = 4,000 + 10V$, which gives $10V = 1,400$ or $V = 140$ cm per sec. The final velocity of the marble is 140 cm per sec, so that its velocity is increased nearly four times.

So far we have considered only the momentum of an object moving with a uniform velocity in a straight line. An

To turn the windmill, force acts through more than one point — the wind provides equal and parallel forces which combine to spin the wheel. A combination of forces of this kind is called a *couple*.

object moving in a circular path also has momentum. However, if its linear velocity is V, its angular velocity, ω, round the circle is different. (The two velocities V and ω are related by the equation $\omega = V/r$, where r is the radius of the circle.) And with an object following a circular path, it is angular momentum that is conserved. So that if the angular velocity of an object moving in a circle changes, then the radius of its circular path will change so that angular momentum is conserved.

Spiralling satellites

As is well known, the moon raises tides on the Earth. Since the Earth is rotating with the period of a day, while the moon takes a month to go round the Earth, the Earth is, as it were, spinning under the tidal bulges. This leads to friction which slows down the rotation of the Earth (that is, lengthens the day) in a minute but observable fashion. Therefore, the angular momentum of the Earth is decreasing. Since the angular momentum of the complete Earth/moon system must stay constant, it follows that the angular momentum of the moon's orbital motion round the Earth must be increasing. This implies that the moon is receding from the Earth.

We have considered motion in a straight line and motion in a circle. There is one other common type of motion caused by the application of forces: rotation about an axis, as for example when we turn on a tap or unscrew a bottle top. In each of these cases, we are applying two equal and opposite parallel forces which tend to cause rotation. Such a combination of forces, which do not act through a single point, is called a *couple* and its effectiveness is the product of one of the forces and the distance separating them.

If only a given amount of force is available, the turning action of a couple can be increased by increasing the distance between the forces. That is why, in old sailing ships, men used to insert horizontal shafts into the capstan (rather like the spokes of a wheel) to push against, to get the maximum benefit from the amount of force available. The longer the arms of the capstan, the easier it was to turn.

A windmill's sails

Of course, only a single force applied to the rim of a wheel will cause it to rotate. This combination, which may be considered as half a couple, is called a *torque* and its magnitude is the product of the force and its distance from the axis.

Common examples of the application of a torque include a crank used for turning a wheel or a motor-car engine; the way in which a finger rotates the dial of a telephone; and a spanner or wrench used to tighten a bolt. The essential difference between a couple and a torque can be seen by considering a windmill and a waterwheel, both of which for hundreds of years utilized the first sources of power known to men. In a windmill, the wind acts on, say, the top and bottom sails and constitutes a couple which causes rotation. In the case of a water-wheel, the water causes rotation by acting on the baffles at one side of the wheel's axis of rotation only, and constitutes a torque.

Artillery before gunpowder exploited in many ingenious ways the uses of potential energy. In the catapults above, the stone-weighted buckets provide the energy to fire missiles and bolts.

Construction plan for a death-dealing piece of machinery, *below*, storing potential energy by bracing two bows. Released, the bows fly apart, tautening the rope and ejecting the boulder.

Floating and flowing

The behaviour of fluids — gases and liquids — is governed by the laws of fluid statics and fluid dynamics. These laws, from Archimedes' Principle on, have wide practical applications.

ACCORDING TO AN OLD STORY, King Hiero II of Syracuse did not trust his goldsmith, and suspected that the latter had diluted his new gold crown with less expensive silver. Not knowing how to confirm his suspicions, he called on the great Greek mathematician Archimedes (c. 287–212 BC) for assistance.

Archimedes pondered the problem for some time without success. Then (so the story goes), while bathing one day at the public baths, he noticed that when people entered the water some of it spilled over the side. He reasoned that if the king's crown and a block of pure gold with the same weight were placed in a container filled to the brim, the same amount of water should spill over the top each time.

Whereupon, as everyone knows, Archimedes is supposed to have leapt out of his bath and run naked down the road to the palace shouting 'Eureka! Eureka!' (I have found it! I have found it!)

Whether or not the story is true, Archimedes certainly did not let his investigation stop there. He wanted to know why the water spilled over the top and whether his discovery had anything to do with the fact that objects seemed to lose weight when immersed in water. It seemed fairly obvious to Archimedes that water could not really cause an object to lose weight. Instead, he concluded that water must push up on any object placed in it, so that objects only *seemed* to lose weight.

Archimedes' Principle

In formal language, Archimedes' Principle states: A body immersed in a fluid is buoyed up by a force equal to the weight of the fluid displaced. This is perhaps the most important law in the science of *fluid statics*. To understand why it is so important, it is necessary to understand what is meant by a 'fluid'.

Matter is usually said to exist in three states: solid, liquid and gas. The major difference between a solid and a liquid is, of course, quite obvious: a solid maintains its shape, whereas a liquid flows. But the difference between a liquid and a gas is not quite so clear-cut because both flow, and for many purposes the similarities between the two are far more important than their differences. For this reason, liquids and gases are frequently classed together as fluids, a fluid being anything which flows and a solid any substance which does not.

The difference between a solid and a fluid is immediately clear if one makes a hole in a material by a single punch. The hole in the solid remains, whereas a hole made in a fluid is quickly filled up again. This helps explain Archimedes' Principle: if any object, say the human body, is placed in water, some of the water is pushed aside, or displaced; the water at

once tries to flow back, but is prevented from doing so by the object in question. The push of the water trying to fill the 'hole' created by the object, and therefore acting against the mass of the object, causes the object to 'lose weight'.

Suppose an object weighing 20 lb displaces 5 lb of water. The object pushes down with a force of 20 lb (its normal weight), against which the displaced water pushes upward with a force of 5 lb. The object therefore *appears* to lose 5 lb, which

is, of course, regained the moment the object is taken out of the water.

Since large objects push aside more water than small ones, it is reasonable to assume that they would appear to lose more weight. This, however, introduces the very important factor of density, which can be simply defined as the weight of an object in relation to its size. To be more specific, density is the mass of a substance per unit volume. For instance, if a chunk of metal has a mass of 10 lb and a volume of 2 cu. ft, its density would be 10 lb/2 cu. ft – or 5 lb/cu. ft. Likewise, a stone block weighing 60 lb, with a volume of 3 cu. ft would have a density of 20 lb/cu. ft.

In metric units, density is calculated in grams per cubic centimetre. Steel, for instance, has a density of 7·8 gm/c.c., which means simply that one cubic centimetre of the material would have a mass of 7·8 grams.

The density of a substance, when using grams per cubic centimetre, is simply written as a single number; for instance, the density of water (1 gm/c.c.) is expressed as 1. This is known as its *specific gravity*, which can be thought of as a measure of

1 Water overflowing from the by-pass at the Genissiat Dam on the River Rhône, France. The pressure of the head of water behind forces the water out in an arc.
2 The laws of fluid statics relate to air as well as to other fluids. Hot air rises because it expands as it heats. These laws are applied in weather forecasting.

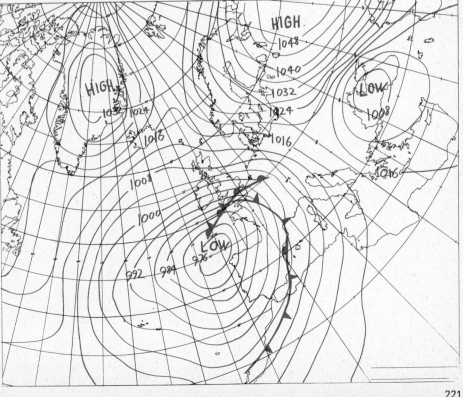

how much heavier or lighter a substance is than the same volume of water. Thus, steel has a specific gravity of 7·8 – that is, a piece of steel is 7·8 times as heavy as the same volume of water.

Because its specific gravity was less than that of water, early ships were made of wood. Today, of course, wooden ships are a rarity, except in the field of pleasure craft. How, then, can big tankers and ocean liners float when they are constructed mainly from steel and other metals which are denser than water?

The problem is easily answered if we bear in mind that density or specific gravity incorporates two components: weight and volume. Given a chunk of steel or any other substance, there is little that can be done about its weight, but there is usually no difficulty about increasing its volume.

Take a cube of solid steel, which has a density of 7·8 gm/c.c. If it is hammered into a flat sheet, and the edges of the sheet folded up to form a steel box, the original cube of steel now has a larger volume but its weight is not altered. If the volume is large enough, the box will float. And for the purposes of this demonstration, we can regard a tanker or a liner as a huge, hollow steel box.

Gas balloons

Because balloons are filled with gas, it is mistakenly believed that a balloon floats in the air for reasons quite different from why a ship floats on water. In fact, however, the reason is precisely the same: the balloon acts only as a container for a gas lighter than air.

When not inflated, a balloon consists only of its fabric, which has a density very much higher than air (air density is in fact only 0·001293 gm/c.c.). However, when pumped up with hydrogen or helium, it occupies a vastly greater volume, and since the gas used is so light, there is relatively little change in the weight of the balloon. As in the case of the steel box, the density of the balloon decreases until it becomes less than that of air, hence it floats. But it is the air outside which forces it skyward, not the gas inside.

If the idea of lowering density by increasing the volume of an object is still difficult to grasp, readers should try the following simple experiment. Place a brimful ice cube tray in a refrigerator until the water freezes, and it will then be noted that the water in the form of ice has risen over the top of the tray. This is because water, unlike most other liquids, expands as it freezes.

It is common knowledge that ice, which is frozen water, does float. Careful measurements show that about 10 per cent of an ice cube, or an iceberg, bobs above the surface when floating because water expands some 10 per cent in volume when frozen.

Air buoys up objects to a much more limited extent than water; very few things float in air. In fact, if all the air in the world were suddenly to disappear, the average person would add no more than 2 gm to his apparent weight – less than the weight of a sixpence.

1 Icebergs float because water expands when it freezes. The ice produced thus has a slightly larger volume than the equivalent weight of liquid water.

2 The Coverack, Cornwall, lifeboat hits the water. Metal boats float because they are hollow and thus occupy more volume than the same weight of water.

1 Soldiers training in snow. By reducing the pressure each foot exerts on the ground, snow shoes make it easier for the soldiers to walk on the soft snow without sinking.

2 Fire-fighting hoses deliver water at high pressure. This gives the water a high speed as it leaves the nozzle so that the jet will travel for a considerable distance.

3 The German *Bernina* balloon in the recent B.B.C. TV Balloon Race. Filled with any gas lighter than air – usually hydrogen or helium – the balloon rises from the ground.

One man who made a major contribution to the study of fluids was the French mathematician and philosopher, Blaise Pascal (1623–62). He asserted: If the pressure at any point in an enclosed fluid is changed, the pressure changes by an equal amount at all points in the fluid.

To understand just what this means and why it is so important, it is necessary first to explore the basic concept of *pressure*. In straightforward terms, pressure is a measurement of how a force is distributed over a surface. Press your hand hard against a flat surface and there is very little pain; now press one finger against the same surface and the pain is much more noticeable. As obviously your arm has not become any stronger, the difference must stem from the fact that the force in question is being applied over a smaller area – the tip of a finger as opposed to the palm of the hand. If a pin is

driven into the surface and you press against that, the pain will be even more noticeable.

Suppose, then, your arm pushes with a force of 60 lb and your palm has an area of 15 sq. in., the pressure is then 4 lb/sq. in. (divide the force by the area). In the case of the finger tip, the force is still 60 lb but the area is very much less – say $\frac{1}{4}$-inch square, that is, one-sixteenth of a square inch. So the pressure at the finger tip becomes 60 lb divided by one-sixteenth – or 960 lb/sq. in.

In the case of fluids, it is useful to imagine that pressure is caused by the fluid mass pressing down on the surface. For instance, 1,000 gm of water in a straight-sided container with a bottom 10 square centimetres in area would exert a pressure of 10,000 gm/10cm² – that is, of 100 gm/cm². If the base had a larger surface area, say of 20 cm², the pressure would

decrease, because the same weight is now spread over a larger area and becomes less concentrated. In this example, the pressure has in fact been halved to 50gm/cm².

Something else has happened. The height of the liquid in the container has also been halved, which seems to suggest a relationship between the height of a liquid and the pressure it exerts.

This supposition is quite correct, and it is not hard to understand why. Area is measured in square units – square inches, square feet, square metres and so on – and in the example given the term 'square' means exactly what it says: the bottom of the container is divided into ten squares each with a side one centimetre in length. Hence, to say that the pressure is 100 gm/cm² means that each of the squares is holding up 100 gm of water. By doubling the number of squares to 20, it follows that each square is now holding up only 50 gm of water. In other words, the pressure has been halved, and this reduction is reflected in a drop in the height of the water in the container by the same amount.

The same holds good for liquids other than water – for petrol, tea, coffee, milk, beer and so on. It is in fact quite easy to calculate pressure from the formula $p=dh$, where p is the pressure, d the density of the liquid and h the height. Moreover, it is often more useful to discuss pressure in terms of height than in actual pressure units (lb/in^2, gm/cm^2). The weathermen on radio and television never report actual pressure, referring instead to so many inches of mercury. Here, inches denote the length of a column of mercury in a barometer.

Odd as it may sound, pressure can be calculated as height × density even where the sides of the container are not straight up and down; the rule still applies even with the most fantastic shapes. This is because when sides are not vertical they take up part of the weight of the water and re-direct the force in different directions.

To imagine pressure as the mass of a fluid pressing down on a surface is useful but also somewhat misleading. It would not be surprising to see the bottom of a cardboard box fall out if it was full of bricks, but it would be most odd if the bottom remained intact while a side fell out. This is because the weight of a solid acts mainly in a downward direction, whereas with fluids pressure acts in all directions at once.

When biting into a cream bun, the teeth press down but the cream filling may squirt out of the front and sides. That is to say, downward pressure has been converted into a sideways pressure on the cream.

In solids, the molecules are bound tightly together, which is why a solid holds its shape. In fluids, however, the molecules are less tightly bound and so move about at random in various directions. It is this molecular motion that accounts for sideways pressure.

Another excellent way to show how fluid pressure acts in all directions is to punch several holes in the side of a tin can, then fill the can with water. It will of course come squirting out through the holes, which would not be possible if there were no pressure to force the water out. The water gushes out with increasing force the nearer the holes are to the bottom of the can, confirming that the pressure towards the bottom is greater than at the top. This shows, incidentally, why divers at great depths must wear protective diving suits: without such gear, the sideways pressure of the water would crush them.

Pascal's Principle is that 'if the pressure

1 Blaise Pascal (1623–62), one of the great figures of mathematics, and discoverer of the principle that bears his name.
2 The bathyscaphe *Trieste* is really an underwater balloon. The cigar-shaped portion is filled with a mixture of oils with about the same density as water. Varying the proportions slightly sends the vessel up or down.

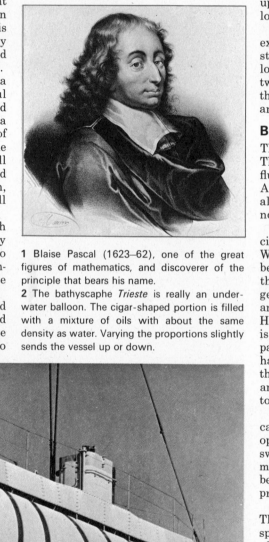

at any point on an enclosed fluid at rest is changed, the pressure changes by an equal amount at all points in the fluid'. This can be understood by looking at an important everyday application of the principle – a car breaking system. In its simplest form, a hydraulic brake system is a fluid-filled tube with branches terminating at each wheel and at a fifth terminal, the brake pedal. Stepping down on this pedal increases the pressure on the enclosed fluid, which in turn causes the brake shoes to tighten against the wheels. In accordance with Pascal's Principle, the increased pressure is transmitted equally to each brake drum, and so the car stops smoothly.

Another common application of the principle is to be found in the hydraulic lifts in garages. This type of lift is mounted on top of a large piston which is pushed up by increasing the fluid pressure and lowered by releasing the pressure.

Here now is a simple but very significant experiment which anyone can try. Cut two strips about an inch wide and ten inches long from a newspaper, and hold them out two inches apart. Now, blow between them. Instead of the strips flying apart, as anyone might expect, they fly together.

Bernoulli's Theorem

This is a simple example of Bernoulli's Theorem which states: 'The pressure in a fluid becomes smaller, the faster it moves.' At first glance, this assertion seems to defy all logic, but closer study shows that it is not quite as improbable as it may seem.

Remember, air is a fluid, and can exercise sideways as well as vertical pressure. When the two strips are at rest, the air between tries to push them apart while the air outside tries to press them together. These conflicting pressures balance, and the strips hang motionless. However, when the air between the strips is accelerated by blowing, it rushes right past the strips and, in a sense, does not have time to press sideways. As a result, the pressure between the strips is reduced, and the outside can push the strips together.

The same thing happens when a small car and a big lorry pass each other in the opposite directions. Momentarily, the car swerves towards the lorry, because the motion of the two vehicles sets the air between them moving and reduces the pressure in the space separating them.

Practical applications of Bernoulli's Theorem are found in atomizers and paint spray guns where, in both cases, a stream of air blowing over a narrow tube reduces the air pressure at the top. This causes the liquid inside to rise until it is caught in the airstream and ejected as fine spray.

Technically, Bernoulli's Principle belongs to the more complicated study of *fluid dynamics,* or fluids in motion, one of the most complicated and difficult of all branches of physics. But however complex the details and however challenging the mental disciplines involved, examples of fluid statics and dynamics in action are often, as we have seen, to be found in commonplace activities. Even so, the everyday applications of science are frequently the most remarkable.

Queen of the sciences

Pure mathematics is a discipline dealing with abstracts, but the results are often applied to practical problems. What are the processes involved, and what criteria are used?

EVERYONE KNOWS, or assumes that he knows, the difference between the inside and the outside of familiar objects. One knows immediately whether one is inside or outside a building, or a room, and the inside and outside of a toy balloon are separated, quite unmistakably, by the material of the balloon itself.

A circle drawn on paper divides the area of the paper into an inside and an outside. Similarly, if a long, narrow strip of paper is joined at the ends, the cylinder so formed has an inside surface and an outside surface. But supposing that same strip of paper is given a half twist before the ends are joined. Does it still have an inside and an outside? A good test of this is whether or not a line can be drawn, joining two points on opposite sides of the paper, without crossing an edge. A simple experiment shows that the strip has only one edge.

This extraordinary twisted hoop is known as the *Mobius strip,* and investigation of its properties is part of one of the newest branches of mathematics, *topology.* Topology, as its name implies, deals with the relationships, on a plane or in space, between geometrical figures, not only the familiar figures of school geometry books, but lines and spaces of any shape or length. It does not deal with lines in terms of length, or shapes in terms of area or volume; it is concerned only with the relationships between them.

Common sense at bay

Subjects such as topology often lead non-mathematicians to query the usefulness of much mathematics and to point out that it bears little relationship to the real world.

To the mathematician, however, this criticism is irrelevant. The pure mathematician does not seek to paint a picture of the real world – that is a task which he leaves to the physicist, the chemist and the geologist. To him, the only criterion of the mathematical system is that it should be a consistent, non-contradictory scheme developed by logical processes from fundamental statements, or *axioms.*

It is this acceptance of results obtained by strict logic which leads to many of the apparent absurdities of pure mathematics. For example, if a mathematician asks how many whole numbers there are, the answer is that there is an infinite number of even whole numbers. In fact, by strictly logical reasoning, it is comparatively simple to prove that there are as many even numbers as there are whole numbers. This conclusion, based on valid mathematical reasoning, goes completely contrary to observation and common sense, but it satisfies the mathematicians' criteria.

Not surprisingly, it has been said that mathematics begins where common sense leaves off, and again, with more than a grain of truth, that mathematics is the science where we do not know what we are talking about.

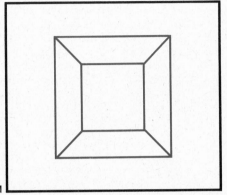

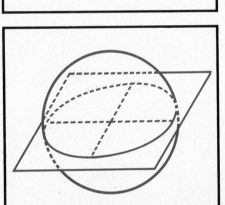

One of the finest examples of this is in the matter of dimensions, and particularly the (or, as the mathematician would say, a) fourth dimension. Suppose the symbol x represents a line of certain length. Then x^2 will represent a square with sides equal

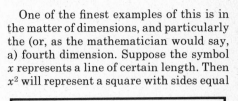

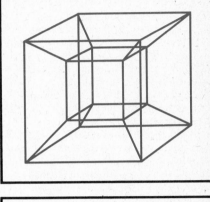

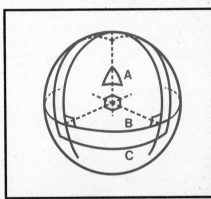

1 To the inhabitant of a two-dimensional world, a cube would look like this.
2 This is a mathematician's impression of a four-dimensional cube, often called a supercube or tesseract.
3 A great circle is generated by a plane cutting a sphere and passing through the centre of the sphere. The equator is a great circle.

4 This drawing of great circles shows how Riemann's 'parallel' lines on the surface of a sphere do in fact intersect and form triangles. These spherical triangles are important in navigation and map-making.
5 Shapes like this modern sculpture are ideal subjects for the topologist, who is only concerned with the relationship between lines and spaces rather than their shape or size.

to x, and x^3 will represent a cube with sides equal to x. But what does x^4 represent? This is a question commonly asked by non-mathematicians, but again, to the mathematician the question is irrelevant. If forced to give an answer, he will probably reply that it represents a *supercube* or *tesseract,* a cube in four dimensions. But such a figure is completely beyond visualizing by people who live in a world of three dimensions.

Problems of number

Pure mathematicians see their work as the establishment of universal proofs for general cases in a particular field. One of the richest fields, in this respect, is the field of numbers, the normal everyday whole numbers, or integers. Much time and energy has been expended by mathematicians in establishing general truths regarding these numbers, and many of the problems posed 200 years ago are still awaiting a solution.

An example of the type of problem which exists in this field relates to prime numbers, numbers which cannot be divided by any other number except one. This is the proof of Goldbach's Theorem, which states that all even numbers are the sum of two prime numbers. It is an easy statement to understand, and it is easily verified for any single even number, but no general proof of its validity has ever been achieved. This theorem together with the problem of finding a general formula for prime numbers, has baffled

many great mathematicians. As indicated by topology, much mathematical research is devoted to geometry, and geometry rather different from Euclid's orderly lines, squares and rectangles. Euclid's theorems, proofs and figures held universal sway for 2,000 years, and nobody dared challenge them. As Plato said, 'If God ever geometrized, then he surely looked to Euclid for the rules.' The formal geometry of Euclid appealed mainly because it was held to be a good representation of the real world. It was useful for measuring the area of fields, for laying out buildings, and for many tasks in elementary surveying.

But by the nineteenth century, mathematicians had begun to realize that Euclidean geometry had its limitations: although it was adequate for surveying and mapping the small piece of land occupied by a Greek city-state, it was far from adequate for producing a similar map of Europe or the United States. It was recognized that Euclidean geometry was only valid in its entirety on a perfectly flat, infinitely large plane, such as did not exist in the real world.

The point at which mathematicians attacked Euclid was on his so-called fifth Postulate, which states that through a given point in a plane, only one line can be drawn parallel to a given line. Riemann, a German mathematician, replaced this postulate with the statement that *no* line can be drawn through a point in the plane parallel to a given line. In other words,

Riemann maintained that every pair of lines in a plane must intersect. Maintaining the rest of Euclid's theorems, but discarding those which depend on the fifth Postulate, Riemann constructed a new geometry, derived by logical processes from his fundamental assumptions. This geometry is now known as Riemannian geometry and it is applicable to a very familiar geometrical figure, the sphere.

Much of Riemann's work is very difficult, but consideration of the surface of a sphere as the 'plane' of his geometry, makes many of his ideas clear. In ordinary geometry, a straight line is often defined as the shortest distance between two points. On the surface of a sphere, the shortest line joining two points is a part of a *great circle*.

Where circles meet

Although the idea of a great circle may be unfamiliar, it is by no means difficult to grasp. If a plane (such as a piece of cardboard) is considered to pass through the centre of a sphere (such as a tennis ball) the circle at which the sphere and the plane intersect is a great circle. So, considering the Earth to be a sphere, the equator and the circle passing through the poles are both great circles. All great circles meet somewhere on the sphere's surface, and so there can be no such thing as non-intersecting 'straight' lines in Riemann's geometry.

Other familiar geometrical ideas, translated to the sphere, acquire some interesting variations. For example, in Euclid's geometry two lines which are drawn perpendicular to the same line are parallel. If two lines are drawn perpendicular to the equator, they meet at the North and

1 Cylinders like these in a children's playground have a clearly defined inside and outside, but the distinction can be difficult to apply to other shapes.

2 Surveyors still use Euclidean geometry in their work. They could apply Riemannian geometry, which is perfectly suitable, but rather more complex.

South Poles. Hence the triangle which they form will have two right angles, and indeed it is possible to draw a triangle on the sphere which has three angles equal to 90°. In Euclidean geometry, of course, the sum of the three angles of any triangle is only 180°, or two right angles.

The development of Riemannian geometry is an excellent illustration of the way in which mathematicians think, and perhaps also illustrates why much of their work is incomprehensible to non-mathematicians. But perhaps the most abstruse, the most pure mathematics is to be found in the theory of numbers, that is the study of whole numbers, or integers.

Starting with 0 (zero) counting in the normal way gives 1, 2, 3, 4, 5... and so on. But supposing the count is taken in the other direction, this is done by subtracting, rather than adding, one at each step. The counting sequence will then be -1, -2, -3, -4, -5... and so on. This is where the mathematician immediately departs from the realm of 'common sense'. In the real world no one has ever seen 'minus three houses' so that it is impos-

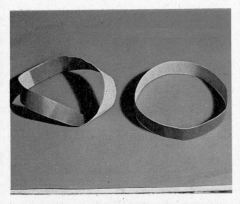

sible to relate these numbers to real groups of objects as can be done with normal positive numbers. However, the mathematician will manipulate these numbers and reach conclusions which are valid, i.e. the reasoning which leads to them is sound.

Negative numbers can be taken a stage further. Square roots are fairly familiar quantities. If $4 = 2 \times 2$, then 2 is the square root of 4. Similarly, 3 is the square root of 9, 4 is the square root of 16 and so on. The concept is one which is readily acceptable to most people. But what is the square root of -9? Can such a number have a square root? Does the idea have any meaning, or is it of any value to applied mathematics? In the sixteenth century the Italian mathematician Cardan set himself a problem which would seem meaningless to the non-mathematician. The problem was to split the number 10 into two parts which, when multiplied together, would give the answer 40. The result which he produced was the two numbers $5+(-15)^{\frac{1}{2}}$ and $5-(-15)^{\frac{1}{2}}$. If these two numbers are added, they give 10 as the result: if they are multiplied, they give 40.

But what is the square root of a negative number? Cardan himself was so uneasy at the idea that he gave them the name *imaginary numbers*, a name which persists to this day. But the odd thing about imaginary numbers, is that they proved

1 A Mobius strip is made by giving a strip of paper shown here with a half twist and gluing the ends together. With it is a normal cylinder. Continuous magnetic tapes for repetitive playing are large Mobius strips.
2 Time is considered as a fourth dimension in some mathematical and physics work. This time-exposure photograph of a Ferris wheel shows the relation between position and time.
3 Fairgrounds provide illustrations of a number of mathematical concepts – e.g. curves of various kinds, statistics and probability, for example.

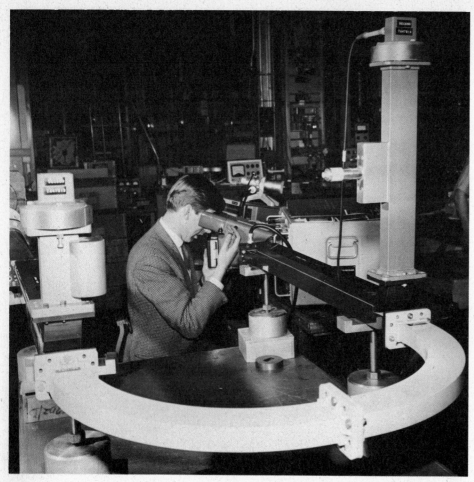

Although the square root of −1 may be an 'imaginary' number, this scientist is trying to eliminate it from electrical equipment, where it signifies an unwanted component.

invaluable in solving problems relating to electricity, so that they are used every day by engineers, giving results which are directly applicable to the design and use of electrical equipment.

In passing, it is worth noting that $(-15)^{\frac{1}{2}}$, for example, is usually written as $j(15)^{\frac{1}{2}}$, where j is the square root of -1. In mathematical terms, j is an operator, an instruction to 'take the square root of -1'. There are many operators in mathematics, one of the commonest being Σ, the Greek letter sigma, which means 'take the sum of'. For example, $\sum_{n=1}^{25} n$, where n is a whole number, means that one must add together all the whole numbers between 1 and 25. Similarly, $\sum_{n=1}^{12} 2n$ is the sum of all *even* numbers between 1 and 25, and $\sum_{n=1}^{13} 2n-1$ means the sum of all the odd numbers between 1 and 25. Much mathematical effort has gone into establishing a way of manipulating operators, establishing the relationship between them; in other words, in building up an algebra of operators.

A good example of this, taking the summations above, is to prove that

$$\sum_{n=1}^{25} n = \sum_{n=1}^{12} 2n + \quad 2n-1.$$

Common sense indicates that this is obvious, and does not require proof, but this is not sufficient for the mathematician, who will produce formal proofs for this and other similar statements.

A very common method of proving mathematical theorems is the method of *reductio ad absurdum*, literally, reduction to an absurdity, or a contradiction. Quite simply, if a theorem is to be proved, the mathematician takes its converse, and shows logically that it results in an absurd conclusion, thus showing that the original theorem is correct. A simple, if not entirely rigorous, example will show how this operates.

Suppose it is required to prove that there is no greatest even number. The mathematician will assume that there *is* a greatest even number, say $2n$, where n is a whole number. But $2n+2$ is also an even number, and as $2n$ is the greatest even number $2n$ must be greater than $2n+2$. This is absurd, and so there is no greatest even number. Although this example is extremely simple, the method is a very powerful and sophisticated one which mathematicians apply to a very large number of theorems in all branches of mathematics.

But despite the apparent seriousness of mathematics, much of it provides recreation for mathematicians and non-mathematicians alike. One of the most famous of these is the 'magic square', a framework of numbers arranged in such a way that the total of the vertical columns, the horizontal rows and the diagonals are in each case the same. Many mathematicians have spent a great deal of pleasant time constructing these squares, although in fact they contribute very little to knowledge of the number system.

Perhaps the most famous of all mathematical puzzles, however, was invented in 1878 by an American, Sam Lloyd. Known as the '*15 puzzle*' or the '*Jeu de Taquin*', people became so obsessed by it that in Germany employers had to post notices forbidding workers to play it during business hours. Tournaments were staged and huge prizes offered for its solution, and according to a contemporary French journalist it became a scourge of mankind, 'responsible for untold headaches, neuralgias and neuroses'.

The Jeu de Taquin consists of a shallow wooden box containing 15 flat wooden squares numbered from 1 to 15. They are arranged so that they form four rows of four, with one space remaining, so that the numbered squares can be moved about and interchanged, one at a time. The problem in the Jeu de Taquin is to bring about a particular arrangement of the blocks, by moving one block at a time. Obviously, the number of possible arrangements of the numbers is very large, but very soon after the game was introduced, two American mathematicians, Johnson and Story, showed that only half of the positions could be achieved. This meant that many of the huge prizes which were offered could never be won.

Mathematical recreations

Mathematicians, and indeed people in general, have been fascinated for centuries by unusual numbers, or numbers with unusual properties. Prime numbers, numbers which cannot be divided by any other number except 1, have already been mentioned. Another class of number which has attracted an inordinate amount of interest are those known as *perfect numbers*. The peculiar property of these numbers is that the sum of all their factors, including 1, is equal to the number itself. An example of a perfect number is 6, since $1+2+3=6$. The next smallest perfect number is 28 since $1+2+4+7+14=28$. Many pleasant hours can be spent working out other perfect numbers.

Many newspapers and magazines carry puzzles of different kinds, and it is commonly supposed that the easiest way to solve these is by mathematical methods. This is by no means always the case; they often resemble problems in mathematical logic, but more often than not there is no real problem once the smoke-screen of words has been cut away.

One of these which forms a fitting conclusion to an article on the mental processes of mathematicians concerns, in its most popular form, a cowhand and currency.

At the border of the United States and Mexico, there was once a strange situation with regard to currency. In Mexico a U.S. dollar was worth only 90 Mexican cents, while in the States, the Mexican dollar was worth only 90 U.S. cents. A cowhand crossed the border into Mexico, bought a ten-cent beer and paid for it with a Mexican dollar. His change was a U.S. dollar. Crossing into the U.S., he bought another ten-cent beer, paid for it with a U.S. dollar, and received a Mexican dollar in change. He carried on like this all day and ended up with a U.S. dollar in his pocket. The problem is: Who paid for the beer?

The world of number

Primitive men counted on their fingers. So do small children. But eminent mathematicians also use a similar technique in examining the amazing properties of everyday numbers.

2

1 The modern decimal system probably owes its existence to the fact that we each have ten fingers.

2 Arabic numerals of the kind in use today are of comparatively recent origin. As this engraving shows, they speed up arithmetical operations compared with the Roman system.

ONE OF THE FIRST THINGS a child learns when he is old enough to speak is counting on his fingers. To his parents, this is a heart-warming accomplishment. One of the first things a child is told *not* to do when he enters school is count on his fingers. To his teacher, finger-counting is puerile and primitive. To a certain extent, both are correct. The ability to count – on fingers or anything else – was a great intellectual achievement in the history of the human race. But this happened thousands of years ago, so it can be considered 'primitive'. Ironically, however, the 'finger-counting' so much frowned upon in many schools has reclaimed a place of prominence among abstract mathematicians.

Counting probably arose as an important human endeavour about the time early Man changed from hunting to farming. As long as his livelihood depended mainly on tracking down and killing a wild animal, counting was of little importance to him. But when he began domesticating animals, and grazing his future food supply on pasture land or growing it from seeds, keeping track of live stock and agricultural yields became imperative.

The idea of numbers came much later. There is evidence gained from primitive peoples in the world today that the concept of numbers required a great leap forward in human intellect. For instance, when we see five oranges, five stones, five dogs, or five people, we recognize that there are five of each. But for ancient Man, it was not so easy. In order to satisfy himself that five sheep and five stones represent the same number of objects, he actually had to place the stones one by one by each animal and check to see that none were left over. But gradually he evolved the idea of numbers. He then turned his attention to ways of writing them.

Pictographic numbering

Several hundred years before the birth of Christ, the Egyptians began writing numbers in the form of pictographs. A vertical staff (|) was one, a heelbone (∩) was ten, a scroll or coil (𓍢) was 100, a lotus flower (𓆼) was 1,000, a pointed finger (𓂭) was 10,000, a polliwog (𓆐) was 100,000. The highest numeral the Egyptians employed was for one million. Since it took the form of an astonished man (𓁨), we suspect that they had little use for numbers higher than this.

Any number could be written by combining the appropriate numerals. For instance, 13 was (∩|||), 34 was (∩∩∩||||), 57 was (∩∩∩∩∩|||||||), and so on. Aside from being rather cumbersome (try writing 95), this way of writing numbers was also a bit haphazard. Thirteen could be written (∩|||) or (|∩||) or (||∩|) or any other possible combination of these symbols. No doubt there was some standardization by convention, but the scope for variation remained inherent in the system.

The Romans were not quite so disorganized. Roman numerals were written with letters of the alphabet, rather than special symbols. To some extent we still use Roman numerals today, such as on public buildings and important documents. In the Roman system, one was I, five was V, ten was X, 50 was L, 100 was C, 500 was D and 1,000 was M. To write a number such as six, one would add five and one and get VI. Unlike the Egyptians, the Romans did not have the option of also writing IV, because this indicated five minus one, or the number four.

Number systems in which the location of one number in relation to another changes the meaning are called *positional notation* systems. Our own Hindu-Arabic (so called because it was pioneered by the Hindus of India and transported to Europe by Arab traders) carried positional notation to its zenith. In the Roman system VI and IV represented two different numbers, but the symbols V and I retained their meaning. VI meant five plus one; IV meant five minus one. In both cases, V still meant five and I still meant one, regardless of position. But in the Hindu-Arabic system, the symbol 2 means two, but in 24 it means 20, in 231 it means 200, in 2,453 it means 2,000. Thus, the symbols of the Hindu-Arabic system (1, 2, 3, 4, 5, 6, 7, 8, 9, 0) appear to have no fixed meaning at all.

Positional notation

We say 'appear to have no fixed meaning' because if the symbols actually had no fixed meaning, they would be useless. But the number 24 really represents $20+4$. Likewise, the numeral 231 really means $200+30+1$; and 2,453 means $2,000+400+50+3$. So our numbers really have a close similarity to both the Egyptian and Roman numerals. Two always means two, but two what? In one case it means two 'thousands' $(2\times1,000)$, in another case it means two 'hundreds' (2×100), in another case it means two 'tens' (2×10) and even when standing alone, two means two ones (2×1).

The Hindu-Arabic number system is what mathematicians call a *base ten* or decimal number system, by which they mean that it is built on powers of the number ten. As already demonstrated 2,453 can be expanded to $2,000+400+50+3$. This can be further expanded to $2\times10\times10\times10+4\times10\times10+5\times10+3\times1$. Or in the shorthand notation of indices $2\times10^3+4\times10^2+5\times10+3\times10^0$. (Note that any number to the zero power is one, so that $10^0=1$.) There are powers of ten everywhere. If the powers of ten are eliminated and only the multipliers retained, this gives the number in its original form – 2,453. This same procedure can be carried out for any number of the Hindu-Arabic system. For instance, 342 expands to $3\times10^2+4\times10+2\times10^0$. Eliminate the powers of ten and one gets 342.

There is nothing sacred about the base ten; numbers could be written in any other base we choose. Electronic computers carry out their calculations in the simplest base of all, the base two. In this base, each position in a numeral represents powers of two, not ten. For instance, the numeral 11 is not 'eleven', but $1\times2+1\times2^0$ or $2+1=3$. And 101 is not 'one hundred and one', but $1\times2^2+0\times2+1\times2^0$, which simplifies to $4+0+1=5$. In order to avoid confusion when writing numbers in bases other than ten, base ten names are not used, but simply the digit names. For

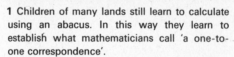

1 Children of many lands still learn to calculate using an abacus. In this way they learn to establish what mathematicians call 'a one-to-one correspondence'.
2 Without a number system and the ability to correlate abstract numbers and real quantities, Man would have been unable to conceive of instruments such as this sundial.
3 Numbers are a universal language. Pigeons, for example, are labelled with numbered rings rather than alphabetical symbols or words which might not be understood in some countries.

example, 110 is read 'one hundred and ten'. In fact, 110 turns out to be $1\times2^2+1\times2+0\times2^0$, which is $4+2+0=6$.

All our base two numbers so far have used only the symbols 1 and 0. These are all that are needed, because every possible number can be written using only 1 and 0. For instance, seven can be expressed as $1\times2^2+1\times2+1\times2^0$. Eliminating all the powers of two and just writing what is left gives 111 (read 'one-one-one'), which is seven. Another example is ten, which becomes 1010 in base two.

While base two has the advantage of requiring only two symbols, it has the disadvantage of having to use these two symbols at great length to express even relatively small numbers. Sixty-eight in the familiar base ten notation is 68. In base two, it is 1000100 requiring seven

digits. Ninety-nine also requires only two digits in base ten, 99, but seven in base two, 1100011. Mathematicians consider that our present base ten system may have evolved because Man has ten fingers. They contend that Man would have been far better off had he been created with 12 fingers, because base twelve has many advantages, even over base ten.

Nearly all elementary arithmetical operations learned in primary school derive directly from the fact that our number system is a positional notation, and the operations are the same in base two as in base ten.

Finger-counting represented an important early step forward in Man's intellectual development, but history repeated itself barely a century ago, when a mathematician named George Cantor carefully

1 Although one of the oldest calculating machines, an abacus in the hands of a skilled operator can still sometimes be quicker than modern calculating equipment.

2 Coins are marked with the number of units of currency which they represent. Most countries, including Britain, are now accepting the logical decimal system, established for so long in the United States and France.

3 Without a number system, there could be few gambling games. This is particularly true of roulette.

re-examined the idea of finger-counting and thereby founded the *arithmetic of infinity*. Cantor did not actually count on his fingers, but he analyzed finger-counting to discover just how it works:

Cantor said that when a person finger-counts, he is actually making *one-to-one correspondences*. For instance, a small boy counting marbles puts up one finger for each marble he has, and then counts his fingers to find the number of marbles. This relationship 'one finger for one marble' and conversely 'one marble for one finger' is a one-to-one correspondence. When a football-score keeper puts down one mark for each goal scored, he is also using a one-to-one correspondence.

To some extent, nearly every counting operation is a one-to-one correspondence. But it is only when very large numbers are used that this idea reveals its true importance.

Since antiquity, mathematicians had been puzzled by the idea of *infinity*. Infinity was conceived as a sort of super-number used for describing things which cannot be counted. For instance, if we start writing numbers in a series:

$$1, 2, 3, 4, 5, 6, 7, 8, \ldots$$

it soon becomes obvious that there can be

1 Counting was not always accepted with the same nonchalance as it is now. This is a reproduction of Pythagoras' table for counting to 100.

2 Of all mathematicians, Pythagoras is probably the best known. Here he is instructing a group of students in the principles and techniques of calculation.

no end, or largest number. To every number, no matter how large, it is always possible to add one and get a number still larger. This example gives two possible meanings to infinity. First, it can be considered to be the last number of a series which cannot have a last number: or as the total number of numerals in the series. Attacking the problem from this second point of view, Cantor discovered some amazing things about the idea of infinity. But first it is necessary to define some important words.

Some odd results

A collection of anything we wish to count can be called a *set*. For example, the marbles the boy counts, or the goals in a football match are sets. Cantor defined the *cardinality* or *cardinal number* of a set as the number of objects in the set. If the boy has one marble for each finger on both hands, then the cardinality of the set of marbles is ten. If the final score of the football match is 4–2 then the cardinality of the set of goals is six.

Which is the larger, the cardinality of the set of all even numbers or the cardinality of the set of all odd numbers? The answer is that the cardinalities are the same; there are just as many even numbers and odd numbers. This cannot be proved by counting all the even numbers and all the odd numbers, because these are infinite sets and do not end. But it is possible to set up a one-to-one correspondence.

Odd numbers   1 3 5 7 9 11 13 ...

Even numbers   2 4 6 8 10 12 14 ...

Since there is one odd number for each even number, both sets must have the same cardinal number.

But now what about the question, 'Are there more even numbers than counting numbers?' One is immediately tempted to say, 'Of course not. There are fewer even numbers than counting numbers. In fact, there are precisely half as many even numbers as counting numbers.' This is to say, according to 'common sense', the cardinality of the set of all even numbers is half the cardinality of the set of counting numbers. But since there is no way of determining the cardinality of all counting numbers and all even numbers, the only thing to do is establish a one-to-one correspondence:

Counting numbers 1 2 3 4 5 6 7 8 9 10

Even numbers   2 4 6 8 10 12 14 16 18 20

But this shows that for every counting number, there is precisely one even number, and vice versa. In other words, there are just as many even numbers as counting numbers! By the same reasoning, there are just as many odd numbers as counting numbers. Furthermore, the sum of all odd numbers and all even numbers together constitute all the counting numbers. So it is apparently possible for something to be equal to half itself, and apparently possible to add two equal things together and get a total no larger than either part.

Certain other interesting things can be done with infinite sets. Again consider all the counting numbers. Now chop off the first ten numbers from this series. Does this new set have the same cardinality as the original set? The answer is 'yes', because we can still establish a one-to-one correspondence:

1 2 3 4 5 6 7 ...

11 12 13 14 15 16 17 ...

Omitting the first million counting numbers would still give a new set with the same cardinality as the original.

Perhaps the strangest thing about infinities is that some infinities do not have the same cardinality as others, rather than that some of them do. After all, if an infinite set is created by continually adding more and more members to it without stopping, how could it be possible that one infinity could be larger than another? Suppose one could find two infinite sets such that when they are put into a one-to-one correspondence, there is always something left over. This is roughly like trying to stuff two pounds of sugar into a bag as large as we want; yet some sugar still spills over the top of the bag.

Mathematical heresy

Cantor not only showed that this is possible, but that there is an endless number of cases in which this occurs. In rather imprecise language, not only are some infinities larger than others, there is an infinite number of infinities larger than each other!

Cantor's ideas, formulated in the nineteenth century, were considered so heretical in some quarters that they were stridently denounced. In other quarters they were considered nonsense, because traditional ideas had been so firmly implanted that people refused to understand or were incapable of understanding. The beauty of mathematics is often obscured by processes which take on the guise of principles. In the case just discussed, the important point to remember is that *numbers* are really ideas; they exist only in the mind. *Numerals* are physical representations of numbers; they are 'meaningless marks on a piece of paper', until we give them meaning. The meaning we give them can change, depending on how we wish to use them. Therefore, to truly understand mathematics, one must forever be ready to adjust to its newer, and presumably better, forms.

Manipulating ideas

Mathematics changes. The concern of much modern work is with underlying patterns and processes rather than with shape or number. So mathematicians learn the manipulation of their own ideas.

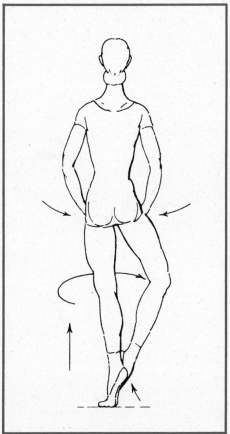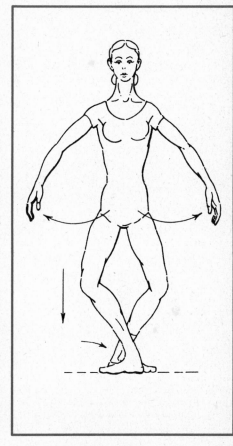

WHAT HAVE the following operations in common: adding odd and even numbers, pressing the switch of a table lamp, and a soldier turning about? Anyone familiar with the ideas of the new mathematics will probably know the answer. In the highly necessary jargon of the mathematician, one would say that all these operations are *isomorphic*. Which means, simply, that all these systems of operations follow rules which have exactly and precisely the same structure or pattern; it signifies much more than a mere resemblance between the systems of operations. To see how this is, first let us glance at the language of the new mathematics. At one and the same stroke we may then reveal some of the crucial differences between the new and the traditional mathematics, as it has come to be known.

Traditional algebra textbooks are concerned with technical problems as 'how to do it'. Modern maths differs in this respect: it is directed to asking 'why'. (It is not, however, a spectator sport. You still need the constant use of pencil and paper.) New maths, like Euclidean geometry, has axioms, definitions and theorems with proofs. But there is a difference. Euclid defined each concept; the modern mathematician has given up the unequal struggle. For example, Euclid defined a line as 'that which has no breadth' – at best a cryptic directive of

A turning ballet dancer demonstrates the idea of 'states' and operations. By repeating the same operation twice she reverts to her original state.

Sphinx-like obscurity. In the new maths, we can discard the definition. 'Line' is now accepted as one of the undefined terms of Euclidean geometry. The acceptance of the undefined, of basic axioms, in fact, is one of the corner-stones of the new maths thinking.

Dr Samuel Johnson, the celebrated lexicographer and wit, was a past master at the art of employing the undefined term. His dictionary defined many strange words in terms of others, equally obscure and undefined. In a modern dictionary we might look up the word 'thingumebob' and be directed to a list of synonyms, 'whatsit', 'thinger', 'thing-ummy', and 'thingumejig'. Look up 'whatsit' and you find the same synonyms listed. Under 'thinger' and 'thingummy' the same list appears. And so on. We are no nearer an understanding of 'thingumebob' – unless it is described in terms of words we already know.

Suppose we are going to build up a mathematical theory from scratch. We must start somewhere. Our first definition cannot be made in terms of words with which we are familiar, otherwise we could formulate an even more fundamental definition. The solution to this impasse:

in all mathematical systems – geometry, modern algebra, topology or whatever – there must be undefined terms. These are our axioms. From this simple beginning derives the so-called axiomatic approach to the new mathematics.

How do the operations already described have the same structure? Let us begin with the lamp. It has, we imagine, a press switch. Begin with the light off. In mathematical terms, this is its state. We can change its state by means of some *operation* we carry out on it; we then become the *operator*. (An operator is a common term in mathematics.) We press the switch: the light goes on. The light is the new state of the lamp, which we are treating as a simple machine. Press the switch once more and the light goes off. We have a system of states and operators; the generators of this system are 'to leave alone' and 'to press the switch'. We can write, then:

	Leave alone	Press switch
Leave alone	OFF	ON
Press switch	ON	OFF

The operators – what you do – are on the outside of the table. Inside are the results of the operations in terms of the final state achieved.

Take another simple machine, a calculator. We may ask it these sorts of questions – What happens when we add an even number to an odd? The result is an odd number. In all we may write:

$$Even + Even = Even$$
$$Even + Odd\ \ = Odd$$
$$Odd\ \ + Odd\ = Even$$

Or, as a table:

+	Even	Odd
Even	Even	Odd
Odd	Odd	Even

In the same way, in the case of the about-turning soldier – if he turns about twice he faces front again, which is the same thing as not turning at all. We call that the 'face front' move. Our generators of the system are this time 'Face front' and 'About turn'. In table form we may write:

	Face front	About turn
Face front	Face front	About turn
About turn	About turn	Face front

Finally, we may consider adding on a special clock. It has one hand and only two hours on its face, 0 and 1. On this clock – it forms the basis of a topic known popularly as *clock arithmetic* and more formally as modular arithmetic – the time is either 0 o'clock or 1 o'clock. Here is the clock:

$$0$$
$$\downarrow$$
$$1$$

Start at 0, say. Add 1 to it. This operation changes the state of the clock from 0 to 1. Add 1 again: this changes the clock's state back to 0. So we can say $1+1=0$ in this arithmetic, called *modulo 2* arithmetic because it has two symbols. Our table looks surprisingly familiar:

+	0	1
0	0	1
1	1	0

States are shown on the outside left column of the table; operators on the top row. Their joint effect is shown in the body of the table.

Isomorphism and correspondence

We said all these mathematical structures were isomorphic to one another. That is, they all have identical patterns. Thus, our final table of this sort, brings out this essential sameness of pattern in a quite abstract way:

	△	□
△	△	□
□	□	△

As can be seen, △ is the 'leave alone' operator (or zero state). Whatever it is

234

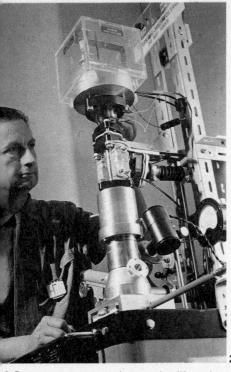

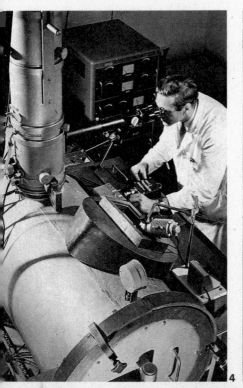

1 Patterns are common in everyday life and on the sports field. Investigation of the patterns underlying different operations has led to the discovery of important relationships in mathematics.

2 As industry becomes more scientifically aligned and production techniques more sophisticated, advanced mathematical ideas play an ever-increasing part. This equipment is used for milling ceramics using an electron beam at Harwell Ceramics Centre, England.

3 Learning is concerned with the establishment of patterns. Programmed learning and teaching machines are based on this technique.

4 Mathematics in action. Precision welding of steel tubes using electron-beam equipment relies on precise mathematical control of current phases.

5 Children often have an instinctive appreciation of pattern and are able to see similarities between apparently dissimilar sequences or objects.

combined with, it leaves it as it is. The $\square$ is the 'changer' (or second state in the game). It changes $\triangle$ to $\square$ and $\square$ to $\triangle$. On this evidence we can make up a mathematical 'dictionary' with some resemblance to Dr Johnson's. For example:

OFF – Even – Eyes front – 0 – $\triangle$
ON – Odd – About turn – 1 – $\square$

Remarkably, the structure is the same in every detail in each of the four real-life situations, all isomorphic to each other. Indeed, our dictionary amply demonstrates a correspondence between their various states. Establishing such a correspondence is an essential prerequisite to proving isomorphism. (Perhaps the most obvious example of such a correspondence is the one familiar to most five-year-olds: that of putting an egg in each

egg-cup on the breakfast table on a one-for-one basis.) Finally there are the abstract symbols of $\triangle$ and $\square$. The last table showed the self-same pattern existing between its elements of triangles and squares. We are now behaving as a mathematician does: we do not bother to affix a real-world meaning to the symbols. They are now divested of any meaning. All that concerns us is their relationships within a basic set of rules.

The structure we have just looked at is the embodiment of a mathematical entity known as a *group*. Basically, a group is a special kind of set of things, ideas, numbers, operations or anything else that is mathematically interesting. In a group the *elements,* the things, can be combined by one operation: with the lamp it was pressing the switch; with odds and evens

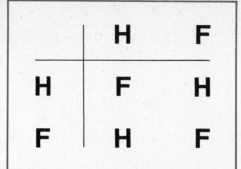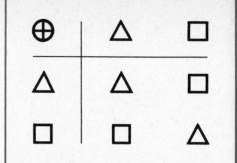

it was adding; with the turning soldier it was turning; with 0 and 1 adding again; with the triangles and squares, some abstract, unspecified operation.

A group is one of the sharpest of the new mathematical tools: it was used to cut through the Gordian knot of explaining the behaviour of atomic particles. Indeed, group theory was used with spectacular success to predict the presence of the Omega-minus particle in 1964.

Our group is a 2-group: it has two elements in it, and they are combined in some way according to the rules of the table. Like all self-respecting groups, ours has the following properties.

(1) *The inbred property*: The result of combining elements of the group must be one of the group's elements. This is rather like the handing out of jobs in the French Court long ago. The same people were always involved, as no outsiders were allowed in. The mathematical name is *closure*.

(2) *The group ad-lib property*: Three elements may be grouped in any way when being combined. Say we want to combine △ □ □. We could combine △ □ first and then combine the result of that operation, that is, □ , with △ , resulting in □ . On the other hand we could combine the same elements by combining □ △ and △ first, giving □ ; then △ □ gives □ , the same result. This is called the *associative property*.

(3) *The stay put property*: For every element there must be an element that does nothing, the 'stay-put' element. In our group this is △ , the *identity* element.

(4) *Undoing element*: For every element there must be an element that undoes what has been done. Each element is its own undoing element, or *inverse*. So □ undoes □ and △ undoes △ , no matter what the initial state.

Perhaps the most famous group in mathematics is the Klein group, a 4-group. The 2-group we have just considered is part of this group, that is, it forms a sub-group of the Klein group. Such a brief review can afford only a glimpse of the direction new mathematics is taking. A trip in this direction will take one on to the topic of *fields*.

A group has one combining operation associated with it. But a field has two. A typical field is the set of *rational* (whole and fractional) numbers; the two obligatory operations are addition and multiplication. Also a field has to have about a dozen properties; the group only has four as we saw. But the same abstract notions subsume both structures. They are the

The discovery of patterns in operations such as the addition of even and odd numbers leads naturally to rules governing all such operations. On the left, the results of adding odd and even numbers is shown. The centre illustration related to the half and full turns of a ballet dancer or a soldier, while the third illustration shows the generalized case.

very breath and spirit of the new mathematics.

We pursue our investigation of mathematical things that are not numbers for two good reasons. In the first place, they are part of advanced mathematics which is interesting in itself. In the second place, they are a significant feature of the new mathematics. They demonstrate with high clarity the rules of the game, so to speak. For mathematics is a game, and particularly the new mathematics. It is played according to certain rules of the structures. Advanced mathematicians play, however, not with rules of one game (structure) alone. They play to see what happens when the rules are changed or broken. They play, in fact, with rules about rules – at a second level of abstraction. But here, at the first rule-playing level, is a simple table game the reader can attempt. It may be intriguing to try to recognize an isomorphism!

Mathematical games

The game requires a supply of coins and paper clips. They are placed on the table in a row to make a 'word'. The ground rules are simple. Rule (1): You may add a paper clip to the right end of a word. For example: ∪ O can become ∪ O ∪ . Rule (2): You may place a coin on either side of any paper clip.
Typically:

O ∪ ∪ becomes O O ∪ O ∪ .

By means of these two simple rules a well-determined 'word' may be constructed. Such constructions are known in mathematics as *derivations*. Building up and breaking down such 'words' affords a concrete picture of proof, a keystone in the new mathematics. Here is one such derivation starting from O.

O
O ∪
O O ∪ O
O O ∪ O ∪
O O ∪ O ∪ ∪
O O ∪ O ∪ O ∪ O .

The game could, naturally, go on for ever. We end it at this point. The steps illustrated here may be regarded as a form of logical calculus, on the one hand, and as a game with operators on the other. The game becomes isomorphic to the 2-group already considered if we add a third rule

even numbers is shown. The centre illustration related to the half and full turns of a ballet dancer or a soldier, while the third illustration shows the generalized case.

to it. Rule (3): You may add or remove two coins *anywhere*, provided they are adjacent. Thus: O ∪ becomes O ∪ O O , and vice versa.

With these three rules we can prove a simple theorem in modern mathematics – that O ∪ = ∪ O .
The proof runs:

	O ∪
Rule (3):	O ∪ O O
Rule (2):	∪ O
Conclusion:	O ∪ = ∪ O .

That completes the proof. In conventional algebraic symbols we would have $xy = yx$. The same steps may be carried out with the △ and □ symbols in our 2-group. Which means, as already averred, that the systems are isomorphic. That is, they have identical structures; the paper clip corresponds to △ and the coin to □ .

This proof is a further demonstration of the power of the new mathematics. Demonstrably, a knowledge of one structure – in this instance, the 2-group – gives us the power to handle many other mathematical systems if they all have the same structure. Our five concrete systems had but one structure between them. A case of killing, so to speak, five birds with one stone (a mathematical structure).

We have paid no more than a passing tribute to the other great cornerstone of the new mathematics – the theory of sets. Suffice it to say that the whole of mathematics can be built up on this idea. Georg Cantor (1845–1918), a Russian-Dane, the creator of the theory of sets, defined a set thus: 'A set is a *collection of things into one total*.' That is, into one new thing. This intuitive demonstration of the concept of a set highlights the fact that a set is a collection of things *into one totality*. Mathematician Richard Dedekind (1831–1916) envisaged a set as a bag of things; what the things are he did not know, except that they are inside and determined. Cantor announced illuminatingly, 'A set I imagine as an abyss.'

In a modern, educational context the point of sets is this: colours, shapes and sizes, weights – indeed all physical and perceptual properties – are attributes of the things themselves. But numbers are properties of sets of things. For this reason alone, sets and the manipulation of sets, must represent the big guns of the new maths armoury.

Shapes of mathematics

Geometry grew out of the need for surveying land and erecting buildings, and for 2,000 years the principles laid down by Euclid for this purpose held undisputed sway.

AT THE TIME when the Roman legions ruled the world the farmers in the fertile valley of the Nile disputed about the ownership of land. This was not a petty squabble, but one which affected their livelihoods, and even the administration of Egypt itself. The custom in those days was to mark off the land owned by a particular person with posts, which served as the boundary between one holding and another.

But each year, when the Nile flooded, many of these posts were washed away, and this led to the disputes about ownership and boundaries.

The man who put the delineation of boundaries on a more secure footing was one called *Hero* of Alexandria. He used a method of surveying, based on a science called geometry, to reinstate boundaries which had been obscured by the floods. Thus it is Hero who is credited with the foundation of a modern system of surveying, but although he was an able mathematician and technician, he was by no means the first to set down and codify geometrical knowledge.

This is a distinction which must be given to Euclid, who lived three centuries before Hero. Euclid is one of the most famous of all mathematicians, and his name is almost invariably linked with geometry. And yet he himself was not the great innovator which many believe him to be.

The great geometer
Euclid took the mass of geometrical knowledge which had grown up over many centuries, simplified it, wove it into a coherent system, and wrote about it in terms that everyone could understand. His great work, the *Elements,* is to this day studied by schoolchildren all over the world, and is the basis of classical geometry.

But, sadly, Euclid's name is much better known to most people than is the science which he sought to explain. And yet Euclid's work, his reasoning and his conclusions are interesting in themselves, quite apart from their practical value.

But what, in essence, is the science of geometry? According to the Greek derivation of its name, it is the science of measurement of the Earth, and this was the function which gave rise to its development in ancient Greece. This definition can be seen to be inadequate, however, in terms of its applications, and it would be more enlightening, but not strictly correct in mathematical terms, to say that it is the branch of mathematics which deals with lines and spaces and the correlation between them.

Most of present-day geometry is based on Euclid and his work, and mathematicians still use many of his assumptions

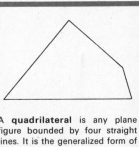

A **quadrilateral** is any plane figure bounded by four straight lines. It is the generalized form of the four-sided figure.

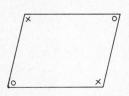

A **parallelogram** is a quadrilateral with one pair of opposite sides equal and parallel. It follows that the other pair are also equal and parallel.

A parallelogram with one of its angles a right angle is called a **rectangle.** All four angles are equal to a right angle. The diagonals are equal.

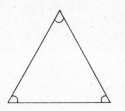

A **triangle** has three straight sides. This is an **equilateral** triangle, which has all the sides and all the angles equal.

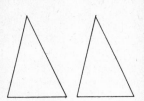

Congruency means that the figures concerned are equal in every respect. Thus the corresponding sides and the corresponding angles are equal.

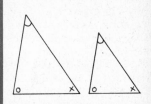

When two triangles have their corresponding angles equal, they are said to be **similar.** This means that they have the same shape.

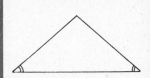

Isosceles triangles have two equal sides. The angles opposite these sides are also equal, while the third angle may be any size.

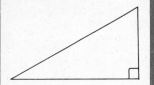

A **right-angled** triangle is any one in which one of the angles is a right angle. The sum of the other two angles will be a right angle.

The line forming a circle is called the **circumference.** A line drawn from a point on the circumference to the centre is the **radius.**

1 These drawings show some of the familiar figures and ideas in classical geometry. Most geometry theorems are concerned with the triangle, the quadrilateral, similarity or congruence. 2 The circle is the basis of sundials. This modern example is outside the headquarters of Times Newspapers in London.

and methods of proof. His definitions are still accepted, on the whole, although the nineteenth century saw a rebellion against many of these which led to the development of new branches of geometry.

Euclid's geometry deals with a flat surface, called a plane, and his definitions and assumptions are based on this plane. It is easy to visualize a plane – a table top, for example – but less easy to imagine a plane of infinitely large extent, as Euclid proposed. On this plane are two main geometrical 'building blocks', the point and the line.

According to Euclid, a point is that which has position on the plane, but no

1 Bees build honeycombs with chambers which are accurate hexagons, six-sided figures, with equal sides. This is one of the most economical ways of fitting shapes together within a given area.
2 This painting depicts a monk teaching Euclidean geometry. On his left is a solid body with 12 faces (a *dodecahedron*), each of which has five sides (a *pentagon*).
3 Triangles are often used in structural work because they cannot be deformed by load without bending the sides. The U.S. pavilion at Expo 67 was designed on this system by the architect, Buckminster Fuller.
4 Core storage units in computers use a grid system based on co-ordinate geometry. Each storage unit is identified by its co-ordinates.

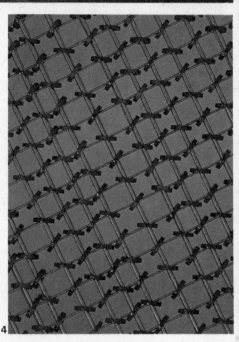

dimensions; a line has length but no breadth and no thickness, a limitation which was extended to apply to all planes.

These concepts worked very well in the world which the Greeks observed. They thought themselves to live on a plane surface, apart from natural features such as mountains and valleys, and if their points and lines did in fact have dimensions and width respectively this was regarded as a limitation in their existing drawing instruments.

With these three basic concepts, Euclid developed a number of *postulates* or *axioms*. Axioms are truths which are accepted as self-evident and thus require no proof, and Euclidean geometry is based on these axioms, which remained unquestioned until the nineteenth century.

Plane figures

In the first of his 13 elements, Euclid dealt with parallel lines. He defined these as lines which would never meet, no matter how far they were extended in either direction. Euclid applied this to straight lines, as these are the only ones which can be said to maintain a constant direction when extended. From this idea of parallelism he went on, in his famous

Fifth Postulate, to say that through a point in a plane, only one line could be drawn parallel to a given line. On examination this is seen to be true, according to common sense, and yet it was this postulate which mathematicians questioned in the nineteenth century.

On the basis of the straight line, a number of common geometrical figures or shapes can be produced. If two non-parallel lines are drawn, they meet (intersect), forming an angle between the lines. Three non-parallel lines will intersect to produce a figure with three sides and three angles, called a triangle. In the same way, four intersecting lines give a quadrilateral.

Generalized triangles, formed of any three non-parallel lines, include equilateral triangles, in which all the sides are equal; isosceles triangles, in which two sides are equal; and right-angled triangles,

with two sides of the triangle making an angle of 90 degrees, or one right angle. Similarly, the four-sided figure, the quadrilateral, becomes a trapezium if one pair of the sides is parallel, and a parallelogram if both pairs of sides are parallel. In the same way, if one of the angles of a parallelogram is a right angle, the figure is then a rectangle, and a rectangle which has all four sides equal is called a square.

This process can be carried out for any number of intersecting lines, but the triangle and quadrilateral are the most common and are the ones which have given rise to many of the theorems of geometry.

It was out of a study of these figures that the ideas of *congruence* and similarity arose. Congruence is best illustrated by imagining two triangles drawn on a sheet of paper. If one triangle can be cut out and made to fit exactly over the other one, then

1 Railway lines are a common example of parallelism. They maintain the same distance between them over very long stretches.

2 Formal gardens, such as this one at Château Villandry, France, are normally laid out to geometrical patterns. In this case great use is made of arcs of a circle (parts of the circumference) as well as more complicated curves based on other geometrical shapes. Laying out such a garden requires a good deal of geometrical skill.

3 Climbing frames for use in children's playgrounds often use a triangular lattice pattern. This gives rigidity under hard use, and great strength with light weight. Frames based on squares need much stronger components.

the two triangles are said to be congruent – they are equal in every respect.

From this simple fact, several useful conclusions can be drawn.

The corresponding sides of the triangles must be equal, the corresponding angles are equal, and the areas of the triangles are equal. These are the consequences of congruency, but what is not immediately obvious is the minimum conditions necessary for two triangles to be congruent. The proof of congruency when given sides and angles are equal forms the basis of a section of Euclidean plane geometry.

Comparison of shape

Similarity, in geometrical terms, means that two figures are the same shape, but that the sides have different dimensions. For instance, two equilateral triangles are similar, regardless of the dimensions of the sides. More generally, any two

figures which have their corresponding angles equal are said to be similar. From this idea follows the proportionality of similar figures, so that if there are two similar triangles, and a side of one is twice the length of the corresponding side of the other, then the other sides will also have the ratio 2:1. This proportionality of similar figures is extremely important in geometry, and gives rise to a large number of important propositions. It is also extensively used in the practical applications of geometry, such as surveying, architectural drawing and civil engineering.

But similarity does not begin and end with figures composed of straight lines. Examination shows that all circles must be similar. They have the same shape regardless of size, and measurement shows that the lengths of the *circumferences* (the circumference is the line bounding the

circle) are in the same ratio as the *radii* (the radius of a circle is the distance from the centre to the circumference). This important similarity led to the conclusion that there is a constant relationship between the length of the circumference of a circle and its radius. This ratio, which is represented by the Greek letter π, has a value of 3·1416, so that the circumference of any circle is 3·1416 × diameter. Also, the area of a circle is 3·1416 × (radius)^2.

Obviously, the early applications of geometry were largely concerned with the measurement of areas, and many methods have evolved for the calculation of the areas of irregularly shaped figures. One of Hero's important contributions to geometry was his formula for calculating the area of triangles from the length of their sides. But the formula which he evolved can be rather cumbersome in use, and it has now been replaced by more convenient methods based on *trigonometry*.

Euclid and his fellow geometers built up a body of geometrical knowledge based on the simple, self-evident postulates or axioms. Beginning with axioms, they were able, by using pure logical reasoning, to draw irrefutable conclusions about the nature of geometrical figures and the relationship between them. This method of reasoning was extended into three dimensions, and dealt with the sphere and the cube rather than the circle and the square, the tetrahedron (a figure whose four surfaces are all triangles) rather than the triangle. The methods used to prove these propositions are similar to those used by medieval scholars in their disputations.

For over 2,000 years Euclidean geometry held almost unchallenged sway, and in time assumed the status almost of Holy Writ; the few who dared question it, indeed, often found themselves facing the wrath of the Church authorities.

The first really major alteration to geometrical method came through the French philosopher and mathematician, *René Descartes*. He devised a system for using algebra to discover and examine theorems in geometry. The system is called algebraic geometry, analytical geometry, co-ordinate geometry or sometimes cartesian geometry, after Descartes. (*Fermat,* a contemporary of Descartes, invented this system independently.) But co-ordinate geometry, or analytical geometry, used the basic postulates of Euclid: the infinite plane, the point with no size and the line with no breadth. Descartes' geometry was thus built almost entirely on the foundations laid down by the master, Euclid.

But the nineteenth century saw a swing away from Euclid. Mathematicians pointed out that real lines and real points bear little relation to those postulated in classical geometry and, what is more important, the world is not an infinite plane. Leading the attack on Euclid was the German mathematician *Riemann,* who abandoned Euclid's fifth postulate and constructed another geometry, a logical, consistent system based on his new ideas. Riemann's geometry is directly applicable to the surface of the sphere, and in these circumstances Riemannian geometry has become extremely useful in navigation and mapping.

Variable shapes

But important as they are in themselves, Riemann's efforts were much more significant in that they encouraged other mathematicians to throw off the restraints imposed by Euclidean concepts, and re-think the whole basis of geometry. But regardless of the reaction against Euclidean notions, most of the systems which have been developed still owe a great deal to his work.

One which bears little relationship to classical geometry, and which at first sight does not seem to be a geometry at all, is *topology,* that branch of mathematics which deals with lines, points and areas without relation to their shape or size, considering merely their spatial relationship. To people educated in Euclidean geometry, this always appears rather odd, because classical geometry is so concerned with dimensions, whether of lines, angles or areas.

A basic concern of topology is the relationship between the number of vertices (points at which lines intersect), the number of edges and the number of faces of geometrical figures. Taking the cube as a simple example, it has eight vertices, 12 edges, and six faces. The tetrahedron, on the other hand, has four vertices, six edges and four faces. An interesting point about these figures is that the total number of vertices and faces is in each case greater by two than the number of edges. This applies to all figures, and is one of the few simple numerical laws in topology.

But the fascinating thing about this law is that it holds good regardless of how the shape or size of the figure is distorted. The edges of the cube may be bent in any way, the cube itself may even be squeezed into a spherical shape, but as long as the body is not broken or cut, the relationship above still holds. Thus, while at first sight topology may appear to be a very limited subject, its findings apply to an enormous range of shapes.

A further extension of geometry has been the development of geometries of four or more dimensions. These are extremely complex and difficult to grasp by people who, after all, live in a three-dimensional world. But mathematicians can see no good reason for stopping at three dimensions, and they have extended their work to the discussion of the properties of four-dimensional spheres and four-dimensional cubes.

1 Modern office blocks, such as the Centrepoint Building in London, are usually built on a three-dimensional grid system. In many of them the individual offices are identified by geometrical co-ordinates.
2 Although it uses curves as well as straight lines, the Pirelli building in Milan also uses a grid system.

Measuring with angles

Trigonometry grew up among ancient peoples as a means of measuring towers, fields and trees. Now, it has become one of the most useful tools of the scientist and engineer.

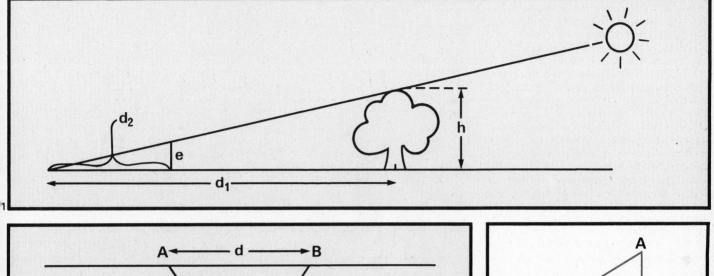

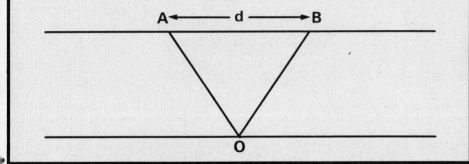

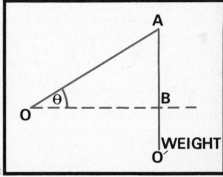

1, 2 Trigonometry is most useful in measuring quantities like the height of a tree or the width of a river without either climbing the tree or crossing the river. Measuring the

angle concerned and knowing the value of the circular functions concerned (the sine, cosine and tangent of the angle) allows a surveyor to calculate the relevant distance.

3 Circular functions are best understood in terms of a rotating rod with a weight hanging vertically on a string, as shown in this diagram. The rod does not vary in length.

EVEN IF it were only good for measuring the height of trees without the necessity of climbing them (disregarding its use in navigation, electrical theory, astronomy, surveying, structural engineering etc., the triangle and trigonometry would still play a leading part in mathematics.

How can one use a triangle to measure the height of a tree? Choose a time in the morning or afternoon when the tree casts a fairly long shadow. Now, hammer a stick into the ground, measure the height of the stick and the length of its shadow, and divide the stick length by the shadow length. Now, measure the length of the tree's shadow, and multiply it by the answer to this division problem. This is the height of the tree. For instance, suppose the stick is 2 ft high, and its shadow is 6 ft long. Dividing 2 by 6 gives $\frac{1}{3}$. Now, suppose the tree's shadow is 30 ft long. One third of 30 ft ($30 \times \frac{1}{3}$) is 10 ft. Thus, the tree is 10 ft tall.

This method of calculating heights depends on the properties of similar triangles. The triangles in this case are the one formed by the stick, its shadow, and the ray of sunlight passing from the top of the stick to the end of the shadow, and the one formed by the tree, its shadow,

and the ray of sunlight passing from the top of the tree to the end of the shadow. They are said to be similar (have the same shape) if each angle in one corresponds to an equal angle in the other.

For example, consider two similar triangles (the angles of one are equal to the angles of the other) such that the sides of the smaller are 2, 3, 4 and the sides of the larger are 6, 9, 12. Now, in the smaller triangle, divide the longest side by the shortest: $4 \div 2 = 2$. Now, divide the longest side of the larger triangle by the shortest side: $12 \div 6 = 2$. The answers are the same. Now, in the smaller, divide the middle length side by the shortest: $3 \div 2 = 1.5$. Do the same thing for the larger triangle: $9 \div 6 = 1.5$. Again the answers match. This will happen no matter what combination of sides in the two similar triangles are used: the answers will always match.

If the process is applied to *right triangles* (triangles containing a 90 degree or 'right' angle), these ratios are *trigonometric functions* and each one is given a special name.

Consider the triangle ABC containing a right angle, an angle of 37 degrees and the third angle of 53 degrees. (If two angles of a triangle are known, the third angle

can be calculated because the sum of the three angles of a triangle is always 180 degrees.) The length of the sides are as indicated, approximately 3, 4, 5. Now a bit of nomenclature. Focus attention on the 37 degree angle. Then the side CB directly across the triangle from it is, quite appropriately, called the *opposite side*. The shorter of the two sides that form the angle, side AB, is called the *adjacent side*. And as in all right angles, the longest side, side AC, is called the *hypotenuse*.

Finding the functions

Now, form the ratio of the opposite side divided by the hypotenuse ($3 \div 5 = 0.6$). This is called the *sine function* of 37 degrees and is written sin $37° = 0.6$. The ratio of the adjacent side divided by the hypotenuse ($4 \div 5 = 0.8$) is called the *cosine function* of 37 degrees and is written cos $37° = 0.8$. The ratio of the opposite side to the adjacent side ($3 \div 4 = 0.75$) is called the *tangent function* of 37° and is written tan $37° = 0.75$.

There are three more *trigonometric functions*. But these are simply the reciprocals of the three just defined. For example, the *cotangent function* of 37 degrees is the adjacent side divided by the opposite side (4÷3=1·333). The *secant function* of 37 degrees is the hypotenuse divided by the adjacent side (5÷4=1·25), and finally, the *cosecant function* of 37 degrees is the hypotenuse divided by the opposite side (5÷3=1·67).

Since all right triangles containing a 37 degree angle are similar, the values of their trigonometric function will be identical. The same thing applies to right triangles containing any other angle. For example, the sine function of 30 degrees in a particular right triangle is 0·5, i.e. sin 30°=0·5. So the sine of 30 degrees in any other right triangle is also 0·5. Tables of trigonometric functions have been produced for each whole degree angle from 0 degrees to 90 degrees and many fractional angles in between.

For simple applications such as measuring the height of a tree, the stick-shadow method is probably just as easy, if not easier, than trigonometry. But for other more important applications – such as determining the location of a ship at sea or the distance to a star – the stick-shadow method would be useless.

Measuring the sun's distance

For example, astronomers need to know the distance from the Earth to the sun, the so-called *astronomical unit*. By a method known as *solar parallax*, it is possible to determine the angles of the right triangle formed by the distance from the Earth's centre to the sun, the Earth's radius, and the tangent from the sun to the Earth. The radius of the Earth is known to be approximately 4,000 miles, and the angle with the sun at the vertex (point) is known to be approximately 8·8 seconds of arc. (Angles are measured in degrees, but a degree is composed of 60 *minutes,* and a minute is composed of 60 seconds. So an angle of 8·8 seconds is extremely small, equal to little more than two-thousandths of a degree.) By using the tangent function, one can derive the equation:

$$\tan 8\cdot8 \sec = \frac{4{,}000 \text{ miles}}{\text{sun distance}}$$

The value of tan 8·8 sec is taken from a table of trigonometric functions, the equation solved, and the answer recorded as the familiar figure 93 million miles. In actual practice, the Earth–sun distance was first calculated by methods other than trigonometry, because a total eclipse of the sun is necessary in order to use polar parallax. However, distances to some of the near stars were first calculated in a similar manner but using the radius of the Earth's orbit (93 million miles) rather than the 4,000 mile radius of the Earth itself (the method for stars is called *stellar parallax*), and a unit of astronomical distance called the *parsec* derives from this method of measuring stellar distances.

But how can these functions be used in other than right triangles? Various equations have been worked out to make this possible, the two most important being the Sine Rule and the Cosine Rule.

The Sine Rule states that the ratios of the sines of the angles to the lengths

1 **Both navigation and the design of ships depend** on trigonometry. Special tables of trigonometric functions are prepared for navigators, these being based on the sphere rather than a plane.

2 **In the pithead machinery at a coal-mine, tri-**gonometry enables designers to calculate stresses and the power of the winding motor. Sinking new shafts is also based on circular functions.

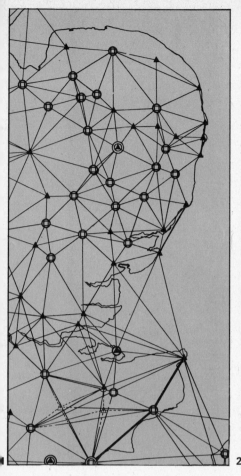

1 Cartographers use trigonometric methods to calculate distances and elevations in map-making. Reference plinths for this purpose are located in various parts of a country.

2 When a motor-cyclist lifts his front wheel off the ground under power, the relevant stresses are a function of the angle between the machine and the horizontal.

of the opposite sides in a triangle are identical. In the form of an equation:

$$\frac{\sin A}{a} = \frac{\sin B}{b} = \frac{\sin C}{c},$$

where the capital letters represent the angles, and the small letters represent the length of the sides opposite the angles.

The Cosine Rule is a bit more complicated:

$$a^2 = b^2 + c^2 - 2bc \cos A,$$

where the small letters again represent the length of the sides and the capital letters represent angles. In this case, there is only one angle, angle A. If one is working with angle B, then the equation becomes:

$$b^2 = a^2 + c^2 - 2ac \cos B,$$

and if one is working with angle C, the equation becomes:

$$c^2 = a^2 + b^2 - 2ab \cos C.$$

So far, only triangles with angles of 90 degrees or less have been considered. But it is quite possible for a triangle to have an angle greater than 90 degrees, so it would be useful to have trigonometric functions for angles greater than 90 degrees.

Mathematicians have defined such functions in terms of a rotating radius circling round a co-ordinate axis. This process may be visualized by thinking of a rod

with a weighted string on one end and the other end nailed to an upright plank (see diagram). As the rod is swung round anti-clockwise, the string is always vertical, like a plumb-line, and so the rod, the string and the horizontal axis (x-axis) always form a right triangle. Soon the rod approaches the vertical axis (y-axis), and passes it. Now the rod and the horizontal form an angle greater than 90 degrees, but the weighted string still hangs so as to form a right angle. It is this right angle, and the triangle formed by the string, the rod, and the left side of the x-axis, that are used to define trigonometric functions greater than 90 degrees.

For example, in the diagram, the radius vector has been rotated 110 degrees from the x-axis. The triangle OCD formed by the radius vector, the string and the left side of the x-axis is a right triangle. Since a straight line contains 180 degrees, the fact that triangle OCD contains a 70 degree angle can be determined simply by subtracting. Thus, $180° - 110° = 70°$. All the trigonometric functions of 70 degrees are already in the table. So mathematicians have defined all the trigonometric functions of 110 degrees to be the same as those of 70 degrees. For instance, cos 70° = 0·342. Thus, cos 110° = 0·342.

Actually, this statement is not quite correct, because it fails to take into account one mathematical refinement. The halves of the x-axis and the y-axis are labelled '+' and '−' depending on location.

For the x-axis, everything to the right side is '+' and to the left '−'. For the y-axis, everything above the horizontal axis (x-axis) is '+' and everything below '−'. This factor must be taken into consideration when determining the trigonometric functions for angles larger than 90 degrees.

In the example, cos 110° was said to equal cos 70°. But the cosine is defined as the adjacent side divided by the hypotenuse. The hypotenuse is always positive, but in this case the adjacent side D is negative. A positive number divided by a negative number gives a negative result, so to be completely correct, cos 110° equals the negative of the cos 70°, i.e., cos 110° = 0·342.

Functions of any angle

Sin 110° is found the same way. By definition, the sine of 110 degrees is the same as the sine of $180° - 110° = 70°$. Thus, sine 110° = sin 70°, which from the table is shown to be 0·939. But is it to be positive or negative? The sine is defined as the opposite side divided by the hypotenuse. The hypotenuse is positive and so is the opposite side; the result must be positive. Thus, sin 110° = 70° = 0 939.

Similarly, tan 110° = tan 70° = 2·747, but positive or negative? The tangent function is defined as the opposite side divided by the adjacent side. In this case, the opposite side is positive (because it is above the x-axis), but the adjacent side is negative (because it is on the left side of the x-axis), so the result is negative. Thus, tan 110° = −tan 70° = −0·939.

In general, the trigonometric functions of any angle between 90 degrees and 180 degrees can be found by subtracting the angle from 180, looking up the value of the function of the resultant angle and affixing the appropriate sign.

There is no real need to stop with angles between 90 degrees and 180. If the rod is allowed to continue its rotation, it will soon drop below the x-axis, giving an angle greater than 180 degrees. Indeed, it could swing all the way round to the starting point, completing a circle and covering an angle of 360 degrees. By imagining the weighted string capable of 'falling' upwards, right triangles can be formed right round the circle, and so trigonometric functions can be defined right round the circle. That is, it is possible to have trigonometric functions for angles from 0 degrees to 360 degrees simply by taking the right triangles formed, looking up the value in the table, and affixing the appropriate sign ('−' or '+'). For instance, what is the sine of 210 degrees? The angle 210 degrees forms a right triangle in the third *quadrant* of the co-ordinate axes. (The four parts of the co-ordinate system are called quadrants and number anti-clockwise.) The required angle, in this case angle OCD, is found by subtracting 180 from 210; $210° - 180° = 30°$. Thus, sin 210° = sin 30°, but positive or negative? Sine is opposite side divided by the hypotenuse. In the third quadrant, the opposite side is below the x-axis, so it is negative. Thus, sin 210° = −sin 30° = −0·500.

If a graph of all the values of the sine function from 0 to 360 degrees is plotted, the result is the *sine curve*. Note that the sine curve first rises to a positive peak above the *x*-axis (graduated in degrees), then descends till it crosses the axis, and then heads back up again. The rise and fall of the sine curve from positive peak to negative peak (maximum to minimum) is periodic; that is, it repeats itself every 360 degrees. For this reason, the sine is called a *circular function,* a name which is also applied to the cosine and tangent, and to the reciprocals of these three, the cosecant, secant, and cotangent.

In a very similar manner, an alternating electric current (one which keeps switching direction and the kind used in ordinary house circuits) also rises and falls through maximum and minimum points in a periodic manner. In fact, if one plots a graph of the behaviour of an alternating current, the result looks almost exactly like the sine curve. So by comparing the graph of an alternating current with the sine curve, it is possible to write trigonometric equations to explain the behaviour of an alternating electric current. This

accounts for the sometimes puzzling fact that equations related to electric circuits often contain angles, when there are no angles apparent in the circuit itself. These angles derive from a comparison of the behaviour of alternating currents with the sine curve (or cosine curve, or tangent curve, or any other appropriate trigonometric curve).

The result can be generalized. Any kind of motion which is periodic (repeats itself according to certain physical laws) is called *simple harmonic motion.* A swinging *pendulum* or a vibrating spring are examples of this type of motion. The graph of a simple harmonic motion also turns out to be a sine curve. So any kind

of simple harmonic motion may be studied by equations involving angles and trigonometric functions, even if there are no angles apparent in the motion itself.

Trigonometry is an almost inexhaustible subject. Its applications are many and sometimes unusual. But like most powerful tools of mathematics, or any other science for that matter, trigonometry stems from basic research. The triangles from which it is derived were studied in detail by the ancient Greeks, more as an intellectual exercise than because they expected to gain something practical from their endeavours. Yet something of great practicality emerged, and it is anyone's guess just how it will be put to use next.

1 Angles and their relation to loads play a large part in modern architecture, such as these additions to the Festival Hall in London.
2 Cranes of the type used in docks provide a good illustration of circular functions. As the jib rises, its length is unaltered, but the angle increases and the length of the vertical cable and the horizontal both increase.
3 Measurement of the sun's diameter and its distance from the Earth are carried out by

trigonometry. These measurements must be made during an eclipse.
4 Although trigonometric functions are usually associated with right-angled triangles, they apply to any triangle. A graph of a sine function makes a familiar curve.
5 Shadows of skaters show how trigonometry can be used to measure the height of inaccessible objects such as trees, mountains, towers and aircraft.

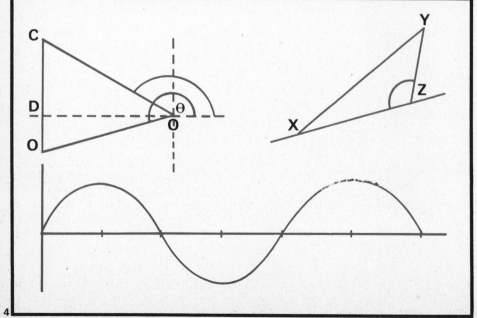

Man must measure

Science and engineering depend on the ability to measure and evaluate with speed and accuracy. What are the standards used, how are they determined, and what are the techniques?

SUPPOSE YOU BUY a pound of meat from a butcher, but when the butcher gives it to you, it doesn't feel like a pound. Just to check his honesty, you take the meat home, weigh it on the bathroom scales and discover that it weighs only 15 ounces. You complain, but the butcher insists that his scale is more accurate than yours and that he gave you a full pound of meat. How do you settle the argument?

If you live in a well-regulated society, somewhere there must be a weights and measures office with a staff of inspectors to check things like this. The inspector arrives with a scale, weighs the piece of meat, and finds that it weighs slightly more than one pound. Now there are three different weights. But the question remains: which is correct? The inspector insists that his must be, because the scale was examined for accuracy just before he left his office. How was it checked? Simply, it was compared with the master scale at the weights and measures office. But how can one be sure that the master scale is correct?

Measurement by comparison

It is obvious what is happening. Every measurement involves comparison with another measurement, and this process could continue *ad infinitum*. Three important facts about the nature of measurement now emerge: (1) all measurements are relative; (2) there must be some measurement arbitrarily set as a standard; (3) everyone must accept the standard.

In the situation just described, the standard would be the scales at the weights and measures office. In actual practice, a mechanical device such as this is never used as a standard. Instead, some physical object or reproducible physical phenomenon is used. As a result of an international conference arranged by the French Government and culminating in the signing of the Treaty of the Metre in 1875, an International Bureau of Weights and Measures was established to define suitable standards, not only for mass but for other important measures such as length, time and volume.

The Bureau reported the results of its efforts in 1889. The international standard for mass was defined as the *kilogram*, which is the mass of a particular cylinder of platinum-iridium alloy kept in a vault in Sèvres, near Paris. There is no question as to whether or not this cylinder actually has a mass of one kilogram, because it is *defined* as having a mass of one kilogram. But if one wants to know if something else has a mass of one kilogram, the way to find out is to put the standard kilogram mass and the object whose mass is to be determined on opposite sides of a delicate

1 The standard 1 lb mass is used to calibrate weighing equipment for both scientific and commercial purposes.

2 Great care must be taken in handling standards to avoid changes in mass or length. This kilogram standard is specially stored.

balance. If the two balance then the object has a mass of one kilogram; if not, then the object does not have a mass of one kilogram. Precise copies of the standard kilogram mass were made and are now held in all countries adhering to the Treaty of the Metre. These are used as the mass standards against which other masses in the country are measured.

From these, other precise copies were made, and very precise part copies of the standard kilogram mass were also made, such as a half-kilogram, a quarter-kilogram, a tenth-kilogram, and so on. So in

3 Drawing instruments must be carefully calibrated as even a small error can lead to serious malfunctioning of equipment. These special drawing tables are designed with this in mind.

each country of the world subscribing to the Treaty, it is possible to determine mass in relation to a standard mass accepted throughout the world.

The international unit of length was defined by the International Bureau of Weights and Measures as being the length of one ten-millionth of the distance from the North Pole to the equator measured on a quadrant through Paris. In more practical terms, a metre is the distance between two lines engraved on a platinum-iridium bar kept in a vault in Sèvres. As with the standard kilogram mass, copies of this bar have been made and distributed to countries throughout the world.

It is necessary to keep these standard kilogram masses, metre lengths and others very carefully protected. If one should be

chipped, or in some other way altered, international difficulties would arise, because what one country accepts as being the proper measurement of a kilogram mass would be different from what another country accepts. For this reason, these copies of the standard kilogram mass, like the original itself, are housed in special, moisture-proof, air-conditioned cases.

But even the most careful handling will not prevent minor changes from occurring in these standards over long periods of time. So in 1960 new standards were adopted which are more reliable.

Degree of accuracy

The metre is no longer the distance between two engraved lines on a platinum-iridium bar, but 1,650,763·73 wavelengths in vacuum of a transition between energy levels $2P_{10}$ and $5D_5$ of krypton-86 atom excited at the triple point of nitrogen. Likewise the standards for other fundamental units such as the second and the degree Celsius have been redefined in terms of physical phenomena. These new standards, though far more complicated than the old, have the advantage that they do not need to be stored anywhere; nor do copies have to be made. The transition wavelength of excited krypton-86 is, as far as modern science has been able to determine, always the same under the given conditions. Thus, whenever a scientist wants a precise metre-measurement, all he need do is excite a krypton-86 atom. The important point about this is that it can be done, at any time, anywhere.

Unfortunately, no way has yet been found to define a kilogram in terms of a completely reproducible physical phenomenon, so the standard kilogram is still the platinum-iridium cylinder in Sèvres.

Assuming that absolutely perfect standards have been created, the science of measurement still faces an enormous difficulty. Suppose you take a metre stick

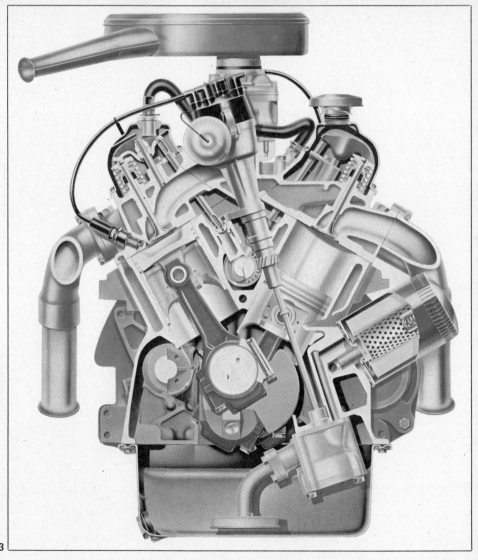

1 Measurement of length in scientific work often involves optical equipment such as this krypton interferometer, which is almost as exact as the wavelength of the light used.

2 Precision weighing is done on balances which are fine examples of modern engineering design and construction.

3 Interchangeability of engine parts depends on the accuracy and tolerance on dimensions with which they are made.

which you know to be precisely one metre long and then measure a table with it. The table turns out to be 2·53 metres long, or does it? A closer look at the metre stick shows that the table is slightly longer than 2·53 metres long. It appears to be, though one cannot be certain, 2·532 metres long. The question now is, does one write down 2·53 m as the length of the table or 2·532 m?

For measuring tables, the difference between 2·53 m and 2·532 m is generally of no consequence; it really does not matter which measurement is used. But for scientific work, this can make a tremendous difference. For instance, it could make the difference between whether a rocket lands successfully on the surface of the moon or explodes on the launching pad.

Rounding forward and back

Scientists, of course, use measuring instruments much more precise than a simple metre stick, so they might be trying to decide between 2·5312 m and 2·53124 m. Nevertheless, the problem still remains.

On first consideration, one might say that the scientist should use 2·53124 m, because it is more accurate. However, to a scientist, accuracy is not a function of how many digits a number has, but what those digits mean. In making his measurement, the scientist knows for certain that his length is at least 2·5312 m, because his measuring device is capable of measuring this with complete accuracy. But when he tries to measure more accurately, he knows that the final 4 is nothing but a guess. He cannot tell for certain whether it should be a 4, a 3, a 5, or what. So he rounds off. If he is inclined to choose 4, this means that the measurement appears to be closer to 2·5312 m than it is to 2·5313 m. Were he tempted to choose 5 or 6, he then would round forward, that is, he would write 2·5313 m.

Of course, the measurement obtained by rounding off is not completely accurate either. But the mathematical study of statistical probability and error analysis has shown systematically rounding back when the measurement is less than half-way between two units, and rounding forward when a measurement is more than half-way between two units, in the long-run produces accuracy which is greater than when simply guessing.

The maximum possible difference between the measurement recorded and what a completely accurate measurement would be (were a completely accurate measurement possible) is called the *tolerance*. For example, if one were to measure a wheat field and reported its length as 302 m, this would mean that the field is no less than 301·5 m and no more than 302·5 m. Thus, the tolerance would be 0·5 m, because the reported length could not be any more than one-half metre more or less than the reported length. Tolerances are often assumed, but they are also often written into the measurement, as 302m ± 0·5m, which is read 'three hundred and two metres plus or minus nought point five metre'.

Tolerance plays an important part in precision machine making and mass pro-

1 The need to measure has been apparent from the very earliest times, as this Egyptian mural shows. International trade was responsible for the creation of international standards of mass and length.

2 Weighing on the level of the housewife is still a matter of high accuracy. Commercial weighing equipment is frequently checked against standard equipment, which is in turn referred to the standard mass.

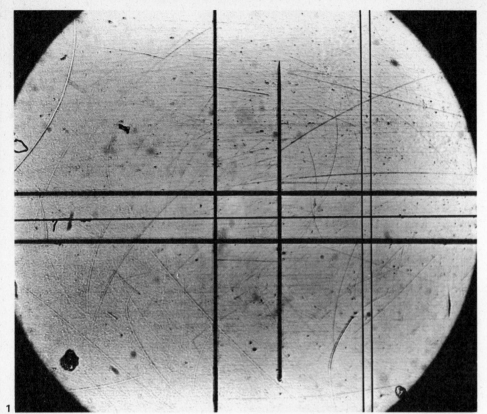

1 This photomicrograph of the defining lines at the end of a standard shows the lengths at temperatures of 0 °C. and 20 °C. Checking must be done at one of these temperatures.

2 Standard lengths are carefully constructed and calibrated so that they are unlikely to vary with use or age. This cross-section has been designed to eliminate bending.

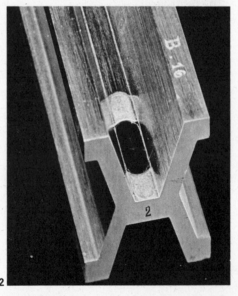

duction. Imagine the difficulties if a piston ring or some other minor part of an engine were to wear out and it were not possible to replace it. You would have to buy a whole new engine. However, engines are made so that they can accept new parts, provided the new parts have the proper tolerance. That is, a new piston ring may be designed to have a diameter of 0·5 inch, but due to normal manufacturing error, it may actually be 0·49 in. or 0·51 in. In other words, it has a tolerance of 0·01 in. so the engine into which it is to fit must be capable of accepting and using a piston ring of these varying dimensions. That is, the engine itself must also have a tolerance of at least 0·01 in., or else one could never be sure that the new part would fit.

As complicated as the science of measurement appears to be today, in one way it is very much easier than it was hundreds of years ago. In those days of poor communications, not only did weights and measures differ from country to country (such as between the U.S.A. and Britain or between Britain and France), they even differed within a country from village to village. The Treaty of the Metre went a long way towards remedying this chaotic situation, but to anyone living in an English-speaking country, it is obvious that not all nations of the world subscribed to the Treaty.

Even some of those governments that did, did so in a rather half-hearted manner. For instance, the United States decided to retain pounds and feet as units rather than using kilograms and metres, but the pounds and feet in the U.S.A. were redefined to be based on the kilogram and the standard metre. Great Britain, however, decided to retain its own standards in use before the Treaty of the Metre. Thus an American pound and a British pound were almost, but not quite, the same. Likewise, an American foot and a British foot were almost, but not quite the same.

For casual use, the difference between American measures based on the Treaty of the Metre and British measures based on British Imperial Standards stored in London were of little consequence. But in industry, especially during the Second World War, the differences became quite significant. The American inch is equivalent to 2·540005 cm. The British inch is equivalent to 2·539995 cm. In more familiar terms, 1 in. U.S.=1·000004 in. British, an almost infinitesimal difference of 0·000004 in. Yet some modern machinery is so

precisely made that even this difference is enough to prevent many British-made machine parts from fitting American equipment, and vice versa. British and American standards were brought largely into line in the early 1960s. Today both countries define the inch as 1 in.=2·54 cm exactly. American and British pounds are also exactly the same.

The metric system of measures is a *decimal* system of measures, meaning that it is based on the number 10. Our ordinary number system is also decimal. This similarity allows for simple calculations.

For example, if a vehicle travels at 40 metres per second, how fast is this in kilometres per hour? Since one hour contains 60 minutes and one minute contains 60 seconds, the number of seconds in one hour is $60 \times 60 = 3,600$. Multiplying 40×3600 gives 144,000 metres an hour. One kilometre equals 1,000 metres, so dividing 144,000 by 1,000 gives 144 kilometres an hour.

Now try a similar problem in the English system of units, which is not decimal. If the speed is 50 feet per second, how fast is this in miles per hour? Again, one hour contains 3,600 seconds, so multiplying $50 \times 3,600$ gives 180,000 feet an hour. But one mile equals 5,280 feet, so one must now divide 180,000 by 5,280. Very few people can do this in their heads, as was done with the metric units. Instead, this division is a long and tedious pencil and paper calculation.

A universal system

The important thing to note about these two examples is that the ease of doing the problem in metric units and the difficulty of doing the problem in English units is inherent in the two systems. It is *always* easier to do problems in the metric system than in the English system, because the metric system was specially designed to make it easier. There is no difficulty in converting 5,240 grams to kilograms. Simply divide by 1000 to give 5·24 kilograms. But there is a great deal of difficulty in converting 5,240 ounces to pounds. So while it may be somewhat painful for people to give up the English system, with which they have grown up, in the long run everyone will be better off when the whole world measures mass in grams and kilograms instead of ounces and pounds, and measures distance in metres and kilometres instead of feet and miles.

Of course, to be absolutely consistent, it would be necessary to invent decimal units for time, in which one hour would be equal to 100 minutes and one minute would be equal to 100 seconds. Similarly, it would be useful to redefine angular measurements so that a circle would have 100 degrees instead of 360 degrees. A degree would then be divided up into simple decimal fractions, instead of 60 angular minutes and 3,600 angular seconds.

These and similar developments are no doubt still very far in the future. But by the turn of the century, the world may still be speaking in 10,000 or more different languages, but finally it will be recording weights and measures in only one.

The means of measurement

Measurement is a vital part of science and engineering, and the degree of accuracy far surpasses that encountered in everyday life. What are the tools of such precise measurement?

OF ALL the semi-scientific activities encountered in everyday life, the most important is measurement. Everyone is at some time or another interested in weighing something or other and the majority of people carry a watch – an instrument of some precision.

Watches and clocks are, without doubt, the most precise measuring instruments which we encounter in everyday life; even a clock of mediocre quality must have a standard of accuracy well beyond that of, say, a set of kitchen scales, or a dress-making tape measure. An error of two per cent (less than two ounces in five pounds) is perfectly acceptable in kitchen scales. The same error in a watch would result in it gaining or losing more than 28 minutes per day, which is an intolerable variation.

It is this matter of accuracy which distinguishes precision instruments used in industry and science from the normal measuring equipment employed by the housewife or shopkeeper. In many industries, an error of a thousandth of an inch in the dimensions of a finished part can be enough to cause it to be rejected as unsuitable for its function. In some, the order of accuracy required is even higher, so that the demands placed on the measuring tools used is onerous indeed.

Measuring problems on the scientific and industrial level resolve themselves into problems of measuring length, mass, and time. This may not at first sight appear

to be so when quantities such as temperature, pressure or acidity are under consideration. Taking an ordinary thermometer as an example, however, it soon becomes obvious that a principal problem in measuring temperature with this instrument is in accurately determining the length of the mercury column.

The first problem is to devise ways of accurately determining length, mass and time. The units in which we measure these

quantities are arbitrary; that is, they are purely convenient parts which have been determined by scientists, and have no absolute significance. It would be perfectly justifiable to divide the day into 100 hours rather than the present 24. Indeed, it is this arbitrariness which explains the fact that there are several different systems of measurement in use.

Standards of accuracy

Measurement comes back to comparison with an agreed standard. Measuring instruments are merely devices which are an intermediate between the standard and the object to be measured. Precision measuring instruments are devices which can do their job with a high degree of accuracy, and maintain that accuracy time after time.

Accuracy and reproducibility are of no value if they are represented in such a way as to be difficult to read in using the instrument. Often, there are very few markings on the face of a watch, so that, although the watch may be an excellent timekeeper, it is difficult for the user to tell the time to within less than a minute with any degree of certainty. A small magnifying glass can be incorporated in the glass of a watch to increase the accuracy of reading without increasing the complexity of the instrument. This expedient is often employed in scientific apparatus.

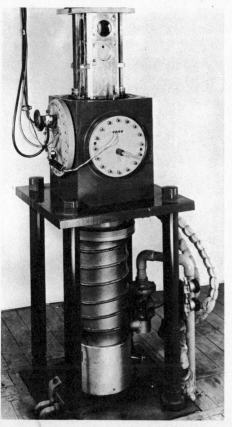

1 Accurate measurement of components normally depends on a micrometer gauge. The rotational displacement of the thimble allows the dimension to be very accurately determined.
2 The caesium clock is used in scientific time measurement. Such a clock varies by less than a second in 1,000 years. Its accuracy depends on sub-atomic vibrations.
3 Errors of less than one twenty-millionth of an inch can be serious in large telescope lenses. Such an error requires years of polishing to correct it.

But one of the most universally applicable devices ever devised in metrology, as the science of measurement is called, is the *vernier scale*. Briefly, a vernier scale is simply a means of increasing the speed and accuracy of reading a normal graduated scale. Consider a rule marked off in centimetres and millimetres. In constructing a vernier scale, a small movable scale marked off in ten divisions each equal to 0·9 millimetre is placed edge to edge with the normal scale. In using a normal centimetre rule, if the length being measured falls between two of the millimetre graduations, the length (if it is to be closer than the nearest millimetre in accuracy) must be estimated, with consequent risk of error. With the vernier, however, the actual length can be read off without this risk of error.

The vernier scale

Briefly, the vernier scale is used thus: the zero on the sliding scale is brought in line with the point on the fixed scale which coincides with the length to be measured. The user then looks along the two scales and finds two graduation marks which coincide. If this coincidence takes place at the seventh graduation on the sliding scale, then the final component in the length being measured will be seven-tenths of a millimetre.

Vernier scales are used in many measuring instruments in the engineering industry, such as caliper gauges, but they are also applied to the more accurate reading of thermometers, barometers and pressure gauges. There is no reason why they should not be applied in any instrument in which the quantity being measured is represented in terms of length or angle. For the vernier scale can be applied with equal facility to angular measurement, and such instruments are in common use. In engineering or scientific parlance, the use of a vernier scale increases the *order of accuracy* of reading such an instrument.

An interesting example of the application of the vernier to very accurate measurement of length is to be found in the micrometer screw gauge, although the vernier is, in fact, only an auxiliary device. The micrometer itself consists of a U-shaped frame, one leg of the U carrying a hardened steel boss or anvil. The other carries a steel nut, internally cut with a very accurate screw thread whose pitch (the distance between successive parts of the thread) is precisely known. This nut carries a bolt with a matching thread, and with a sleeve which is graduated along its length. Each turn of this bolt within the fixed nut either increases or decreases the distance between the bolt and the anvil by a fixed amount, which can be read off on the longitudinal scale. Similarly, each part of a complete revolution of the bolt can be measured and expressed as the equivalent length, by means of a scale and datum mark engraved on the barrel of the micrometer. This scale, in instruments of high accuracy, is a vernier, so that instruments of this type can read to an extremely high accuracy within their working range.

The screw principle of measuring lengths

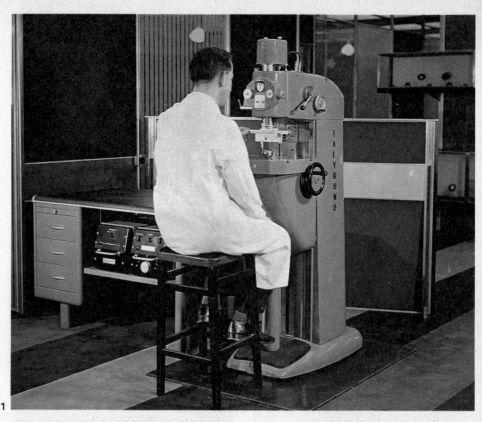

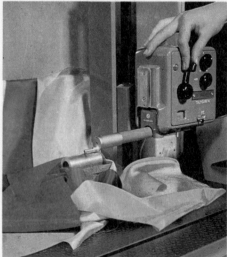

1 Roundness measurement is a complex task which today makes use of advanced equipment working to closer tolerances than normal engineering gauges.
2 Automatic print-out of results is a feature of advanced measuring equipment. It combines the speed necessary for mass production with accuracy of a high order.
3 The quality and durability of cloth depends on close control of the fibres. The diameter of individual strands is monitored by equipment of this kind.

is used in a variety of applications, one of the oldest of which is in astronomical equipment. In this case, a screw micrometer is used in conjunction with a telescope to measure the angular size of the sun, or the angular distance between two heavenly bodies.

It is probably true to say that, of the high-precision techniques for measuring length, the micrometer screw principle is the most widely used, whether with or without the refinement of a vernier scale. For the accurate measurement of small distances, this type of movement is used in conjunction with a microscope to give an instrument known as a *traversing microscope*. Instruments of this type are used to measure the sizes of such things as watch parts, biological specimens and a wide range of engineering parts. It relies for its accuracy largely on the excellence of the optical system with which it is associated, a condition which also applies to the astronomical micrometer.

These systems described so far are applicable only to relatively small distances. For greater distances when the accuracy obtainable by normal surveying methods is not sufficient, the scientist or engineer must employ electromagnetic waves.

The principle employed in radar (which stands for RAdio Direction And Range) is to transmit a short pulse of electromagnetic waves at the object whose distance is required. These waves are reflected by the object and return to a suitable receiver placed alongside the transmitter. Together they incorporate electronic equip-

1 Supersonic aircraft such as the Concorde depend for their speed, stability and safety on accurate dimensional control of both equipment and airframe. Inaccuracies can be disastrous.
2 Within the Concorde's cockpit the numerous gauges must be highly accurate and frequently checked. They must be designed to withstand harsh operating conditions.

ment for measuring the lapse of time between the transmission of the wave and its return to source. Knowing this interval and the speed of the wave (equal to the speed of light) it is a simple matter to compute the distance between the transmitter and the object.

Range-finding using radar is a very accurate process, and it is used with great success in aircraft and ships; indeed, it is now standard equipment in all commercial aircraft and ships. A later technique using the same principle has been developed using the *laser,* a device which produces a narrow beam of coherent (that is, with the light waves in step) light of a certain wavelength.

This light is in fact only a shorter wavelength variety of the electromagnetic pulse emitted by the radar transmitter, and the associated timing equipment is very similar. But there are two differences. Because of the shorter wavelength, the ultimate accuracy obtainable is greater; but visible light is obstructed by fog, so that laser equipment is unsuitable for conditions of poor visibility.

As can be seen, even sophisticated length measurement depends on an *analogue,* the comparison of one quantity with another. In this case length is represented in terms of time.

In basic weighing equipment, such as a spring balance of the type used in a kitchen, the analogue used is between weight and the extension which it causes in a spring. Such spring balances are also used

by scientists, but only for very rough work. Unfortunately, they suffer from a drawback which makes them unsuitable for fine work.

The extension of a spring is caused by the gravitational pull of the Earth on the object being measured, and this gravitational pull varies as the distance between the object and the Earth's centre varies. Thus an object on a spring balance will give different readings at the top of a mountain and in the depths of a mine. Even the discrepancies caused by a change in élevation of a few hundred feet is sufficient to make a spring balance unsuitable for accurate work.

Instead, scientists revert to the comparison between the weight of the object under consideration and a set of standard

weights. The standard chemical balance, in almost universal use, is basically a metal beam mounted on an almost frictionless and durable pivot carrying two weighing pans of identical weight on either end of the beam. The beam is mounted exactly in its centre, so that when a balance is reached between the object under test and the standard weights in the other pan, the weight of the object is completely independent of altitude, as the pull of gravity is equal on both scale pans.

An improvement in the chemical balance has taken the manipulation of the counterweights out of reach of moisture and dirt by placing them within a case, where they are operated by remote control. This also enables the designers to provide a numerical display, which allows the weight to be determined much more easily than by the former method of counting the total of the weights in the balance, as well as removing influences which can affect the accuracy of the weights.

Curiously, the gravitational drawback of the spring balance also becomes apparent in the measurement of time. Clocks which depend on the pendulum for their timekeeping were found to show discrepancies at different altitudes, so that they had to be adjusted to take altitude into account. This, together with their susceptibility to changes in temperature and movement, soon made them obsolete in the world of precise time measurement.

It is apparent from this that measurement of time also depends on an analogy, in this case between the passage of time and the mechanical movement of a pendulum. The pendulum has been replaced in modern clocks and watches by a balance wheel to sidestep some of the drawbacks of the pendulum, but the analogy remains.

In the quest for a method of time measurement compatible with the demands of scientific research, horologists looked for an easily reproducible natural phenomenon occurring at precisely determined time intervals. A method which was used for a long time was the clock based on a *piezo-electric* crystal, that is, a crystal which vibrates at a standard frequency whenever an electric current is applied to it. In many ways, this phenomenon is similar to the action of a pendulum; the impulses emitted by an oscillating quartz crystal have the same pattern as the oscillations of a pendulum, but they are very much less dependent on external circumstances.

Quartz clocks have attained a very high degree of accuracy, the best of them maintaining their timekeeping to an accuracy of within one second per year. But even this is not good enough for some scientific purposes.

Regular atomic pulses

Further research led to the development of atomic clocks, and in particular to the caesium clock. It was found that, under certain circumstances, atoms of caesium emit pulses of electricity at extremely regular intervals. Fortunately the necessary conditions are, in scientific terms, easily reproducible, so that this gives scientific workers an extremely dependable instrument for measuring the passage of time. The pulses are added by electronic means to give a total interval which is as accurate as the natural vibrations of the caesium atom. One particular advantage of this type of clock is that it does not have to be compared during construction with a standard timepiece. Clocks like this are used for standardizing less sophisticated instruments for use in observatories, scientific laboratories and in space research and broadcasting.

One outstanding watch, however, has become available which is driven by an entirely different method from the usual. The inventor sought a method of timing depending on an invariant and easily reproducible natural phenomenon. He settled on an electrically driven miniature

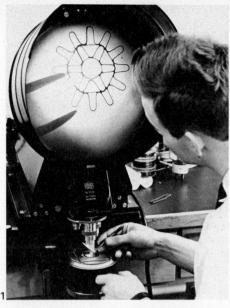

1 A magnified image of an engineering part facilitates rapid checking of dimensions to close limits. Screens often carry a scale superimposed on the image of the part.

tuning fork, whose oscillations are solely dependent on the physical characteristics of the fork. Using this principle, he produced a watch which provided a standard of accuracy of an unprecedented order, and which is immune to many of the factors, such as vibration, shock, or moisture, which interfere with the proper functioning of more conventional watches.

Developments in the latter half of the twentieth century have made it possible to relate dimensions to invariable physical phenomena rather than Man-made standards.

Precision instruments, by their very nature, demand skilful design and construction as well as the most careful handling if they are to give their best. In the early days of science, this often meant that they had to be protected within sealed cases, or located in special buildings, strictly limiting their usefulness. The latter half of the twentieth century has seen the development of instruments which are very accurate, yet are able to withstand the normal hazards of everyday use in the laboratory and workshop.

2 Automatic machine-tool control often incorporates a means of feeding back information to a computer during the manufacturing process, resulting in an accurately machined component.

3 Gear teeth must be checked for curvature, pitch, width and surface smoothness. This is generally done while the gear wheel is still undergoing machining.

Two and two make why

Calculation plays a large part in modern life, particularly in business. Analysis of the methods we use to work out calculations reveals many interesting facets of numbers.

CALCULATION IS so much a part of modern life, indeed it is an essential adjunct to the very business of living in society, that we tend to take it for granted, and tend to ignore the underlying ideas and techniques which shape our arithmetic.

But it was not always so. The step towards counting, enumerating, listing and quantifying the objects around him was a vast one for early Man, but systems and the control which they gave him over his life have culminated in the great scientific achievements of the twentieth century.

Study of the numbering and counting systems of primitive tribes has shown that the first step in counting was to establish a 'one-to-one' relationship between sets of objects, whether it was between the sheep in a flock and a number of pebbles; or between the children in a family and the fingers of the hand. This apparently simple one-to-one relationship implied in the first place the recognition of an abstract number relationship between sets of totally dissimilar objects; the subsequent steps towards manipulation of the numbers were small in comparison.

1 This picture, a vignette from a multiplication table published in 1650, shows a merchant and clerk using a calculating table – a sophisticated type of abacus – for multiplication.
2 The man in the foreground of this tavern scene is holding a tally. Making marks on a stick known as a tally has been used for centuries as a way of keeping totals.
3 Calculation long ago became one of the military arts. This is a primitive way of measuring the elevation of a cannon. More recently, war stimulated the development of computers.

Counting on the fingers is still a valid method, but it has largely been replaced by establishing a one-to-one relationship between the objects to be counted and the 'natural' numbers (that is, 1, 2, 3, 4, 5, 6, 7, etc.). When bank clerks and shop assistants count money, this is what they do.

In fact, watching people at work in a bank can give a valuable insight into the techniques of calculation as they are used in everyday transactions. A bank clerk counting a large number of coins of one denomination, for example, will not count them singly, but in groups of three, four, five, or even ten. For groups up to four, he will normally place one finger on each coin and move them to one side in groups of four. Accomplished bank tellers can recognize much larger groups with ease, and can thus count in large numbers.

To do this they need to be able to recognize rapidly the number of objects in a group. Children acquire this ability at an early age; under the age of five, if they play board games like Ludo or Snakes and Ladders, which involve the use of dice,

children quickly learn to recognize the number pattern engraved on the dice. Not only do they recognize these conventional patterns, but they are also able to recognize four, five or six objects when the group is haphazardly arranged, without having to count.

The abacus, which embodies this principle, is still a respected instrument of calculation, particularly in the East. Bank clerks in Japan who use the abacus for calculation are able to read off the answer to their calculations almost at a glance without having to count the individual beads.

Cumulative addition

Counting, even in ones, can be regarded as cumulative addition, and this is a convenient way to think of it, because the series of natural numbers is itself constructed by successively adding one to the previous number in the series.

Adults add and subtract by using a set of rules acquired in early childhood. Thus, when one is adding 7 and 9, one does not normally count 7, 8, 9, . . . 16, in units of one, but takes the answer 16 from the store of arithmetical results in the memory. Subtraction, which can be regarded as the converse of addition, makes use of the same set of stored results; this process is perfectly straightforward so long as the result of the subtraction is one of the 'natural' numbers.

Much of the calculation of normal life is concerned with problems such as the total cost of, say, five gallons of petrol at six shillings per gallon. Such a calculation is normally done almost subconsciously, as the numbers involved are small, and the result familiar to most people. But it is worth examining the processes involved in such multiplications.

In effect, what is required is that we set aside six shillings for each gallon of petrol, that is five groups of six, and find the sum of all the shillings. Multiplication then, is a form of addition, and any multiplication sum can be so represented. In ancient Rome, this was the only possible way of multiplying, as the Roman number system did not permit the manipulative technique used with the modern Arabic numbers and positional notation. The concept of multiplication as a repeated addition is also applied in digital computers, which perform multiplications by adding in rapid succession.

With numbers greater than 12, multiplication becomes a matter of manipulative technique, for few people carry the result of, say 27 multiplied by 86 in their heads as they would the result of six times five. The method used depends on the positional notation used for our number system. The 8 in 86 represents eight tens and the 6 represents six units. In the actual multiplication, the number 86 is multiplied firstly by the 2 of 27. This gives the result 172, that is, 172 tens, giving 1720. Secondly, 86 is multiplied by 7 (seven units). This gives 602. Adding these together gives the result of the calculation as 2322. Many of the errors involved in multiplications of this type are caused by people misunderstanding the processes involved, so that tens are added to hundreds, units are added to tens, in a completely meaningless way.

Distributive law

Multiplication by splitting one of the numbers into tens and units, or hundreds, tens and units, is an example of the distributive law of multiplication. This states that, for example, $8 \times 27 = 8 \times (20 + 7) = 8 \times 20 + 8 \times 7$. It is completely unimportant how the number is split, and the technique is used by bankers, accountants and others to reduce fairly complex multiplications to the level of simple mental calculation.

Some numbers, of course, lend themselves readily to easy manipulation. The most obvious is multiplication by ten, which is done merely by adding 0 to the number to be multiplied. Thus, 10×27 is 270, 10×316 is 3160.

These results open the way to even more short-cuts. Multiplication by five by adding 0 and dividing by two; hence, 5×46 is 230. Similarly, multiplication by 25 can be performed by adding two zeros (multiplication by 100) followed by division by four.

But what are the processes involved in division itself? When a pack of playing cards is used to deal four bridge hands, the pack is divided into four equal parts. Each

player received 13 cards. The available number of units, in this case cards, is allotted equally among four, which in arithmetic is called the divisor. In the case of bridge hands, each player gets exactly 13 cards, and there are no cards left over. But if the normal deck of cards contained 55 instead of 52 cards, there would be three cards left over. If it were absolutely necessary to share all the cards, one would have to resort to breaking (or fractioning) the surplus cards. Suppose each extra card were cut into four pieces. Each player would then receive one fourth-part of each card, or a total of three-fourths of a card. This is expressed mathematically as $\frac{3}{4}$, which simply means three parts, each of which is a quarter of the whole. The parts

1 These children are being taught to recognize the relations between numbers. Modern ways of teaching mathematics stress the need for the child to find out himself.

2 Bookmakers need to be able to calculate complicated odds in their heads. Many are very adept at this. They have a special form of semaphore for signalling the odds.

3 A shop assistant in a supermarket using a modern till. This machine can work out the total of a set of purchases very much more rapidly than the average shop assistant.

4 A child being taught by the Montessori method. This technique illustrates very clearly the connection between volume and length. The beads are one unit across.

5 Persian astronomers in their observatory. Arabic mathematics gave the world its present system of numerals and greatly simplified the process of calculation.

indicates that the answer *may* be correct.

Another time-honoured method of adding columns of numbers is 'casting out nines'. Basically, this is just a means of simplifying the task of remembering the sum of individual additions, but many variations of it are used throughout the commercial world.

A recurring problem in arithmetic is that of taking averages. If one is asked to calculate the average age of a number of people, the normal method is to find the total of the ages and divide it by the number of people. For example, if the ages are 26, 18, 42, 38 and 36, the total will be 160. Dividing by five gives the average age as 32.

But a glance at the figures shows that the average age will probably be about 30. Thus $30-26=4$; $30-18=12$, giving a total of 16 'below the line'. In the same way, there is a total of 26 'above the line'. This works out at $26-16=10$ above the line. Dividing this result by five gives 2. Thus the average will be two above the line, that is, 32.

Obviously, any other number than 30 could have been chosen as the mean, and the system would have worked equally well. But the closer one can get to the actual average in choosing this number the easier, generally speaking, will the calculation be. Obviously this does not hold if the numbers involved are 8, 11, 9, 15 and 326. In this case it would be marginally easier if a number such as 10 were chosen.

Counting by weight

It is perhaps a sad commentary on our techniques of calculation that when a large number of similar objects is to be counted, the best method is to dispense with numbers and rely on weight. It is common in banks to see a teller weigh a bag of coins rather than counting them by hand. If he knows the number of coins in, say, a pound weight, it is an easy matter to estimate the number of coins from the weight. This method may appear to be rather crude and liable to error, but for the bank clerk without mechanical aids, it may literally be that the weighing machine is worth its weight in gold.

Mathematics can indeed claim in this scientific age that it is the 'Queen of the sciences'. It penetrates every aspect of modern life. And at the basis of mathematics is the process of computation – simple in its basic principles, often difficult in execution. In these days it is no longer fashionable, as it once was, to claim that one is 'no good at figures'. A knowledge of the elements of arithmetic is, of course, taught in schools, but many people are so to speak mathematical cripples, and some of the blame for this may lie with the methods by which mathematics was taught in the past. Mathematics and arithmetic are not really the property of an élite, and everyone, in some way or another, consciously or unconsciously, makes use of these sciences every day. They represent big human conquests and there is no doubt that in the future they will come to play an increasingly important part in the everyday life of human beings.

1 The stocking counter at the huge GUM store in Moscow. The assistant is using an abacus. This extremely ancient calculating instrument is still used in many parts of the world.
2 This bank clerk at the Fuji Bank in Tokyo is one of the most skilled in Japan. Bank clerks frequently become highly adept with figures and able to calculate very rapidly.

of the unit thus expressed are called fractions, and $\frac{3}{4}$ itself is also called a fraction.

By far the greater number of calculations result in fractions, that is, the result is seldom a whole number. But it is often useful when beginning a division to be able to tell whether the answer will, in fact, be a whole number. Many rules of thumb can be applied. The most common and the most obvious is that numbers which end in 0 (38760, for example) are divisible exactly by 10. They are also divisible by 5. More importantly, numbers which do not end in 0 are not divisible exactly by 10. Numbers which end in 5 are also divisible by 5, and even numbers are, by definition, divisible by 2.

Denary system

Obviously, these and similar rules will only work for our number system, which is based on the number 10 (the denary system), but similar rules can be devised for number systems which use the base 12, or any other base for that matter. The tedium of adding long columns of figures is often a major cause of errors, and people like accountants and bank managers who have to perform large numbers of such operations have devised systems to lighten the load. One of the best known techniques is 'adding in fives'. Suppose one is asked to add the numbers 56, 73, 49, 22 and 13. The normal method is to add the units, which gives 23. The two tens are then transferred to the tens column and the second addition is made. This gives 21 (21 *tens*), so that the answer is 213.

But suppose the addition is performed like this: six is one more than five – now

we have plus one; three is two less than five – plus one and minus two gives minus one; nine is four more than five – minus one and plus four gives plus three; plus three and minus three is zero; zero minus two is minus two; two less than five is three, and so the number to be entered in the units column is 3. There are five numbers; five fives are twenty-five, so that in the final step we have in fact subtracted two from twenty-five, and hence the number of tens to be added to the tens column is two. Repeating this process for the tens column gives the answer 21, and so the total is again 213.

Checking the addition is again an easy matter. Add the digits in each number thus: $5+6=11$, $1+1=2$, $7+3=10$, $1+0=1$, $4+9=13$, $1+3=4$, etc. Then add $2+1+4+4+4=15$, and again, $1+5=6$. Now add the digits in 213, $2+1+3=6$. Unfortunately, like so many other checking systems, this one is not an infallible guide. If the totals of digits are the same, it only

Not and except or

An apparently abstruse nineteenth-century branch of mathematics, based on an attempt to codify the laws of thought, now plays a major part in the design of modern computers.

1 Boolean algebra plays an important part in the planning of military campaigns. The manoeuvres of these American Grant tanks in the Western desert are organized by rules of logic.
2 Charles Dodgson, better known as Lewis Carroll, author of *Alice in Wonderland*, was a leading mathematician. Many of the bizarre stories in his books have a logic basis.
3 All logical processes can be expressed according to the rules of Boolean algebra. The court-room process of deciding guilt or innocence is a typical example.

MOST PEOPLE know the old rhyming riddle made famous in the Peasants' Revolt:

When Adam delved and Eve span
Who was then the gentleman?

The answer to this riddle is obvious, and most people might leave it at that. But it is interesting to see how a logician would tackle it.

In the first instance, Adam can be described as a member of the class of people who delve (or dig). Eve is a member of the class of people who spin (apart from being female, which puts her in addition in the class of people who are female). The gentleman is a member of the class of people who do no manual work. Anyone who *does* perform manual work is by definition *not* contained in the class 'gentlemen'. Thus neither Adam nor Eve (quite apart from her disqualification on

the grounds of sex) can be described as a gentleman.

This relationship can be expressed in symbols. Let a be the class of people who dig. Let b be the class of people who spin; and let g be the class of gentlemen. Then we can say that neither a nor b is contained in g. This can also be written:
$$a.g=0,\ b.g=0,$$
which means 'no diggers are gentlemen, nor are any of the spinners'. This is an example of the techniques of Boolean algebra, which is concerned with classes, groups and types of objects and the relationships between them. Unlike the familiar algebra of the schoolbooks, it does not deal with numbers, powers and roots, etc. Instead of operations like *plus, minus, divide, multiply,* it uses relations like *and, or, not, except.* In other words, Boolean algebra uses the common words

and phrases of everyday speech, but it gives them an exact and invariable meaning. Boolean algebra is named after an English mathematician, George Boole (1815–64). Boole's book, *The Investigation of the Laws of Thought,* published in 1854, sought to establish the methods by which the human mind reasons and to express them in mathematical form. Boole set down the rules of his new algebra in straightforward terms, and his work was improved and extended by two other logicians, John Venn and Ernst Schroder.

In many ways, Boolean algebra is simpler than ordinary algebra, as it is primarily concerned with *classes* (types, groups, or kinds of things), and *statements* about these classes. Everyone is familiar with classes: 'dogs', is a class, although in Boolean algebra one will perhaps speak of 'the class of all dogs'. Other classes

might be men, women, human beings, sparrows, flowers, houses or any other collection of objects which have something in common. To understand the basis of Boolean algebra, it is useful to consider the inter-relationship of some of these familiar classes. Consider the class of all human beings, and let us represent this by U (the significance of this symbol will be apparent later). This class can be divided into males, m, and females, f. It can also be divided into people below the age of 21, p, and those over the age of 21, s.

Obviously, the class of people contained in m will also be contained in U. In Boolean algebra this is written:
$$m \subset U.$$
Similarly,
$$f \subset U; p \subset U \text{ and } s \subset U.$$
This symbol $\subset$ means 'is contained in'.

The universe class

Again, class U will consist entirely of the people in class m and class f. This is written:
$$m \vee f = U,$$
which means 'the class of things contained in m or f or both is the same as the things contained in class U'. Similarly,
$$p \vee s = U$$
and there is no reason why this cannot also be written
$$m \vee f \vee s \vee p = U.$$
The symbol which is here used for all the people in the world, U, is the Boolean algebra symbol for 'all', or the *universe class,* the class of all things which are contained in any particular discussion.

The symbol for *and* is usually a dot between the letters representing classes. Thus $m . f$ means 'the class of things contained in both m and f. From our knowledge of the human race we know that there is nothing which is both male and female, and so
$$m . f = 0,$$
where 0 represents the 'null class', the class which contains nothing.

1 The methods of classification used in compiling library catalogues owe much to mathematical logic. Books are classified into categories denoted by numbers.

2 The animals in this photograph of African wildlife are classified in various ways by zoologists. The method of classification — by species — can be expressed mathematically.

Turning back for a moment to ordinary speech, one can say that within the human race everyone is either male or female, and that a man is by definition not a woman. The symbol, in this notation, for 'not a woman' is f'. (The symbol for 'not a man' is m'.) Thus
$$m = f', \text{ and } f = m'.$$
(The class of all people who are men is the same as the class of all people who are not women, and vice versa.) Other relations which can be established are:
$$m \vee f' = m; f \vee m' = f.$$
All the people contained in the class of males and the class of females constitutes the same class as those who are either over 21 or under 21.

Thus $m \vee f = s \vee p$.

Strictly speaking, on the information available about the universal class (all human beings) there is little that can be said about its composition. But four other classes might be defined. These are: (a) males over 21, denoted by t; (b) males under 21, denoted by d; (c) females over 21, denoted by g; and (d) females under 21, denoted by h.

Hence, $t \vee d = m$; $g \vee h = f$; $t \vee g = s$; and
$$d \vee h = p.$$
It must be borne in mind that the sign '=' used here has a different meaning from that given to it in ordinary algebra. In algebra the expression $a = b$ means that the numerical value of a is the same as the numerical value of b. In Boolean algebra, however, $a = b$ means that the members of

258

class *a* are identical with the members of class *b*. In other words, they are the same. Roughly speaking, in our discussion, regarding population, the numerical value of class *m* is the same as the numerical value of class *f*. But *m=f* is *not* true, since the members of the class are not identical.

Another common symbol is that used for non-identity. This is the same symbol as is used in ordinary algebra for inequality, thus: $a \neq b$ means '*a* is not identical with *b*'. This can be used in a number of ways, one of the most common being $a \neq 0$, meaning '*a* is not a null class, *a* is not empty'.

George Boole based his work on the system of logic which had been developed over the centuries since the time of Aristotle. One of the cornerstones of this system is the syllogism, the method of reasoning drawing a conclusion from two premises, or statements, which are connected.

An example of the syllogism is: 'All squares have four sides. This is a square. Therefore this has four sides.' This reasoning is valid, but often a similar type of argument is put forward which runs: All squares have four sides. This has four sides. Therefore this is a square. The second version is obviously wrong in this case. But sometimes the fallacy is not so easy to spot. Expressed in Boolean algebra, the error becomes clear immediately.

Spotting the fallacy

Suppose the class of all squares is represented by *s*. Then let all four-sided figures be represented by *f*, and the object under discussion be a member of the class *q*. In the first case: All *s* are *f*, or $s \subset f$. Similarly, $q \subset s$ and the conclusion is $q \subset f$. If all *q* are contained in *s* and all *s* are contained in *f*, then obviously all *q* are contained in *f*. In symbols, if $q \subset s$ and $s \subset f$, then $q \subset s \subset f$, hence $q \subset f$.
Taking the second case, however, the statements become: $s \subset f$ and $q \subset f$. There-

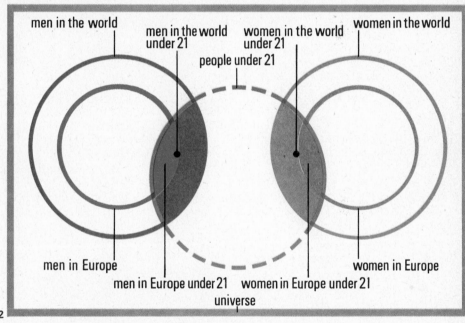

men in the world
men in the world under 21
women in the world under 21
people under 21
women in the world
men in Europe
men in Europe under 21
women in Europe under 21
women in Europe
universe

2

fore $q \subset s$, which is wrong, or at least the conclusion does not follow logically from the propositions. One can establish the validity of the conclusion from a large number of such connected statements by writing the statements in Boolean symbols and then seeing whether a chain can be established. Thus, one might finish up with a chain $a \subset b \subset c \subset d \subset e \subset f \subset g$ from which it is possible to conclude that $a \subset g$. If no such a logical chain can be established, then the argument has a flaw.

John Venn, who built on Boole's work, developed a graphical method of representing classes and their relationships. Diagrams based on his method are called *Venn diagrams,* and they are often valuable in clarifying a problem. The usual

way of setting up a Venn diagram is to draw a rectangle to represent the universe class, the class of all things under discussion, say all the people in the world. A circle can then be drawn within the rectangle to represent the total number of men in Europe, and another can be drawn to represent the total number of women in Europe. These two circles will not intersect, as there are no members common to these two classes. If, however, a circle is drawn to represent all people under the age of 21, then this third circle will intersect the other two, as this third class will contain members of the first two. If yet another circle is drawn to represent all the males in the world, exclusive of origin, then this circle must include the first completely. Again, if a fifth circle representing all the females in the world is required, it should include all European females, and should also include that part of the circle representing children not included by the circle representing all men. This is, in fact, impossible to draw accurately, but it can be done by dispensing with circles and making the areas any shape.

It should be noted that the area outside the two circles 'all males' and 'all females' represents an empty or null class. This is usually denoted on a Venn diagram by shading the empty area. By using Venn diagrams, many of the rules of Boolean algebra can be diagrammatically verified, and they offer a simple means of checking the validity of sets of statements. Boolean algebra has found a large number of uses. One of the most important is its application to switches and switching circuits, which in turn has led to it being used in the design of digital computers, which make extensive use of electronic switches.

Stairway switches

A simple example is the light on the stairway of an ordinary house. Very often, such a light is controlled by two switches, one at the top of the staircase, and the other at the bottom. Suppose the condition 'top switch on' is represented by a then 'top switch off' will be represented by a'. Similarly, for the two possible states of the bottom switch the symbols will be b and b'; for light on and light off we shall have c and c'. In the normal working of these switches we have:

$a.b=c'$; $a.b'=c$; $a'.b=c$; $a'.b'=c'$.

In another notation, the two states of the switches could be denoted by 1 and 0,

1 The interior of a digital computer. A large computer contains thousands of 'logic components', each of which can be either 'on' or 'off' thus storing information.
2 A technician examines punched cards carrying medical data. Each space on the card can be either punched or left intact, and the cards carry information in binary code.
3 Another application of binary logic to computation. This is an electronic Russian-English dictionary. The words, in binary code, appear as notched lines which are read electronically.

where 1 means 'switch on' and 0 means 'switch off'. 'Light on' and 'light off' will also be represented by 1 and 0. It is then possible to draw up a table showing the state of the light in terms of the state of the switches.

top switch	bottom switch	light
0	0	0
1	0	1
0	1	1
1	1	0

This is an arrangement known as parallel switching. It is also possible to arrange the circuit so that the light will be on if, and only if, both switches are in the 'on' position, known as series switching.

If, instead of operating a light, the two switches were arranged so as to operate a third switch (perhaps a relay, valve or transistor), then another table could be drawn up which would be similar to this.

The process of drawing up tables can be carried out for complicated banks of interconnected switches such as are found in computers. Normally a designer working on computers will draw up the logical requirements of the system, using tables like the one above, and will then design the circuit to give the necessary logical operation.

Two important points should be noted in connection with the simple table above. The first is that the notation which we have used is the same as that used in the binary counting system; and, secondly, it tells us the conditions prevailing in the light when either the top or the bottom switch is on, but not both together. In a similar manner, if two switches are wired in series, so that both must be on before the light will operate, this is called an *and* circuit, and a table which we would draw up would tell us that the light is on when the top switch and the bottom switch are on. These circuits are, in fact, exactly the types of circuit used in electronics computers.

Successive banks of these switches, as used in a computer, allow calculations to be made and logical operations to be carried out. Suppose, for example, we want to know whether the outputs from the two switches in our parallel circuit are on. A glance at our table once again will show that the light being on or off gives us an infallible answer.

A table such as the one which we have produced is, in the world of computers, called a 'truth table', and this is, in fact, a truth table for a 'binary comparator'. If one wanted to go back and determine the statement in Boolean algebra which would apply to such a table, one could say

$(a.b')\vee(a'.b)=1$ (i.e., there is an output) and $(a.b)\vee(a'.b')=0$ (i.e., there is no output).

Although at first sight the ideas and principles of Boolean algebra may appear to have little relevance to the computer, yet they are fundamental to both its design and operation. The laws of this strange, simple and yet powerful branch of mathematics are an invaluable part of the machines which have made much of modern progress possible.

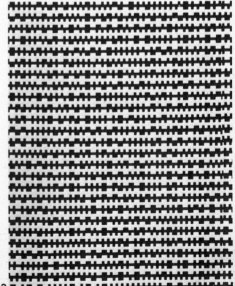

Man-made brains

The advent of the computer has changed the nature of many activities. Complicated calculations have become child's play and information handling is completely revolutionized.

SCORES OF THOUSANDS of electronic computers are now in service in the world, and the present time has rightly been dubbed the computer age. The modern computer, however, is only the latest in a long line of mechanical aids to calculation devised by mathematical Man.

The earliest aids probably resembled the abacus or counting frame. This, in its earliest form, was a tray with grooves cut to hold pebbles which later was developed into a rectangular frame supporting wires with beads threaded on them. The abacus was used all round the Mediterranean in the first millennium B C. It is known to have been used by the Aztecs and by the Chinese at the time of Confucius.

The abacus is used even today in many parts of the world and, with a skilful operator, it is still a powerful tool. In an open contest in 1946 between a Japanese abacus operator and an expert American operator using the latest electronic desk calculator, the Japanese won convincingly, using an abacus costing only a few shillings, in five types of calculations covering the basic arithmetical operations.

A big advance in calculating technique was made with the invention of the logarithm by John Napier. Napier's invention was publicly announced in a book published in 1614. His contribution made it possible to multiply and divide, the two most difficult computations, merely by adding and subtracting. And by 1621 William Oughtred, using the new principle of logarithms, had produced a working slide rule which was the precursor of the modern instrument.

The first mechanical calculator

The first truly mechanical calculator appeared in the seventeenth century. The beads of the abacus, in effect, became teeth on gear wheels. Instead of beads being moved individually by hand the teeth on the gear wheels were notched round as the calculation proceeded. Early examples of mechanical calculators built by Blaise Pascal who died in 1662 are still preserved in Paris. Leibniz, the great German mathematician, produced a machine about 1671 which could multiply as well as add and subtract. In 1810 the first commercially available mechanical calculator was developed by Charles Thomas of Colmar, Alsace, and 1,500 machines based on his design, using the Leibniz principles, were made over the next 60 years.

The distinction between a mechanical calculator and an automatic one is important. All the calculating aids so far discussed need the constant attention of an operator. He has to move beads on a frame, set dials, or punch keys for each part of the calculation. The speed of calculation is therefore determined by the rate at which the human operator can manipulate the input to the machine rather than by how fast the machine reacts internally. This was recognized by the Englishman Charles Babbage (1791–1871) who set about designing an automatic calculating machine which could conduct intricate mathematical computations without attention.

Babbage is recognized as the father of modern computing. His first computer – first in the world – was the Difference Engine, to be used for computing tables of mathematical functions. His second, the Analytical Engine, was truly universal, unlike the Difference Engine which was designed for a specific set of calculations.

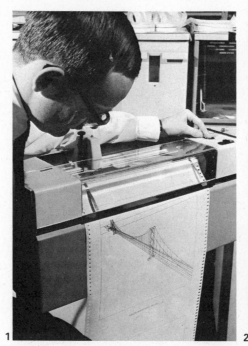

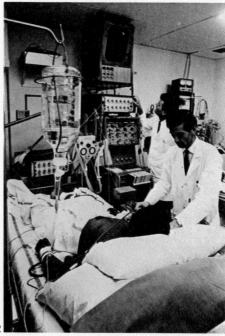

1 The designer's job is made easier by computers. With appropriate information, this Elliott 900 model can produce in a few minutes designs that would otherwise have taken weeks.
2 Medical computers aid doctors to diagnose and follow the course of disease. This model automatically keeps track of heart rate, respiration and other body functions.
3 A VC 10 airliner landing in fog at London's Heathrow Airport. Computers linked to the plane's instruments keep the pilot constantly informed of his position and speed.

The Analytical Engine could be used for any type of calculation – in today's parlance it was a General Purpose Computer.

Unfortunately, neither of these machines was completed but the principles were sound. Charles Babbage had designed into his machine the five fundamental functions of a computer system, the store (or memory), arithmetic unit, control unit, input devices and output devices. His machines were a mass of gear wheels, rods and levers. The mechanical standards required to construct the machines were far too precise for the engineering methods available in the nineteenth century. Part of the Difference Engine can be seen at the Science Museum in London.

If Babbage was the father of the modern computer, Lady Lovelace (1815–52) was the mother of a necessary adjunct to it – the computer program. The computer, as we shall see, is capable only of the most elementary action without instructions. Lady Lovelace, the only child of Lord and Lady Byron, knew Babbage well and devised typical programs, some of which were very advanced. A computer program is stored in the computer and instructs it at every stage of a calculation.

Babbage's 'engines' were a concept far ahead of their time. We had to wait for the technical revolution of the twentieth century before the practical realization of the universal computer. In particular it was the rapid development of electronics that made the modern high-speed computer possible.

The breakthrough came almost simultaneously in Britain and the United States when researchers in several laboratories demonstrated working stored-program computers. The pioneer machine, developed in the United States, was ENIAC which used 18,000 electronic valves and consumed 150 kilowatts of electric power. Completed in 1946, it weighed 30 tons. Another pioneering computer was a small laboratory model designed by Professors F. C. Williams and T. Kilburn at Manchester University. This was operated successfully in June 1948. Other work was going on at London and Cambridge Universities and at the National Physical Laboratory.

Commercial machines

The early computers designed in the United States and Britain were the prototypes for commercial machines that began to appear in 1951. These machines, bearing such acronyms as EDSAC, ACE, DEUCE and LEO, had a hitherto unprecedented speed of operation and calculating power but were unreliable and consumed vast quantities of power. The invention of the point-contact transistor in 1948 and the subsequent development,

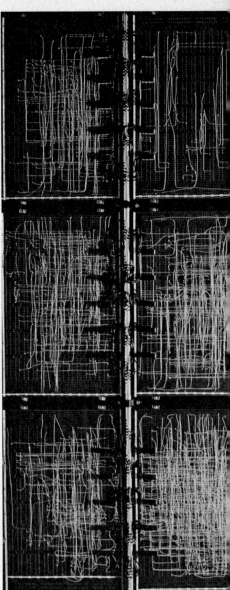

in 1957, of the planar silicon transistor transformed the situation. Computers became much smaller and faster in operation. The latest electronic development, the integrated circuit, has made computers yet smaller, faster and more powerful than those with planar transistors. These 'third-generation' machines using integrated circuits can compute at a rate of a million instructions per second.

It is important to remember that even the most modern and powerful computers cannot think. The work they do is, in fact, trivial in nature, but they do it quickly. A good computer can do simple arithmetic ten million times faster than a man, but it calculates only under orders determined by the program.

Let us look again at the five basic elements of a computer. These are: the store (or memory) unit, the arithmetic unit, the control unit, input devices, output devices.

Imagine a person sitting at a desk starting a calculation with paper and pen and a common desk calculator. The calculator is equivalent to the arithmetic unit in a computer. It performs the mathematical calculations. The person doing the calculations is equivalent to the control unit, and the pen and paper, on which are written intermediate results of the

1 The internal circuits of a large modern computer are exceptionally complex, and their manufacture involves a large amount of highly skilled labour. For this reason, computers are still very expensive.

2 The computer is formed of a number of units like this one. The maze of small wires linking various components together can be clearly seen in this view. Together, the various units compute and store information.

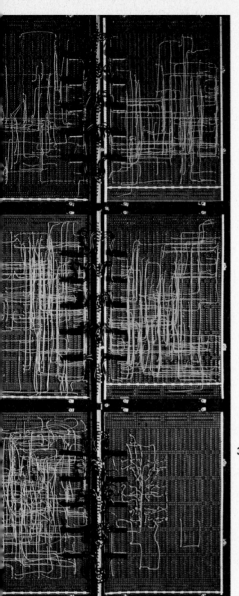

complex calculation, are equivalent to the computer store or memory unit.

Input and output devices are not necessary with a human operator because he is able to interpret directly his input data, the figures he feeds in, and the answer he needs, from the machine. The computer, however, must have input and output devices for the machine to interpret the input data in machine language and re-interpret it in understandable and usable form for the human beings at the output.

Perhaps Babbage's main failing in the design of his 'Engines' was to use the decimal notation of numbers. All modern computers use the binary system in which numbers or letters are represented by simple on-off states of electrical circuits and represent the digits 0 or 1. In the binary system, numbers are represented to the base 2 instead of to the base 10. Thus 13, which is $(8+4+1)$ or (2^3+2^2+1) becomes 1101 in binary notation. This is the simplest of all mathematical forms and the two main binary components in all digital computers are binary switching elements and binary memory elements.

A single digit in computer parlance is known as a bit and five bits commonly constitute a word. The word, then, is a set of digits of standard length, which can represent a number or an instruction to

3 The memory element of a modern computer. This tiny element contains about 650 components and measures only 0·11 in. by 0·105 in. Thousands of such elements are required for a large computer.

4 The computer as artist. A drawing executed by an IBM 7090 computer according to a program by Kunio Yamanaka. Many artists have looked towards the computer for fresh sources of inspiration and mathematical designs.

the computer. Numbers and instructions can be held in the main store and are accessible by addressing each 'pigeon hole' or register, as it is known, in the store.

Let us consider the simple operation of adding 1 and 2 in the computer. The first operation is to feed the figures into the input device where they are encoded into binary form and entered into the store. The computer must then be instructed to take them from the store, add them together in the arithmetic unit, and pass the answer back to the store. The final instruction tells the computer to pass the answer through a decoder to the output device where, for example, it might be printed out on an electric typewriter. More complex operations are simply continuous repetition, at very high speed, of the four basic arithmetical functions of addition, subtraction, multiplication and division. But at each stage the computer needs instructions from its program.

Even the fastest input/output devices of a computer installation are very slow compared with the speed of operation of the central processor. Where punched cards are used as the input the reading speed can be 1,000 cards a minute. Printed pages pouring out of a line printer at the output end appear far quicker than they can be read. Electric typewriters print far faster than a human operator could type. Even so, if a computer could be put into slow motion so that it carried out only one operation per second, the equivalent speed of a computer typewriter would be only one character per day. Modern computers are therefore designed to operate simultaneously with several input/output devices and do computation between times.

1 The minute square at the centre of this picture is an integrated circuit – a basic element of computer construction. The circuit's mounting dwarfs the circuit itself.
2 Computers are now used to predict weather. This model, at the U.S. Airforce Data Center, prints out a map of the world with tomorrow's weather indicated on it.

A significant development was the device known as the 'program-interrupt'. This device announces the arrival of important information in the input/output sections and stops the computation until the data is transferred, after which the computer carries on with its former activity. The most important modern development, however, is time-sharing, a system whereby several users can use the computer simultaneously, each working on separate problems. A large system of this type used at the Massachusetts Institute of Technology has 160 remote operating terminals of which any 30 can be in use simultaneously. What happens in this type of installation is that each user of the computer gets access to it for only a thirtieth of the time but the speed of switching from user to user is such that each individual gets the impression that he is the sole user. This is possible, of course, only because the computer works at a speed so much greater than the human mind.

Similar large installations are in operation in Britain, and the general public can get access to them through ordinary Post Office lines provided they have the necessary terminal equipment and pay

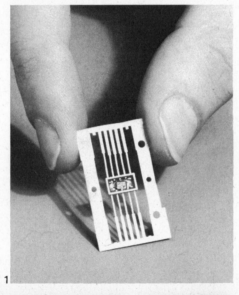

fees to the computer bureau. A number of universities have developed their own time-sharing systems (or multi-access systems, as they are sometimes called).

Time-sharing multi-access systems demand very large machines with enormous storage capacity. The Massachusetts system, for example, has stores containing a million words, 100 basic computer programs and a variety of special-purpose programs. In addition, users can insert their own private programs and one of the features is that a user can compile a program in conjunction with the computer.

Security is a major problem with computer installations of this type. Many contain vast amounts of stored information which may be quite private and confidential. Companies or individuals using the system must be guaranteed absolute privacy. One method of ensuring this is to have a secret password which alone allows access. After the initial call to the computer in which the subscriber states his name and project, the computer responds by asking for his password. If this does not correspond with the subscriber's name and project, the machine prints out a 'no access' message and denies further access.

What does a modern computer installation look like? This can be seen from the accompanying illustrations. A modern large installation, like the British ICL 1906A, has a main store with 256,000 words capacity, and the central processor chugs along happily at a million operations a second. The peripheral processor unit can sustain a total transfer rate of up to five million characters a second through the bank of additional stores, interrogating visual displays and other input devices and the banks of output devices. Among the input/output devices, the graph plotter can print out answers in graph form and the visual displays give the answers on the face of cathode ray tubes, rather like television sets, either in printed or graphical form.

Entering the computer age

In the 20 years since the high-speed electronic digital computer became a reality Man has had to learn how best to use this new and very powerful tool. In the early days, many computers were under-utilized and their full potential was not realized. Even now, we are only scratching the surface of possible computer applications. Today, there is practically no aspect of civilized life which is not at some stage under the control of a computer.

For the future we may expect that most homes will have a computer terminal just as today they have a telephone. Vast quantities of information will be stored in the computer system, which can be many miles distant. Dialling the appropriate code would enable the information required to be displayed on a TV tube. This type of transaction is known as information retrieval. But in addition to this the computer, with all its calculating power, will be available to all for working out mathematical problems.

As yet, we have only begun to penetrate into the Computer Age.

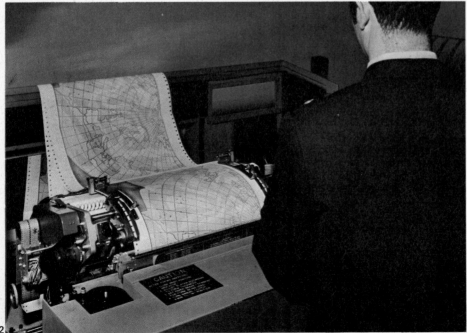

Mathematics in art

Greek philosophers early recognized the close connections between mathematics and the arts. Today, the conclusions of the Greeks and of their Renaissance successors are still applied.

Greeks, for instance, used the triquetra as a symbol for three-cornered Sicily. The swastika is based on the number four, another magical number. The five-sided pentacle was revered by the Greeks and used by Dr Faustus to banish Mephistopheles, the Devil.

Equally powerful is the mathematical concept of symmetry in art. And of all the various kinds of mathematical symmetry, the bilateral (left-right) sort is the most ingrained in our appreciation of art. According to Hermann Weyl, a leading mathematician and physicist, artists tend to sacrifice naturalness to produce pictures with left and right halves mirror images of each other. Striking examples are to be seen in Sumerian designs and in the two-headed eagle in the coat of arms of Tsarist Russia and the Austro-Hungarian Empire.

It can be claimed with some justification that it was the Greeks who created works of art as we know them now. They

ARTISTS DO NOT USUALLY think of themselves as mathematicians: nor do other people think of mathematics and art as being connected. Indeed, art as we understand it is a comparatively recent idea. Many of the Greek buildings that we consider to be outstanding works of artistic expression were originally regarded simply as practical solutions to everyday problems.

Early mathematics was also severely practical. Number ideas were invented to count herds of sheep and goats; then written symbols made it possible for early man to record such counts and make an inventory of his possessions.

As early as the Stone Age mathematics and art fused in the geometric patterns decorating pottery, weaving and carpentry. The word 'line' probably derives from 'linen', thus reflecting the fusion of weaving and geometry. Again, in a very different sphere of activity, there has always been a strong link between mathematics and art on the one hand, and magic on the other. The aesthetic appeal of patterns based on the prime numbers three, five and seven is often matched by the magic aura that attaches to them. The

1 This Assyrian marble slab showing two eagle-headed gods picking fruit appears to be bilaterally symmetrical, but it is not. Both are using their right hands to pick the fruit.

2 The Baptisterio at Pisa in the foreground of this picture is a brilliant example of Renaissance architecture, embodying many degrees of rotational symmetry.

3 The design of the Greek Parthenon displays the proportions of the Golden Section as calculated later by Fibonacci. The distances marked A and B are in the proportion 1:1·618.

restored the wholeness and completeness to the pictured image – it was the custom in Egypt to mutilate all likenesses in deference to the local deity. In the sense that mathematics is a completely abstract picture of the world, it can be said that the Greeks' 'conquest of space in art' mirrored their triumphs in Euclidean geometry. As a consequence of the Greek artistic revolution, copies of original Greek works of art were made and displayed in the houses and gardens of the Romans. In them was sown the seed of the art of reproduction which flowered into the invention of the printing press some 1500 years later.

Consider the Assyrian picture shown here of two eagle-headed gods picking fruit. At first sight this appears to have left-right symmetry – or bilateral symmetry, as mathematicians call it. Closer inspection reveals that this is not so however. If the left half of the picture is reflected in a mirror the reflection will not be the same as the right half of the picture. For the picture to have bilateral symmetry the man on the left must be extending his left hand, while the man on the right must put forth his right hand. In early art and in most modern formal architecture bilateral symmetry is strictly observed. In art symmetry signifies rest and stability: asymmetry implies motion and a loosening of ideas. One evokes a sense of rigidity, the other of play life and freedom. Symbols for truth and justice are usually shown from a frontal symmetrical viewpoint.

To see how deeply embedded in our consciousness is the idea of left-right symmetry, take any photographic transparency and turn it over. Unless there is a clue, such as a printed sign or a man with a handkerchief in his breast-pocket, it is impossible to tell that anything has happened to the picture. But reflect the same picture about a horizontal axis and the effect can be most disturbing. Something of this effect is created when one looks into an utterly calm pool of water or at a painting of such a scene. Our preference for left-right symmetry rather than up-and-down symmetry is no doubt due to the pull of gravity, but there are, nevertheless, subtler forces at work which painters and writers capture in their works of art.

People in most countries shake hands with their right hands only. In most languages right is associated with good and left with evil. A case in point is the word 'sinister' which derives from the Latin word for 'left'. We see God extending his right hand towards Adam in Michelangelo's *Creation of Adam*. In describing the Last Judgement St Matthew records that sheep – the good people – shall go to the right while the goats – the bad – shall

go to the left. Of the two robbers flanking Jesus on their crosses, it was the one on the right who ascended to Heaven.

But there is another equally powerful side to mathematical symmetry: rotational symmetry. The ancient sign of the triquetra, recalled today in the three-legged symbol of the Isle of Man and in a ship's propeller, has perfect threefold symmetry. The test of whether an object has rotational symmetry is simple and decisive. Ask someone to rotate the object behind your back and if you cannot tell that it has been so moved, then it has rotational symmetry. The number of times this operation can be performed before the object has been turned full circle determines the order of the symmetry. The triquetum, for example, can be turned in three stages to present the same 'picture' each time before it returns to its original position. Thus it has threefold symmetry.

5

4

1 Landscape by Wang Yuan-k'y. Classical Chinese artists do not use 'true' perspective. Instead, objects intended to appear as part of the background to a picture are painted further up the picture.

2 The Sydney Opera House is an extravagant example of the use of mathematics in architecture. The curves of the roof were drawn up by a computer, but it has proved almost impossible to reproduce them exactly.

3 Leonardo da Vinci's *St Jerome,* now in the Vatican, is a classic example of his use of the Golden Section. Da Vinci took special delight in what he called 'geometric creations'.

4 Mathematics has always played a considerable part in the theory of music. The Pythagorean philosophers of ancient Greece studied musical scales produced by stretched strings of various lengths, and linked them with the design of the Universe.

5 *The Annunciation,* painted by the Venetian artist Carlo Crivelli, illustrates what is meant by 'true' perspective. It contrasts with the Chinese version of perspective shown in Wang Yuan-k'y's picture on the previous page.

The swastika has fourfold symmetry and something more. A simple equal-armed cross is identical to its mirror image, combining rotational and bilateral symmetry; but not so the swastika. Perhaps its lack of bilateral symmetry endows it with its fabled magical qualities.

Despite the fact that the Egyptians ran the gamut of all the possible symmetrical patterns in their ornamental art – 17 in all – they seemingly hit on them purely by chance. The Arabs fumbled around with patterns based on fivefold rotational symmetry. Great masters of the geometric art of ornament that they were, they never succeeded in handling designs based on the regular five-sided pentagram, once the sign of good luck to Pythagoras and his followers. The reason is simple: it is geometrically impossible to cover completely a flat plane with pentagrams and leave no gaps.

After the Greeks launched Western art on the Euclidean principles of the

Golden Section in *St Jerome,* an unfinished canvas, taking special delight in what he called 'geometrical creations'. More recently Le Corbusier, the French architect, devised a design philosophy based on the Golden Section. He designed buildings on a system of Golden Rectangles, which he called *le modulor,* and showed how this proportion is related to the dimensions of the human body, much as da Vinci had done earlier. A confessed failure at mathematics in school, Le Corbusier once said: 'Mathematics is the majestic structure conceived by Man to grant him comprehension of the Universe.' In contemporary architecture, whether functional or decorative, the application of such complex mathematical curves as the hyperbolic paraboloid are practically commonplace. Buckminster Fuller, probably the leading exponent of mathematically designed architecture, has revolutionized our concept of building structures with his now famous geodesic dome, based entirely on equilateral triangles. In contemporary painting, the influence, if not the practical use, of mathematics is coolly apparent.

Not surprisingly, there have always been undertones of mathematics in European music. The average audience enjoys the emotional content of a piece of music; but the more perceptive discover an added delight in mathematical formality. The Pythagoreans, in addition to finding the law of pitch and tension in a stringed instrument, initiated the mathematical science of musical harmony. One might not suppose that symmetry plays a role in music. But if one thinks of a line of music stretching out in time, its mirror image is got simply by playing it backwards. Music can also be turned upside-down in the sense that high notes become low and low ones high. Bach's fugues are a sophisticated example of such mathematical composing.

Mathematical jokes

As a joke, Mozart composed a canon in which the second melody exhibited both types of reflection – it was the same as the first melody inverted and read backwards. The same 'reversals' can be seen in literature. Lewis Carroll's *Alice* books and his poem *The Hunting of the Snark* abound in mathematical jokes and conceits.

That mathematics has strong and sometimes unexpected links with art is undoubted. Even in the classroom this seems to be borne out. Experiments in Australia, Canada and Great Britain have given clear indication of such links being established in children's learning processes. Much of the so-called modern activities in the mathematics classroom has been mirrored by creative work in the art class.

The appreciation of the relationships between art and mathematics is difficult. On the one hand mathematicians claim to create in their theorems complete systems which do not refer to natural phenomena.

On the other hand, the artist sees the function of mathematics in Le Corbusier's terms: '. . . the structure conceived by Man to grant him comprehension of the Universe.' However, generally they have been mutually beneficial.

exclusive use of the straight-edge and compasses, the next major mathematical impetus to artistic creation came with the Renaissance. Then artists such as Albrecht Dürer threw away the Euclidean crutches to discover that they could stand on their own feet. For when Dürer developed the art of perspective, he at the same time created an entirely new sort of geometry – projective geometry. As the name implies, he projected images on to a plane rather than copying the original object in the round. You can get a good idea of his technique by looking through a window with one eye closed. You see the scene because light rays from it travel to your eye. Each ray from an object outside the window passes through some point on the pane. If you mark each point with a pen you would re-create the scene 'in the flat' or 'in section'.

As we have said, an off-shoot of this artistic work was the discovery of the theorems of projective geometry. A projection of a circle, for instance, could be an ellipse. When we see an ellipse in a picture drawn in perspective, the mind's eye supplies the answer to the question: is it meant to be an ellipse or a circle? The effect of foreshortening on artistic values is strikingly illustrated by a comparison of a typical Chinese 'perspective' and an Early Renaissance example of 'true' perspective.

Leonardo da Vinci made significant contributions to the art and technique of painting alike. He recognized, for instance, the spreading effect in trees and propounded the mathematical law: in a drawing of a tree, the total thickness of all twigs cut by a circle of a given radius must equal in sum the thickness of the tree-trunk. In the field of Renaissance architecture, the Baptisterio at Pisa in Italy stands out as a brilliant example embodying many orders of rotational symmetry.

This period also saw the arrival of another equally profound influence on art. It came from a mathematician who lived in the Middle Ages – Leonardo of

1 Albrecht Dürer's woodcut, from his book *The Art of Measurement* shows a man using a mechanical device to draw a lute in perspective. The string cuts the canvas at the required point.
2 The hoop in this Victorian lithograph is not circular but elliptical. The eye sees the hoop as a circle, however, because that is what we expect to see.

Pisa, nicknamed 'Fibonacci'. He established a remarkable connection between a mathematical series and a pleasing rectangular shape known to the Greeks as the Golden Section. This is simply a rectangle whose length is in the same proportion to its breadth as half its perimeter is to its longer length, which works out at 1·618:1. The harmony of the Golden Section is evident in much Greek architecture. Artists of all ages have instinctively used its pleasing proportions and it appears in the human body and in many living things. Modern painters, Impressionists and abstract artists, have especially made use of this mathematical ratio.

Certainly da Vinci made use of the

Mathematics in industry

Modern industry requires advanced mathematical techniques at almost all stages of the process of production. Designers, engineers and salesmen all rely on the mathematician.

IN THE EARLY DAYS of the motor car, it was common practice among manufacturers to make a rough chalk drawing on the floor of the workshop showing the size and shape of the finished product. Craftsmen then put the car together on top of this sketch, often using any suitable components which came to hand. Not unnaturally, the finished products owed more to art than to technical design, with the result that these cars tended to reflect the defects as well as the talents of the 'artist'.

This situation was understandable when cars were made for a small minority and when the industry was in its infancy. But as the industry developed, better products, and more of them, were demanded, and the supply of 'artists' having the peculiar talents which were necessary was insufficient. So car manufacturers turned to science, and to mathematics, the universal language of science.

This trend has been repeated in almost every field of industry – ships, bridges, road building, aviation – as manufacturers turned from inspired artistry to reliable scientific techniques.

The ordinary person who is not involved in this field can readily understand the importance of mathematics in such things as motor cars, aeroplanes, radios and bridges. The complexity alone indicates this. But it is not so self-evident how mathematics has helped to produce one of the simplest yet one of the greatest achievements of twentieth-century industry – the ball-point pen. As Chesterton once said, when a thing is too familiar, we see it but don't take notice. This is the

1

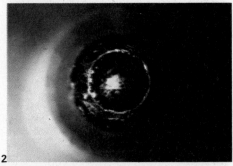

2

3

case with a ball-point; the methods which are used in its manufacture involve many diverse applications of mathematics.

Few manufacturers would dare to begin making a new pen without first establishing the size of the market for it. This is done by market research, a technique which involves questioning potential buyers about the features which they would like to see in the article to be produced. Obviously it would be too costly to ask all the potential buyers, so a sample of the public is taken. But to be reliable, the sample must be representative. To ask 100 millionaires for their views might lead one to the conclusion that there is a market for throwaway pens costing several pounds! Instead, the market researchers use a statistical technique known as *random sampling,* so that the sample is representative of the population as a whole.

The manufacturer now knows with some degree of certainty the number of pens which he can hope to sell in, say, the next year. His market research department will also probably have supplied him with a numerical table showing how the sales will vary at different times of the year. This seasonal factor is probably of little importance for ball pens, but in the car industry there is a severe slackening of demand during the winter months.

Projected sales

This graph of projected sales serves as a guide to the production staff, who must, ideally, make enough pens, but no more, to satisfy the demand. The design of the pen will already be established, but might be varied slightly if market research shows that these changes would be desirable. The typical ball-point has three main parts: an outer casing, usually of plastic; an inner reservoir which holds the ink; the tip which transfers the ink to the paper, and it will probably also have a mechanism for retracting the ball when not in use. Once the shape of the casing has been decided draughtsmen will draw accurate diagrams showing it from every angle and specifying such things as length, diameter, thickness of wall and the taper of the case. This will be a scale or proportional drawing, several times actual size. In producing it, the draughtsman will use classical geometrical constructions together with his knowledge of circle and tangency theorems. He will also produce drawings which show how the reservoir and mechanism will be accommodated within the barrel.

The engineer responsible for designing the mechanism must calculate the stresses which will fall on the mechanism when it is being used. He will know how hard people push on the retracting button, and

1 The elegant functional simplicity of the modern ball-point pen owes much to careful mathematical design. Before the pen is made, detailed large-scale plans of all the major components are drawn up and tested. The design of the ball, **2**, is especially important. This must be machined to very fine tolerances.
3 Scale model of a Ford Capri being tested in a wind tunnel. Thousands of tests are required to ensure design accuracy.

from this, using the Principle of Moments, vector analysis or calculus, he will calculate how strong each component must be to withstand normal use.

At the same time, the size, shape and material of the writing ball and its socket will be calculated. The ball must run easily; frictional forces must be calculated and the gap between ball and socket must be neither too large nor too small. In the first case, too much ink might be released, and in the second it is quite possible that none at all will reach the page. This is one of the most tricky calculations in the whole operation, partly because the viscosity, or resistance to flow, varies from one ink to another, and also because the viscosity drops as the temperature rises, and vice versa. Assuming that the ink is a new one, tests must be made to determine its viscosity. There are a number of instruments for doing this, but one of the simplest is merely a wide glass tube and a ball-bearing. The tube is filled with ink, the ball-bearing is dropped into it, and the time taken for the ball to fall a specific distance is measured. From this figure, and the weight and diameter of the ball, the coefficient of viscosity can be calculated.

This test is repeated at a number of different temperatures, and a graph is drawn showing the variation of viscosity with temperature. From this, the dimensions of the gap between the ball and its socket can be calculated to give satisfactory performance under almost all conditions.

Planning production

The production director is now able to calculate the quantities of the various materials, plastics, metal components and ink, which he will need, and, knowing how long the delivery is on each, can draw a graph showing how much of each he must buy, and on what dates. Generally speaking, the barrel of the pen will be made by *injection moulding* or *extrusion*. In the first case, the plastic is forced at a high temperature into a cavity which is the same shape as the finished item; in the second case (a technique which is particularly suitable for objects of this type) the hot plastic is forced through a hole which has the same cross-section as the barrel, and comes out looking rather like plastic spaghetti. In each case, the temperature and pressure of the plastic during forming must be controlled within close limits. If either is wrong, the resulting product will be defective. Both can be calculated from the shape of the mould or former, and from these the strength and dimensions of the mould are calculated.

Similar calculations are made for the press tools which will stamp out the working parts of the mechanism. Once these have been made, the factory can then be equipped for production. But before any items are made available to the public, the engineers concerned check their calculations by ordering a pre-production batch of pens. This may run into several thousands, and each pen is put through a series of rigorous tests.

Surprising as it may seem, the engineers

responsible expect a number of these pens to be unsatisfactory, either initially or after a period of service. In any mass-produced item, there are invariably a few which are bad. But the production engineers will be aiming at a proportion of satisfactory articles or 'yield' of something over 99 per cent, and if the pre-production batch matches this, they will be satisfied.

During testing, the time at which each part of each pen fails is noted, and a chart of failure rates is drawn up. From this, engineers can draw conclusions about the performance of the production pens in the hands of buyers, using statistical techniques. A common method which is used is to assign to the article a 'lifetime' or average before-time failure. This figure is purely statistical, and in fact says nothing about the reliability of any individual pen, but it allows the manufacturer to make a statistical prediction. For example, he may be able to say that 95 per cent of all pens produced will have a life of between 20 and 22 working hours. He will be able to predict with a high degree of accuracy the number of complaints of faulty goods which he will have, and also the replacement rate, as people buy new pens to replace the old which are exhausted.

1 Mathematics plays a predominant part in the design of bridges such as the Forth Road Bridge. Stresses have to be carefully calculated to ensure that they will be safe.
2 Power combined with elegance is the keynote of this hydrofoil. The foil is designed so that the hull will leave the water at a predetermined speed.
3 The screw of the liner *Queen Elizabeth 2* seen during the liner's construction. A propeller of this type requires careful design to avoid wear and 'cavitation'.
4 Workmen riveting the hull of a boat. The sheet steel will later be bent into shape according to a design worked out carefully in advance by mathematical means.

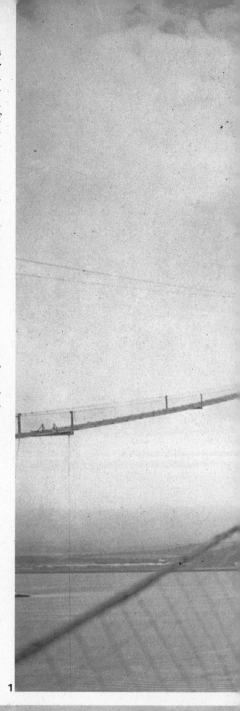

The time which it takes to produce each component will vary with the complexity of the manufacturing operation. But as the components must be produced at rates which give the same total number of each component, the resources which must be applied to each stage of production will vary.

To match production rates, the pen is broken down into as many components as possible, and a production time is allotted to each. With this information, the production controller will then use a comparatively new mathematical technique – *critical path analysis* – to determine the rate and order of manufacture and assembly. From it, he will also know how many injection moulders, for example, he must provide in relation to die-stamping equipment for the metal parts.

Reducing production time

Critical path analysis is, in principle, a simple technique with a forbidding title. It can be applied to almost every activity from making a cup of tea to building a vast ocean liner. Its objects are to reduce the time and effort which it takes to perform a task, or a complex of tasks, by showing how best use can be made of available resources. In the shipbuilding industry it has been particularly effective, as it spotlights areas where tasks may be duplicated, or men and machinery may be standing idle while waiting for another part of the work to be completed. On this scale, however, the job of performing the analysis is given to a computer, as it is too complex to be easily done by a mathematician.

On a simple level, critical path analysis involves drawing lines on graph paper to represent various parts of a task, and making the length of the line proportional to the time which each part takes. Some activities can be carried out simultaneously – for example, in making tea, the teapot can be warmed while the water is coming to the boil – while other tasks can only be carried out when a preceding one

is completed. By drawing these parts of the total task, and linking them together, a working routine requiring the shortest possible time can be easily worked out.

In the manufacture of something as simple as a ball-pen, many different branches of mathematics are employed – algebra, Euclidean and co-ordinate geometry, arithmetic, calculus and Boolean algebra among them. These are what are often called by engineers applied mathematical subjects to differentiate them from pure mathematics, which is often thought to have no practical applications.

But this is far from being the case. In the nineteenth century, a mathematician called Riemann developed a geometry which looked to most observers as if it had no practical application. Riemannian geometry is based on the sphere, whereas the familiar geometry of Euclid is the geometry of flat surfaces and lines drawn on them.

With the beginning of rocket and space research, however, scientists realized that, since space is curved, Riemannian geometry is directly applicable to calculations

involving the flight of rockets. In this context it is much simpler to use than Euclidean geometry.

An even more interesting point is that the theoretical work of Einstein on relativity has been applied to rocket calculations. On Earth, where speeds are comparatively low, the mathematical methods of Newton, which take no account of mass change, are sufficient. But at the immense speeds and distances involved in deep-space flight, Einstein's methods are necessary. Because of the peculiar interrelation of time and space implied in Einstein's theories, four-dimensional geometry is used in the solution of many problems.

Almost every aspect of every industry uses mathematics in one way or another. Since the computer was first used in decision-making by industrial managements, that activity has depended on Boolean algebra, although decision-making has always been regarded as a non-mathematical function. Throughout an industry, at every level, designs are chosen, production and sales are planned, machines installed, wage rates fixed – all by mathematics. The wide application of this science at every level in industry has transformed even the most backward processes.

Without the wide range of mathematical techniques, industry as we know it, and mass production in particular, would be unthinkable; and we can expect even greater use of mathematics as industry progresses.

1 A tunnel for the Victoria Line of London's underground railway. Such tunnelling demands exact design so that the tunnel follows the course planned for it.
2 Checking the production of motor cars at the Chrysler factory in Detroit. Mathematical techniques such as critical path analysis are used to speed up production lines.
3 Engineers examining charts during the manufacture of the Concorde airliner. Projects like the Concorde pose enormous problems for designers.
4 This precision viscometer is used to measure the viscosity of fuel oils. Oil companies spend a great deal on laboratories which standardize their products.

Watchers of the sky

Star-gazers of prehistory were primitive ancestors of the astrologers. Early beliefs and superstitions promoted study of the heavens and led to the foundation of scientific astronomy.

IT IS IMPOSSIBLE to say when the stars came to mean anything more than twinkling spots of light to our primitive ancestors. Palaeolithic hunters must have caught nocturnal animals by the light of the moon and may have learned to find their way back to their caves by the light of a familiar star. But it was not until the hunter settled down to grow food and the first farming communities came into being that Man took a more personal interest in the heavens. He could not but realize that the periods of the moon and the regular succession of the seasons must in some way be connected with what he saw in the sky.

Yet for these people who lived before the dawn of history, there was no such thing as a solar system. To them the world in which they grew their meagre crops, hunted and fished, were born and died was just a small patch of land bounded by distant hills or the line where sea and sky met. Above it all the sky formed a roof from which a mysterious yellow ball gave light and warmth by day, while at night a silvery disc shone with a paler light and tiny dots of light pierced the black sky.

Watchers of the sky

In time a few adventurous minds began to think more deeply about the daily and nightly drama of the sky: why did the moon change its shape and sometimes shine wanly by the light of day? Why did a few stars move amongst the others? Why did the sun rise in one part of the sky and set in another? Why was the light of the sun shut off by a black shadow sweeping across its surface? Why did stars suddenly shoot across the sky? All these questions tantalized our distant ancestors; and in the often fumbling search for answers lie the origins of astronomy.

So men set up primitive observatories, where without telescopes or other optical aids they watched the sky and made the first crude observations. Curiously enough, these tentative steps in astronomy were for strictly practical purposes.

By counting the days between full moons, the first calendars were compiled; and with calendars history was no longer old men's tales but became chronological records. By observing the sun's position at solstice and equinox, the changes of the seasons were understood which led to a better development of agriculture.

Most of the great civilizations of the ancient world gave star-watchers an honoured place in the social scale. In this connection it is interesting to discover that the Chinese were less advanced in astronomy than is generally supposed. There is no record of their observations earlier than the fifth century A D.

Probably the most enthusiastic star-gazers of the ancient world were the Sumerians, the Babylonians and the Egyptians. They built observatories and with their clumsy instruments managed to amass a great deal of valuable information. As long as 4,000 years ago the Babylonians were keeping records from which they could calculate the occurrence of eclipses. They had a fairly good idea of the *ecliptic*, the *zenith* and the *nadir*, and were the first to think in terms of an equator.

Once the early astronomers had established what they conceived to be the movement of the sun, moon and planets, and could predict these movements with reasonable accuracy, they were able to build up a strange hotch-potch of fact and fiction. They had no understanding of the true nature of the phenomena they observed. To them the Earth was flat, and as Man was lord of the Earth, the Earth must be the centre around which everything else revolved. The sun, moon, planets and

1 Ptolemy, the ancient geographer and astronomer, used astronomical observations and results in the production of his maps, as this engraving illustrates.

stars were accepted exactly as they appeared to be, and their motions were equally accepted without any serious questioning of what caused these motions.

By keeping track of the sun's annual motion north and south, the astronomers of Mesopotamia correctly linked it with the progress of the seasons. Counting the days after the sun's furthest retreat towards the south, they were able to predict when the life-giving floods would sweep down the rivers. Predictions of this nature were bound to be successful because floods depend on the seasons, which in turn depend on the sun.

Even more surprising was the fact that the astronomers of 4,000 years ago had linked the moon with the tides, though the real cause of tides escaped them. All they could say with any confidence was that the tides seemed to depend on the shape of the moon at certain periods of the month.

Astronomy and religion

From these solar and lunar observations developed the religious cults of sun and moon worship. It was thus inevitable that the early astronomers began combining their studies with the functions of priests. This gave them tremendous political power, and in Babylon their importance reached such a peak that they constituted a separate and noble caste.

It was equally inevitable that the astronomer-priests should carry matters a stage further. If the sun controlled the seasons and the moon moved the oceans, was it not probable that events on Earth and the people inhabiting it were influenced by the 'wandering' stars – the visible planets Mars, Venus, Mercury, Saturn and Jupiter? In fact, might not the movements of these wandering stars make possible prediction of the future?

2 El Caracol observatory, in Mexico, was built by the Aztecs. Like many peoples, they used astronomy purely as a tool for astrological work.

Careful observation and the keeping of detailed records enabled the priest-astrologer-astronomers to fix the positions of the planets at specific times in the past and future. Their records told them where planets such as Mars or Saturn would be when a king planned to go to war. These were the war planets, and if the astrologers told their royal master that their positions were unfavourable, the campaign would be called off. Solar and lunar eclipses and the appearance of the comets were even greater portents because of their relative rarity, and it was for the astrologer to say whether these phenomena meant good or evil. The destiny of a new-born child and the success of business or matrimonial ventures depended on what the astrologers read in the sky. Astrologers were never short of clients, and prospered accordingly.

Although study of the heavenly bodies was thus made in the cause of astrology rather than for the advancement of astronomy, it would be a mistake to dismiss these early astronomers as merely practitioners of a completely pseudo science.

1 Until the Renaissance, the common view of the heavens was a sphere with the stars and planets inset as permanent objects, as in the Mausoleum of Galla Placidia at Ravenna.

2–5 Ancient India was the birthplace of many astronomical and astrological techniques, and as such was rich in observatories. The periodicity of the movements of the sun, the moon and the planets led to the building of structures used in calculations and the construction of calendars. The first step was the construction of astronomical stonework whose shadows would indicate date and time. This developed into more compact and exact instruments such as those shown in the bottom two illustrations. Development along these lines is apparent in a number of different cultures. This primitive approach to the movement of the sun survives to the present day in sundials, which are now used almost exclusively for decoration rather than accurate timekeeping.

1 Comets have been regarded as objects of awe throughout history, as shown by this section of the Bayeux tapestry. They were held to portend disaster.
2 The Aztecs, who were sun worshippers, produced calendars like this which were surprisingly accurate in view of their limited equipment.

Their craft was often of direct benefit to serious astronomy. It was astrologers who measured the angle of the ecliptic, checked the relative brilliance of the stars and introduced the sine function in trigonometry. In Samarkand, astrologers built a great observatory with a quadrant having a radius of 190 feet and compiled a catalogue of over 1,000 stars.

Many astronomers were outstanding mathematicians, and it was not unusual for men whose real interest was pure astronomy to practise astrology simply as a source of income. Knowledge of the stars garnered by astrologers made possible the first tentative voyages out of sight of land. Much of the data which enabled astronomers to calculate the recurrence of comets came from astrological records.

It was the Greeks who first divorced astronomy from astrology and raised it to the level of a true science. Although the Greeks had a pantheon of gods ruling their lives, they disliked relying on the supernatural to explain natural phenomena. Above all, they were mathematicians.

Almost from the beginning of their astronomy the Greeks rejected the flat-Earth theory. They reasoned that the world must be round because ships sailed below the horizon. Also, a flat Earth was inconsistent with the Earth casting a circular shadow on the moon. On the other hand, they held firmly to the belief that the Earth was the centre of the universe and that the sun, moon and planets were smaller bodies moving around it.

Pythagoras, who lived in the sixth century BC, was the first Greek to declare that the Earth was a sphere. As this fitted well with the Greek passion for spheres and circles, they adopted the idea to explain the movements of the sun, moon and planets. They envisaged a system in which the heavenly bodies were prevented from falling on to the Earth by invisible concentric spheres or circles that rotated and carried them around the Earth on circular courses.

Before long this theory ran into trouble since observation by improved sighting devices showed that the planets wandered about the sky and behaved in a way that no single arrangement of spheres and circles could account for.

Consequently, the spherical theory had to be bolstered by later Greek astronomers who visualized secondary spheres attached at varying angles to the primary ones. By this concept, a planet carried along on a secondary sphere would appear to follow a non-circular course which resembled its observed movements. Even so, two spheres per planet was not the answer to something that the mathematically minded Greeks knew to be a mathematical problem.

Eudoxus of Cnidus, who lived in the third century BC tried to solve the problem by giving each planet 27 spheres. Aristotle (384–322 BC), who was a staunch believer in the geocentric theory, gave each planet a complex arrangement of 55 spheres. Aristotle's spheres were of a pure and transparent crystal, but only a few actually carried planets. The function of the others was to adjust the bodies' movements.

Heracleides of Pontus, a pupil of Plato and a member of the Greek Academy appears to have contributed much to serious astronomy. Although most of his writings are lost and there is some controversy regarding the interpretation of the surviving fragments, it is possible that he discovered that the Earth rotated on its axis. He seems also to have solved the problem of why Venus and Mercury are sometimes further away by suggesting that they are revolved around the sun and not around the Earth. To his contemporaries this was rank heresy and raised such a storm that Heracleides abandoned astronomy.

Aristarchus of Samos was another Greek whose theories were far in advance of his day and earned him the scorn of his contemporaries. Teaching in Alexandria about 270 BC, he maintained that the sun was a motionless body in the centre of the Universe with the Earth and planets revolving around it. He also stated that the moon revolved around the Earth, and that the Earth had a double movement – rotation on its axis and rotation around the sun. Denial of the Earth's traditional position as centre of the Universe brought on him a charge of impiety, a significant forerunner of what was to happen to Copernicus 1,800 years later.

Undeterred by the tirades of his contemporaries, Aristarchus wrote a treatise *On the Size and Distance of the Sun and Moon* in which he calculated the distance of Earth from the sun to be 19 times greater than that of the Earth from the moon.

After Greek science became centred at Alexandria, a long line of brilliant astronomers produced a mass of observational and theoretical data. Hipparchus invented trigonometry and used it to measure the distance of the moon from the Earth. He first observed eclipses of the moon and noted the time lapse as the moon passed through the Earth's shadow. He then compared the apparent diameter of the moon with the diameter of the cone of shadow projected by the Earth on to the moon. Having established an approximate relationship between the apparent diameter of the moon and the diameter of the shadow cone, a trigonometrical calculation gave the distance between Earth and moon as 30 times the diameter of the Earth. Today's instruments and methods show how close Hipparchus came to the actual distance.

Ptolemy was another giant of the Alexandrian school of astronomy. He wrote a textbook called *Almagest* which, although perpetuating the geocentric theory, suggested that the planets are much closer to the Earth than are the fixed stars. He also compiled a new catalogue of 1,030 observed stars and *Geographia,* listing places on the Earth according to their latitude and longitude.

Ptolemy's *Almagest* was a brilliant exercise in attempting to prove mathematically the phenomena of astronomy as understood in his day. It is not generally acceptable in the light of modern knowledge, but it was taken as dogma until Copernicus propounded his heliocentric system some 1,800 years later.

Measuring the Earth

One of the most remarkable achievements of Greek mathematical astronomy was the measurement of the Earth's circumference by *Eratosthenes,* who learned his mathematics at Alexandria. He set up an obelisk at Alexandria and another of identical height at *Syene,* 5,000 *stadia* away. He noted that at mid-day the sun shining on the *Syene* obelisk threw no shadow, whereas at the same hour of the day the Alexandria obelisk cast a measurable shadow. He calculated the distance between the two obelisks as one-fiftieth of a circle. Multiplying the distance of 5,000 *stadia* by 50 gave the circumference of the circle as 250,000 *stadia:* in other words the circumference of the Earth. Although the exact length of the *stadium* used by Eratosthenes is uncertain, it is probable that 250,000 were approximately equal to 25,300 miles. As the circumference of the Earth at the equator is now known to be 24,901 miles, Eratosthenes' figure is a striking tribute to Greek mathematics.

Ptolemy's *Almagest* was the swan song of Greek astronomy and science in general. For a few centuries science struggled against the decadent materialism of Imperial Rome, but little original work was achieved. The Dark Ages plunged science into a morass of superstition in which astronomy became the handmaiden of astrology. Nowhere was astronomy studied any longer for its own sake. Even the great observatories in India and Arabia served astrologers rather than astronomers. Nevertheless, astrologers continued to make some contributions to astronomy. Astrologers at Baghdad observatory, founded in the eighth century, discovered lunar libration, and in the thirteenth century Arab astrologers drew up a reasonably accurate chart of the night sky. But, in general, for many years astronomy was eclipsed by the shadow of superstition and religious intolerance of scientific thought.

1 The orrery, a mechanical model of the solar system, has been used extensively from the early eighteenth century for instruction and demonstration.

2 For several centuries Greenwich, in England, was the home of modern astronomy. This old print shows the viewing room with astronomers at work.

Giant eyes on the sky

Optics has opened up new fields to the astronomer, but even the best conventional telescope has given way to the radio telescope, which can detect and examine that which the eye cannot see.

1 This replica of the original Newton reflecting telescope, at the California Institute of Technology, has a magnification of 38. It was the forerunner of modern instruments.
2 For complete accuracy, the errors in a telescope movement must be constantly checked and corrected, as shown here.

ALTHOUGH THE HUMAN EYE is a masterpiece of evolution and unrivalled for keeping its owner in visual contact with his immediate and changing surroundings, it is a poor instrument for detailed observation of the very minute or the very distant.

From the astronomer's point of view, the limitations of the human eye stem from the fact that the visible light to which it is sensitive comprises only a small segment of the electromagnetic spectrum. That is, its *resolving power*, or ability to separate close sources of light and so observe and distinguish fine details, is far too coarse for the purpose of stellar or planetary observation.

Father of the telescope

The telescope was the first instrument to transcend the limitations of Man's natural distance-vision. Some doubt exists as to who invented the telescope, but the consensus of opinion gives the credit to Hans Lippershey, a young Dutch spectacle-maker, who in about 1600 discovered by accident that when two lenses were held some distance apart, objects seen through them appeared larger and nearer to the observer. The first telescopes were simply crude spy-glasses for looking at objects on land or sea and their magnification was little more than double that of normal sight.

Then in 1609 Galilei Galileo, 'the father of modern astronomy', turned a telescope to the sky. His instrument had only 20

magnification, but it did find a chink in the blind that hitherto had hidden so much that was invisible to the unaided eye of Man.

When Galileo looked through that primitive telescope more than 350 years ago, he saw things that the astronomer-astrologers of Babylon had only dreamed might be there. He saw mountains on the moon, and found that the planet Venus had phases similar to those of the moon,

proving that the planet had an orbit centred on the sun.

Despite advances in the optical telescope and the assistance it receives from the camera, this method of observation can of itself do little more than bring the stars and planets nearer and pinpoint their positions relative to the Earth. The optical telescope and the camera attached to it cannot tell the astronomer a great deal about the physical conditions of the objects observed, what they are composed of or their temperatures. Neither can the optical telescope give accurate figures relative to the distance of the observed object nor, in the case of moving objects, their speed. To obtain that kind of information, the astronomer requires a number of additional instruments, some of which function independently and some as components of the telescope.

When the eye cannot see

Another disadvantage of the optical telescope as now used in ground-based observatories is that there is a limit to the distances to which it can carry the human eye into the vastness of space. Many astronomers believe that the Mount Palomar telescope is the ultimate in optical observation and that ground observatories have now seen all that is ever likely to be visible to them.

For years astronomers have dreamed of being able to do just that. Since 1950 tests with rockets and satellites have demonstrated the crystal clarity of space where

3 The huge radio telescope at Arecibo, Puerto Rico, uses a man-made depression in the ground as the dish. This makes the instrument extremely rigid despite its enormous size.

there are no atmospheric conditions to distort long-range vision. But the dream of putting an observatory in that astronomer's paradise did not become reality until 1962. Curiously enough, it was not done with a spaceship or rocket, but with a balloon – the pioneer of all aircraft.

Weighing nearly three tons, the telescope and its auxiliary equipment of cameras and other instruments was suspended from a huge nylon balloon inflated with helium gas. The whole complex was launched from the National Scientific Balloon Flight Station at Palestine, Texas, and reached an altitude of 100,000 feet, just within the fringe of the Earth's atmosphere, extending the range of astronomical visibility by several light years.

When the balloon reached its designed ceiling, technicians manning a tracking

The Vostock and subsequent satellites are valuable astronomical tools. This model of a Vostock at a Moscow exhibition shows the radio atennae and optical equipment.

The 250-foot bowl of Jodrell Bank radio telescope framed by the control-room window. This single operator can position the aerial to pick up signals from anywhere in space.

station on the ground sent radio signals which operated relays in a 'black box' on the telescope. These caused the telescope to turn round until it pointed towards the object to be observed. Other radio-controlled relays operated mechanisms to focus the lens.

Called a *stratoscope,* the space-borne telescope can be locked on to a star or planet simply by pressing a button on the ground level panel. The stratoscope's first mission was to collect information about Mars in preparation for a future landing on that planet by astronauts. It has since been used to photograph Betelgeuse, Sirius and other stars.

The tube of the stratoscope is 18 feet long and the lenses are powerful enough to distinguish two objects 30 miles apart from a distance of 5,000 miles. The tele-

scope itself is mounted on the main arm of an L-shaped frame. The shorter arm carries the control mechanism.

Immediately the telescope is directed on to the object for observation and is in correct focus, its own transmitter radios a signal to the ground station that everything is ready for observation. Ground control then sends a radio message that sets in operation the camera that photographs everything the telescope 'sees'.

Incorporated in the stratoscope are a television camera and transmitter which send back to Earth a picture of everything in the telescope's line of sight. By watching the transmitted pictures on the screen of a television receiver, astronomers on the ground can signal the telescope and its camera to move from side to side or up and down until some particular object or feature that they want to photograph appears on the screen. Anything seen by the telescope can be held in focus for photographic exposures of one second to one hour. All is done simply by pressing buttons on panels in the ground control station.

Each mission by the stratoscope lasts for approximately 12 hours. At the end of the mission, the ground control transmits a radio signal to release from the balloon the L-shaped frame carrying the telescope, camera and other instruments. Another radio signal opens a parachute which brings the whole complex back to Earth. The films exposed by the cameras are then developed ready for examination by the astronomers.

Because of the stratoscope's success, astronomers envisage the observatory of the future as a stabilized platform-satellite placed in an orbit beyond the Earth's atmosphere. It would be equipped with all the latest instruments for visual

The Surveyor soft landing craft is powered by wings bearing the solar cells which derive energy from the sun. They are completely automatic.

observation and manned by a team of astronomers who would work and live in space for periods of weeks. United States astronomers have gone as far as tentatively scheduling a family of orbiting observatories with 36-inch telescopes searching the skies by 1980.

Not that orbiting space observatories are likely to render the ground-based telescope obsolete. It will remain for many years to come the most convenient instrument for obtaining data relative to, for example, the distance of the stars. This is measured by what is called *parallax*.

Parallax is a measure of the amount by which an object appears to move in relation to its background when an observer looks at it from two different places. A simple example of judging the parallax of something such as a vase on a table in relation to an adjacent wall, is to look at the vase first with one eye and then with the other. To judge the parallax of, say, Jupiter, the astronomer sights it at different times in a single night against the background of the stars. Due to the rotation of the Earth, his telescope has moved a few thousand miles to a new position

1 The 200-inch telescope at Mount Palomar, California, is one of the most advanced optical instruments. The versatility of the mechanical movement is almost as important as the excellence of the optics in equipment like this.
2 A *planetarium* represents star and planet motions, greatly speeded up. This instrument is at Griffith Park, Los Angeles.

relative to the stellar background at each sighting. Parallax of a star is fixed by observing it during opposite seasons of the year, so that the Earth's revolution round the sun gives a base line of 186 million miles. Theoretically, parallax could give the distance of movement of stars up to 400 light years away from the Earth. Just what that means will be appreciated when it is remembered that a light year is the distance that light, moving at a speed of 186,326 miles per second, travels in one year.

For judging the brightness of stars the astronomer uses instruments based on the properties of the photo-electric cell and other light-sensitive devices. This has resulted in stars being grouped into definite classes, each of which has the same degree of real brightness. In this way the distances of stars can be estimated by measuring their brightness one against another.

Studying the spectra

To establish the composition of celestial bodies, the astronomer uses a *diffraction grating*. This consists of a glass plate across which are closely ruled lines. When light from an observed body passes through the grating it is broken down in the same way that light is broken down by a glass prism. Since laboratory experiments have demonstrated that every element when heated emits its own characteristic line in a diffraction grating, examination of such lines enables the astronomer to establish the elements in objects light years away from the Earth.

Other instruments for analysing stellar light give reasonably accurate estimates of the speed of stars moving towards or away from the solar system. *Magnetic sensors* can measure the strength of a star's magnetic field. It is also possible to measure the speed of stellar rotation and to calculate the amount of invisible gas adrift in space between a star and Earth.

For accurate measurement of the surface temperature of bodies millions of miles away from the Earth, astronomers have developed their own special thermometers. One of these is the observatory *thermo-couple,* which was invented in 1922 by the American physicist Coblentz. Light from the observed object is concentrated on to two wires of dissimilar metals which are welded together and placed in the focus of a large reflector. Filters separate the light from the infra-red rays which heat the wires of the thermocouple but to slightly different temperatures. This causes the wires to generate a minute electric current, the strength of which is an indication of the temperature of the heat source. One of the first facts established by Coblentz's thermocouple was that the temperature of the planet Mercury is 420 °C. on the side of the planet exposed to the sun, and

−220 °C. on the surface of Neptune.

An even more sensitive instrument for measuring distant heat is the *germanium bolometer* invented by Dr Low of Arizona University. The germanium crystal is enclosed in a glass tube and registers heat by contact with infra-red radiation. Electronic relays actuate a pen that traces the readings on a chart. The bolometer can detect one hundred-million-millionth of a watt. This is equivalent to sensing the heat from a lighted match at a distance of 15,000 miles.

Dr Low's first use of his bolometer was to measure the temperature of Jupiter, which proved to be higher than had been thought and gave rise to a theory that the planet may have its own heat source.

Probably the greatest advance in the development of astronomical instruments since the invention of the optical telescope is the radio telescope. Radio astronomy may be said to have begun in the 1930s when radio amateurs using new types of highly sensitive receivers repeatedly picked up weak signals which they knew could not have originated from any known transmitter on the Earth. Simultaneously, an American astronomer named Jansky was propounding a theory that there might

be a radio source in the Milky Way.

The outbreak of the Second World War prevented any serious attempt to link the unknown radio signals with Jansky's theory. It was not until after the war that astronomers and radio technicians gathered sufficient evidence to prove that the transmissions were coming from objects in space. Much more was then known about nuclear energy, and it was suggested that the mystery signals were natural transmissions of stellar energy. Like everything else in the Universe, stars consist of matter, and their matter is made up of atomic particles in a constant state of movement. This movement emits radiation which travels through space in the same way that a broadcasting station transmits radio programmes.

Careful search with optical telescopes failed to find any known stars in the right position to be making the transmissions. From this fact emerged that the stellar radio does not appear to be transmitted from any star or other object that can be seen or photographed through the most powerful of optical telescopes. To find out more about the source of the transmissions, the first movable radio telescope was built in 1952 at Jodrell Bank in Cheshire. It is, in fact, a super radio-receiver with a bowl aerial that can be aimed at any point in the Universe. The aerial is 250 feet in diameter and supported between two 165-foot towers. The towers are mounted on electrically driven bogies running on a circular track so that the aerial can be positioned at any point of a circle, while the aerial itself can be raised or lowered. In this way, the aerial can be pinpointed to pick up signals from any direction in the Universe.

Computers and the sky

All movements of the aerial are remotely controlled by a single operator at a switchboard in a building which also houses instruments for measuring the strength of the signals. The information is then processed by computers and appears in the form of graphs.

Although the Jodrell Bank radio telescope is now 17 years old, it is still the biggest instrument of its kind in existence. It is used by astronomers from all over the world and has been the model for several similar but smaller installations in different parts of the world. There are radio telescopes with much bigger aerials at observatories in the United States, Australia and Russia, but the aerials of these are fixed and designed for examining some specific part of a galaxy.

The computer has revolutionized the study and evaluation of data collected by astronomers. Modern astronomy is very much a matter of long and complicated calculations in higher mathematics. Not so very long ago this consumed an inordinate amount of the time which astronomers would have preferred to devote to direct observation. Now every important observatory has its own computer which can be programmed to work out in minutes abstruse calculations which previously took weeks or even months of tedious labour with pencil, slide rule and paper.

1 Arrays of antennae are often used rather than paraboloid dishes in radio telescopes. They can be made in larger sizes, increasing their power, but they are not so versatile.

2 *Coronographs* such as this one at Pulkovo, Russia, are used to study the sun's outer edge. In effect, it simulates the optical conditions of a solar eclipse.

Nine worlds in orbit

Life, warmth and energy come to us from the sun. Other planets in the solar system are in the same position. Are the sun's rays sufficient to give them the vital energy for animal life?

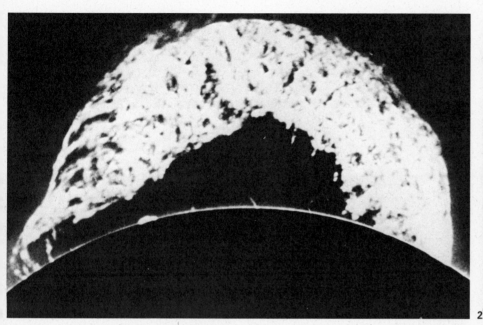

IT HAS BEEN SAID that astronomers get over the problem of trying to conceive of the inconceivable distances and forces at work in the Universe by deliberately not thinking about them at all. Radio astronomy has enabled them to detect galaxies at a distance of some 12,000 million light years (one light year being 5,878,500,500,000 miles), but they can offer little or no guidance on how the imagination can cope with such a scale.

Nor does this problem begin with distant galaxies. Our own solar system, though an insignificant feature of the Universe, is set on a scale which to human beings is stupefyingly vast. The distance from Earth to the moon is only 240,000 miles: but the solar system has a diameter at least 40,000 times greater. Alpha Centauri, the nearest star group to our sun, lies at a distance of 4·3 light years, or 25,000,000,000,000 miles.

The Milky Way galaxy, to which the solar system belongs, contains at least 100,000 million stars in a lens-shaped spiral with a diameter of 100,000 light years, with the sun some 27,000 light years from the densely packed centre. The collection of planets, moons, asteroids and comets which, together with the parent sun, comprise our particular system can thus be regarded as a closely knit heavenly family, held together by the gravitational influence of the parent.

Many attempts have been made to explain the vastness of the solar system in terms which ordinary people can understand. One of these states that, if the sun was reduced to the size of a beach ball 12 inches in diameter, then the planets could be represented as follows:

1. Mercury: a grain of mustard seed, 164 feet away;

1 Solar flares like this one observed from Boulder, Colorado, are clouds of burning hydrogen which billow hundreds of thousands of miles from the sun's surface.

2. Venus: a pea, 284 feet away;
3. Earth: a slightly larger pea, 430 feet away;
4. Mars: a currant, 654 feet away;
5. Jupiter: an orange, half a mile away;
6. Saturn: a tangerine, four-fifths of a mile away;
7. Uranus: a plum, just over a mile away;
8. Neptune: a plum, two and a half miles away; and
9. Pluto: a grain of rice at a mean distance of three miles.

On the same scale, Alpha Centauri would be 8,000 miles away.

Birth of the planets

All the planets, and the belt of asteroids lying between Mars and Jupiter, revolve round the sun in the same direction and in roughly the same plane (which is known as the *ecliptic*). However, Mercury and Pluto (respectively the nearest and furthest planets from the sun) each have highly eccentric orbits which are inclined to the plane of the ecliptic at 7° and 17° respectively. Orbital speeds of the planets also vary with the distance from the sun; a planet near the sun has to travel faster in order to remain in orbit. Thus, Mercury orbits at 107,030 mph, while Pluto can remain at its appointed distance with a speed of only 10,800 mph.

Uranus – to mention only one planet – rotates in the opposite direction to all the others because its polar axis is tilted at an angle of 97°53′ to the ecliptic; some astronomers believe this to be true also of Venus,

2 Central body in the solar system is the sun, which presents different aspects at different places. This photograph was taken from Captain Scott's base near the South Pole.

about which not very much is known for certain because of the thick layer of cloud which obscures its surface. Another curiosity is the path of Pluto, which at one point comes inside that of Neptune, though there is no danger of the planets colliding.

Among the many things still unknown about the solar system is the manner in which it was born. One theory which was very popular for a long time is that thousands of millions of years ago another sun passed within the gravitational field of our own. According to some astronomers, this resulted in a cigar shape of material being torn from the intruder. Eventually, the material condensed into 'blobs' which were the *proto-planets*. According to other astronomers, it was the intruder which tore away a portion of the sun, but the result was the same.

For various reasons, both these theories are no longer popular, having been replaced by the hypothesis that the solar system began as a huge mass of dust and gas drifting through space. Gradually, about 5,000 million years ago, the gravitational attraction between the molecules and particles in the cloud caused it to contract and, as contraction continued, the whole mass began slowly to rotate. Eventually, this took the form of a sphere rotating at a furious speed, thereby generating an enormous temperature, especially at the centre of the sphere.

At the same time, in the same way that planets bulge slightly at their equators as a result of centrifugal force, the fantastic speed of rotation of the protosphere caused

PLUTO

ASTEROIDS

CERES   JUPITE

MARS   SUN
MERCURY
EARTH VENUS

JUPITER

NEPTUNE

MERCURY   VENUS   EARTH'S   EARTH
                    MOON

NEREID

MARS

URANUS

MOONS OF SATURN   PLUTO

TITAN

SATURN

GANYMEDE   10

CALLISTO   EUROPA

2

4

1 Relative sizes of the planets of the solar system. Earth is the fifth largest planet, slightly larger than Venus, but far smaller than the four massive planets Jupiter, Saturn, Uranus and Neptune. The other objects in the diagram are the various minor bodies in the solar system, large asteroids and moons.

2, 3, 4, 5 Eclipse of the sun, showing the progressive obscuring of the sun's disc by the moon. Under these conditions it is possible to examine the fringe of the sun (the *corona*), which is not possible under normal circumstances.

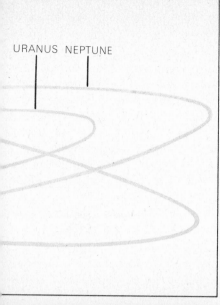

URANUS NEPTUNE

discs to form at the equator. One by one, the theory goes, these discs were thrown off into space to become the proto-planets, while the rest of the sphere became the proto-sun.

If true, the theory has one implication of enormous significance, which is that it vastly increases the probability of there being other 'families' like our own, not only in the Milky Way but in the billions of galaxies in the known Universe and beyond. Hence, it vastly increases the probability of there being life like our own elsewhere.

All life, as well as motion, in the solar system depends on the sun. Scientifically, it can be regarded as a globe of gas 865,000 miles in diameter, or as a gigantic nuclear pile with a temperature of 5,500 °C. at its surface but rising to nearly 14,000,000 °C. at its centre. Yet, astronomically speaking, the sun is only an average star as far as dimensions, brightness and tempera-

ture are concerned.

The sun, which is 330,430 times more massive than Earth, derives its energy from the enormous atomic furnace at its centre where atoms are moving so rapidly that nuclear reactions take place upon collision, converting hydrogen into helium; more than 90 per cent of the energy so generated takes place in a sphere which has only 20 per cent of the total diameter of the sun. Already, it has been carrying out this process for an estimated 5,000 million years, and it is thought to be capable of carrying on for the same length of time again before it becomes a burnt-out black cinder drifting pointlessly through the heavens.

The planets of the solar system fall conveniently into two groups: there are the inner planets, Mercury, Venus, Earth and Mars, and the outer or Jovian planets – Jupiter, Saturn, Uranus and Neptune. Pluto, which behaves more like a comet

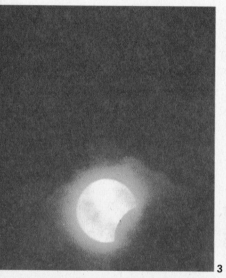

3

© California Inst. of Technology & Carnegie Inst. of Washington

6

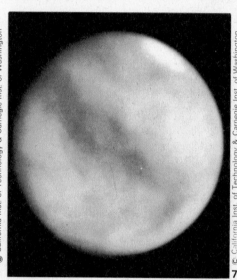

© California Inst. of Technology & Carnegie Inst. of Washington

7

5

8

Jupiter displays the characteristics of both a planet and a sun, and many astronomers believe that nuclear processes within the core maintain its surface temperature. Jupiter (Jove) gives its name to the outer planets.

Mars – the 'Red Planet' – appears to have both water and vegetation. It is these observations which led early astronomers to presume that life might exist on this planet.

The Earth photographed from space. It reflects light on the moon rather in the way the moon lights the Earth, but six times brighter.

than a planet, seems to be the only cuckoo in the nest: it may, however, be the remains of a large Jovian planet which suffered a catastrophic nuclear explosion.

Of the inner planets, Mercury is the sunniest, being both nearest the sun and having little or no atmosphere (at least in comparison with Earth) to shield its surface. At one time, it was thought that Mercury, during its 88-day journey round the sun, presented the same face to it all the time. Astronomers, as a result, thought that the sunlit surface had a temperature of about 415 °C., while that of the hemisphere turned away from the sun was put at near absolute zero (−273 °C.).

In 1965, however, the huge radio telescope in Puerto Rico discovered that Mercury rotates every 59 days instead of every 88 days. This explained why temperature measurements of its dark side showed a comfortable 21 °C. Days and nights are long but not permanent, the sun rising at intervals of 170 days.

Other worlds

But we simply have no idea of what Mercury's landscape contains. It may be bleak and inhospitable with a thin, unbreathable atmosphere, or there could be forms of life based on sulphur and silicon instead of on oxygen and carbon. As one astronomer said, 'Mercury may be eminently suitable for life as we do not know it.'

Even more mysterious is Venus, the Earth's twin, whose mysteries are shrouded in a thick atmosphere containing carbon dioxide, water vapour and possibly nitrogen. Moreover, because of this permanent shroud, we know nothing of the planet's rotation or of the inclination of its axis to the ecliptic, the two vital factors determining surface temperature and the existence of seasons. Estimates of its rotation period vary from 20 hours to 249 days; likewise, estimates of its axial inclination vary widely.

In the same way, the surface of Venus has been variously described as swampy jungle, barren, hot desert and unbroken ocean. However, at 67,000,000 miles from the sun, Venus ought to have a reasonable period of rotation, and the water vapour in its atmosphere strongly suggests some form of water on its surface. Again, with a diameter of only 300 miles less than that of Earth and a mass four-fifths that of our

planet, one may expect the chemical composition of both to be substantially the same.

By contrast, the surface of Mars can be easily observed through its thin atmosphere, composed largely of nitrogen and carbon dioxide. This planet, which has half the diameter and one-ninth the mass of Earth, is generally considered to be the most likely supporter of life forms among the other planets. Such life, however, is likely to be very different from that of Earth for three main reasons: (1) the Martian atmosphere is much thinner and chemically different; (2) Mars is half as far again from the sun; (3) it has a mean density of 4 compared with Earth's 5·52, suggesting a different rock structure and core.

Even so, water vapour exists in the Martian atmosphere and liquid water may exist in relatively small amounts on and below the surface. Moreover, the planet enjoys the same axial inclination and the same rotational period as Earth, giving rise to clearly defined seasons. Snow, or frozen hoar frost, can be clearly seen at the Martian poles, and these polar caps shrink in summer just as on Earth; unlike Earth, however, atmospheric pressure on Mars is so low that the ice turns directly into water vapour. Again, certain surface areas change colour during spring and summer on Mars, suggesting that some form of vegetation grows there.

Finally, there are the two moons of Mars, Phobos and Deimos. Each of them is tiny and orbits close to the planet: in the case of Phobos, the diameter is five miles and the height of orbit only 5,800 miles, while Deimos is only three miles in diameter and orbits at a height of 15,000 miles. Again, calculations have shown that, if not hollow, each moon must be composed of some material much lighter than any solid known on Earth or any porous material that could hold together.

The outer planets begin with Jupiter, though it is believed that there was once a planet orbiting between Mars and Jupiter which was shattered by the latter's gravitational field. The remains of this planet, at least part of them, are thought to be the

asteroids which orbit in this band of space. Some 1,500 of these have been detected, the largest being Ceres with a diameter of 480 miles.

The Jovian planets all have a similar atmosphere, consisting of a mixture of hydrogen, helium, ammonia, methane and perhaps some water. However, hydrogen predominates because these planets are massive enough and far enough away from the sun to retain the lighter gases.

Jupiter, with a mass of more than 318 Earths and an equatorial diameter of 88,700 miles, is the greatest of the Jovian planets in all senses of the word. No one can tell yet where its solid surface begins and its atmosphere ends, but it is known to be the scene of violent storms and is a great emitter of radio waves, as befits the God of Thunder. It is also the proud possessor of a Great Red Spot in its south tropical zone which seems to be a coherent feature suspended in some form of liquid or gas. It measures some 25,000 miles in length by 8,000 miles in breadth. The planet also boasts 12 moons, and is not unlike a solar system in miniature. For all that, Jupiter's density is only 1·33 times that of water.

Planet or sun?

Many astronomers believe that Jupiter lies somewhere between a planet and a tiny sun, a body in which nuclear processes are going on but are insufficiently strong to make it luminous. Hence, it is argued, although the outer atmosphere is incredibly cold through lack of heat from the sun, its surface may receive considerable heat from the nuclear reactions at the core, and may indeed be warmer than the surface of the Earth. A similar argument applies to the rest of the family: Saturn, Uranus and Neptune.

There is little doubt that Man will soon be visiting some of the inner planets. Apart from the fact that voyages like these will constitute the greatest and most exciting challenge ever presented to the human spirit and mind, it will be also fascinating to find out how far the reality of these planets accords with what we think we know of them today.

1 Saturn boasts six satellites, four of which are clearly shown here. They supply information about the size, mass and movement of Saturn.

2 At one time total (annular) eclipses of the sun were held to be omens of disaster. Now they are observed by people all over the world, as this picture shows.

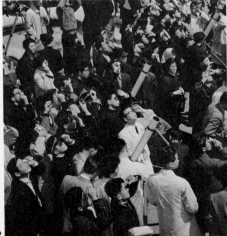

The Universe around us

The sun is only one of 100,000 million to 200,000 million stars in our galaxy. If the properties and relationships of Earth and sun are duplicated elsewhere, Man may not be alone in the Universe.

1 About 80 per cent of known galaxies are spirals. Spiral nebula Coma Berenices is seen here photographed 'edge-on' by the 200-inch Hale telescope at Mount Palomar.

2 Comets, occasionally visible from Earth, can be the most spectacular and brilliant phenomena in the sky. The comet Jurlof-Achmanof was a brief visitor in 1939.

JUST AS HYDROGEN comprises the raw material of the Universe, stars are its main product. In our own galaxy, the Milky Way, the number of stars is estimated at between 100,000 million and 200,000 million, while the number of galaxies in the detectable Universe is put at anything between 100,000 million and one million million. With figures like these, it would indeed be strange if the sun was the only star to sustain life.

Yet the sun does seem so different from the other stars in the sky that most people probably do not think of it as a star at all. We see it as a bright yellow disc and are conscious of the heat and light it provides, but only because it happens to be much nearer than any other star. The mean distance between sun and Earth is only 93 million miles, compared with 25 million million miles (4·2 light years) to the next nearest star, Proxima Centauri. Altogether, some 6,500 stars can be seen with the naked eye, and a large number of these would look very much like the sun at the same distance.

The science of astronomy abounds with unproved theories, some about when and how the stars were formed. It is believed that some stars were formed only a few million years ago, while others, including the sun, are thought to go back 5,000 million years and more. As to the manner of their birth, no theory has so far successfully challenged that called 'the nebular hypothesis', propounded by the German philosopher, Immanuel Kant, in 1755.

Kant believed that stars evolved from enormous clouds of dust and gas drifting about in space. These clouds were originally cool, but began to heat up as gravitational attraction between the particles came into play and the clouds began to condense and contract.

The planets are formed

According to Kant, the primitive cloud would begin to rotate: it grew hotter and hotter as it contracted until it began to glow like a giant proto-star. Meanwhile, the rate of spin reached a point at which centrifugal force began throwing off rings of glowing dust and gas which in time cooled and formed themselves into planets.

A similar theory was advanced independently of Kant some 40 years later by the French scientist, the Marquis de Laplace. In the opinion of Laplace, however, the cloud would be hot and rotating from the very beginning: contraction alone, he argued, could not have caused the cloud to rotate. But in any case, although it has been modified somewhat since, the nebular hypothesis is accepted in principle today.

Stars have been discovered which have more than 10,000 times the mass of the sun and more than one million times its volume. There are other stars which, in comparison with the sun, are dwarfs. Yet the remarkable fact is that more than 99 per cent of all stars in the Universe are thought to belong to the Main Sequence – that is, they can be grouped together according to their various properties to form an orderly progression from the biggest and hottest to the smallest and coolest. When this is plotted as a graph, the result is a straight diagonal line.

This progression of the stars was recognized more than 50 years ago independently by two astronomers, E. Hertzsprung and H. N. Russell. Each prepared versions of what is now known as the Hertzsprung-Russell (H-R) diagram, in which the Main Sequence stars form the straight line just mentioned. This line suggests a smooth and continuous change in the intensities of the absorption lines of the stellar spectra.

Stars in the Main Sequence have been grouped into ten main groups or classes, designated by the letters O, B, A, F, G, K, M, R, N and S with each group sub-divided by the numbers 0 to 9. The Class O stars, which are very rare, are the most massive and hottest with surface temperatures up to 90,000 °F. (50,000 °C.); the coolest and

smallest are the Class S stars whose surface temperatures can be as low as 5,400 °F. (3,000 °C.). The sun, classified as a G2, and called a yellow dwarf, has a surface temperature of about 13,500 °F. Its absolute magnitude (its luminosity at a distance of 32·6 light years) is +5, which means that at this distance it would be an inconspicuous star, just slightly more visible than the faintest stars which can be seen with the naked eye. Compare this with some of the stars in the Large Magellanic Cloud which have a magnitude of −10, and therefore shine with the light of one million suns!

The brightest stars

The simple analogy of a red-hot poker helps explain what the Main Sequence is about. If left in a fire for an adequate length of time, the tip of the poker should be white hot, perhaps even blue, whereas the further away from the tip, the duller the heat-glow. White turns to yellow, to orange and to red. Similarly with the stars: the hottest look blue to the naked eye, the coolest look red. This explains why the sun is called a yellow dwarf.

Stars in the Main Sequence are in the stable period of their existence, during which hydrogen is being converted into helium at a steady rate owing to nuclear reactions taking place at the centre. After they have consumed a certain amount of their available hydrogen (with the sun the

proportion is thought to be 12 per cent) stars expand rapidly into cool 'red giants' and leave the Main Sequence.

Ultimately, they become hot white dwarfs', stars perhaps no bigger than a planet but of incredibly high density. In the evolution towards this ultimate condition, the star may suffer a dramatic loss of mass through a 'nova' or 'supernova' explosion during which it gains a fantastic increase in brightness for a few days.

Despite immense gravitational pressures, stars keep their shape through the opposite, outgoing pressure of radiation. However, the processes of thermonuclear fusion and neutron capture gradually transform hydrogen into heavier elements, and there comes a point at which the thermonuclear reactions grow so weak that the radiation pressure surrenders to that of gravity. As already explained, the star then collapses inward, during which process the larger stars become supernovae and for a short period may shine with the light of 1,000 million stars. Less massive stars are thought to contract into superdense white dwarfs by the same process.

What happens, briefly, is that the process of nuclear fusion during a star's life in the Main Sequence is followed by a process akin to nuclear fission. According to V. A. Firsoff, one of the leading writers on astronomical matters: 'Old galaxies must contract too. Their nuclei are found

1 The spiral mist in the constellation Canes Venatici is ten million light years away. Such nebulae are clouds of diffuse gas within the Milky Way system of stars.
2 Pleiades is a star cluster within the constellation Taurus, about 300 light years from the solar system. Nebulosity is probably caused by rarefied matter made luminous by radiation.

to spout forth hydrogen. A gravitational collapse of their superdense stars should eventually follow, most probably to yield a quasi-stellar radio source, or quasar, which is to a galaxy what a supernova is to a star. In a quasar, dense matter seems to be converted to hydrogen, but the processes and the forces involved in this are not at present understood.'

The middle way

The more massive a star, the more rapidly it burns up its stock of hydrogen, hence the shorter its stay in the Main Sequence. Stars in the O class may in fact remain there only for a few million years, which is a very short time in astronomical terms and certainly not long enough for life to develop on any planets attached to such stars. By the same token, stars in the classes M to S are due to stay in the Main Sequence for a prodigious length of time – perhaps for 100,000 million years – but may not emit enough energy to start life on their satellites.

As ever, where life is concerned, the

middle way seems to be the best way. Our sun is estimated to be 5,000 million years old and to have at least another 7,000 million years to run, most of them in the Main Sequence. Similarly, it is hot, but not too hot, massive but not too massive. Thus, for various reasons to do with age, temperature and mass, it is thought that the stars most likely to support some form of life on satellite planets are those lying between F2 and M2 (inclusive) in the Main Sequence.

From star counts and classifications, it is believed that 25 per cent of all stars lie in this sector. Out of every 10,000 stars, more than 7,300 lie in the M spectral class; that is, nearly three-quarters of all the stars are small and dim. As the spectral class increases, the number of stars in each decreases: thus, of every 10,000 stars, 1,500 are in spectral class K, 730 in G, 290 in F, and so on until at O there is only one star in every 50,000.

At this point, the importance of the nebular hypothesis becomes apparent because, if true, it means that most stars – even double, treble and quadruple systems – are likely to have attendant planets. What this means in the case of the Milky Way, to name only one galaxy, has been summed up by the well-known astronomer, Isaac Asimov:

'The total number of stars in our galaxy,' he writes, 'has been estimated at 135 billion (one American billion equals 1,000 million). Therefore, the total number of stars in the range of the spectral classes F2 to M2, representing all stars that might conceivably have habitable planets, is 34 billion.

'The total number of stars in the range

3 A seventeenth-century copper-plate engraving showing the positions of the stars and their pictorial astrological representations. The names have been adopted for the constellations.
4 The Andromeda galaxy among the stars of the Milky Way contains 100,000 million stars and is 100,000 light years in length. It is the only extragalactic object visible to the naked eye.

of spectral classes F2 to K1, which can have habitable planets without special satellites (and this is the important range) is 17·5 billion. In sheer numbers, then, there is no lack of suitable stars in the galaxy.'

If we apply the Main Sequence classification to the 20 brightest stars in the sky, we find that six are too massive to be on it. These are Capella, Arcturus, Aldebaran, Pollux, Betelgeuse and Antares.

The Milky Way

Six more are of spectral class B, five of A, two of F and one (by a lucky chance, Alpha Centauri, the second nearest) of spectral class G, like our own sun. Sirius A, the brightest star in the heavens, is a white dwarf of spectral class A; at a distance of 8·7 light years, it has an apparent magnitude of −1·58, and an absolute magnitude of 1·3. Magnitude increases logarithmically, so that a star of the fourth magnitude is 2·512 times brighter than one of the fifth. However, a star of the first magnitude is 100 times brighter than one of the fifth.

But Sirius is by no means the most interesting object among the brightest stars. The second brightest, Canopus, some 650 light years away, is a fantastic body with an estimated absolute magnitude of −7·4 (one million times brighter than the sun), yet it is thought to belong to spectral class F. Canopus is not visible from all parts of the northern hemisphere. Another remarkable object is Rigel (spectral class B) with an absolute magnitude of −5·8; there is also Deneb with one of −5·2.

The sun is, of course, a modest member of the Milky Way, a star system some 80,000 light years in diameter which is often referred to simply as the galaxy. The Milky Way is actually spiral in shape, but in cross-section it looks like a disc with a central nucleus of stars (some 13,000 light years in thickness). In this nucleus, many stars are thought to be as little as one light year apart. In 1926, the galaxy was discovered to be rotating, the galactic rotation of the sun being about 200 miles a second, but speeds are higher at the centre.

The sun lies some 26,000 light years from the centre of the galaxy and just north of its central plane; at this distance, the thickness of the galaxy is only 2,000 light years. Within 22 light years of the sun, there are only 111 stars, the closest being Proxima Centauri, a very small star some 4·2 light years away. It is part of a triple star system of which Alpha Centauri (4·3 light years' distance) is a G star like the sun. Other 'near' stars include Barnard's Star (6·2 light years away), Lalande 21185 (8 light years), Wolf 359 (8·1 light years) and Sirius (8·7 light years).

According to Asimov, only 14 of the 111 nearest stars enjoy a probability greater than one in 100 of having a habitable planet (that is, a planet which is habitable from the point of view of human requirements). However, Asimov also states that 'the combined probability of the existence of at least one habitable planet in the whole volume of space out to a distance of 22 light years from the sun is about 0·43. That is to say, in gambler's parlance, the odds are about 3 to 2 against our finding even a single habitable planet in the entire list of 14 candidates.' On the other hand, we are talking about only a very tiny fraction of the stars in the Milky Way.

The probability of finding some form of life within 22 light years of the sun is, of course, vastly higher. The existence of several planets attached to nearby stars has been inferred from a study of the motions of the stars in question. In 1944, for example, the binary 61 Cygni C system showed irregularities which could be due only to the presence of a dark companion about eight times the size of Jupiter. Similar studies have shown that Barnard's

Star and Lalande 21185 A, the stars second and third closest to the sun, also have dark companions.

It is, of course, impossible to detect the existence of planets outside the solar system by optical means because the distances involved are so vast. The unit of measurement generally used in the case of stars is the parsec, which is equal to 3·26 light years. At this distance, the angle between the Earth and sun amounts to only one second of arc; and a telescope mounted in space could not detect the separation of a dim body from a bright one at an angle smaller than two seconds of arc.

Undiscovered phenomena

Space contains many strange objects, strange, anyway, in the sense that we do not yet properly understand them. There are, for instance, the quasars, phenomena many times smaller than the average galaxy but which emit more than 100 times the radio energy of a galaxy. Again there are the cepheid stars, objects which glow bright then dim at regular intervals and the pulsars which emit radio energy at regular intervals. No doubt there are other celestial phenomena awaiting discovery.

Yet when one bears in mind the distances and the forces and the time scale involved, Man has a remarkable amount of knowledge about the stars – enough anyway to be practically certain that he is not alone in the Universe. With an estimated 7,000 million stars of the same spectral type as the sun in the Milky Way alone, how can we dismiss the possibility of there being creatures similar to us sharing this corner of space? We are as we are because Earth and sun are as they are. What if their various features and their distance relationship were duplicated elsewhere in space?

1 The great nebula in Andromeda. Working with the 100-inch Mount Wilson telescope in 1925, Edwin Hubble showed a resolution of the nebula into stars. One million galaxies have been photographed at Mount Wilson. Hubble classified them according to their shape.
2 A great nebula in the constellation of the Swan consisting of clouds of rarefied gases.

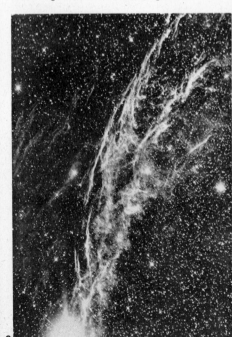

The enigmatic Cosmos

Powerful new techniques such as radio-astronomy now enable scientists to look deep into space. But many basic questions about the Universe we live in remain unsolved.

IF WE LOOK at the sky on a clear night, we can see some of the myriad bodies that make up the Universe. Astronomers, who are able to look far more closely at the heavens with the aid of telescopes than we can with the naked eye, are able to see many of the components that make it up. The objects visible from Earth are stars and galaxies. The separate stars belong to our own galaxy: the Milky Way. The galaxies are more distant and are very numerous.

The stars that make up our own Milky Way are visible as a band across the sky. The reason for this is that the Milky Way is a spiral galaxy, shaped rather like a disc, with the sun and the solar system placed towards the edge of the galaxy. While the stars appear in this way, the other galaxies are uniformly distributed, so that in whatever direction one looks one can see the same number of galaxies, provided one counts sufficient numbers. The galaxies show a tendency to occur in clusters.

The only way we have of estimating the relative distances of the galaxies we can see is to estimate how faint they look. The fainter they are, the further away they are likely to be. Estimates of the distribution of the galaxies based on faintness suggest that the Universe is uniform, that is, it is generally the same in all directions.

The uniformity of the Universe suggests that we are in fact looking at a fair sample section of the Universe, although we cannot see it all.

Speculation about the Universe has naturally occupied a great deal of human attention for many centuries. Many of the problems associated with an understanding of the Universe involved difficult concepts: the concept that space is, as Einstein maintained, 'finite but unbounded' has been one that has long puzzled laymen.

There is a second problem of this nature – namely, the Universe may be eternal, or it may have come into being thousands of millions of years ago. There is evidence to suggest that all the galaxies, and the stars and planets within them, the quasars and the supplies of interstellar gas, are in perfect balance, and may have reached this condition an infinite number of years ago. On the other hand, there is equally good reason to believe that the Universe is changing and evolving, that it is subject to cosmic laws of evolution.

For the moment at least, then, there is little we can state with certainty. The known Universe has been variously estimated to be as large as 10,000 to 12,000 million light years, while the number of galaxies has been put at anything from 3,000 million to one million million. Such discrepancies are only to be expected when we are dealing with distances far, far

beyond the range of the most powerful telescopes. Even so, the earliest discovery of galaxies beyond our own goes back 1,000 years to the time of the Arabic astronomer, Al-Sufi, who recorded Messier 31, the modern name for the spiral galaxy in Andromeda, the most distant of all the heavenly bodies visible with the naked

eye from the surface of the Earth.

In 1923, the famous American astronomer, Edwin P. Hubble, discovered six Cepheid variables (stars whose brightness fluctuates regularly and so allows them to be used as standard known light sources) in this spiral, and calculated that their distance was in the region of 750,000 light

1 A medieval view of the Universe. The print shows an explorer reaching the point at which the Earth meets the heavens. Behind the bowl of stars are the various wheels to drive the bowl.

2 Ancient Egyptian picture of the cosmos. The sky-goddess Nut arches over the reclining Earth-god Qeb. Shu, the air-god, stands between, supported by two ram-headed gods.

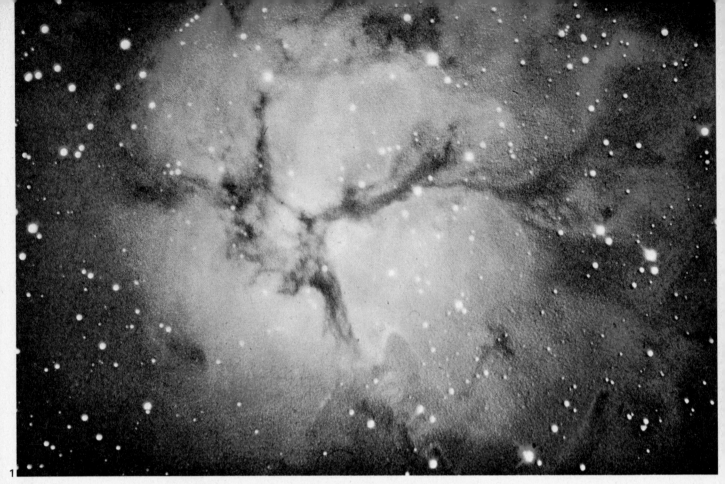

1

years, a staggering figure in those days; in 1952, another American astronomer, W. Baade, found that the true distance was even greater – about 2 million light years. Yet these distances are a mere fraction of those separating us from the most distant galaxies. Radio astronomers have detected objects which may be 6,000 million light years and more from the Earth (one light year being 5,878,500 million miles).

Theories of the Universe

Today, three main theories of the Universe are popular among astronomers, but while these opinions should be treated with respect, it must be emphasized that none of these theories is necessarily correct.

All these theories accept that the Universe is uniform, and that it is now expanding. In other words, the bulk of modern cosmological theory rests on the observations of astronomers that the light from distant stars is red-shifted, and that this indicates that they are moving away. Much of the theoretical work that led to the formulation of these theories was carried out by such leading mathematicians as Albert Einstein, Willem de Sitter Friedmann and Sir Arthur Eddington.

The first of the three is known as the 'steady state' or 'continuous creation' theory. Put forward in 1948 by Hermann Bondi, Thomas Gold and Fred Hoyle, all of them British astronomers, it maintains that the Universe is eternal – that is, it has always existed – and must appear to be essentially the same from whichever point of time or place it is studied. Matter, states the theory, is continuously created out of apparently nothing at the rate of 62 atoms of hydrogen per cubic inch of space every 1,000 million years. This is sufficient (and one can well believe it because there are a lot of cubic inches in

1 The Trifid mist in the galaxy Sagittarius. A mass of gas and dust 3,200 light-years away, it contains many hot newly-created stars.
2 Diagram of the 'big bang' theory of the evolution of the Universe. A dense supercondensate exploded giving rise to the Universe's expansion.

3 The 'oscillating' theory. The Universe is pulsating, expanded to a maximum and then contracting to a dense mass again.
4 Diagram of a 'steady state' universe. The Universe is expanding, but new matter (ringed) is created continuously and density maintained.

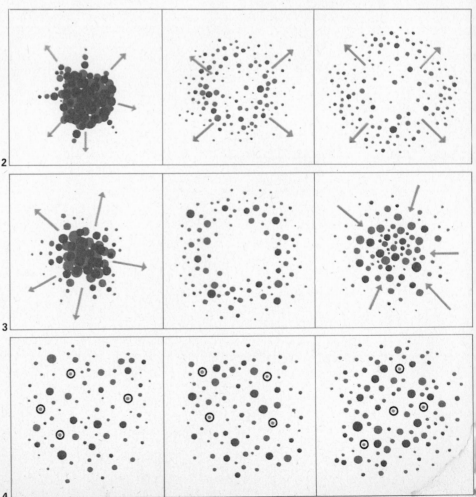

2

3

4

1 During the Middle Ages, astronomy declined in Europe but study of the Universe was developed in Moslem countries. Here, Persian astronomers measure the movements of heavenly bodies.

space) to form new galaxies to fill in the gaps caused by the fact that the Universe is expanding.

One major test of the steady-state theory is that because light travels at a finite speed, and because vast distances separate us even from the nearest galaxies, the light we see now from very distant galaxies was in fact emitted hundreds or even thousands of millions of years ago. Some of these observations tend to show that the Universe then was different from now thus contradicting the steady-state theory.

The second theory, and one which should appeal to all lovers of science fiction, is the 'big bang' theory, advanced in 1930 by the Belgian astronomer, Georges Lemaitre. The theory maintains that about 10,000 million years ago, all matter in the Universe was packed into one superdense sphere – the primeval atom – so that one cubic inch of the material weighed several thousands of millions of tons. Not surprisingly, the body exploded, its various fragments becoming galaxies moving apart at fantastic speeds.

The third explanation, known as the 'oscillating' theory, was revived in 1965 by the American astronomer, Professor Allan Sandage. It is essentially a special case of the 'big bang' theory, maintaining as it does that the Universe is today 10,000 million years along the expansive stage of an 80,000 million years' cycle of expansion and contraction. Thus, the theory claims, the Universe will continue to expand for another 30,000 million years, after which the gravitational attraction between the galaxies will gradually overcome the centrifugal force of the big bang. As a result, all the galaxies will move towards each other at millions of miles per hour until finally they re-form into the primeval atom, which will again explode. In this way, the Universe is fated to undergo an infinite series of explosion-implosion cycles.

Fantastic as some of these theories may sound to the layman, it must be remembered that, to human beings, the Universe is a fantastic phenomenon. Ordinary people must have been equally perplexed when some early Greek first maintained that the Earth was round. It will be noted, however, that the steady state and the big bang theories are mutually exclusive: if one is right, the other is wrong, because the Universe cannot at one and the same time be in a steady and an unsteady state. Yet if, in a steady-state universe, galaxies are moving apart and matter is being created to fill the gaps so created, then we have the apparently contradictory notions of an eternal Universe with dynamic features. However, what appears contradictory on Earth may be perfectly valid on a cosmic scale.

2 The solar system after Ptolemy. In this picture, the planets are orbiting the Earth. Until the sixteenth century, Earth was thought to be the centre of the Universe.

If it could be established beyond doubt that the Universe is, or is not, expanding, at least a lot of time and thought could be saved. In 1920, an American astronomer, V. M. Slipher, discovered, while working at Flagstaff in Arizona, that the light from certain distant galaxies was, in astronomical terms, 'exhibiting Doppler shifts to the red end of the spectrum'. Subsequent work by Edwin Hubble showed by 1929 that the amount of red shift was directly proportional to the distance of the galaxy concerned – in other words, the greater the shift of the light to the red end of the spectrum, the further the galaxy. It was as a result discovered (to the satisfaction of most astronomers at least) that galaxies were receding and that the more distant the galaxy, the higher its speed of recession. It has been estimated, for instance, that the pair of galaxies in Boötes, known as 3C295, are receding at over 300 million miles per hour, and are therefore assumed to be 6,000 million light years away. By such reckoning, galaxies nearing the circumference of our Universe would be receding at the speed of light.

Is the Universe expanding?

Most astronomers accept that the Universe is expanding because of the evidence of the red shift, but it is only fair to add that a number of them question not the evidence but the interpretation. Various other reasons have been put forward, but have never found wide acceptance, as explanations of the phenomenon, among them the suggestion that light on a long journey through space will be affected in an otherwise unknown way by gravity, or by electric and magnetic fields so as to exhibit a red shift. This, the so-called 'tired light' theory, is rejected by almost all astronomers because it would necessitate an entirely new physical principle which is not supported by any other evidence. Moreover, the Doppler shift has been successfully interpreted as a velocity effect in measuring the period of rotation of Jupiter which has been confirmed from

1 A modern reconstruction of Dondi's astronomical clock. The original was built in 1364. In addition to telling the time, the clock shows the positions of the sun, moon and several planets.
2 Technical experts at a flight research centre in the United States work on future space projects. The laboratory produces 'flight hardware' to protect instruments during exploratory missions.

other scientific evidence.

Nothing, then, is certain yet. We can, however, claim to be much further along the path of universal understanding than the Greek cartographer, Anaximander, who 2,500 years ago held that the Universe consisted of a sphere of fire enclosing a cold, moist mass from which it was separated by a layer of mist. Eventually, Anaximander thought, the fire became the light of the stars, the mist became the atmosphere, and the cold moist mass was transformed into Mother Earth. If we laugh at this, we should bear in mind that it was not until after Columbus had discovered the New World that Copernicus, in 1512, put the sun, and not the Earth, at the centre of the solar system.

The galaxies

Only four galaxies are visible from Earth with the naked eye. These are the Milky Way, the Large and Small Magellanic Clouds which lie at a distance of about 170,000 light years, and the Andromeda Nebula at 2 million light years. The Magellanic Clouds are a different type of galaxy from the Milky Way and Andromeda: true, they probably have a basic spiral structure, but it is not nearly so prominent. Other galaxies lack an orderly structure, taking an overall elliptical form with their brightness diminishing from the centre outward.

Galaxies also tend to be found in

clusters. Those nearest the Milky Way, for example, form a small team of about 20 members, known as the 'Local Group'. They also vary considerably in size: large galaxies will have a star population ranging from about 10,000 million to more than 100,000 million. By these standards, the Milky Way (with anything between 100,000 million and 250,000 million stars) is one of the largest.

However, Andromeda, our second closest galactic neighbour, is much bigger. With a real diameter of 200,000 light years (the Milky Way's is 80,000 light years), as well as two satellite galaxies, it is undisputed king of the Local Group. It boasts all or most of the various stellar phenomena, including Cepheid stars, young stars in the nucleus, older stars in its spiral arms, compact globular clusters, novae and supernovae. By comparison, the Magellanic Clouds are small indeed, having a diameter of 25,000 light years. These include young clusters of very hot blue stars, and super stars with absolute magnitudes many times greater than the sun.

As well as moving away from its neighbours, the galaxy is rotating. In our own part of the Milky Way, the speed of rotation is about 140 miles per second, so that in its total lifetime the sun has made anything from 20 to 50 circuits; simple arithmetic will demonstrate the vastness of the scale being discussed. This rotation is not uniform like that of a wheel, but the inner parts complete a circuit much faster than the outer parts.

Important discoveries

Much of our recently added knowledge of the Universe has come from the techniques of radio astronomy, through which we can turn an ear into space where the eye cannot reach. Such techniques are, of course, based on advanced aerial systems, such as steerable paraboloids, of which the 250-foot diameter disc at Jodrell Bank and the vast moveable array of the Cambridge astronomers are examples. These, and systems based on large aerial complexes, have been responsible for a number of important discoveries, including the rotation of Mercury, the rotation in the central region of the galaxy and the identification of quasars, or quasi-stellar radio sources.

No look at the Universe, however brief, should ignore these phenomena, if only because their discovery indicates there may be many strange objects in the Universe of which we have yet no inkling. As far as can be inferred, quasars are objects possessing the same mass as galaxies, but much, much smaller in volume; hence they seem to be collapsing under intense gravitational attraction, and at the same time releasing almost inconceivable amounts of energy. It is as if they are the source of minor big bangs, generating energy the equivalent of 100 and more exploding stars.

It is easy enough to pose questions about the Universe but practically impossible to find conclusive answers. Man must be content as an insignificant spectator of the vast cosmic drama around him.

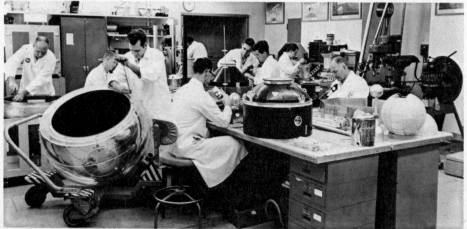

The mystery of cosmic rays

The Earth is under continual bombardment from cosmic rays coming, it is believed, from exploding stars. But how these rays obtain their phenomenal penetrating power and energy is not yet known.

IN 1893 Charles T. R. Wilson, who later became professor of natural philosophy at Cambridge and shared with Arthur Compton the Nobel Prize for physics in 1927, was studying the rings or haloes of coloured light which in hilly districts sometimes surround a shadow thrown on mist lying on slopes below the position of the person shadowed. Such haloes are caused by condensation of water vapour and Wilson wanted to find out the reason for the water vapour condensing.

He carried out a series of experiments to prove that most of the water drops were formed on dust particles in the air, but that a few of them appeared to be formed on electrified molecules, or *ions*. After further experimentation, Wilson concluded that some ions may result from some kind of radiation originating in outer space and penetrating the Earth's atmosphere. About the same time the German chemist Friedrich Giesel was carrying out experiments similar to those of Wilson and reaching the same conclusion.

No one was particularly interested in the Wilson-Giesel experiments until the beginning of the present century when physicists began turning their attention to the properties of X-rays, electrical discharges through gases, and radioactivity. The measuring and detecting instrument used in most of these studies was the gold-leaf electroscope. This consists of two tissue-thin leaves of beaten gold which, when they receive an electric charge repel each other and diverge; the degree of divergence being dependent upon the value of the charge. The electroscope was well insulated, to prevent the charge on its leaves from leaking away.

It was discovered, however, that if the electroscope was placed in the path of X-rays or radiation from a piece of radioactive material, the leaves of the instrument immediately fell together. The reason for this was that the X-rays or other radiation had ionized the air around the electroscope, so allowing the air to conduct the charge away from the leaves.

When there was no radiation to ionize the air around the electroscope, the air acted as a reasonably good insulator, but certainly not as a perfect one. No matter how carefully the leaves were insulated to prevent a charge on them from leaking away, they eventually lost their charge and came together. In other words, some invisible and unknown medium was conducting away the charges on the leaves of the electroscope.

In 1910 Victor Hess, an Austrian physicist, by going up in a balloon armed with a gold-leaf electroscope, proved beyond question that the mysterious radiation was not of terrestrial origin. The greater

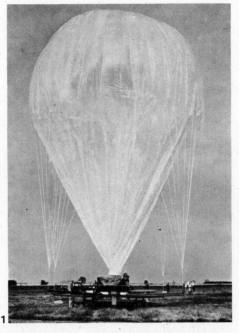

1 This balloon – when launched with its payload of instruments for measuring cosmic radiation – will travel across Britain at an altitude of 23 miles for about six hours.
2 On collision with a nucleus in a photographic emulsion, the high-energy cosmic ray particle causes it to explode into fragments. These produce a track of their own in the emulsion.

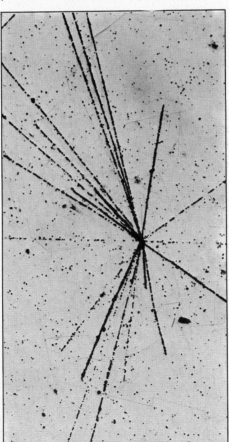

the altitude, the more quickly the gold leaves fell together, showing that radiation intensity increased with height. Subsequent experiments with balloon-borne electroscopes revealed an even more remarkable fact. Radiation intensity progressively increased up to an altitude of 15 miles, then steadily decreased between altitudes of 15 and 25 miles. Above 25 miles the radiation remained constant with altitude.

It was one thing to establish that this radiation did not originate on Earth, but it was much more difficult to establish just from where it came and what caused it. To find the answers to these questions, more and more physicists began studying the mysterious radiation. One of the outstanding of these inquirers was Robert Millikan, professor of physics at the Californian Institute of Technology and winner of the 1923 Nobel prize for physics. It was he who christened the radiation 'cosmic rays'.

By means of various detecting and measuring devices, more and more information was gathered about cosmic rays, although there still remains much to learn. It has been established that cosmic rays are continually pouring down on the Earth and we are all under constant bombardment from them. They have tremendous penetrating power, and will pass through most known materials. They are a form of energy but they behave quite unlike any other form of energy radiation.

Penetrating power

Ordinary light, for example, penetrates only a very short distance into opaque matter. X-rays and radiation generated by nuclear fission have a greater penetrating power, but even the latter can be stopped by a wall of lead and concrete. On the other hand, cosmic rays will to a considerable extent pass through a barrier of lead 6 ft thick and will penetrate to the bottom of mine shafts. Cosmic rays continue their bombardment on the tops of mountains, in the frozen regions of the Arctic and Antarctic and in the hottest parts of the tropics.

During the early period of cosmic-ray research it was thought that all cosmic radiation emanated from the sun. Since intensity of radiation varies with solar flares at least some cosmic rays must originate in the sun, but the vast bulk come from some source outside the solar system: possibly from a super-nova explosion.

Instrumentation carried into the upper atmosphere by balloons and, later by rockets and satellites has provided physicists with a mass of information relative to cosmic rays, though it has as yet failed to answer all the questions. The most important result of modern research is

1

that cosmic rays are particles with initial energies of anything between ten million and billions of millions of electron-volts. An electron-volt is the energy acquired by an electron when accelerated through a voltage difference of one volt. Cosmic-ray radiation energy is, therefore, infinitely greater than anything Man can produce with his most sophisticated equipment for artificially accelerating particles.

All the instruments used to detect and evaluate cosmic rays are based on the rays' ability to produce ions in the matter they penetrate or traverse. The chief instruments operating on this basis are the ionization chamber, the Geiger-Müller tube, cloud and bubble chambers and photographic emulsion.

In the ionization chamber, the current carried by the ions produced by the rays passes between two electrodes through a gas. The ionization chamber, no longer used, is not sufficiently sensitive to detect single particles of radiation. This sensitivity is accomplished by the Geiger-Müller tube. This latter instrument is a highly sophisticated version of the Geiger counter used for the detection of nuclear radiation and measuring its intensity. In the Geiger-Müller tube, single ion pairs, created in the space between a cylindrical electrode and an axial wire, trigger or release a temporary discharge. By the simultaneous employment of a battery of tubes it is possible to trace the trajectories of single cosmic-ray particles through great thicknesses of matter.

Other forms of cosmic-ray instrumentation are cloud and bubble chambers, scintillators and photographic emulsions. Cloud and bubble chambers are particu-

larly valuable in analysing the rays by making their tracks visible through droplets or bubbles formed on the ions created in gases or liquids. Scintillators make use of the light produced by the recombination of ions after the passage of the cosmic particles or by the radiation created by charged particles of high velocity. Another method to give visible proof of the existence of cosmic rays is the exposure of photographic plates coated with highly sensitive emulsion. The presence of the rays is indicated as tracks in the form of silver grains.

Counters and cloud chambers

One of the first tasks towards an understanding of cosmic rays was to establish whether radiation consisted of uncharged particles such as gamma rays, or charged particles, such as electrons and protons. It was at first thought that cosmic rays were all exceptionally energetic gamma rays of very short wave-length, but this was soon disproved. Experiments with counters and cloud chambers showed conclusively that most rays reaching the Earth's surface carried electric charges.

With the development of high-altitude instrumentation, it became possible to distinguish between two kinds of cosmic rays: primary and secondary. Primary rays are those originally coming from outer space and striking the top fringe of the Earth's atmosphere. Secondary rays are produced by the collision of primaries with the atoms in the atmosphere.

Experiments with counters and emulsions taken by rockets and satellites into the higher reaches of the atmosphere and beyond into space have shown that the

primaries consist essentially of bare nuclei of light elements, chiefly hydrogen, and, possibly, a few gamma rays of very high energy. The particles constituting primary rays are very quickly modified by collision with the atomic nuclei present in the atmosphere. The secondary cosmic rays are thus created, and these are composed of many other fundamental particles. Of these the pions (pi-mesons), muons (mu-mesons), photons (gamma rays], and negative and positive electrons are the most important.

Conversion of primary cosmic rays to secondary cosmic rays is generally initiated by a collision between a high-energy proton and the nucleus of one of the atoms constituting the atmosphere. This leads to the production of protons, neutrons and pions, and, much more rarely, some heavy elementary particles: the heavy mesons and hyperons. The pions so produced can be charged or neutral.

Secondary protons and neutrons can initiate further collisions and are then finally slowed down. The charged pions mostly decay in flight, but each produces one much with the same charge and one neutrino. The muons show little reaction with atomic nuclei, but can penetrate great thicknesses of matter. The muons eventually decay into one electron and two neutrinos.

Electrons and photons resulting from these decay processes produce new electrons and photons, and it is repetition of these processes that results in showers of cosmic rays. The intensity of cosmic radiation at sea level varies with latitude, proving beyond doubt that cosmic-ray radiation is charged. Thus rays reaching

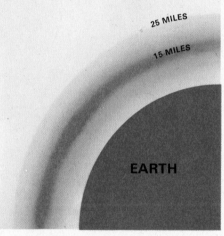

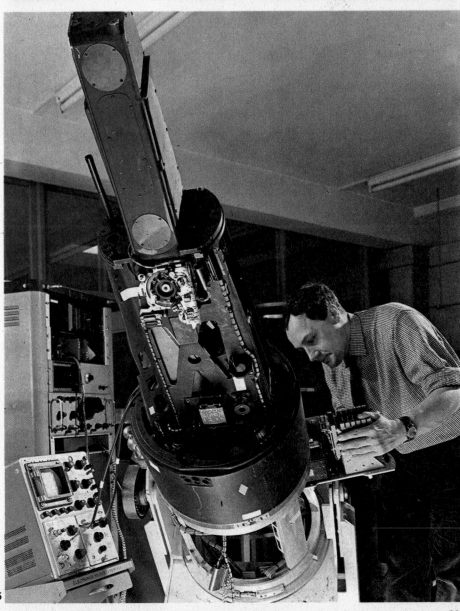

25 MILES

15 MILES

EARTH

1 By measuring cosmic radiation at the Poles, physicists have discovered that the cosmic rays reaching the Earth are much more intense near the Poles than at the Equator. This deflection by the Earth's magnetic field suggests that the cosmic particles are charged.

2 Sir William Crookes (1832–1919) was the first to suggest that cathode rays were fast-moving negatively-charged particles. With his X-ray tube he performed experiments that led to the discovery of the electron.

3 The gold-leaf electroscope was one of the first instruments used to detect cosmic radiation. In 1910 Victor Hess took one up with him in a balloon and showed that the higher he went the more intense was the radiation.

4 Up until 15 miles above the Earth the radiation progressively increases, but then, from 15 to 25 miles it drops steadily. Once above 25 miles the radiation remains constant with altitude right out into space.

5 To make spectroscopic observations of the sun scientists at Britain's Culham Laboratory prepare electronic equipment that can be mounted into the cones of Skylark Rockets. The mounting is easily removable for any adjustments.

the Earth are about one-tenth more intense near the Poles than they are at and near the Equator. This suggests that the rays reaching the Earth near the Equator are deflected away by the Earth's magnetic field. From this it was deduced that as the rays could be deflected by a magnetic field, they must be moving charged particles.

The atmosphere as protection

The Earth is, in effect, a gigantic magnet and by means of its magnetic field it attracts towards it some of the cosmic-radiation particles constantly pouring through space. Primary rays usually penetrate about ten miles through the Earth's atmosphere before being turned into secondary cosmic rays. Primaries are made up of approximately 86 per cent hydrogen nuclei, 13 per cent of helium nuclei, and the remaining one per cent is made up of nuclei of heavier elements, such as calcium, iron, lithium and carbon. Most of the primary particles travel at a speed very near to that of light.

Very few primary cosmic rays penetrate through the Earth's atmosphere to reach the surface of the Earth. Nearly all of them collide with particles in the atmosphere to produce the secondary cosmic rays. Occasionally primaries generate very large showers in the atmosphere so that many millions of particles strike the ground over an area of several acres. One primary can produce a shower of secondaries which zig-zag to earth like forked lightning.

Study of the secondary particles and the curvature of their tracks as revealed by photographic plates enables their energies to be measured. The maximum energies so far registered in any atomic process are those of the primaries responsible for the very large showers of secondaries. Some of these showers have energies of billions of millions of electron-volts.

How do primaries obtain their fantastically high energies? Physicists have not yet found a conclusive solution. Some theories attribute the energy of primaries to the violent star explosions that create super-novas. Another school of thought inclines to the view that the particles' energy is built up and accelerated by their interaction with variable magnetic fields in space, in much the same way that particles are artificially accelerated on Earth by synchrotrons and other types of particle accelerators.

Because primary cosmic rays appear to arrive in equal intensity from all parts of space, it has been suggested that their trajectories undergo strong deviation in the magnetic fields of the galaxy. This has further suggested that the action of the galactic magnetic fields can trap the particles inside the galaxy for millions of years, so rendering cosmic radiation less directional and more intense.

Study of cosmic rays is helping science to make important discoveries in nuclear physics. In their experiments with synchrotrons and other accelerators, physicists are producing particles in an attempt to find out the more minute details about the structure of the nuclei of atoms. Yet with

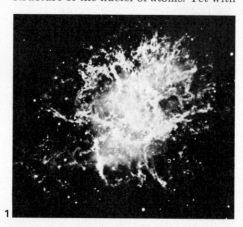

1 The Crab nebula is thought to be one of the sources of cosmic radiation. It is the remnant of a star seen to explode by ancient Chinese astronomers in 1054 A.D.
2 By setting up a series of counters, like this one in operation at a London University field station, the number of cosmic rays striking the Earth can be measured.

cosmic rays there free for the asking, physicists can penetrate far deeper than they can with particles produced in machines costing millions of pounds.

Bearing in mind the unbelievable energy in cosmic rays, it is not surprising that power engineers are tantalized by the possibility of harnessing cosmic energy. As yet, however, they have been unable to provide any practical solution.

It was during investigation into cosmic rays that radiation belts surrounding the Earth were discovered. In 1958 counters were sent up in the satellite Explorer I to measure cosmic-ray intensity and to transmit the results back to Earth. When the signals started coming in from the satellite it was found that an unexpectedly high amount of radiation was overloading the counters and jamming them.

Later satellites, carrying more sophisticated instrumentation, established that the overloading of Explorer I's counters was caused by two radiation belts surrounding the Earth and trapped in space. It was further established that the radiation belts consisted of either protons or electrons trapped in the Earth's magnetic field and spiralling around it.

Electrons, much lighter than protons, are more easily trapped and forced to spiral around the Earth in an outer belt some 12,000 miles above the surface. On the other hand, protons have a greater mass and can, therefore, penetrate deeper into the Earth's magnetic field before they, too, are trapped and forced to spiral in a lower belt about 1,000 miles above the surface. These two radiation traps are the Van Allen Belts, named after James Van Allen, the American physicist in charge of the research teams which discovered them.

The region in space influenced by the Earth's magnetic field is called the magnetosphere. A curious thing about the magnetosphere is that it is not symmetrical like the field surrounding an ordinary bar magnet on Earth. This would seem to be due to variations in the strength of the Earth's magnetic field.

Icarus and Apollo

Flying — a long-held dream of human beings — is now an everyday experience. Men have now gone outside the Earth altogether and flight to the planets is a real possibility.

THE LEGEND of Icarus, whose presumptuous flight ended in disaster, shows that Man has for long dreamed of soaring like a bird. To the mortals confined on the surface of the Earth, the freedom to rise and descend as they please seemed a very desirable goal.

But like so many of Man's cravings, the early attempts at flight came to nothing. During the Middle Ages, brave adventurers trusted their lives to home-made wings in jumping from tall towers.

In the fifteenth century, Leonardo da Vinci designed the first helicopter, the parachute and studied aerodynamics and air resistance. Da Vinci never built any of these devices; he approached them in a theoretical spirit which was yet completely scientific and realistic.

By the seventeenth century Giovanni Borelli had shown, on the bases of anatomy and physiology, that it was impossible for Man to fly by his own muscle power alone. However, this did not deter the many pioneers who were determined to fly. It is interesting to reflect that, although the dream throughout the centuries had been of flight in a 'heavier-than-air' machine, it was the gas envelope, a 'flotation' or lighter-than-air device (first tried in Paris in 1783), which first carried men into the sky. The development and use of balloons fired the imagination of inventors and drove them to new efforts to devise other types of flying machine.

The father of the aeroplane

Prominent among these pioneers (and, indeed, he has been called 'the father of the aeroplane') was Sir George Cayley (1773–1857). Cayley investigated the aerodynamics of the wing, showing how lift could be derived from the forward motion of a wing through the air, and at the same time considered the resultant drag which would operate on that wing. Incidentally, he also foresaw the internal combustion engine, which was eventually to make powered flight possible. Cayley, in fact, built a moderately successful glider on the principles which he expounded and, unlike some early powered aircraft, it was an inherently stable machine.

Cayley's wing was little more than a flat sheet. If a plate is held at an angle of, say, 15 degrees and is propelled through the air with the higher edge leading, the mass of air passing along the lower side will tend to lift the plate. The plate is a simple wing, and the angle between it and the horizontal is referred to as the 'angle of attack' by aerodynamicists.

If the plate is bent into an arc, rather than flat, and the convex side is held uppermost, it is found that the lift, given the same forward speed and angle of attack, is increased. This follows a theorem

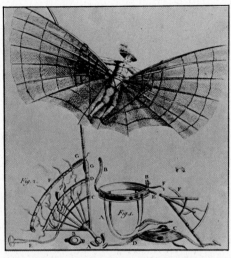

Flying machine with beating wings designed by General Resnier. Constructed about 1788, the machine was tried out (unsuccessfully) at Angoulême, France, in 1801.

in aerodynamics, called Bernoulli's theorem, which states that the pressure of a moving stream of air is inversely proportional to its speed. Thus, as the air passing along the top of the wing has further to travel than that which is on the underside, its speed will be greater, its pressure will be lower, and the difference in air pressure will give lift to the wing.

At a later stage the bent plate wing was refined into a flattened 'tear-drop' shape. This was done initially by enclosing the bottom side of the bent plate wing to make it flat and smooth. This increased the lifting effect of the wing and reduced the air resistance or drag.

But the fully enclosed, aerodynamic wing was a fairly late innovation in the pioneering days of flight. The first men to fly a powered machine successfully, the brothers Orville and Wilbur Wright, used a simple curved wing on their aircraft. In 1900, after a great deal of theoretical study, the Wrights constructed a full-size glider with which they made a number of successful flights. Much of the work which they carried out with this glider was concerned with the problems of stability and control. They knew that, to be practicable, a flying machine would have to be steerable, like a ship, and be able to ascend and descend at the wish of the pilot. They worked out a method whereby their craft could be controlled by twisting the wings, using wires controlled by the pilot.

Work on these gliders and on the theory

Hot-air balloon steered by sails, similar in design to that of the Mongolfier brothers, who made the first balloon ascent in 1783. The model here was used about 1785.

of control continued, until in 1903, on 17 December, Orville Wright made the first true flight at Kittyhawk in the aptly named 'Wright Flyer'. The flight lasted only 12 seconds, but it was enough to demonstrate the capabilities of the machine. Later the 'Wright Flyer' flew for longer periods.

This first practical powered aircraft was a biplane, that is, it had *two sets of wings,* one mounted above the other. The Wright brothers had worked out that the total lift available depended on the length of the wing (the wingspan), but the limitations of the materials available to them severely limited the length which they could construct without the wing bending. Consequently, they made two wings, one above the other, which theoretically would give the same lift as a single wing equal to the combined lengths. This is not strictly true, owing to various aerodynamic factors, notably the aerodynamic interference between the wings, but until the 1950s biplanes were fairly common, as they conferred advantages of lift and manoeuvrability especially in low-speed aircraft.

Driving an aircraft through the atmosphere is a complex business, and it would have been quite impossible without the internal combustion engine, which is very powerful in relation to its weight. This power had to be transferred to the air, and this was done using the propeller or airscrew. Shaped rather like a twisted wing the airscrew is attached at its centre to the driving shaft of the engine, and propels the aircraft by screwing its way through the air as if it were solid matter.

Jet propulsion

Between them, the airscrew, the wing and the internal combustion engine provided most of the essentials for successful flight. But one thing still remained, something which exercised all the Wright brothers' ingenuity – namely the problem of stability. Stability is, briefly, the ability of the aircraft to right itself automatically if its level attitude is upset by, say, a gust of wind. Many early designs lacked this essential quality, and even in the 1930s there were a number of craft which lacked stability under certain conditions of flight.

If a gust of wind were to lift one wing of an aircraft, the aircraft would slip downwards through the air-sideslip. By tilting each wing slightly upwards towards the outward tip, the designer ensures that there is greater aerodynamic lift on the lower of the two wings, so that a level attitude is automatically restored. This tilt of the wings is called the dihedral, and it confers stability in roll.

For about 45 years the type of airscrew used by the Wright brothers to propel their 'Flyer' was universal in aircraft, with modifications and improvements. But during the Second World War, a young Royal Air Force officer, Frank Whittle, devised a new means of propulsion, the jet engine. Basically, this is a chamber with an intake at the front and a nozzle at the rear. The front intake admits air, which is then mixed with fuel (generally kerosene) and ignited. The rapidly expanding gases are

expelled through the rear nozzle and drive the aircraft forward. Contrary to a common but erroneous view, this propulsion is not caused by the ejected gases driving against the air, but by the conservation of momentum as described in Newton's Third Law of Motion – 'To every action there is an equal and opposite reaction.'

This type of jet engine is known as the ram jet or 'stovepipe' jet, the simplest form of jet propulsion. Obviously, such an engine will work efficiently only when the craft is moving with sufficient speed to ensure that the engine is supplied with adequate air. Other versions of the jet have been devised and used with the object of making this method of propulsion more effective at low speeds.

But despite the advent of the jet engine and its wide use in modern aircraft, the propeller still survives although in some cases in a curious and unfamiliar form. The airscrew drags the aircraft along by screwing the air. The helicopter achieves its lift by using an airscrew which works on the same principle but rotates in a horizontal plane. Helicopters can rise into 1

1 The launching of Sputnik 1, the first artificial Earth satellite, in November 1957, marked the opening of the Space Age.

2 A 'walk' in space. U.S. astronaut White is tethered to his Gemini space-craft by a gold-covered lifeline. His pressurized space-suit protects him from the vacuum of space.

3 A U.S. astronaut is put through his paces in a space simulator. This machine enables the conditions of space to be reproduced on Earth. A test of driving ability is in progress.

4 Saturn-Apollo IV rocket after lift-off. This rocket was launched in November 1967 on a course for the moon. The tail of hot gas from the rocket is 300 yards long.

5 The Earth as seen from behind the moon. This remarkable photograph was taken by the U.S. astronauts Anders, Borman, and Lovell during their moon-flight at Christmas 1968.

the air without having to attain a forward speed. In effect, the wing is moving through the air by being rotated, rather than by being driven bodily forward, for an airscrew is in fact merely a rotating wing. However, there would be little point in a helicopter which could only rise and descend: it must also be capable of moving in a forward direction.

This is achieved by tilting the rotor forward, when the effort of the airscrew will then have a horizontal as well as a vertical component. By simply changing the angle of direction of tilt, the speed or rate of climb or even the direction of motion, can be altered. In fact, the versatile helicopter can be made to fly both backwards and sideways at the wish of the pilot. Stability, again, is a problem in a helicopter, but is usually taken care of by a small subsidiary airscrew mounted near the tail and rotating in a vertical plane.

Apart from the helicopter, there are other aircraft which do not require a lengthy accelerating run. These are so-called VTOL (Vertical Take Off and Landing) craft. Although there are a number of different approaches to this problem, all use the same basic principle. During take-off, the jet engines are pointed downwards, so that the thrust lifts the plane off the ground. The engines are then gradually returned to the horizontal position to provide forward thrust, while during landing the procedure is reversed.

While Whittle was experimenting with his jet engine in the early 1940s, scientists in Germany were working on the V2 rockets which were to carry high explosive loads to Britain.

The V2, despite its original purpose as a weapon to terrorize Britain's cities during the war, was in fact a major breakthrough in rocket technology. It was the first large rocket to leave the ground. Weighing 14 tons, and rising to a height of 50 miles, it had an engine which developed more than half a million horse-power. As Dr Werner von Braun realized in developing the rocket, it was the beginning of the Space Age.

In terms of the driving principle, the conservation of momentum, rocket engines are similar to jet engines, but they differ in that the oxygen supply necessary for combustion is contained in the fuel, so that they are capable of working at very high altitudes where there is little or no atmosphere. Rockets are thus ideally suited for high-altitude, high-speed research aircraft, and for launching space-exploration shots.

Vestigial fins

Whilst the jet engine is capable of driving aircraft at up to several times the speed of sound (called by aero engineers Mach 1, which is about 750 miles per hour at sea level), it is completely inadequate to drive a space rocket, which must exceed a speed of 22,500 miles per hour before it can escape from the Earth's gravitation pull. As space rockets operate in an airless space, they cannot rely on aerodynamic lift, and so must depend entirely on the lifting ability of the rocket motor. In the near total vacuum of space, the rocket must be controlled by the reaction propulsion principle. That is, the exhaust gases expelled backward drive the rocket forward. One day this may be done by atomic particles from a nuclear engine.

These conditions determine the design and the launching attitude of space rockets. Instead of having wings, they are long, slim and pencil shaped, and carry only small vestigial fins on the first stage which operates within the Earth's atmosphere. Rockets are also launched from a vertical position, and rise vertically into the air.

Because of the enormous amounts of power required, and because each pound weight of rocket requires fuel to drive it, space rockets are made in several stages. The first, which is used for launching, is used to accelerate the complete vehicle within the Earth's atmosphere. When the fuel in this stage has been exhausted, it drops away and the second stage ignites and takes over propulsion. This process can be repeated as often as necessary, depending on the required range and speed of the rocket. The speeds of each stage are added, giving a final speed equal to the sum of the various velocities.

Outside the Earth's atmosphere and the Earth's gravitational field, there is no resistance to the motion of the rocket, and so fuel can be conserved. The rocket will continue to travel in its initial direction at its original speed until its engines are restarted or until it comes within the gravitational field of another planet.

Rockets of this type use either liquid or solid fuels, each of which has advantages. For most of the space rockets launched in the 1950s and 1960s, liquid hydrogen was the fuel used. A wide range of different fuels are available for specialized purposes.

In space, the range and manoeuvrability of a rocket, and, of course, its ability to make the return journey, depend on an adequate supply of fuel. Conventional fuels are very heavy in relation to the power which they supply, and thus research workers have developed a nuclear power unit. This power pack uses the stream of sub-atomic particles released in a controlled nuclear reaction as the propulsive force. Engines of this type will doubtless supply the driving force for the first rockets to carry men beyond the solar system and into deep space.

For space journeys beyond the solar system, the speeds necessary will be enormous, far beyond those attainable by present-day rockets. This condition is dictated by the vast distances involved in space travel. These distances are so great that they are seldom measured in miles, but rather in light years. A light year is the distance which light will travel in one year. When it is remembered that light has a speed of 186,000 miles per second, the magnitudes involved will be apparent. In fact, it is true to say that, when the first space explorers take off for another galaxy, it will not be they, but their descendants, who will complete the journey. In the meantime we have been privileged to see the start of it all with the journey of the three-man Apollo space-craft round the moon.

1 Kittyhawk, North Carolina, 17 December, 1903. Orville Wright, watched by his brother Wilbur, pilots the 'Wright Flyer' — the first manned heavier-than-air machine to fly.

2 A wartime V2 rocket on its launching pad in Germany. The V2, developed as a terror weapon by Werner von Braun, was a major breakthrough in rocket technology.

What is engineering?

Whether building bridges, designing machines, developing new materials or constructing complex electronic devices, the engineer is a central figure in the progress of a modern industrial society.

ENGINEERS PRODUCE most of Man's material wealth, change the face of the Earth, create every new product of modern technology and increasingly make life easier, safer and more convenient.

According to one wit: 'an engineer does for half a crown what any fool could do for five bob'. And, in the same vein, an aeronautical engineer has been described as 'a man who designs a part weighing eight ounces that any fool could design to weigh a pound'. Clearly, engineers have to be cost conscious, and some have to be weight conscious; almost all of them are deeply concerned with how long things will last, what they will accomplish and with what efficiency; their reliability, safety and a thousand other factors. An engineer's whole life is spent balancing conflicting factors like these, weighing one against another and coming up with the best possible answer. Each of his products is a compromise: it could always be improved if it were made more expensive; it could always be made lighter, if reliability was unimportant, and much cheaper if it did not have to last long. But what are engineers like, and what do they actually do?

Wrong notions about engineers

Most people have a hazy, and usually quite wrong, notion about engineers. It is still common to find engineers thought of as men in boiler suits or overalls, with oily hands holding a monkey wrench. Today's engineer may look like this, but only on Sunday when he (or increasingly, she) is doing jobs about the house. On Monday he puts on a smart suit, or sports jacket and flannels, and goes to work. He may go to an office that looks much like a thousand other offices except for pieces of 'iron-mongery' – pistons, turbine blades, bearings or broken pieces of metal – decorating the desks and filing cabinets. He may go to a drawing office and take his place behind a huge bench or drawing board. He may go 6,000 miles by jet to see something 'on site' or visit a customer. Wherever he goes, within five minutes of his arrival he will probably have his jacket off and be engaged in intense discussion with colleagues, customers, university professors, government officials or suppliers of material or components. Their talk would be unintelligible to most people, but out of it may come a better answer to

a problem, or a possible answer where none existed before.

And this leads to the heart of engineering. All engineers create something out of nothing. Sometimes, as with suitcases or even motor cars, the engineering design is not really a dramatic step into the unknown; the new product is technically very similar to what has been made before, and most of the effort is concerned with making it look attractive while keeping

down the production cost. But other engineers spend their whole lives pushing out the very frontiers of human achievement. Aircraft are made to carry greater loads, trains to go faster, telephone systems to handle more traffic with fewer breakdowns, newspaper presses to work faster at lower cost, home sewing machines to be more versatile yet smaller and neater than before, life-support systems to enable an astronaut or aquanaut to go where Man could not go before, and a bridge to span a great river previously thought unbridgeable. The engineer's creations are of steel, aluminium, glass, glass fibre, plastics, concrete and every other material used by Man. The engineer must have a deep knowledge of these materials and may be skilled at fashioning them; but to do so is not his job. His own tools are a drawing board and notebook, pencils and pens, slide rules, typewriter, test equipment, computer, instruments and dozens of volumes of reference books, catalogues and articles from the technical press.

The oldest category of engineer is the civil engineer. Civil engineers conceived the pyramids of Egypt, the roads of the Roman Empire and the castles and cathedrals of the medieval and Renaissance periods. Today's 'civils' design and oversee the world's motorways, hospitals, airports, harbours, power stations, factories, dams, bridges and tunnels. The civil engineer builds to last; his products will often

1 Developing a method of controlling machine tools by laser beam. Many engineers spend most of their working lives in laboratories developing new applications of technology.
2 The skeleton of the Forth Road Bridge provides a magnificent walkway for construction workers. This was the first bridge for which the suspension cables were spun on site.

outlast his own life many times over. The Egyptian engineers who designed the pyramids 5,000 and more years ago demonstrated an amazing mastery of mathematics, structural stability and precision. The task of hewing, transporting and erecting the stone blocks – in the case of the Great Pyramid, 2,300,000 blocks each weighing $2\frac{1}{2}$ tons – took 100,000 slaves 20 years, working three months each year. No civil engineer today could dream of such a labour force. He deploys machines instead of men, so that the task of constructing the Great Pyramid could now be done by 200 men working for three months in all; but they would need a lot of special equipment. Every big civil engineering job today has to be costed carefully beforehand; woe betide the engineer who tells his employers or clients a project will cost £3,500,000 and proves to have underestimated by £1,000,000! Cost and time are vital, and closely interrelated, and careful analytical techniques and computerized management are essential to control all phases of the design, building, testing and commissioning of all giant schemes in modern civil engineering.

Mechanical engineering

Perhaps the central branch of the profession is mechanical engineering, and a mechanical engineer's degree is the most common type of engineering degree. The mechanical engineer lives in a world of machines which either generate power or consume it. While the civil engineer is concerned with the stability of subsoil, the physical characteristics of rocks, wind loads on structures, the properties of concrete and the cheapest way to tunnel safely through a mountain, the mechanical engineer designs engines, gear wheels, printing presses, wine presses, laundry presses and presses that stamp out the body of a car at one blow. In 1800 the apprentice mechanical engineer soon acquired horny hands from learning how to file pieces of iron to an exact profile. Today's engineer does not make things himself but creates the concept; he does not file iron but might design a system in which a piece of iron plays a part. If he does, he will also develop the production schedule for every part, and today hand filing is obsolete, except in the 'hand finishing' of some cast or forged items made in very small numbers.

A century ago iron was the dominant material for ships, trains, rails, bridges, tunnel linings and a hundred other structures, and for the great machines and machine tools that made them. These were among the most obvious products of the Industrial Revolution, and mechanical engineers trod carefully over new ground every day, making a ship that was larger, a steam engine running faster, a boiler operating at higher pressure and a crane that would lift a greater weight than any before it. They designed conservatively, applying a 'factor of safety' (often justifiably called a 'factor of ignorance') to make everything two, five or 100 times as strong as their calculations showed it had to be. Today engineers have greater understanding of the properties of their materials

under all conditions of stress, temperature, corrosion, fatigue and other adverse influences and are able, with the help of computers, to design heavily loaded components with extreme accuracy so that they need the least amount of material, production time and labour yet will do their job reliably throughout their work-

1 Nuccio Bertone, Italian designer of the Pirana sports car, with the car and his team of craftsmen behind him. One engineer may control the work of many men.
2 Assembling valves in Mullard's Blackburn factory. Mass-production techniques and more efficient ways of producing goods are the concern of a growing number of engineers.

kept on punched cards or tape.

Just one example from the thousands of types of problem encountered in mechanical engineering is the design of a bearing to support a rotating shaft. A century ago the only bearing available was what today is called a plain bearing: the shaft, of iron or steel, is supported by a fixed shell of softer metal, such as brass or a special alloy of lead and bronze, with an intervening film of lubricating oil. Engineers discovered how to make the shaft ride up automatically on the oil film so that, no matter how heavily it was loaded, the fixed and moving metal surfaces could never actually touch each other. But by 1900 developments with bicycles and later the first cars had led to ball and roller bearings in which a 'cage' containing perfect metal balls or hardened rollers supported the central shaft with very little friction, thus opening the way to more efficient machines running at higher speeds. Today ball, roller and tapered roller bearings have been developed to support heavy loads at extremely high speeds with total reliability, while in recent years completely new forms of 'gas bearing' have appeared in which the shaft is supported by a thick film of air or other gas passing through under pressure. Other more efficient bearings are sure to be invented by mechanical engineers in the future.

Theory and practice

Bearing design, like the whole of engineering, requires a knowledge of the basic laws of physics, metallurgy and either hydrodynamics or aerodynamics; and the engineer must combine this theory with a hard practical appreciation of the job in hand. He designs every new type of bearing in great detail so that when the first example is made it unfailingly fulfils the performance required of it; and, if it is to be made by the million, its design must provide for the cheapest possible mass production with the fewest 'rejects'. Test bearings are made in the metals that will

ing life. Even 15 years ago mechanical engineering meant armies of designers, stressmen, calculators, analysts and mathematicians laboriously working out the correct figures and writing them in volumes of design and production books to be kept as a record. Today the computer does the arithmetic and the records are

1 Engineers wearing surgical gowns and caps swarm over the uncompleted shell of the Apollo lunar module, in which astronauts will go to the moon. Contamination of space must be avoided.
2 A Swiss watch-maker, a highly skilled engineer, at work on a watch. Many engineers work in highly specialized fields, requiring a great deal of practical experience and knowledge.
3 A young engineer in training. Engineering students are given wide practical experience in handling machinery as well as rigorous mathematical training to equip them for their work.

be used in production and also in transparent plastics or polarized glass so that the patterns of strain when in use can be rendered visible. Every eventuality must be allowed for – the need for the different parts of the bearing and its housing to expand by different amounts over the whole range of temperatures that might possibly be encountered, the probability that some bearings will at some time be overloaded or overspeeded, the pros and cons of making the whole assembly in the form of separate halves each of which could continue to run should the other half fail (to give what is called 'fail safe' design), the need to inspect and perhaps remove the installed bearing with least difficulty, the need to prevent chips or parts of a failed bearing from causing further damage – all these and many other considerations must be taken into full account and weighed against each other. And when the bearing is in production the engineer may help in preparing the technical manuals and servicing instructions, while special 'service engineers' may go out on visits to customers.

1 Many thousands of engineers work on the design side of the profession. Here a designer climbs on to the table to mark out a curve on a plan of an engineering part.
2 Super-clean conditions are essential in some types of precision engineering. In this case, the

What applies to bearings also applies to a million other engineering items. The same principles and techniques are used in every case, according to the end product that is wanted. For example, a valve controlling a Freon circuit in a home refrigerator poses few design problems apart from the fact that it must be profitably sold at about sixpence; but the valve doing the same job in a manned spacecraft must never fail even under the most severe environmental conditions, and the fact that it may in consequence cost thousands of dollars is less important.

Other branches of engineering

What about the other branches of engineering? There are many hundreds, and new fields are opening up all the time as scientific discoveries find their way into useful industry. One big and long-established branch is electrical engineering, but these engineers do not merely perpetuate old designs. Far from it: every electrical engineer is engaged in making things newer and better, from exotic 'superconducting' distribution systems operat-

engineer is assembling a gyroscope at the British Aircraft Corporation factory.
3 Overhauling one of the vast turbines at London's Fulham power station. The design of these large components poses many challenges for engineers, not always solved successfully.

ing near to absolute zero temperature to designing multi-core ribbon cables suited to service in the turret of an army tank. The newer breed of electronic engineers are even more diverse, and an increasing number of them spend their time creating circuits so small that they cannot be seen except under a microscope.

There are aeronautical engineers, marine engineers, railway engineers, vehicle engineers, pneumatic and hydraulic engineers, mining engineers, acoustic engineers, and yet newer varieties. Nuclear engineers bring cheaper power, as well as many new techniques in medicine and industry. Communications engineers are improving telephones and radio and may before long give us 'picturephones' worn like a wristwatch. Environmental engineers not only ensure that modern buildings have comfortable lighting, temperature, humidity and noise level but also design equipment for people to work well at the bottom of the ocean or on the moon. Ocean engineers design equipment and develop techniques for exploring the Earth's oceans and reaping whatever harvest of marine life or minerals may be economically possible. In doing so they parallel the modern agricultural engineers whose aim is to revolutionize an ancient science and double, treble or multiply by ten the world's annual production of food for an 'exploding' population. A very new species are the medical engineers – half-electronics specialists and half-doctors. And perhaps the fastest growing family of all are those concerned with complex dynamic systems. One group of these are the computer, control and cybernetic engineers who design computers, automated measuring and control devices and all kinds of operating systems which involve 'feedback loops' which may include human beings as operators.

There are never enough engineers, except perhaps in the Soviet Union where it is one of the most exalted professions for both men and women. In Britain, as I remarked earlier, people who are not engineers tend to look down on anybody who is. But this is not the case in the United States, Germany or Japan, or in any other of the swiftly growing, technology-based nations.

Bridging the world

Bridges and dams, pyramids and skyscrapers, tunnels and fly-overs, all are produced by the labour of construction engineers. Their proud boast that they 'shape the world' has more than a grain of truth in it.

NO ONE who has seen the Tennessee Valley irrigation scheme, the polders which the Dutch have reclaimed from the sea, the Aswan high dam on the Nile or the Simplon Tunnel under the snow-capped Alps can fail to be awestruck by the sheer scale of these projects. Beside them, the achievements of aero or electrical engineering, while still technically outstanding, pale into insignificance in terms of spectacle. The construction engineer takes over where geology left off; he uses the natural features of the Earth for the benefit of men, and he specializes in overcoming the obstacles which nature has created. If a mountain range is in the way, he will span it with roads, viaducts and causeways, or he will drive a tunnel through it; an impassable river or gorge presents little problem, as the many beautiful bridges throughout the world testify. If a city or farmland needs water, the civil engineer will construct massive dams to store it and tunnels to carry it to its destination, even though the distance involved may be hundred of miles. During the last 700 years Dutch engineers have performed what is perhaps the most remarkable construction engineering feat of all – reclaiming 1½ million acres of land from the sea bed, more than two-fifths of their whole country.

But construction engineering, although today it uses highly advanced planning and engineering techniques, is by far the oldest branch of engineering. The pyramids, the Roman aqueducts, Stonehenge, the standing statues on Easter Island and the causeways of Mexico City are monuments to the skill and persistence of early

1 The world's largest prefabricated concrete span is the Medway Bridge, in Kent, on the M2 motorway. The 1,300-yard bridge was built by the cantilever method, and is seen nearing completion.
2 At 1,107 feet, the John Hancock Building, Chicago, is only 143 feet shorter than the Empire State building. This view shows the steel lattice which forms the building's frame.
3 A tunnelling machine in operation during the construction of London's Victoria underground railway line. Modern tunnelling machines do much of the heavy work previously done by men.

constructors. Even today, the methods which were used to build these structures are unknown to us, erected as they were in an age which lacked modern mechanical aids.

It is to the Romans, the inveterate builders of bridges and aqueducts, that we owe the invention of one of the basic materials of modern construction – concrete. Not only did the Romans use it to bind blocks of stone, but they also erected buildings entirely of concrete, an art which was lost with the decline of the empire and was not redeveloped until many centuries had passed.

Despite the variety of work undertaken in construction engineering, it depends almost entirely on two structural materials – concrete and steel. There are few structures of the twentieth century which do not employ one or other, or generally both, of these materials. In fact, one of the greatest advances in civil engineering has been the use of these materials in a composite structure known as reinforced concrete.

Concrete itself, although it is immensely strong when used as a pillar, breaks comparatively easily when subjected to a bending load. Engineers describe this by saying that concrete is strong in compression, but weak in tension. When concrete is used as a pillar to support a weight, it is in compression and serves its purpose well. If, however, a concrete beam is supported at the ends on pillars, and a load is applied to it, the beam will tend to bow downwards. The top of the

beam will tend to shorten in length (it is in compression) while the bottom will tend to lengthen (it is in tension), and, unless it is particularly massive, the beam will give way. Obviously this is a severe drawback, because even when concrete is used as a vertical pillar, say in the structure of a bridge, it will still be subjected to side loads from the wind which will put it in tension. The result of this is that simple concrete structures have to be made very large to support these loads, and very often a large part of this unwanted mass is there to merely support the weight of the concrete itself.

But if the lower side of the beam could in some way be strengthened with a material which is strong in tension, this problem would be overcome. Not only could the weight of the beam be reduced, but the appearance of the structure would be slimmer and more gracious. Ordinary reinforced concrete is made by embedding steel rods in the concrete beam or slab while it is being cast. Firstly, a wooden mould, generally called shuttering, is set up. The steel rods are then placed in position and the mixture of cement, sand and stones, in the correct proportions, is poured into the mould. Various methods are used to ensure that the concrete adheres firmly to the steel, including shaping the steel surface, but more often the rods are allowed to corrode in the open air to provide the necessary grip. Since its introduction in France in the early nineteenth century, reinforced concrete has taken over many of the functions which were once the province of ordinary concrete, stone and cast iron, and has made possible structures which would at best have been uneconomic before.

However, ordinary reinforced concrete does have a number of drawbacks. The concrete surrounding the reinforcing rods contributes very little to the total strength of the beam; it does little more than enclose the reinforcement. Thus the beam will still be more massive than the load requires.

Prestressed concrete

This drawback can largely be overcome by a technique known as prestressing, which can be carried out in two ways. The first method employs steel cables in addition to the normal reinforcement. The cables are put in tension by applying a pull at both ends, and the concrete beam or slab is cast round them in the normal way. When the concrete has set, the tension is released. The forces thus set up in the cables tend to make the beam curve like a bow. When the beam is then put in position, the applied loads will merely serve to reduce this bowing effect, so that the strength of the beam under load is immense. The stresses imposed on the reinforcing cables are calculated so that they will be larger than any load which will be applied to the beam.

Another method of increasing the tensile strength of a beam is by post-tensioning. Here, the beam is cast with holes or channels passing through it. After the concrete has set, the cables, or tendons, are threaded through the channels and are then tensioned by hydraulic jacks and anchored at the ends of the beam.

Steel is used in tensioning concrete because of its great strength under tension. It is used alone in many structures, especially bridges, but it has the great drawback that it rusts when exposed to the elements. Since this would lead to serious weakening of the structure, steel bridges, such as the Forth Bridge in Scotland and the Golden Gate Bridge in San Francisco, require an army of more maintenance men to paint them.

Apart from the materials of construction engineering, there are a number of basic types of structure which recur again and again, particularly in bridge building. One of these, the arch, is a means by which a span made of materials such as brick and stone, with low tensional strengths, can support quite heavy loads. A load applied vertically to the top of an arch is transmitted to the stones forming it as compression loads, and the limitation on the load-carrying capacity of bridges built on this principle is usually the strength of the foundations.

For many centuries bridge and viaduct builders used the arch in all major structures. It is seen at its finest in Roman

1 The Pont du Gard at Nîmes, Provence, was built in 19 B C by Marcus Agrippa. The aqueduct carried water 155 feet above a valley to the prosperous Roman city of Nemausus.

2 Stonehenge, on bleak Salisbury Plain, Wiltshire, is one of the oldest civil engineering works in Britain – and still one of the most impressive. Some stones were brought from west Wales.

aqueducts such as the spectacular three-tiered Pont du Gard.

Although at first sight the resemblance is not obvious, the retaining walls of dams are curved for exactly the same reason as the arch is used in bridges. The mass of water pressing against the outside of the curve sets up almost purely compressive forces within the wall. When one looks around, one can see many applications of the arch principle: doorways, brick-lined railway tunnels and the vaulting of cathedrals and churches are good examples. Bridges are the most obvious examples of the construction engineer's work, and many of them are both beautiful and spectacular. Basically, there are four types which are used by the engineer according to circumstances. Termed the beam, arch, suspension and cantilever types, they can usually be easily identified although sometimes a bridge will be seen which is a hybrid, or mixture of different types.

Simplest of all is the beam, which works on the principle of a plank over a stream, surely the simplest of all bridges. For short spans this type of bridge is economical and easy to build, but where long distances are involved intermediate supports must be provided unless the beam which carries the deck (load-carrying surface) is not to be unduly heavy and

1 The Maya Pyramid and Temple of the Magician at Uxmal, Mexico, is only one of the many huge edifices built by pre-Columbian civilizations in Central America.

2 The arch of the Hoover Dam on the Boulder River on the border of Arizona and Nevada is one of the highest in the world. The pressure of the water tends to maintain the arch.

3 Wells Cathedral, Somerset. Much of the civil engineering effort of medieval builders went into the construction of religious buildings, combining function and beauty.

4 Tower Bridge has retractable leaves to allow shipping into the Pool of London. The leaves are steam operated, and give an opening 250 feet wide.

A modern cathedral under construction in Liverpool. This building makes use of prestressed concrete spars to achieve an unusual and attractive design.

expensive. Opening bridges across canals and narrow rivers are normally made on the beam principle, although a steel lattice-work forms the side of the bridge to give added stiffness.

In arch construction, before either iron or prestressed concrete were available, the bricks or stones forming the arch were built on a temporary wooden frame-work – falsework – which was removed after the keystone, the stone at the apex of the arch, was put in position. The arch then 'settled' and was ready to have the roadway built over it. This method is still used when concrete is employed, but iron, steel and prestressed concrete have made it possible to build the arch and then suspend the deck of the bridge below it. This often improves the appearance of a long bridge as well as allowing the engineer to vary the height of the deck to suit the elevation of the approach roads.

This latter type of bridge obviously does not have the load applied above the arch, but the weight of traffic is imposed from below by the cables suspending the deck. However, the stresses in the arch are the same. An excellent example of this type of bridge is the Sydney Harbour bridge in Australia, whose high, clear, wide span allows large ocean-going liners to pass underneath.

For wide spans where it is undesirable to have too many intermediate supports, cantilever or suspension bridges are usually chosen. In cantilever construction, two supporting pillars or piers are constructed in the river or ravine. These are located so that the distance between them is about half the total completed span. Construction then proceeds by building outwards in both directions from each pier. During this work, the weight of the deck on each side of the pier balances, so that only compressive loads (apart

The giant scoops of this 7,600-ton excavator can move more than 200,000 tons of earth in one day. Such machinery cheapens considerably many big construction projects.

from wind loads) are imposed on the piers.

In suspension bridges, the piers which support the structure are built a good deal higher than the final height of the deck, and again are located some way from the ends of the span. Steel cable is then suspended from the piers to anchorage points on firm ground and also between the piers, where it forms a curve known as a catenary. Round this pilot cable is spun a series of others making up an immensely strong cable with multiple strands. There are two such cables and the load-bearing deck is finally suspended beneath them by a series of vertical cables.

Building the piers for a bridge, no matter what its final form may be, is a very difficult operation in its own right. Frequently the piers have their foundations under water in the bed of a river or estuary. So that the work can be done in comparatively dry conditions, the engineers either construct a temporary

dam or sink a caisson or diving bell within which the work can be carried out.

Modern tunnelling depends to a large extent on a device invented by the great engineer Marc Isambard Brunel (1769–1849). This is a combined tunnel excavator and shield known as a drum digger, which supports the tunnel while at the same time digging out the clay or sand. It allows progressive lining of the tunnel and prevents dangerous roof falls. But while the drum digger is very useful in soft strata, when rock is encountered the tunnellers must resort to explosives. A special technique using concentric rings of explosive charges fired in sequence has simplified this difficult work, although progress is still slow.

Because of the time factor in rock tunnelling, engineers insist on a highly detailed geological survey of the proposed site before work begins. It is often possible to avoid rock by altering the course of the tunnel slightly. Whereas 40 or 50 years ago engineers would drive a tunnel under comparatively small hills, the development of really powerful earth-moving machinery in the 1950s led to another method which can be used when the depth involved is not too great and when the surface is not built on. This is the cut and cover method, which means scooping out a huge trough, lining it, putting a roof on, and replacing the soil. Modern machinery makes this an economic alternative to tunnelling in a large number of cases.

Construction and environment

A hazard which was recognized only in the late 1950s is that large structures may modify their environment to such a degree that actual damage can be caused either to the structures themselves or to existing structures in the vicinity. Good examples of this are the high winds and turbulence caused by tall buildings and the disturbance of tide patterns by man-made harbours. While the engineer may design a tall building for existing wind loads, he may find that his structure will have to deal with much greater loads caused by its very presence. Conditions like this are called 'mini-climates', and although once again computers are being used to give adequate warning of such conditions, it is still good engineering practice to over-design, just in case.

As in many other fields, the computer has transformed design procedures in construction engineering. In bridges, dams, tunnels and harbours the variables encountered are so complex that manual mathematical analysis is out of the question. Using a computer, however, it is possible to take all variables into account, with the result that structures are both stronger and much less wasteful of time and materials.

In the end, though, the success of a project comes down to the experience and skill of the man on the job, the site agent. The motto of engineers used to be: 'If it looks right it probably is right.' To this the construction engineer could add the motto of the old Roman builders: 'Build to endure.'

The road-builders

Road-building is almost as old as human society, closely linked both with conquest and trade. But the modern demand for good, fast motor-roads poses serious problems for builders and designers.

SINCE THE DAWN of recorded history the building of roads has been a prominent human activity. Necessary for trade and for the development of contact between communities, they have played a formative part in the progress of civilization.

In an age when we are accustomed to regard roads as essential for civilization, it is difficult for us to imagine a society which does not depend on roads for its transport. But primitive Man must have relied largely on tracks and blazed trails which would not now be dignified by the name of roads. The road-builder's task in those days no doubt largely comprised of blazing trails round obstacles and clearing paths which could be recognized by others. Preparation of the surface and actual road-building came later.

The societies of the Tigris and Euphrates valleys, which flourished about 3000 BC, are known to have had a widespread system of metalled roads, many of them surfaced with bitumen, a substance which has only in relatively recent times been 'rediscovered' for road surfacing in the West.

But perhaps the most tireless road-builders were the Romans, whose construction was closely tied up with the exploitation of their military conquests. Many Roman roads are still admired as notable feats of civil engineering, and in its heyday the Roman road system spanned Europe, Asia Minor and a large part of North Africa with straight, efficient, fast roads. The engineers of the Roman roads were the Legions, which frequently made use of local pressed labour to build the

roads which were constructed of whatever materials were locally available. The most favoured road surface was stone flags, but where these were not available, as in forested areas, the Romans would make ingenious use of tree-trunks instead. Marshy areas presented serious problems, particularly as these were often used as hide-outs for recalcitrant tribes. In the Fens, for example, the Romans tried at first to build a road across the marshes by filling in the marsh with stones. The stones were swallowed up, but it was found that the road could still be built on the basis of tree-trunks used as a floating platform for the road surface. Remains of such roads still exist in some areas.

After the decay of the Roman Empire, road-building fell into a long period of disuse and the ancient arts were largely lost. Even during the medieval period, European states were content to rely largely on the old Roman system for their transport, and not unnaturally the system became worn through constant use. Chronicles of the period are full of complaints about the bad state of the roads, many of them little better than mud tracks, dusty in summer and impassable in winter, which served as the main highways of the country.

One of the features of the Roman roads was that they were linked to an efficient system of horse transport, served by staging stations along the route. A rider could change horses regularly along the road and arrive much faster at his destination than would otherwise be possible. This type of system was retained by the Arabs, who set up caravanserai along the main trade routes in their dominions. The medieval economy, with its self-sufficient peasant units, relied less on good roads and trade than the Romans, who were mainly concerned with speeding the flow of tribute to Rome and maintaining their grip on the scattered outposts of their empire. It was not until the beginning of the modern era, therefore, with the spread of trade and the development of mercantile relations on a scale embracing whole nations and continents that the need for

1 The art of the pavier lies in cutting the cobble-stones so that they fit together to form fan-like patterns. Although labour costs are high, the results are very durable.
2 A Roman road at Mamhilad, Monmouthshire. Even in this remote outpost of the Roman Empire, roads were carefully paved and provided with gutters for drainage.
3 The overhead section of the M4 London–South Wales motorway during construction. More than 35,000 tons of pre-stressed concrete were required to build the mile-long flyover.

good roads again became pressing and agitation about the state of the roads began to gather force.

The passing of the Turnpike Act marks the first significant step in Britain to improve the roads. The first Act of this type was passed in 1663, and its application was extended to the whole country in 1767. The levying of tolls, despite wild abuses, made it possible to find money to improve certain sections of road and led to the development of more enlightened methods of road-making. The same type of development occurred in France after the revolution, when the road system of the country, previously the product of the hated *corvée* system, of forced peasant labour, was changed radically under Napoleon, and the foundations of the present road network laid.

But the turnpike system in Britain rapidly became a medium for the worst type of abuses, and very little of the money collected from passers-by was actually applied to improving the roads. The abolition of the turnpikes, carried out progressively from the beginning of the nineteenth century, made it possible to build more convenient and less expensive roads.

Two men figure pre-eminently in the early period of modern road-building. Thomas Telford, a shepherd's son from Eskdale, Yorkshire, became a prominent road engineer after he had carried out surveying and other road-making com-

missions for the county of Shropshire. He soon became nationally known for his application of scientific principles to road construction.

An even more important influence was that of the Scot, John Loudon McAdam. McAdam was in many ways the founder of modern scientific road-making, and the first to realize that roads had to be designed so that the wear caused by the passage of vehicles would assist rather than destroy the development of the road surface. He argued that a surface composed of small stones and dust would become compacted by wheeled traffic and that the foundation of a good road should be made by exploiting the natural elasticity of the sub-soil.

Water-bound roads

McAdam's method, using crushed stones, made it possible for the first time to make roads of adequate quality fairly cheaply with local materials and labour. This type of road is known as a water-bound road, because the force holding together the surface of the road is the surface tension of water on the small stones and dust of which the road is composed.

Until the beginning of this century, when the demands of motor transport began to make themselves felt, a combination of the methods devised by Telford and McAdam was generally used in the construction of roads. Foundations would

be prepared according to the rules put forward by Telford, who favoured laying down a layer of large stones about seven inches deep and filling the spaces between them with smaller stones. Other ways of providing a foundation include the laying down of *hardcore* and the provision of a concrete slab.

Having laid the foundations, larger stones would be broken to provide a surface layer of material which would be raked together with the stone dust and watered. The cohesion provided by watering the stones provided the means that held the road together. The iron wheels used in the period would crush the broken stone still smaller and the weather could be relied on to keep the stones moist most of the year.

This method of road-building was no doubt adequate for the period and for the type of traffic which was then common, but the advent of the motor-car spelt the end of this type of road except in a few isolated country areas. Fast, wheeled traffic tends to break up the surface of such a road and to scatter the small surface stones.

The fault lay not so much with the method of construction as with the use of water to bind the road together. Other means of binding were therefore sought, and a return was made to bituminous materials which were used by the ancient Babylonians to surface their roads. By the time the question of new surfacing

1

2

3

1 The Kingston by-pass, a dual-carriageway development on the outskirts of London, represents a partially successful attempt to speed traffic flow into and out of the capital.

2 The asphalt lake in Trinidad, West Indies, supplies a considerable proportion of the world's asphalt requirement. Other sources are the Val de Travers, Savoy, and coal-tar residues.

3 A rock-crushing machine being operated by British army engineers in Aden, provides gravel for road-making. Historically, many roads have been built for military purposes.

4 The German autobahn system of fast motorways linking industrial and commercial centres is widely copied by other countries. Despite high initial costs, such roads cut transport overheads.

5 Laying tarmac on the road surface of the Severn Bridge, in Britain. The tarmac mixture is carefully calculated to give good conditions for car tyres to grip the road surface.

materials became a pressing necessity bitumen could be obtained in large quantities and fairly cheaply as a by-product of the refining of coal-tar. Other sources were found in various parts of the world, such as the Val de Travers in Savoy, where there are bitumen-containing rocks, and Trinidad, where there is a large natural outcrop of asphalt, a mixture of pitch and small pebbles.

Other types of surfacing were also tried, and for a time there was a fashion for wood blocks. It was found that creosoted blocks of reasonably soft wood laid in sand with the grain vertical, made a fairly durable surface for traffic. In many town centres, these wood blocks are still the basis for many of the streets, although most of them are covered with bitumen to prevent the slipping which was their main

disadvantage in wet weather.

Another type of surface which was also popular for a period was what is known as *sett paving*. This is based on the principle of the cobblestones found in many old towns, although the cobbles are far more regular and carefully shaped. Unless the setts are carefully laid, however, they become worn rather rapidly and create a noisy surface. They also tend to give a very bumpy ride when worn. On the continent of Europe, sett paving is used much more extensively than in Britain or the United States, and various forms of synthetic blocks are used. Many of the mountain passes in Switzerland and Germany are paved in this way.

One of the many objections at present to sett paving is its high initial cost. The blocks must be laid by hand, and high labour costs make this a big initial outlay, although the upkeep of sett paving, when well laid, is low.

Despite various roads of this type, the great majority of modern roads make use of bituminous materials for surfacing. They have the great advantage that they can be laid relatively easily, that they cost less than stone surfaces and that they can relatively easily be renewed when the surface becomes worn.

But bitumen or asphalt by itself is insufficient to make a road. Foundations must be laid to take the weight of the traffic and spread it as evenly as possible over the width of the road. On a well-designed road, the weight of the traffic is borne not only by the portion of the road directly underneath the wheels of the vehicle, but by a considerable part of the underlying foundations. In modern use, there are generally two types of foundation.

Hardcore is frequently used, consisting of materials such as bricks from demolished buildings, pieces of broken concrete and the like. It is generally laid over a bed of cinders or some similar material to discourage water from rising into the foundations and undermining the road. On top of the hardcore may be laid a more regular course of stones and the whole covered with a layer of asphalt or with a mixture of gravel and tar. A road of this sort must be rolled a number of times to ensure that the foundations are tightly packed and that the tarred surface is smoothly laid over them. This method is widely used for medium roads that do not have to bear continuous heavy traffic.

For roads like the motorways, more elaborate and expensive methods have to be used. The foundations may be built up of one or more layers of concrete, perhaps laid on a foundation of hardcore. The concrete will probably be reinforced with steel mesh, to provide a resilient basis for traffic flowing over it. Much of the building work on such roads is carried out with specially designed concrete-laying and tarring machinery.

The advent of this machinery has taken much of the backbreaking drudgery out of road-building. Many of the roads of the last century, and of most of this century, were built by vast gangs of labourers working with pick and shovel. Much of the work has now been mechanized and the gangs of 'navvies' replaced increasingly by massive earth-moving machinery and road-laying and rolling machines.

The growth of traffic over the past 50 years has meant that much more attention now has to be given to planning the road network as a whole than was formerly the case. Roads in the past were often laid down almost haphazardly along the lines of century-old tracks. This, perhaps, and not Chesterton's 'rolling English drunkard' was responsible for the meandering lines of many of the old roads. The tendency is now for new roads to be planned so that the traffic can travel rapidly from place to place in the greatest safety.

Road design

Modern road design has to take into account not only the need to make the roads safe but the likely pattern of future road use. Roads have to be designed with the needs of future motorists in mind. The task of the road-designer is a highly complex one, and since road-building also involves vast expenditures of public money, mistakes are hard to correct.

But the design of roads extends not only to the overall view of the needs and requirements of motorists. The road-designer must take into account also such details as the provision of a suitable surface for the high-speed motorist. A great deal of research in recent years has concentrated on making safer surfaces for tyres to grip better and to prevent skidding and 'planing' when there is water on the road. Many surfaces which are perfectly adequate for traffic moving at low or medium speeds in good weather become dangerous when used at high speed in adverse conditions.

Road signs have also to be designed so that they can easily be read, service stations sited where they will be most convenient for the driver, and many other aspects of the design have to be integrated to make a good road. The trend towards motorways, restricted to motor traffic and with fast lanes, isolated from the rest of the road system, has in many ways made this task easier, as it enables the road to be designed as a whole rather than as several separate sections.

Because roads need to cross country and to penetrate sometimes into areas of natural beauty, the road must also be carefully landscaped to conform with the lie of the land and not to obtrude on the view. This can be done, but is often relegated to a low priority.

Road-building is an important part of the modern world. Like sewers, water-supply systems and hospitals, roads are a public necessity and good roads should enhance rather than retard this need. The complex relationship between the road, the road user and the vehicle needs to be better understood if we are to have roads which will become lasting monuments to our civilization rather than merely regrettable necessities.

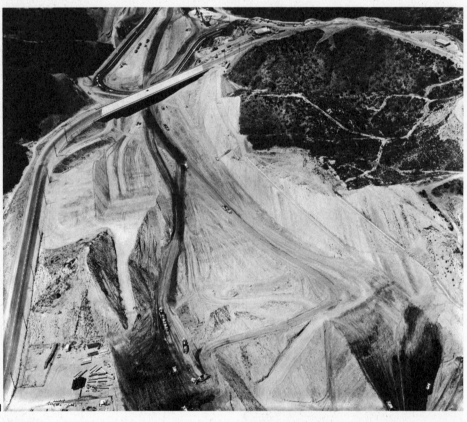

1 A huge scar on the earth marks the site of construction of California's San Diego Freeway. Road-building sometimes involves the remoulding of mountain contours.

2 Prefabricated steel sections being lowered into place on the Frankfurt–Kassel autobahn, Germany. The portable steel slabs form a serviceable surface while the road is under repair.

The car makers

The motor-car, which everyone takes so much for granted, is in reality an engineering marvel with a long history. Modern car manufacture makes use of the latest techniques of automation and mass production.

CARS HAVE DEVELOPED from carts and carriages which, through the centuries, had been drawn by animals. In Europe the horse was most common and the first cars were known as horseless carriages. What needed invention was not the carriage but the engine to drive it.

As well as being a great artist, Leonardo da Vinci (1452–1519) was also a fertile inventor and devised a self-propelling carriage driven by a large spring. This carriage could not be realized in practice at the time, but was notable for its geared mechanism which compensated for the different speeds of rotation of the driving wheels when going round curves. We now call this the differential gear.

James Watt (1736–1819) had started work on the development of high-speed steam engines by 1760 and a horseless carriage driven by a steam engine ran in 1769. The real birth date of the modern car, however, was probably 1886 when a light-weight internal combustion engine designed by Karl Benz was fitted to Daimler's first motor bicycle.

The internal combustion engine, far and away the most usual form of car propulsion today, did not have a runaway victory over other forms of propulsion until well into the twentieth century. Steam and

electricity were both serious rivals. At the turn of the century an electric car held the speed record at 65·62 mph, while seven years later, in 1906, a Stanley steam car won the world speed record with a top speed of 127·38 mph, a truly remarkable achievement. Even today the internal combustion engine still has its rivals for certain applications.

With the increasing availability of engines came a long process of innovation and, with it, a continuous and accelerating process of applying new technologies and, indeed, science to the design and manufacture of cars. By 1910 Britain, France, Italy, Germany and the United States were all producing cars, and the motoring age had really begun.

In the early days car manufacturers were not interested in bodywork. The building of carriages was a craft occupation best left to craftsmen who knew their jobs. The car manufacturer made the engine and transmission and built the complete chassis on which a body, built

by a specialist firm, could be fitted. Today almost all cars are of unitary construction in which the bodywork and the chassis are in one piece.

The greatest single influence on car design was mass production. In 1914 at Dearborn, Michigan, Henry Ford introduced a moving belt on which the component parts of Ford Model T chassis were assembled. Each worker had his own modest assembly job to do as the car moved slowly past. The bodies were built on another conveyor and the two major components, chassis and body, met at the gates of the factory and were joined together into a complete car. By 1915, using this original assembly technique, Ford had already completed his millionth car. Ten years later his factories were still turning out the Model T and had built up production to a rate of nearly 10,000 vehicles a day. In these ten years, however, technical developments elsewhere had overtaken the Model T and the record production run had to cease. The Model T

1 The gas-turbine car is a fairly recent innovation. The world's first, called Jet I, was built by Rover in 1950. Shown here is the later BRM-Rover mark II gas-turbine racing car.
2 The first petrol-driven motor-car. Built by Karl Benz in 1886, this chain-driven three-wheeler laid the basis for the advanced vehicles we know and use today.
3 The body deck at Ford's Highland Park factory, Detroit, in 1914. Ford's was the first motor firm in the world to make use of the conveyor-belt system for mass producing its cars.

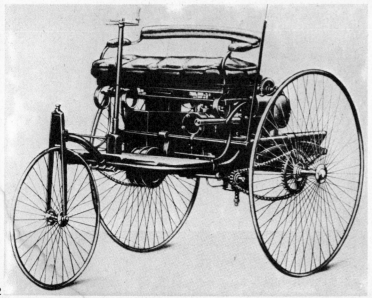

had become a very old-fashioned motor car.

While the mass producers of the 1920s and 1930s were meeting the needs of the mass of motorists there were still plenty of creative designers who, in the smaller companies, were forcing the pace of technological advance.

The basic components of a car are its frame, either chassis and body or all-in-one, its suspension system, braking system, steering, and the engine and transmission. All have been continuously improved throughout the years but even in the case of very specialist designs, such as racing cars, every one of the basic components is subject to some compromise in design.

A decision on the positioning of the engine would appear to be quite simple to make. And, indeed, it was on the earliest cars. The obvious thing was to position the engine at the rear with a chain transmission to the rear axle. Coaches were high and there was plenty of room beneath to store the small single- or twin-cylinder low-powered unit of the day. But with the introduction of large multi-cylinder engines and a need to lower the bodywork for greater stability, a new position was needed, and ahead of the driver seemed best. Unfortunately it was not possible at the time to solve economically the mechanical problem of driving the steerable front wheels and so the drive was still taken to the rear wheels, first by long chains but soon by the Cardan shaft, named after the Italian inventor Cardano who devised it as early as the sixteenth century. This special type of shaft, with spline and universal joints, is needed because the engine has to be sprung relative to the wheels.

Rear-mounted engines

The front-mounted engine, however convenient for access and for its cooling system with the radiator facing into the wind, was not the cheapest or necessarily the best position. The rear-mounted engine was to re-enter the popularity race because it dispensed with the Cardan shaft and could be built as a unit complete with drive and rear suspension. It also allows the car a flat floor. The siting of the engine is not only a matter of economics but also affects handling of the car because of the way the weight is distributed. Ideally, the engine should be beneath the floor in a central position with drive to all four wheels. The drive would be hydraulic in which the fluid flow can be reversed to provide smooth and powerful braking.

The conventional reciprocating engine in which a piston moves up and down in a cylinder followed the pattern set by James Watt in his steam engines. The difference essentially is that in the internal combustion engine instead of steam, the fuel, in the form of an explosive mixture, is sucked into the cylinder, compressed, and then ignited, the resultant explosion forcing the piston down in the cylinder and, through the connecting rod and crankshaft, converting the linear motion of the piston into rotary motion.

Although the principle has been main-

1 Production of a modern mass-produced car involves years of planning and development before the first model rolls off the production line. Here Ford technicians examine a mock-up Capri.
2 Protecting an unfinished Ford Capri against rusting. The car body is dipped mechanically as a unit into a large vat containing a red protective paint.
3 Modern car designs undergo extensive testing under extreme conditions. Here a prototype of the Ford Capri is being rigorously tested in the arctic weather of northern Finland.
4 Part of a modern production line at the Ford factory in Halewood. This machine, called a multiwelder, joins together several sections of the cars' bodies in a single controlled operation.
5 The chassis of a battery-driven electrical car shows its attractive simplicity. Despite the obvious advantages, however, such as lack of exhaust gas, there are still development problems.

tained, modern engines are vastly different from those of the early pioneering days. Weight, for example, is important and the technologists and engineers had to devise methods of improving performance without adding to the weight of the engine. One way of doing this is to increase the speed of rotation and, whereas the early engines had running speeds as slow as 100–500 r.p.m., many of the smaller modern engines run at 5,000 r.p.m. To achieve this took the combined energies not only of general engineers but also metallurgists, chemists and other experts. New alloys had to be developed for engine parts; valve gear and carburation had to be improved; and fuels and oils of better quality had to be developed.

The reciprocating internal combustion engine will be hard to displace as the most commonly used power unit, but two challengers are already on the scene. First is an old invention called the rotary piston engine. Quite clearly it would be a big improvement if the reciprocating motion of the piston could be a rotary motion. Although the rotary principle had been used for years in pumps it was found that to reverse the process and use the force of combustion to do work demanded an unrealizable degree of hermetic sealing.

Felix Wankel, an engineer who has specialized in pressure-tight sealing, has now solved the problem and, in conjunction with the German firm N.S.U., has developed the first practical rotary piston engine. Its advantages are compactness, low weight and, because it only contains rotary parts, smoother and quieter running.

The second development is the gas-turbine engine, which has already been used in racing cars and is now finding applications in heavy goods vehicles. This engine, originally developed for use in aircraft by Frank Whittle, uses expansion

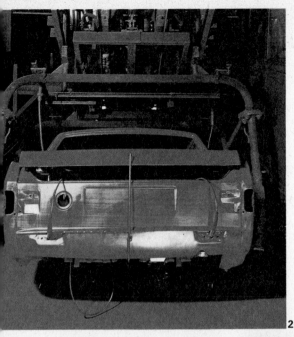

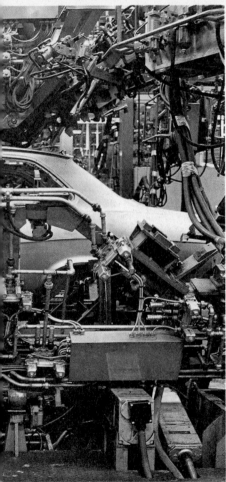

of gases caused by combustion to be expanded across a turbine to convert the chemical energy of liquid fuel into mechanical energy. It has no reciprocating parts and therefore has great smoothness of operation, but it needs an elaborate control system and is not as immediately responsive to control as piston engines.

Along with engine developments from the earliest days has been a parallel development in suspension systems and springing. Even with horse-drawn carriages it was found necessary to isolate the body from the axles carrying the wheels if frequent breakages were to be avoided. The problem is one of absorbing road shocks, and the ideal, from the point of view of comfort, is that the vehicle body should 'float' steadily on an even keel whatever road irregularities or dynamic forces from wind, acceleration or braking encountered.

One of the great inventions was unquestionably the pneumatic tyre invented for the bicycle by John Boyd Dunlop in 1887. It is basically an air spring contained in an elastic rubber container which also constitutes the running surface. In addition to the tyre, which can only absorb minor shocks, it is necessary to have springing and shock absorbers. Springs store shock energy when compressed and release it again in returning to their normal shape. If a car had only springs a hard shock would lead to a long-lasting vibration and give a very bouncy ride. If, however, we can make the shock energy harmless by absorbing it in some way a much smoother ride is obtained. The shock absorber takes the energy from the spring and disperses it in heat rather than back through the spring in mechanical energy.

For many years the most popular type of shock absorber has been the hydraulic type in which a piston with a number of

1 The 1969 model Brabham formula 3 car makes its debut at Brands Hatch. The two aerofoil 'wings' – one over the tail and the other over the nose – act as stabilizers to keep the car on the road at speed.
2 A Dunlop technician demonstrates the dangers of worn tyres. Despite the 800-pound load, the smooth tyre floats on the thin water film and stays still while the drum moves at 60 mph.

tiny holes in it is moved against oil pressure. To absorb a shock the oil is forced through the holes and heat, generated by molecular friction, is dissipated to the surrounding air through the metal casing of the absorber.

The first cars had very indifferent springing and shock absorption, but developments have been rapid both in materials and the way in which they have been applied. The first springs were of the leaf type and were a carry-over from the old coaching days. They are still used in some cars but have been modernized by the use of better steel. Coil springs are also extensively used as they take up little room, and torsion springs are used where there is insufficient vertical height for coils.

The feature of the hydropneumatic system is that a detector unit controls the amount of hydraulic fluid in each cylinder to keep the car, whatever the load, at a constant height above ground. The driver has a manual override and can, if he wishes, actually lift the car to give greater ground clearance, a useful facility for travel over rough terrain. If the adjustment is set for maximum ground clearance and a block is put under one side of the car and the lever is then set for the lowest level, the wheels on that side will rise off the ground automatically, thus dispensing with the need for a jack for wheel changing.

The first cars, like the carriages before them, had brake blocks which could be applied externally to the rim of the wheels. Rising speeds soon called for more efficient means of stopping quickly, and the internal expansion brake has proved the most economical and effective general solution. The brake is used to dissipate, in

the form of heat, the kinetic energy of the moving vehicle and bring it to a standstill.

The internal expanding brake came into general use in the 1920s and consists of two or sometimes three brake 'shoes' faced with a compound with good frictional properties which press outwards against the rim of a shallow drum attached to the wheel. The heat generated by friction is conducted to the air through the outer rim of the brake drum. The first brakes were operated by a cam action controlled by levers or cables. All modern systems are hydraulically operated through a small cylinder with two opposed pistons which, under hydraulic pressure, move the shoes outwards into contact with the drum.

Disc brakes are old in principle but are only now finding favour with car designers. They consist of a flat disc and the braking action is achieved by caliper pads which grip the periphery of the disc when the brake is applied. By careful design, disc brakes can be made to brake more evenly than internal expansion types, and brake 'fade' is less of a problem. Disc brakes are not very suitable for use in

parking so it is common to have internal expansion brakes at the rear and discs at the front. This is another example of compromise in car design.

Although cars have developed comparatively slowly to their present state of development over a period of some 60 years, this does not mean that intensive effort is not put into improving design. However, each new move forward becomes increasingly difficult and costly. Science has given us new materials for detailed improvement. No car is produced today, for example, without plastic fittings and some plastic furnishing. Some cars have complete bodies built from glass fibre. But while striving for perfection the designer is hampered always by the need for compromise, not least being consideration of whether it can be sold at a competitive price and if it can be mass produced efficiently.

The Ford *Capri,* announced in February 1969, is a typical new car with old features. The engines are common to other Ford models and so is the gearbox. The engine is forward mounted and the rear wheels are driven. Disc brakes are fitted forward and drums at the rear. And yet Ford's investment to make the car amounted to £20 million when tooling as well as research and design costs were included.

The car of the future

If there is a revolution to come in car design what may we look for? Technology has already taken care of many of the chores of driving. The automatic gear box on the more expensive models has dispensed with the need for changing gear, and power-assisted brakes and steering are already commonplace.

We may yet see a return to steam propulsion and, almost certainly, the scientists will crack the problem of electric traction, the development of which is still hampered by the weight of batteries. The fuel cell, once thought to be a good solution when fully developed, is not now thought to be suitable for private cars according to one study carried out in the United States in 1968. Instead, a high-temperature alkali-metal battery is suggested.

Whatever the shape of the car of 2000 A D and its type of propulsion, it will be a safer and better car than today's. Car design is no longer a hit and miss affair. Analogue and digital computers, wind tunnels, test tracks, finely equipped laboratories, strain-recording gear and many other aids are available to the designers at the assembly plant. The component suppliers making brakes, tyres, headlamps, carburettors, clutches and a host of other essentials which go to making up the complete car also have their individual research and development programmes. And so do the oil and petrol companies in their search for better fuels and lubricants.

If we now take our cars for granted as essential, economical and trouble-free daily work-horses we not only have to thank the manufacturers but an army of scientists and technologists who have made it all possible.

Power within the pile

Whether in conditions of peace or war, nuclear power will clearly play an increasingly important role in our lives. What are the basic mechanisms of this potent but threatening energy source?

Small· nuclear generators like this one are now widely used in remote weather and research stations and may in future provide electric power for space craft. This model weighs only 1·5 tons.

A general view of the well of the fast reactor at Dounreay nuclear power station in the north of Scotland. The tower in the centre is a machine for removing radioactive fuel elements.

These six precision-machined carbon rods form the outside of a fuel element for the Dragon Reactor at Winfrith. A uranium rod fits inside the six carbon rods, forming the element's core.

ON 2 DECEMBER 1942, a group of British and American physicists were gathered in a large shed that had been set up in the Chicago University squash court. They anxiously watched Professor Enrico Fermi operating switches and levers controlling a strange piece of equipment submerged in a pool of heavy water. The equipment consisted of uranium embedded in a big block of graphite from which projected cadmium rods. The whole was submerged in the heavy water, but the cadmium rods could be moved up and down in the graphite by linkages with the control panel. The complete apparatus was called a pile.

As the minutes ticked away on the laboratory clock, the audience became more and more tense, while Fermi calmly operated the control panel. Then at 3.25, one of the dials on the panel flickered and an instrument began ticking. Professor Fermi relaxed, turned to his audience and smiled; 'Gentlemen,' he said, 'the chain reaction is self-sustaining.' That historic statement announced the birth of the world's first nuclear reactor. It was the culmination of lines of research by physicists of all nationalities which had begun nearly 25 years before when Lord Rutherford, professor of physics at Cambridge University, had first demonstrated the possibility of obtaining energy from the spontaneous disintegration of the atom.

Fermi's demonstration set in motion the vast Manhatten Project which cost £700,000,000 and employed 500,000 people; all dedicated to the production of an atomic

bomb. But his great experiment pointed to the harnessing of atomic energy for peaceful purposes as well as to a nuclear explosion designed for mass destruction.

The difference between an atomic bomb and a reactor for the generation of useful power is that in an atomic bomb the nuclear action is rapid and uncontrolled, whereas in the reactor the nuclear fission releasing atomic energy is slowed down and can be controlled to within fine limits. If neutrons were not controlled in a reactor, which is the heart of an atomic power plant, there would be a devastating explosion, just as there is when an atomic bomb is exploded.

In simple terms, a nuclear reactor is a furnace in which a nuclear fuel such as uranium is 'burned' to produce heat. The heat so produced can then be used to raise steam to drive turbo-generators. Alternatively, the heat from a reactor can be utilized to heat and so expand a gas to power a gas-turbine. The basic distinction between a conventional furnace using solid or liquid fuel, such as coal or oil, and a nuclear reactor is that the latter does not need air to 'burn' its fuel. Moreover, a few pounds of nuclear fuel in a reactor releases as much energy as would the burning of thousands of tons of coal or oil in a conventional furnace.

In 1939 the German physicist, Otto Hahn, showed that when uranium is bombarded with neutrons some of the atoms split into lighter fragments. As some of the mass of the atoms is lost during their break up, some part of each uranium

atom must be converted into energy, according to Einstein's famous equation. One neutron is needed to split an atom, and even that neutron is not lost but will in turn split another uranium atom. This continuous splitting of the uranium atoms sets in motion a chain reaction.

In practice, many of the neutrons fail to split another atom, so that every time a neutron misses its target the chain reaction is weakened – if energy is to be released from nuclear fuel on a large and useful scale, there must be some means whereby the chain reaction becomes self-sustaining. In other words, the reactor must operate in such a manner that enough neutrons reach enough atomic nuclei and split them.

Chain reaction

Fermi established that slower-moving neutrons are more effective in bringing about fission (atom-splitting) than are those travelling at high speed. On the other hand, most of the neutrons released by the disintegration of an atomic nucleus are fast moving. The problem was to slow down fast neutrons to a velocity whereby they would be effective in inducing fission and so maintaining the required chain reaction.

Fermi knew from his own and other physicists' experiments, that the nuclei of graphite, a pure form of carbon, resist absorbing neutrons. In fact the nuclei rebound from the graphite just as a billiard ball rebounds from another ball after a collision. Conversely, there are certain substances which will attract nuclei and absorb them as a sponge absorbs water. By using absorbent nuclei Fermi discovered how to use the properties of different substances to maintain and control the chain reaction in much the same way that the accelerator on a car enables the driver to increase or decrease speed at will simply by pressing or depressing a pedal.

Professor Fermi's solution to the problem was relatively simple. He embedded the uranium fuel in a great mass of graphite. When fission took place the fast neutrons released by disintegration of the uranium atoms richocheted off the graphite, so slowing them down and giving them a better chance of hitting the uranium nuclei. The chain reaction thereby created was prevented from getting out of control by inserting cadmium rods into the graphite.

What happened inside Fermi's pile was that enough neutrons were slowed down to sustain the chain reaction while sufficient were absorbed by the cadmium to prevent the reaction getting out of control. If a pile were built without the cadmium rods there would be an uncontrolled fission reaction and all the energy in the uranium would be released instantly as a violent and devastating explosion. That was exactly what Fermi's pile was meant to demonstrate, and its further development was towards making a pile small enough and light enough to be carried by an aircraft; in other words, all effort was mobilized to producing a bomb.

Nevertheless, the Chicago University demonstration had proved beyond doubt the possibility of harnessing and controlling nuclear fission as a source of power for peaceful use. Although Fermi's pile was crude, its principle is the basis of the nuclear reactors now producing an appreciable amount of the electric power consumed in Britain, the United States and other countries.

Reactor design

Designing a nuclear reactor entails the solving of many difficult and complicated engineering and scientific problems. There must be an efficient source of energy; the chain reaction must be safe and controlled; the reactor must be shielded to prevent dangerous radiation from escaping; and there must be an efficient and economic method of using the nuclear energy for the production of useful power. During the past 25 years these problems have been solved in brilliant fashion and current development is primarily concerned with reducing the size and cost of reactors, adapting new fuels, and designing more efficient ways of utilizing the nuclear energy created by their fission.

Uranium is still the fuel most commonly used in reactors. Naturally occurring uranium is a mixture of various isotopes; that is, it consists of atoms of the same element but of different masses. Uranium-238 accounts for over 90 per cent of uranium in its natural state, while the lighter isotope, uranium-235, makes up less than one per cent. Only uranium-235 can create the chain reaction in a

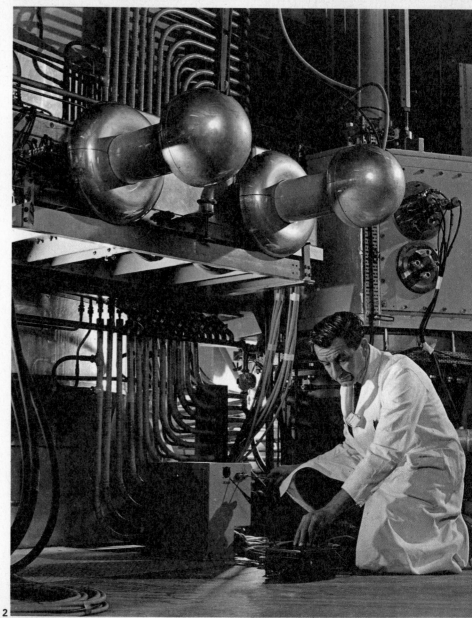

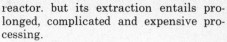

reactor. but its extraction entails prolonged, complicated and expensive processing.

Production of nuclear power would be less complicated and much cheaper if the reactor could use uranium in its natural state. The solution to this problem is to design the reactor in such manner that fission of the uranium-235 takes place and at the same time the unwanted uranium-238 is prevented from interfering with the fission process. The actual fission process is very complex, but it can be stated briefly and simply as follows.

If a piece of uranium is under bombardment by neutrons moving at different speeds, the uranium-235 will absorb the slow-moving neutrons and fission occurs, but the uranium-235 will not be affected by the fast-moving neutrons, which simply pass over it. At the same time the atoms of the uranium-238 disintegrate when bombarded by fast neutrons. Unfortunately only a few fast neutrons reach the uranium-238 so that that isotope is of little use in the pile. Moreover, the uranium-238 has the undesirable property of absorbing slower-moving neutrons without fission taking place. In other words, uranium-238 steals neutrons which otherwise would be useful in bringing about fission in uranium-235 nuclei. But it will not absorb very slow-moving neutrons.

Ideally the reactor would have only very slow neutrons moving about in the pile. The slow-moving neutrons would not be absorbed by the uranium-238 but would keep on circulating until they met uranium-235 nuclei. In practice, however, the neutrons released in the fission reaction travel at very high speeds and are absorbed by the uranium-238 nuclei and so lost to the chain reaction unless slowed down by a moderator.

A moderator is a mass of some material that has the property of slowing down fast neutrons without absorbing them. Amongst the most efficient moderators are carbon, in the form of pure graphite, and deuterium oxide or, as it is commonly called, heavy water. Whatever the moderator used it should be a material with light atoms because a light atom will take away more of the neutrons' energy than a heavy atom when neutrons collide with it. The moderator is mixed in with the uranium metal, so that any fast neutrons released by the fission of the uranium-235 or uranium-238 are slowed down by the heavier isotope and easily absorbed by the lighter one.

Selection of the current moderator ensures an adequate supply of neutrons which move at the right speed to maintain the chain reaction. It is no less important to design the pile so that neutrons are not lost through its walls. If the pile were too small, a high percentage of the neutrons would be lost. For that reason the pile must be made larger than the *critical size* (the size necessary to induce fission). Provided the pile is big enough and the right moderator is used, the reactor is said to be *critical,* and a chain reaction can be initiated and maintained.

Describing a reactor as being critical is somewhat confusing to the layman. What

1 Two artificial elements – nobelium and lawrencium – were first created in this ten-million-volt electron accelerator at Berkeley, California.
2 Very high voltages are used in this cyclotron to accelerate atomic particles to very high speeds. These high-voltage terminals are located close to the point where the high-speed particles leave the cyclotron.
3 Technicians at this atomic power station stand on a bridge over the deep water surrounding the reactor. The blue glow is given off by the water when it is bombarded with neutrons.
4 The chamber with which the English physicist, James Chadwick, discovered the neutron in 1932. The original nuclear research was done on a shoestring, until its military uses became apparent.
5 This specially designed furnace is used for preparing uranium pellets to be used in nuclear reactors. Contamination must be carefully avoided.

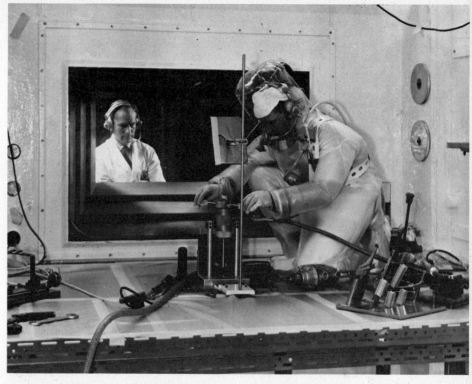

Special protective clothing is needed to work in highly radioactive areas. The plastic suit, inflated under positive pressure, prevents this worker from coming into contact with 'hot' material.

it actually means is that the pile is larger than its critical size so that there are more neutrons in it than are needed to maintain a controlled reaction.

The basic design problem with all reactors is to keep the neutrons under control at all times so that the pile remains critical throughout its lifetime. One of the components that does this is the *reflector* – a shield completely surrounding the pile which reflects back to the fuel those neutrons which otherwise might leak out. As reflectors must scatter but not absorb neutrons, they are generally made from the same materials as moderators.

Reactor fuel or fissionable material is usually in the form of rods, the uranium or other fuel material being alloyed with other metals to increase its strength and heat-conductivity and to minimize corrosion. In what are classed as *homogeneous reactors,* the fuel is uniformly distributed in a fluid to form a slurry.

Because of the intense heat generated by nuclear fission, the reactor temperature must be kept under control by a substance called a *coolant.* Common coolants are carbon dioxide gas, liquid sodium, helium, certain organic liquids and even water. The coolant is pumped through the hot reactor and absorbs a large part of the heat. In power stations this heat is used to raise steam in a boiler. The steam in turn drives turbines linked to electric generators. In some power stations using gas coolants, the hot and expanding gas is used directly to drive turbo-alternators. After serving the boilers or turbines the coolant, whether gas or a liquid, passes through a system of heat exchangers and condensers which reduce its temperature so that it can be pumped back to the reactor to repeat its cooling function.

In fact, it was the necessity for a coolant that led to the development of the nuclear power station. The first reactors were built during the Second World War to make the plutonium used as the explosive in atom bombs. Plutonium is a synthetic element specially manufactured by physicists. It is capable of splitting up easily and so starting a chain reaction.

Plutonium derives from the bombardment of uranium-238 by fast-moving neutrons and is highly fissionable in a reactor using a mixture of uranium-235 and uranium-238. The fissionable material is 'burned' directly, but an even larger amount of fertile uranium can be converted into plutonium fuel. This is the principle of the *breeder reactor* which nuclear engineers believe to be the most promising type for producing atomic power in the future.

The first reactors were built only to provide the explosion element for atom bombs, and the intense heat generated was just so much waste. Heat from one of the experimental reactors built by the United Kingdom Atomic Energy Authority at Harwell had been used to warm laboratories and workshops, but as a general rule reactor heat had been wasted.

Nevertheless, engineers resent useful energy being thrown away, and after various experiments with reactors designed to produce elements for atom bomb material, it was decided to try and convert reactor heat into useful power. The result was Calder Hall in Cumberland, officially opened on 17 October 1956. Calder Hall was the world's first atomic power station. The heat from its reactors was harnessed to drive turbo-alternators which fed electric power into the United Kingdom's national electricity supply network.

Dounreay

In 1955, the United Kingdom Atomic Energy Authority began building the great liquid-cooled reactor at Dounreay, near Thurso, in Scotland. Dounreay is a breeder reactor, and like Calder Hall its chief purpose is the production of nuclear explosives but its liquid sodium and potassium coolant is used to drive turbogenerators.

Experience gained from Calder Hall and Dounreay led to the development and construction of a number of reactors in Britain designed for the production of electric power. These now contribute a substantial proportion of the United Kingdom's electricity needs for heating, light and power.

Building work in progress on an atomic power station near Naples. Such designs have to be tailored to the special requirements of stations running on atomic fuels.

Atoms for peace

Atomic energy, with a vast potential for destruction, can also be used to solve many problems in industry, medicine and engineering previously beyond the scope of conventional methods.

IN 1910 Ernest Rutherford, professor of physics at Manchester University, was conducting a series of experiments to demonstrate the radioactivity of elements and to show that certain elements which are not radioactive can be made so by bombarding them with radioactivity. Amongst Rutherford's pupils was Georg von Hevesy, a Hungarian who later won a Nobel Prize for his work on radioisotope indication.

During one of his experiments, Rutherford showed that if a speck of radioactivated lead is placed in any substance or material traces of its radioactivity persist for some considerable time. That gave the Hungarian student an idea.

Hevesy was, at that time, living in a boarding house run by a 'cheese-paring' landlady who, her boarders suspected, was using scraps of the Sunday joint left on the lodgers' plates to make the stews and pies served throughout the rest of the week. One Sunday the landlady served roast beef for dinner and Hevesy introduced a tiny speck of radioactive lead into a scrap of the meat he left on his plate. Throughout the remainder of the week Hevesy took back to the laboratory samples of all the meat dishes served up. Appropriate tests then proved beyond question that every sample was radioactive and that his landlady was indeed using scrapings from her lodgers' plates.

Trace elements

Hevesy's successful venture into scientific detection had done something more than expose a dishonest landlady: he had given the first practical demonstration of what are now called *trace elements* and suggested one of the most important of the peaceful applications of the atom. This was all the more remarkable because it was achieved long before the release of nuclear energy and the development of atomic power.

Hevesy's trace element was radium D, a radioactive form of lead. Radium is an element which in the course of time turns into another substance, lead. But throughout the centuries that the conversion takes, the lead retains some radioactivity inherited from its radium origin. Radium D is not a particularly good trace element: it is scarce, costly and poisonous. Moreover, when Hevesy used radium D to unmask the mysteries of the boarding-house dinners, very little was known about trace elements. Consequently Hevesy could not develop his meat-scrap experiments into anything of much use in everyday affairs.

Now vast quantities of trace elements or, more, correctly, *isotopes*, can be produced easily and relatively cheaply in reactors. In fact isotope production has

1 A geologist prospecting in the field can use a small but accurate spectroscope to locate the radioisotopes characteristic of the rock sample he is testing. This gives him a knowledge of the likely economic value of the rocks.
2 A gamma-radiograph, shown here testing for faults in the metal hull of a Thames tug, allows on-the-spot detection of cracks and strains in metal parts by passing radiation through them.

become a profitable side-line of nuclear fission for atomic weapons and power. Radioactive isotopes are now produced artificially by bombarding a non-radioactive element in a nuclear pile. Isotopes are produced in this way from carbon, nitrogen, iodine, sodium, phosphorus and hydrogen. Bombarding the element alters its atomic structure by adding or subtracting from it.

Whatever the element from which an isotope is derived, its presence can be detected in any substance into which it has been introduced. A quick and easy method of detection is by photography, but in liquids, and certain semi-solid substances, such as the human body, isotopes move about. In such situations they are best detected by a Geiger counter, which gives a continuous signal while it is trailing the isotope.

A radioactive material sends out a stream of fast particles which detach electrons of any material from their parent atom and so make insulating materials into temporary conductors. The isotope of any particular element emits its own kind of radiation which labels it, rather like the call-sign of a broadcasting station. Instruments can distinguish between all the different isotope call-signs and so immediately identify what kind of isotope they are tracking.

Medicine was one of the first sciences to use isotopes, which have proved to be a wonderfully versatile tool in the treatment and prevention of disease. An example is diagnosis by isotope, which depends upon the fact that the human body, like everything else in the world, is made up of various elements and compounds of elements. These atoms and molecules are in constant motion and contact with each other, and there is a continuous attraction and repulsion going on. In a healthy body, repulsion and attraction follow a pattern, but the pattern alters if some part or organ of the body is diseased or injured.

When an isotope is put into the body, either by injection or in the food, its passage through the body is trailed by the Geiger counter. If all is well, its movement registered by the counter shows no variation in its signals. On the other hand, if there is an irregular signal from the Geiger counter, the doctor knows that there must be something interrupting the healthy rhythm; perhaps a disease or an injury. Using isotopes in this way a disease can be diagnosed before the symptoms are apparent.

By injecting the isotope sodium 24 into a vein, the medical practitioner can measure with great accuracy the rate at which the blood flows through a patient's body. As the isotope travels with the bloodstream, its radiation is registered

on the Geiger counter and the speed at which the blood is flowing through the body recorded. Measuring the speed of the bloodstream with isotopes plays an important part in the prevention of blood-clot formation after an operation.

Money-savers

Isotopes are now saving industrialists and engineers huge amounts of money every year by quickly and cheaply gathering information about things which they suspect may be happening but which they cannot see.

Oil refineries use isotopes to save time and money in the operation of their pipelines, where it is the practice to pump several grades of oil through a single pipeline for filling into separate storage tanks according to quality. At one time lengthy and complicated analyzing and sampling had to be carried out on the oil to decide precisely when the change-over from one storage tank to another should be made. Now, by injecting a suitable isotope into the oil as each grade enters the pipeline, the front of each grade flowing through is effectively labelled.

1 This radio beacon on the Scottish island of Benbecula is powered by an isotope generator, which gives long periods of trouble-free electrical generating, though at a high initial cost.
2 Chromatography is used to separate radio-isotope compounds before packaging them for sale. The method uses the fact that different compounds travel at different speeds down a column of starch-gel.
3 To obtain information on kidney function, a small amount of isotope (iodine 131) is injected into the blood and detectors placed over the heart and kidneys. These measure the radio-activity in each organ.

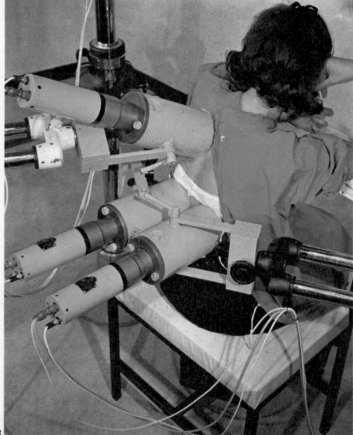

A Geiger counter at the end of the pipe-line immediately indicates when the new grade of oil arrives.

Using isotopes has solved one of the most time-wasting problems in surveying, when it is often necessary to drive marking-pegs into the ground for future reference. If the survey is over farmland, the pegs must be driven several inches below ground level so as not to interfere with ploughing. When the marking-pegs are again required, considerable search and digging are needed to find them. Now surveyors fix into the top of the marking-peg a disc containing an isotope. The presence of the isotope and the peg bearing it can then be detected years later by a Geiger counter – even if the peg is covered by several feet of earth or with thick vegetation.

Paper mills

Many paper mills use isotopes for the automatic testing of paper thickness during manufacture. An isotope is put into the paper pulp and the strength of the radiation received by the Geiger counter indicates the thickness of the paper during its manufacture. The paper passes over the counter which is linked through relays to a brake that automatically stops the machinery if the paper is above or below its predetermined thickness.

Another important application of isotopes is in tracing leaks and their source. An example of this occurred at a large colliery in the north of England, where it was suspected that water might be seeping into the mine from a nearby lake. If so, expensive pumping equipment would have to be installed and extensive structural alterations made to the mine galleries. Before committing themselves to the

expense, the colliery officials threw into the lake a pound of salt containing a sodium isotope. A Geiger counter was then mounted in the mine where the seepage occurred. The counter immediately picked up the isotope's call-sign, proving beyond doubt that water from the lake was filtering into the mine. When a similar problem arose in a mine close to a river, a sodium isotope and a Geiger counter proved that leaks in the roof were not from the river but due to

natural seepage. In that case the mine was able to avoid expenditure on new pumps.

Thread used in the textile industry must have a very thin but even coating of oil before it is woven into cloth. If the oil-coating is not spread evenly along the length of the thread, the fabric woven from it will be faulty and the finished cloth will look patchy when dyed. Until recently, the only method of measuring the amount of oil on the thread was to take the average coating on several

1 The 'target' end of the cyclotron at the Radiochemical Centre, Amersham, Buckinghamshire. Materials placed at the target are converted into isotopes by bombarding with atomic particles.
2 Technicians at a glass furnace can study the convection currents inside the molten glass in the furnace by adding small amounts of radioactive glass and tracing the radioactivity.

inches of it. This rule-by-thumb method gave no guarantee that the thread was evenly coated. Now, however, a minute quantity of isotope-labelled compound called *ethylene dibromide* is added to the oil. The thread is then passed in front of a Geiger counter which registers the oil thickness on every one-hundredth of an inch of thread.

At one time it was thought that foodstuffs could be preserved indefinitely by irradiation, but practical tests proved that although irradiation was more efficient than refrigeration for preventing the bacterial growth that induces decay, the process destroyed flavour and nutrient value. This type of irradiation has, however, been found highly efficient for sterilizing medical and other equipment after it has been packaged.

Bearing in mind the devastation caused by atomic explosions and despite the Test Ban Treaty, engineers have been tantalized by the problem of harnessing atomic explosions for industrial blasting. The Russians are said to have developed a technique of nuclear blasting and used it for cutting channels to divert a river in Siberia. In the United States serious consideration is being given to applying nuclear explosives to irrigation and flood-control projects; for canal, harbour, road and railway construction; for surface mining and for the release of natural gases and petroleum deposits; and for the release of the Earth's internal energy. According to the United States Atomic Energy Authority, 10,000 tons of rock could be blasted by nuclear explosives for a cost of £125,000.

America's first practical project for nuclear blasting, as yet not started, was for cutting a path through the Bristol Mountains in California to take a motorway and a railway. The path will be 300 ft wide and 300 ft deep, and will be blasted from the solid rock by 22 atomic bombs with a total explosive effect of 1·73 megatons. When plans to build a second Panama Canal mature, it is likely that the ditch will be blasted out by nuclear explosives.

Archaeology, the study of the ancient world, is linked with nuclear physics, the latest of sciences, by the technique of radioactive dating. Radioactive dating is the use of radioactive isotopes that occur naturally on the Earth to determine the period of time that has elapsed since certain events took place in the world's history. Radioactive dating is based on the fact that all radioisotopes have a characteristic decay rate, and it is believed that this rate has not changed since the formation of our planet.

Isotope dating

When atoms of a radioactive element decay, atoms of a new element are formed. Consequently, if the rate of decay (half-life) of a specific radioisotope in a given sample of rock, for example, is known, and the resulting amount of the new element can be determined, the age of the sample can be calculated.

Radioisotopes that occur naturally on the Earth and which have proved most useful in geological and archaeological dating are of three main groups: those of long half-life that have been present since the formation of the Earth; those continually produced by the decay of other radioisotopes; and those produced by reactions between cosmic rays and stable isotopes.

The first group of isotopes includes uranium 235, uranium 238, thorium 232, rubidium 87 and potassium 40. These isotopes must have half-lives of thousands of millions of years or they would have decayed away completely since the formation of the Earth. They have been successfully used in establishing rock ages ranging from thousands to millions of years.

The second group contains thorium 230 and radium. Both these are proving invaluable for dating the sediments of the ocean beds.

Carbon 14 and hydrogen 3 appear to have shorter half-lives, for they are continually being produced; a process that balances the loss by decay. Carbon 14 is the most important of the dating isotopes in the third group as it enters into the life cycle of all living matter, but this process is terminated by death. Hence the proportion of carbon 14 to ordinary carbon 12, which is a known constant for living matter, remaining in a sample is a measure of the time that has elapsed since death occurred. Carbon 14 dating can be applied to a wide variety of once living materials, including wood, cloth, parchment, glue and animal, including human, remains. Carbon 14 has made possible very accurate archaeological and geological dating of events within the past 50,000 years.

It was dating with carbon 14 that resulted in the reappraisal of the age of the human skull found at Florisbad, South Africa, in 1932. Using conventional tests, archaeologists had fixed its age at approximately 30,000 years, but carbon 14 analysis showed that the skull must be at least 41,000 years old.

Radioisotopes are used in agricultural research to study plant and animal diseases, to develop better diets for farm animals and to improve strains of food plants. If, for example, a research worker wants to study the uptake of fertilizer by a plant, he puts a small amount of an isotope in the fertilizer and traces its movement through the earth and into the plant.

Maintaining adequate supplies of fresh water for domestic and industrial use is becoming a major problem in many parts of the world. Atomic energy can play a part here, in providing energy for turning sea water into fresh water. Such plants are planned in many arid areas.

1 Another industrial application of radioactivity allows workers in this Doncaster glass factory to measure the level of molten glass in the furnace by detecting radioactivity from a source on the opposite side of the furnace.
2 Tumour growth can be arrested by irradiation.

Apparatus at a Guildford, Surrey, hospital, enables powerful radiation to focus on tissues.
3 A worker at the Radiochemical Centre takes a sample from a pile of gold grains retrieved from radon seeds. The radioactive gas decays fairly rapidly to give the precious metal.

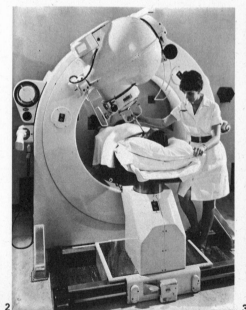

Down to the mines

Mining for coal, metals and precious stones was one of the earliest forms of large-scale industry. Although modern mines are deeper, mechanization is doing away with much of the danger and drudgery.

AMONG THE MANY endearing rags-to-riches stories, one of the most appealing is that of Dick Whittington, the poor boy who rose to fame and fortune through the ownership of a half-starved cat. The tale loses some of its charm, but in compensation becomes credible, when it is realized that the 'cat' or 'catch' refers in reality to a type of ship used to carry coal from Newcastle to London. Whittington was a forerunner of the mine-owners who made vast fortunes from coal in the eighteenth and nineteenth centuries, and even of the few miners who made fortunes in the Alaskan 'gold-rush', and who frequently lost them within months in shanty-town saloons.

But Whittington was by no means the first to benefit from mining, the extraction of useful minerals from the Earth's surface. Ancient civilizations extracted gold, silver and copper for making into decorations and utensils; precious and semi-precious stones were used both in jewellery and as items of barter long before money was in general use; and iron and bronze were used for weapons and body armour.

To most people, mining almost invariably means coal mining; the familiar picture is of dark underground tunnels with men labouring in hard and dangerous conditions to extract the valuable black fuel. Coal was, until comparatively recently, almost a universal fuel and it is in coal mining that almost all modern techniques of location and extraction have been developed.

It is not clear when the organized extraction of underground coal really began. By 1200 AD there were coal pits on the southern shore of the Firth of Forth, near Edinburgh, and in Northumberland. About this time, the importance of coal in trade was increasing rapidly, so that people in all parts of Europe were beginning to dig for the precious mineral, although in a haphazard way.

Early methods

Two methods of mining were in general use: digging pits or burrowing into the side of a hill in search of a seam. Of the two, the first method was the more widespread. But although these coal workings were called pits, they were in fact only relatively shallow holes in the ground. When all the coal had been extracted from the pit, the digger would move off a few yards and dig another, and so on until he reached the end of the seam or the coal became too deep for him to reach.

Much more productive was the technique of hill tunnelling. Here, diggers tunnelled into a hillside until they reached a coal seam, and then excavated horizontal branching tunnels along the coal. These coal quarries often developed into quite complicated systems of passages in which the miners dug the coal by the light of rushes. Despite the fact that mines of this type supplied large quantities of coal as a fuel both for ironworkers and domestic hearths, their yield was severely limited by roof falls which often closed down the workings altogether.

One of the most spectacular of the early mines was that at Culross, in Fife, started by monks and referred to by them as a 'carbonarium'. Although worked by men who had nothing more than primitive wooden and cast-iron tools, this mine had many miles of galleries early in the seventeenth century. One such gallery extended for nearly half a mile out under the sea, and ended in a vertical shaft which emerged on an artificial island. Coal was brought up the shaft to this island, where it was loaded directly on to boats for transport to London and Europe.

The quarrying method used for coal in the early days of the industry was also in common use in the extraction of other minerals, notably tin and gold. In North America, gold was still being mined by this method as recently as the 1930s, although with the addition of modern aids such as pit props and infilling which reduced the risk of roof falls and allowed extraction

A train of heavy trucks loaded up with ore from a chute in the Nkana copper mine near Kitwe, Zambia. The train will take the ore to the foot of the main shaft, for transport to the surface.

Washing for gold in the Australian outback. Ore placed on the chute is washed over 'riffles'. The heavy specks of gold are trapped while the lighter dirt is washed away.

to be more complete. In the seventeenth century, when the supply of minerals readily available near the surface was beginning to run out in Europe, men began to sink shafts in search of deeper deposits. This was at first merely an extension of the old pit method, except that the shafts were sunk deeper, often to a depth of several hundred feet, and the mines were equipped with windlasses for raising coal and miners.

At the bottom of the shaft, in the coal seam, digging took place in every direction, as far as it could go before the roof caved in. From their shape, these pits were known as 'bell' pits, and became common in most European countries. But although bell pits were much more productive than older systems, they were also extremely dangerous. Not only did the roof fall frequently but many miners lost their lives from fire, explosion or simply lack of air. In a coal mine, there are two main causes of explosion: methane, which is found in coal seams, and which is highly explosive when mixed with air, and coal dust, which also forms an explosive mixture with air. In addition, the deeper workings were subject to flooding, and many otherwise suitable coal seams had to be abandoned because there was no convenient method of removing the water.

The development of modern mines depended on the recognition of these problems and the devising of solutions. All deep workings are now designed to make mining as safe and as comfortable as possible, while ensuring that extraction is efficient.

A modern mine

A modern mine is designed around two shafts, known as the upcast and downcast shafts. In the sinking of a mine, work starts by digging one of these shafts towards the mineral deposit. This shaft is usually between ten and 25 feet in diameter, although some mines have elliptical shafts whose larger axis is greater than this. As the digging progresses, the shaft is lined with casing to prevent rock and earth falls and to exclude water which might seep in from the surrounding earth. Progress through the topsoil is usually fairly rapid, but when rock is encountered it used to be necessary to blast a way through, nowadays high-speed rock drills are used.

When the shaft has reached the working level, another similar shaft is sunk nearby. One of these two is termed the downcast shaft, that is, the route by which air is drawn into the workings, while the other is used for extracting stale air and gases. This upcast shaft is also the route by which the extracted mineral reaches the surface, while the downcast shaft is used for taking the miners to and from the workings. As fresh air must be circulated to all parts of the mine, the bottom of the downcast shaft is always the lowest part of any mine. Although the shafts are connected by a tunnel, this is sealed by an air-tight door, so that the air must circulate completely round the mine before being mechanically removed.

In most modern mines, roads or tunnels

1 A derelict coal mine at Tylorstown in the Rhondda Valley, Wales. Large numbers of British coal mines have been abandoned in favour of relatively few highly-mechanized pits.
2 An open-cast copper mine at Chingola, Zambia. Heavy earth-moving equipment makes it possible to extract very large amounts of ore cheaply where it occurs fairly near the surface.
3 A more primitive type of open-cast mining is seen at this West African gold mine. Gold was mined in Alaska and California by similar methods in the early days of the great gold rushes, though most surface gold is almost exhausted.

by wooden supports or props, or filled in with rubble. This method is now used in conjunction with hydraulic pit props and the wastage has been considerably reduced. Generally speaking, during the nineteenth century the 'room and pillar' method was superseded by the 'long-wall' method of working. Tunnels are driven towards the working face, and another tunnel at right angles to these is then cut, exposing a long 'wall' of mineral deposit. As this wall is cut away, props are inserted to support the roof, generally with cantilevered plates which extend as far as the working face. As extraction proceeds, the props are moved forward, along with the conveyor belts which carry the mineral away from the face.

The miner's pick is now giving way rapidly to machinery, although in Europe this has been a recent development; indeed, there was virtually no power coal cutting in Britain until after the Second World War. By contrast, in 1950, 91 per cent of all bituminous coal mined in the United States was extracted mechanically, which accounts for the enormous American output per man-shift.

Mining machines

The simplest type of mechanical aid to mining is the cutter which weakens a coal deposit by gouging out a slit at floor level. Explosives placed in this slit are used to bring the coal down, and a machine pushes the broken coal on to the conveyor belt. This method is closely analogous to the 'shot firing' technique for loosening coal deposits; although the use of explosives can be dangerous in the confines of a mine, it eliminates the need for hewing the coal with picks. Machines which are more nearly automatic in operation fall into two main types: cutters and gougers. One of the most successful of the coal cutters is the Anderson Boves trepanner. Looking rather like a giant power-driven apple-corer, it cuts deep into the coal with a rotating motion. Unlike most other mechanical cutters, it produces a high proportion of large coal, which is still demanded by many users.

Strangely, one of the latest machines to be devised for this work imitates the action of a miner with his pick. Blades resembling pick-heads are mounted on a wheel which rotates horizontally into the seam, cutting and pulling out the coal in one action. Although regarded as an entirely up-to-date machine, this cutter bears a striking resemblance to the Gillot and Copley coal cutter of the mid-nineteenth century.

Mining ploughs were developed principally in the Rühr coalfields in Germany, where the coal is soft and easily worked. These machines are very similar in action to agricultural ploughs with steel blades 'turning' the coal. Coal is brittle, and falls away in pieces, and as many of these ploughs have driving tracks which double as conveyors, the coal is automatically collected by the track and removed from the working face, as they crawl forward along the seam. Although ploughs tend to produce small coal, they are widely used because of their speed. Some will

1 Another view of the Chingola open-cast copper mine. The ore in this region is so rich that it has proved economic to excavate virtually a whole mountain to extract the copper.
2 Drilling for diamonds at a mine in Uganda. The diamond-bearing rock is blasted with explosives and brought to the surface, where it is broken down and searched for the precious stones.
3 A tin dredger in operation near the Jing Jang mine at Kuala Lumpur, Malaysia. The heavy metal-bearing mud on the river bottom is a rich source of tin and of smaller amounts of antimony and other metals.

are driven from the bottom of the shafts along the direction of the mineral-bearing stratum. These roads are in groups of three: the first is a passageway for the miners, the second is for extracting the mineral, while the third is primarily for ventilation. At an early stage in the sinking of a new mine, powerful pumps are installed to extract water from the workings, and the winding machinery at the pithead and the huge air extractor fans are erected.

Three principal methods of deep mining are in use today. By far the oldest of these is the 'room and pillar' method, in which the seam is worked in passages at right angles to each other, with the pillars between the seams being left in position to support the roof. Although a safe method, and in fact the only one which was feasible before pit-props and plates to support the roof were used, this method is very wasteful. As the demand for coal became greater, however, various methods were devised for extracting these pillars. When the 'rooms' were worked out, the pillars were then removed and replaced

327

remove a strip of coal a foot thick, while the faster versions skim from two to six inches in one rapid pass.

During the Second World War, when coal was in urgent demand, mining engineers reverted to a method of extraction similar to that used by early miners. Known as strip or open-cast mining, this technique involves removal of the overlying strata by mechanical diggers, extracting the coal and then replacing the top layers of soil. The coal obtained by this method is generally of poor quality since it lies fairly close to the surface but strip mining lent itself to mechanization using existing earth-moving plant. Even now when deep mines are using highly automated equipment, open-cast mining is still vastly superior in terms of yield per man.

In an age when the machine has taken over most of the dirty, arduous tasks in industry, it seems a little incongruous that men should still have to work in unpleasant and dangerous conditions deep in the Earth. What prospect is there for fully automatic mining? Equipment is already in existence which can detect coal and guide the cutters using gamma-ray detectors. The machine will then cut and load entirely automatically so that it is possible to bring coal to the surface without it being touched by hand. But development of such equipment is still in its comparatively early stages and at present the large amounts of dirt brought out with the coal make the process uneconomic. Mining by water-jet, although it has been used for many years in gold-mining, is now being adopted for extracting many minerals. Jets of high-pressure water are directed at the face, and the force breaks

the mineral down. Although the resulting mud is generally loaded on to conveyors for transport to the surface, the slurry might also be pumped to the surface. Another possibility is that the mineral can be transported using the latest fluid-bed techniques, already used for transport of solid materials on the surface.

But as the demand for solid coal as a fuel diminishes, another more interesting prospect is opened up – underground coking of the coal to produce coal gas and extract the valuable chemicals. Apart from the prospect of completely automatic mining, this process would allow the exploitation of coal deposits which would be uneconomic to work by other means. Although underground coking and gasification has been used from time to time in the United States and Europe, it is used on a large commercial scale in Russia.

Fires are started at the coal face, and a carefully controlled supply of air is pumped

to the burning face, while the gas is drawn off through a second shaft.

World demand for minerals is increasing rapidly every year, and although known reserves are still substantial, there is great interest in the rich deposits which are known to exist in the Antarctic. Previously, these had been considered uneconomic because of their remote situation and the difficulties which would be experienced in exploiting them, but modern technology has made these deposits an attractive proposition to mining interests.

It has also been proposed that an incidental benefit of space exploration will be new sources of mineral wealth on the planets. Whether these will ever in fact be used is a matter of debate. Mining on Earth may have come a long way from the shallow pits of the Middle Ages, but there are few mining engineers who would suggest mining the moon before Earth techniques become fully automated.

1 The interior of a coal mine in India. Despite using a modern coal-cutting machine, the miners have neither boots nor helmets to protect them from falling rock.
2 A diver prospecting for gold in the fast-flowing Chaudiere River, northern Canada. The divers dredge gravel from the river bed and its gold content is analyzed.
3 A woman tungsten miner in Burma uses a crowbar to chip metal-rich rock from outcropping tungsten seams. Tungsten is used to make specially hard steels and in light-bulb filaments.

Energy from underground

Coal and petroleum, despite their different modes of extraction, are both fossil fuels. The by-products of these two great sources of energy are the basis for chemicals, dyestuffs and plastics.

1 Liquefied propane gas, a petroleum by-product, is used in Tokyo, Japan as fuel for taxis. The gas is considerably cheaper than petrol and is said to give longer engine life.
2 Drilling for oil on Zakynthos Island, off the coast of Greece. The oil-field on this island was known to the ancient Greeks, who used asphalt seepages to caulk their ships.

THOUSANDS OF YEARS before a drilling rig darkened the Texan sky, the infant Moses was consigned to the Nile in a basket which, so the Bible tells us, was made comparatively waterproof by caulking with bitumen, mineral oil which seeped through the sands of the Middle East. At about the same time, the natives of Glamorgan, in Wales, were incinerating their dead on pyres fuelled by coal.

From these beginnings, coal and oil have developed to become the primary fuels of civilization, and what is more, are in the twentieth century the source of an enormous range of raw materials which have changed the whole concept of chemical manufacture. It has been said that coal and oil between them provide all the materials necessary to feed, clothe and house us. Although this may, when it was said, have been slightly premature, it

is by no means the wild exaggeration which at first it appears.

Many people think that coal is formed from some type of rock, but its origins lie in the dank tropical forests of the Carboniferous Period, which ended about 270 million years ago. These were not like the present forests, but were rather huge areas covered with giant ferns and club mosses. In the tropical conditions prevailing at the time, these plants grew rapidly. They reached maturity, decayed and finally fell, to be superseded by a new generation. Over many centuries, masses of rotting vegetation, estimated to have reached heights of several hundred feet in places, built up. In time, perhaps due to volcanic action, the forests sank and the sea inundated the land. As the cycle continued, new forests arose on the sea-borne silt, and frequent repetition led to a layered structure of vegetation, silt and sometimes rock thrown up by volcanic action or earthquakes.

Over millions of years the enormous heat and pressure engendered by the overlying rock wrought a change in the masses of rotting vegetation. Like the plants of today, those strange ferns and mosses of the Carboniferous Period were composed almost entirely of carbon, hydrogen and oxygen. Heat and pressure combined to drive off much of the hydrogen and oxygen, so that the proportion of carbon increased.

It is interesting that the deepest layers of coal, subjected as they were to the greatest pressure, and also of greater age than those above, are very rich in carbon compared with layers nearer the surface. In extreme cases, notably in Switzerland, the process has produced pure carbon in the form of graphite. But normally, the coal with the highest carbon content is anthracite, a hard, shiny, almost smokeless fuel. Anthracite contains 94 per cent carbon, but at the other end of the scale, lignite, a young brown coal, contains only about 66 per cent carbon. The youngest form, which is not really coal at all, is peat, used as a fuel in many parts of the world.

Oil formation

Similar accidents of nature brought about the formation of oil, although it is of animal as well as vegetable origin. Millions of years ago when the Earth was mainly covered by water, millions of tiny marine creatures lived and died and left their remains on the bed of the sea. Over the ages these deposits reached great depths and the accumulation, supplemented by plants washed down from the land, formed a thick slimy ooze on the sea bed. Mud brought down by river action mingled with this ooze, and the animals and plants slowly turned into oil and gas. The pressure of the seas eventually turned the mixture into oil-bearing limestone or sandstone, both of which were porous and retained the oil rather as a sponge holds water.

By a fortunate accident, many of these oil-bearing rock formations were later roofed with impervious rock layers which retained the oil. As the Earth dried out, many of these deposits were topped by land formations, but there are still a great many rich oil-fields under the bed of the sea. But whereas pressure and the passage of time has made coal almost entirely carbon, oil still retains its hydrogen and is a mixture of compounds of hydrogen and carbon.

Although oil has been under the Earth for millions of years, it was not until the nineteenth century that it was commercially exploited, much later than coal. People had gathered the oil which seeped to the surface through cracks in the rock cap and a few enterprising men went to the length of digging pits to concentrate the seepage.

In 1859 an American, Willard Drake, drilled the first oil well, which fortunately was a producer, and founded the modern oil industry. This was at Titusville in Pennsylvania, and his discovery led to a tremendous upsurge in drilling in that

The acetic acid plant at British Petroleum's Salt End, Hull, chemical factory. Acetic acid, an important constituent of a number of plastics, can be produced from petroleum.

area of the United States.

By the time Drake struck oil, the Industrial Revolution was well under way, running on coal. And coal was already being processed to yield its chemicals as well as driving the engines of industry. At a very early stage in coal-mining it was noticed that along with the coal occurred a highly explosive gas called methane, which caused a large number of deaths among miners through the use of naked lights in mines. It is by no means certain who first distilled coal to produce coal gas and use it in lighting, but it is recorded that an Englishman, George Dixon, lit one of the rooms in his house with coal gas – an experiment which came to an end with a spectacular explosion.

William Murdock, a Scottish mill-wright's son, was the first to produce gas in commercial quantities at a price less than that of candles – then the normal means of illumination. He constructed gas-making plants for sale to commercial firms, and also designed gas holders. But no history of the development of coal gas is complete without mention of Samuel Clegg, a former pupil of Dalton the famous chemist. To celebrate a visit of foreign royalty to London, he erected an 80-ft-high wooden pavilion illuminated by 10,000 gas jets. As an incidental bonus the spectators had the pleasure of seeing the whole structure burnt to the ground.

Widespread use of gas for heating and lighting depended on the availability of efficient retorts for distilling the coal, and it was in retort design that William Murdock made his greatest contribution. There are now two main types of retort, vertical and horizontal, but the latter is more useful in large plants because it can be loaded and discharged automatically

1 Aerial view of the Salt End chemical plant. Note the storage tanks for liquid and gaseous products in the background and the maze of pipes linking the various processes in the plant.
2 Drilling for natural gas in the North Sea. New areas of exploitation for oil and natural gas are constantly being opened up, though prospecting costs are very high.

by conveyors. These retorts produce gas by heating the coal in the presence of limited quantities of air. The gas is drawn off and passed through chambers which extract ammonia, coal tar, benzole and naphthalene. The residue in the retort is coke, which is itself an excellent fuel.

But the economics of the simple retort depend on a large steady market for coke. While houses were heated by open fires, the disposal of the coke was no problem, but the growth of central heating often makes these large supplies of coke an embarrassment. The coke can be converted to another gas, water gas, by passing steam and air over the red-hot coke. Water

has, however, is of a lower grade than coal gas and must be mixed with methane before being fed into the mains for distribution to consumers.

Large stocks of unsaleable coke are avoided by using the Lurgi process, which has the added advantage of using low-grade coal rather than the expensive and scarce coking coals used in other processes. The plant is run at a pressure of about 25 atmospheres. Coal is heated and a mixture of oxygen and steam passed through it. The high pressure and temperature cause the formation of a mixture of carbon monoxide and methane, which is an excellent fuel. When the gas has been purified, it is ballasted (its density is adjusted) by adding nitrogen and generally some butane. The advantage of the Lurgi process is that it produces gas at high pressure so that it can be fed directly into

the main or into high-pressure storage without pumping. Of the by-products of coal distillation, coal tar is the most important from the economic point of view. Not only is it used for tarring roads, but under distillation it gives more than 200 useful chemicals. An interesting sidelight on one of these products, naphtha, is that in the early nineteenth century Charles Mackintosh used it to dissolve rubber which he then used to waterproof cloth. This was the beginning of the Mackintosh waterproof coat.

To describe the production and use of all the products of coal would take a sizeable book, but some idea of the diversity of products can be gathered from the fact that coal is the source of detergents, explosives, drugs, dyes, alcohol, paints, lubricants, motor spirit and even food. The last two are of particular interest, as many countries have no oil deposits of their own and many more countries suffer from lack of adequate food. Research into the manufacture of motor spirit started as early as 1916, but the cost was always too high in comparison with petrol produced by distillation of crude oil. In the late 1960s, however, a team of German chemists succeeded in bringing the price down almost to that of naturally produced spirit.

Food from coal

Protein research has shown that it should be possible to synthesize simple proteins from the elements in coal, and indeed this has been done. Although these do not taste like normal food, they have become a valuable animal feeding supplement, and further research should produce something which is acceptable as a supplement to the diets of the poorer countries. These proteins are also produced from oil, and since many of the oil-rich areas of the world are desperately short of food, it will be possible for the people to eat part of their crude-oil output.

But whereas there has always been a large demand for coal, when the first barrels of oil were filled there was only a tiny market. Most of the oil produced was used for caulking ships, oil lamps or for lubrication. However, during the eighteenth century many research workers investigated the possibilities of constructing an internal combustion engine, one that would dispense with the cumbersome boiler of the steam engine. Oil came to the market at just the right time, and road transport now runs almost entirely on oil products.

Oil as it comes from the well is not immediately usable, however. It is a mixture of light and heavy hydrocarbons – light oils, like petrol and paraffin; heavy oils, such as those used for lubrication, and heavy waxes. Before oil can be put to its many uses, these parts or fractions must be separated. This is done in a fractionating column, which employs the different temperatures at which these fractions

331

vaporize to separate them.

In the fractionating tower, the temperature is carefully controlled so that at each level, at a temperature slightly below the vaporizing temperature of each main fraction, there is a collecting tray. The hot crude-oil vapour is brought in through the bottom of the column, and the heaviest fraction condenses at the bottom. The remainder progresses upwards, as the temperature is still too hot for it to condense. But the temperature decreases further up the tower and one by one the fractions condense to liquids and are tapped off and stored. At a refinery many fractionating towers may be in use simultaneously and the crude oil is pumped in sequence through them to give complete separation.

This, however, is only one of the stages involved in oil refining, although it is the most important one. But simple fractional distillation gives an abnormally high proportion of heavy hydrocarbons – the lubricating oils and waxes – much more in fact than can be absorbed by the market. The main need is for the lighter oils for motor and aviation spirit.

The invention of the catalytic cracker (cat cracker) enabled the refineries to redress this balance between supply and demand. In a catalytic cracker, the heavy hydrocarbons are broken down by chemical action to give light hydrocarbons. In this way, the output of motor spirit per barrel of crude oil can be doubled.

During the Second World War a new industry, the petro-chemical industry, grew up on oil. Because of the war, the rubber plantations of the Far East were not available to British and American industry. As the armies needed rubber desperately for tyres and components in many pieces of equipment, scientists developed synthetic rubbers from oil. This was only a beginning, but by 1960 synthetic rubbers were being used in the majority of tyres, and the type of rubber used was adjusted to suit the tyre characteristics required.

Synthetic rubber production, however, is only a small corner in this vast industry. Like coal, oil is the starting point for an amazing variety of products, drugs, paints, explosives and plastics among them. The last is perhaps the most important of all and the development of plastic materials has transformed twentieth-century living. Although natural gas is often found in the same deposits as oil, there is also a demand for gas made from oil by a further cracking process; this is used in many countries to supplement supplies of coal gas or natural gas.

The coal and oil industries grew out of the demand of people for power – power to keep themselves warm, power to drive their transport, and power to generate electricity. But as the primary purpose of these fuels was warmth, it is interesting to note that scientists have established that the carbon dioxide produced by burning these fuels is forming a layer over the Earth and raising the atmospheric temperature slightly but steadily each year. Coal and oil are extremely versatile commodities; but it is the final comment on their utility that, even after they have been used, and the waste products have escaped from the control of Man, they should still be, accidentally, producing the end result for which they were first used.

1 Naphthalene, used for moth-balls and the basis for other chemicals, is a by-product of the coking process. Here solid naphthalene, separated from oven gases, is drilled out of a tank.
2 A technician at a South Wales plastics factory produces a test moulding by spraying resin and glass fibre on to a mould. The resin, a thermoplastic, is formed from petroleum by-products.
3 Horizontal 'retorts' like these were at one time used to produce gas in Britain's major cities. A great deal of coal was used to produce coal gas for domestic and industrial use.

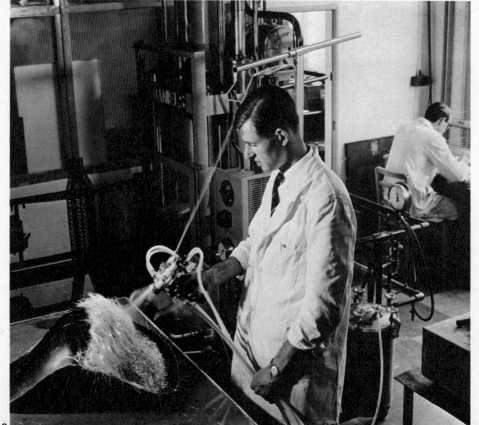

Inside the engine

Millions of years ago, Nature began storing energy by creating petroleum from the decaying remains of prehistoric life. Now this energy is being tapped and put to work in heat engines.

THE CAPACITY for doing work is usually called energy, and heat is a form of energy which has (like any other form of energy) the capacity of being partially transformed into useful mechanical work. This is the basis of the First Law of Thermodynamics. Since it was established, Man has consciously tried to use this knowledge to find ways of turning this capacity of heat to his advantage. An obvious way that this can be done is to build machines which can effect the transformation of heat energy into work. Machines which do this are called 'heat' or 'thermal' engines.

The Second Law of Thermodynamics says there is a definite limit to the amount of mechanical energy which can be obtained from a given amount of heat energy; within this limitation engineers have always tried to make their engines more efficient – to convert the heat generated into the maximum possible amount of mechanical work. When we say that an engine has 40 per cent thermal efficiency we mean that it converts 40 per cent of the available energy into mechanical work of one kind or another – the other 60 per cent being wasted. However, size and running costs are other practical considerations which the engineer must consider and very often they are as important, if not more so, than thermal efficiency.

Designs for efficiency

When the compression ignition engine was first introduced with a thermal efficiency approaching 40 per cent, it was said that it would displace steam plants in power stations, which then had an efficiency range of 30 per cent. But in fact this has not happened, because steam plants were found to be more reliable, more suitable for continuous working and less liable to breakdown.

While there are many different designs of heat engines, they all work on a common principle. Gas or vapour which is heated expands rapidly, and this is used to provide energy in one of several ways. In the steam engine, or the conventional internal combustion engine, the expanding gases impart motion to a movable piston, which then transfers this motion by mechanical linkages to driving wheels, airscrew, or ship's propeller. In a turbine, whether of the steam variety or fuelled by some other material such as kerosene or diesel oil, the gases, moving at high speed, convert their energy into useful mechanical work by driving what is, in effect, a sophisticated windmill. Jet engines, on the other hand, use the energy in the gas much more directly. These gases are allowed to escape at high speed through a nozzle so that they transfer energy to the vehicle (usually an aircraft) according to Newton's

The development of commercially practical steam engines transformed human society. *Top,* the elegant steamship *Britannia* here sets out on her maiden voyage from Liverpool in the year 1840. *Above,* steam locomotives opened up the American west, accelerated the Industrial Revolution and, as a result of train schedules, dramatically sharpened Man's awareness of time.

Third Law of Motion (action is equal to reaction). In these various ways the energy in the hot gas is made to do useful work.

The first practical heat engine devised was the *reciprocating steam engine,* in which a piston is pushed to and fro in an enclosed cylinder by an expansion of high-pressure steam. The steam is produced by evaporating water in a boiler heated by a fire in which any fuel may be burned.

The admission of steam to the piston cylinder is controlled by a valve which opens when the piston is at one end of its stroke, remains open for a short time to pass the required amount of steam – which starts to push the piston along – and then closes while the steam expands and pushes the piston to the other end of the cylinder. This process is then repeated, with steam now pressing against the other side of the

piston to push it back along the cylinder, while an exhaust valve opens to allow the surplus steam on the other side of the piston to escape. This cycle is known as *simple expansion* and is the most common method of driving steam locomotives.

However, in their continual quest for greater thermal efficiency, designers have sometimes made use of the exhaust steam, drawing additional work from this 'waste' which still contains a considerable amount of energy. In these engines, partly expanded steam from the high-pressure cylinder is put to work in an additional low-pressure cylinder before being allowed to escape into the air. This is known as *compound* or *double expansion.*

A further development is *triple expansion,* in which the steam passes from the high-pressure cylinder to an intermediate cylinder and thence to a low-pressure cylinder, so that minimum pressure is wasted. This system is too cumbrous and space-consuming for most locomotives, but at one time was widely used in ocean-going ships where, cost notwithstanding, it is important to obtain the maximum amount of work from each ton of fuel.

Internal combustion engines are so called because the burning or combustion takes place inside the engine – in the cylinder, unlike the steam engines, where it takes place outside the engine in the boiler which produces the steam.

All internal combustion engines work on much the same principle whether they use petrol or diesel oil. The fuel is mixed with air and is ignited in the cylinder in which there is a piston. When the mixture ignites, the expanding hot gases produce a sudden pressure in the cylinder. This pressure against the piston forces it down in the cylinder. Connecting rods attached to the piston transmit the work generated to other parts of the engine. Once again the First Law of Thermodynamics applies – heat energy is converted into mechanical work.

Most petrol engines in use today are *four stroke* – that is to say there are four strokes or phases which go to make up one work cycle.

At the *induction* stroke, the piston is drawn down in the cylinder and as the piston goes down a mixture of petrol and air is sucked in with it. This mixture consists of a mist of petrol suspended in air. It enters the cylinder through a valve called the inlet valve, which is automatically opened by the working of the engine. When the piston reaches the bottom of its stroke, it is pushed up in the cylinder by a crank to which it is attached. This is the *compression* stroke. During this stage, both inlet and exhaust valves are closed and the cylinder is tightly sealed. On its upward journey, the piston compresses the mixture into a space as much as 14 times less than it occupied before. When the piston nears the top of the cylinder, a spark is generated between the points of the spark-plug, which explodes the mixture.

Two-stroke simplicity

Because petrol or diesel oil is highly inflammable, it burns rapidly and the burning mixture heats to a high temperature and a high pressure. These gases exert great pressure on the walls of the cylinder and piston head. As the piston head is the only moving part of the cylinder, it gives way before the pressure and is pushed to the bottom of the cylinder. This is the *expansion* stroke.

The *exhaust* stroke occurs as the driving force of the explosion ends and the piston is driven upwards again by the momentum of a heavy flywheel. Meanwhile, the exhaust valve at the top of the cylinder opens and the burnt gases are swept out by the upward-moving piston. When the piston reaches the top of its stroke the exhaust valve closes and the cycle begins again.

The thermal efficiency of the internal combustion engine depends very largely

Top, automobiles have brought Man the freedom of wide-ranging mobility and the irritation of nerve-racking traffic jams. In addition, petrol engines pollute the atmosphere, so many nations are seeking to replace them with large rapid-transit systems and battery-powered mini-cars. *Above,* an artist's conception of Britain's new *Queen Elizabeth II,* a modern luxury ocean liner.

on the amount of compression given before ignition. The higher the compression, the greater the possible efficiency. This is one reason why it is uneconomical to run a large engine continuously at small loads. This does not entirely apply to the diesel engine, however, which is not throttled and which is much more economical of fuel than the petrol engine under partial loads. The fraction of the heat supplied to the engine which is converted into useful work (known as the *brake thermal efficiency*) diminishes rapidly as the load is reduced even when the indicated thermal efficiency remains the same.

The *two-stroke* engine is comparatively cheap and its structure is very simple, hence its popularity for motor cycles. It differs from other combustion engines because it needs no valves. The induction inlet and the exhaust outlet are opened and closed in sequence by the piston.

When the piston reaches the top of its upward stroke it has compressed the fuel mixture and also closed both the transfer and the exhaust port. Only the fuel inlet into the crankcase remains open and a mixture of petrol and air is sucked through it in the form of an 'atomized' mist. Immediately the explosion takes place, the piston is forced down rapidly. As it goes down it closes the inlet and exhaust ports and starts to compress the fuel-air mixture in the crankcase. Towards the end of this stroke it opens the exhaust to the suction ports to allow the exhaust gas to escape from the cylinder and a new charge of mixture to pass from the crankcase to the cylinder.

The compressed mixture enters the cylinder through the suction port, sweeping the burnt gases out through the

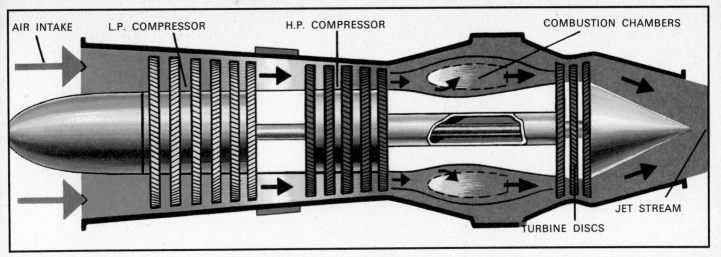

AIR INTAKE · L.P. COMPRESSOR · H.P. COMPRESSOR · COMBUSTION CHAMBERS · JET STREAM · TURBINE DISCS

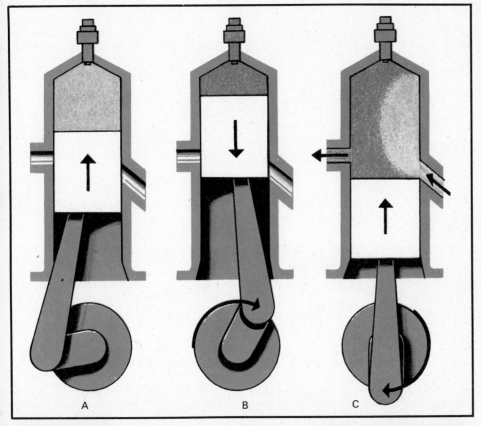

A   B   C

Above, a turbo-jet engine is little more than a hollow tube. Air taken in through the front passes through compressors, mixes with fuel in the combustion chamber, and then ignites. Propulsion is produced by the force of gases exhausted through the rear. *Left,* in a two-stroke engine, a mist of petrol mixed with air is compressed as the piston moves up in the cylinder (**A**) and ignited by a spark-plug (**B**). The piston is forced downward by expanding gas, which is exhausted out of one port as more fuel enters through the other (**C**). *Below,* two-stroke engines are most commonly found in motor cycles.

exhaust port at the same time. The piston then moves up again, closing all the ports. It compresses the mixture in the cylinder and a fresh explosion takes place.

Another type of internal combustion engine is the *diesel engine,* invented by the German Rudolf Diesel (1858–1913). It is now widely used in heavy lorries, motor ships and railway locomotives which are powered by diesel engines. The diesel engine works by burning diesel fuel oil, which is not as expensive as petrol. A diesel engine has neither carburettor nor spark-plug, but instead an injector which forces fuel oil under high pressure into the cylinder through a fine nozzle. Although the diesel engine is slower and heavier than the petrol engine, it is more economical and needs less maintenance.

At the induction phase the piston moves downwards and sucks air into the cylinder through the inlet valve. On its upward journey (the compression stroke) the piston compresses the air. This compression heats the air to temperatures as high as 1,100–1,300°F. At the injection stroke oil is injected through a nozzle into the cylinder above the piston, forming a fine mist in the hot air. Because of the very high temperature the mixture burns and the gases which are generated push the piston down. This is the expansion, or working stroke. Finally, the piston rises again and expels the burnt gases.

The gas turbine is another form of heat engine which is based on the same principle as all other heat engines, namely that when a gas (in this case air) is heated, it exerts more pressure. Gas turbines normally utilize paraffin or diesel oil, and although they often seem to be very complicated because refinements are added for greater efficiency, their operating principle is very simple.

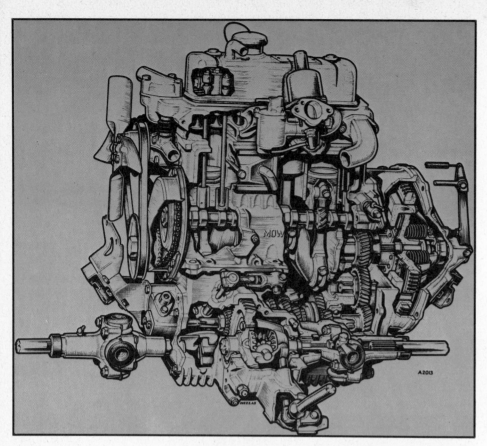

is used to work the compressor. When built on a large scale, a great volume of air is forced to the engine and as it escapes backward is concentrated as a jet which can be used to propel a vehicle – usually an aircraft. Engines of this type are called *turbo-jet* engines and can develop so much thrust that they have supersonic capabilities.

In addition to aircraft, gas turbine engines are used in hovercraft, hydrofoil marine craft and they have been used experimentally in cars. An established industrial use for the gas turbine engine is in remote-control power stations which can switch in electricity at peak times to supplement the conventional supply.

The advantage of the gas turbine engine for aircraft is that they are lighter than piston engines of equivalent horsepower and can be designed to reduce wind resistance; the fact that they usually run on paraffin also reduces the fire hazard.

One of the earliest jet engines was the *ram-jet*, which is very much like the pipe described earlier to demonstrate the principle of the gas turbine engine – indeed it has been called the 'flying stove-pipe'. A ram-jet is simply an open tube with no moving parts. As the aircraft moves forward, the air forced into one end of the tube is then mixed with fuel and ignited. The expanding gases cannot escape out at the front because more air is being 'rammed' into the tube. Thus the gases are forced out at the back and the reaction then drives the aircraft forward.

The ram-jet can be very powerful but it has one great disadvantage: it cannot work at less than about 200 miles per hour, because at speeds less than this the air in front of the plane is not scooped up fast enough to meet the demands of the igniting fuel. For this reason, planes or missiles which use a ram-jet engine must be launched with a booster before the ram-jet can be brought into action.

Strides towards perfection

Although the gases which leave a modern gas turbine engine may be forced out at speeds of more than 1,300 mph, the speed of a plane depends not only on the speed of expulsion of the exhaust gases, but also on the weight of the expelled gases. Some jet engines take advantage of this fact by injecting a mixture of water and alcohol into the combustion chamber. This injection adds weight to the exhaust gases and gives an extra thrust to the engines.

Jet engines need air to burn their fuel and for this reason will only work within the Earth's atmosphere. The *rocket* engine carries oxygen in tanks with it, so it can be used outside the atmosphere into the vacuum of space.

Designers are continually working towards the greater efficiency of heat engines and at the moment engines, such as the fuel cell, are being developed which will increase efficiencies even further. So far we are nowhere near achieving maximum thermal efficiency from our engines. Incomplete combustion, an inevitable loss of heat from the cylinders – and particularly friction losses – prevent an attainment of the theoretical maximum.

Top, to the non-mechanic, an internal combustion engine can be a frightening conglomeration of gears, wheels, cylinders and pistons. But to the mechanic, it is a masterwork, translating abstract physics into practical reality. *Above,* the world's introduction to jet-powered flight was anything but auspicious. But the V-1 flying bombs led the way to Man's adventure into space.

Basically the gas turbine engine is a piece of pipe. At one end of this pipe is a small fan which draws in air and blows it along the inside of the pipe. At the rear end, a similar fan is arranged pointing in the same direction. When the front fan is rotated, the air which is pushed into the pipe can escape only by passing the rear fan. As it escapes this air will turn the blades of the rear fan with a force which is almost equal to that used by the front fan in pushing the air into the pipe.

The flying pipe

Now imagine that in the middle part of the pipe there is a small hole through which a tiny jet of fuel is pumped. When the jet is lit, the flame heats the air inside the pipe and in consequence the air expands. To escape from the pipe this larger volume of air must flow past the rear fan more quickly than the smaller volume of cold air and thus the blades of the rear fan are turned more rapidly. Work which the rear fan can do exceeds that needed to

turn the front fan, and if the two fans are mounted on a single shaft, the power obtained from the rear fan is enough to turn the front fan, yet leaves sufficient power in the shaft to provide energy for some form of work.

In practical applications the front fan is replaced by a compressor. This is simply a more complex type of fan which usually consists of several different sets of blades designed to draw great quantities of air into the engine. The air passes into the combustion chamber where it is heated by a flame of paraffin or diesel oil. It increases in volume and escapes past the *turbine,* the rear fan turning at a tremendous speed. The turbine turns the compressor which as a result draws in more air.

In some gas turbine engines the power in the shaft is used by means of a series of gears to drive a conventional propeller. Such engines are called *turbo-prop* engines and have use in aeroplanes. In others, however, almost all the power in the shaft

The steam age

Many people do not realize that despite the advance of the internal-combustion engine, steam power continues to play a prominent part in the production of electricity and even in nuclear submarines.

AS THE FIRST of Man's many forms of mechanical power, steam is today commonly regarded as archaic. We even use the adjective in derision to mean something crude or outdated. Although it is no longer widely used by railways, steam propulsion has never ceased to be a dynamic technology. Steam power generates almost all the electricity used in Britain; it is a highly competitive method of driving large ships and is the almost universal method of using the heat from nuclear reactors. Steam is immensely important in many branches of industry in 'process plant' in which some form of physical or chemical reaction is involved. This wide use is all based on the fortunate fact that on Earth we have an abundant supply of water, a relatively dense liquid that is non-poisonous, cheap, easily pumped through pipes and valves and that can absorb a great deal of heat energy in being converted to vapour at high pressure.

The inventors of the first steam engines at the start of the eighteenth century were mocked and abused when they tried to make steam do the work previously done only by muscles. A century later those who tried to put steam engines to work driving carriages, trains and ships were

also treated as madmen. Most of their critics tended to equate steam power with the fires of Hell, and complex and ingenious arguments were often put forward to show that such fearsome engines would pollute the air, poison humanity physically and morally and destroy the wholesome agriculture by which nations lived.

The first steam engines also had to contend with the powerful influence of Aristotle who had decreed that 'Nature abhors a vacuum'. This was because the

only way Man knew how to use steam before about the year 1725 was to admit steam to a cylinder closed by a piston and then condense the steam back to water (for example, by pouring cold water on the cylinder). The cylinder full of steam would rapidly return to a volume of water about 1/1300th as great and the pressure of the atmosphere acting on the piston would then drive the piston down to fill up the volume previously occupied by the steam. Denis Papin, a Huguenot refugee from

1 This watercolour by Rowlandson shows one of the first steam trains on a demonstration track near Euston Square, London. It was built in the early nineteenth century by Richard Trevithick.
2 James Watt's first steam engine revolutionized the use of steam power. By adding a condenser to the cylinder containing the steam, Watt was able to prevent waste of heat in the engine's cycle.
3 Early steam carriages, such as this 1860 model, were extremely clumsy, very slow, and had to stop at regular intervals to get up steam. There is renewed interest today in steam power for cars.

Blois working in Germany, built various model engines on this principle from 1690 on; and the Englishman Thomas Savery devised a water pump he called 'the miner's friend' which had the same action. The strange name was given because all these early steam engines were constructed to pump water out of mines.

These early steam engines were often called 'fire engines', and it was not uncommon for preachers to pray for the souls of the misguided men who sought to raise water with the power of fire. The engines were extremely inefficient machines, because the cylinder was heated by the steam one moment and then deliberately cooled down by cold water the next, so that rather more than 99 per cent of the heat from the original fire was wasted. The man who first saw the cause of the inefficiency and did something about it was the poor Scots laboratory instrument maker James Watt. Legend has it that he was first set thinking about steam by wondering what power lifted the lid of his grandmother's kettle as it boiled away on the fire. He made a thorough study of the properties of water and steam, calculating the temperatures, pressures and quantities of heat needed to boil given masses of water at different pressures and the quantities of cold water needed to condense a given volume of steam. In 1763 the University of Glasgow, where he worked, asked him whether he could make the university's Newcomen engine work better.

Increased efficiency

Watt realized that the inefficiency lay in wasted heat in cooling the cylinder and then heating it again. He made a working model of the first engine ever to have a condenser, a separate vessel in which the steam is turned back to water while keeping the cylinder itself as hot as the steam from the boiler. It was obvious to Watt that he now held the key to steam engines far more efficient than any built before; he then set about writing a patent for his method of 'lessening the consumption of steam, and consequently fuel, in fire engines . . .'

Unlike so many others, Watt happened to find a way to turn his ideas into reality. He had once met Matthew Boulton, the young owner of the great engineering works at Soho, Birmingham. Boulton was one of the few men at that time with the talent and money to back Watt, and soon the firm of Boulton and Watt was established. The ironmaster John Wilkinson devised a way then accurately casting boring large cylinders six feet in diameter that 'did not depart from absolute truth in the worst part more than a thin sixpence', and in 1774 the first of the new engines was on test. It soon proved its power and efficiency and orders came thick and fast. At first most were required by British mines and factories, but gradually the fame of the new steam engines spread overseas and by 1800 Boulton and Watt had delivered 500 engines – a figure that grew to 10,000 sold in Britain alone by 1824. Watt incidentally, spent months in courts of law, trying to protect his firm

against unscrupulous rivals who stole his ideas as soon as they were seen to work.

The steam engine swept through industry, replacing the waterwheel that stopped during a dry summer, the windmill that worked when the wind blew strongly enough, the treadmill that worked when unfortunate beings were forced to turn it, and the power of the ill-used beast of burden or labourer. Steam power helped Britain to become the 'workshop of the world'.

One of the first to utilize steam for transport was a French artillery officer, Nicolas Joseph Cugnot, who in 1769 pro-

pelled himself about Paris in a steam tractor – until he ran into a wall. Then in 1801 Richard Trevithick, helped by Watt's assistant William Murdoch, completed a more practical steam carriage and ran it up to Camborne Beacon summit with seven or eight men hanging on to it. Three years later he won a £500 wager by making a steam locomotive move a load of ten tons; in fact it pulled a train laden with this weight of iron as well as 70 passengers. By 1808 he had run a train at the amazing speed of 20 mph.

There was no great success in making a railway for public service until 27 Septem-

1 Diagram of a gas-cooled nuclear reactor. The hot gases from the reactor are made to turn water into high-pressure steam in a heat exchanger. The steam can then be used to drive turbines.

2 The *Flying Scotsman*, perhaps the world's most famous steam engine, on its last run out of King's Cross Station. British Rail have now abandoned steam in favour of diesel and electric power.

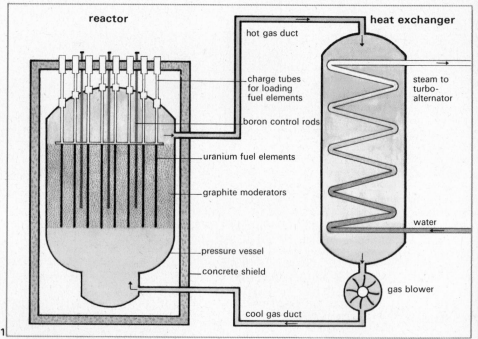

reactor — heat exchanger
hot gas duct
charge tubes for loading fuel elements
steam to turbo-alternator
boron control rods
uranium fuel elements
graphite moderators
water
pressure vessel
concrete shield
gas blower
cool gas duct

1 The Burrell traction engine *Princess Royal* on display at the annual traction engine rally near Cambridge. Steam engines of this type are still used on fairgrounds, and also as steam-rollers.
2 The heyday of the Mississippi steam-boats was the end of the nineteenth century. But a few examples of these large paddle-steamers survive, like Cincinnati's *Delta Queen*.

3 Nowadays, the steam engine is often regarded as a toy. This simple engine demonstrates clearly the principles involved in much more complex and larger steam engines.
4 The nuclear submarine H.M.S. *Dreadnought* moored in Portsmouth Harbour. Like other nuclear submarines, *Dreadnought* uses steam power to propel the turbines which drive her propellers.

ber 1825, when the Stockton to Darlington Railway opened. The line was built by the son of a poor mineworker who taught himself to write when he was 19: his name was George Stephenson. The first train was made up of 34 trucks carrying old mail coach bodies. The first six were laden with coal and flour; the next was occupied by the directors of the new railway company; 21 coaches of guests came next (there were almost 450 of them); and at the rear were another six coaches full of coal. The ten-mile trip took just over an hour.

The idea of the railway could at last be seen to work, but when the much larger cities of Liverpool and Manchester tried to join each other by rail there were riots, protests of all kinds and endless obstruction in Parliament. It took nine years for the opposition from landowners

and the road carriage owners to be overcome; then Stephenson built a masterpiece of engineering called *Rocket* to haul trains on the 30-mile route. *Rocket* was a great advance on earlier steam engines and it drew passengers at 26 mph and ran light at 35 mph. To the amazement of the onlookers, Stephenson's lungs were not sucked inside out, nor did the devil make off with him. As early as 1843 the British rail companies were carrying more than 18,000,000 passengers a year – as many as the rest of the world combined.

In contrast steam never really gained a foothold on the roads. Although by 1810 at least a dozen steam coaches had run successfully, all attempts to use them commercially from 1831 to 1860 were handicapped by the terrible roads. These crumbled under the weight of the smoky monsters, and the tollkeepers, seeing this,

slapped on crippling charges which can still be read on the old toll boards preserved in many British museums. While an ordinary coach might have to pay a toll of a shilling, a steam driven 'horseless carriage' might be levied five shillings *per wheel*. So, even though steam driven lorries and cars were occasionally built they never caught on.

At sea, after a few halting attempts in the eighteenth century, the steamship became the normal method of marine propulsion. At first steamships were thought to have little advantage over sail apart from the fact that they could sail up a river without having to tack from side to side; and, in any case, they always retained their full rig of sails. But by 1860 bold designers began to leave the sails off, and improved steam engines driving better paddle wheels or screw propellers enabled ships to run a greater distance in a day than even the best sailing ships, and to do so with far more certainty. All the first steamships had what are known as reciprocating engines, the only type of steam engine then being built, in which the steam drives pistons up and down in their cylinders and thus, via connecting rods, turns a crankshaft round

1 Early motor vessels, like Bell's *Comet* in this photograph, had steam engines but also retained their sails. This ship is driven by paddle wheels on either side of the hull.

2 The British destroyer H.M.S. *Viper,* seen here during trials in 1900, reached a speed of 37 knots with its revolutionary turbine engine. This was far faster than any previous naval vessel.

and round. But in 1884 Sir Charles Parsons made his first steam turbine and it is the turbine, in which the steam acts directly on blades on a spinning shaft, that has today become the most important type of steam engine.

Although it is one of the most modern types of engine the steam turbine is also perhaps the most ancient, because Hero (or Heron) of Alexandria made a toy steam/turbine in about 100 AD. But Parsons triggered off the modern steam turbine, and he put it in the public eye by fitting turbine engines into a small boat he called *Turbinia* which was so successful that the Admiralty ordered Parsons to make a turbine-engined destroyer, and the resulting vessel, H.M.S. *Viper,* did 37 knots – far faster than any previous naval ship in the world.

Steam turbines

Today the steam turbine is the main means of driving the largest ships and much of the world's electricity generating plant. Modern turbines work just like those installed in *Turbinia* except that they are much larger and use steam of a very different quality. The basic aim in any steam engine is to take as much as possible of the original heat – liberated by burning coal or oil, for example – in order to put it to work heating the water and turning it into steam with as little wastage as possible. Just how successful the engineer is in doing this has always depended on the materials available, how

much money can be spent on designing and building the plant and how safe it should be in use.

A century ago it was considered daring to make a boiler deliver steam at 40 lb pressure per sq. in. The *Britannic* and *Titanic,* huge passenger liners built just before 1914, had piston engines taking steam at 215 lb per sq. in. pressure while the world record 50 megawatt electricity generating plant installed in Chicago in 1928 pushed the pressure up to 600 lb. Soon after the Second World War the standard generating set in British power stations was rated at 200 megawatts and was driven by steam at over 1,000 lb. per sq. in., while today we use 500 and 660 megawatt sets (each capable of supplying a million people with all their domestic electricity) driven by steam at 2,350 lb pressure per sq. in.

The increase in pressure is not merely beneficial in itself but comes coupled with higher temperature, just as it does in domestic pressure cookers. At ordinary atmospheric pressure water boils at 212 °F., and on a high mountain it may boil at a temperature of no more than 180° or even 170°. But at 1,000 lb per sq. in. the temperature exceeds 1,000 °F. The boilers that generate such steam in modern power stations are as big as the largest 30-storey office blocks. They burn pulverized coal or oil with flames 100 feet long and the steam is generated in hundreds of miles of special stainless-steel pipe. The steam is then admitted to the blades of the high-pressure

turbine. The steam expands through dozens of rows of whirling blades, each row larger than the last.

Not only is a steam turbine plant of this type extremely efficient, with an overall 'thermal efficiency' of about 40 per cent compared with a thermal efficiency of 1 to 2 per cent for the steam locomotives and steam engines of a century ago, but it is designed to run continuously for many years. The first turbine built by Parsons in 1884 would have needed 22 lb of coal burned in the boiler for each unit of electricity it could generate. By 1900 the earliest big steam turbines actually put to use in generating electricity had reduced the figure to about 3 lb. In 1969, despite a general worsening in the quality of coal, the giant 500 megawatt installations generate a unit of electricity for not much more than half a pound of coal burned.

Now these machines are in competition with nuclear power, where the amount of nuclear fuel burned in making a unit of electricity is millions of times smaller. A nuclear reactor is simply a vast generator of heat. Unlike the traditional boiler it does not have to be fed with huge quantities of coal or oil but will run at high power for years on a single charge of fissile material. It contains no moving parts, apart from a cloud of neutrons which are the actual carriers of the energy from the heart of each atom. Once the reactor has been made 'critical' it will continue to generate heat until a material that absorbs neutrons is inserted to slow down the reaction. If no means were provided to withdraw the heat, the reactor would get hotter and hotter and eventually melt. In practice the reactor is made to behave as a furnace heating a steam boiler. In most British reactors the heat is taken out by carbon dioxide gas, which is pumped round and round a sealed circuit, giving up some of its heat to the water boiler on each circuit. In America's nuclear power stations the water is usually passed right through the reactor according to two methods, the 'pressurized water reactor' (PWR) or the 'boiling water reactor' (BWR). In either case, the nuclear power is turned into steam power, and it is a steam turbine that drives the electric generator.

Nuclear ships

Nuclear ships, nearly all of which so far are naval vessels, are thus all 'steam driven'. In this case it is important to make the propulsion machinery compact as well as absolutely reliable and efficient. All the latest and largest submarines have steam turbine propulsion with the heat provided by a nuclear reactor, and in this case there is the added need not to contaminate the atmosphere.

Finally, many designers in the United States have since 1960 been trying to decide what sort of machinery will be needed in future space stations to generate electricity and serve other functions. There is no doubt the most efficient arrangements use rotating machines of various kinds driven by a form of steam power. Their steam will probably be vapour produced by molten metals.

Age of automation

Man has embarked on a second industrial revolution. Not only is automation increasing the productivity of manufacturing processes, it is transforming the way of life of the industrial worker.

THE DEVELOPMENT OF HUMANITY has hinged on the continual effort to make labour more productive. From the use of tools by the most primitive men to the rise of modern industry, changes in social life have been founded on advances in technology by which the same amount of work could be done with a smaller effort.

Automation (the word, coined in 1946, is not very precise in its meaning) implies that this process is taken to the point where hardly any human intervention is required in production. The implications of such a development for the lives of men and women are incalculable.

Mechanization in its broadest sense can be traced through various stages. At its simplest, tools held in the hand replace the use of bare hands themselves. Then comes the use of an outside source of power to move the tool. The first of these machines were water or steam driven and they had to be controlled by hand.

Soon after their invention, machines such as these were being used in factories to perform complex sequences of operations, like cotton spinning or weaving. The machines were harnessed together in a rigid, inflexible system; anything interrupting the smooth working of the process – changes in raw material for example – meant that an operator was needed to intervene, adjusting the machine.

Governors

But the speed of a steam engine can be controlled by an automatic device – a *governor* – and with this a machine can be allowed to run by itself to some extent unsupervised. Invented by the Scottish engineer, James Watt, a governor basically consists of weights attached to a shaft which spins faster or slower according to the speed of the steam engine. The faster the shaft rotates the more the weights fly out from the axis, and the more they pull on a mechanism for shutting off the steam. Thus, if the engine runs too fast, the steam pressure is automatically reduced while, if it slows down, the weights fall inwards, opening the steam valve. The speed of the engine may, therefore, be *self governed*.

A self-governed steam engine is an early example of the *feed-back* principle. The governor measures engine speed and uses the measurement to correct any changes which occur. Information about the departure of the process from a pre-set state is fed back to cancel out the discrepancy.

Such processes, later called *servo-mechanisms,* are capable of replacing human control of machines. The study of their properties developed in the 1920s and 1930s.

With the rise of electronics, servo-mechanisms have really come into their own. All kinds of measurements, and

1 At a railway siding control room near Munich, Western Germany, automatic electronic controls sort wagons, apply track brakes and estimate speed and weight.
2 On the station at Ulm, southern Germany, a businessman uses a coin-operated express copying automaton. Within a few seconds it produces a good copy of any document.

observations can be translated into electrical currents. Electronic circuits then amplify and transform variations in such currents to control highly sophisticated mechanisms.

However, feed-back devices are by no means all electronic. Pneumatic and hydraulic means are also widely employed in servo-mechanisms. What is involved here is merely the form through which information is signalled back to the system being controlled.

In nature there is nothing new in the idea of feedback mechanisms. They are used all the time, unconsciously in human activity, in fact in all living processes. When a man reaches out his hand to pick up an object special sensory devices continually register the state of contraction of the muscles and control their movements to co-ordinate the picking up of the object seen by his eyes. This information is 'processed' by the brain and by the spinal cord and is fed back to the muscles controlling the hand.

The flexibility and adaptability of human activity depends on a complex hierarchy of such mechanisms. The application of similar principles to the control of machines has given Man a means of making machines carry out activities and tasks formerly thought of as essentially human. Indeed when many such mechanisms are linked together, whole industrial processes can be made to carry out production – continually checking themselves and selecting procedures required to meet various eventualities.

However, the full possibilities of developments like this could only come about because of the electronic computer. First constructed to make complex and repetitive calculations at high speed, it was realized in the 1940s that they could have much wider applications. Basically, a sequence of numbers is used as a code, and when a programme of instruction is fed in code into the machine, it is converted by the electronic circuits into a set of operations comprising numbers. One operation may mean that certain instructions are followed again and again until they have been carried out the required number of times. Then a new operation comes in and a new sequence is begun.

The *digital computer,* so called because it deals with digits or figures, is one type of computer. Essentially it is a device for storing numbers, and adding and multiplying them at high speed. It can also compare two numbers and according to whether they are equal or not, set different courses of operation in process.

Once Man recognized the versatility of the computer he began to use it to control a variety of processes, and even make decisions. True automation was now a reality. It was not merely a matter of getting a process to follow a fixed pattern and of correcting it when it departed from this set path. By transforming data on the working of the process, the computer could 'make decisions' about how it should be changed.

An oil refinery is a highly complex establishment. Complicated chemical reactions may be taking place simultaneously, and to control them at the correct pressure and temperature thousands of valves are needed at various points in the system.

Remote control

In the 1940s and 1950s refineries were built in which valves were controlled by servos to maintain pressures and temperatures at set levels. Measurements were automatically made of these levels, together with the chemical composition of materials flowing past various key points. All of this information was transmitted electrically to a central control room and changes in the working of the vast complex – including breakdowns – could thus be corrected rapidly, perhaps without the operator leaving the controls. An entire refinery of this sort can thus be controlled by a handful of men. Similar automation equipment is also widely used in the chemical processing industries.

The computer is now making even such sophisticated plants obsolete. By feeding all measurements directly into a computer, calculations can be made of how the controls may be simultaneously altered so as to produce a better result. Whereas in the non-computerized plant the operator often has to make decisions on the basis of 'hunch' or 'experience', the computer can be programmed to do the same thing but systematically.

Moreover, it is quite feasible to *programme* (instruct) the machine so that it 'learns' from its errors. It can be made to experiment with various changes, selecting the best possibilities for future action, and adapting itself to meet changes in conditions.

The chemical processing industries have been the most successful in applying concepts like these, but all sections of industry are susceptible to similar applications. The transfer machine, moving material from one stage of production to another makes it possible to integrate entire factories and consider them as a single system. All repetitive operations, so common in manufacturing industry, can, in principle, be mechanized and automatically controlled and checked. Computers can then take over the 'management' of the entire system of operations.

In the metal industry the *lathe* – the basic tool of metal-working – can be controlled by electronic devices. The piece of metal being machined is automatically moved about, while a programmed

sequence of tools works on it. Measurement by optical or electrical means, may be continuously carried out, and fed back to servo-mechanisms controlling the various movements.

The entire system can be made very flexible by using a programme consisting of nothing more than holes punched in paper tape. The tape is produced by a computer, which calculates the sequence of instructions required to produce a given shape. Thus, by coding an original blueprint, the modern 'numerically controlled' machine tool can be made to carry out the necessary engineering work.

Processes like packaging, sorting or mixing are not difficult to control. Assembly of complex components is harder. Only in the last few years has any advance

1 The whole complex of a waterworks in Düsseldorf is operated, and breakdowns rectified, from this automatic control room.
2 At a modern wine-bottling factory, the bottles on a moving conveyor belt are automatically filled, corked and labelled by machine.
3 This machine tool in a British factory cuts with great accuracy patterns in steel plates to be used for shipbuilding. It is electronically controlled by a programmed computer in a nearby control booth.
4 A robot tub with trailers steers a pre-set course round a British warehouse. It stops and starts as needed for loading, and can automatically open and close doors.
5 Automatic control valves and meters operate the blending system at an oil refinery in Denmark. The rate of flow and temperatures are maintained at set levels and measurement of the chemical composition is made automatically.

been made on this front. The items to be assembled have had to be redesigned, and the relative orientation of two components being fitted together has had to be measured and programmed.

Not only manufacture may be 'automated' in this way. The 1950s saw the development of the 'electronic office'. Many clerical operations may be broken down and reorganized so that a computer can carry them out according to instructions. Many airline companies use computers to deal with seat reservations and to keep records of future flights. Cheques are sorted in some banks by automatic methods which also keep accounts and print statements.

Pay-rolls, for example, in many large enterprises are now produced by computer.

Each employee has a card, bearing coded information on his wage-rate, overtime worked, and tax code. The programme can produce the amount to be paid, allowing for such items as tax and insurance, and can also indicate how many notes and coins of different denominations are required.

The 'automation' of an office produces a phenomenon which occurs quite often in this field. Before a computer can carry out the work at present being performed by a group of clerical workers, the work they do must be looked at systematically. This process frequently brings to light routine operations whose purpose was long ago forgotten.

Pieces of information may be recorded, forms filled out, copies of documents made,

merely because 'that is how we always do it'. Only when the entire process is analysed for conversion to computer working is it discovered that a simple reorganization will make the whole operation doubly efficient.

Systems analysis, as it has come to be called, is now an essential part of automation. Because of such analysis the designs of plants and offices from the start have been affected.

The application of automation is still far behind the theory. As early as 1948, the American mathematician, Norbert Wiener published his book *Cybernetics: Communication and Control in the Animal and the Machine,* which was still about four or five years before the first computers were being produced commercially.

In his book Wiener introduced the basic principles of automatic control, computer control and information theory. Information regarding an error in, for example, the path of a guided missile or a human body temperature, is fed to the controlling device which acts to correct the error. He showed the relevance of these conceptions to biology, psychology and economics and pointed out their tremendous implications for social and industrial development.

Many of the possibilities he discussed are still far beyond what is technically achievable. But he was able to lay the basis for the mathematical examination of the properties of automatic devices.

Wiener and his fellow mathematician, John von Neumann, considered abstractly many of the implications of the construction of computers. For example, von Neumann asked the question: could a machine be made so complex that it could construct one more complex than itself?

He decided that there was a critical level of complexity above which this was possible. The implication of machines which programmed themselves raised the spectre of a robot conquest of the world. Someone suggested that this danger could always be countered by pulling out the plug. A pessimist answered him: by that time, you will find it has been cemented to the wall. These notions reflected the social issues raised by automation.

A great controversy began about the effect of automation on unemployment. Wiener and many others foresaw the danger of the rapid displacement of human beings by machines in a 'second industrial revolution'. At first, as automation began to affect the motor industry especially, it looked as though these dangers were immediate. Soon millions of people would be out of work.

Then, in the 1950s, the idea spread that automation, in fact, meant an increase in the demand for highly skilled manpower. All that was needed was the retraining of the former unskilled men.

Transforming industry

No investigation has supported this contention although a few specialist maintenance men are needed; electricians must be replaced by electronic engineers, for example. In any case, it is quite conceivable to carry out even these tasks automatically. Machines already exist which check their own working automatically, correcting errors and replacing faulty components when necessary.

But the bulk of production workers can and will be displaced, as automation takes over many repetitive processes. Even if its advance is slower than might have been anticipated in 1948, the automatic factory is technologically inevitable. It may well be that, when the present period of economic upheaval is considered in the future, one of the basic factors will seem to be the changes in this direction that have been occurring since the end of the Second World War.

It is sometimes said that automation is only mechanization taken a bit further. But, as always, it is this change of degree which makes the decisive difference. All the problems of transforming industry are magnified enormously by the extent and rapidity of the changes implied by the application of automatic control.

Will the spread and extension of automation mean economic ruin, as markets fail to expand, unemployment rises and productive potential soars? Or will the new machines be the servants of men, removing all drudgery and unpleasantness from the labour process?

The answers to such questions are not technical but social and political in character. One thing is certain: in the age of automation, nothing can remain the same for human life.

1 The control room of a natural gas production platform in the North Sea. The panel consists of computers, recorders, controllers and encoders which control gas flow and pressure.

2 A guard at the master control panel of an electronic system which keeps watch on factory premises. Lights warn of an emergency and information is relayed to the panel.

Refining natural products

Petrol tanks and sugar basins the world over are filled with the products of refineries. Modern refineries are highly automated chemical factories, in which wastage is cut to the minimum.

FEW NATURAL SUBSTANCES are found in a pure state. Almost all are contaminated to some degree or another by other substances, some of which may not only be undesirable but actively harmful in the final product. The canes from which sugar is produced, for example, contain not only sugar but cellulose, proteins, chlorophyll and other colouring chemicals and salts, as well as water. The sugar we put into our tea is made from sugar cane by a complicated process in which the chemicals contaminating the sugar are removed by chemical and physical processes.

These processes come under the collective heading of refining, a word which is applied chiefly to the process of purifying crude oil. Refining originally meant the removal of impurities, but its meaning has been extended to cover the very complex operations which take place in a modern oil refinery.

Crude oil is rather like a conjurer's hat: if you are clever enough you can make it produce almost anything you want. In fact, the story of petrol refining is an excellent example of the economical pressures of demand causing a changing pattern in the supply of commodities produced by different refining techniques.

This comes as rather a surprise to people who have only a sketchy knowledge of the workings of a modern refinery. A common misconception is that crude oil is composed of the same materials always in the same proportions.

Constituents of crude

But oil varies enormously in composition, depending on its place of origin. The constitutents of crude can be divided roughly into three classes, together with a number of impurities present in small amounts, but the ranging proportions of the classes of compound give each crude a definite character.

All the main compounds found in crude oil are hydrocarbons, formed solely from carbon and hydrogen atoms. Of these, one of three main groups is the *paraffins*, or saturated hydrocarbons, which embrace products from methane, a very light gas, to heavy waxes. Paraffins have the special characteristic that, if the number of carbon atoms in the molecule is denoted by n, then the number of hydrogen atoms is $2n+2$. They are called 'saturated' hydrocarbons because each carbon atom is united with the maximum number of hydrogen atoms.

Containing fewer hydrogen atoms per atom of carbon, the *naphthenes* are distinguished by having the carbon atoms arranged in rings, giving a slightly closer packing of the atoms in the molecule, reflected in a higher density. In the *aromatics*, however, the carbon atoms arrange themselves in rings of six, and the molecule contains six fewer hydrogen atoms than the corresponding naphthene. From this indiscriminate mixture of so many different compounds, the refinery produces a large number of substances for varying purposes, and in amounts depending on the demands made at any one time in any place. In the early days of oil exploration the principal requirement was for kerosene (better known in Britain as paraffin) for heating and lighting. Natural

The oil refinery at Kirkuk, Iraq. The taps in the foreground regulate the flow of crude oil and oil fractions through the refinery's stages. In the background are stills.

gases and the lighter parts of the crude oil, which we now use as petrol or gasoline, were burnt as unusable waste products.

Early in the twentieth century the development of the petrol engine changed all that, however, and together with the use of gas for heating and lighting, led to an upsurge in the sales of petrol and, locally, of natural gas, while paraffin was regarded as an encumbrance at the refinery. But again, in the 1950s, jet and jet turbine engines began consuming vast quantities of kerosene, which is a much better fuel for these continuous-burning engines than the lighter and more volatile gasoline fractions. So the pendulum of refining swung back once again. Fortunately, refinery techniques had by this time reached a very advanced stage of development, so that subsequent unexpected demands, such as for the raw materials for the plastics industry, posed few problems to the refineries.

As with any item intended for mass consumption, the economics of oil products are particularly critical. Profit per gallon is low, and so the siting of a refinery, for example, is of the utmost importance. At first sight, since the volume of saleable products is only nine-tenths of the volume of the original crude, it would appear to be best to site the refinery near the well to save transport cost.

Since wage rates in the consuming countries are also generally higher than in the producing countries, there would

An engraving by Stradamus of the production of olive oil. In the foreground tyre-like baskets are filled with olives ready for the oil to be pressed. The oil is decanted into barrels.

appear to be a double saving. However, the risk of contamination of the end product and the problems of distribution more than offset these two factors, and so the refineries are almost always built near the markets.

In Europe, most crude oil arrives by tanker, and so refineries are usually on the coast or on an estuary which provides a deep-water berth for these vessels. But there is a second reason why a refinery should be built near the sea: vast quantities of water are needed for cooling and raising steam for the separation processes.

Modern refineries are operated on the stream system, in which the crude is processed continuously. This is distinct from the older batch method in which reaction vessels were filled with crude, the process run to completion, stopped, the vessel emptied and the process begun again. The high capital cost of modern refinery equipment, with its automatic control gear, makes it necessary for operation to be virtually non-stop.

Feedstock, the crude oil, must always be available, and each refinery has large storage tanks so that the refinery will continue to operate for a period of weeks even in the event of a breakdown in supply. Oil from the tankers is discharged directly into these tanks, which in turn feed the first refining stages.

Refining techniques

Refining processes can be divided naturally into two groups: physical separation, which depends on the physical characteristics of the constituents of the oil such as specific gravity and volatility (the best known of these processes is fractional distillation), and processes in which a chemical reaction is used to change the character of the constituents. Among the latter are cracking, reforming and polymerization.

The oldest of all techniques for reducing crude oil to usable compounds is distillation, a process similar to that used in producing fresh water from sea water.

In refineries these stills are known as fractionating columns, and they can be anything up to 50 ft in diameter and 180 ft high, as tall as the drilling rig at an oil well. Stills operate in banks, through which the raw material passes in sequence.

Normally, the first column operates at fairly high pressure, usually about 100 lb/sq. in., to give the first separation of light and heavy fractions. Crude oil, previously heated to about 425 °C., is pumped into the bottom of the tower, which contains a number of catchment trays at various heights. As the crude enters the column, the lighter fractions, with their lower boiling points, ascend as vapour while the heaviest parts of the crude condense at the bottom of the column and are run off. As the vapours ascend the column, each liquefies out at its own boiling point, so that each can be extracted from the

tower at the appropriate level. The fractions which are taken off at this stage are known as side-cuts, and they also contain a proportion of lighter fractions. These are further separated outside the column, and the light vapours are returned to the column by pumping them in from the top. Not only does this increase the purity of the side-cut, but it also improves the 'sharpness' of separation within the column.

Normally, only constituents which boil in the gasoline range, that is, the fractions which will eventually go to drive our cars, will be extracted in this first column. At least two other columns are necessary before the distillation is complete.

The second column in the bank is run at atmospheric pressure, and it is fed by the liquid run off from the bottom of the first column. In this second column, kerosene and the middle distillates are extracted and the 'bottoms' are run off to a third column. Because of the higher temperatures involved in the second column, it is fed by steam which is subsequently separated from oil products by an overhead condenser which is cooled by water. This explains why so much water is necessary for the operation of refineries, and why they are located near the sea.

When it has passed through a heater, the heavy fractions from the second column are fed into a third column, which is the vacuum column, operated at a pressure well below atmosphere. This partial vacuum is secured by injecting steam and rapidly condensing it. The third column gives separation of the heavy fractions in the crude oil, and completes the distillation process.

Besides the hydrocarbons in crude oil, there are certain impurities which can be either unpleasant or dangerous if included in the finished product, particularly if this is a fuel. Two of these impurities are sulphides and a class of compounds called mercaptans, which are rather like alcohols except that they have sulphur atoms replacing the oxygen atoms. The process

used for the extraction involves dissolving out the impurities and perhaps the most common is the Eldeanu process, which uses liquid sulphur dioxide at low temperatures as the solvent. An advantage of this method over chemical treating processes is that it yields valuable by-products.

Liquid sulphur dioxide is used to cool a kerosene fraction (known as the kerosene feed) and the kerosene is fed into the bottom of a chamber known as a contacting column while the much heavier liquid sulphur dioxide is allowed in through the top. The difference in density causes a mingling of the two liquids. The result is that a mixture containing 80 per cent purified oil and 20 per cent sulphur dioxide is extracted at the top, while

A water de-salinization plant on Grand Canary Island. Where water is scarce, sea water can also be refined to remove the salts and impurities and provide fresh water for drinking.

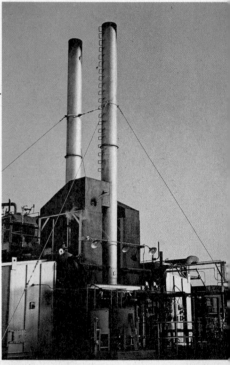

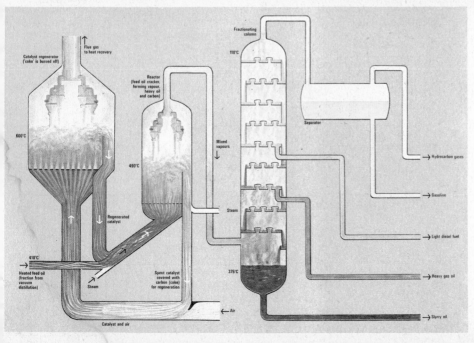

Catalyst regenerator ('coke' is burned off)

Flue gas to heat recovery

600°C

410°C

Heated feed oil (fraction from vacuum distillation)

Steam

Regenerated catalyst

Reactor (feed oil cracker, forming vapour, heavy oil and carbon)

490°C

Spent catalyst covered with carbon (coke) for regeneration

Catalyst and air

Air

Fractionating column

110°C

Mixed vapours

Separator

Steam

375°C

Hydrocarbon gases

Gasoline

Light diesel fuel

Heavy gas oil

Slurry oil

1 A worker in the oil refinery at Abadan, Persian Gulf, threads his way through the maze of pipes which carry the oil products from the fractionators to the catalytic cracker in the background.
2 A diagrammatic representation of a 'cat' cracker. Oil, with catalyst and steam, passes into a reaction vessel where it is broken down into smaller hydrocarbons suitable for motor vehicles.

another mixture of sulphur dioxide and impurities is run off at the bottom. Depending on the fraction being treated, other solvents may be used. For example, with lubricating oils, the common solvent is furfural.

In extractive distillation, which is a related process, the solvents used act as catalysts which change the boiling point of some of the constituents, so simplifying separation.

One of the oldest methods of improving the yield from a crude oil is thermal cracking, which was first used with batch stills, but which has been developed into a process with continuous plant. In

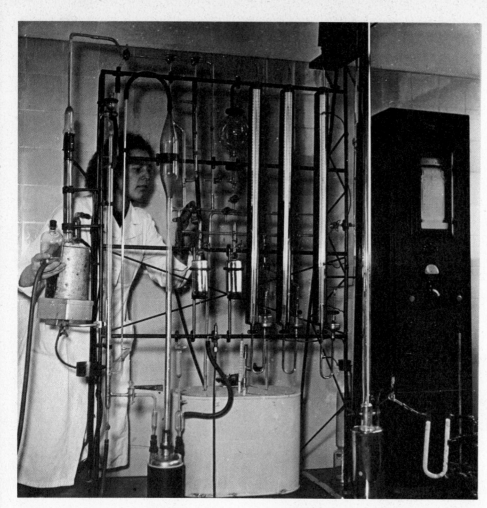

Refinery products have to be checked constantly to ensure purity and consistency of the products. A scientist at a West German refinery tests the characteristics of oil samples.

thermal cracking, the heavier molecules are broken down by heat into simpler, lighter substances. The new substances produced by this method are of a type not found in the naturally occurring oil, called olefins. These olefins contain fewer hydrogen atoms than the corresponding paraffin, and they have the unusual property that they improve the anti-knock properties of petrols which contain them. Knocking is the detonation of the fuel/air mixture in the cylinder of an engine, before the spark has been applied. Apart from making the engine run roughly, it can also cause long-term damage. Compounds which reduce this tendency are added to all modern petrols, but they are particularly important in the high-compression engines used in high-powered cars.

For most purposes, the anti-knock quality of motor spirit is expressed as its octane rating, which is merely an expression of the resistance of the fuel to detonation relative to a standard fuel under specified conditions. As fuels of high octane numbers are in great demand, processes have been developed which are specifically aimed at yielding high-octane products.

One of these processes is thermal reforming; the feedstock material in this process is naphtha, which has a low octane number. This is reformed by heat to give naphtha of a much higher octane rating.

A catalytic cracker at Rotterdam, Holland. 'Cat cracking' makes it possible to obtain a higher yield of valuable motor and aircraft fuels than would otherwise be available.

Of all the many processes carried out in oil refining the one which is usually best known, at least by name, is catalytic cracking, or cat cracking. A catalyst is a material which alters the rate of a chemical change without itself undergoing any change, and various catalysts are used in oil refineries to reform and reduce crude fractions into usable and valuable products. Catalytic cracking is also used to remove sulphur from naphthas.

Sulphur removal, in the form of its naturally occurring products, sulphides

and mercaptans, is termed sweetening, and forms an important stage in the final preparation of commercial oils. Modern refining processes generally produce a fraction which is itself sweet, the impurities having been removed during the refining stages, but it is still sometimes necessary to carry out a final purification, especially in kerosene, where sulphur in the product causes an extremely unpleasant odour when it is used as a lamp fuel.

When the crude oil has at last been fully processed, it is almost ready for sale, but, particularly with motor spirit or petrol, it must be blended in the correct proportions to give the desired characteristics. Motor-spirit blending is mainly carried out to adjust the octane rating of the fuel. High-octane products, such as olefins, are mixed with natural light fractions with a lower octane number. As the olefins are comparatively expensive, oil chemists are always searching for ways of producing a high-octane fuel which uses less of these compounds.

This can be done by adding a little tetra-ethyl lead (TEL) to the fuel. This has the effect of increasing the octane number of the fuel at little extra cost, and TEL has in fact been the means by which low-cost high-octane fuels have been produced for high-performance cars.

During the blending stage, each product receives additives, which may vary from stabilizers to prevent decomposition of, say, the olefins, to simple dyes in lubricating oils. These dyes, apart from serving as a ready means of identification, are often a good sales point. Many users of motor lubricating oil equate a slightly blue fluorescent appearance with a high-quality oil, and so the manufacturer will often add this to the mix.

Finally, the various commercial products are shipped to the point of sale by pipeline or tanker. Some will go directly to garages or commercial users, and while the fuels and lubricating oils are end products, a large part of the bulk deliveries will be destined for the petrochemical industry, to be used as the feedstock in manufacturing plastics.

Refinery management

During the whole process of refining from crude to finished product, the refinery engineers must always be aware of the fluctuating demands of the users. Modern equipment and automatic control systems in today's refineries make it possible to change the balance of the finished range of products quickly in response to changing demands. This, in fact, is one of the main advantages of the modern, automated refinery.

For the better part of the twentieth century, oil has been a major source of power, overtaking coal even in the generation of electricity. Almost all commercial lubricants are derived from oil, and with the growth of plastics, many of the goods which we use are also products of the refinery. It is only modern refining techniques which have made these advances possible, and which keep the cost of the products at a steady level.

Metals in the service of Man

Simple tools gave primitive societies the means of cultivating the land. Sophisticated jet aircraft now span the globe at supersonic speed. The metals are the bright and enduring basis of both.

METALS ARE the most important structural materials in the world of Man. Many of them are beautiful and virtually indestructible, so that today we look with wonder at bronzes from Ur of the Chaldees and at exquisitely-wrought gold ornaments from ancient Egypt. Bronze gave its name to an age, as did the much stronger and keener iron. We are today still in this Iron Age, though the word 'steel' would be more appropriate.

Apart from gold and silver, the metals of the ancients were valued mainly for their utility. Bronzes could be beaten into shape to make weapons and tools and vessels not easily broken. It was a *manageable* material and probably its earliest form was almost pure copper. But very early on, Man began to smelt rocks and so make copper and tin from their ores. It was smelting that enabled Man to produce iron, which does not occur naturally as the metal.

This early iron of prehistoric times was a crude product, probably a sort of rough steel, and it varied from place to place according to the quality of the ore available and the closely guarded know-how of the artificers, some of whom came to have more than local fame, as the astonished Crusaders found millennia later when they faced the swords of Damascus.

For thousands of years the known metallic elements could be numbered on two hands. They were gold, silver, copper, iron, tin, lead (thought to be another form of tin), zinc and bismuth (both confused with lead and other metals). Mercury was known as an oddity as early as 300 B C.

The upsurge that gave us so many of our modern metals came in the great days of the experimental chemists, in the eighteenth and nineteenth centuries. Metallic elements were isolated and named, though only in the search for truth. They were not produced in bulk.

Metals and non-metals

Cobalt was isolated in 1735, platinum at about the same time, manganese in 1827, tungsten in 1783 and nickel in 1751. Caesium was isolated in 1861 and germanium in 1886. Aluminium came in 1827. Even a metal such as titanium, regarded as an exotic modern metal, was discovered in 1789. Today, out of the 92 natural elements of which everything in the Universe is made, some two-thirds are classed as metals.

Many of them were not recognized as metals; they were just elements to be named. Today it is difficult to make an exclusive definition of what is or is not a metal in a way that will satisfy the scientist. Half a century ago a bright schoolboy would have had a ready answer.

He would have said that a metal was a material that was malleable (i.e. workable, some needing to be hot for this property to be obvious), ductile (it could be drawn into rod or wire), had a metallic sheen and was a good conductor of heat and electricity.

This seems so obvious but it is not really satisfactory. The 60 or so elements classed as metals vary very much in their properties. Cast iron, and indeed many alloys, are not malleable; they are brittle. Some are not ductile and cannot be made into wire. Some are dull to look at. The metals vary tremendously in their properties. Some have great Ultimate Tensile Strength, frequently called just the 'Strength', which is the force that will make them give way finally under tension. Some are 'tough'. The melting points range from a mere 70 °C. for an alloy of bismuth called Wood's metal to 3,370 °C. for tungsten.

Their densities range from 0·53 for lithium to 22·4 for a platinum alloy. These properties are important in all

A number of metals were first used by the alchemists and doctors as remedies for various diseases, as this seventeenth-century engraving shows. Gold was often used in medicine, and it was widely believed that the metal transmitted some of its own properties to the patient.

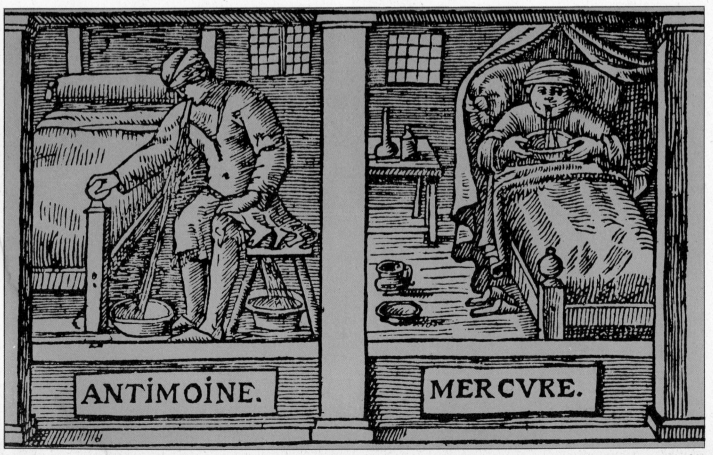

ANTIMOINE.   MERCVRE.

1 Copper ores are often extracted from open-cast mines such as this one in Zambia.
2 Electrolytic extraction of the metal from its ores involves the use of large electrodes. When an electric current is passed through a solution of the ore in water, copper is deposited in a highly pure state.
3 Because of its property of transmitting heat very readily (good thermal conductivity), copper is used in radiators of motor vehicles, and in industrial heat-exchange equipment such as these vast turbo-generator coolers. For the same reason, it is also used as a base for cooking utensils.

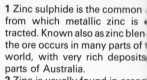

1 Zinc sulphide is the common from which metallic zinc is tracted. Known also as zinc blen the ore occurs in many parts of world, with very rich deposits parts of Australia.
2 Zinc is usually found in assoc tion with other metals such as ver and lead. When the ores ha been extracted, often by und ground drilling as in this A tralian mine, the metals are refin and separated.
3 External steel structures I this pier at Scheveningen Holland are coated with zinc protection against corrosion. T technique is more effective th painting.

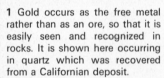

1 Gold occurs as the free metal rather than as an ore, so that it is easily seen and recognized in rocks. It is shown here occurring in quartz which was recovered from a Californian deposit.
2 Its use as the basis of international currency means that gold must be available in an easily handled form. It is melted and cast into bars of a standard size and shape for storage by treasuries throughout the world.
3 The perfect state of this Peruvian gold mask after more than 700 years convincingly demonstrates the metal's resistance to corrosion. It was this property which first led to its use in currency.

practical applications. Aluminium alloy is used for aircraft frames because of its strength combined with lightness. But it melts at just above 600 °C., so it would not do for supersonic aircraft travelling at 1,500 miles an hour or more. Titanium, melting at 1,800 °C. and with a relative density only about half as much again as aluminium alloy, here comes into its own. Nor would magnesium alloy do for canning the uranium in a nuclear reactor because it would melt. So stainless steel is used.

What about the metals' good conduction of electricity? A table of the values of the resistivity, which is the resistance in millionths of an ohm per cubic centi-

metre, shows some peculiarities. Silver has a value of 1·59 at room temperature, copper 1·72, gold 2·44 and aluminium 2·82 – all very low resistivities and therefore high conductivities. This shows why copper, which is so much cheaper than silver, is generally used for electrical conductors and power cables. Hard rubber, on the other hand, has a value of very many millions of millions and is thus a non-conductor, or insulator and it is a non-metal.

An electronic distinction

But what about hard carbon with a figure of 5,000? This is a non-metal and yet is a much better conductor than germanium,

which is classed as an element with more metallic properties than non-metallic. This has a resistivity of 46 million. It is in fact called a semi-conductor and was the earliest material to be used for transistors.

Attempts have been made to combine all the properties that are specifically metallic into a reasonable definition. One depends on the atomic structure of elements. Every one of the 92 natural elements consists of a nucleus with a positive electrical charge surrounded by moving negative electrons that exactly balance the nuclear charge.

Thus iron has a nuclear charge of +26 balanced by 'shells' or circular layers of 26 negative electrons. Each shell has its specific number of available places, like a

1 Aluminium is by far the most abundant metal on Earth. It normally occurs as bauxite, which is aluminium oxide. This ore is formed by the weathering of rocks such as mica or feldspar. Aluminium also occurs as cryolite.

2 Bauxite is easily mined, as it occurs in such large quantities on the Earth's surface. After the top layer of earth has been removed, the ore can be dug out and loaded by machine.

3 Its lightness, strength and attractive appearance make aluminium a common metal in households as well as in industry. It is easily rolled into thin foils and can be anodized in attractive colours.

1 Iron is second only to aluminium in abundance. But as well as occurring on the Earth, it is also a constituent of meteorites, as this fragment which was found in Australia indicates.

2 Extraction of iron from the ore is done by smelting, which reduces the oxide to the metal and separates out impurities such as silicates. Generally, this is only a first step, the iron then forming the basis of various steels.

3 Iron and steel have been used for armour and helmets throughout history. As this picture shows, stainless steel still has something to contribute to unusual types of clothing.

bus. When all the shells, from the nucleus outwards, are filled, the element is inert. It is therefore classed as a non-metal.

Elements with only one or two in the outermost shell are willing to give them up and so as a result become positively charged. Such an element, say the physicists, is a metal. But hydrogen has only one electron and can give it up very readily. So sometimes it acts as a metal and yet it is a gas and a non-metal.

This explanation agrees with another physical concept of the metallic state, one which conforms to the idea of 'true metals'. The identical atoms of the metal arrange themselves in an orderly way as closely as possible, rather like a lot of billiard balls, in rows and layers. The outer free electrons then act as if they are interchangeable between atoms, and their attractive force binds the atoms together.

Structure and strength

They act as a sort of cloud of glue. When an electrical pressure is applied, these free electrons are available to drift along. They constitute the electric current, and their movement also allows easy conduction of heat. This explanation shows the sharp distinction between metals and non-metals.

In non-metals either all the shells are filled completely, or almost completely filled, so that there is no tendency to provide free electrons; or the atoms may be held together by strong chemical bonds which maintain the electrons in the molecular pattern.

Sir Lawrence Bragg once gave an elegant demonstration of how such a system might work. He made a raft of identical tiny soap bubbles on the surface of water. With ingenious gadgets he showed how he could make one row of bubbles slither over another layer touching it. Very little force was needed. He then showed that if the raft was distorted so that the bubbles separated into groups with random lines of separation between the groups, then it was more difficult to make a row slide over the other because there were fewer

Iron gave its name to an age, and early iron workers used simple furnaces to refine and work the metal to make primitive tools, weapons and ornaments.

bubbles in a continuous row.

In addition, there was a sudden break at the separation of one group from another and this prevented further sliding. He also showed that if a larger or smaller bubble was inserted into the otherwise homogeneous raft this would also cause irregularities with the same effect as the distortions he had previously demonstrated.

This explanation can be transferred to real metals. Sir Lawrence was working with only one layer, whereas a real substance has many layers, so that the effects he showed operate in three dimensions instead of two. The creation of grains or crystals with separation boundaries strengthens the metal so that it is more difficult to stretch it; the smaller the grains or crystals and the more boundaries there are, the stronger the metal. On the other hand, a metal is very soft when there are very few grains. In addition, if foreign atoms are introduced into a metallic element its characteristics are changed. In some cases, such as the addition of the larger tin atoms into copper, the result is an increase in strength, so that bronze is stronger than copper.

These explanations, however, are not enough to provide a complete explanation of metallic properties. For example, selenium has spiral chains of atoms and can exist as a red amorphous (non-crystalline) material or as a grey metallic material. The first is a non-metal and the second more nearly a metal. Then again, bismuth and tin and lead can be alloyed to make a metal that melts several hundred degrees below the melting point of the separate elements. It is Wood's metal, which one can melt by the heat of a match. And everyone has used solder, which is an alloy of lead and tin which melts well below the melting point of either metal.

Thus the metallurgist is driven eventually to a classification that includes *true metals, pseudo-metals* (which are more like true metals than non-metals) and *hybrid metals* (which have the properties of both to about equal degrees). This discussion may seem academic and of interest only to the pure scientist, but it is not.

Out of the detailed investigations has come understanding of what was for so long a rule-of-thumb branch of engineering. From inquiries into the solid state have come means of making all sorts of metals with special properties, such as magnetic materials not made of iron. One alloy of platinum and cobalt, for example, is the most powerful magnetic material, and is used for tiny devices such as hearing aids.

Shaping the properties

Skilful alloying can also produce metals that will withstand extremes of environment, metals that resist atmospheric corrosion (special stainless steels) and so on. There are more metallic materials available today than ever before and there is a more precise understanding of them as a result of scientific investigation of the metallic state. In this work the most advanced and sophisticated instruments are used.

The atoms-all-in-a-row explanation also clarifies some of the practices and phenomena of metals engineering. One of the commonest of these is *work-hardening*. If a man tries to break a piece of copper wire with his hands, as he would string, he fails. But if he bends it backwards and forwards a few times it breaks like a biscuit.

What he has done is to apply stresses that create more and more crystal boundaries until the metal becomes brittle and snaps. This is a simple example of work-hardening, a process which takes place when metal is forged or hammered or rolled, and allowance has to be made for this in the quality of the metal in the first place. It often occurs when a metal is being used in a moving device, and often leads to failure of component parts in metal structures and machinery.

Another useful method of altering the characteristics of a metal is heat-treatment. Heating does many things to a metal, one of them being to reduce the crystal boundaries and make the metal tend to flow. But if the hot metal – red hot perhaps – is suddenly quenched in water there is no time for the heat to diffuse out naturally and myriads of crystal boundaries are formed, so that the metal often becomes glass hard.

How would one make a file hard enough to cut other hard metals? Is there a tool hard enough to cut the ridges? The answer is easy. The ridges are cut when the steel is comparatively soft and then the file is hardened by heat treatment. Naturally, there are many other things to consider in an alloy, or a metal, such as the existence of true compounds (for example, iron carbide in some steels) but the grain-boundary explanation accounts for many of the phenomena.

Tough alloys of iron

By far the most important field of metallurgy is concerned with steel, or rather steels, for there are many. Steel is the cheapest structural metal in the world and the most widely used – 500 million tons of it every year. The basis of all steels is iron with the addition of other compounds to give the steels their particular properties. With the addition of a small percentage of carbon, iron becomes mild steel.

Increasing the amount of carbon gives medium steel, and the addition of chromium and nickel results in one form of stainless steel. Chromium, molybdenum, silicon, nickel, manganese among other metals are used to give properties of toughness, stainlessness, hardness and rollability to steels.

The steel industry throughout the world has replaced the skill of the old operators by computer control and advanced scientific testing techniques. Steel-making now uses oxygen instead of air to cause fierce combustion of the carbon and impurities in the raw material – scrap and pig iron and alloying materials. Above all there is the continuous casting of steel from furnaces into the billet form required by steel fabricators.

Electric-arc furnaces for the batch production of really large quantities of special steels are now in use. Analytical instruments of the most sophisticated sort are in continuous use to detect impurities present in only a few parts per million.

From their use in ornaments and jewellery, weapons and cooking pots, the metals have become the most useful and widespread materials known to twentieth-century Man. No office, home or city could serve its functions in the technological age without the metals in their many forms. The glitter and durability which attracted men so many thousands of years ago are among the properties which make the metals the most useful materials of the present day.

Continuous production of steels from the iron ore in one operation is now reducing both the capital cost of plant and the price of the end product.

The steelmakers

Man has surrounded himself with steel. Ranging from the stainless steel knife or can-opener in a kitchen to the stress-resistant rockets that probe space, it is the basis of modern civilization.

OF THE MANY crafts and skills developed by primitive Man, the exploitation of metal-working has outstripped all others in its contribution to the material basis of present-day society. An early reference to the craft is found in the Old Testament and archaeologists say that iron-ore has been reduced to forms of pig iron for nearly 4,000 years.

Ancient Man probably discovered iron-making by accident. By lighting a fire on or close to an outcrop of iron-ore he would have seen a shiny liquid form. From this initial discovery he developed the process for iron-making. Using the wind as a draught and a hole in the ground for a furnace he could make pig iron. By using charcoal in his simple furnace, the quality of the product was improved. This process of increasing the carbon content of wrought iron by heating it with carbon, with no air present, is the method known as *cementation*. By heating and quenching the iron, sharp-edged weapons could be produced.

The first successful use of bellows originated in Spain. Made of a skin bag, with a tube into the furnace, the bellows were used to increase the supply of wind to the furnace and so enable higher temperatures to be reached. Catalonia became an important centre for steelmaking in Spain and Toledo steel became world-famous. The furnace developed became known as the *Catalan forge*. Small lumps of ore were heated in a charcoal fire, with lime and marl binding them together and acting as a flux. The product, after repeated hammerings, gave a suitable metal that could

During processing, flat slabs of steel are fed into a heating furnace and passed through mills to produce this hot rolled strip which moves along a cooling bed.

Steel for special uses can be shaped with an accuracy equivalent to splitting a human hair 270 times. These mechanical seals have been made for space rockets at a Los Angeles factory.

be worked by the blacksmith.

Shortly before the close of the Middle Ages steel was first made by heating iron-ore together with charcoal in an air-free tube. This steel was known as *blister steel*. Further heating and hammering produced *shear* steel, which was a more homogeneous, uniform product. The steel produced was used by the blacksmith, armourer and cutler, for the production of small everyday items such as knives, locks, hinges, bolts, nails and weapons.

The great leap forward in steel production came in about 1340 with the development in Germany of the *Stückhofen*, an early form of the blast-furnace. This enabled the iron producer to control his process better, to reach a higher temperature and made it possible to run the molten iron into big moulds.

With this single development iron and steel production raced ahead in size and quality. By the sixteenth century rolling-mills were being used in Germany and the Low Countries. The only factor which held back iron production at this time, the dependence upon timber as fuel, was overcome during the eighteenth century with the use of coke. After many decades of effort to develop an alternative to wood as fuel, Abraham Darby in 1709 first used coke successfully in smelting. The blast-furnaces worked at higher temperatures and were able to produce better, finer castings for more varied uses.

Modern blast-furnaces based on the same principles are used to produce pig iron for the steel industry. The ore, mixed with limestone and coke, is fed into the upper part of the furnace and is at once acted upon by the gases coming up from below. The principal gas is carbon monoxide and the temperature at the top of the furnace is between 200 °C. and 500 °C. Reduction continues with increasing speed as the charge of ore descends to the lower region of the furnace where the temperature is about 1,000 °C. The hot, spongy iron meets the rising carbon monoxide and decomposes. The iron dissolves and absorbs carbon as it passes down the furnace. It eventually trickles down and collects, below the level of the *tuyères* (openings) in a well. In addition to carbon, the molten iron absorbs phosphorus, silicon and manganese, which are also absorbed by the *slag* (the impurities which

In a shower of sparks, steel chain links are moulded by this semi-automatic machine. The strength and durability of the final product depends on the type of steel used.

1 The strength and flexibility of steel can be increased by repeated heating and cooling. Here ceremonial swords are reheated to produce a hard cutting edge.
2 A huge steel plant at Indiana in the United States. Situated on Lake Michigan, ore, coal and other materials are brought by rail and water to feed the blast-furnaces.
3 At an up-to-date mine in Sweden, television is used to watch and control the transportation of iron-ore to the surface.
4 A huge piece of red-hot steel is squeezed into shape between the jaws of an 8,000-ton press at Sheffield. This method of forging increases the strength of the steel.
5 In an electric-arc furnace, extremely high temperatures are reached when an electric charge jumps or *arcs* between the electrodes and the melting metal. Here the red-hot electrodes are raised above the roof of the furnace.

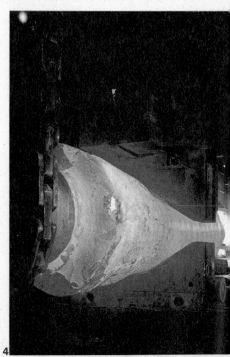

rise to the surface).

In the 1740s Benjamin Huntsman realized that by using the old cementation process and raising the cemented steel to melting-point, a better-quality steel could be produced. His idea was tried out in a large crucible and the slag impurities skimmed off the surface as they floated to the top. The metal was then poured into a mould and left to solidify into a mass which could be worked into the desired shapes. The steel was found to be homogeneous and free from slag and dirt. It was immediately recognized that for producing superior steels this process was the best and it was quickly adopted.

Developments in engineering helped the steel-maker and with the coming of the steam-engine larger blast-furnaces and mills were the order of the day. Pig-iron output rose in Britain from 20,000 tons a year in 1700 to 1,500,000 tons by 1850. At least half of this went to the railways.

The next step forward in steelmaking was in the 1840s and 1850s by two men working independently in different countries: Henry Bessemer (1813–98), an Englishman and William Kelly (1811–88) an American. Bessemer discovered that by blowing a current of air through molten pig iron, unwanted chemicals, such as carbon and silicon, were oxidized out of the melt. Bessemer used tuyères in the bottom of the refractory-lined crucible of molten pig iron to blow pressurized air through the melt. The product of the Bessemer process was *mild steel* which had

a low silicon and carbon content and which could not only be used for implements needing temper, such as springs, knives and tools but also for the railways, engineering and shipbuilding industries.

The process in the Bessemer converter receives energy in the form of heat from the endothermic oxidization of the impurities. About ten tons of molten pig iron are run into the large converter made of iron plates lined with siliceous bricks, and provided with holes at the bottom through which a powerful blast of air can be blown. The carbon monoxide which is formed burns at the mouth of the converter. By observing the flame, the correct moment to stop the blast can be determined. When the blast has been stopped the right amount of *spiegeleisen,* a ferro-manganese containing a known quantity of carbon, is added. Then the blast is turned on for a few moments and then metal poured into moulds. Unfortunately this process can only be used with phosphorus-free pig iron since, if phosphorus is present it is oxidized but not removed, and the steel is brittle and useless.

In 1877 Sidney Thomas and Percy Gilchrist showed that if the converter is lined with lime then, by blasting with air for a little longer, the oxides of phosphorus, sulphur and silicon which form remove themselves from the furnace by combining with the lime. Basic slag arises in this case, and is used as a fertilizer, due to its rich phosphorus content. If the lining of the Bessemer converter is siliceous, the

operation is called the *acid Bessemer process,* and if dolomite, the *basic Bessemer process.*

The melted iron from the blast-furnace is run into the Bessemer converter and the blast turned on. The silicon and carbon react with the iron oxide formed, then the carbon reacts, and large flames appear at the mouth of the converter. When the flame dies down, the molten metal is nearly pure iron with a small amount of dissolved oxide. The addition of spiegeleisen is made and the normal Bessemer procedure followed. This produces mild steel containing up to 0·25 per cent of carbon. Before the 1850s, axles, crankshafts, piston-rods, shafting, bars and plates were made of wrought iron. When Bessemer found how to make steel on a large scale, directly from blast-furnace pig iron, all these items were qualitatively improved. Gilchrist and Thomas improved on Bessemer's original converter for the handling of high-phosphorus ores 20 years later, by introducing a basic lining.

Open hearths

The next important development in steel technology came in 1864, when the Martin brothers in France first successfully worked the open-hearth process. This had been suggested initially in 1722 by René de Réaumur in France and by John Payne in 1728. The Martin brothers used an invention of Sir William Siemens to reduce heat losses from the furnace with the *regenerative gas furnace.* This utilized the waste heat in the burnt gases coming from a furnace to pre-heat the air needed for the burning of the fuel, and allowed for higher furnace temperatures.

The open hearth was able to save on costs and became widely popular since another advantage it had over the Bessemer converter was that large quantities of scrap metal could be used. Siemens's open hearth consists of a large flat hearth

enclosed in a furnace heated by producer gas. The air and gas are supplied through different regenerators of chequered brickwork. The hearth is either *acid lined* with silica, or *basic lined* with dolomite or calcined magnesite, depending on which process is being used.

The charge used is pig iron, steel scrap and haematite, with limestone added for the basic process. Part of the carbon is burnt out of the cast iron by the action of haematite, and fluid steel remains. The subsequent operations in the hearth are the same as those in the Bessemer process. The furnace can be tilted and a portion of its contents discharged into a ladle. Usually eight to ten hours are needed for the full operation of the hearth, from start to finish.

The open hearth is more easily controlled than the Bessemer process and is used widely. Both processes, however, have certain limitations when the special high-quality steel is needed as the finished product. A high-quality steel is usually called an *alloy steel,* but the two processes described are incapable of producing alloy steel commercially, because of the whole process of oxidation, limited control of slag, and use of deoxidizers.

To overcome these difficulties, electricity is used for heating. All oxidizing gases are eliminated by the use of electrical energy and the character of the slag can be changed from oxidizing to reducing conditions, enabling the addition of alloys without loss in the slag. The principal type of electric arc-furnace was first used commercially in France in 1902 by Paul Héroult. In this process electric current is conducted into a covered furnace through three large electrodes made of carbon or graphite. Very high temperatures are obtained as the electricity *arcs* or jumps between an electrode, the metal and another electrode. These furnaces have a very large output of high-grade carbon or alloy steel.

In the *high-frequency* or *induction furnace* the charge of scrap metal is put into a crucible of refractory material, surrounded by a coiled conductor. An alternating high-frequency current passing through the coil induces a secondary current in the charge of material and raises the temperature. The hearth of the arc-furnace may be acid or basic lined, according to necessity and is of the same design as the open-hearth furnace.

Basic-lined furnaces are used mainly for electric steel production, and acid-lined furnaces for the refining of semi-finished liquid steel. The latter is of greatest value to the steel manufacturers. The high-frequency furnace is used mostly for steel melting, not for refining, and the capacity of the furnace is less than the arc-furnace, being from a quarter of a ton to five tons. Carefully selected scrap and alloys are used and the steel produced made into articles like ball-bearings.

Duplexing and cascade casting

To combine the cheapness of the Bessemer process with the high-quality control of the open hearth or arc-furnace, steel is made sometimes by refining in the converter and finishing in one of the other furnaces. This method is known as *duplexing.* For some refined steels vacuum furnaces, first developed for non-ferrous metals, are used. Melting is carried out under high vacuum and an arc is used to heat the charge. The electrodes themselves are made of steel and they are eaten away as the current is passed. Titanium is one metal with a special application to this method.

A technique which has been developed since the 1930s is that of continuous or *cascade casting.* Initially developed for non-ferrous metals, by 1956 it was being used on an industrial scale in 12 countries. The continuous casting process starts when liquid steel from the furnace is poured into a water-cooled jacket of copper or brass, in the shape of a tube, with a round, rectangular or oval cross-section. The metal cools, solidifies, shrinks from the mould and is drawn out of the mould by rollers which grip the ingot at the lower end. It is cut or *sheared* as it emerges into the required lengths, and the ingots rolled or forged as needed. The metal is more homogeneous when cast in this way, and ingot pits and moulds are eliminated from the foundry. This method is now used for the casting of large slabs and sheets.

At each stage of production of steel, many tests are made to control the contents and qualities, from the raw materials to the finished products. Altogether over 35 tests may be carried out on the molten steel in the furnace. In the past, the steelmakers had to depend entirely on their own experience and judgement. Now steel plants contain a huge array of instruments to control the furnaces, the temperatures and flow of fuels. Samples of steel are taken from the furnace for testing. When cool, they are examined and analysed in laboratories with such instruments as X-ray machines, electron microscopes and spectroscopes. They are also tested for strength, durability, resistance to wear and hardness.

Thousands of different kinds of steel are made by varying the chemical composition or the processing after the steel leaves the furnace. *Carbon steels,* the most widely used of all steels, contain up to 1·5 per cent of carbon with small amounts of manganese to make the steel less brittle. *Alloy steels* contain carbon and other chemicals, such as chromium, manganese, molybdenum, tungsten and vanadium, according to the properties of steel required. Nickel, for example, is added to steel to increase toughness and resistance to acids and heat. Nickel and chromium are used to make stainless steels which do not rust or corrode. *Tool* or *high-speed steels,* which usually contain tungsten and chromium, remain hard and sharp at high cutting speeds which produce temperatures sufficient to soften many other steels.

From the small, primitive beginnings, the production of steel has grown into a huge international industry with an output of over a million tons of steel a day of thousands of different types to be used in millions of manufactured products, ranging from sewing needles to space rockets.

Liquid steel from a furnace is poured from a continuous casting machine into water-cooled moulds. As the metal cools, it shrinks and can be drawn out of the moulds.

Thousands of types of steel can be made by varying the ingredients. This piece of transparent steel – still a laboratory curiosity – was produced by research scientists.

Before the breaking point

As aeroplanes go faster and faster, as buildings rise higher and higher, the question, 'Will they hold together?' becomes more and more important. The answer comes from stress analysis.

IT IS NOT UNUSUAL to hear someone talk about 'the stresses and strains of modern life'. But many people using this expression are probably unaware that it has been borrowed from the world of physics, and that stress and strain are in fact quite different from each other.

To understand this difference, consider a rubber band hanging from a hook. If we pull on the rubber band it will stretch. The force of the person pulling it is a *stress* and the increase in the length of the rubber band is a *strain*. Stress is the cause, and strain is the effect.

In addition to this casual connection between stress and strain there is a mathematical relationship, discovered by the English physicist Robert Hooke (1635–1703). He made careful measurements of the strains produced in vertical coiled springs by attaching various weights to them. He found that doubling the weight on a spring doubled the increase in the spring's length. In other words, doubling the stress on the spring will double the strain produced. If we plot a graph of the stress against the strain, we get a straight line. In other words, strain is proportional to stress and this is known as Hooke's Law. Substances obeying the law are known as *elastic* solids.

Compressing and stretching

Hooke's Law also applies for strains produced by forces other than stretching stresses, such as those produced by compressing stresses or twisting stresses. In every case, so long as the law holds, the strain is proportional to the stress producing it, and if all stress is removed, the strain will become zero. This fact means that any deformation – a stretch, a twist, or a bend – will disappear if the stress producing it is removed.

The ratio of stress to the strain it will produce is an indication of the strength of any substance, and is known as a *modulus*. For instance, the modulus which indicates resistance of a material to stretching or compressing was defined by the English doctor and physicist Thomas Young (1773–1829), and named after him. The Young's modulus of steel is about four times as great as the Young's modulus of glass – which indicates the greater resistance of steel to compressing, stretching, or bending.

But we cannot go on stretching a material for ever. For every solid there is a limit to the force that can be applied without producing a permanent deformation. Beyond this *elastic limit*, removal of all stress will still leave the solid with some strain. This residual strain in an object stressed beyond its elastic limit is called a *permanent set*. For instance, if a piece of rubber is stretched and then released, it springs back to its original length. But if a piece of copper wire is stretched too far, it keeps its new length because the elastic limit of the material has been exceeded.

When the elastic limit has been passed, further increase in stress will take the solid to its *yield point*. A stress beyond the yield stress produces a change in the internal structure of a solid, and groups of atoms start sliding over each other. Usually this internal breakdown takes place in one part of the solid which is weaker than the rest. For instance, if a metal rod is put under a stretching stress beyond the elastic limit, one weak part of the rod usually stretches more than the rest, and becomes thinner. This thinner part is called a *neck*.

If the stretching stress on a rod is continually increased beyond the elastic limit, and beyond the yield point, it eventually reaches a point where the rod breaks. This value of the stress is known as the *ultimate strength* of the material in the rod. The ultimate strength of steel is a stress of about 100,000 pounds per square inch. This means that a steel rod one square inch in cross-section could support more than 40 tons.

When engineers are designing structures which have to bear loads, such as bridges and aeroplanes, it is obviously very important to avoid making the stress on any part of the structure come near its ultimate strength. In actual practice, engineers are careful to avoid stresses coming even remotely near the elastic limit, to minimize the risk of breaking any part of the

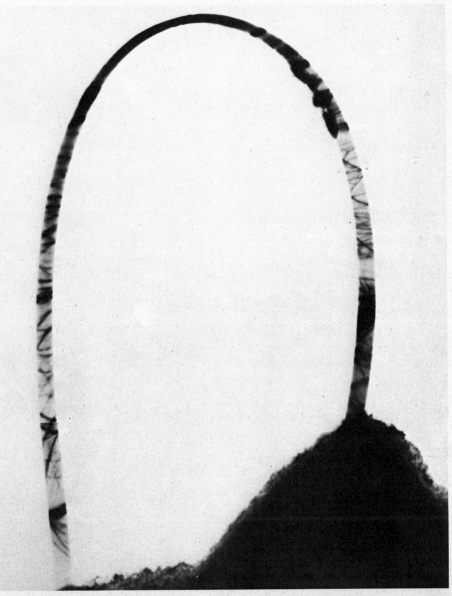

Whiskers, long hair-like growths in crystals produced from super-saturated solutions, give added strength. In tin, for example, strength can be increased by more than a thousand times.

structure, however apparently trivial.

To discover the distribution of stresses within a structure, a design is often tested by *experimental stress analysis*. This involves measuring the strain at various parts of the structure, and applying Hooke's Law to calculate the stress. A model or prototype of the structure is made, and strain gauges are attached to it at the positions under investigation. A strain gauge measures the variation in the distance between the two points at which it is attached to the structure. The change in distance is measured through its effect on some electrical property of the gauge, and this change in electrical property is used to calculate the strain in the structure at the position of the gauge.

Another method of stress analysis depends on the principle of *photo-elasticity*. Some transparent solids, such as glass and celluloid, have a special effect on light when they are subjected to stress. If a glass model is made of a structure which is to be tested, the model can be put under stress and the distribution of stress within the model studied by looking at its effect on light.

Laying the lattice

As a very simple example of the effects of stress analysis on design, imagine a beam of square cross-section supported at both ends and carrying a load in the middle. The beam will bend. The lower layers of material in the beam will be stretched and the upper layers will be compressed. Between these two extremes are the middle layers which are under very little stress. Thus the top and the bottom layers take most of the load, and so a beam of cross-section like a letter I is very nearly as strong under bending as one resembling a hollow square in cross-section. The I-beam is, of course, lighter than a hollow square one of the same outside measurements, and is therefore easier to transport. This reduction in weight is also important in constructing bridges, big buildings, aeroplanes, etc., which must bear their own weight as well as a useful load.

1 The world-famous Eiffel Tower stands as a monument to the daring French engineer who designed it and to the advances in metallurgy which made it possible. When it was erected in 1889, it was condemned as both ugly and dangerous; people were afraid that it would collapse. Time has shown that Gustave Eiffel's faith in the steel girders that went into the construction of his tower was well-founded; opinion is still divided over its beauty. 2 Los Angeles, the sprawling giant of southern California, for many years prohibited high-rise buildings because the city is subject to earthquakes. Recent advances in structures and architecture have caused this restriction to be lifted, so Los Angeles is now beginning to grow upwards instead of outwards. 3 Stress on a structure of insufficient strength can produce terrible results, as in the Tay Bridge Disaster. 4 Modern bridges are much stronger than their predecessors, both in materials and design. 5 Even diamond, the hardest substance in the world, cannot stand against the piercing energy of a ruby laser. 6 A microphotograph of a type of metal used in automobile construction reveals a typical stress pattern. Knowledge of such stresses ensures greater safety.

The strength of any piece of metal depends on the metal's internal structure. Metals are made up of closely knit grains or crystals. Each of these grains has a very regular internal arrangement of atoms into a pattern which is called a *lattice*. At the boundaries between grains, the lattice is distorted. If there are many boundaries, they provide the metal with great strength. In other words, the smaller the grains, the more boundaries there are between them and the stronger is the metal. For this reason, engineers always try to make grains as small as possible to produce strong metals.

The faster a liquid metal is cooled, the smaller will be the grains which form as the metal solidifies, as large crystals do not have time to grow. Hence moulds for metal castings are usually made of materials which conduct heat away as quickly as possible, to increase the strength of the metal being cast. The part of the metal which solidifies close to the mould has very small grains, but further inside the body of the metal the cooling is slower, and the grains have more time to develop.

The tendency is for the grains to develop as columns running at right angles to the wall of the mould. Grain-formation like this eventually leaves the last of the liquid metal in the middle of the mould. This portion contains most of the impurities present in the liquid metal, and when it eventually solidifies, the impurities make it a weak spot. For this reason, the middle of a cast-iron object is often weaker than the rest.

Weaknesses can also develop in cast objects if there are sharp corners in the mould. The tendency for the inner grains to grow at right angles to the mould walls produces a line of boundaries between grains. This line leads from the sharp corner into the body of the metal and the weak area in the middle. Thus sharp corners are a source of weakness and are avoided wherever possible in the design of cast metal objects.

Although engineers make sure that no part of an object they design will ever be subjected to a stress near its ultimate strength, they cannot avoid breakages entirely, because of the phenomenon

known as *fatigue*. If an object is repeatedly stressed, even well within its elastic limit, fatigue will inevitably cause it to break sooner or later. The continual stressing gradually distorts the structure of the grains. Eventually minute cracks develop and slowly grow. If the cracks are not noticed they will eventually grow large enough for breakage. Metal fatigue is the cause of many aeroplane and railway accidents, and some car breakdowns. For this reason, many railway and airline companies use portable X-ray equipment to look for flaws in metal structures.

Another phenomenon which can cause failure in materials over a length of time is *creep*. An object under constant loading will very gradually increase its deformation due to a very slow sliding or flow of its atoms across each other. Creep can be a considerable problem with concrete when it is used to support heavy loads, as in many modern buildings. With metals, resistance to creep decreases with rising temperature. For this reason, metal parts for use at high temperatures – for instance, turbine blades in jet engines – are liable to creep. Special non-creep alloys have been developed to combat such structural failures.

The internal behaviour of a metal is very similar in nature when it is undergoing creep and when it is 'necking' (producing a neck) under a stress greater than its yield stress. In both cases, the atoms comprising the metal are sliding or flowing across each other. There are some substances which undergo this flow at extremely low stresses, in the phenomenon called *plasticity*. Plastic solids have a very low yield stress, and continually deform if subjected to a force greater than their yield stress. The graph of stress against strain for a plastic solid is a short straight line up to the yield stress, exactly like an elastic solid obeying Hooke's Law.

Two types of plastic

However, beyond the yield point, it is a straight line parallel to the strain axis, showing that at the yield stress, the plastic will deform indefinitely. This behaviour was first described mathematically by B. de St. Venant (1797–1886). A solid which exhibits plasticity is therefore known as a St. Venant solid. Examples include modelling clay and lead solder. The synthetic substances known as *plastics* were originally given this name because of their plastic behaviour. However, they are not all St. Venant solids, and many of them are very elastic.

At high temperatures, but below their melting points, most metals will deform plastically. This is because a stress breaks up the crystal structure of the metal grains, and a new crystal structure cannot form until the metal is cooled. The new crystals then formed are unstressed and so the deformation produced by the stress is permanent. Use is made of this effect in the forging or hot rolling of metals, as when a blacksmith makes horseshoes from hot iron.

Plastic materials are defined by their ability to flow, but so are liquids. In that case, what is the difference between a

359

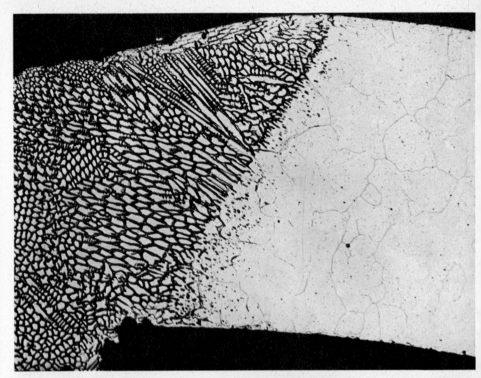

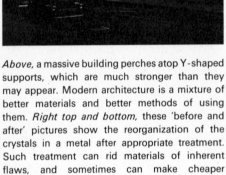

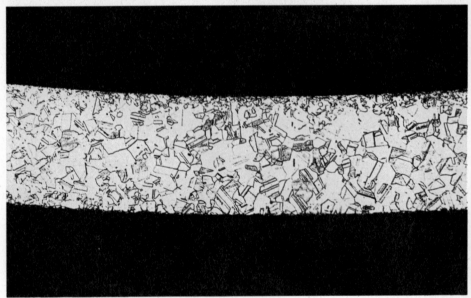

Above, a massive building perches atop Y-shaped supports, which are much stronger than they may appear. Modern architecture is a mixture of better materials and better methods of using them. *Right top and bottom,* these 'before and after' pictures show the reorganization of the crystals in a metal after appropriate treatment. Such treatment can rid materials of inherent flaws, and sometimes can make cheaper materials serve in place of more expensive ones.

liquid and a plastic solid? The only difference is that a liquid does not have a yield point – it will flow and deform under any stress, including its own weight. Tar (pitch) at room temperature is a borderline case between a solid and a liquid. It is in fact a liquid since it will flow under its own weight (though this may take weeks).

The study of flow within objects under stress is called rheology (from the Greek word *rheos* meaning 'a stream'). The distinctions between an elastic solid, plastic solid, and liquid just described are rheological distinctions – in other words, distinctions which depend on flow characteristics.

An interesting rheological problem is deciding whether or not glass is a liquid. Glass window panes which have been in position for a long time show definite evidence of flow under their own weight. The lower parts of the glass are thicker than the upper ones. This fact is often quoted as evidence that glass is a liquid. However, the 200-inch reflector in the famous Mount Palomar telescope is made of glass. (The reflector glass is the mechanical support for a very thin film of aluminium which acts as a mirror.)

When the telescope was built, the reason given for the choice of the glass as the material for the reflector was that it would retain its shape more permanently than steel or concrete. The telescope's designers evidently regarded glass as more of a solid than steel or concrete.

The stresses can be 'frozen' in some photo-elastic solids. For instance, epoxy

resins show a normal photo-elasticity pattern if subjected to a stress at a temperature of 75 °C. However, if the resin is cooled to room temperature with the stress still applied, the photo-elastic pattern is 'frozen' so that if the stress is removed, the photo-elastic pattern remains in the resin. The strain, produced by the stress at 75 °C., has become a permanent set. Furthermore, the resin can be cut without affecting the frozen photo-elastic pattern. This enables the strains in all directions to be studied, and in this way Hooke's Law can be used to get a fuller picture of the distribution of stress throughout an object (or a model of it made in resin) than could be obtained by any other method.

Freezing stress patterns

The explanation of this phenomenon is found in the structure of the epoxy resin. At room temperature, the resin can be thought of as resembling a metal spring frozen in ice. When the temperature is raised, the 'ice' part melts, and so the spring is the only part which can resist

any stress. If the 'spring' is now extended by a stretching force, and the temperature allowed to fall, the 'ice' will again freeze around the spring, holding it in its strained position. The part of the resin which corresponds to the 'ice' is rigid at room temperature, and able to flow plastically at 75 °C. The other part is rigid at both temperatures, and provides the resistance to stress at the higher temperature. Thus at 75 °C., an epoxy resin can be thought of as a mixture of elastic and plastic solids.

The subject of stress and strain analysis is yet another example of how theoretical science contributes to modern technology. It is not enough to know that materials stretch or break or flow when stresses are applied to them. The physicist must know *why*. As usual, the answer requires a knowledge of the microscopic atomic structure of materials. But once he is armed with this knowledge, the scientist can design materials which will have the physical properties he requires. In this way, modern metals and plastics are tailor-made for the jobs they have to do.

Putting chemistry to work

Switching on a battery sets off chemical reactions which are converted into electricity. The same kind of electro-chemical reactions are used for refining metal, electroplating and electrodialysis.

EVERY TIME you press the button on an electric torch and the bulb lights up you have a demonstration of electro-chemistry: for electro-chemistry is the science that relates chemical changes with the passage of electricity. There are scores of practical applications of electro-chemistry. Some, as in the torch battery, depend upon chemical changes to produce an electric current; others as in electro-deposition, depend on electrically charged particles of a substance depositing on a desired surface.

The *primary cell* of a torch battery is one of the simplest examples of electro-chemistry. Such cells are variously called *voltaic*, *galvanic* or *electromotive*. Devices in which the opposite occurs and electricity is used to induce chemical changes are called *electrolytic cells*.

There are various types of primary cell, but all depend on the principle that when chemicals react together they produce chemical energy which can be converted into electrical energy. If two metals, one positive and the other negative, are placed in an electrically conductive solution, called an *electrolyte*, the positive metal attracts electrons from the negative metal.

Gradually the negative metal is eaten away, while the movement of electrons to the positive metal produces a current, since an electric current is a movement of electrons. The two metals in the cell may be in actual contact, or they may be connected through a wire or through the filament of a lamp. The glowing filament of the torch bulb is visual evidence of electron movement in the cell.

A simple type of primary cell is the *dry cell*. One type consists of a zinc cup containing a carbon rod surrounded by ammonium chloride paste to form the electrolyte. A little manganese dioxide is added to act as an oxidizing agent. The zinc and the carbon are called the *electrodes*; the carbon being the positive electrode or *anode* and the zinc the negative electrode or *cathode*. The carbon anode or *positive pole* of the cell is a good electrical conductor and the zinc is the cathode or *negative pole*.

When the poles of the cell are connected, the zinc produces ions and releases electrons. As the zinc ions are formed they are dispersed in the electrolyte. The electrons flow through the external wires, and when they reach the carbon rod they combine with hydrogen (positive) ions to form hydrogen atoms. The function of the manganese dioxide is to oxidize the hydrogen to prevent the latter from forming a coating of insulating bubbles on the carbon rod, thereby reducing the efficiency of the cell.

Eventually so many zinc atoms are converted into ions that the zinc cup becomes

thin and finally breaks down altogether. That is why a torch battery has a limited life. It cannot be recharged, although the action of a very moderate heat may temporarily revitalize it.

Because of its relatively short life the primary cell has many limitations as a practical source of current. These disadvantages are overcome by the secondary cell or, as it is often called, the *accumulator* or storage cell. The secondary cell can act in two ways: it can run down or discharge, or it can take up electricity and recharge. For that reason, secondary cells are used to provide current for the electrical system on motor vehicles. While the car or other motor vehicle is travelling, a dynamo driven by the crankshaft generates a supply of direct current which recharges the battery.

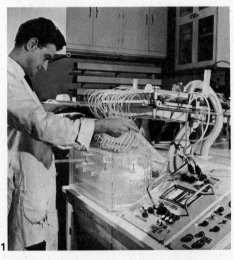

1 At a medical research institute, electrophoresis is used to sort proteins. When a voltage is passed across a solution of proteins, they are sorted according to their electrical charge.
2 Telephones run on electric batteries. In one of the telephone exchanges in London two of the staff check the specific gravity of the batteries by measuring their acid levels.

Many heavy-duty storage cells, such as those fitted in electrically propelled road vehicles, in submarines and in small, self-contained lighting and power plants, work on the principle that when a piece of lead is dipped in water a few atoms on the surface of the lead ionize and dissolve. Each ion leaves behind two electrons clinging to the surface of the lead. But there is a saturation point – or state of equilibrium – when the concentration of lead ions in solution remains constant, as does the negative charge left on the metal. The result is that the piece of lead has an overall negative charge, while the solution carries an overall positive charge. Although a potential difference now exists between the lead and the water, there is no current movement because there is nowhere for it to go.

Storage cells

It is this potential difference that is exploited to produce current in the storage cell. A lead storage or secondary cell consists of two plates: one, the negative plate, is a grid filled with spongy lead, and the other, the positive plate, is a grid filled with brown-lead dioxide. Both plates dip in a container filled with diluted sulphuric acid. When the cell is connected to an external circuit, electrons flow through the circuit to the positive plate in an effort to compensate for the deficiency there. But they cannot compensate because the electrons are taken up by certain chemicals immediately they arrive. Consequently more and more electrons flow and the result is a continuous current.

Lead atoms dissolve at the negative plate, leaving the plate negatively charged. The lead ions formed immediately react with the sulphate ions from the sulphuric acid to create lumps of lead sulphate and these stick to the lead plate. Electrons which have flowed round the circuit and arrive at the positive plate instantly combine with lead dioxide and the hydrogen ions from the sulphuric acid. Once again lead ions are formed, and as before they combine with the sulphate of sulphuric acid to produce lead sulphate which forms a coat on the lead dioxide plate.

Ultimately, because no more electrons can leave the lead electrode, the cell ceases to generate a current and becomes discharged. The cell can be recharged by connecting it to a source of direct current. The chemical action that then takes place is the reverse of that which occurred when the cell was discharging to produce a current. During discharge of a lead storage cell, removal of the sulphate ions tends to reduce the concentration of sulphuric acid in the solution, so that in time the solution or electrolyte contains less sulphuric acid. Water loss in the electrolyte is made good by adding distilled water.

No matter how big the plates of a single primary or secondary cell, the voltage produced by a single cell is constant. For a primary cell it is 1·5 volts and for a secondary cell it is 2 volts. Voltage can be increased only by joining several cells together to form a battery. The weight of batteries, particularly batteries of storage cells, is excessively high in relation to the duration and value of the voltage produced and it is this that hitherto has precluded their use for the propulsion of long-distance vehicles. At present electric traction dependent upon batteries is limited to milk floats, and other vehicles serving short routes.

Several types of light-weight storage batteries have recently been developed, but the metals used for the electrodes are, as yet, far too expensive and have too short a life between charges to be practical for long-distance road transport. Light-weight batteries using silver, cadmium and nickel have been used experimentally for the propulsion of cars, and as a power source in electric shavers, photographic equipment, rechargeable electric torches and in space craft.

Coating base metals

Electroplating is essentially a kind of *electrolysis,* whereby electrical energy causes a chemical change in a conducting medium. The medium may be either molten or a solution. The electrical energy enters and leaves the electrolytic medium through pieces of metal that act as electrodes. The electrons enter the solution at the cathode, and leave it at the anode. Positively charged ions, called *cations*, are attracted to the cathode, and negatively charged ions, called *anions,* are attracted to the anode.

Most electroplating is done to increase the value of an object made from a base metal, to give additional durability, or to render it resistant to rust and corrosion. To coat a base metal with silver, it is placed with a block of pure silver in a solution of either silver potassium cyanide or silver nitrate. The article to be plated is the cathode and the block of pure silver the anode. Passing an electric current through the electrolytic solution from one electrode to the other causes pure silver to dissolve and particles of the metal are deposited as a film on the object being plated.

Electroplating baser metals with copper is done in a similar manner. The article to be plated is connected to the negative terminal of an electric supply and becomes the cathode, while a block of pure copper forms the anode. Both are immersed in an electrolyte of copper sulphate. When current is switched on the copper from the copper-sulphate solution is deposited on the article being plated and is simultaneously replaced from the copper of the copper anode. In this way the strength of the electrolyte solution is maintained until the whole of the copper anode has fully dissolved.

Electroplating chromium on to steel in order to render the latter metal resistant to corrosion is somewhat more complex.

1 In 1868 a Frenchman, Georges Leclanché invented the prototype of the modern torch battery. The electrode is zinc, and the electrolyte is a special zinc chloride paste.
2 A battery-driven car like the Ford 'Comuta' may well be the answer to traffic exhaust pollution in the cities. The batteries are designed to be recharged from the mains.
3 Tinplate does not rust and is used for making tin cans. In one type of manufacture a pressed steel sheet is coated with a layer of tin as it passes through a special electrolyte.
4 When submerged, submarines cannot use fuels which use up oxygen and give out exhausts. Instead they run on batteries. The state of charge of these batteries must be checked constantly.
5 Special lightweight batteries using silver, cadmium and nickel have been developed for use in space craft. In space the problem of not using up oxygen is much the same as in submarines. **1**

2

Although chromium gives an exceptionally efficient tarnish-free surface, it does not adhere well to steel when directly electroplated on to it. Moreover, minute crevices are left in the chromium film through which moisture can pass and make the metal below liable to corrosive action. Accordingly, good-quality chromium-plated steel is first electroplated with copper, which provides a good adhesive surface. This surface is then electroplated with a film of nickel to give protection against corrosion. Finally, the nickel surface is electroplated with chromium to produce the tarnish-free finish.

Electrotyping is a form of electroplating used in the production of the engraved copper plates for printing. An impression of the plate is taken in a plastic material which is then covered with a layer of graphite, silver or other substance that will readily conduct electricity. Next, the plastic mould is connected to the negative terminal of an electricity supply and

3

4

placed in a solution of copper sulphate in which there is a sheet of copper connected to the positive terminal of the current supply. When the electric supply is switched on, the current passes from the copper plate to the silver- or graphite-covered mould through the electrolyte and deposits a film of copper on the plastic. When the mould is removed a copper plate is left with the desired impression on it.

For successful electroplating, the objects to be plated must be absolutely clean, and the vat containing the electrolyte must be lined with glass or other material of good insulating qualities to prevent the current from leaking through it. The strength of the applied current must be carefully controlled: this is very critical as the thickness of the metal film deposited on the article being plated depends upon it. The time taken to electroplate varies between a few minutes to over an hour.

Large-scale electroplating is carried out in huge tanks of electrolytic solution with several anodes so that batches of a hundred or more articles can be plated simultaneously. By using suitable solutions, a wide range of metals can be electroplated.

Electro-chemistry can be used in the smelting and refining of metals. The extraction of aluminium from its bauxite ore is basically an electro-chemical process. Bauxite is first subjected to a series of chemical and heat treatments to extract the alumina or aluminium oxide. The alumina is then placed in the 'furnace' together with molten cryolite, which is an aluminium compound. Although alumina has a high melting point, over 2,000 °C., it will dissolve in molten cryolite at a temperature of about 1,000 °C. to form a solution which is electrically conductive. The furnace which is basically a type of electrical cell, consists of a steel bath lined with carbon. Dipping into the alumina-cryolite electrolyte are a number of carbon blocks or rods. The carbon lining of the furnace forms the cathode of the 'cell' and the carbon blocks or rods are the anodes.

When a strong electric current at a pressure of six volts is passed through the electrolyte from anode to cathode, molten aluminium from the solution is deposited on the bottom lining of the tank, the cathode. From there the molten aluminium is drawn off and poured into ingot moulds. The electro-chemical process consumes an enormous amount of electricity: 20,000 kilowatt-hours of current are needed to produce one ton of aluminium. That is enough electricity to keep a two-bar electric fire burning for 10,000 hours.

Electrodialysis is an electro-chemical process mainly used for the demineralization of water. It employs an electric current to induce migration of salt anions and cations in sea-water through an electrolytic solution and a barrier of membranes. The membranes, which contain permanent charges of ions are permeable to the water solvent and to either the anions or the cations, but not to both. By passing sea-water through successive tanks containing the membranes and using electric currents at each stage, the saline content of the water is completely extracted, rendering the water fresh.

Electroforming is an electro-chemical process similar to that of electrotyping. It consists of the electrolytic deposition of metal on forms or moulds made from graphite-coated wax, metal or plastic, and

is used in the production of medals and master gramophone records. Electroforming differs from electroplating in that the metal is not actually joined to the base on which it is deposited.

The *photoelectric cell* is an electrochemical device which exploits the effect of light on certain elements. The cell consists of a glass tube from which the air has been evacuated, although a low-pressure gas is sometimes added to increase the current output of the cell. A curved metal plate coated with caesium is fitted inside the evacuated tube to form the anode. The atoms of caesium vibrate so violently under the influence of light that some of their electrons fly off. Close to the cathode is the anode, a thin metal rod. The anode is connected to the positive terminal of a battery or other source of electronic current and the cathode to the negative terminal of the current source.

When light falls on the cathode, electrons are knocked off the caesium and stream across to the anode, so providing a conductive path for the current from the battery and completing the circuit. The

photoelectric cell can be kept in operation continuously by keeping a light shining on it, or intermittently by shining a light on it at intervals.

Photoelectric cells are the basis of many burglar alarm systems. When the burglar approaches a door or safe so protected, his body interrupts a beam of invisible infra-red radiation, so cutting off the light shining on the cell. The interruption of the current through the cell operates relays which can be made to ring a bell, close a grill, or even operate a camera to photograph the intruder.

Photographers' exposure meters incorporate a photoelectric cell to move a pointer on a scale according to the brightness of the light in which the photograph is taken. Photoelectric cells are also used for counting mass-produced articles and components as they are carried on conveyor belts and interrupt a beam of light falling on the cell. Doors which automatically open when a person approaches are controlled by photoelectric cells, as are the garage doors which open automatically at the approach of a vehicle.

1 Electroplating base metals to make them more valuable, durable or rust-proof began in the last century. This scene is of a French electroplating factory in the 1870s.
2 Electrodialysis can be used for demineralizing water. At this plant in Italy sea-water passes through stacks of membranes and at each stage gradually loses more and more of its salt.
3 Alumina, the oxide of aluminium, is fed to an aluminium reduction furnace. The furnace works on an electro-chemical basis, with molten aluminium being drawn off as the end product.

Keeping in step with time

To keep in step with time, Man has devised beautiful and ingenious instruments to measure the intangible. Today, he has clocks that will not lose or gain a second in three thousand years.

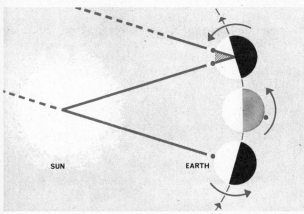

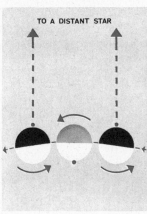

TO A DISTANT STAR

SUN   EARTH

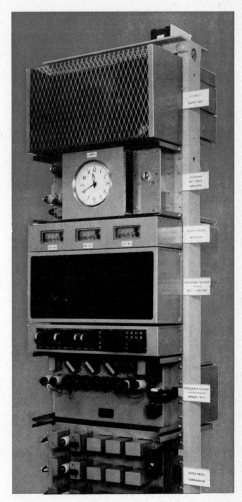

WE ARE MADE conscious of the passage of time by noticeable events. Time elapses between two happenings of which we are made aware. For example, if we are sitting reading this article, we are aware of when we start reading a page, and we may notice when we turn over the page. Between these two events, all the while we were reading we have been made aware of no other happening, and an interval of time has passed. But if someone rang the doorbell when we had read only half a page, we would be aware of two time intervals: the time that passed from when we started the page and the doorbell rang, and the time that passed from then until we finished the page.

Early man did not have books to read or doorbells to interrupt him, but certain natural events made him aware of the passage of time. The existence of night and day, the succession of the seasons, the birth, life and death of his animals – all these events made him conscious of time. He observed the phases of the moon, the rise and fall of the tides, and the apparent rotation of constellations of stars in the night sky. Today scientists still use natural events to measure time precisely.

The first attempts to measure time were based on the motion of the Earth, moon, sun and stars. Originally, men thought that the Earth remained stationary and the moon, sun and stars moved round it in the heavens. We now know that this is not so; the moon orbits round the Earth, and the Earth-moon system orbits round the sun. And the sun, together with its attendant planets (including the Earth), is itself moving in the arms of the large spiral nebula that forms our galaxy – the Milky Way.

The fundamental astronomical units of time are the day (the time it takes the Earth to spin once on its axis) and the year (the time it takes the Earth to orbit once round the sun). Another unit, the month, is the time it takes for the moon to orbit once round the Earth. The lengths of the day and the year vary, however, depending on what reference point we take for timing the measurement of one complete rotation

Man measures time by observing the recurrence of natural events – chief among them the passage of day and night and the cycle of the seasons. There are two ways to calculate a complete revolution of the Earth. *Above left,* we calculate a revolution by reference to the sun. This gives us a *solar* day – the time taken for one place on Earth to make a complete revolution and return to the same position facing the sun. But because the Earth is moving round the sun, the solar day is four minutes longer than the time taken for a complete revolution. To measure the rotation of the Earth without reference to the sun, we can consider its position in relation to a distant star. This calculation, *above right,* gives us a *sidereal* day. The time taken for a fixed point on Earth to complete and face the star again is 23 hours 56 minutes 4 seconds. Other natural phenomena, like the vibrations of a quartz crystal, can be used in the clock, *right,* to keep time accurate to one second in three years. An alternating electric current causes the crystal to oscillate at the rate of 100,000 times a second.

of the Earth on its axis or one complete orbit round the sun.

For example, we may measure the time taken for one place on the Earth directly facing the sun to make a complete revolution and come back to the same position facing the sun. This time is called the *solar* day. But because the Earth moves round in its orbit during the time taken for it apparently to spin once on its axis, the solar day is a little longer than exactly one revolution. The difference is about four minutes.

The moving shadow

The speed of the Earth in its elliptical orbit round the sun also varies (it travels fastest when it is nearest the sun and slowest when it is furthest away). For this reason, the distance the Earth moves along its orbit during one revolution varies during the year. So the length of the solar day, measured in the way just described, also varies. The average value, taken over a whole year, is called the *mean* solar day (or mean time). This is the time which clocks are designed to keep, although clocks are in perfect agreement with solar time only four times a year. A mean solar day contains exactly 24 hours.

The errors of solar time can be avoided if we measure the rotation of the Earth without reference to the sun. Instead of timing how long it takes for the Earth's rotation to bring a point on Earth back into a position in which it exactly faces the sun, we can consider the position of a point on Earth directly facing a remote star. Because the star is so far away, there will be no error due to the movement of the Earth along its orbit during one revolution on its axis. This time interval is called the *sidereal* day, and it is equal to 23 hours 56 minutes and 4 seconds.

A year is the time taken for the Earth to make one complete orbit round the sun. It is equal to 365·2422 days, or 365 days 5 hours 48 minutes and 48 seconds (that is, mean solar days – days by the clock). In practice, we call a year 365 days and every four years have a leap year, which contains an extra day in February. In doing this, we have corrected too much, and have to omit leap years every hundred years, at the change of centuries. A final correction is made by retaining the leap year when the number of the century is an exact multiple of four. The year 1900, for example, was not a leap year, but the year 2000 will be.

The most accurate clock in the world until 1962, the atomic-powered device, *above,* was used to check the accuracy of the quartz crystal clocks used at Greenwich Observatory. This atomic clock was accurate to one second in 300 years – but its successor is at least six times as accurate. Atomic clocks are based on the known rates of oscillation among the electrons of certain elements.

Water turned a paddle-wheel to operate a clock created by Chinese craftsmen in A D 1092. The model above reconstructs the device. Water clocks had one main disadvantage – they froze in winter.

The first instruments for telling time made use of the sun. In about 1000 B C, the Egyptians devised a shadow clock consisting of a horizontal bar mounted above and at right angles to a rod calibrated in hours. The shadow bar was faced towards the sun (eastwards in the morning and westwards in the afternoon) and the position of its shadow gave the time.

Various types of sundials were also constructed in ancient times. The simplest consisted merely of a stick pushed into the ground; the position and length of the shadow gave the time. More elaborate types have a *gnomon* (replacing the stick) and a calibrated dial. This might have been the function of some of the large vertical stones in monuments such as Stonehenge. Finally a triangular plate called a *style* replaced the gnomon. For accurate measurements, the angle of the style should be chosen to correspond with the latitude of the sundial's location, and it should be lined up exactly north–south, so that it casts no shadow at noon.

Sand, water and candle flame

Other early clocks made use of escaping water or sand. In the simplest water clocks, the rate at which water runs out of a hole in the bottom of a container is used to measure time. The container can be calibrated on the inside and the water level read off against it, or the level of the water can operate a float which controls the movement of a pointer – or, with the aid of cog wheels, a hand. The ancient Greeks built a large water clock called a *clepsydra* in Athens.

More elaborate water clocks have automatic means for refilling the chamber, or work paddle-wheels which drive hands round by means of cogs and pinions. A sort of water clock in reverse, invented more than a thousand years ago and still used in some parts of the world, has a bowl or cup with a hole in the bottom. The bowl is floated in water and the time taken for it to fill up and sink is used as a measure.

Another natural process used by man for time-keeping is burning. In a candle clock, traditionally invented by Alfred the Great, a long candle of uniform thickness is calibrated by coloured bands on the outside. A wooden lantern round the outside protects the candle from draughts.

Swing of the pendulum

If the time taken for the candle to burn down between the bands is known, the device can be used to tell the time. In an extension of the same idea, the reservoir of an oil lamp is calibrated and the time found by reading off the oil level against the calibration. Sand-glasses use a similar principle to that of water clocks, but they are less messy and do not freeze solid in cold weather. They were often made in sets of four to record an hour in quarters.

The next great step forward in recording time came with the invention of mechanical clocks. The earliest mechanical clocks were powered by weights. In such a clock,

This simple Egyptian water clock allowed water to escape from a hole in the bottom of a vessel at a fixed rate. The passage of time could be read against the sinking water level in the bowl.

the weight is attached to one end of a cord, which is wound round an axle. As the weight falls, the cord unwinds and the axle turns. Although the rotation of the axle can be transmitted to other wheels by means of gears, some method of regulating the fall of the weight is needed if the clock is not to require rewinding every minute or so. The earliest regulator consisted of an *escape* wheel and a balance-governor or *foliot.* The whole arrangement is called an *escapement.*

The escape wheel with foliot balance came into use in the late 1200s. No further advance was made in escapements for weight-driven clocks until the Italian mathematician Galileo Galilei (1564–1642) made his famous study of pendulums. In 1581, Galileo discovered that the time taken for a pendulum to swing through small angles depends only on the length of the pendulum and is independent of its mass. According to tradition, Galileo's interest in pendulums was aroused when he saw the chandeliers swinging in Pisa cathedral. He probably thought of applying the constant swing of the pendulum to clock escapements and a drawing made by Galileo's son in 1641 (the year before Galileo died) shows such an escapement. It is doubtful whether a clock of this type was actually made by Galileo, but later clocksmiths were able to make clocks from his original design.

Christiaan Huygens, a Dutch scientist, is generally credited with making the first successful pendulum clock, in 1657. In his escapement, a pair of pallets alternatively engage and disengage in a crown (escape) wheel, as in the verge escapement, but the crown wheel is mounted with its axle vertical and the movement of the pallets controlled by a swinging pendulum.

About 13 years later, the British scientist Robert Hooke invented the anchor escapement for pendulum clocks, and his method is still in use today. In this

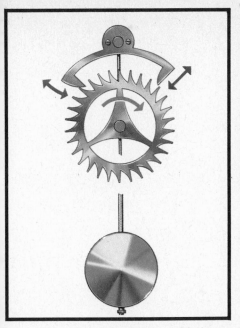

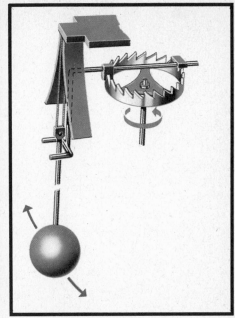

In a clock powered by weights, a device to regulate their fall is needed. In the anchor escapement, *above*, the swinging pendulum rocks a claw-shaped anchor to stop and release the wheel.

The hairspring (*A*), coiled on the same axle as a balance wheel (*B*) is the escapement device used in most watches. The spring turns the wheel back and forth to control a rocking lever.

Christiaan Huygens, the Dutch scientist credited as the inventor of the first pendulum clock, used an escapement in which a pair of pallets alternately engage and disengage a 'crown' escape wheel.

escapement, the swinging pendulum rocks a claw-shaped anchor which alternately stops and releases the escape wheel. The anchor escapement was improved by another Englishman, George Graham, who produced his 'dead-beat' escapement in 1715.

While these developments of weight-driven clocks were taking place, inventors were also turning their attention to clocks driven by springs. To turn an axle, the spring is attached to it and coiled tightly round it. Then, as the spring is allowed to unwind, it turns the axle round. The first problem which had to be overcome stems from the fact that a fully wound spring turns the axle faster than when it is nearly uncoiled – the turning force varies with the tension in the spring. The problem was solved by a device called a *fusee*. Neither the exact date of its invention nor its inventor is known with certainty. It may have been in use in the late 1400s, but some historians give the credit for inventing it to a man called Jacob the Czech in the 1500s.

Hairspring and balance wheel

The fusee compensates for the varying force from a coiled spring by making it exert less leverage on the driven axle when the spring is fully wound than when it is nearly unwound. To do this, the spring pulls in a cord or chain which is wrapped round a stepped cone-shaped pulley. The fully wound spring pulls on the narrow part of the pulley, and the nearly unwound spring pulls on the wide part.

Springs were also used to regulate a clock's escapement, in the form of a hairspring. It is also difficult definitely to credit one man with this invention, the two main claimants being Huygens (1674) and Hooke (1675). The hairspring replaces the function of the pendulum in controlling the stopping and starting of the escape wheel. The hairspring is coiled on the

same axle as a *balance* wheel, which turns first in one direction and then in the other. The oscillations of the balance wheel control a rocking lever with two teeth which alternately engage and disengage with the teeth of the escape wheel, in rather the same way as the anchor of an anchor escapement works. The hairspring and balance wheel are still used today in most watches.

All the inventions which we have just described resulted in more and more accurate clocks. The culmination of this progress was the development of the chronometer by two Englishmen, John Harrison (who worked from 1735 to 1773) and Thomas Earnshaw (1782). The important application of the chronometer is in

navigation. A ship's captain can find local time at the ship's position by using the sun or stars. If he compares that time with the time showing at the same instant on clocks at his port of departure, he can calculate from the difference in times how far east or west of his home port he has travelled. (Each 15 degrees of longitude he sails east or west corresponds to a time difference of 1 hour.) So by keeping on the ship an accurate chronometer, which always shows the time at his home port, he can easily calculate his longitude.

The next advance in time-keeping came with the invention of the electric clock. At first electricity, used to work electromagnets, was employed to drive the pendulum regulating the clock. This was the

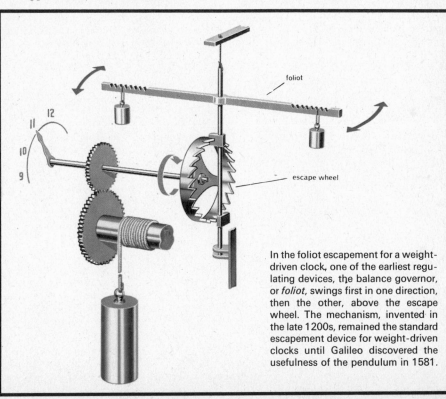

In the foliot escapement for a weight-driven clock, one of the earliest regulating devices, the balance governor, or *foliot*, swings first in one direction, then the other, above the escape wheel. The mechanism, invented in the late 1200s, remained the standard escapement device for weight-driven clocks until Galileo discovered the usefulness of the pendulum in 1581.

basis of an invention by Alexander Bain, a Scotsman who worked with Charles Wheatstone and who patented the first electric clock in 1840. Two years later, a Swiss clockmaker, Mathias Hipp, freed the pendulum somewhat, so that it was only driven by electromagnets when it swung less than a certain amount. Electro-magnetism was replaced by electromagnetic induction, which was used to drive the pendulum in Fery's clock of 1900. Finally in 1921 W. H. Shortt made an electric clock in which the pendulum was virtually free.

After the 1920s, alternating current (AC) mains electricity became generally available and was used to drive motors to power clocks. These clocks keep good time by relying on the constancy of the alternating frequency from the generating station – 50 cycles a second in Britain and much of Europe, 60 cycles a second in North America. If the frequency of the AC supply varies, then the clocks also vary. But all AC electric clocks connected to the same supply keep perfectly in step with each other, and the electricity authorities keep a check on any variation in mains frequency, making sure that such variations are averaged out over a period.

Atomic clocks

Conventional electric clocks make use of current electricity to work magnets or motors. In the late 1920s, W. A. Morrison of the Bell Telephone Laboratories in the United States, developed a clock based on the electrical properties of a crystal of quartz. When a quartz crystal, carefully cut so that its crystal axes run in specified directions, is deformed by 'squeezing' it across its faces, an electric current is generated. This phenomenon is known as the *piezoelectric effect*. If an alternating electric current is applied across the faces of such a crystal, the crystal will change its dimensions by a microscopic amount in step with the applied current – the inverse piezoelectric effect. In a quartz clock, the crystal is made to oscillate at a rate of

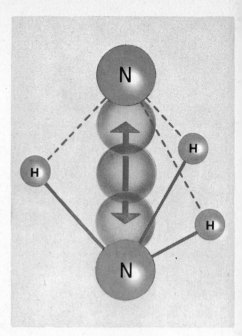

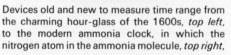

Devices old and new to measure time range from the charming hour-glass of the 1600s, *top left*, to the modern ammonia clock, in which the nitrogen atom in the ammonia molecule, *top right*,

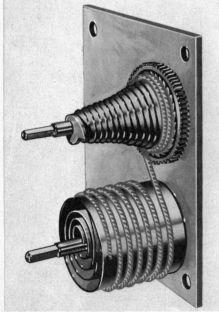

The fusee, an elegant mechanical solution to a problem, stops a fully wound spring from turning an axle faster than a spring nearly unwound.

100,000 times a second. It keeps accurate time to within one second in three years.

More recently, scientists have used the natural frequencies of oscillations of molecules and atoms as time standards for clocks. The ammonia molecule contains one atom of nitrogen and three atoms of hydrogen, arranged in the form of a pyramid with the nitrogen at the apex. When stimulated by radar waves, the nitrogen atom flips through the plane of the hydrogen atoms, effectively turning the pyramid inside out. These oscillations of the nitrogen atoms in ammonia take place with absolute regularity 24,000,000,000 times a second. A clock based on this phenomenon – requiring a whole cupboard full of ancillary electronic equipment – was made in 1948 by the American scientist Harold Lyons. It keeps time to within one second in 1000 years.

Under certain conditions, similar oscillation takes place among the electrons of the atoms of some metallic elements.

oscillates backwards and forwards through the plane of the hydrogen atoms. *Above left*, an alarm clock for Italian monks of the 1400s; *above right*, clock by the clockmaker, Tompion.

These oscillations are responsible for the characteristic spectral lines used in identifying the metals. A clock has been made using the oscillation of caesium atoms, which takes place at a frequency of 9,192,000,000 cycles a second. It is claimed that the caesium clock will keep time accurately to within one second in several thousand years.

Apart from their phenomenal accuracy, molecular and atomic clocks are completely independent of external influences as well. Unlike even the best craftsmanship of the world's most famous clockmakers of past ages, today's instruments work unhampered by factors such as gravity, temperature and pressure. They can be used to calculate the timing of space-rocket launchings and manoeuvring, and are so reliable that they can detect the tiniest variations in the movement of the Earth, the motions of which probably gave Man his earliest ideas on time and its measurement.

Plastics revolution

Is the age of metals giving way to the age of plastics? More and more uses are being found for these very versatile materials, while new forms with useful properties are still being discovered.

UP TO the end of the Second World War, it would have been largely true to say that civilization rested upon a rubber cushion. Rubber had become a universal shock absorber; it not only protected mankind from many a physical jolt – as in the motor-car tyre, crash helmet and upholstery of all kinds– it also protected him from the elements – as in waterproof clothing, roofing and the like.

Since 1945, however, the role of natural rubber has dwindled considerably, in some cases almost to vanishing point. Its place has been taken to a great extent by a group of materials called plastics, which are now used everywhere in the machinery of our daily lives – from ball-point pens to domestic plumbing; table-tennis balls to aircraft construction.

Versatility is clearly the essence in plastics, and equally a number of manufacturing substances – not only rubber – have been displaced or reduced in importance by them. For plastics to be suitable for such a wide range of uses, they must individually possess very different properties. So first, how are plastics to be defined?

Very briefly, all have the following features in common. They are completely man-made and cannot be found in nature. Next, they consist of large molecules of organic compounds. Then at some point of their production they are liquid, during which time they can be moulded or otherwise shaped. And lastly, they are solid in final form.

This basic definition covers the wide variety of plastics as we know them. The variety of form depends on the skill with which the manufacturing chemists blend the constituent materials. The plastics story can therefore be regarded as one of the most important examples of 'putting science to work' in the twentieth century.

Carbon chemistry

The basic chemistry of plastics is carbon chemistry. It used to be thought that the chemical changes which take place in the development of living organisms were peculiar to such living organisms. So the study of these mysterious chemical happenings was at first called *organic chemistry*. But later it was realized that the reactions were no different in essence from those which take place in non-living materials; on the other hand, scientists found that most of the substances involved in the chemical changes of life contained carbon.

Organic chemistry therefore became carbon chemistry. It was research into an aspect of the latter that led to the discovery of nylon, a very widely used form of plastic. In the 1930s, an American chemist called Wallace Carothers was investigating the presence of large ring formations

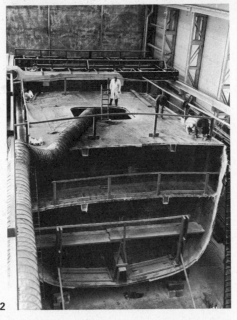

1 Polyethylene is replacing traditional materials in a wide range of applications. Here barrels are in use at a Derby, England, fruit factory. The older wooden barrel is on the right.
2 Part of an all-plastic ship under construction. The hull, bulkheads, decks and bearers of the 600-ton design are all made from various types of plastic materials.

of carbon atoms in some natural substances (civet and musk) used in the perfumery industry. As a result, he began to wonder whether or not it was possible to take long carbon-containing chains of molecules constructed in the laboratory and cause them to join together so as to make similar rings.

He tried the experiment – only to discover that comparatively few rings were formed: the vast majority of the chains joined up to form even longer chains. Such superchains are called polymers, each

chain being made up of hundreds of repeating molecular sub-units (monomers), and Carothers knew that what gives natural fibres like silk and cotton their fibrous properties, is the essence of giant polymers. It took him no time at all to realize that he had stumbled upon a way of making a new artificial fibre.

Even so, it was not all plain sailing. The fibres he first produced were weak and he set out to discover why. One reason he found was that water was produced during the mixing process, so he overcame this by carrying out polymerization at very low pressures. In consequence, the water vaporized and could be removed after condensation.

The second cause of the unwanted weakness was found to be that the polymers in the first fibres were laid down randomly – not smoothly, side by side. And to overcome this a process called cold drawing was found necessary. This means that the extruded nylon fibre is drawn out, while cold, to several times its own length and, as a result, the polymer chains rearrange themselves so as to lie side by side. The emergent fibre is now as bright and sheer

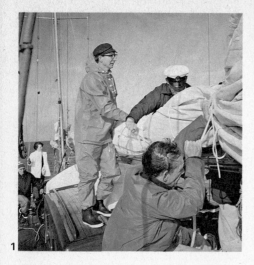

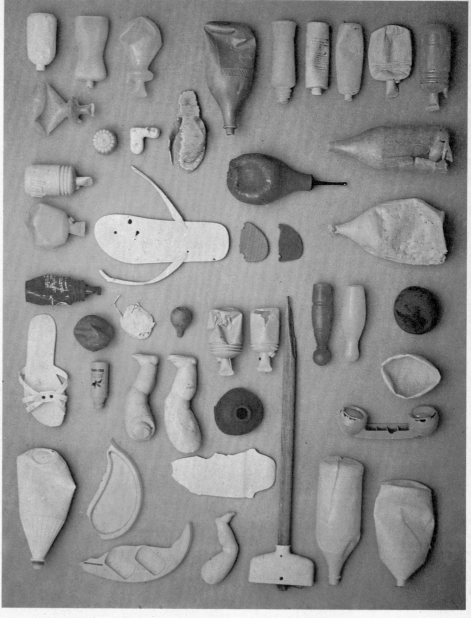

1 Rot-proof ropes and sails, water-proof clothing and boots and the yacht itself can be made with plastics. Plastics now have a wide range of uses in the sporting-goods field.

2 Relics of the age of plastics. A collection of plastic litter picked up on an Italian beach gives some idea of what our epoch may look like to archaeologists of the distant future.

as silk, and very much stronger.

Polymerization is the structural basis of the production of nylon and other plastics. But the constituents of the polymerizing materials are just as important. So, what are the basic materials which go to make nylon?

The nylon chain molecule consists of only four elements: carbon, nitrogen, hydrogen and oxygen. Carbon and nitrogen atoms form the central backbone of the chain, while the hydrogen and oxygen are attached on either side. This pattern is found in each of the sub-units, over 100 of which join to form the chain molecule.

These basic building bricks are relatively cheap and easy to come by. First, the nitrogen and hydrogen are taken from the air and turned into ammonia. Carbon and more hydrogen come from the inevitable by-products of the coal, oil and even natural gas industries. Oxygen comes from the atmosphere.

Nylon production

But to see just how all this works in practice, let us take a look at the production of one variety of the fibre, nylon 6:6. (The numbers denote the fact that there are six carbon molecules present in each molecular sub-unit or monomer.) This particular form of nylon is made by mixing two monomeric substances, hexa-methylene diamine and adipic acid. Both stem from synthetic phenol which is in turn made from benzene. And with benzene we find ourselves well and truly concerned with the coal or oil industries. For benzene is produced either when bituminous coal is destructively distilled to produce coal gas or coal tar, or when heavy oils are broken down ('cracked' is the technical term) to produce lighter oils.

The actual production of nylon 6:6 goes like this. Ammonia is built into hexamethylene diamine during its production and this latter substance is mixed with adipic acid to form nylon 6:6 salt. The salt is then mixed into a 60 per cent

aqueous solution and heated under pressure in a stainless steel container to a temperature of 280 °C. The water vapour which Carothers found such a nuisance is driven off as the reaction continues, and when all of this has been removed, the molten nylon is extruded under pressure by means of nitrogen.

It appears first as a ribbon and is sliced into chips and dried by tumbling in a stream of hot air. Finally, it is remelted and forced through small holes, or spinnerets, and the resultant fibre is cold drawn – in this case from four to seven times its original length.

This is only one form of nylon. Other varieties are made by using other constituents, but the general production method is the same. It can be produced both as fibre and in solid form for uses ranging from women's stockings, through parachutes to bearings of various kinds. The production process is also that used to manufacture all the other man-made fibres, and these, like nylon, show great resistance to dampness, to staining and to hard wear.

Like nylon, the raw materials for all other plastics – substances as different as Perspex, Bakelite, polyvinyl chloride

(PVC) and polythene – are the organic chemicals produced by the oil and coal industries. And here, the monomers join together to form polymers when subjected to heat, pressure or catalysis. (A catalyst is a substance which hastens a chemical reaction without itself taking part in that reaction.)

The properties of any particular plastic depend on three things. First, there is the actual length of the polymer chain involved. Second, there are the kinds of atoms employed and their arrangement in the chain. Finally, there is the way the chains are arranged in relation to one another. It is the variation of one or more of these factors by the chemist which gives rise to different properties in the eventual plastics.

Contrast, for example, the molecular chain structure of one of the oldest plastics, Bakelite (it was discovered in 1909 by the Belgian-born chemist, Baekeland), with that of another which came 20 odd years later, Perspex. The first is used widely for electric light fittings; the second for aircraft canopies. The constituents of each are very different but both emerge as tough and brittle plastics. Yet, Bakelite is the tougher, since its

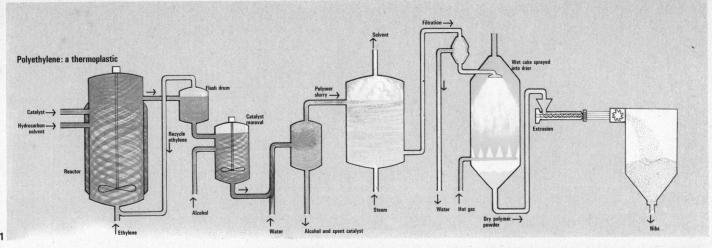

Polyethylene: a thermoplastic

Catalyst
Hydrocarbon solvent
Reactor
Ethylene
Recycle ethylene
Alcohol
Flash drum
Catalyst removal
Water
Alcohol and spent catalyst
Polymer slurry
Steam
Solvent
Filtration →
Water
Hot gas
Wet cake sprayed into drier
Extrusion
Dry polymer powder →
Nibs

1 Stages in the production of polyethylene, one of the most versatile of today's plastics. Continuous production is normally carried out under automatic control.

2 Fun with plastics. This plastic dome, inflatable like a giant beach-ball, makes an ideal and unusual playground.

3 Plastics in the building industry. Their strength and versatility make them ideal materials for many functions in building. This portable bathroom unit, in plastic and fibreglass, can be added on or into an existing building.

molecular structure when set consists of a chain of rigid rings and it is also opaque. Perspex, on the other hand, possesses molecules with long side chains, which, while inherently a weaker combination, does allow light to pass through. Once the raw plastic of whatever kind has been manufactured, it still has to be turned into usable commodities. And in this respect, the methods used are very much the same as those employed in working metals.

First there is moulding, useful for mass producing articles of fixed shape and size like electrical fittings, washing-up bowls and toys. The mould is, of course, in the shape of the desired article, the molten plastic is injected into it and held there for something like 30 seconds. During this time the plastic sets hard enough to retain its shape and it is then automatically ejected from the mould for the process to begin again.

Polyethylene, or polythene for short, is much used in this field – look around any kitchen. It is also suitable for working with the second process, extrusion. Forced through a suitable *die* (former) in the extrusion machine, polythene can be used

to produce continuous tubing – anything from 1 in. to 40 in. in diameter – and this, cut into suitable lengths, is much used in the packaging industry. Other extruded plastics provide the tubular covering for electric cables and large-diameter pipes for sewage or drinking water.

Finally, there is the process known as rolling in the steel industry and calendering in plastics. Here sheet plastic is produced by squeezing the molten material between two rollers, both of which are hollow and heated. One of the rollers rotates a little faster than the other and the speed differential serves to smear the surface of the plastic as it passes through, imparting a very smooth finish to the

sheet. Inflatable beach toys, rainwear and curtaining are some of the goods in which calendered plastics are found.

The study of polymerization has also played a significant part in the production of synthetic rubbers and other substances with no chemical resemblance to natural rubber but with rubber-like qualities. (This last group are known as elastomers from 'elastic polymers'.) The search for these synthetics or alternatives was given great impetus by the two World Wars, during which the highly industrialized combatants were to a greater or lesser extent cut off from sources of natural rubber.

It has been understood for some time

Producing tubular Lupolen plastic film at a factory near Cologne, Germany. Raw plastic chips placed in the hopper at the top appear in front of the machine as a continuous transparent tube.

that the natural rubber molecule was in fact a natural polymer. Except in this case, the chain was not straight but twisted up, like tangled string. It only straightens on stretching, and in this lies rubber's natural elasticity.

The basic constituent of rubber is a substance called isoprene and to find a substitute for this in the manufacture of synthetics, the chemists had once again to turn to the oil industry. It was recognized that both butadiene (a direct product of petroleum cracking) and styrene (manufactured from two other petroleum products) were very similar to isoprene. German researchers thereupon experimented and found that they could get molecules of butadiene and styrene to polymerize. The result was called Buna S, and by 1943, the Germans were manufacturing over 100,000 tons per year without having to go near a rubber plantation.

But the synthetic rubber story does not end there by any means. For example, a substance called neoprene was developed in the United States during the 1940s. Here the basic molecule resembles natural isoprene, but chlorine atoms are substituted for certain parts of the natural molecule. The result is a synthetic rubber which is resistant to oils and petrol and does not soften or swell as much as the natural commodity. Then there are silicone rubbers in which the backbone of the chain consists of atoms of silicon and oxygen. These rubbers remain tough and flexible even in extremely high or low temperatures. And there is the plastic, polyethylene, which can be rubberized by adding chlorine and sulphur to the mix. These substances allow the polyethylene molecules to move more freely and hence impart rubber-like properties to it. Rubberized polyethylene is used for coating fabrics and in the manufacture of whitewall tyres for motor cars.

The list of artificial substances produced

Lightweight plastic pipes, resistant to chemical corrosion, are replacing lead, iron and copper tubes in many applications. Plastic is cheaper, lighter and easier to handle.

Plastics can be moulded into a huge variety of shapes. High-density polyethylene is being moulded here to form a strong, rigid plastic milk-bottle crate.

by the chemist continues to grow – not only in the field of synthetic rubbers, but in fibres and other plastics as well.

By applying his knowledge of the molecular structure of substances and his ability to manipulate that structure, the chemist is producing materials often far superior to those which nature can supply. In putting his science to work so effectively, he becomes truly a creative artist and as such is helping to change the quality of our lives by supplying a huge range of useful, durable and often, cheaper substitutes for natural materials.

From fibre to fabric

Since the Stone Age, Man has used the fibres from animals and plants to weave cloth. Science and technology and the invention of man-made fibres now provide a remarkable choice of fabrics.

THE FIRST CLOTHES were most probably made from animal skins but the availability of such clothing depended upon the availability of the right animals. Quite often, substitute materials would have been useful – and eventually Man found them in the shape of leaves and plant stems.

These it seems he interlaced to make clothing of a kind – but it could not have been very effective for comfort, protection or fit. But these unknown and primitive technologists of prehistory were experimenting in other directions. At some point, they discovered that bundles of long grass could be twisted together to make rope. The ropes could be made of varying thickness and from there it was a relatively short step to the weaving of crude cloth.

The small fibres contained in the structure of plants were the most suitable materials for such uses and it is upon fibres that the twentieth-century textile industry depends. Now, however, it is not only plant fibres that are involved, but animal and man-made fibres as well.

In the early days of textile production, the people involved were craftsmen rather than scientists or technologists. The producer knew that he could obtain certain effects by handling the fibres in certain ways but he often did not know why he got such results.

Since then science has lent a hand by elucidating the physical and chemical nature of the fibres. Such basic research was important in discovering new and improved manufacturing techniques and also in the quest for man-made fibres.

Fibres of cellulose and protein

But what do we know about fibres? Natural fibres come from two sources: plants (where they exist as a kind of skeleton binding together the fleshy parts of the plant) and animals (where they occur in the hair, skin and flesh). Plant fibres, such as cotton, linen and flax, are made of a substance called cellulose, the chemical components of which are carbon, hydrogen and oxygen. Animal fibres consist of various types of protein, mixtures of carbon, oxygen and nitrogen, sometimes with sulphur added.

These chemical facts lead to the most important consideration of fibrous matter – its molecular construction. The chemical substances in all fibres are arranged in units called *monomers,* which link together to form very long chain molecules called *polymers.* The polymers are laid down in roughly parallel lines, and the structure as a whole means that the fibres are strong and very flexible.

This is how fibres are built and the way they are put together. The result of this building process is a variety of outward

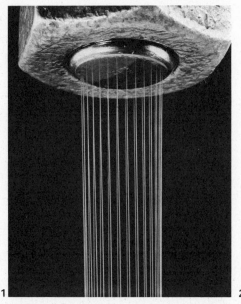

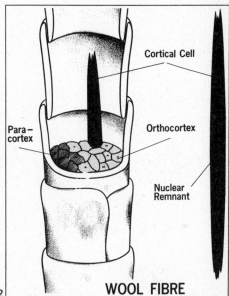

WOOL FIBRE

Cortical Cell

Para-cortex

Orthocortex

Nuclear Remnant

1 The man-made fibre, rayon, can be produced in strands of any thickness. Made from the cellulose of wood or cotton, the thick liquid is forced through jets to form continuous filaments.
2 A diagram of wool fibre. Under the microscope wool is seen to have an outer skin of overlapping scales. Because of this roughness, the fibres cling together during spinning into yarn.
3 A fully automatic cotton-spinning machine. The spun yarn is examined by a photo-electric cell, faults are cut out and the yarn re-tied as it is wound into packages for weaving.

forms, providing the qualities which the textile producer needs in different combinations. The cotton fibre is almost pure cellulose and is a single cell which in length varies from $\frac{1}{2}$ to $2\frac{1}{2}$ in.; it is many thousand times thinner than it is long. Under the microscope the fibre appears flattened like a hair ribbon, but it is also twisted. The twists occur when the cell walls collapse during ripening and there can be as many as 300 twists to the inch. It is these twists that makes the fibre such a good material for spinning, the roughness imparted by the twists causes the fibres to cling together.

Cotton fibres are strong, become even stronger when wetted, and they are absorbent. A natural resistance to boiling water, and bleaches, also makes cotton extremely washable. On the other hand cotton fibres have little stretch or elasticity so that the cloth creases and tears readily. Finally, cotton fibres are inflammable, weaken in strong sunlight and are prone to mildew.

Wool is a protein – in this case, the protein is keratin and contains sulphur. In length the wool fibre varies much more than cotton: fine wool may be anything from $1\frac{1}{2}$ to 5 in. long; coarse varieties run from 5 to 15 in. in length (and the average thickness would be about 40 microns).

The structure of wool

There are two qualities of the wool fibre which make it a good spinning material and a warm cloth as well. First there may be as many as 30 natural waves or *crimps* to the inch and these ensure that the various fibres hang together well when the yarn is spun. Second, there is the surface of the individual fibre itself. Under the microscope, the wool is seen to be an outer skin or *cuticle*. The cuticle consists of overlapping scales (epithelial scales), the unattached ends of which point towards the tip of the fibre. The roughness implied by this means that the fibres cling together during spinning into yarn. Both crimp and scales tend to trap air in the yarn which acts as an insulator.

At the same time the crimp gives the fibre a natural spring, making it both stretchable and elastic, and although the weakest of the natural fibres, wool can be bent a great deal without breaking. It is also extremely resistant to creasing and crushing. Wool, however, has its disadvantages; for example, it shrinks. If the fibre is rubbed from tip to root, the rubbing surface catches on the projecting edges of the scales and tips them backwards. They then become jammed together and the fibre curls back towards its root. Shrinkage in woollen cloth is due to the fact that when rubbed – during washing, for example – some of the fibres curl or 'creep' towards the root end and the cloth becomes deformed. Wool is particularly susceptible to insect attack – hence the damage which the grubs of the clothes moth can do. And although it is not highly inflammable, it deteriorates in dry heat. Boiling and some bleaches also cause weakening.

These are two very common natural fibres, both of which have their drawbacks as well as advantages. And the same can be said for the other natural fibres. As a

1 A small loom can be used to produce a huge range of colourful weaves. By varying the thickness of the warps and wefts that make up the lattice work, different textures and patterns can be obtained.

2 When sheep's fleeces arrive at the factory they are sorted and passed through a series of wash bowls. This process of scouring removes the dirt, sweat and grease.

3 The highly magnified fibres of a nylon stocking. First produced in the 1930s, nylon is about twice as strong as cotton and is resistant to insect and bacterial attack.

4 A high-speed worsted cloth weaving machine. To produce worsted, fine wool yarns with the fibres lying as parallel as possible are used.

5 Silkworm cocoons being prepared for unwinding. Silk is an extremely strong, continuous filament that is smooth and elastic. Each cocoon may provide as much as 1,300 yards of silk which can be twisted directly into yarn.

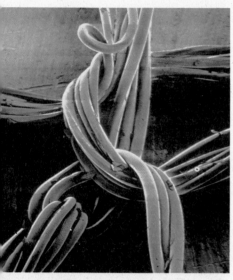

result scientists have looked round for a means of making fibres artificially, fibres into which all or most of the required qualities can be built. First came the viscose and cellulose acetate rayons. In the former, cellulose is obtained from spruce wood and poor-quality cotton. It is then treated with caustic soda and carbon bisulphide to form a thick treacly liquid, which is forced through tiny holes to form a thin filament or fibre and hardened in an acid bath.

Cellulose acetate rayons employ poor-quality cotton treated with acetic acid and acetic anhydride to form cellulose acetate. The acetate is then dissolved in acetic acid to form a thick liquid which is pushed through tiny holes into air where the filament hardens. Both types of rayon are lustrous and strong, and therefore were given the name 'artificial silks'. Both have ridged surfaces which improves the spinning capability, and the filaments can be manufactured into any length required. But the rayons also have one distinct drawback – although they will absorb water, they weaken when wetted.

In the 1930s an American chemist produced a fibre which was to be much more successful. The chemist was Dr Wallace Carothers and the fibre he produced was nylon. He took the chemical substances produced and involved in the oil and coal industries and found – during carefully planned experiments helped in the end by a fortunate accident – that they could be induced to form monomers (repeating sub-units) which in turn could be linked together to form long chain molecules – or polymers. In other words, he repeated in the laboratory a process used by Nature to impart the

fibrous quality to fibres. Nylon was found to be about twice as strong as cotton and water-repellent to a great extent. What water it did absorb had no effect on its strength. It was also resistant to insect and bacterial attack. There were, however, problems in weaving and dyeing.

Having once picked, caught or constructed a fibre, the next step is to spin it into yarn. Taking cotton as an example, there are a number of steps involved. After picking, the raw cotton is baled and sent to the spinning factory. Here the compressed fibres are loosened on a machine which also causes heavy impurities to fall out. It is spread out into a sheet (called a *lap*) and is now in a suitable state to be pressed on to the carding machine. This not only removes the remaining impurities and weeds out weak or otherwise imperfect fibres, but also combs the fibres so that they lie fairly parallel to each other.

The machine consists basically of a number of cylinders, the largest of which is covered with numbers of fine wire points. The cotton is fed to the larger cylinder and the points take up the fibres in a fine layer. This layer is then combed again by another device and passed on to a final cylinder called the *doffer,* where it is gathered together in a loose skein or *sliver* and finally coiled into tall cans. To provide a uniform quality of cotton yarn, several slivers are drawn out thinner and thinner – the loose-packed nature of the fibres allows this – until the required thickness is achieved. The drawn fibres are then twisted tightly together to make the yarn. If very fine yarn is required, the slivers are combed again before drawing.

The process for wool is rather more complicated and depends upon the kind of

5

yarn required. Sheep get very dirty and they also sweat. Two processes, scouring and carbonizing, are used to remove the impurities from the fleece when it arrives at the factory.

In the scouring phase, the wool is washed in a series of vats of soapy alkaline water, the mixture decreasing in strength as the wool moves through the series. This removes dirt, oils and sweat (called *suint*) and also the natural colour of the wool. Vegetable matter, like burrs and tough grasses, are the target of the carbonizing process. Here the wool is subjected to a very weak solution of acid. The excess liquid is extracted and the wool is then dried. While the wool is unharmed by its dousing in acid, the vegetable impurities begin to disintegrate. When the wool moves on to a crushing machine the burrs become powdered and can be shaken clear. At this point the preparation of wool yarn becomes a forked path. One branch leads to a type of yarn called *worsted*, employing the finer wool fibres and intended to make fine cloths; the other branch leads to a type called simply *woollens*, which utilizes coarser fibres and ends as coarser cloth. The two types of yarn also differ in that the fibres in worsted yarns must be as parallel as possible, in woollens the parallelism is much reduced.

Both cotton and wool are what is known as short staple fibres (that is, the actual fibre is relatively short). Silk and man-made fibres, however, have continuous filament yarns. For example, the two threads spun by a silkworm can be as long as 1,300 yards, while the man-made fibres can be produced to any length required. Both are therefore twisted directly into yarn. With man-made fibres, the exact process employed differs according to the material employed, and there may here be some further complications. If, for example, a 'stretch' artificial yarn is required for garments like socks or stockings, the yarn itself must be twisted even further and the twist is heat set. It is then unwound and as a result has a spring-like form which gives it 'stretch'.

Cloth consists of a lattice-work of threads at right angles to each other. Those running the length of the piece are called the *warps*, while the crosswise ones are called the *wefts*. The warps are stretched in parallel lines (perhaps 60 warps to the inch) from one roller called the *weaver's beam* to another called the *cloth beam*. On the way each warp passes through an individual eyelet on one of two wire frames called *heddles*. The odd-numbered warps (one, three, five and so on) pass through the eyelets on the first heddle; the even numbers pass through those on the second and both heddles are movable in the vertical plane.

Heddles, shuttles and reeds

To weave, one heddle is raised and the other lowered, and the weft (carried by a *shuttle*) is passed through the gap between them. The weft, therefore, passes over half the warps and under the rest. After each pass, the weft is pressed back against its forerunners with another wire frame called a *reed*, to make the texture of the material tight. The position of the heddles is then reversed, and the process repeated. This produces the simplest kind of weave; different textures may be achieved by varying the number of warps.

The second major fabric-making process is knitting, and here again the basics are simple – although modern technology has provided some very complicated machines to do the job quickly and efficiently. Basically knitting depends upon forming the yarn into a series of loops; the free end is then passed back through these loops so that it not only stops the first line from pulling straight but also forms a second row of loops. The manoeuvre is then repeated over and over again.

What of colour? This is imparted by either dyeing or printing. Dyeing can be carried out during any of the stages of fabric production. Loose fibres are evenly packed into a perforated drum and the dye is injected. Yarn is hung in a vat in which the dye is circulated by a propellor. Woven fabrics may be *jig dyed,* which means that the material is opened out and drawn back and forth through a dye trough; knitted fabrics are put on to a *winch dyer* which gently dunks them in the liquor (the jig dyer would stretch them).

Multi-coloured fabrics, like carpeting, may be made by weaving together yarns which have previously been dyed. Otherwise, printing can be employed and, for large runs – that is, extensive lengths of material – roller printing is used. The material is passed between a series of rollers each of which is engraved with part of the pattern and each of which carries one of the colours in the form of a paste of pigment and gum. The component parts of the pattern are printed on contact with the cloth, the colour is heat set, and the gum washed out.

The finishing processes, of which there are a great many, are designed to improve one or more of the qualities of the cloth. If some non-shiny cloth, like cotton, is to be given a shiny finish, the material may be *calendared* – passed through heavy rollers which both flatten and polish the yarn. There is also shrink resistance. In the case of cottons it may be done mechanically – the weft threads being closed up together with a high degree of compression, so that shrinkage can cause them to close up no further. But with wools such a process is less effective, for here the shrinkage comes about through *felting* (the scales on the fibre interlock). The trick in this case is to cause the edges of the scales to disintegrate slightly so that the surface of the fibre is smoothed. The wool is, therefore, treated with any one of a number of chemical agents – chlorine gas is often employed – to carry out this work of controlled destruction. Boosted crease resistance can be brought about by impregnating the fibres of the yarn with resin so that they become stiffer. Fabrics can also be treated with chemicals to make them resistant to fire.

It is just one of the 'tricks' which science and technology have brought to the job of providing and improving materials which also bring comfort, protection and colour into our lives.

When wool is rubbed during washing, it shrinks and felts. This is caused by the scales of the fibre interlocking. Here wool is experimentally treated for shrink resistance.

A skilled operator ties a broken thread on a weaving machine that can weave two or more cloths at the same time. Such machines can be adapted to produce a variety of textiles.

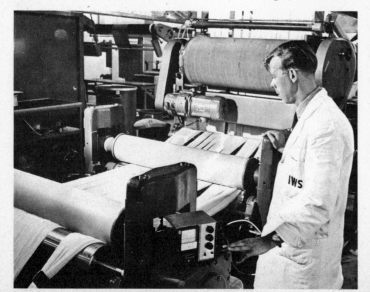

Fast and fugitive colours

Wear, washing and weather may all ruin a carefully chosen colour. The range and fastness of modern dyes and paints is the result of constant testing and experimenting by a complex industry.

FOR THOUSANDS OF YEARS, the naturally dull colours of cloth, leather and other materials have been brightened with dyes, derived from plants and animals. These dyes were probably stains rather than true dyes. Little progress could have been made in the art of dyeing as distinct from staining, until the property of *mordants* was discovered. A mordant is a substance which is either applied to a material before it is dyed or is mixed with the colouring agent to *fix* or hold a dye permanently to a fabric. The mordant, often a hydroxide of a metal, causes a chemical reaction to take place between itself and the dye to form an insoluble substance called a *lake*. The lake is permanently fixed into the fabric and it is the lake that gives the colour.

That mordants were known at a very early period in the history of dyeing is proved by an Egyptian collection of technical recipes compiled some 34 centuries ago. One recipe gives instructions for the preparation of alum to prevent dyes from wearing off cotton fabrics. Careful analysis of dyed fabrics found in ancient Egyptian tombs reveals traces of the aluminium from the alum used as a mordant.

Ancient Egyptians extracted their dyes from roots and herbs, tree bark, berries, nuts and lichens, while rich reds were

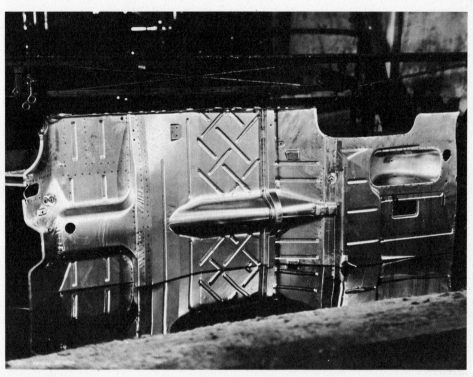

The floor of a car on an assembly line is sprayed with a rust-resistant paint. Later the entire body will be covered with colourful cellulose paints that are baked to harden them.

obtained from insects and molluscs. With these dyes the Egyptians were able to give silk, wool, linen and cotton a wide range of beautiful shades. By using different mordants, they produced different colours from the same dyeing medium. For example, the red dye called *madder,* obtained from the climbing plant *Rubia tinctorum,* gave a rich red when used in conjunction with an alum mordant, while it dyed purple in association with a salts of iron mordant.

Dyes derived from the indigo or woad plants and used to colour fabrics blue, were developed in Thebes nearly 3,000 years ago, where an industry existed for dyeing clothes for the living and wrappings for the dead. Since very early times, soldiers' clothing was coloured red with a dye extracted from an insect called kermes. After the discovery of America, the chief source of red dyes was the cochineal insect.

Tyrian purple, the most splendid of all the ancient dyes, came from the yellowish juice of the murex shellfish. The Phoenicians discovered that exposing the juice to the sun causes it to go through all the colours of the rainbow until it finally becomes a rich and unfading purple. Its name derives from Tyre, where it was first made. It was so expensive to produce that only the rich could afford it.

Although many vegetable- and animal-derived dyes gave good and lasting colours, they tended to be variable in quality and shade, and it was impossible to produce a standard shade or subtle variations. Moreover, most of the natural dyes have little

affinity with textile fibres, which must be pre-treated with a mordant if the colour is to remain fixed.

Modern dyeing techniques date from the mid nineteenth century, when the English chemist William Perkin made the first synthetic dyes from coal-tar derivatives. From this developed an entirely new industry which now synthesizes thousands of colours and shades. For brightness and durability these shades far surpassed the best that had derived from vegetable and animal sources.

Early synthetic dyes were relatively easy to produce, but the vast range of colours and shades now available involve long chains of processes. Nevertheless, modern synthetic dyes derive from much the same materials used by Perkin and his immediate successors. Chief of the raw materials of synthetic dyes are anthracene, benzene, toluene and naphthalene, all yielded from the distillation of coal-tar. Intermediate substances made as steps in the chain of processes between the start of synthesizing and final production of the dye include trinitrotoluene, picric acid, benzaldehyde and toluene sulphonic acid, while the chemicals necessary to produce the intermediate substances include chlorine and phosgene.

To most laymen a dye is just a dye, and all that is needed to colour something red, for example, is a red dye. That is an over-

Painting metallic objects that are exposed to the weather helps prevent them from rusting. A covering of paint does not exclude oxygen, but it does repel moisture.

1 Painted wood is set outdoors to see how the paint withstands the weather. Under such conditions, an inferior paint will quickly crack, chip or peel off.
2 The special anti-fouling paints for ships' bottoms contain chemicals which repel seaweeds and barnacles. Some paints are made resistant to insects and bacteria.
3 Laboratory machines facilitate rapid and well-controlled dyeings. A dyer must decide which

dye to use for a specific material, what the material is to be used for and the conditions it will have to withstand.
4 A mechanical stirrer mixes paint in a factory. Some paints contain poisonous lead, and some countries have laws forbidding their use on surfaces that might be exposed to children.
5 Brightly dyed wool hangs to dry in the dyers' market in Marrakesh, Morocco. The Egyptians used dyes over 34 centuries ago.

simplification of what is, in fact, a highly technical craft. No one dye, whatever its colour may be, will successfully colour all textile fibres. A dye must be chosen that has chemical affinity with the material to be dyed, whether it be cotton, silk, wool, linen or one of the man-made fibres such as rayon, nylon or terylene.

Dyes come into two main categories: *fast* and *fugitive*. Fast dyes are those which retain their colour after the fabric to which they have been applied has been repeatedly laundered and do not fade in sunlight. Fugitive dyes are those which tend to lose colour under such conditions. To meet the dyer's varying requirements according to the material to be dyed, there are some ten principal classes of dyes: acid, basic, direct, chrome, sulphur, vat, azoic, acetate, solubilized, and oxidized.

Acid dyes are applied from a bath containing acid and give best results on silk and wool. Their light shades are the most successful, but they are not completely fast. Basic dyes are preferred for wool and silk, but they take equally well on cotton

that has been mordanted with antimony salts. They hold their colour well after washing, but are liable to fade and rub off after exposure to sunlight.

Direct dyes take well on cotton, rayon, wool and silk without a mordant. Their best result on cotton is when salt or soda ash is added to the dye bath, while acetic acid in the bath gives the most satisfactory result on silk. Direct dyes are exceptionally resistant to washing and sunlight.

Chrome dyes are a class of acid dyes and are normally confined to dyeing wool. The wool has to be treated with potassium dichromate either before or after dyeing to ensure the dye being fast to light and washing. Sulphur dyes are applied from a bath containing sodium sulphide and are chiefly used for cotton and rayon. Although the colours lack brilliance, they are fast to light and laundering.

Vat dyes include the fastest colours known. Many of them deepen rather than fade in strong sunlight, and they all withstand prolonged boiling in soap solutions. The dyes are insoluble but after treatment with sodium hydrosulphite they become soluble in the caustic-soda solution that constitutes the dye bath. When the dyed material is exposed to the air, the dye becomes insoluble again and is firmly fixed on and in the fibres. Vat dyes are colourless when applied to the material, but subsequent oxidation produces the required hues. Oxidation can be achieved by exposure to the air, but it is normally accelerated by dipping the dyed fabric or other surface into vats containing a solution of oxidizing agents.

Azoic dyes are used mainly on cotton. Although fast, they are liable to rub off easily. The colours are formed on the

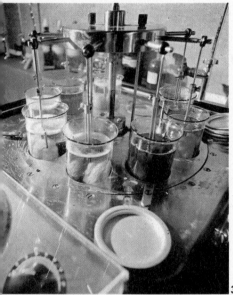

surface of the material by impregnating with two intermediates in succession which combine to fix the dye in and on the fibres. Acetate dyes were developed for cellulose acetate fibres. They consist of fine dispersions of water-soluble dyes applied from a soap solution and have good qualities of fastness.

Solubilized vat dyes are ordinary vat dyes chemically modified to be water-soluble. After-treatment of the material reforms the insoluble dye. Although the expense of this type of dye limits its application to high-quality fabrics, it is easy to apply and has exceptional fastness.

Oxidized dyes are a mixture of salts of aniline and its related compounds applied to a fabric which is then treated with chromic acid or other oxidizing agents, to render the dye insoluble.

Although chiefly used for fabrics and clothing, dyes have an enormous range of applications. Food and beverages are coloured with specially tested and selected dyes of guaranteed purity. Medical uses of dyes include the tinting of parts of the human body when taking X-ray photographs, while chemical laboratories employ various types of dyes as indicators.

Although dyes and paints perform a similar function in that they impart colour to an object, there is a sharp distinction between them. A good dye incorporates itself within the substance to which it is applied. The best of paints, however, does no more than cover the surface to which it is applied and does not penetrate. And, unless paint is given a protective coating of varnish it will 'wear' badly, flake and

discolour, and fade in sunlight. A dyed article can be distorted by creasing, folding, stretching or crumpling without affecting the finish imparted to it by the dye. But a painted surface will crack or flake under such distortion, though some of the rubber, synthetic rubber and plastic paints do withstand certain distortion of the surface to which they are applied.

Nevertheless, modern paints do perform a limited protective and preservative function. A skin of paint on a metal surface provides a protective layer against rust. The protection is mainly chemical, as the constituents of the paint increase resistance to attack by oxygen and other gases in the atmosphere. Paint does not exclude oxygen; it repels moisture. That is why it is essential that metal surfaces be re-painted immediately the existing coat shows signs of cracking and flaking. Such defects permit moisture to come into contact with the metal and so initiate corrosive action.

More than 20,000 years ago, men used colours obtained from natural earths to paint on the walls of caves in France and Spain pictures of their hunting exploits. For thousands of years natural earths were the sole source of the colouring matter in paints. These natural pigments were usually clays containing the iron oxide which gave yellowish or brownish tints and pigments derived from limestone, shale, charcoal, graphite and chalk. All the early paints were purely decorative, as they contained no oil or other constituent to give them preservative properties.

The two principal ingredients of a

modern paint are the *pigment* and the *vehicle*. The pigment is the colouring agent and the vehicle is the liquid in which it is colloidally dispersed. Pigments are generally classed as *prime* or as *extenders*. Extenders are substances added to cheap paints to increase their bulk, and paints containing them are deficient in covering properties. One of the most extensively used pigments is white lead, a basic lead carbonate prepared by the action of carbon dioxide and moisture on finely divided lead with acetic acid as a catalyst. Alternative white pigments are titanium oxide, zinc oxide and compounds of zinc sulphide and barium sulphate. Red lead is the pigment used in the red paint employed as an undercoat for the protection of steel structures. Other first-class pigments are lead chromate, or chrome yellow; Prussian blue, which is a complex iron compound; and oxides of iron such as ochre and rouge. Extenders are derived mainly from byrates, magnesium silicate, limestone and various clays.

Laws against lead

As lead is poison, it is important that lead-based paints are not applied to toys or other articles which children are likely to put in their mouths. In fact there are legal prohibitions of lead-based paints to surfaces likely to be handled by children or which are unprotected against contact with food and drink.

The vehicle or liquid constituent of a paint is mainly an oil. Raw linseed oil is the usual vehicle in paints for exterior application. The linseed oil is a mixture of unsaturated esters and when the paint is exposed to air, oxygen combines with the unsaturated carbon in the paint to form a hard and glossy substance which is resistant to moisture. The paint mixture normally contains resins and substances that act as thinners and driers.

Resins help to bind paint together and make it easier to apply with a brush. The resins can be natural gums or synthesized from chemicals. Driers accelerate the hardening of oil-based paints and are mostly oxides and acetates of lead, cobalt or manganese. Driers have a catalytic effect by increasing the rate of oxidation and polymerization of the oil vehicle. Polymerization in this context means the effective combination of the various molecules of which the paint's constituents are formed; that is, the molecules of the oil vehicle are induced by the drier to form a more complex molecule with the same empirical formula as the simpler ones. Efficient polymerization of a paint produces a tough, resistant and more or less permanent film. Thinners such as turpentine and paraffin make the paint more fluid and easier to apply, particularly by spraying. Fractionation and synthesis of oils have made available new paint vehicles that are inexpensive and adaptable to a wide variety of uses.

Ageing of paint is a measure of its durability, and a paint that ages badly is one that deteriorates rapidly after application, resulting in the film cracking, chipping or peeling off. Weather and light soon affect poor-quality paints, causing them

to age quickly. Chalking, the progressive powdering of the paint film from the surface on which it has been applied, is sometimes considered a desirable form of ageing, since the paint film is kept clear of cracking, chipping and peeling, leaving the surface in reasonable condition for repainting.

A recent development in paint that has become popular with the 'do-it-yourself' decorator is the latex emulsion paint which contains synthetic rubber. It is easy

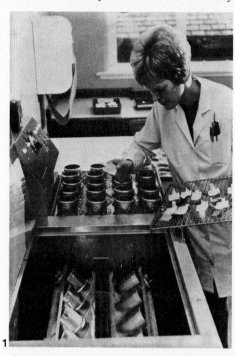

1 Knitted wool is tested to determine how the colour stands up to repeated washings. Until modern dyeing techniques were discovered it was impossible to attain uniform quality or shade.
2 The fastness of dyed wool is tested under intense light in a laboratory. *Fast* dyes are those which retain their colour after many washings and exposure to sunlight.

to apply; does not drip, is nearly odourless, flows well on the surface, dries quickly. In some instances it is sufficiently flexible to resist limited distortion by bending, twisting and stretching. There are also paints containing chemicals which are germicidal and insect-repellent; others can be treated to prevent the growth of fungi or be made resistant to fire and heat.

Water paints for interior application contain casein or synthetic resins. Their high proportion of pigment, together with the thickness of the coat that has to be applied, gives them good covering qualities. Whitewashes for exterior use consist of a mixture of slaked lime, water and glue or casein. Emulsion paints consist of an emulsion of oil in water and may contain casein as the emulsifying agent.

Varnishes differ from paints in being transparent and when they are coloured they contain dyes instead of pigments. Varnishes are either spirit or oil. Spirit varnishes are a solution of resins in a volatile solvent such as benzene or alcohol. Their drying after application involves a chemical reaction, as the solvent evaporates to leave a thin film of resin on the surface to which the resin has been applied. Resins in varnishes are now mostly synthetic as they are of more uniform quality than natural resins and give a better and more durable finish.

Oil varnishes consist of natural or synthetic resins dissolved in linseed, tung, castor, soya-bean or fish oil. Lacquers, which vary widely in their composition, resemble paints by containing pigments, but like varnishes dry by evaporation of the solvent. Motor-vehicle bodies are most commonly painted with cellulose lacquers containing synthetic resins. A plasticizer is added to make the lacquer tough and pliable. The lacquers dry to a hard-wearing and shiny finish which is unaffected by water, oil or petrol.

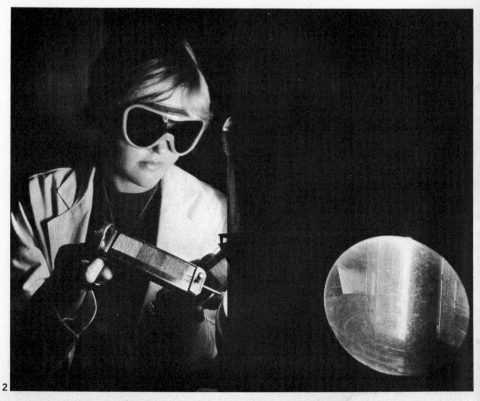

Glass and ceramics

Revolutionary breakthroughs in the development of glass and ceramics have transformed these basically fragile materials into a specialized range with important applications in science and industry.

WINDOW-PANES AND TUMBLERS, crockery, roofing tiles and countless other articles made of glass or ceramics are all visible links with our distant ancestors' tentative ventures into the arts of manufacture, or the crafts of making things from naturally occurring raw materials.

The term ceramics comes from a Greek word meaning 'potter's clay', and a ceramic product is anything made by shaping a mixture of clay and other materials into a desired form, drying it and then baking it hard by firing in a kiln. Bricks, cups or priceless porcelain vases are all basically the same.

Over a period of thousands of years pottery developed into the clay bricks used by the ancient civilizations of the Euphrates for building their temples and palaces. It was realized that a design impressed on soft clay became hard and permanent after the clay had dried. Men were soon to write their records on clay tablets and from these the history of ancient civilizations can be pieced together.

The first clay pots and bowls were dried hard in the sun but they became soft again when filled with water. Then it was discovered that this could be remedied by drying the clay pot or bowls and firing them at red heat. That marked the turning-point of craftsmanship in pottery: ceramics had been made durable.

When clay is hardened by firing, the tiny particles of clay lose water and in doing so change their structure. There is also a certain amount of melting, particularly of the felspars and micas present in the clay. On cooling, the silicates in the clay *vitrify*, that is, they become glass-like, and act as a binder to cement the clay particles together so that the clay becomes hard and strong.

The first ceramics were earthenware. In the earthenware process, ordinary clay is moulded to the required shape and fired to approximately 800 °C. Because only a small percentage of vitreous material is present in the clays used for earthenware, there is very little recrystallization and, unlike other ceramics, it tends to be porous. Earthenware can be made waterproof by covering it with a substance, or mixture of substances, which melt during firing to form a glazed surface. One of the first substances used for this purpose was salt, and articles were said to be salt-glazed. Wash-basins and other cheap chinaware are made in this way.

Bricks and tiles

Clays used for bricks and other outdoor building-components require carefully controlled drying. This is to prevent too rapid an escape of moisture during firing which would cause excessive shrinking and cracking. Clays used for bricks and tiles contain iron compounds and the final colour of the fired articles depends upon the atmosphere in the kiln during firing. A plentiful supply of oxygen oxidizes the iron compounds to give a red colour, less oxygen gives a blue colour, and further adjustments a brown or mottled appearance.

Ceramic products designed to resist melting at temperatures in excess of 1,000 °C. are called *refractories* and include the heat-resistant bricks used for lining furnaces. Many types of bricks and other industrial ceramics must, in addition, be able to withstand the corrosive action of chemicals. They are made from sands and clays having a high proportion of silica and are mixed with lime to produce a binding medium. Firing at a temperature of 1,400 °C. converts the normal silica crystal formation into one that remains stable when subjected to high temperatures.

For certain special applications, refractories are made from dolomite, a double carbonate of magnesium and calcium. Fireclay, one of the most common of heat-resistant ceramics, is derived from carboniferous rock and obtains its heat-resistant property from its alumina content.

Porcelain, which is the highest quality of all ceramics and is used for electrical insulators, vases and other decorative articles, is made from kaolin, or white china clay. It is composed almost entirely of the mineral kaolinite, a hydrated silicate of aluminium, and is formed by the decomposition of granite felspars. In the making of porcelain the kaolin has added to it quartz, felspar and, sometimes, ball clay. Ball clay also derives from granite felspar, but during its formation the kaolinite grains leave the parent rock. It is finer grained and more plastic than china clay and contains quartz and mica.

Porcelain was first made about 200 BC by the Chinese. Kaolin is a Chinese word meaning 'high ridge' and the clay was originally dug from the sides of hills. The Chinese also discovered another material called petunce which, when added to kaolin enabled porcelain vases and other objects to be fired at relatively low temperatures and they become hard and glass-like. For centuries the Chinese were able

At this plant in Tennesee, a continuous sheet of glass is drawn out of the furnace and rolled on to a grinding and polishing line. After cleaning and inspection, it is cut to size.

A large porcelain electrical weather-shield is turned vertically at a factory in Britain. Its basic material is kaolin which is fired at extremely high temperatures.

to keep the ingredients of their porcelain secret. Then, in 1718, a traveller returned to England with samples of kaolin and details of how to make the pottery. European potters attempted to make porcelain from the coarse clays then available but were unsuccessful until 1758, when the Cornwall china-clay deposits were found in England. Chinese porcelain reached its greatest perfection during the Ming dynasty (1368–1644), when wonderful colour effects were achieved. Other notable periods of Chinese porcelain are the Tang and Sung dynasties.

Porcelain is fired at temperatures ranging from 1,200 °C. to 1,400 °C. These temperatures ensure maximum vitrification and, therefore, great impermeability, making porcelain invaluable for insulators and chemical equipment.

Bone china, used for high-quality household crockery, consists of china clay mixed with fluxes and calcium phosphate, or calcined animal bone; hence the name bone china. The addition of the calcium phosphate gives bone china its characteristic translucence.

Before shaping and firing, most clays have various non-clay ingredients, chiefly white mica and felspars added to them. These melt easily and lower the firing temperature of the clay. On recooling, a glass-like substance forms to give the ceramic extra strength and make it waterproof. Excessive shrinking of ceramics after drying and during firing is prevented by the addition of a quartz filler.

Certain industrial and scientific applications of ceramics demand hardness, strength, heat resistance and an ability

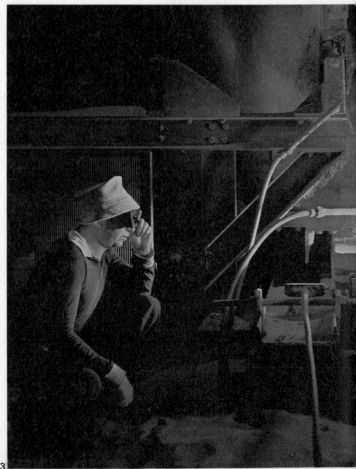

4

5

1 An inspector examines plates made on moulds by a fully-automatic machine at a pottery in Staffordshire. Glazed and dried, the plates are then fired in kilns.
2 Molten glass, which resembles thick, sticky toffee, flows between patterned rollers to produce flat glass with a textured surface. It is then slowly cooled to avoid cracking.
3 His eyes protected from the glare, this glass-worker checks the glass mixture in a furnace.

Any impurities in the ingredients can discolour and spoil all the glass in the melt.
4 Ceramics are packed into a kiln, lined with heat-resistant bricks, before firing. Kiln temperatures ensure maximum vitrification and great impermeability of the porcelain.
5 Red-hot molten glass is extruded from an automatic machine to form soft-drink bottles. The glass is made from carefully measured quantities of sand, soda ash, lime and other materials.

to withstand sudden changes of extreme temperatures, which ordinary clays cannot meet. Accordingly, an entirely new range of ceramic materials has been developed, amongst them oxides of beryllium, aluminium, thorium, zirconium and magnesium, and certain synthetic nitrides and carbides. Beryllium oxide ceramics are employed in the casing for the rods of nuclear fuels in reactors. Aluminium oxide ceramics, which can resist temperatures up to 2,100 °C are used as insulators for sparking plugs and heat shields on space rockets. Zirconium-oxide ceramics are essential in metallurgy and chemistry where temperatures up to 3,000 °C are encountered. Non-organic binders are added to non-plastic ceramics materials in order to hold the shaped article together while it is soft. During the firing process, the binder is destroyed, while the grains of the non-plastic material are *sintered* (bound together by the heat).

The chief tool in ceramics used to be the potter's wheel. Although still used for the shaping of high-quality articles, it has been largely replaced by automatic moulding machines for crockery and similar ware, and extrusion-moulding for pipes. Ceramics for certain industrial uses are shaped by putting semi-plastic clay mixtures on a lathe and turning the material like soft metal. The article is then fired in the usual way.

After ceramics, glass was Man's major

step towards the development of industrial crafts. There are no reliable records as to when or where it was discovered that a transparent material could be produced by fusing together sand, soda and potash, but the art appears to have been established in Syria some 7,500 years ago. From there it was introduced into Egypt, and by the seventh century BC glass was being made in Europe. The Egyptians initiated many technical advances; they were the first to make glass vessels, they invented glass-blowing, and they produced coloured glass by adding copper to the molten materials to obtain a red tint.

Much of the glass used now is made from the same materials. Sodium or window glass, which is the cheapest and most extensively manufactured, is produced by heating a mixture of sand, soda ash and limestone at a temperature of 1,500 °C. The intense heat causes sand to replace carbon dioxide in the soda ash and limestone and so form silicates. The molten glass is then a mixture of the silicates of calcium and soda. If molten glass cools too quickly it sets up internal stresses which result in cracks and bubbles. To prevent this, the articles being moulded or blown are passed through annealing ovens to bring them gradually down to an atmospheric temperature.

Glass does not crystallize on cooling; nor does it appear to have any definite temperature at which it may be said to solidify. Consequently glass is classed as an *amorphous solid* which retains some of the properties, particularly transparency, of a highly viscous fluid. Chemists describe glass as a *super-cooled liquid*, thereby emphasizing that it is not actually a solid, but a fluid of almost infinite viscosity.

Modern glass-works melt the ingredients in tanks built up from fireclay slabs. Before the ingredients are added a proportion of broken glass, called *cullet,* is put in to hasten the fusing process. As the mixture melts and fuses, impurities rise to the surface from which they are mechanically skimmed. The molten glass is allowed to cool until it resembles a thin, sticky toffee. It is then ready for drawing off to go to the mechanical moulding and blowing machines or for rolling into plate glass.

One of the most difficult tasks in glass-making is to ensure that the ingredients are free of impurites and that they are mixed in the correct quantities. A tiny piece of iron in a mixture for making plate glass will discolour every particle of glass in the melt. Cheap glass frequently develops a greenish tinge due to ferrous compounds in the sand. This can be overcome by adding manganese dioxide. Alternatively, small quantities of compounds are added to give a colour which offsets the green.

Glass can be coloured to any desired shade by adding to the melt appropriate metal oxides. Copper or gold produce ruby glass, cobalt gives blue glass. Manganese colours glass in a variety of shades from pink to purple according to the amount added; chromium gives shades of green; uranium gives green and yellow shades and copper colours glass red or black, depending on the quantities.

Cut glass contains a considerable amount of lead silicate, but an excess of lead in the melt destroys its characteristic brilliance and sparkle. It is this care in the mixing of ingredients of the right quality and the careful addition of colouring agents that has made the techniques of quality control so essential in the glass industry.

Hundreds of varieties of glass have been developed by technologists to meet the ever-expanding demands of industry

Chemists have produced many special types of glass for particular uses. The glass of this tank has been tempered to have the strength and durability of steel.

and science. There is heat-resistant glass for smelters and convertors; glass which shields against nuclear radiation; glass to allow the passage of the ultra-violet rays in sunlight, optical glass ranging from spectacle and microscope lenses to the huge mirrors for telescopes; glass bricks for the walls of buildings; splinter-proof glass for windscreens and bullet-proof glass strong enough to resist machine-gun fire.

Ribbons of glass

Grinding and polishing processes to produce plate glass began in 1688, when the glass had to be cast in sheets at least 50 per cent thicker than the final product required. Later the molten glass was poured into shallow moulds on a rotating table and ground with metal discs working in a mixture of fine sand, emery and water before being polished with rouge and water. An improved method was the Bicheroux process, in which molten glass was fed through rollers on to a flat surface and then annealed before polishing, but the area of the glass remained limited. Then, in 1920 the Ford Motor Company and the English glass-making firm of Pilkington Brothers invented a method of rolling plate glass in the form of a continuous ribbon as it left the furnace. Five years later Pilkington Brothers developed a machine that ground and polished sheets of plate glass continuously, first on the top surface and then on the bottom surface.

In order to avoid having to turn the glass over, in 1937 they introduced a machine in which the ribbon of glass passed between grinding heads so that its two sides are worked on simultaneously. In this way, a sheet of glass 1,000 ft long and 100 in. wide could be ground and polished at the rate of 200 ft a minute. Even so, they still had to discover how to support the hot, fluid glass without strain, so that a truly flat, distortion-free sheet could emerge of any desired length. The problem was finally solved in 1952, when

Alastair Pilkington invented the float glass system, whereby the continuous ribbon of glass passes from the furnace to float on the surface of a molten metal at a controlled temperature. It emerges as sheet or plate glass with a brilliant lustrous finish on both sides.

There is also glass that can be drawn into fine thread, and woven into a fibreglass cloth, and glass that can be combined with resins to make fibreglass, for car and aircraft bodies. Many plastics tend to elongate under tension, crack under bending or impact, or turn soft under heat. Reinforcing them with fibreglass increases their strength, much as concrete strength is reinforced with metal rods. Fibreglass plastics enable large structures to be made of plastics without risk of collapse or other failure.

Another type of glass is low-expansion glass designed to withstand sudden changes of extreme temperatures. One glass of this type even resists fracture when placed on a block of ice and molten iron is poured on it at a temperature of 2,600 °C.

Applications of glass seem endless. There is glass that can be folded or crumpled; glass that bounces like rubber; glass that can be cut with a saw or have nails driven into it; glass sutures for surgery; and glass fishing-rods and lines. Transparent cooking utensils are made from glass mixtures to which boric and aluminium oxide have been added. They can withstand great changes of temperature without cracking.

Glass is a bad conductor of heat, but it has a good compression and tensile strength, and is unaffected by most acids. Finally, glass cannot be corroded by the impurities in the atmosphere: an all-glass building would never need painting and would probably last indefinitely.

Glass is blown and shaped to make scientific instruments. Resistant to acids and other corrosive chemicals, it is widely used for laboratory apparatus and storage containers.

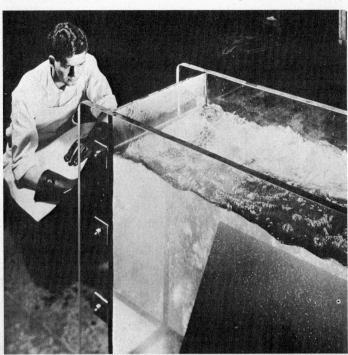

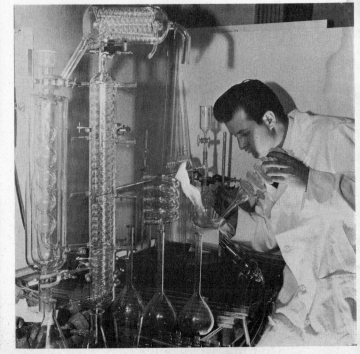

Quinqueremes and Queens

From the crude rafts of early Man to the quinqueremes of Mediterranean traders, through steamships to modern Cunard Queens, the history of shipping is a dramatic story of struggle with nature.

THE SHIP has had a profound effect on the progress and spread of civilization. 'Trade follows the flag', said the comfortable Victorians – and of course the ship carried both to all corners of the Earth. Because of their importance, ships have received a great deal of attention from inventors: in ship design and building, science has been put hard to work.

The modern ship has evolved from the very much simpler craft of ancient times – craft like the canoe, raft and coracle. But Man first ventured on the water in something much simpler even than these. He must have noted that trees or branches which fell into water floated and consequently reasoned that these would probably bear his weight as well. Here lies the first scientific principle of the ship. Although the early sailors did not know it, they were demonstrating Archimedes' principle – that an object will float if it displaces a weight of water the same as or greater than its own – many hundreds of years before it was formulated by the great Greek engineer. They also discovered that collections of fallen branches made a more stable floating platform and that large logs could be hollowed out to form dug-outs.

We have more information about the early ships of Egypt than any others. There were papyrus reeds in plenty, and the

1 Clay model of an ancient Greek ship, found at Mochles, Crete. The high prow and stern and the typical curve of both ends are well shown.
2 The *Great Eastern,* built in Britain in the 1850s, had paddle-wheels, propellers and sails. For 40 years she remained the largest ship ever built.
3 Henri Beaudout, Gaston Vanackere and Marc Modena took 88 days to reach Falmouth from Nova Scotia on this primitive raft in 1956.
4 The control room of one of the first nuclear-powered merchant vessels. The N.S. *Savannah* can go round the world without refuelling.

Egyptians built rafts by weaving them together. Their early ships were therefore shallow, and very broad in the beam, like rafts. There was also a scarcity of suitable wood. The most available wood was acacia, which grows as hard brittle timber, and which could be cut only in relatively short lengths. So the early Egyptian ships were not only broad and flat but were also constructed of numbers of short pieces of wood about 3·5 feet in length; there were no continuous planks running from stem to stern of the vessel.

The Greek historian, Herodotus, tells us that these pieces were put together like bricks and then dowelled or dovetailed. The 'bricks' were clamped together by long gunwales which often swept upwards and backwards at the bow to form a spring and gave added resilience to the structure. The spring often terminated in a carved figurehead; a characteristic feature of the pharaohs' ships.

The Egyptian vessels had no keel – they

depended on their great beam for stability and this, added to the shortness of the hull components, brought problems of longitudinal strength. The second characteristic of their ships was a long truss which was placed overhead and stretched the length of the ship. It was of course secured at the bow and the stern to provide the needed stiffening.

Propulsion for these unwieldy vessels was usually by oars. Square sails were nevertheless developed and these were used to supplement the oar power when the wind was suitable. Here, 'square' does not refer to the shape of the sails but to the fact that they were set across the centre line of the boat from left to right. The sails were therefore suitable only for running before the wind.

Biremes, triremes, quinqueremes

The Minoans of Crete who dominated the sea trade of the Eastern Mediterranean at an early period, developed their ships from a different tradition. Crete was extensively covered with huge cypress forests, some of which grew very tall. The very early Cretans therefore adopted the dug-out as a means of travel and, about 2000 BC, discovered that they could make this type of craft even more effective by building up the sides with planks.

Cretan ships were lighter in relation to capacity than the Egyptian vessels and the fact that the heavy dug-out section was situated at the bottom of the hull meant that stability could be maintained without resorting to great width in the beam. In fact the concept of the keel developed from this stabilizing dug-out section. The Cretan ships, and those of the Greeks and Romans, were faster as well as being narrower, than the Egyptian vessels.

The main worry of the Cretan shipbuilders was to make the built-up planking watertight where it joined at stem and stern. They overcame this problem by setting the stem and stern posts back from the ends of the keel or dug-out section. Such an arrangement meant that the projecting keel took the major force of the water rather than the planking joint at the post. The resulting two-pronged bow is called a *bifid bow*.

The Phoenicians ousted the Cretans as the dominant sea power. Like the Romans they travelled as far as Britain, but it has also been suggested that they may have been the sailors employed by King Necho of Egypt in 600 BC to circumnavigate Africa, a marathon journey which took three years. The early Phoenician ships had straight keels and high end posts; they were lightly built for speed and were perhaps the first ships to have two banks of oars on either side (this kind of ship was called the *bireme* – later Grecian and Roman versions had three banks and were called *triremes;* there were even five-banked ships – the *quinqueremes*). The Phoenicians may also have built upon the bifid constructional ideas of the Cretans and developed the bow ram for their fighting ships.

In more northern latitudes ships appear to have developed more recently than in the Mediterranean, yet in some ways they

seem to have evolved in a similar manner. The Norsemen did, however, pioneer a totally new method of boat construction in which the planks used to build up the dug-out were not laid edge to edge as in the Mediterranean ships, but overlapped. Boats constructed in this way are said to be *clinker-built* (the edge-to-edge method is called *carvel* construction) and such partial lamination provides extra strength and watertightness.

Steering in the Viking ships, and indeed all the early ships so far mentioned, was by one or two oars at the stern.

In these early ships can be seen a number of scientific principles put to work. First, there is the exploitation of buoyancy as described in Archimedes' principle. Then, with the development of the pointed bow and sleeker lines to the hull, we see early application of hydrodynamic ideas. Oars are simple mechanical levers, and the development of the keel shows that shipbuilders early understood that the lower the centre of gravity in a vessel the more stable it is likely to be.

Most of these considerations have remained important to the shipbuilder right up to the present day in constructing conventional craft. Others have, of course, disappeared from the scene with the arrival of new materials – like iron, steel and glass fibre – and new methods of propulsion.

As ships became steadily bigger, they became more and more difficult to move by

means of oars. The early sailors had a ready-made answer to their problem in the sail, but for a considerable time they could only see one aspect of its usefulness – for catching winds blowing from astern. The sail to them was nothing more than an auxiliary propulsion system.

The Vikings developed a system by which their ships were able to sail close to the wind. They turned their square sails edge-on to the approaching wind, so that in effect they ran 'fore-and-aft'. The pressure of the wind caused the fabric of the sail to form an aerofoil section; the sail adopted the curved shape similar to the upper surface of an aeroplane wing. An aeroplane is able to fly because the air has to flow faster over the upper surface than the lower one. Because of this, a partial vacuum is formed above the wing which, together with the higher pressure under the wing, tends to lift it upwards. The same

1 The *Queen Elizabeth 2* during construction at John Brown's shipyards on Clydeside. The internal structure of the massive hull with its honeycomb of rooms is taking shape.
2 Tugs towing *Queen Elizabeth 2* down the Clyde after launching. The superstructure – the funnel and deck fittings – has still to be finished and there is still unfinished work below decks.
3 The liner *Queen Elizabeth 2* undertaking her first trials on the Firth of Clyde. Her trials were marred by problems with the complex turbines which drive her huge screws.

1 Wooden model of an ancient Egyptian funerary boat, found at Thebes. The shape of the ship, with its two pointed ends rising out of the water, is derived from boats made of papyrus reeds.
2 The *Cutty Sark,* probably the most famous of all sailing ships. This beautiful clipper was used for many years on the eastern run, bringing tea to London from China.

is true of the aerofoiled sail except that the force is horizontal.

The exploitation of this aerodynamic principle – whether it came by accident or design – opened the way for the age of sail. The next step was the invention of the truly fore-and-aft sail, that is one which is permanently set more or less along the centre line of the vessel. It is thought to have been invented in the eastern Mediterranean or the Indian Ocean.

Sail shapes

Various shapes of sail were then developed to perform in different fore-and-aft conditions. For example, where the vessel was required to do a great deal of its work close to the wind the sails were often triangular; where some of the trip at least was to be accomplished by exploiting strong following winds the sail remained four-sided so that it would catch the maximum amount of wind when pushed out over the *beam,* or side of the vessel.

The fighting ships of Sir Francis Drake, the Spanish galleons and the mighty clippers, used both triangular fore-and-aft and four-sided 'square' sails in various combinations for greater flexibility of operation. Others, like the many-masted trading schooners of the United States' eastern seaboard, used only the fore-and-

The four-masted barque *Lawhill,* built in 1892 for the Far Eastern case-oil trade. A number of windjammers were still in use on the Borneo run until well into the 1920s.

A modern oil tanker, the *Esso Bernicia*. Built in 1968 at Kiel, Germany, she is more than 1,000 feet long and has a dead weight of 190,600 tons. The crew's quarters in the stern are fully air conditioned.

aft kind, all of which were triangular.

Sail remained in the ascendancy for many hundreds of years and the designers concentrated on improving the hull shapes of their craft so that while they carried the maximum amount of payload they were also speedy and stable. They also used iron, copper, bronze and steel to clothe the wood; the first completely iron ships were built early in the nineteenth century. But nothing they did could really make up for the fact that the sailing ship was at the mercy of the wind.

Steamships

The advent of the steam engine in the early eighteenth century sounded the death knell of the sailing vessel. Steam soon became a reasonably efficient means of moving a ship through water. The steam engine became more refined, and eventually the steam turbine began to replace it.

Concurrently with the appearance of the steam turbine (Sir Charles Parsons patented the first in 1884), the internal combustion engine began to show its promise. The version which has been most widely used is that invented by Rudolf Diesel in 1892 and which bears his name – as does the fuel which it uses. Unlike the petrol engine this needs no spark to ignite the mixture of air and fuel in the cylinder. Instead, the diesel engine draws in air on the down-stroke of its piston. On the up-stroke, the air is compressed and its temperature is raised sufficiently to spark the injection of diesel fuel and so provide the necessary internal combustion.

But the power story does not end here. The Americans, Russians and Japanese are harnessing the nuclear reactor for propelling ships.

The early steamers used the power of their engines for propulsion by mechanical extensions of the oar concept. The closest to the original was the American John Fitch's *Experiment* which employed the power of the steam engine to work what have been called 'duck leg' paddles. Simply,

these were no more than three vertical oars set at the stern of the vessel. They were plunged into the water in rotation and then 'pulled' by the power of the engines.

More usually, however, the early steam-boats were propelled by paddles arranged around a wheel. These wheels were set either at the stern as in the famous Mississippi riverboats, or on either side of the hull – as in the *Great Western* which from 1837 did 12 years on the trans-Atlantic run.

But none of these ideas was as effective as the propeller screw. The latter works like the windmill; the angled blades of the propeller press the water backwards away from the ship and consequently force the ship itself forwards. Of course, the paddle produces the same effect, but the important difference is that the three or four blades of the screw are all totally immersed in the water and thus are all doing useful work for the ship as long as the propeller is turning. The major part of the paddle wheel, however, is out of the water during any given revolution. During this time the 'dry' paddles are nothing but passengers.

In 1839 the efficiency of the screw principle was demonstrated by the small British steamer, *Archimedes*. Today, without exception, the major vessels which go down the slipways of the world are screw-driven.

Most modern conventional ships then are powered either by steam turbines or diesel motors; they are propelled by screws; they are constructed of steel. In addition, the marine architect has brought to a fine art the design of hull shape for effective travel through the water. But already there has been a new synthesis of the principles of flight and traditional ship design. It is to be seen in the emergence of the hydrofoil and the hovercraft.

In the first case, the ship does become a kind of aircraft. It rides over the surface of the water on stilts which terminate in ski-like foils. These work in water just like the wings of an aeroplane in air; they provide sufficient lift to raise the main body of the ship above the surface. The drag of the hull in the water disappears, and hydrofoils are therefore capable of very high speeds (up to 70 knots).

The hovercraft sucks air in through a giant fan on its upper side and pumps it out beneath the flattened hull. Flexible skirts contain this expelled air so that the hovercraft rides on a cushion of air over almost any surface. It is propelled by aero-engines mounted on the deck, and is in effect a very low-altitude vertical-take-off aircraft.

Container vessels

In the realm of the cargo vessel, important work has been done on the development of the container ship. In its most sophisticated form, this consists of three sections: a bow, a stern, and a central portion for cargo. The three are detachable and engines and steering equipment are situated either in the bow or stern. These are used to bring the full container into port, whereupon they are unbolted and reaffixed to another cargo section which has already been loaded – so that the cycle can begin again. Turn-round time is dramatically cut.

At the same time, oil tankers are becoming ever larger, and their length puts great strain on the middle of the hull in heavy seas. To overcome this, designers are looking at the possibility of hinged vessels, which 'give' to the violence of the waters.

The submarine may soon take the tanker's place as a cargo-carrying vessel. The important principle is that varying buoyancy enables it to sink or rise. But problems of water pressure must also be met and these, with the necessity of cheap and simple life-support systems, make submarines a complicated matter for the designers.

While the application of science to seafaring has taken Man to all corners of the globe, a great deal of work remains to be done. Probably the principal effort will now be directed at exploiting the possibilities of undersea transport. But for surface shipping there remains a vast potential, only now being fully tapped with the development of container ships.

Storehouse of the sea

To meet the growing need for food, fuel and minerals, Man is turning to the sea. Through intensive study of the oceans, he is learning where this wealth is stored and the means to extract it.

THE OCEANS of the Earth – that is the actual water itself – contain more gold than all the land mines put together. In fact, sea water contains all the known elements. Some occur in high concentrations – sodium chloride (common salt), if totally removed from the water and spread out evenly, would cover the surface of the globe to a depth of some 450 ft. Others, in spite of their intrinsic worth, are diluted with such a vast quantity of sea water that extraction would be uneconomic. Still others, such as magnesium and bromine, are both useful and exist in large quantities.

The oceans have enormous potential as providers for mankind. Indeed, the elements dissolved in and extractable from the waters are just one aspect of the whole. The sea also provides food, energy and minerals from the sea bed – and the list is growing apace. The progress achieved in unlocking the door to the ocean treasure house rests to a great extent on the work of a group of scientists, called oceanographers. These scientists come from a wide range of fields: among their group are geologists, geophysicists, chemists and biologists.

Marine geophysicists and geologists are basically interested in elucidating the Earth's history. For this they need to know the topography of the ocean bed, so maps have to be made. They also examine the kinds of rock and sediment that occur in various places, and the ways in which these materials are arranged. Taken together, this may suggest ways in which the topography has changed during the Earth's history.

Mapping the sea floor accurately is generally carried out from a surface vessel. This presents a major problem; sea water is comparatively opaque to light and it is impossible to see the bed except in the shallowest of waters. The oceanographers, however, have overcome this by 'seeing' with sound – that is they employ the echo sounder. Equipment of a kind was in operation as long ago as 1922. Since then, primarily because of developments during the Second World War, equipment has improved. As a result the oceanographers have discovered many new underwater features – from vast underwater chasms to towering mountains.

Sounding the waters

The echo sounder basically consists of a noise source – nowadays an electric oscillator situated below the hull of the ship – and a receiver. When the oscillator is activated, a short ultrasonic signal is directed down to the sea bottom. There it is reflected and returns to the receiver as an echo. Since the speed of sound through water (about a mile a second) is well known, the depth of the sea bed can be worked out from the time it takes the signal to make the two-way journey. The depths revealed by a continuous series of signals are automatically marked on paper to give a profile of the sea bed over which the ship is passing.

Echo sounding becomes less accurate in very deep waters. In a great thickness of sea water there are likely to be other recording surfaces like shoals of fish, and the beam of sound waves spreads out as they move away from the ship. This means that the further the reflecting surface is away from the emitting source, the greater

1 During seismic surveys, small surface explosions generate sound waves from which the number of layers on the sea bed and their depth can be identified. The geologist on a survey ship interprets the results from a continuous trace.
2 H.M.S. *Challenger* sailed around the world from 1872 to 1876, gathering information about the oceans, much of which is still relevant.

will be the area of it upon which the sound waves impinge. This area could be a mile across, and the returning echo could come from any part of it. Echo-sounding equipment mounted in submersibles, such as the all-aluminium *Aluminaut,* may provide the answer here, since the carrier can travel relatively close to the sea bed, and the crew can carry out visual checks.

In a great many areas of the ocean bed, the surface consists of sediment. To discover the depth of the underlying rock layers and their spatial relationships to each other, the oceanographers use a technique called seismic sounding. This is very similar to the echo kind, but relies for its sound source on the explosion of small charges on the surface of the sea. Thus a greater sound energy is emitted, part of which goes straight back to the receiver. But some of the explosive sound passes through the topmost rock layer before being reflected back to the receiver. A further proportion continues downwards until it reaches the next layer and some of it is reflected. By relating the time taken for the return journey by various parts of the signal to the known speeds of sound through various media, the scientists can work out the depths of the various layers.

Civil engineers also use such techniques for a multitude of purposes, such as to picture the kind of underwater terrain in which a communications cable must be laid, to monitor the build up of silt in harbour entrances and channels, and to reveal whether a particular geological structure is compact enough to allow some weighty construction like a bridge to stand upon it.

Tapping the oceans

The techniques amassed by the oceanographers have been used most spectacularly in the search for sea oil and offshore natural gas. Both of these valuable commodities tend to collect under humps of some impermeable material – it may be rock, clay or even salt – forced upwards in the sea bed by giant pressures from the interior of the Earth. The oceanographers' techniques can reveal such structures – as proved by the amount of oil which is being piped ashore from the sea bed around the United States and in the Persian Gulf, and the gas which comes ashore in Britain and Europe.

To establish the kinds of rock and sediments existing in various areas of ocean bed, the sea scientists have mostly had to rely on samples brought up by corer and dredge. But once again, the new submersibles come into the picture. Many are fitted with external manipulators which allow the scientists to gather samples at considerable depths in a much more accurate manner than before.

Nevertheless, surveys carried out by the old methods have revealed important deposits of valuable materials. Some have been exploited in a big way. Gravel extraction is a case in point, and even diamonds have been dredged up from the sea bed off the southwest coast of Africa. In South East Asia, tin comes from the same watery source.

Other important finds have yet to be

1 For centuries fishermen have used bright lights to attract fish into their nets. This method is being used on the Sea of Galilee, which, as in the time of Christ, still teems with fish.
2 In the search for oil off the west coast of Vancouver Island, a geologist takes core samples of the ocean bed. By taking regular samples he can trace the course of any oil-bearing rock.
3 Once they have matured sufficiently, artificially raised salmon and trout are transferred from their tanks into floating cages. The tides then ebb and flow over the fish.
4 When artificially rearing salmon and trout the breeder must accustom them to salt water. After the fry have hatched he transfers them to a tank into which he pumps salt water.
5 Mussels comprise one of the rich sources of food from the sea bed. They tend to collect on silt, and a dredger need not go far from shore to gather in its harvest.
6 Using an aqualung, the oceanographer can investigate the sea bed for himself. However, there are limits beyond which the diver cannot go in safety; he must then resort to other methods.

exploited. Oceanographers have located a phosphate of calcium called phosphorite in extensive deposits in comparatively shallow waters (averaging about 1,000 ft) off the coasts of the United States, Japan, South Africa, Australia and Spain. Phosphorite is vital to modern agriculture as a fertilizer and so will be in ever-increasing demand in the future.

Black lumps

There are also manganese nodules. These valuable black lumps, which also contain iron oxides, copper nickel and cobalt, were discovered on the ocean bed 100 years ago during what must be one of the most ambitious oceanographics expeditions ever to be mounted – that of the British corvette H.M.S. *Challenger.* The voyage lasted from 1872 to 1876 and ranged through the waters of the world in almost all latitudes, producing 50 volumes of information, much of which is still relevant. Later surveys have shown that

great areas of the ocean floor, particularly in the Pacific, are carpeted with these nodules. The Pacific's tally, according to the Institute of Marine Resources, University of California, stands at something like 1·5 million million tons.

But how to raise this wealth? Manganese is particularly vital in the making of many of the special steels used by industry. The trouble is that the nodules lie at depths around 14,000 ft and ordinary dredging methods are obviously unsuitable. One solution which has been suggested is that they should be sucked up by machines like giant underwater vacuum cleaners which are suspended beneath the mining vessels.

The biologists among the oceanographers are interested in the animal and plant life, particularly in establishing the links in the food chain and learning the

habits of the undersea creatures. For instance, how often and how does a species breed? Do they migrate? And if so, where? The commercial fisheries of the world need to know the answers to such questions.

The widespread use of sonar for fish hunting has helped to increase catches. Other methods – more novel – are also used. In the Caspian Sea, the Russians are operating boats which have electric lights, electrodes and a large-bore pipe hanging from the hull. The lights are switched on to attract the fish – mostly sardines – in the murky depths. An electric field is set up between the electrodes, and the current paralyses the lured fish. A shipboard pump then sucks up the massing fish in great quantities through the funnel-ended pipe.

Although the food resources of the

oceans are very great, technical improvements like these may soon irreparably harm fish stocks. Indeed, some areas of the ocean are already barren, due to over-fishing even without the use of lights, pumps, or electric fields. Marine biologists have given frequent warnings about these dangers. But better still they have also come up with a possible solution, a way of reconciling conservation with the need for a rising food yield.

Thousands of years ago, the human being obtained his food in much the same way as other animals; he either hunted and killed it, or gathered it where it grew. Then he learnt to grow animal and vegetable foods for himself.

By contrast, fishing is still a hunting gathering process, in spite of the sophistication of modern methods. Now a number of scientists are urging that a radical

change should be made. The seas must be farmed, just like the land. In essence, fertilizers should be added to the waters to promote plant growth, and since plants start the food chain, the size of fish populations would be boosted as well.

It is a pretty theory and appears to have sound practical backing at first sight. The Chinese proved that they could grow more, bigger and better carp by adding manure to the carp ponds. During the Second World War the fish yield of certain lochs in Scotland was improved by the addition of other fertilizers. The situation at sea, however, is very different. Currents would quickly disperse even the largest amounts of fertilizer until the concentration dropped to quite useless levels. But even if the fertilizers did work, they would also increase the pest population. In this context, pests mean the creatures which compete with edible fish species for food, yet are inedible themselves. The kind of inroads which such creatures can make into food resources is demonstrated by the discovery in Denmark that some 75 per cent of food material suitable for flatfish does not, in Danish waters, reach them. Instead it is eaten by such creatures as inedible starfish and sea snails.

The real answer may not be cultivating the sea, but fish farming. Here suitable adult fish are brought together in enclosed stretches of water for breeding to take place. Afterwards the eggs are collected in their thousands and put into hatcheries – large tanks with a steady flow of fresh sea water, no predators and no competitors. In carefully controlled conditions the hatched young are reared to a size at which they can be returned to the sea with a good chance of survival.

Some success and some failure has been reported from the, as yet, fairly small-scale attempts at seeding the sea, but the scientists involved are optimistic. One hopeful factor is the sheer quantity of young and sturdy fish which can be reared in this way. At the Marine Biological Station, Port Erin, Isle of Man, where experiments have been made for some years with young plaice, as many as a million have been successfully reared in a year.

The movement of ocean waters is of practical importance, and has been exhaustively studied by oceanographers.

1 Using an underwater camera lowered down from a ship, the oceanographer photographs the sea bed. Details can be seen of the terrain and underwater life as far down as a mile or more.
2 Seismic sounding in the North Sea from a survey vessel. Depth charges are fired about 200 yards astern of the ship at the rate of one a minute during tests.
3 Two divers check their exit and entry from a United States submarine workboat. They are preparing for when they will be diving in the deep ocean environment off the Californian coast.

The great ocean current systems, for example, have considerable effect upon the migratory habits of fish and other animals such as eels. To observe animal life within the Gulf Stream was one of the aims of the 30-day submerged drift northwards up the east coast of the United States by the research craft, *Ben Franklin.* The findings of Dr Jacques Piccard and his colleagues who crewed the vessel are likely to produce important new information.

Knowledge of the currents, their speed and direction is important to the mariner and on the surface they are fairly well charted. Below surface, the picture is not so clear. Even so, the oceanographers have established that great systems of submerged currents do exist.

The significance of this to submarine commanders is easy to see. One current complex in the Straits of Gibraltar was well exploited during the Second World War by U-boat commanders in the Atlantic who wished to slip out into the Mediterranean. Evaporation in the Mediterranean causes the water to become more saline and therefore more dense. It tends to sink and runs out into the Atlantic as an undercurrent, while less dense water comes into the Mediterranean as a surface current from the Atlantic. The U-boats were able to evade the Allied ships stationed at the Straits by switching off their engines and allowing the undercurrent to carry them through the opening.

Upwellings

Upwellings are also important movements of water for food yields. Caused by complex interactions of currents of various kinds, they bring to the surface mineral nutrients utilized by the plant life at the surface. The flourishing of plant life causes a population explosion among the fish. The discovery of such upwellings by the oceanographers is a matter of considerable interest to the world fishing industry. And some ocean scientists have seriously suggested that nuclear reactors could be sunk to the bed in barren areas of ocean where the heat they produce would cause up currents. In this way mineral nutrients would be brought to the surface artificially; the marine desert would bloom.

Oceanographers have now amassed a great deal of data on the wave behaviour of water under a great variety of wind conditions and in relation to different kinds of sea bed and beach. From this data it is possible to predict wave conditions, provided one or more of the variables involved is established. The Normandy landings in 1944 were postponed for 24 hours as a result of an adverse wave prediction – one which turned out to be correct.

These have been some of the practical benefits which oceanographic research has brought. And clearly the oceanographers and the men who have built upon their work have only just begun to understand how to tap the ocean's resources. Both the developing and the technically advanced nations are watching developments with interest as they turn to the oceans to meet their needs.

Mass production test-tubes

Chemical manufacturing is a vast industry which plays a vital part in modern civilization. Many of the things we take for granted — synthetic fibres, petrol, fertilizers and drugs — are products of this industry.

THE DISCOVERY that fire could be produced by rubbing together two dry sticks was one of Man's first steps in the science of applied chemistry, because the wood had not only altered its chemical structure but had created new chemical compounds. The first firemaker did not know that he had given a demonstration of applied chemistry, he was only delighted to have found a way of keeping himself warm. Neither did he know as we do now that everything he saw, ate or used was the result of some chemical action.

Later, primitive Man discovered that leaving certain substances to ferment produced a chemical action resulting in alcohol, and that by heating clay objects he could turn a soft material into a hard one. Fire, fermentation and pottery-baking were the tentative and pioneering steps in harnessing chemistry in the service of Man.

The early civilizations of Egypt, Mesopotamia, India and China carried chemical progress forward and came, in some cases, to the modern concept of chemistry concerned with the composition of things. As a scientist, the chemist wants to know what things are made of and how Nature goes about making them. The industrial chemist takes matters another stage by

trying himself to build things with chemicals and thus gains knowledge of how to produce new substances or make old ones in a new way.

The ancient civilizations knew how to make enamels, how to refine gold and how to use natural dyes. The ancient Egyptians were able to embalm and so preserve the bodies of their Pharaohs that the mummies resisted decay for thousands of years. Although they knew the art of smelting metals and the forming of alloys this did not mean they were aware of all the chemical processes involved. These arts may well have been the results of chance discovery, and those who applied them were artisans rather than scientists.

Glass-making

It was probably by accident that Man discovered that certain sands or flint or quartz turned into glass when melted with ashes. When he wanted to make glass himself, he had to look for the right kind of materials and then proceed by trial and error. There were no chemical formulae or text-books to help him. Glass-making also requires an alkali, but the pioneers of industry knew nothing of the chemical properties of lime or potash or soda. They did discover, however, that the materials used to make soap would also help in the making of glass. So the glass-makers used the soap-makers' lye, which happened to contain lime and potassium carbonate; but it never occurred to them to add

any calcium compound as a separate ingredient.

The tanning of leather, baking of bread, soap-making and hundreds more of the ancient crafts were all forms of applied chemistry, but the tanner, the baker and the soap-maker knew little of the chemistry their trades involved.

There was no system of chemical analysis whereby the product of a trade could be properly tested. It was impossible to agree on any chemical specification, and the purchaser had only his own rough and ready knowledge of what a product should look like and what it should do to assess its value.

Study of chemistry for chemistry's sake has been a science discipline for several centuries, whereas industrial or applied chemistry has been practised as a profession for less than 200 years. The conditions under which the pure chemist and the industrial chemist worked tended to maintain a sharp distinction between these two branches of chemistry.

Modern industrial chemistry has as its prime purpose the initiation of research programmes for the specific purpose of producing a chemical or a chemical result that either will fulfil some material need or become the mainspring of a commercial

An eighteenth-century engraving of Eskimos making fire with a fire-drill. Burning, among the first chemical processes mastered by Man, formed means for glass-making and other arts.

Mummification was one of the first large-scale industries with a chemical basis. This well-preserved mummy of a young girl, thought to be about 1,900 years old, was found near Rome.

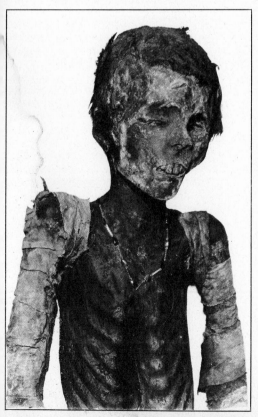

venture. The industrial chemist carries out his work for a business organization which pays his salary and provides his laboratory and other equipment. Much of his work is routine analysis required for the control and improvement of industrial processes and the development of new products. Sometimes his work results in new developments of chemical theory and in that way becomes linked with pure chemistry. In general, however, the industrial chemist is not encouraged to follow lines of research that do not offer prospect of profit to his employers. Conversely, the pure chemist working in the rarefied atmosphere of his university laboratory can become isolated from the industrial world and its needs.

This distinction between the industrial chemist and the pure chemist was particularly rigid until this century when there has been a tendency for it to break down, at least to a limited extent. Appropriately enough, the barrier has been breached by industrial chemistry. Commercial firms and organizations dependent on chemistry are steadily increasing in size and numbers and have come to realize that pure chemistry may have much to offer that will benefit their commercial expansion. So they encourage the pure chemist to work in their laboratories and carry out research work that appears to bear little relation to their commercial needs. In addition they support university laboratories for prestige reasons and thus maintain touch with lines of research which, although very remote from industry, may eventually have commercial value. All this has resulted in a phenomenal growth of industrial chemistry which has transformed the world.

Chemical reactions

Chemical reactions can be divided into four main groups: combination, decomposition, replacement and double replacement. These are the simple types of chemical change, but the industrial chemist often has to deal with far more complex processes. Indeed, certain reactions are so complex that they are not completely understood by the industrial chemist himself: hence the immense amount of research involved in running an industrial chemists' laboratory.

Apart from routine analysis of raw materials and the products obtained from them by chemical reactions, the industrial chemist's work has three main purposes. First the chemist endeavours to obtain simple substances from the more complex mixtures or compounds occurring in Nature. Examples of this are the distillation of petroleum or bituminous coal for the extraction of by-products; the separation of gases; and the extraction of metallic elements from their ores and the combining of the extracted metals to form alloys.

Conversion processes by which the chemist produces new substances by replacement and double replacement form a second category. In this type of work, the size of the molecules used does not differ very markedly from the size of the molecules of the substance produced. Amongst the many examples of conversion processes are the production of soaps, fats and the heavy chemicals, including acids and bases, essential to the production of domestic and industrial materials. Third are synthetic processes, which are fundamentally aimed at building bigger and more complex molecules from smaller ones. In principle this procedure is the opposite of that used in extraction processes, and is the basis of synthetic chemistry, including man-made fibres, plastics and synthetic dyes. The production of synthetic materials is without doubt the greatest achievement of industrial chemistry.

Father of industrial chemistry

Nicholas Leblanc, a French physician, was the first to prove the commercial value of chemistry and he may be considered the father of industrial chemistry. In 1775, the Paris Academy of Sciences, concerned at the high price of soap and the consequent spread of dirt-induced diseases in the Paris slums, offered a prize of 2,500 gold louis (about £5,000) to anyone who could find a cheap way of producing sodium carbonate. Better known as washing soda or soda ash, sodium carbonate is used in the manufacture of soap, glass and paper. The Paris Academy not only was anxious to cheapen soap, but also thought that more and cheaper glass would mean bigger windows to let extra health-giving sunlight into the houses of the poor, while cheaper paper would allow the printing of more books to reduce the illiteracy of the masses.

Leblanc, whose medical practice in a poor district of Paris had never been very profitable, was attracted not only to the money prize but also by the prospect of combating the disease so rife in the slums where he worked. Accordingly, he spent all his spare time trying to evolve some process to cheapen sodium carbonate. But although he had a good knowledge of chemistry, it required 14 years of hard work before he succeeded in perfecting a process using chalk, salt, charcoal and sulphuric acid.

When, however, Leblanc announced his formula to the Academy and claimed the prize, he was refused the money on the grounds that the academicians did not consider the process practicable. Undaunted, Leblanc approached some of his wealthy friends, who advanced him 200,000 francs to set up a sodium-carbonate plant in the Paris suburb of St Denis. By 1794 the Leblanc factory was producing 700 pounds of the chemical daily.

Leblanc's factory covered an area of nearly two acres and in order to keep down the cost of the new product, was laid out on lines which reduced handling of the materials to a minimum. In fact, it was not only the first real chemical factory, but it was the first to operate on the modern system of constant flow of the ingredients. The process began by heating common salt with sulphuric acid to produce sodium sulphate. This was then heated with carbon and chalk to form a mixture of sodium carbonate (soda) and calcium sulphide, to which water was added. As only the soda dissolved out of the solution it could be

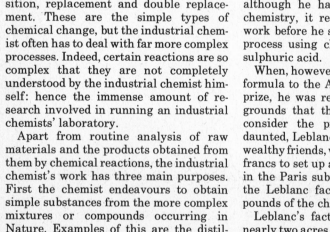

separated and evaporated to yield crystals of sodium carbonate (washing soda).

Leblanc's sodium carbonate process is no longer used, but it was of great importance in his day and was the first example of factory methods being applied to the making of a chemical.

Another important step in the development of industrial chemistry was made in 1832 by Jean Dumas, professor of Chemistry at Paris University. One evening while working in his study he noticed that the candles were emitting irritating fumes and an unusually thick and pungent smoke. To find out the cause he subjected the candles to a series of chemical tests in his laboratory. He was able to identify the fumes as hydrochloric-acid gas created by the chlorine which the chandler had used to bleach the candle-wax. He further established that joining the chlorine and the wax had replaced some of its hydrogen atoms to form a new compound.

Combustion of the candle broke up the new compound and in doing so united the chlorine atoms in it with the remaining hydrogen atoms, so forming the pungent hydrochloric acid gas. Carrying his experiment a stage further, Dumas began a series of reactions of chlorine with other organic substances, and was able to show that the chlorine could replace hydrogen in some compounds, atom for atom. He obtained the same results with iodine and bromide. From all this he deduced that the elements in an organic compound can be successively displaced and replaced by others.

Dumas's experiments provide the basic knowledge of the substitution reacting

1 Oil forms the basis of many modern synthetic chemicals. Oil refineries, like this B.P. plant at Westernport, Australia, break down crude oils and provide raw material for chemical factories. .
2 Another stage in oil treatment. Superheated steam passing through pipes at Esso's Fawley refinery reduces heavy oils into lighter ones for everyday use – a process known as 'cracking'.
3 Emptying a coke oven. Crushed coal is heated in a closed oven for about a day at a temperature of 1,000 °C. The tars and gases are driven off, and the coke is left behind.
4 Analysing chemical samples for traces of elements at the Amsterdam laboratories of Shell. Detailed analysis plays an essential part in modern industrial chemistry.
5 Testing a new synthetic dye and moth-proofing agent at an industrial laboratory. Small-scale pilot plants are frequently set up to test the feasibility of using new products.

2

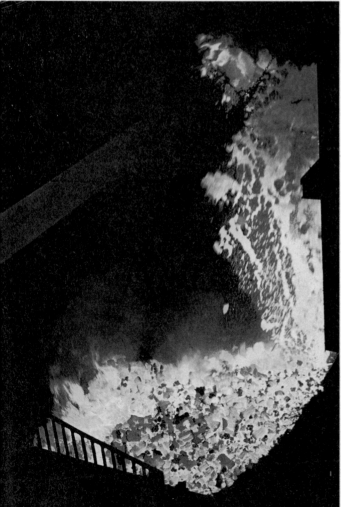

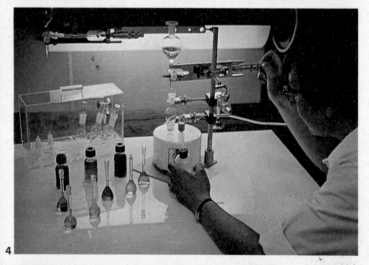

4

5

now so vital to industrial chemistry. But his experiments were never more than exercises in chemistry and it was left to industrial chemists to provide the means of turning them to commercial profit. Substitution can produce a vast number of carbon compounds which, despite their common origin, are very different from each other. Dumas's work was a striking example of pure chemistry pointing the way to a vast field of industrial chemistry.

Conversely, there are equally striking examples of a chemist deliberately experimenting to achieve some specific result. Herman Frasch, for example, had the commercial aspect before him when he evolved his process of mining sulphur by forcing super-heated steam into the deposit from the surface and then pumping out the melted sulphur. In this way the expensive digging out of deposits was avoided. Similarly, Alfred Nobel began experimenting with the deliberate intention of rendering nitro-glycerine safe as an explosive and so produced dynamite and blasting gelatine. Baekeland was concerned with the industrial problem of making a synthetic varnish when his experiments developed the first self-hardening plastic, called after him Bakelite. From that developed the vast modern industry of plastics, all of which are the result of industrial chemists juggling with molecules.

William Perkin can be considered the

1 A beaming machine at the Pontypool nylon fibre plant of ICI Fibres Ltd. Synthetic fibres — many of them produced from oil derivatives — now occupy a large part of the chemical industry.
2 Measuring the acidity of a solution during the manufacture of emetine at the Wellcome Chemical Works, Dartford. Emetine is used to treat amoebic dysentery in tropical countries.
3 A typical industrial chemists' laboratory, showing apparatus for distillation, controlled heating, drying and maintaining temperature. The scientist on the left is using a thermometer.

first of the great English industrial chemists, although the product that started him on his career was discovered by accident rather than by design. In 1849 Perkin was an 18-year-old laboratory assistant to August von Hofmann, the German director of the Royal College of Chemistry, London, who was then attempting to synthesize quinine. Hofmann was experimenting with coal-tar from which he had succeeded in obtaining toluidine, a benzene derivative which appeared to have a chemical structure similar to that of quinine. Hofmann was, however, far from satisfied that toluidine provided the solution to his problem and he abandoned it for another line of research. Perkin was not so sure and decided to continue the toluidine experiments in the modest laboratory he had set up in his home. He tried various reactions based on toluidine, but the only product was a reddish-brown sediment at the bottom of the flask.

Perkin was far from dejected and started a new series of reactions, this time with aniline, another, but more simple, derivative of coal-tar. The final state of his reaction was the addition of potassium dichromate, the oxidizing agent that precipitated in his flask a black powder. This was a most un-quinine-like product: but it roused the youthful chemist's curiosity and in order to see what would happen he dissolved the powder in alcohol. The result was a brilliant purple liquid. The liquid was not unfamiliar in laboratories, but chemists who had previously found it had always thrown it away as waste from unsuccessful experiments in other lines of research. Perkin did not do so. The sheer brilliance of the purple liquid suggested to him that it might have commercial possibilities as a dye. So he applied it to some strips of silk with results that surpassed everything he had expected. The dye stuck fast to the silk, it did not fade in strong sunlight, and repeated washing in soap and water failed to affect its colour. Repeated tests proved that Perkin's dye was far superior to any derived from vegetable sources. Perkin patented his process and founded the industrial chemistry that eventually evolved a whole variety of fast dyes obtained from coal.

Modern chemical industry

From this in turn developed the experiments which enabled industrial chemists to use coal as the basis of detergents, flavouring agents, explosives and plastics. Industrial chemistry has made gigantic strides on the basis of the work of the early pioneers. Today, vast chemical plants turn out thousands of tons of plastics, dyes, drugs, heavy chemicals and synthetics of all types. The chemical industry is now one of the largest sections of industry in the world. Scientific chemical theory is now applied to processes as varied as steel-making and the manufacture of stockings. Although the layman may not be aware of the full extent to which industrial chemistry has changed everyday life, he is still the recipient of countless benefits which flow from the chemists' activities. Without industrial chemistry our lives would be very different indeed.

Farming with machinery

Agriculture depends on tilling and cultivating the soil and collecting the harvest. Modern machines, which can perform highly specialized operations, are causing a revolution in farming.

1 In many parts of the world traditional methods of agriculture are still used. Too poor to buy machinery, this Asian farmer uses water buffalo to drag a plough through the rice fields.

2 The Russians have developed a tea-harvester, which does the work of countless labourers. This harvester not only cuts the leaves on the bushes but also 'selects' the tender ones.

3 Picking machines, which strip the ripe bolls from rows of cotton plants, move slowly across a large plantation on a collective farm in the Pushkin District of the U.S.S.R.

WHEN OUR DISTANT ANCESTORS ceased to be nomads and began to settle down in agricultural communities to grow their food instead of hunting for it, they tilled the ground with a pointed stick which was pushed through the soil to cut furrows two or three inches deep. The pointed stick was the first farm implement and from it stemmed the host of ingenious and complicated machines which now serve the highly mechanized industry of farming.

Machinery in a factory does its work more efficiently, quickly and cheaply than a human worker, but mechanizing a farm poses many more problems than installing factory machines. A machine in constant use is always much more economical than are human hands, so explaining why many highly mechanized factories work shifts to

keep the machinery operating as long as possible. On the other hand, few farm machines, except tractors, can be found tasks that keep them in action for more than a week or two every year.

Yet the variety of tasks that could be done by machinery on the farm is far greater than in a factory. On a farm each of the scores of different tasks suitable for machinery needs its own specific machine designed for a specific job. Thus a mowing machine may be used for not more than ten days in the year on the average farm, while a trailer binder may work for only a fortnight every 12 months. This means that a mechanized farm has a variety of expensive machines which lie idle for most of the year and the conditions under which they must work change from season to

season, from hour to hour and even from field to field. Changes in weather and soil conditions are always liable to interrupt their smooth working.

It was the modern tendency towards larger farms that inspired much of the agricultural machinery now in use. Although so many agricultural machines are in operation for comparatively so little time, the farmer finds them more economical than employing large numbers of labourers. A farm machine works hour after hour tirelessly and efficiently so long as it is supplied with motive power and has someone to operate it. During harvesting, for example, one machine with a crew of two or three men will complete in a day the amount of work that would occupy ten men for several days; the time saved is worth far more than the price of a machine and the cost of operating it.

One of the most revolutionary agricultural machines was the self-propelled combine harvester. As the machine moves forward, revolving arms in front pull the growing grain towards a platform, where a row of scissor-like clippers cuts the crop about three inches from the ground. The cut stalks are then carried by a conveyor and elevator to a spiked cylinder in which the grain is threshed. The grain then falls on to a vibrating pan across which blasts of air from a fan blow away the chaff. Next the cleaned grain falls through a sieve into a chute and on to an endless screw to a storage bin. In some machines the bin delivers the grain to a device that pours it into sacks, or the grain may be fed into a tractor-drawn waggon for delivery to a silo. The straw is carried on racks to the rear of the harvester where it is baled and dropped on the field.

Combine harvesters developed from a machine called the crop stripper invented in Australia in 1845. At that time Australia was embarking upon large-scale wheat-growing for export, but the labour needed for traditional harvesting was both scarce and expensive. The stripper was the answer to cheap harvesting. As the machine moved forward, drawn by a team of horses, revolving blades geared to the transport wheels stripped the wheat from the ears, which were then winnowed mechanically and the grain shovelled into waggons for carriage to the bagging sheds. As the grain was the only part of the crop considered worth harvesting, the straw and chaff were left on the field and later ploughed in. Australian strippers were exported to the United States where they were greatly improved and developed into the combine harvesters, which were in general use by about 1917.

The first combine harvesters were towed by teams of as many as 30 or 40 horses or mules. Later, steam tractors were used until the internal-combustion engines enabled the combine to be completely self-contained and self-propelled.

Steam tractors

Until the invention of the steam engine, ploughs had for thousands of years been drawn by horses one furrow at a time. The first attempt at mechanization was a steam engine at both ends of the field which hauled the plough by a steel cable. The engine moved across the ends of the field as each furrow was cut. Later, steam traction-engines were used to pull a battery of two or three ploughs. But the engines were so heavy that they rolled the ground and made it difficult for the following plough-shares to cut into.

The introduction of the internal-combustion-engined tractor made possible efficient and economical mechanical ploughing. The tractors now in use can pull a plough having six or more shares, so enabling one man to plough a field in a fraction of the time that would be needed by a horse-drawn plough.

Without the tractor, much of modern mechanized farming would be impossible. Bigger and more effective reapers and mowers, harrows and rollers, drilling and

had a rake at the rear which covered the seed with soil as it was planted.

From the horse-drawn seeding machines developed the tractor-hauled, multi-purpose planters now in use. Seed and fertilizer are contained in hoppers from which tubes lead to the soil. In front of each tube is a steel drill. As the machine moves forward, each drill punches a hole into which the seed falls through the tube. Behind the tubes are devices that cover the seed with soil. The flow of seed and fertilizer is controlled by the opening and closing of shutters which are mechanically adjusted so that the right amount of seed and fertilizer are put into the ground according to the crop and type of soil. The drills are also adjusted to ensure that the seed is planted in the correct quantity at the best depth to ensure germination and growth. Some of the more sophisticated seeding machines also deposit herbicides and pesticides and have meters that register the amount of seed sown per acre and the number of acres sown from each filling of the hoppers.

Somewhat similar to the seeding machine is that used for planting seedlings and small and tender plants. The machine opens a broad furrow of even depth and width wherein the roots of the plants are deposited by a continuous chain of rubber fingers. An automatic device then presses the soil around the roots. One seeding or planting machine can do in one day the amount of work that formerly required the labour of 20 skilled men.

One of the most ingenious seeders now coming into use on large vegetable-growing farms is the tape-planter. The seeds, together with appropriate fertilizer, are enclosed in long gelatine, plastic or petroleum-based tape. The tapes are wound on to drums carried on a machine that cuts a furrow. At the same time drums

1 Before the advent of modern machinery, land clearing was laborious and slow work. Now scrub land and young saplings can be felled and pulped in one single operation.

2 On small farms where a combine harvester is too cumbersome, the ripe corn is still cut with a 'binder'. The sheaves are collected and stacked by hand and threshed at a later stage.

3 Some processes on farms are still only semi-automated. Young kale plants are fragile and they must be fed individually into the machine which plants them in the ground.

4 Until relatively recently sheep were sheared by hand. Power-operated clippers are now widely used with the result that a single labourer can shear several hundred animals a day.

5 A combine harvester cuts the corn and threshes it in one single operation. The grain, free of the straw, is either put in sacks or, as here, blown into a separate trailer.

sowing machines, and manure and fertilizer distributors can all be towed by a tractor. And as two or more of any one type of machine can be hauled by a single tractor, acres of ground can be treated in a working day.

Sowing seed by hand is inevitably a wasteful process, as some parts of the soil receive too much seed and some none at all. One of the first attempts to mechanize sowing was made in the early eighteenth century by the Englishman Jethro Tull, a barrister turned farmer, who did much to encourage a scientific approach to agriculture. Unfortunately, Tull's machine was not only very costly but it was far too complicated for use by unskilled labour.

It was not until the mid-nineteenth century that a really efficient machine was designed for sowing seed. It consisted of a long hopper mounted on two wheels and drawn by a horse. Projecting downwards from the hopper containing the seed were a number of evenly spaced tubes each ending in a hollow spike. As the machine was drawn across the field, the spikes dug ridges into which the seed fell through the tube. Sometimes the machine

unwind the tape, laying it in the furrow, which a scraper at the rear of the planter covers with soil. The moisture in the soil then dissolves the tape, leaving the seed free to germinate. The machine is capable of laying a dozen or more tapes of seed simultaneously.

Devising a machine for lifting potatoes efficiently was a problem that for long defied solution by agricultural engineers. The trouble was that machines could lift the potatoes but they also lifted stones and clods of earth. Various devices were tried to separate the potatoes from unwanted material, but none was really successful and entailed a great deal of hand-picking.

The problem was eventually solved by the electronic potato-harvester which became available to farmers in 1969. As the potatoes, stones and clods are lifted they fall on to a belt where they are spread out by mechanical fingers and carried past a battery of 16 X-ray beams each shining on to a form of photo-electric detector cell. The detector cells can recognize the differences in the densities of objects passing between them and the X-ray source. Stones and clods are identified by the detector cells as being of greater densities than potatoes. Through electronic relays, the cells signal to mechanical finger-units which then push the stones, clods or other material of greater density than the potatoes off the belt.

By using the electronic potato-lifter, one man can do the work that formerly employed six men in sorting. Equally ingenious machines are available for harvesting carrot, beet and other root crops. There are also machines for harvesting fruit in orchards and for picking tomatoes and peas.

If fruit- and vegetable-picking machines are to operate efficiently, the objects they gather must be of approximately the same size and shape. This has led to the development of, for example, rounder and smaller tomatoes and potatoes.

The raising of fruit and vegetables under glass has made tremendous strides of recent years through the use of electronic and mechanical devices. Glasshouses can be equipped with photo-electric cells that switch on infra-red and other beneficial illumination when natural light fails through overclouding; thermostats turn on artificial heating when the temperature drops below a certain reading; and time-controlled sprays provide artificial rain exactly when it is needed. By these means

1 The first machines on farms were steam driven. The steam engine itself, like the modern tractor, was multi-purpose. Here, by means of a belt-drive it is working a threshing machine.
2 This potato picker can harvest 17 acres per day. Electronic detector cells in the machine distinguish between clods of earth and potatoes, which are then separated.
3 Intensive farming calls for more and more technology. In this modern feeding and dairy unit in East Germany, a herd of cows can be milked simultaneously by machine.

many fruits and vegetables, once considered strictly seasonal, are available nearly all the year round at economic prices. This availability is increasing due to new methods of controlled ripening which irons out the seasonal glut which follows the harvest, and the fruit can be marketed out of season. Better storage methods and pest control also benefit the year-round sale of some vegetables.

Contented cows

On dairy farms the traditional milkmaid with her bucket and stool has been replaced by milking machines which deliver the milk direct into tanks for storage until pumped into road or rail tankers for transport to the pasteurization or other processing plants. On many farms the cattle are kept in heated byres and fed on a carefully balanced diet brought to them on conveyors. Contented cows mean a rich and plentiful milk yield and to keep their cows contented many dairy farmers provide their herds with soft lights and soothing music.

One of the most highly mechanized branches of agriculture is poultry farming, as exemplified in the battery system. The fowls are automatically fed at fixed intervals and the eggs they lay are stamped with the date and carried directly to the packing sheds. Automatic counters record the individual laying of each hen.

What will farming be like in the future? Judging by the tremendous strides that have been made in mechanization during the past 50 years, farms of the future will bear little resemblance to those of today. According to the survey carried out by a panel of agricultural scientists and engineers, much farming will become completely independent of the weather by erecting huge glass or plastic domes to cover areas of ten or more acres. The moisture of the soil within the domes and the amount of heat and light it receives will be automatically controlled merely by turning dials. In this manner the best possible environment will be created for the growing of crops.

Electronic-eyed machines will plant seeds by pneumatic injection and the seeds will be coated with chemical fertilizers, herbicides and insecticides. Machines fitted with electronic devices and computerized fingers will decide when a crop is ripe for harvesting.

On wheat fields and other areas too big for covering with glass or plastic domes, machines will be pulled by driverless tractors controlled by computer tape, buried wires or sensing devices. Hovercraft will be used for spraying, and there will be machines able to harvest one crop and simultaneously plant another.

Techniques for breeding plants designed for mechanical harvesting will make tremendous advances. Tall wheat stalks will have given way to new, squat plants like miniature fir trees. In this way they will absorb more energy from the sun and the ears will be concentrated at the top for easier harvesting.

Livestock farms of the future will bear little resemblance to those of today. Instead of grazing land, the landscape will be dotted with many-storeyed buildings, like blocks of flats, occupied by cattle, sheep, pigs and poultry. The temperature, air, light and humidity within the buildings will be precisely regulated to provide the stock with the best possible environment. Waste products from the animals will be pumped directly to plants for conversion into solid and liquid fertilizers.

According to the agriculture futurist, farmers will have to have an expert knowledge of big-business management, electronics, computers, botany, biochemistry and biophysics while farm labourers will have to be technicians with the professional skills needed to operate the sophisticated equipment.

Farming with chemicals

Farming, traditionally the most backward industry of all, is undergoing its own 'Industrial Revolution'. New chemicals — insecticides, fungicides and plant hormones — are changing the face of the farm.

FARMERS WERE THE FIRST manufacturing chemists, although the modern farmer would be very surprised indeed if he were told so. When a farmer sows a field he plants thousands of tiny chemical compounds and the soil acts as a laboratory in which mass chemical reactions take place to produce the crop that will be harvested. For thousands of years farmers knew nothing of the actual chemistry of agriculture and were content to accept that something went on in the soil to give them a crop: they let nature do the actual chemistry, their only contribution to the actual processes being the application of manure. Insects were laboriously removed by hand, while weed pests were suffered unmolested, as were most of the plant diseases.

In order to achieve healthy growth, plants need in varying degrees some 22 of the 92 natural elements. The most important of these are hydrogen and oxygen (present in water) and sulphur, chlorine, potassium, phosphorus, silicon, magnesium, iron, sodium, nitrogen, calcium. Most of these occur in the soil in the form of soluble compounds. About ten more elements, including zinc, copper, boron and iodine have a marked influence on plant growth. These are called *trace elements,* because only very small quantities or traces of them are needed for plant development and in general they are always present in the soil in sufficient amounts. Many of what might be called the agricultural elements are normally present in sufficient quantities in most soils that are well watered by the rain and given sufficient fresh air by periodical ploughing.

Essential elements

Nitrogen, potassium and phosphorus are the most essential of all the agricultural elements as they supply plants with the food that makes them grow. Although these elements are naturally present in the soil, they are soon depleted by plant growth. By the time a ton of wheat is ready for harvesting, it has taken from the soil in which it grew 47 pounds of nitrates, 18 pounds of phosphates and 12 pounds of potash, with a consequent reduction in the soil's fertility. Each of these elements has its own particular function in ensuring the growth of a healthy plant. Potassium is essential to the production of seed, and also inhibits many of the fungoid diseases. Phosphorus is mainly a root food, while nitrogen is necessary for the development of root, stem and leaves. Yet any one of these elements is useless without the other two. Thus a soil exceptionally rich in nitrogen but with a low potassium or phosphorus content would not produce healthy plants.

On wild and uncultivated land, the elements taken from the soil by growing plants are replaced when the plants die and fall to the ground. This is because phosphorus, for example, forms part of the living substance of plants and returns to the soil when they decay. Similarly, soils consisting of clays and feldspar normally contain an adequate supply of potassium which is restored when the plants wither. On farmland, however, plants are grown to be removed when they ripen. Consequently, the elements taken from the soil during their growth are not replaced, which is why agricultural land has to be re-fertilized artificially.

When Man first began to cultivate the soil, he found that crops would not grow in the same soil year after year. He realized that something was wrong with the soil, but he did not know what or why. So he solved his problem by abandoning the land and cultivating a new piece. Then he discovered that if ground that had grown crops was left for a couple of seasons the soil again became fertile. So he learned about letting ground lie fallow.

1 Fleecing without shears. After treatment with a growth-prevention drug, the sheep's wool can easily be removed by hand.

2 Scientists at a plant pathology laboratory examine wheat seedlings to test the results of treatments for leaf rust disease.

covery of the large deposits of guano or seabird droppings on the shores and islands of the South American coasts.

But agricultural scientists soon realized that the deposits of natural fertilizers were not unexhaustible, and that if farming was to keep pace with increasing population something must be done to manufacture fertilizers. To meet the demand, the now gigantic fertilizer industry was established as a result of research by chemists who devoted their energies to solving the problem.

Although farm manure is still the best enricher of agricultural land, it plays a steadily decreasing part in modern farming, particularly since horses have been largely replaced by tractors. By far the greater part of the fertilizers now applied to farmland are manufactured, and the annual production runs into hundreds of millions of tons. One of the great advan-

It was the farmers of ancient Rome who found that their land produced bigger and richer crops if farm waste was spread on the ground and ploughed in. That was the beginning of artificial fertilization and the start of agricultural chemistry. Among the fertilizers which have been used since Roman times are sewage, farm manure, wood-ash, mussel and lobster shell, powdered limestone and marble. The latter is a form of soil consisting of clay and carbonate of lime. For centuries the chief source of applied phosphates was raw bones, which were ground into powder and then spread over the soil. Wood-ash provided the soil with the essential potash. But the most valuable of all the early applied fertilizers was farmyard manure. A ton of farm manure contains on average 20 per cent potassium, 15 per cent nitrogen and 10 per cent phosphorus. In addition to its fertilizing properties, farm manure improves soil by retaining moisture.

Although the need for fertilizing farmland was, therefore, being slowly appreciated, very little was understood about the actual chemistry involved. Even by the mid-eighteenth century virtually all that was known was that certain salts, especially potassium nitrate (saltpetre) promoted growth. It was wrongly thought that plants obtained their carbon from the humus content of the soil in which they grew.

It was fortunate that science turned its attention to agriculture when it did, for world population has steadily increased since the mid-nineteenth century. Had not science shown the way to grow bigger and better crops, there would have been worldwide starvation by the beginning of the present century. Long before that, the supply of farmyard manure and the production of potash from wood-ash would have supplied only a fraction of the increasing need for fertilizers.

Some alleviation of the shortage of fertilizers, that was steadily becoming more alarming, was provided by the dis-

1 A modern version of the old sheep-dip. Sheep channelled into the metal trough are sprayed with insecticides and fungicides developed experimentally by agricultural chemists.
2 Spraying vines in Champagne, France. Growing grapes require careful attention to ensure that they do not fall victims to a variety of fungus and insect-borne infections.
3 One side-effect of over-use of fertilizer is to encourage the growth of algae in nearby ponds and streams. These 'blooms' consist of millions of tiny green organisms.

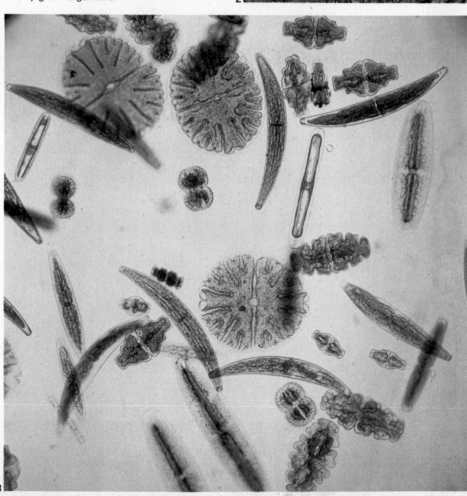

tages of synthetic fertilizers is that they are generally easier to apply to the soil than are natural fertilizers, especially when mechanical spreaders are used. Moreover, synthetic fertilizers can be tailor-made to specific types of soil or crops.

But the most efficient of natural or synthetic fertilizers would be useless to the farmer if his crops were to be weed-ridden, devoured by insects and stricken by disease before they could be harvested. The chemist has now provided agriculture with increasingly effective weapons in the farmer's constant war on these pests.

Practically every plant disease can now be prevented or limited by chemical means. An example is wheat, one of the world's most important food crops. Not so very long ago, one or other of these fungoid diseases, rust, smut and bunt, were present to a greater or lesser extent in every wheatfield. All three diseases cause greatest damage on well-fertilized land. This is because the richer the soil the more the wheat growing on it can provide nourishment for the fungi, which multiply very rapidly.

Various fungicides were compounded to combat rust, smut and bunt, but they all proved ineffective. The problem of defeating the depredations of these fungi seemed insoluble until scientists hit on the idea of treating the wheat seed with chemicals that destroy the spores before the wheat is sown.

Once upon a time the only way to keep weeds in check, and prevent them from either overcrowding the growing crops or taking nourishment from the soil and depriving the crop of wanted nutrients, was to remove the weeds by hand. The development of efficient herbicides was a particularly difficult problem, because weeds are themselves plants and any spray applied to a crop is just as likely to kill the crop plants as the weed plants. One solution to the problem is to spray the field with a weed-killer before the crop is sown. By the time the field is ready for sowing, the herbicide has destroyed the weeds and become mixed with the soil so that it is harmless. .

Selective herbicides

Another type of weed-killer depends upon the fact that certain chemical compounds destroy plants at a specific stage of their growth. Fortunately, most weeds grow faster than food plants, so the field is sprayed with a herbicide that kills the more advanced weeds without seriously harming the young crop. The herbicide is then dispersed throughout the soil and becomes innocuous long before it could damage the crop. Considerable success has also been achieved in the development of selective herbicides that destroy weed plants and leave plants unharmed.

The development of insecticides has also been successful. Some selectively kill pests, while others render the males or

1 On a modern Texas ranch, a high-pressure jet of an anti-parasitic fluid is wielded by a cow-hand. Modern chemicals greatly assist the rancher and cut cattle losses.
2 An entomologist weighs a locust using a specially sensitive insect balance. Careful studies of insects assist farmers in their constant war against destructive insect pests.

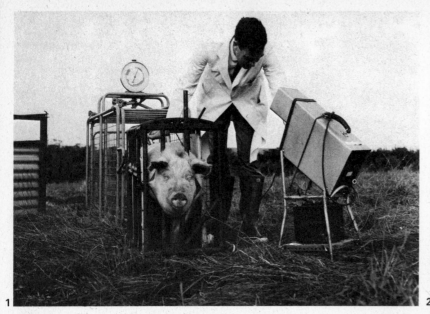

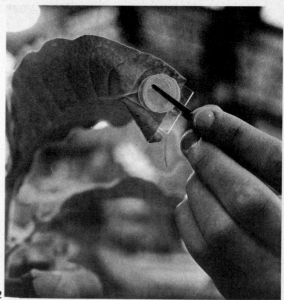

1 An electronic meter in use to test the amount of lean meat on a pig. Scientific aids like these are developed by agricultural scientists on experimental farms throughout the world.

2 Testing an insecticide for use on tobacco plants. The tiny Perspex and nylon gauze cage prevents aphids and other insects escaping from the chemically treated plants.

females sterile and so prevent the pests from breeding. Some insecticides destroy the eggs or grubs. Even more remarkable are the systemic insecticides, such as *octamethyl pyrophosphoramide,* which render plant juices poisonous to insects but are non-toxic to the plants or to the mammals that feed on them. These types of insecticides hold considerable promise of solving the problem of the serious effects which many of the insecticides now used have on wild life, particularly birds.

Rodents destroy a considerable amount of crops, and various poisons have been evolved to keep them in check, but most are unselective and prove just as fatal to farm stock as to rodents. Attempts have been made to introduce selective and contagious disease among rodents. Myxomatosis was an example of this against rabbit pests, but it had the disadvantage of driving foxes, which normally hunt rabbits, into chicken runs in search of food.

Besides providing farmers with an unlimited supply of fertilizers and efficient pesticides, scientists have been working on plant hormones to provide bigger and better crops in a shorter time and to grow larger crops on smaller areas of land. It has been found that certain relatively simple organic substances, which can be synthesized cheaply and in quantity, have considerable effect on plant growth. Some of these synthetics promote root formation and are revolutionizing the propagation of plants from cuttings. But the application of scientific knowledge to farming has not been wholly beneficial. Many of the chemicals now being used are extremely powerful, and are not always applied with sufficient caution. Nitrate fertilizers, for example, can, if over-used, drain into rivers and lakes, where they encourage the growth of algae. The algae in turn can form a dense, thick mat of vegetation, hindering navigation and lowering vital oxygen levels of the water. If this process is allowed to go too far the lake or river can be rapidly exhausted and unable to absorb sewage and waste.

Again, some insecticides and weed-killers are known to be long-lasting in the soil and poison animals much higher up the food-chains.

Some agricultural scientists foresee a day when the farmer will be free of the soil and independent of the vagaries of the weather. This Utopia will be brought about by growing plants without soil. The seeds are sown in beds of fibre or gravel through which circulates a solution containing all the fertilizing and nutrient elements essential to plant growth. The plants can be sown in beds or trays several tiers high in air-conditioned buildings which can be maintained at the correct temperature for any particular crop. In this way crops can be raised in any kind of climate from the torrid heat of the tropics to the zero conditions of the Arctic or Antarctic.

Composition of the nutrient fluid varies according to the type of plants under cultivation. Moreover, ripening can be accelerated by adding to the fluid high levels of appropriate nutrients. After the nutrient fluid has passed through the fibre or gravel beds, it drains into tanks and is pumped back on to the crops.

Amongst the many advantages of *hydroponic* cultivation, intensive application of the principle enables normally annual crops to be harvested two or more times a year; the properties of the bedding material being constant, the constituents of the nutrient fluid can be standardized to within fine limits for any particular type of plant; there is greater control over weeds, disease and insect pests; greater plant yields are obtained than with plants cultivated in conventional conditions; and much larger crops can be raised in a smaller space.

In some parts of the world, tomatoes, cucumbers, and even wheat have been grown by hydroponic culture, and large-scale production of other plants has been undertaken in India, America and the

At a research station, the grass yield of a field is measured after fertilizer treatment. In this experiment grass from a treated area is compared with that from a similar non-treated area.

Middle East. As yet such crops tend to cost more than those grown in the normal way in soil, but many agricultural chemists are convinced that eventually the cost can be lowered below that of conventional farming.

Such a method of farming would have far-reaching social effects. For one thing, it might well be possible to grow more food in less space than is used at present, while the full resources of mechanized harvesting could be used to reap the hydroponic crops. Again, if the cost of hydroponic and similar artificial crop-growing methods can be brought down, the benefits in terms of feeding the Earth's potential population increase would also be considerable. For the first time, farming would cease to be dependent on the vagaries of the weather, and could be dealt with in the same way as any other industrial process. Whether or not hydroponic farming can be made sufficiently cheap to be practicable on a mass scale, we can be certain that science will have an increasing impact on agriculture.

The chemicals we eat

Modern society has an insatiable appetite, and a vast industry has grown up to serve it. The science of food chemistry studies the composition of food and seeks ways to improve its quality.

ALL THE TIME that a human or any other body is alive it is expending energy and that energy is obtained from food. While food is in the body it is undergoing chemical changes which, in effect, release energy. Without that energy no one could breathe, walk or perform any function at all. In exactly the same way, a motor car cannot move until the energy in the petrol has been released by combustion.

For countless centuries men were content to hunt and grow their food without any thought of its nutritional value. So long as he had enough to satisfy his hunger, Man did not worry as to whether he was getting from his food the energy he needed for his body activities. He knew that some things made him ill or even poisoned him, but he did not realize that the lack of certain elements in his diet could affect his health.

This lack of an understanding of the nutritional values of food was one reason for the diseases that afflicted our ancestors. It was once thought that because primitive Man lived close to Nature he was always strong and in good health. Modern science exploded that theory when skeletons thousands of years old were examined and revealed that early Man was victim of toothache, rickets, bone malformations and other diseases due to deficiencies in his diet.

It was not until the beginning of last century that scientists began to appreciate that there is a chemistry of food, and that it is the quality and composition of food, rather than its quantity, that keeps people in good health.

Nutrition is a great deal more than just eating enough food to provide the body with energy. Food must contain specific elements and compounds to nourish and sustain the myriads of individual cells of

1 Gutting chickens in a Canadian processing plant. By mass-production methods, the plant can deal with as many as 1,500 birds an hour. Most of these are frozen for household use.
2 'Hot dog' sausages are packed in sealed bags at this Canadian factory. Food processing and presentation is now a vast industry, conducted on factory lines.

which the body is composed. Every cell in the human body, whether it is a muscle, blood or nerve cell, has a specific function to perform, and the cells can do this only if they are fed with the appropriate food. Dieticians estimate that at least 40 chemical elements or chemical compounds are essential to health. These 40 or so *essential nutrients* must all be present in a properly balanced diet, either directly or in the form of raw materials from which the chemical processes of the body can extract them.

Feeding the cell

Every living cell is itself a unit, and the cells are composed into tissue and the tissue into body organs. Connection between cells, tissue and organs is maintained by a constant interchange of substances, a change and interchange which forms the pattern of construction and maintenance that we call the living body. Biochemists have found that much of the body consists of *enzymes*: complex substances that are continually assisting in the process of building and rebuilding tissues. As there is a constant wastage of tissue-making material, losses must be made good by regular intake of fresh substances from the food we eat.

Chemical analysis has shown that no single food provides all of the 40-odd elements or compounds, though all of them are essential to the proper and

healthy functioning of the body. The lack of any one of the chemical elements or compounds in the diet leads to ill-health, while a permanent lack of some can be fatal. Consequently, the work of the nutrition chemist is concerned with analysing foodstuffs to identify the presence and quantity of essential nutrients and to devise a balanced diet of the various foodstuffs that will provide proper amounts of the necessary nutrients.

One of the great achievements in food analysis was to identify specific nutrients and classify them into four main groups: minerals, proteins, carbohydrates and fats. Each of these groups belongs to a distinct class of chemical compounds and each has a specific function. The most important elements in the mineral nutrients are iron and calcium. Iron combines into a complex blood-substance that carries oxygen throughout the body, while calcium forms and hardens teeth and bones.

Proteins provide a certain amount of the body's energy, but their prime function is the growth and repair of the whole body, because muscles, bones, skin and all other tissues and organs are themselves composed of protein compounds. Proteins are large chemical molecules consisting of chemical units called *amino acids,* which in turn comprise mainly oxygen, hydrogen, nitrogen and carbon. Meat, fish and dairy foods are particularly rich in proteins, and these are separated into their constituent amino acids by the chemical processes of digestion. Chemical reactions induced by digestion reconstruct the amino acids into proteins inside the body tissues.

Carbohydrates and fats are the chief sources of fuel for the body. In other words, carbohydrates give us the bulk of our calories, and their chief sources in diet are sugars and starches in fruit and

vegetables. Carbohydrate sugars provide glucose, either directly or as a product of chemical reactions in the body. Butter and oils are the chief sources of the fats group and consist almost entirely of carbon and hydrogen: the great energy producers. Linoleic acid and substances called triglycerides are also found in fats. Both substances are a source of calories, although their exact functions in the body have not yet been fully established.

Vitamins

There is also a fifth group of essential nutrients: the vitamins. These occur in foodstuffs in such minute quantities that their presence was unsuspected until 1881, when the Russian biochemist Nikolai Lunin conducted a series of experiments that suggested some unknown factor governing the nutritional value of food.

Lunin fed six guinea-pigs on a starch diet containing very little milk, and another group of six on a diet rich in milk. Within a month, four of the first group of guinea-pigs were dead, while the two survivors were sickly and ill-developed. On the other hand, the six guinea-pigs fed a milk diet were all healthy and thriving at the end of the month. Lunin analysed hundreds of samples of food to try to find an answer to the phenomenon. It was all to no avail, and he could only conclude that milk must contain some substance indispensable to animal health.

The mystery was finally solved and the first vitamin isolated in 1911 when the Polish-born biochemist Casimir Funk was experimenting with fowls to find a cure or preventative for beriberi. During one of his many prolonged analyses, he discovered a chemical compound with which he successfully cured a pigeon that had been ill with beriberi. Further experiments convinced Funk that there was a group of amine compounds which appeared to have such a vital part in nutrition that their absence in food could be injurious, if not fatal. Funk christened the substances *vitamins* from 'vital amines'.

No one whose food is of good quality and in sufficient quantity need fear serious vitamin deficiency, but for the treatment or prevention of certain deficiency diseases, the daily intake of the appropriate vitamins has to be increased, either by taking vitamin tablets or by eating foods rich in the required vitamins. People who have to subsist on diets restricted to one or two foods do not get their full vitamin quota and develop deficiency diseases.

Vitamin A is found only in animals but the chemical parent, carotene, occurs in green plants and is converted into Vitamin A in the intestine. The main sources of Vitamin A are fish liver oils, milk, cream, butter and egg yolks. Carotene is found in carrots but is destroyed by cooking and sunlight. This vitamin is stored in the liver, assists physical growth and helps resistance to infection, besides playing a part in activating the light-sensitive cells in the eyes.

Often called the B complex, vitamin B was for some time thought to be one specific vitamin, but chemical analysis has shown that it is a group of different vitamins, which are signified by numerals.

Vitamin B_1 is found in the whole ears of grains and in yeast, nuts, peas, soya beans and green vegetables. It is essential in preventing certain nervous diseases and in some instances deficiency may lead to paralysis of the limbs. Beriberi is the most serious and widespread disease caused by B_1 deficiency.

Originally called Vitamin G, vitamin B_2 (riboflavin) is found in liver, milk, yeast, eggs, poultry, fish and green, leafy vegetables. Its deficiency leads to loss of weight, stunted growth, and affects the skin round the mouth and nose and ears. Pellagra, a wasting disease, results from a diet poor in nicotinic acid, another B vitamin. Vitamin B_{12}, the chief source of which is liver, is essential for the formation of red blood cells and its deficiency leads to pernicious anaemia.

Vitamin C, also called ascorbic acid, is derived from fresh fruits and vegetables, especially oranges, blackcurrants, tomatoes and rose hips. It is essential for sound bones and teeth, and a deficiency delays the healing of wounds and joining of

broken bones. The body cannot store the vitamin for any length of time and it must be replenished by appropriate diet. Vitamin D is essential to a baby's diet, as deficiency of it results in loss of calcium and increased liability to develop rickets. The chief sources are fish liver oils, liver, eggs, milk and butter. Vitamin E is believed to be necessary to the reproduction of animals and the main sources are wheat germ oil and the green leaves of spinach, watercress and lettuce.

Vitamin K, which is contained in green-leaf vegetables, particularly spinach, kale and cabbage, is essential to normal blood

4 Deep freezing is increasingly used for preserving, not only in industry, but in the home. Jams and fruit juices can be kept fresh for long periods at low temperatures.

5 Another preserving method is freeze drying, in which moisture is removed at very low temperatures. Here, a freeze-dried meal is weighed against an egg. The meal weighs less. **5**

clotting.

If adequate vitamin content and nutrient value are to be obtained from food, the food must be fresh or at least adequately preserved to retain its freshness. Little more than 150 years ago, foodstuffs such as meat, fish, vegetables and fruit were seasonal and when they were out of season people had either to go without them or make do with salted or dried foods. Until comparatively recently, such methods of preserving were extremely primitive and destroyed most vitamins. Since the beginning of last century, however, chemists have made tremendous strides in the techniques of preserving foodstuffs so that they retain the bulk of their nutritional qualities.

The chief cause of food going bad and becoming not only toxically harmful but losing essential dietary qualities is pro-

longed exposure to fluctuating temperatures. The first step to overcome this was taken in 1809 by a French confectioner Nicolas Appert, when he won a prize offered by Napoleon I for a reliable method of preserving troop rations to prove the Emperor's dictum that 'an army marches on its stomach'. Although Appert was neither a chemist nor a bacteriologist, he did know that air caused food to spoil and that high temperatures applied to fresh food neutralized the organisms responsible for decay.

Appert's process consisted of putting cooked meat, fish, fruit or vegetables into glass bottles, which were then sealed and immersed in boiling water so that the food was sterilized. While Appert worked with bottles, an Englishman, Peter Durand experimented with metal cans and from this developed the great canned-food and processing industry.

Low temperature is another method of halting bacteria responsible for decay, and in the days of the Roman Empire wealthy citizens brought snow from the Alps to preserve perishable foods. This was the ancestry of the icebox, first introduced in homes in the early 1800s. The high cost of cutting and transporting blocks of ice for the boxes led engineers to devise some method whereby iceboxes could be kept cold without the necessity of replenishing the blocks of ice. The result was mechanical refrigeration, which was first used about 1860 in wholesale meat-stores and later was installed in ships carrying meat. Refrigerators for the home began coming into use in the 1920s.

To overcome the disadvantage of conventional refrigeration, chemists developed deep-freezing. This prolongs the preservation of foodstuffs and has made possible the wide range of frozen foods that now can be purchased from storage cabinets in shops. Solid carbon dioxide, popularly called dry ice, is the refrigerant and is obtained as a byproduct of ammonia manufacture.

Another method of preserving both liquid and solid foods is dehydration, which involves extracting the water from food. The oldest method of drying food was in the sun. When dehydrated food is required for cooking or for consumption, it is reconstituted by adding water. Although dehydration is an extremely

effective preserving technique, it tends to affect taste and nutrition value.

Still in the experimental stage, ultrasonics may one day become a standard treatment for rendering liquid food bacteriologically sterile. Ultrasonic treatment entails generating high-frequency sound waves which set up vibrations which virtually batter bacteria to destruction. As yet, however, ultrasonic vibrations tend to disrupt the structure of foodstuffs and so reduce their nutritive values.

At one time it was thought that irradiation of both liquid and solid foods by radioactive substances was the final solution to the problem of cheap and indefinite preservation Irradiation is a relatively simple process and easily combined with food packaging. But it is still in its experimental stages.

Most methods of food preservation entail some loss of nutritive value or a reduction of vitamin content. But chemistry has made it possible to 'inoculate' the food with appropriate additives. Vitamins lost in milk through processing are replaced by vitamin additives, while certain foodstuffs, such as margarine which does not contain the essential vitamin D, are given quotas of vitamins they do not contain naturally.

Thanks to general wealth, agricultural chemistry and engineering (fertilizers and irrigation) and food chemistry, civilized communities have never been better fed than they are now. Refrigeration and canning to prevent food from spoiling have brought the produce of every country and season to the nearest supermarket all the year round.

1 *Haute cuisine* meals being prepared at a French restaurant. After sealing, the individual packages are rapidly cooled below freezing point and need only be reheated.
2 Bottling milk in a Hungarian automated dairy. The bottling machine can handle 80,000 bottles a day and is more hygienic than older methods of filling milk bottles.
3 A canning machine in operation. Cooked fruit is automatically ladled into cans while still hot. The cans pass to another machine which seals on a lid and they are then sterilized.

The body's chemical crutches

Drugs and their use are as old as Man himself. Some are derived from plants, some are made within the body, and others manufactured by the chemist. All play their part in modern medicine.

FOR HUNDREDS of years, South American Indians tipped their arrows with a brown, sticky liquid which they extracted from plants. Anyone unfortunate enough to be struck by one of these arrows quickly became paralyzed, so that the addition of this compound represented a real improvement in the normal arrow.

This substance, or more accurately, group of substances, was known as *curare.* In 1938, it was isolated by scientists, and it is now used for its curative properties.

Curare is only one of many drugs which have become part of the doctor's normal equipment in his fight against disease. Many of them, like curare, are merely refined and improved versions of drugs which had been known for centuries. Others have only been isolated in modern times, while still more are purely synthetic products of the organic chemist's art. But all of them, in their respective ways, have a large part to play in life and death, sickness and health.

The use and abuse of drugs

Among these chemicals are two groups of substances derived originally from plants and animals. The first group, the *alkaloids,* was once known simply as plant poisons and included drugs which in the hands of doctors are used to prolong human life and prevent suffering. Unfortunately, in the hands of addicts the same drugs can be responsible for much crime, misery, and even death. The second group, known as *steroids,* includes some of the body's chemical messengers, the hormones. These particular hormones control a person's sexual characteristics, which we sum up as masculinity or femininity.

Many of these chemicals are poisons, such as *belladonna* from deadly nightshade; some are narcotics, such as opium from poppies; and others, such as quinine from the bark of the cinchona tree, have long been used as drugs. When chemists came to examine the structures and properties of these plant poisons, they found that they all gave an alkaline reaction, and so they were called alkaloids.

Alkaloids have complex molecular structures, often containing rings of atoms. They are therefore difficult to classify. Before their structures were known, they were grouped according to the plants which produce them. For instance, the nightshade family *Solanaceae* includes such plants as deadly nightshade, potato, tobacco, thorn apple, henbane, pepper and

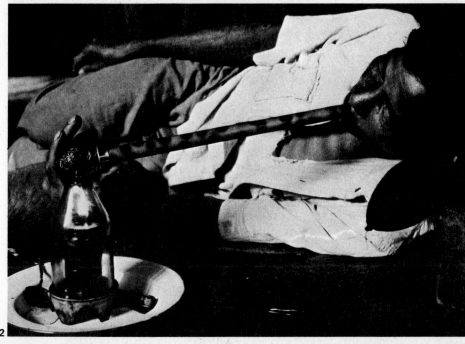

1 When poppy flowers are cut, the white liquid which oozes out is collected and used to make a number of useful drugs.

2 Opium smoking is legal in several countries in the East. Over-indulgence in this habit leads to death from respiratory failure.

tomato – all of which give rise to alkaloids. Another method of classification reflects the action of alkaloids on the human body. For example there are anaesthetics (*curare, cocaine*), hypnotics (*morphine, codeine*), stimulants (*caffeine, strychnine, ephedrine*), hallucinogens (*lysergic acid, ergometrine*) and antimalarials (*quinine*).

These methods of classification are not completely satisfactory. For instance, atropine and cocaine are chemically quite similar but derive from totally unrelated plants – atropine from deadly nightshade and cocaine from the tropical coca tree.

Similarly, caffeine and strychnine (in small doses) have much the same physiological effects but they are chemically and botanically quite different.

Chemists now classify alkaloids in terms of their molecular structures. Often, such a grouping does bring together compounds from similar sources (morphine, codeine and *thebaine* are chemically related and all derived from poppies) or of similar medical uses (the alkaloids from the fungus called ergot are chemically similar, and all produce strong contractions of the womb and may be used in gynaecology). Once

their structures have been worked out, the most useful alkaloids such as quinine may be made synthetically in the laboratory instead of being extracted from plants.

Nicotine is an alkaloid with one of the simplest chemical structures. It was first isolated from tobacco leaves nearly 150 years ago and it is a derivative of the chemical pyrrole, which has a five-membered ring, containing four carbon atoms and one nitrogen atom. It forms a colourless oil which dissolves in water. Nicotine stimulates the nervous system and greatly increases the blood pressure; it is extremely poisonous and is used as an insecticide. It may be used in medicine as an antidote for paralytic alkaloids such as strychnine.

A related group of alkaloids are based on *pyridine,* which has a six-membered ring with five carbon and one nitrogen atom. Hemlock, a common plant of the hedgerow that looks like parsley, contains the highly poisonous alkaloid called *coniine* which acts on the muscles and nerves causing paralysis. It was used by the ancient Greeks for executing criminals, and Socrates is supposed to have died of hemlock poisoning.

Sedatives and anaesthetics
A similar alkaloid called *arecaidine* occurs in betel nut, which is chewed habitually by many natives of South East Asia. It stimulates the flow of saliva, staining the gums and lips bright red and making the teeth black.

The next group of alkaloids in terms of chemical complexity have structures based on a seven-membered carbon ring with a nitrogen atom bridging it. These alkaloids include atropine, cocaine, and one called *pelletierine* which occurs in the bark of the pomegranate tree and has the usual property of curing parasitic worms in men and animals. Atropine occurs in deadly nightshade and other plants of the same family. It dilates the pupil of the eye and is widely used in ophthalmic surgery. The closely related alkaloid *scopolamine* (hyoscine) is used as a sedative in treating mental illnesses.

Cocaine occurs in the leaves of coca trees, which grow in South America and Indonesia. It is used as a local anaesthetic in surgery and dentistry, when it acts by paralyzing the nerve endings. It was introduced into medicine in the 1890s by Karl Koller and Sigmund Freud. In small doses it is a stimulant and can be habit-forming. The leaves of the coca tree are chewed by South American Indians and the white cocaine powder, sometimes called 'snow', is inhaled by drug addicts. Its continued use leads to death.

Another South American tree, the cinchona, gives rise to the important alkaloids quinine and *cinchonine,* used for

1

2

1 Common hedgerow flowers like deadly nightshade often produce useful drugs; some have been in use for hundreds of years. Often, the drug was extracted simply by chewing the plant.
2 One of the most poisonous of the alkaloids is nicotine, a constituent of tobacco. Fortunately, the quantities taken in by a smoker are extremely small.

1 Cholesterol is derived in animals and Man from the acetate, shown here in a photomicrograph. Accumulations of this steroid cause a number of diseases, including gall-stones.
2 Foxglove is the source of digitalis, a drug which is used in the treatment of a number of diseases of the heart. It strengthens the action of the heart muscle and slows the pulse.

treating malaria. Known locally as the 'fever tree', its leaves and bark have long been used in this way, but the alkaloids were not discovered until 1820. Chemically they are based on the substance *quinoline*, which has a six-membered ring (five carbons and one nitrogen) with a bridge containing two carbon atoms. Quinine kills the malarial parasites and lowers the temperature. It has a bitter taste, and in small doses it is a stimulant and temporarily increases stamina. The leaves of the cinchona tree, like those of the coca tree, are used for this purpose by South American Indians. In western countries, small amounts of quinine are added to various bitter drinks.

An organic compound consisting of three benzene rings fused together at an angle is called *phenanthrene*. With various side groupings, including one containing nitrogen, it gives rise to an important series of alkaloids derived from poppies. The juice from crushed poppy seeds is called opium. It contains about 25 alkaloids, of which the most important are morphine, codeine and thebaine.

Morphine acts on the central nervous system. In small doses it is a sedative, and in larger doses a pain-killing narcotic. It produces sleep and unconsciousness (and is named after Morpheus, the Greek god of dreams). It is a dangerous habit-forming drug, addicts generally taking it in the form of its derivative *heroin*. In the Orient, it is taken by smoking opium. In large doses, morphine causes death by respiratory failure.

Codeine, which differs from morphine only in having an extra CH_2 group, is not a narcotic and has no habit-forming effect. As a result, it is commonly used in preference to morphine as a pain killer because its repeated use cannot lead to addiction. It is also used for treating coughs. Its only disadvantage medically is that it tends to cause constipation.

One of the antidotes for opium poisoning is another alkaloid, caffeine. It occurs in coffee (up to $1\frac{1}{2}$ per cent) and tea (up to 5 per cent) and accounts for the stimulating action of drinks made from these substances. Caffeine is also found in cola nuts, used in various proprietary soft drinks, and in Paraguay tea or *maté*. It is used in medicine as a diuretic. In large doses it causes insomnia and headaches.

The compound *phenanthrene*, common to the morphine alkaloids, also gives rise to another whole series of biologically active substances called *steroids*, which include the bile acids and sex hormones. The best-known steroid in Man is *cholesterol* which occurs in the blood, in the cells of the brain and nerves, and is the main constituent of gall-stones. It is manufactured in the liver and is passed into the gall bladder with the bile. It is taken into the body in foods such as eggs and animal fats. In some people, cholesterol is deposited on the walls of arteries where it restricts the blood flow and causes a disease called *arteriosclerosis*. This disease, and the occurrence of gall-stones, is commonest in people who eat a lot of fatty foods.

Sexual characteristics

The chemically related bile acids play an important part in digestion. They break down fats and emulsify them ready for attack by enzymes from the pancreas. Their action is similar to a washing-up detergent which emulsifies the fats from dirty dishes. The bile acids also keep cholesterol in solution and prevent the formation of gall-stones.

Also of similar chemical composition to cholesterol are the steroids which constitute the sex hormones in men and women. The principal female sex hormones, produced mainly in the ovaries, are known as *oestrogens* and *progestins*, and the male sex hormones, produced in the testes, are called *androgens*. They are responsible for Man's sexual make-up, and are excreted in the urine. Similar hormones occur in animals – for instance, most of the female sex hormones used in medicine are extracted from the urine of stallions (which, curiously, contains more female hormones than does the urine of mares).

The oestrogens (or follicular hormones) control the female sexual cycle. In most mammals this takes the form of the oestrous cycle when the female animal is 'on heat' and may mate and conceive. In women and the higher primates, the hormone controls the menstrual cycle. The basic natural hormone in this group is *oestradiol*. Its production during puberty causes the development of secondary sexual characteristics in girls. Adult women excrete about a thousandth of a gram of this steroid in their urine every month. Its formation and excretion increase sharply during pregnancy, and its higher concentration in urine is the basis of most forms of pregnancy testing.

Oestrogens have also been produced synthetically. They are used to reduce the distressing symptoms of the menopause (hot flushes and nervousness) and to bring on puberty in girls who have not developed naturally by the age of 17 or 18. Lactation in women who have lost a baby may also be prevented by large doses of oestrogens.

The progestins are produced in the *corpus luteum*, the mass of yellow cells left in the ovary after the egg is expelled at ovulation. The principal hormone of this group is progesterone, which controls physical changes in the womb during the menstrual cycle, and during pregnancy it is responsible for the development of the *placenta*. The placenta itself then secretes the hormone, which prevents further ovulation taking place. For this reason, progesterone is the active ingredient of many types of contraceptive pill – it prevents ovulation and so a woman taking the pills regularly cannot conceive. It is also used in treating women who have repeated miscarriages.

Among the androgens (the male sex

1

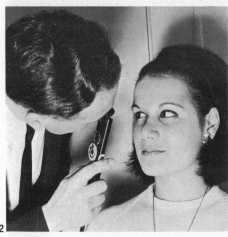

2

hormones), the most important steroids are *testosterone* and *androsterone*. They are produced in the testes in men and adolescent boys and excreted in the urine. They control the development of secondary sexual characteristics in puberty.

Chemically, testosterone differs from the female hormones oestradiol and progesterone only in the positions of two or three atoms in a molecule containing more than 50 atoms. And since normal adult males also possess some female sex hormones, it is easy to see how an imbalance of hormones or a breakdown in the biochemistry of their formation can lead to individuals who have incomplete sexual characteristics or elements of both male and female in their make-up. Carefully used, sex hormones may be administered to such people to make them more feminine or more masculine as required.

Finally there are some plant poisons which are not alkaloids like the ones considered earlier, but are steroids. Typical of these is *digitalis*, which occurs in the leaves of foxgloves. Chemically, it is a compound called a *glycoside* which has a structure very similar to that of the bile acids and sex hormones. It acts on the nerves of the heart, and doctors give it to patients with heart disease. Similar compounds called *saponins*, which are also found in plants, especially in horse chest-

1 Coniine, derived from hemlock, was used by the Greeks for executing criminals. Socrates died in this way when he was accused of corrupting the youth of Athens.
2 Atropine causes dilation of the pupil of the eye and is used by specialists to make it easier to examine the eye with an ophthalmoscope. It is a relaxant drug.

nuts, are deadly poisons. In water they froth like soap and get their name from this fact (*sapo* is Latin for soap).

Drugs against disease

Alkaloids and steroids make up a group of physiologically active compounds that occur in plants and animals. In more than trace quantities, they are practically all deadly poisonous, but in small amounts, they produce marked and widely different reactions in the human body and are an indispensable part of the doctor's armoury of drugs. Some alkaloids dilate the pupils of the eye, others contract them. Some cause paralysis, others are relaxants. Some are sedatives, others are narcotics. The sex hormones produce remarkable changes in a person's make-up and indeed largely determine whether the person is to look like a man or a woman. And yet the wide differences in their actions are often reflected by only the slightest differences in their chemical structures.

Many of the physiological and biochemical effects of the alkaloids and steroids are only now being investigated in detail. Investigation on this scale, often concerned with the sub-microscopic mechanism of the cell, has necessarily been dependent on the development of suitable scientific equipment and techniques.

Out of these investigations has arisen a deeper understanding of the function of drugs in the control of both physical and mental disease, and many maladies which were formerly regarded as incurable are now yielding to treatment. As work progresses, there is hope that still more progress will be made in the development of new drugs to fight the diseases which, so far, have proved to be resistant to treatment.

A breath of ´fresh air´

Man lives more and more in artificial environments – in outer space, under the sea, in large office blocks. To survive he must be supplied with clean air, warmth, pressure and humidity.

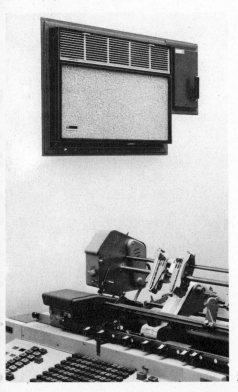

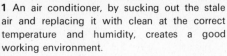

1 An air conditioner, by sucking out the stale air and replacing it with clean at the correct temperature and humidity, creates a good working environment.

2 Prefabricated buildings erected in tunnels bored out of snow provide American servicemen with a cosy refuge from the bitter winds and cold of Greenland's Arctic wastes.

TO STAY ALIVE, in addition to food and drink, Man needs a suitable environment. His natural environment consists essentially of a breathable atmosphere of gases in certain proportions and a climate which is neither too hot nor too cold. Suitable clothing plus artificial heating enables Man to survive extremes of terrestrial climatic temperatures, but he cannot survive for long in an atmosphere lacking the correct proportions of oxygen and other gases.

The atmosphere in a healthy environment, as well as being neither too dry or moist nor too hot or cold, must not be heavily polluted from extraneous sources. The air we breathe at the surface of the Earth and for a few thousand feet above it provides an adequate atmosphere, although a completely unpolluted atmosphere can now rarely be found. Despite the provisions of clean-air regulations and the enforcement of smokeless zones, the atmosphere in cities and urban areas is heavily polluted by carbon monoxide from motor vehicles and chemical and other fumes released from factory chimneys.

In large buildings, such as hotels, office blocks, cinemas, theatres and factories where large numbers of people congregate, the atmosphere becomes germ and bacteria ridden as the air is breathed in and out. In food processing plants a

fresh atmosphere free of bacteria and unwanted odours is essential to hygiene. On the other hand certain industries require a damp and humid atmosphere for the successful processing of their products. One of these is cotton-spinning, where an excessively dry atmosphere causes the thread to become so dry that it snaps in the spinning machines. The damp atmosphere of Lancashire was one of the reasons for that county becoming the centre of England's cotton industry. Some industries, such as those making delicate instruments and precision machines, need an atmosphere that is neither too damp nor too warm, to avoid the corrosion or alteration in size of small metal parts.

But the most serious of all pollutants of the atmosphere is dust. Ever since the world solidified out of its original cosmic gases and diffused materials, dust has been suspended in varying degrees in its atmosphere. It is these minute particles of dust that help create fog and smog in and around large cities and industrial complexes. Even in rural districts far removed from urban centres, the air carries an alarmingly high percentage of dust which pollutes the air we breathe and contaminates the food we eat.

Without dust, however microscopic in quantity, the atmosphere would be hygienically clean, for dust distributes bacteria and other impurities in the atmosphere. Nevertheless, by using sterilizing sprays, the atmosphere can be rendered clean and bacterially sterile.

One way of providing a reasonably clean

and unpolluted atmosphere in buildings and other enclosed spaces is through air conditioning. Basically, air conditioning consists of withdrawing air from an inhabited space, cleaning and purifying it, as well as bringing it to the correct temperature and humidity before it is returned to the space from which it was withdrawn.

The kind of air conditioning required can be varied. The equipment ranges from small, portable units for cleaning the air in a single room or a car to the huge plants that clean the air circulating throughout a building of many storeys. There are also the medium-size air-conditioning plants to maintain a normal and wholesome atmosphere in the pressurized cabins of airliners, within the hulls of submarines, and in the coaches of long-distance railway trains and road coaches.

A complete air-conditioning plant needs a mechanical ventilator, a filter and a unit to add or to remove heat and moisture. The temperature is regulated by thermostatically controlled heating or cooling units or by a combination of both. Heat is generated in the conditioned air either by the combustion of fuels or by electrical-resistance elements. Evaporative and refrigerative units are used for cooling. While refrigeration indirectly produces cooling by the air being in contact with a cold fluid, in the evaporation unit, as moisture evaporates into the air, it both cools and humidifies it. The hotter the air the more water vaporizes and the cooler the air becomes.

The moisture can be taken out of the air by condensing it over a cold surface or by passing the air over a desiccant which draws out the moisture. The quality of the air is regulated by forcing the air through filters to remove suspended particles. Although the air circulates naturally through any area, it is usually helped on its way by a mechanical pump. Extractor fans draw off the old air through ducts to a filter where dust and other solid impurities are removed. The air can be filtered in various ways. One depends upon changing the velocity at which the air is drawn through the ducts. Thus air may be drawn through the collecting ducts at a velocity of 4,000 ft per minute to be discharged into a chamber through an expanded duct which reduces the air speed to 40 ft per minute. Because the air is now travelling more slowly, the relatively heavy and solid impurities fall out and deposit on the bottom of the collecting chamber. A series of baffles prevents the currents or eddies induced by the moving air from sucking the deposited solids back into the slowly moving air stream.

Silent filters

Another type of filter incorporates an electrically or mechanically driven centrifuge, through which the air passes, and which forces all solid contents outwards. Air-conditioning engineers prefer to use non-mechanical filters as they contain no moving parts and are, therefore, less liable to deterioration or to be noisy. A simple filter of this type consists of a textile material stretched on a frame across the duct through which the stale air is passing. Filters of this kind collect a high percentage of solids but they are difficult to clean.

One of the most efficient of non-mechanical air-conditioning filters consists of a number of small cylinders placed side by side across the airflow to provide a honeycomb. The surfaces of the cylinders are coated with a viscous oil over which the air flows freely but to which its solid content clings. The oily surfaces of the cylinders become increasingly rougher with the deposition of the solids, but this merely increases the filter's efficiency in extracting solids from the air. When the solid depositions become so thick as to impede free flow of the air, the filters are easily cleaned by washing in hot soda-water and renewing the oil films.

After filtering, the air passes through a chamber where it is washed and its temperature raised or lowered by fine sprays of water. This dual function is possible because the temperature of air depends upon its water content and air's humidity can be increased or decreased by spraying water into it.

When the air being conditioned has a low solid content, filtering can be combined with washing and temperature and humidity adjustment. The water sprays are installed in front of the air inlet so that the

1 Men in a submarine may spend many hours submerged. Because they are breathing in a closed system the air must be constantly filtered and the exhaled carbon dioxide removed.

2 Water at depth exerts an immense pressure and a diver, supplied with air by a life-line to the surface, would suffer total collapse of the lungs unless wearing a helmet and suit.

3 As well as being airless, the moon is at the mercy of the sun's radiation. To keep cool the astronauts carry a special refrigeration unit in the packs on their backs.

4 By creating carefully controlled 'tropics' in a glass house at Kew Gardens in England, botanists grow the beautiful South African plant *Strelitzia reginae*.

5 Natural fibres become brittle and unusable when too dry. It is essential that during manufacture relatively high humidity is maintained in factories.

stale air passes immediately through them. This saturates the solids in the air so that their weight increases and they either fall into a sediment tank or are separated from the air by baffles.

After such treatment, the air still requires 'reviving'. This can be done by passing the air through carbon filters or, more efficiently, by treating it with an ozone generator. Ozone, which eliminates objectionable odours and is an antiseptic, is a condensed form of oxygen. When used in air-conditioning systems it reduces the amount of outside air required for re-circulation.

Ozone generators are simple to operate and resemble static capacitors with air as the dielectric. A capacitor, often miscalled a condenser, is an electrical device consisting of electrically conductive plates separated by a dielectric or insulating substance. In an ozone generator the capacitor plates are given an electrical charge, while the cleaned air passing through the conditioner acts as the dielectric. If, however, the charge on the plates is increased sufficiently, the insulating properties of the air break down and an electric spark passes through the air between the plates. The production of the spark ionizes the air and it is this that constitutes the source of the ozone. The ozone in fact derives from the oxygen in the air.

Threat of pollution

As a concentration of ozone in the atmosphere much in excess of 12 parts per million by volume would be harmful, only a fraction of the air handled by the conditioning plant passes through the ozone generator. The ozonized air is then injected into the main stream of conditioned air.

Industrial Man is so polluting the atmosphere of his environment that some health experts foresee the day when whole cities and industrial complexes will have to be enclosed in great plastic domes through which clean and conditioned air will be circulated to provide the inhabitants with a breathable atmosphere. They even go further and forecast farms covered by huge plastic domes in which plants will grow in an artificial environment independent of the natural, and often polluted,

atmosphere. Such farms will be free of the vagaries of weather and will be provided with carefully controlled ultra-violet and infra-red radiation to ensure healthy development of plant and animal life.

When Man ventures out of his natural environment to move under the sea or into space he must take with him an artificial environment which reproduces as nearly as possible his natural one. For astronauts and aquanauts, the artificial environment is not just a matter of providing a breathable atmosphere. The aquanaut must be able to survive pressures hundreds of times greater than the 14·72 lb to the square inch exerted on his body by atmospheric pressure at sea level on the Earth. The astronaut must take with him an artificial environment that enables him to survive fantastic extremes of heat and cold.

Since the earliest times men had been tantalized by the possibility of exploring the underwater world; but they first had to solve the problem of taking with them the breathable atmosphere. The earliest written reference to a device for breathing under the water is a passage in Aristotle (384–322 BC) which describes divers taking down with them weighted cylinders filled with air which they breathed through tubes.

Later Pliny (23–79 AD) tells of divers who drew air through a tube, one end of which they held in their mouths and the other made fast to a sphere floating on the surface of the water. Vegetius, a Roman author of the fourth century AD shows a drawing in one of his manuscripts of a diver wearing a tight-fitting helmet to which is attached a long leather tube leading to the surface of the water where its open end is kept afloat by a bladder. Throughout the succeeding centuries many other ingenious devices were invented for diving but none of them could have been used at depths much below 20 ft as they made no provision to counteract the pressure of the water which increases by approximately 4 lb per square inch for every ten feet below the surface. It was not until 1837 when Augustus Siebe introduced his closed diving dress and helmet which supplied the wearer with air pumped from the surface that really deep diving became possible. All diving suits now in use are based on the Siebe principle.

The pressure of the water on a diver working at, say, a depth of 100 ft would be 60 lb to the square inch and his muscles would not be strong enough to expand his chest to breathe in and out the air pumped to him from the surface. Therefore the diver is surrounded by compressed air pumped into his suit from the service ship on the surface. The compressed air is always delivered to the diving suit at the same pressure as the depth of water to which the diver has descended. Consequently, the pressure in the diver's body always equals that of the water outside his suit. By using special gas mixtures, including helium, suited divers can work for short periods at depths of 400 ft, where the water pressure is about 200 lb per square inch.

A new development in deep-diving is

independent diving or skin diving. In this type of diving the diver wears a skin-tight suit and a breathing mask. His air supply is contained in cylinders on his back and the pressure of the gases he breathes in can be adjusted according to the pressure of the water. The breathing equipment, called an *aqualung* is *self-regenerative*; that is, the exhaled air is purified of carbon dioxide by passing it through a suitable absorbent.

With the modern diving equipment, men can go down to depths of over 1,000 ft. Experiments have also been made with undersea houses provided with an artificial environment whereby divers can work and live far down in the sea for weeks at a time.

Survival in space

Astronauts voyaging into space require a much more elaborate artificial environment than aquanauts venturing into the depths of the ocean. A spacecraft's artificial environment or *life-support system* must be designed for an extended stay in completely airless outer space; as the craft clears the lower atmosphere in less than a minute after rocket blast-off, the artificial environment must come into immediate operation.

To survive in outer space the astronaut must have a pressurized cabin with means for replenishing oxygen, removing carbon dioxide and unpleasant odours, and maintaining within the cabin of his craft an ambient temperature and humidity approximating that which the crew would normally experience on Earth. Contour seats for the crew protect their bodies from the effects of high accelerations and decelerations during launching, mid-course manoeuvering and re-entry into the Earth's atmosphere. A heat shield on the outer surface of the spacecraft base prevents the craft and crew being incinerated by friction with the atmosphere during re-entry. A pressure suit for each crew member ensures his survival in the event of breakdown of the equipment maintaining cabin pressure and is worn when the astronaut leaves his craft during the voyage or when he lands on the moon or a planet.

Protection against radiation is also needed, according to the length of the mission and the flight path. A prolonged stay in the Van Allen Belts or a long interplanetary voyage, as from the Earth to Mars, requires greater radiation protection than does a low-altitude orbit flight. There also must be protection for the craft against the possibility of collision with meteor showers that could damage it.

Great as were the problems that had to be solved to enable astronauts to live in a spacecraft, the whole complex of equipment had to be so miniaturized that men who landed on the moon were able to carry their artificial environments on their backs. When manned observation posts are set up on the moon, the personnel will have to live in sealed buildings inside which will be an artificial environment similar to that provided for spacecraft, but on a much larger and more lavish scale.

1 The modern aeroplane flies at altitudes of 30,000 feet and more, where the air is far too rarefied to be breathed. The cabin must therefore be pressurized and the air conditioned.
2 Large modern buildings, such as airports and office blocks, are highly artificial environments. The air is forced to circulate continually and is cleaned during the process.
3 The floor of this furniture factory has never to be swept clean of sawdust. Extractor fans linked to a system of ducts do the job more efficiently than a team of sweepers.

The cleaning revolution

Detergents, plastics, dust- and water-repellent substances, and labour-saving devices have transformed the housewife's work and the methods by which she now keeps her house clean and polished.

SINCE THE BEGINNING of the present century, and particularly since the 1950s, scientists and engineers have completely revolutionized the average home and changed out of all recognition the methods of keeping it clean and of performing a host of what were once laborious domestic chores. Yet the many labour-saving devices now available to the housewife were not specifically invented for her benefit but were simply adaptations of mechanical and chemical principles which had long been commonplace in industry and the laboratory.

Why did this sudden revolution come about in the household? The increasing shortage of domestic servants and the rise in the average family income accelerated demand for machines and chemical compounds to replace the labour of human hands. As a result, the washing-machine, the vacuum cleaner, the food mixer, the stainless-steel utensil, non-stick pots and pans, heat-resistant polishes, the impregnated duster and the high-speed cooker became commonplace in the home.

Machines and detergents have had an enormous impact on the housewife's quest for cleanliness. Doubtless one of the greatest revolutions was brought about by detergents. In this connection, however, the name detergent is not restricted to the cleansing powders and liquids sold under a variety of trade names. Ordinary soap is a detergent, so that any cleansing substance is a detergent. The word detergent comes from the Latin *detergere*, meaning 'to wash off'.

Soap was the first detergent. No one knows when or by whom it was discovered that a mixture of ashes and animal fat had

1 All manner of tests, including resistance to scratching and heating, are carried out on furniture finishes at the British Research Industry Association Centre at Stevenage.
2 Aerosol sprays have been a useful innovation in the home. Trousers sprayed with a thin layer of silicones after ironing become water-proof and they retain their creases.
3 Silicone polishes have many advantages over wax polishes; they give a brilliant shine without hard rubbing, they are durable, dust-repellent and water-resistant.

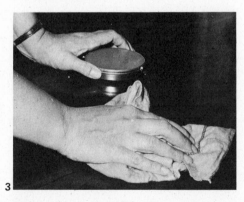

a cleansing action. But since early times our ancestors had been making soap by mixing lye with hot grease or fat. They obtained the lye by letting hot water drip through wood ash. The making of soap was for centuries a major home task and until quite recently the lye hopper was a familiar sight in the backyards of rural communities.

Because the alkali used in soap-making was potash, the resulting soap never hardened, while the crudity of its manufacture was such that its alkali content was so highly variable that its efficiency

as a dirt remover varied from household to household. When soap-making became an industry the result was a better and more uniform quality, while the substitution of soda for potash enabled the soap to be hardened into solid cakes.

It was a long time, however, before scientists discovered how soap performed its work of helping to keep things clean. Soap is basically a compound of an alkali with the fatty acid of an oil having a high emulsifying property. Its primary action is to allow water to wet greasy surfaces and thereby emulsify and remove grease and dirt. Because of its alkaline nature, soap is not always satisfactory for this purpose and there was a need for acid wetting agents.

With a better understanding of the action of soap on dirt, chemists were able to compound new synthetic detergents, or soapless soaps, which were to prove much more versatile and efficient than any conventional soap. The same cleansing principle, however, is involved in both soaps and synthetic detergents, in spite of the fact that soaps are made mainly from fats and vegetable oils, whereas synthetic detergents are compounded from the by-products of petroleum refining from coal tar and other sources.

The molecules, of which soaps and the majority of detergents are composed, have a dual action. One part of each molecule is attracted to water, while the other part is attracted to oil or grease and repelled by water. Thus when a conventional soap or detergent is used for washing clothes, the oil-seeking part of the molecule is attracted to the grease and dirt on the clothes, while the other part is attracted to the water in which the clothes are being washed. This induces a kind of chemical tug-of-war in which the particles of dirt are broken up and fall into the washing water. The detergent then coats the particles with a skin, so preventing them from forming clumps with other loosened bits of dirt. In this way, a detergent slides the dirt off the soiled surface and prevents it from settling on it again. Rubbing, wringing or agitating help to loosen the dirt so that it floats away.

To carry out its cleansing function, a detergent must also be a good wetting agent. This means that clusters of its molecules must crowd the surface of the water, so reducing surface tension and thereby making it easier for the water molecules to penetrate deep into the fibres of the fabric being washed. But it must be able to do this without damaging the fibres. A strong alkaline soap will deeply penetrate the fibres of a woollen garment but in doing so it will shrink the wool: if the alkaline concentration is strong enough, it will actually dissolve the wool fibres. An acid detergent has scarcely any detectable effect on wool fibres.

Soap detergents have many other serious disadvantages. It is almost impossible to obtain a lather in cold, salt or acid water, or in water that is very *hard*. Hard water is water that has absorbed an excessive amount of minerals, such as calcium and magnesium. When used with hard water, soap combines with the minerals to form a deposit or scum on the surface of the article being cleaned, which is very difficult to rinse out completely. The scum also forms on the sides of the vessel in which the clothes are being washed. This can be a particularly serious matter where the laundry is being done in a washing machine. Moreover, using soap in hard water is uneconomic, for the soap that combines with the minerals to form scum performs no cleansing action and is wasted.

Until comparatively recently, manufacturers were so anxious to provide detergents with high lather-making pro-

perties because housewives believed they were necessary, that they overdid it. Detergent suds became a menace, clogging drainage and sewage systems, and when water containing the suds was discharged into rivers they formed a blanket which deprived marine animals and plants of the oxygen on which their life depends. The danger was appreciated and new detergent formulas were evolved which kept sudding within reasonable bounds.

From these formulas developed special sudless detergents for cleansing solid surfaces such as floors and walls. There are also special detergents for the cleansing of stained or polished surfaces which otherwise would be damaged by washing.

'Digesting' dirt

One of the more recent developments of synthetic detergents is the so-called biological detergent. It is very effective for the removal of stains and other forms of deep-seated soiling against which the conventional detergent is often ineffective. Biological detergents react chemically with the dirt and 'digest' it out of the soiled surface. Some people consider that their action is very drastic and that fabrics left to soak in water containing biological detergents may be damaged. Some dermatologists are also critical of biological detergents on the grounds that they can be harmful to human skin and may be the cause of certain skin disorders.

There have been moves in the United States to ban the use of biological detergents pending an inquiry into their potentiality as a health hazard. In some other countries the strong biological detergents used in industrial processes are prohibited unless workers handling them are protected by gloves and clothing. Great care must be taken to avoid what could be a health hazard to workers in the factories producing biological detergents.

Synthetic cleansing detergents were first made in Germany and quickly found favour with textile manufacturers because of their effective cleansing of raw wool. The first of the many household deter-

gents now in use was put on sale in 1936. The effectiveness of any cleansing detergent depends upon, amongst other factors, the temperature of the water in which it is used, the mechanical or manual agitation of the water and the article being cleaned, and the length of time to which an article is exposed to the detergent's action.

It is not only in the kitchen and the washing-machine that detergents have a place in the home. They are found in shampoos, hand lotions, medicines, in cleaning vegetables such as cabbage and broccoli, and even in the milk bottle.

Many shampoos incorporate special detergents to increase foaming and froth effect. Most hand lotions contain talcum powder to make the lotion smooth and incorporate a detergent to break up the talcum particles into still tinier particles. In this manner the talcum particles are coated by the detergent in exactly the same way that detergents coat dirt particles in washing and prevent them from forming into clumps. Other detergents have a place in certain emulsions, such as solutions where oil and some other liquid, with which oil does not easily mix, have to be brought together. Tasteless detergents are used in place of eggs in cake-making.

Amongst the most useful of detergents are those called *quats*, or quaternary ammonium compounds. They have the dual property of not only acting as cleansers but also as bactericides. Since they are particularly effective against the bacteria present in milk, they are finding increasing application in sterilizing milk bottles and other containers. In weak solution, 'quats' destroy any of the harmful bacteria found in drinking water.

One of the most remarkable substances which has gained an increasingly prominent place in the home is called silicones. This is the name given to a range of manmade chemical compounds the main component of which is silicon – one of the most abundant elements found in the Earth's crust. Some of these silicones are ex-

THE BIOLOGICAL WASHING MIRACLE

3

5

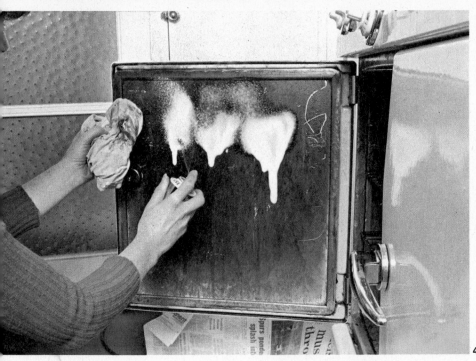

4

6

1 Synthetic materials, such as plastic, have proved a great boon to the housewife. Attractively printed, they can be used to cover any hard-worked surface, and they do not stain.

2 Clothes soaking in a biological detergent. These detergents, containing enzymes which 'digest' dirt, are very effective against certain types of stain.

3 Cooking on non-stick surfaces has made cleaning up much easier and no fat need be used. Scientists discovered the formula of a non-stick surface as an offshoot of space research into a water and heat-proof substance.

4 A powerful synthetic detergent, which is effective against ingrained and burned-on fat, is sprayed from a pressurized aerosol container on to an oven door.

5 Stale cooking smells and dust are removed by this small air-conditioner which draws out all the stale air from the kitchen and keeps the atmosphere fresh.

6 Detergents dissolve away dirt and grease by making them emulsify with water. Detergent foam in this carpet cleaner lifts the dirt from the pile and dries on the surface.

tremely useful because they repel water, do not react with other chemicals and do not easily decompose when heated.

Scientists had for long been tantalized by the possibility of so treating absorbent materials, such as fabrics and leather, so they would have the water-repellent and stain-resistant properties. The early experiments consisted in coating materials with a thin film of glass, but this only succeeded in making the materials far too brittle to be of any use.

Eventually, however, a team of British chemists obtained from silicon a very fine substance that could be sprayed, painted or otherwise applied to the surface of any material without altering its appearance, colour or texture. It is this fine substance that we call silicones, and its great advantage is that it does not stick to other substances and they do not stick to it.

The surfaces of frying-pans and cooking pots coated with a chemical compound prevent the food sticking, while baking pans and cake tins coated with it do not

need to be greased to prevent the dough from adhering. Car and furniture polishes containing silicones give a brilliant shine without hard rubbing; they are durable, dust-repellent and waterproof.

Silicones

Articles plated with chromium, silver and other metals can be given a silicone polish which will remain bright and tarnish-resistant in all weather. Adhesive tapes can be wound in rolls because one surface has a silicone coating. Paint containing silicones is sufficiently heat-resistant for it to be applied to the hot-plates of electric stoves and ovens. As such paints do not blister they can be used for fireplace surrounds and for application to hot-water pipes.

Silicones' resistance to water has been exploited in many ways. Fabrics treated with them can be of the finest possible texture, as each thread in the fabric is coated separately. Nylon stockings and the thinnest of dress materials treated with

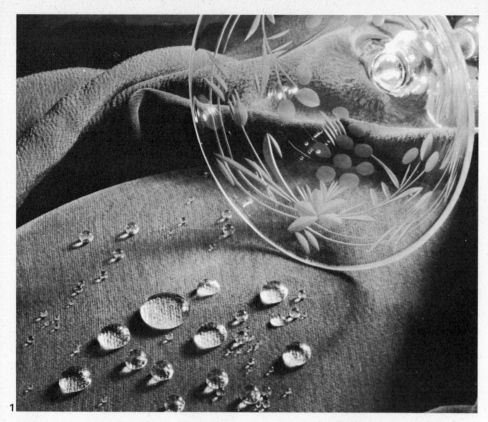

silicones withstand the heaviest rain, which simply rolls off the fabric. Garments made from nylon and other synthetic fibres continue to shed water even after they have been laundered or dry-cleaned.

Siliconized wallpaper can be used in bathrooms or kitchens without being damaged or dissolved by water or steam. The paper can have a rough or smooth surface or carry a coloured pattern and it does not have the shiny appearance of conventional papers rendered damp-proof by varnishing. Even the outer walls of a house can be made proof against damp by application of a silicone lotion. The lotion can be coloured or colourless; the latter is an important consideration when the lotion is applied to old and mellowed brick and stone work.

Silicone-treated articles are able to withstand extremes of heat and cold. Rubber articles, for example, normally melt at relatively low temperatures, but when treated with silicones they can withstand temperatures ranging up to 250 °C. and remain flexible at temperatures as low as −70 °C. Silicones have also exceptional electrical insulation properties. Voltages of up to 14,000 have been passed for periods as long as 12,000 hours through wiring sheathed in silicone rubber without the slightest leakage of current.

Probably the most striking development in the packaging of certain household materials is the aerosol bottle. The bottle is, in effect, a pressure vessel and depends for its action upon containing a substance which is liquid under high pressure, but immediately the pressure is released it turns into a gas. There are aerosol bottles containing sprays of starch, deodorizers, fly-killers, paint, furniture polish, hair lacquers and disinfectants.

Very fine particles of the substance to be sprayed are suspended in the container in a liquefied gas called the *propellant*. When the button on top of the bottle is pressed, the valve is opened and pressure forces the starch, paint or other substance out through the jet-nozzle at the top of the bottle in a very fine mist. When the button is released, the valve closes and the contents of the bottle return to a high pressure. The container is then effectively sealed off again.

Aerosol bottles are made from tin-plate or aluminium and have to be able to withstand a pressure of 20 lb or more to the square inch. The substance sprayed may be poisonous as, for example, in aerosol-sprayed fly-killers and other insecticides, and should not be allowed to come into contact with food.

The most usual propellant is dichloro-difluoromethane. This is the same liquid used in most refrigerators as it is a gas that easily liquefies. To a lesser extent, the hydrocarbon, butane, C_4H_{10}, is also used.

There seems no end to the applications of science and technology to the modern home. But for cleaning, in particular, technology has caused a revolution in both materials and in methods to take the drudgery out of the housewife's work.

1 A fabric coated in silicones is effectively water-proofed and water runs off or can be shaken off. Because it cannot damp the material the water forms spherical drops.

2 The days of housemaids and 'dailies' are practically over and a housewife looks for labour-saving devices. This dish-washing machine washes and dries a full load in 35 minutes.

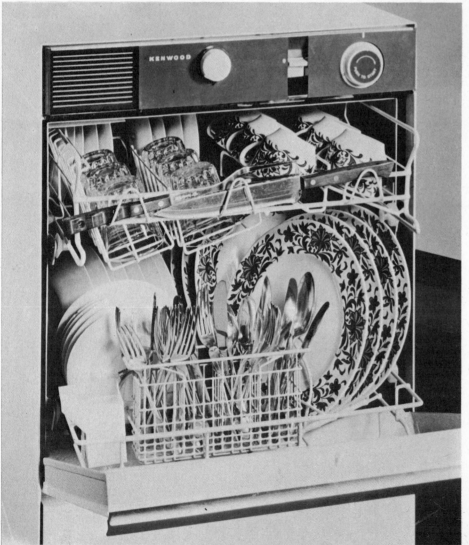

Levers of power

Modern everyday life is made easier by machines. But not everyone realizes that many of the simple gadgets we use to open bottles, dig gardens, or cut paper can also be regarded as machines.

THE INDUSTRIAL REVOLUTION began in the mid-eighteenth century. Two centuries later we are almost completely dependent on machines. Gadgets run our lives, yet many persons today know little more about how machines operate than do African tribesmen who have yet to discover the ox-plough. Anyone who has looked under the bonnet of a modern motor car can readily understand why: machines can be quite complicated. But even the most complicated machines still adhere to a few simple laws of physics.

Whenever a job must be done, energy is required to do it. If the job is accomplished by manual labour, the energy comes from the food we eat. If it is done by machine, the energy may come from burning petrol in an engine, the flow of electricity through a wire, water falling over a paddle-wheel, or 'splitting' the atom. But wherever it comes from, it must be transmitted from its source to where it is needed.

The pulley

Suppose a large crate must be raised from the ground to a platform three feet high. A good husky man could probably bend down and lift it, but he might risk straining his back if it were heavy or awkward.

In such a case, a better way would be to tie a rope to the crate, pass the rope over a wheel called a *fixed pulley,* and then pull on the rope. In this way, the energy generated by the muscles in the man's arms passes to the rope, which in turn transmits it to the crate, which then rises off the ground. Because a fixed pulley is used to transmit energy, it qualifies as a *simple machine.*

Alternatively, instead of using a pulley, one could use an *inclined plane.* The crate could be placed on a trolley and drawn up the slope to the platform.

The fixed pulley and the inclined plane are examples of machines which change the direction of an applied force. With the pulley, one pulls down on the rope instead of up on the crate. With the inclined plane, one pushes sideways instead of pulling up.

Often, simply changing the direction of a force is not enough to accomplish the job at hand. In removing the clip cap from a bottle, for instance, few people would try to pull it off from above, nor would they have much success if they tried pushing it off with their thumbs from below. What is needed here is a machine that does more than change direction; it must actually increase the force on the cap. To see how a bottle opener does this, it is first necessary to take a closer look at the idea of mechanical work.

In physics, 'work' or 'mechanical energy' is defined as the quantity found by multiplying an applied force by the dis-

tance through which the force acts. In lifting a crate of 100 pounds by three feet, the force is the 100 pounds needed to move the crate, and the distance is the three feet the crate moves upwards. The work or mechanical energy expended is thus 100 pounds × 3 feet, which gives 300 foot-pounds of work. If the 100-pound crate were lifted four feet, then the work would be 100 pounds × 4 feet = 400 foot-pounds, and so on.

In general, the amount of work necessary to accomplish a task is found from the formula $W = FS$, where W is work, F is force, and S is the distance the force moves. The force need not be straight up and down

to calculate work, though most of the examples in this article will use vertical forces, because they simplify the mathematics.

Notice that 'work' has two parts or components: force and distance. This is fundamental in understanding the mechanics of a bottle opener.

As the bottle is being opened, the hand at one end of the bottle opener moves a fairly large distance, while the cap at the other end moves hardly at all. Suppose the hand applies a force of 20 pounds and moves its end of the bottle opener three inches. Then the work transmitted to the cap is 20 pounds × 3 inches = 60 inch-pounds. ('Inch-pounds' and 'foot-pounds' are both units of work.) Now, suppose the cap moves one inch before it can be removed. One inch is the distance. What force times one inch gives 60 inch-pounds of energy? The answer is 60 pounds, because 60 pounds × 1 inch = 60 inch-pounds. So the force of 20 pounds supplied by the hand at one end of the bottle opener has become a force of 60 pounds applied to the bottle-top!

The same principle explains the mechanics of an ordinary nutcracker. Squeezing at one end of the nutcracker causes the nut

1 The principle underlying the operation of the screw is that of an inclined plane. Instead of being laid out in a straight line, the plane is formed as a spiral on the surface of a cylinder.
2 The principle of the lever was applied in the construction of this seventeenth-century post mill. One man can turn the whole mill round on its pivot to face the wind.
3 Leonardo da Vinci was fascinated by the practical applications of mechanics. In this sketch from his notebooks, levers and pulleys are shown in a variety of uses.

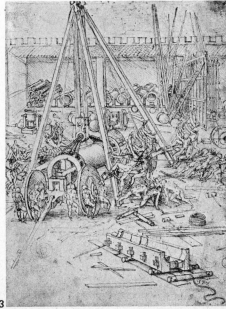

to crack at the other, because the end being squeezed moves much further than the end where the nut is, and so the force is greatly multiplied.

Both the bottle opener and the nut-cracker are examples of a whole class of simple machines called *levers*. In essence, a lever is a straight rod designed so that one end will move more than the other, thus multiplying forces. Other examples are spanners, crow-bars, scissors, shovels, pliers, brooms and wheelbarrows. Levers, of course, are not the only types of machines that multiply forces. Moveable pulleys, blocks and tackles, screws, hydraulic lifts and many others do so as well. But no matter how complicated a force-multiplying machine becomes, the fundamental physics involved remains the same as with the lever. A large force implies a small distance, and vice versa.

Work and heat

So far, work has been discussed in foot-pounds and inch-pounds only. These are English units. In the metric system, used by most scientists, force is measured in newtons (about 4·5 pounds) and distances in metres (about 3 feet). The difference in units does not affect the basic definition of work. To lift a 10-newton crate three metres would require 10 newtons×3 metres=30 newton-metres of work. To lift a 15-newton crate 4 metres would require 15 newtons×4 metres=60 newton-metres of work, and so on. Work is still force times distance, $W=FS$.

In fact it would be more correct to say that *mechanical* work is force times distance. An electric fire does work when it heats a room, an oven does work when it cooks a roast, your body does work keeping you alive. In these situations, the work energy takes the form of heat, not a force moving through a distance.

The fact that heat is essentially the same thing as mechanical work was formally established in the middle of the last century, when James Prescott Joule, a British physicist, determined the *mechanical equivalent of heat*. Joule produced heat mechanically by friction, and measured both the work put in and the heat (measured in calories) produced.

According to Joule's experiment, one calorie of heat represents the same quantity of energy as 4·19 newton-metres of work, that is, 1 cal=4·19 newton-metres. Thus, if an object weighing 4·19 newtons were lifted one metre, the work required could be expressed as either 4·19 newtons ×1 metre (4·19 newton-metres) or as one calorie, whichever were more convenient.

The relationship 1 cal=4·19 newton-metres, which relates heat to work, is the mechanical equivalent to heat. In honour of Joule's work in establishing this relationship, his name has been adopted as the metric unit of energy, replacing the phrase 'newton-metre'.

Since mechanical work is a form of energy, it must abide by the fundamental law which governs all other forms of energy: energy can be neither created nor destroyed; it can only change from one form to another. This is known as the *Law of Conservation of Energy*. When applied

The rigging of old sailing ships – like Nelson's flagship H.M.S. *Victory* shown here – consisted of a complex system of pulleys to make it easier to raise and lower the sails.

to machines, it leads to the rather startling conclusion that it actually requires more work to accomplish a task with a machine than without it!

Returning to the example of lifting the 100-pound crate to a three-foot platform: if this had been done directly, the work would have been 100 pounds×3 feet, or 300 foot-pounds. For convenience, a rope and a pulley were used. Instead of lifting only the crate, it was necessary to lift the crate plus the rope tied to it. Suppose the rope weighed one pound, then the total weight lifted was 101 pounds, not just 100 pounds. So the work was 101 pounds×3 feet, or 303 foot-pounds. Thus, by using the pulley and rope, three extra foot-pounds of work had to be done in lifting the crate. This work was of no real value; it was wasted.

While it is true that were the job done directly, without the intervention of a machine, the expenditure of energy would have been much less, it is equally true that most jobs would not be done at all were there no machines to do them. So no matter how much work machines 'waste' (and they all waste some), they are generally worth the investment.

The notion of wasted work leads quite

naturally to the idea of *efficiency*. Mechanical efficiency is expressed as a percentage. If all the work done by a machine were useful and none were wasted (which cannot happen), the efficiency of the machine would be 100 per cent. Anything less than perfection is indicated by a percentage less than 100.

In the example of the pulley and the crate, the efficiency was 300 foot-pounds useful work divided by 303 foot-pounds total work, an efficiency of about 99 per cent. Efficiencies as high as 99 per cent are extraordinary; indeed, efficiencies as high as 50 per cent are rare.

Efficiency of the machine

The first steam engines had an efficiency of less than four per cent. Engineers constantly seek ways to improve efficiency, but even today a good steam engine cannot be expected to have an efficiency much beyond 15–20 per cent. Motor-car engines generally waste more than half the petrol they burn. The prospects of realizing the utopian value of 100 per cent efficiency are non-existent. This fact has not prevented hundreds of people trying: the goal of 'perpetual motion' continues to attract people who attempt to invent a perfect machine. Such a machine would overthrow the basic laws of physics as they are now known.

But not everyone is concerned primarily with the efficiency of his machine.

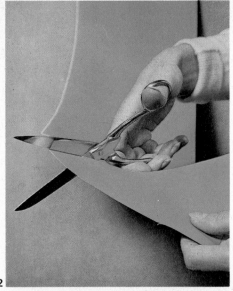

A motorist who wants to overtake on a busy road, prefers to do so in the shortest possible time to prevent a collision with traffic flowing in the other direction. At a moment like this, the motorist is not concerned at all with the efficiency of his engine, that is how much petrol it will burn in making this manoeuvre. All he cares about is whether or not the car has enough power to do it.

Power, like work and efficiency, has a precise mathematical definition. In particular, power is the amount of energy a machine consumes or generates in a unit time.

Imagine two children helping their father move books from the ground floor to the first floor. Each child can carry the same number of books, say 12. But John returns for another load every two minutes, while Mary returns for another load every four minutes. Thus, each child expends the same amount of energy per trip (the energy needed to carry up 12 books), but John is working twice as fast as Mary. Since John removes 12 books every two minutes, his average rate of working (his power) is six books a minute. Mary's average rate of working is only three books a minute.

In physics, energy is measured in joules, and time is usually measured in seconds. If a motor car expends 8,000 joules of energy in two seconds, what is its power? By definition, power is energy expended

1 The crowbar is a simple type of lever in everyday use. Here it is being used to open a case, but it could equally be used to lift a heavy object.
2 Scissors are an application of the principle of the lever. The arrangement of handles and blades makes it possible to apply a strong cutting force without much effort.
3 A can-opener is another form of the lever. The force exerted at the tip of the opener is many times the force which is applied to the handle of the can-opener.
4 Cog wheels, like these examples from an old water mill, transmit power by using the lever principle. In fact, the cog wheel lies at the basis of gearing and complex machinery.
5 A worker at the marble quarries in Carrara, Italy, driving in a bar to split open the block of marble. The bar will then be used to lever the blocks apart.

in unit time (one second), so the power is 8,000/2=4,000 joules per second. The phrase 'joules per second' is usually replaced by the single word 'watt' in honour of the British engineer James Watt, who perfected the steam engine. So an engine which generates 8,000 joules of energy in two seconds has a power of 4,000 watts.

It may be surprising to learn that one can measure the power of a petrol engine in watts. Watts are usually associated with electricity, but power is power, whether it comes from a petrol engine or an electric circuit. It is merely custom which restricts the unit 'watts' to use in electricity.

A much more common unit of power (in English-speaking countries) is 'horsepower'. One horsepower represents precisely what it says – the approximate power of a horse. More specifically, it is the expenditure of 550 foot-pounds of energy per second. Thus, an engine which produces 1,100 foot-pounds of energy in one second would have a power rating of 1,100/2=2 horsepower.

This rather odd unit has an interesting origin. When James Watt tried to sell his newly-perfected steam engines for use in British mines in the late 1700s, the mine owners wanted to know how many of their horses would be replaced by one engine. Watt spent a considerable time experimenting with horses, and found that on

the average a horse could do 550 foot-pounds of work per second. Thus, any machine which could do work at 550 foot-pounds per second was equivalent to one horse, or had a power rating of one horsepower.

It should be mentioned here that just as watts can measure engine power, so horsepower can measure the power of a light bulb. One horsepower equals 746 watts. By simple mathematics, an ordinary 150-watt light bulb has a power rating of just over one-fifth of a horsepower. Either term is quite acceptable, but do not be surprised if you get an odd look when asking for a 'one-fifth horsepower bulb' in an electrical supply store.

Machines are therefore devices for transmitting energy from one place to another; they make it possible to do jobs which otherwise could not be done; they are all inefficient, and the more powerful they are the faster they can do a job.

When these four points are clearly understood, machines (however complicated) lose some of their air of magic. But an understanding of the way in which machines operate can help us to master the increasingly complex modern world.

1 Bicycles, shown here in the World Professional Cycling Championship, at Heerlen, Holland, are machines for converting leg-power into rapid movement.
2 An inclined plane. Here, the work of the children in climbing the staircase is dissipated in a controlled way when they come to slide down the chute.
3 Levers again – this time the spanner. The force exerted at the nut by a spanner is much larger than the force applied to the handle by the operator.
4 Yet another form of the lever. The spade makes it possible to lift large amounts at a distance by exerting smaller forces. The worker's right hand is the fulcrum.

Help for the housewife

Technology has brought vast changes to the average home. In the future, capsule kitchens, mobile furniture, computers and photo-electric cells will all be part of the housewife's domain.

IN THIS CENTURY, science and technology have brought about a revolution to the home. But what of the future? What kind of homes will people with average incomes live in by the end of the century? Will the changes be as great as they were between 1900 and 1970? The answer is undoubtedly 'yes'. The household of today will be developed and many devices which are now regarded as curiosities, or are in the experimental stage, will become part of everyday domestic life. The housewife will have more leisure and will spend less time on household chores.

One example of this is the amount of time taken to cook a meal on a gas or electric stove. Conventional gas and electric ovens and grills cook the food by convection or radiation. The ordinary electric grill is mainly a radiator of heat, the heating element radiating the energy that does the cooking in the form of electromagnetic waves. When the current is switched on, the elements in the conventional electric stove or grill glow and emit visible light. But more important than the visible light is the infra-red radiation from the element. Although invisible to the human eye, infra-red radiation can be detected because of the heat it carries.

Concentrated radiation

Infra-red radiation is induced by vibrations of electrons, atoms and molecules. When these are suitably excited, the radiation travels at the speed of light and heats objects in its path by causing vibration of the electrons, atoms and molecules constituting the object being heated. Much of the heat from the elements in a conventional electric stove or grill is lost because the heat tends to disperse and only a relatively small proportion of it reaches the food being cooked. The infra-red grill concentrates the infra-red radiation so that the maximum amount reaches the food and the heat loss due to radiation is reduced to a minimum.

Convection heat loss can be eliminated by enclosing the element in a glass tube or bulb and so creating an infra-red lamp. To direct the infra-red radiation in the required direction, part of the inner surface of the tube or bulb is coated with a substance which reflects infra-red radiation and helps to beam it in one direction. Infra-red rays are exceptionally effective in their heating property because their energy is absorbed by objects to a much greater extent than is the energy of shorter wavelength radiation of visible light.

One of the advantages of infra-red radiation is that the speed with which it heats up an object depends to a major extent on the temperature difference between the emitter of the infra-red and the object absorbing the heat. With an infra-red

1 Nuclear energy for the home. This prototype device converts heat produced by the radioactive decay of a small amount of polonium-210 into electrical energy.

2 Cooking by infra-red radiation – microwave cooking – is a very speedy process. Within minutes large pieces of meat can be cooked from the inside out.

heater the temperature difference may be as high as 2,000 °C; the object under the radiation, therefore, warms up very rapidly.

In the conventional grill or oven, the heat from the element is conducted and convected through the food to its centre. With an infra-red grill, however, the radiation is able to penetrate throughout the meat or other food. Instead of the centre of the meat taking the longest time to cook, the centre may be cooked more quickly than the outside. This is because heat can escape from the outside, but not from the centre.

Amongst other applications of infra-red radiation which will become increasingly commonplace in the future are infra-red cabinets for tenderizing meat, for the quick drying of clothes after washing, for the quick thawing of frozen packaged-foods, and for the rapid but controlled heating of greenhouses.

There is little doubt that the home of the future will make increasing use of ultra-violet radiation – the range of electromagnetic radiations extending from the violet (short-wave) end of the spectrum to the beginning of the X-ray spectrum. Ultra-violet radiators consist of a special glass tube or bulb filled with mercury vapour and argon gas. The radiations emitted are invisible as the vibrations they produce are so rapid and the wavelengths so short that the human eye cannot detect them. Ultra-violet lamps can be used to produce a cold radiation which preserves foodstuffs. A tube six in. long can protect a larder shelf with an area of 12 sq. ft. Another application would be as a barrier against bacteria, viruses and moulds.

Many homes of the future will have airconditioning, and an ultra-violet lamp placed in the air ducts would protect the whole household against airborne disease. Tests have shown that 80 per cent of airborne viruses and bacteria can be destroyed by inserting a single ultra-violet lamp in the ducts of a heating or airconditioning system.

Applying the principle of photochromism to glass-making will eventually provide houses with windows that shut out glare on sunny days. *Photochromism* means change in colour through exposure to light. During the manufacture of the glass, tiny, light-sensitive crystals of silver hidide (a compound of silver and either chlorine, fluorine, iodine or bromine) are added. When light strikes the window, the silver compound breaks up into the silver and the other constituent, so causing the glass to darken. According to the intensity of the light, the glass can darken until only 1 per cent of the light striking it penetrates. As the light intensity decreases, the silver and other elements rejoin, so clearing the glass and allowing more light through. The speed and intensity of the darkening and brightening of the light can be controlled from a fraction of a second to several minutes by varying the proportion of silver to the other element of the compound. Optical glass can be treated by the photochromism technique so enabling spectacles to become sunglasses in strong light.

What is claimed to be the greatest advance in room-lighting since the invention of the gas-filled electric bulb is now being developed and may eventually displace today's conventional methods of illuminating the house. The new lighting element consists of a flexible ribbon made up of a sandwich of a thin strip of aluminium foil, a layer of phosphorescent material, and a transparent coating of a substance able to conduct electricity. When current is applied to the aluminium foil and the coating, the material between them glows and emits a soft, clear light. The ribbon is one-sixteenth of an inch thick and has been made in widths of up to 12 in. and lengths of up to 150 ft. It can be bent, coiled, twisted and formed into any shape, and it does not generate any heat.

Lengths of the ribbon have been tested to give constant light for 12,000 hours before burning out. This means that a ribbon lamp used six hours a day would last for two years. One probable development of the ribbon lamp is to make it in sheet form for fixing to walls and ceilings.

As a large proportion of the energy going into an electric lamp is dissipated in the form of heat, scientists have been seeking ways to reduce this wastage. A major step towards this has been made by the development of a new type of gas-discharge lamp which will, in time, find its way into the home. This lamp consists

of a ceramic tube made from pure aluminium oxide pressed from a fine powder into crystalline solid. The tube is filled with sodium vapour through which a high-intensity electric current is discharged. Conventional sodium-vapour gas-discharge lamps emit a yellowish-orange light but the light of the new lamp is a clear white. This is because the sodium is heated to such a high temperature that it reverses its range in the light spectrum. In other words, the heat wasted in the ordinary electric lamp is utilized to heat the gas in the ceramic tube. As yet, the ceramic-tube lamp averages only 6,000 hours of lighting before burning out. This is considerably better than the life of 750–1,200 hours for the conventional incandescent filament lamp, but compares unfavourably with the mercury-vapour

1 An automated living area embodies many revolutionary ideas: a chair that moves on a cushion of air, inflatable furniture and a multi-purpose robot.
2 This kitchen of the future is designed to give maximum flexibility. The circular worktop with sink, cooking and storage units is motorized to revolve through 360°.
3 An innovation in central heating is a silicated carbon paint which, when connected to a low-voltage electricity supply, produces heat. The paint is sprayed on to the walls.
4 Computers in the home will take away many of the problems of running a house – preparing shopping lists, making orders from supermarkets and coping with household finance.
5 The glass in the windows of this London building has been treated during manufacture to screen 20 per cent of light and 60 per cent of heat from passing through.

4

5

lamp's life of 16,000 hours.

At an International Television Symposium in 1969, electronic engineers delved into the future to forecast probable developments of domestic television, particularly the types of receivers that will be in use. According to the experts, the trend will be towards small and very compact receivers, made possible through the greater use of micro-circuitry, transistors and greatly improved screens.

Instead of looking at the present large and cumbersome tube, programmes will appear on a thin, electro-luminescent panel which can be cut to any desired size. This, in conjunction with miniaturized printed circuits, will make it possible to have viewing screens in several different rooms of the house which all take the programme from a single, central receiver. That missing a television programme will

become a thing of the past is indicated by experiments now being made with a device for attaching to a television receiver. This will record on tape all the vision and sound of a programme. The tape with the sound and vision tracks is then put into a recorder which plays back the sound and projects the picture on to a screen.

Closed-circuit television, which is at present limited to large-scale industrial and hospital applications, will eventually be miniaturized for use in the home. This will enable a mother working in her kitchen or relaxing in her sitting room to keep a close watch on her children in the nursery or while they are playing in the garden.

The photo-electric cell, which comes into action when a beam of light shining on it is interrupted, promises to have many applications in the home. Linked to suitable relays, it will open doors; enable the driver of a car to open gates and the doors of his garage without leaving his seat; give instant warning of an intruder breaking into the house through a door or window; and ring a warning bell if a child falls out of bed.

In the United States experiments are being carried out which promise to revolutionize the whole concept of the home telephone. For example, a housewife out shopping will be able to telephone the kettle in her kitchen to boil water for a cup of tea when she gets back. Again, if a family is out visiting friends or at a theatre and a telephone call is put through to the empty house, the call will be automatically transferred to the nearest telephone wherever the family happens to be. This is done by electronic switchboards at the telephone exchange.

The instructions which an electronic switchboard needs to transfer calls and perform services, such as ordering a kettle to boil, are punched on thin aluminium sheets which are inserted in the switch controlling the subscriber's number. For example, one of the punched notes on a subscriber's card contains instructions for the kettle. The subscriber dials her home number followed by a code number. When the home telephone rings, even if no one answers it, the dialling of the code number operates a relay connected to the power switch on an electric kettle, so turning on the current. There is no risk of the water boiling away as a thermostat automatically cuts off the electric supply. In the same way, an electric oven can be connected to the telephone exchange, and by ringing the number followed by an appropriate code number the dinner starts cooking.

Even more remarkable results can be achieved by linking an electronic telephone exchange to a computer. A housewife, whose card at the exchange has a coded shopping list, can telephone a supermarket. The supermarket's telephone is linked to a computer which prints her order; an assistant collects the items she has ordered and parcels them for her to take away.

With electronic switching it will not even be necessary always to dial the number required for ordinary calls. Numbers frequently used can be punched on plastic cards, one card for each number. To telephone the number, the appropriate card is put in a slot on the telephone and the caller is instantly connected to the number required. An electronic switching and telephone exchange system is already

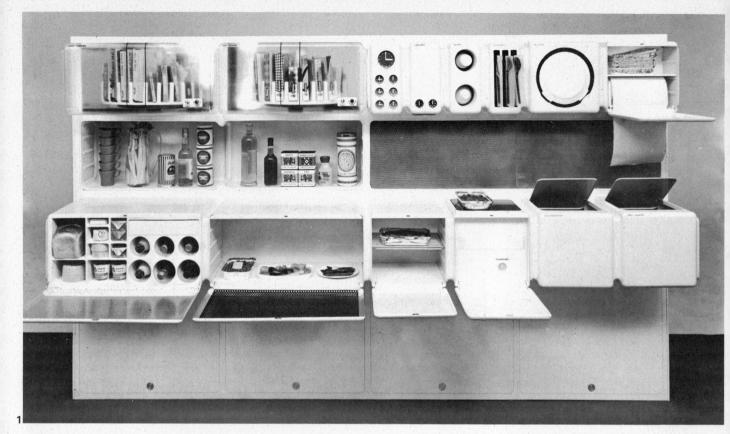

on trial at Syracuse, in the United States, and serves 200 private and business telephone subscribers.

Miniaturized computers will have their place in the home of tomorrow. Suitably programmed, the miniature computer will ease the task of the head of the household making out his income-tax return, while the housewife will use the computer's memory to store such information as cooking recipes and knitting patterns.

Miniature nuclear reactors

As yet atomic power has made little direct impact on the home except for the electric power supplied from nuclear generating stations. But the successful use of a miniature reactor in space satellites holds promise of an atomic power-plant in the house. Called SNAP, from the initials of its name, System for Auxiliary Nuclear Power, the pocket reactor used in satellites weighs $4\frac{1}{2}$ lb. It produces a continuous supply of power for five years on one load of fuel. The fuel consists of a small pellet of plutonium which, as it decays, releases heat. The heat is picked up by a thermocouple which induces a direct electric current.

Although the current is very small it can be stepped up by a small transformer. The ultimate current obtained is equivalent to that from five tons of storage batteries used on motor-cars. At present, a SNAP generator costs £500,000, but it has been estimated that mass producing the midget power-plants could reduce the cost to £100. Nuclear engineers are now experimenting with a more sophisticated SNAP capable of producing 500 watts of power for three years on a single charge of fuel. Amongst the advantages of SNAP are that it has no moving parts, so reducing maintenance to a minimum, and the relative cheapness of the fuel, as the pluto-

1 The capsule kitchen is completely self-contained and can be put anywhere in the house. There is no need for a separate room or for the cook to be isolated from her guests.

2 'Intercom' systems in the home enable parents to keep a constant check on their children. They can also 'baby-sit' for other parents connected to the network.

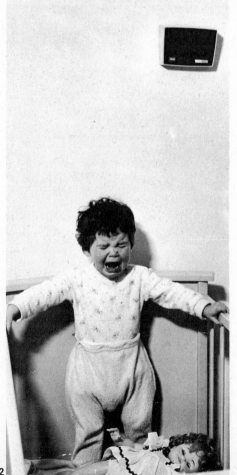

nium pellets are extracted from waste material left by conventional nuclear power stations.

By the end of the century, man-made materials such as plastic, stainless steel, glass and anodized aluminium will be more widely used in the structure of the home. Coloured plastic will replace many fixtures now made of wood. Doors, window-frames, floor skirting and picture rails will not require repainting; if a new colour scheme is wanted, plastic skins in any colour can be applied like a paint and will harden in a few minutes. Stainless steel and anodized aluminium fittings will not tarnish, while toughened-glass sheets will provide easily-cleaned work tables.

Although silverware has been prized for its elegance, strength and durability, most housewives regard their silver with mixed feelings because of the regular polishing it needs. But silver polishing will become a thing of the past. This will be achieved by rhodium-plating. Rhodium is one of the platinum group of precious metals and is exceptionally resistant to chemical action and to atmospheric corrosion. Silverware plated with rhodium has a hard, non-tarnish and permanent finish with all the appearance of silver plate. The only attention needed to retain the brilliant finish is occasional washing in warm, soapy water.

Oven-cleaning, the housewife's most unpopular chore, is now becoming a simple matter. A new type of oven on the market is coated inside with a special surface enamel. To clean the oven, the door is shut and the heat turned full on. In little more than a minute the grease and other dirt is reduced to a fine ash which can be brushed away. Experiments are also being made with an interior coating which reacts to oxygen and destroys grease splashes as they are made.

Extensions of the human eye

Few branches of physical science are as useful in everyday life as optics. Not only is it the basis of spectacles, but it is a fundamental part of photography, television and the cinema.

NEARLY EVERYONE at one time or another has wished that the days were longer, especially when lolling on some sun-drenched beach during summer holidays. This is a rather selfish wish, however. The days already are longer, due to a physical phenomenon called *refraction of light*.

During most of its journey to the Earth, sunlight travels through the vacuum of space, and so travels in straight lines. But when it approaches the Earth, it is confronted with the Earth's atmosphere, which causes it to *refract* (bend). Since the air is denser near the ground, the sun's rays proceed from empty space through gradually denser layers of air to the ground. Particularly when the sun is low in the sky, the rays meet these layers at almost glancing incidence, and are then bent through substantial angles. The rays therefore arrive at the ground from a direction that differs from the true direction to the sun.

The sun is therefore not seen where it actually is, but where the direction of the arriving ray seems to indicate. In the morning, then, the sun is 'seen' breaking the horizon several minutes before it actually does, and in the evening it is 'seen' lingering on the horizon several minutes after it has actually set.

Another more familiar example of refraction can be had by placing a spoon into a drinking glass half-filled with water. The spoon will appear to be bent, but of course it isn't. What is bent is the light rays from the spoon as they travel from the water into the air and then into the eye of the viewer.

Light travels fast through the vacuum of space (low optical density), but is slightly impeded by the Earth's atmosphere, so it slows down a fraction and bends. At the surface of the Earth, light

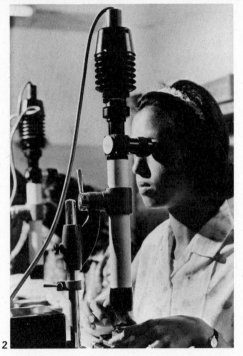

travels faster through air than, say, water. Thus, water is more optically dense than air, and light will refract in passing from one medium to the other. This accounts for the apparent bending of the spoon in the drinking glass.

It is quite easy to determine the direction a light ray will bend from the Fundamental Law of Refraction: a ray of light passing from a medium of low optical density to one of high optical density will bend *towards* the normal (perpendicular), and passing from a medium of high optical density to one of low optical density will bend away from the normal.

For instance, in the case of light passing through a glass prism, the imagi-

1 Enormous lenses like this one are similar in design to a telescope. They enable detailed photographs to be taken at long distances. They are classed according to focal length.
2 Camera lenses must be carefully checked to ensure that the image formed by the lens falls exactly on the film plane. The instrument used for this is a collimator.

nary line perpendicular to the surface is called the normal (see diagram 3 overleaf). The angle between the incoming (*incident*) ray and the normal is the *angle of incidence*. Because glass is more optically dense than air, the light ray will refract towards the normal as it enters the prism, forming the *angle of refraction*, the angle between the refracted ray and the normal. As it passes out of the prism on the other side, the light ray goes from optically dense glass to less optically dense air, so it bends away from the normal.

In general, the larger the angle of incidence, the greater the degree of bending. A light ray entering the prism at an angle of incidence of 40 degrees will bend much more than a light ray entering at 20 degrees. At normal incidence (zero angle of incidence) there is no bending at all. But there is no obvious relationship between the size of the angle of incidence and the angle of refraction. Knowing the angle of incidence is 20 degrees implies nothing about the number of degrees in the angle of refraction. However, according to Snell's Law, the ratio of the *sine* of the angle of incidence and the sine of the angle of refraction is a constant, called the *index of refraction*.

For example, the index of refraction between air and water is 1·333. Suppose a light ray from the air should enter the water with an angle of incidence of 30 degrees. What is the angle of refraction?

From Snell's Law:

$$\text{Index} = \frac{\sin i}{\sin r} = 1 \cdot 333,$$

where i stands for angle of incidence and r stands for angle of refraction. In this example, i is 30 degrees. A table of trigeometric functions gives sine $30° = 0\cdot500$, so:

$$\frac{\sin 30°}{\sin r} = \frac{0\cdot500}{\sin r} = 1\cdot333.$$

Solving the equations:

$$\sin r = \frac{0\cdot500}{1\cdot333} = 0\cdot375.$$

The table of trigonometric functions shows that the angle whose sine is $0\cdot375$ is 22 degrees.

The index of refraction may also be interpreted as the ratio of the velocity of light in a vacuum (or air) which differs little from vacuum to its velocity in the refracting substance. Thus, since light travels at 186,000 miles per second in a vacuum, its velocity in water may be found from the equation:

$$\text{Index} = \frac{c}{vw} = \frac{186,000}{vw} = 1\cdot333,$$

where c is the velocity of light in a vacuum and vw is the velocity of light in water. Solving the equation gives $vw = 139,548$ miles per second.

Total internal reflection

The fact that light bends away from the normal on passing from high optical density to low optical density leads to a rather interesting phenomenon called *total internal reflection*. As the angle of incidence of a light ray travelling from, say, water to air, increases, so does the angle of refraction. Eventually, the angle of refraction becomes so large that the ray just skims over the top of the water (angle $r = 90$ degrees). If the angle of incidence is increased still further, the light ray bounces directly back into the water by reflection at the surface, and does not enter the air at all.

Total internal reflection can be easily demonstrated. Fill a wide-mouth glass with water and wrap your fingers round the glass. Now look down through the top of the water. You will not be able to see your fingers, because all light rays coming from them are reflected back into the water. Now, look up into the water from the bottom of the glass. Your fingers will be seen clearly at the water's under surface, just as if they were being reflected in a mirror.

The phenomenon of total internal reflection finds ready application in optical instruments such as the periscope, prism binoculars and the single-lens reflex camera. In a periscope, a light ray at the top enters the tube into a right-angled prism. It is then reflected straight downwards to the bottom of the tube, where it enters a second prism and is reflected into the eye of the viewer. A similar sequence of events happens in prism binoculars. In the single-lens reflex camera, light enters through the lens and is reflected by a mirror straight up into a

pentaprism (five-sided prism) which in turn reflects the ray round until it enters the eye of the photographer. Thus, the photographer sees in the viewfinder precisely what passes through the lens and will register on the film. By this means, composing the picture is greatly facilitated. What he sees is exactly what he will get on the film.

However useful, the mirror and pentaprism in cameras are only convenient accessories. The real heart of the camera is the lens, because that is what forms the image the film records. A good camera lens, or any other good lens for that matter, is often quite expensive, because a really good lens is not easy to make. Ideally for a *converging* lens, every ray of light that emanates from a given point

on a distant object should be refracted towards each other just enough as they pass through the lens so that they all cross one another at precisely the same spot on the other side. This cross-over point lies in the so-called *focal plane* and is the place where a sharp, clear image is formed. This double meaning for image can cause trouble, so throughout this discussion it is important to recognize when 'image' means focal plane and when it simply means any light picture, clear or blurred.

Knowing where a sharp image is going to be produced is of obvious importance to the designers of cameras, as well as designers of other types of optical instruments. Since all rays from a given point cross at the same place, two rays are sufficient to 'find the image'.

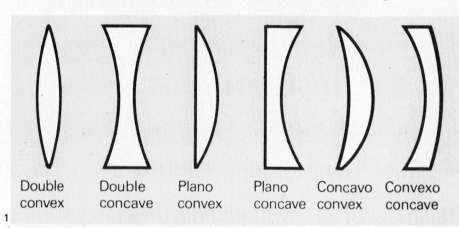

Double convex Double concave Plano convex Plano concave Concavo convex Convexo concave

1

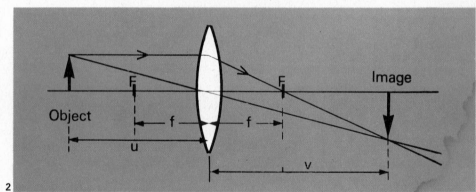

Object F f F f Image u v

2

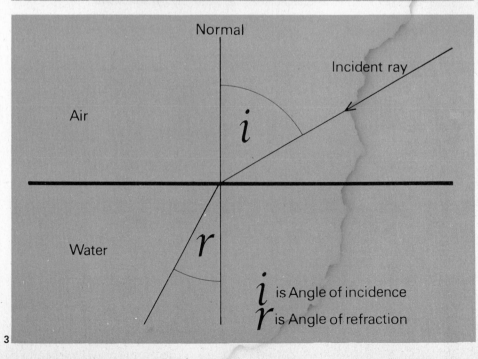

Normal
Air
Incident ray
i
Water
r
i is Angle of incidence
r is Angle of refraction

3

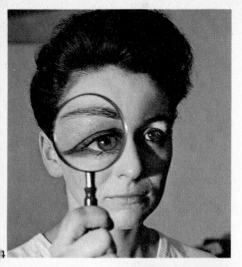

In the diagram, the point in the middle of the lens is the *optical centre* and has the special property that rays pass through it undeviated (without bending). The *principal axis* is a line through the optical centre and perpendicular to the faces of the lens. The point on the other side of the lens marked *principal focus*, a special place on each side of the lens. through which all light rays parallel to the principal axis will pass.

Suppose an object is placed 4 cm away from a lens with a *focal length* (distance from the lens to the focus) of 3 cm. Find the image. First, from any point on the object, draw a ray through the optical centre. It will pass straight through without bending. Next, from exactly the same point, draw a ray parallel to the

principal axis.

At the lens, bend the ray so that it passes through the principal focus, and continue until it crosses the first ray. Repeat the process with another point on the object until two cross-over points are obtained. The image (focal plane) is located on the line joining the two cross-over points, in this case 12 cm from the lens.

The focal plane may also be located mathematically from the lens maker's formula:

$$\frac{1}{f} = \frac{1}{u} + \frac{1}{v}$$

where f is the focal length, u is the distance of the object from the lens, and v is the distance of the image from the lens. In this example,

$$\frac{1}{3} = \frac{1}{4} + \frac{1}{v}.$$

Solving the equation gives $v = 12$ cm, i.e. the image (focal plane) is 12 cm from the lens. If a piece of film inside a camera were placed 12 cm from the lens, one could get a photograph that is 'in focus'. Similarly, a screen placed 12 cm from the lens would show up a sharp image.

It will be noted from the diagram that the image is inverted (upside down) and magnified. The inversion is a direct result of the way the image is formed. Light rays coming from the top of the object are refracted downwards so they form the

1 Different types of lenses are used in optical equipment. Those shown are the most common simple types.
2 Image distance, object distance and the power of the lens are related mathematically. A diagram showing the path of a light ray through a lens is a useful aid to calculations.
3 When light goes from one medium to another (from air to water, for example) the rays are bent (refracted) as shown. It is this property which is the basis of all lenses.
4 A reading glass or 'magnifying glass' is the commonest lens in normal use. As can be seen, its function is to produce a large image of a close object.
5 Astronomical telescopes are extremely powerful instruments with large object lenses to collect as much light as possible from faint, distant heavenly bodies. This instrument is at the Royal Observatory, Hurstmonceaux, England.
6 Refraction of light makes a spoon standing in a glass of water appear to be bent.
7 At sunset, the sun appears flattened on the bottom edge due to refraction by the atmosphere.

bottom of the image. Conversely, light rays from the bottom of the object are refracted upwards so they form the top of the 'image'.

Magnification depends on the location of the focal planes. The further the image from the lens, the larger it is. More precisely, the magnification of the image is the same as the ratio of the image distance to the object distance. In our example the image is 12 cm from the lens and the object is 3 cm from the lens, so the image is $\frac{12}{3}=4$ times as large as the object. When the image distance and the object distance are equal, the image and the object are the same size, so the magnification is 1. Should the image distance be less than the object distance, then the image will be smaller than the object and the magnification will consequently be less than 1.

In general, the closer the object to the lens, the further away the image, so the greater the magnification. However, when the object is placed so that its distance from the lens is less than the focal length, i.e. when it is 'inside the focus', focal plane seems to disappear altogether. No matter where a screen is put, the image is always unclear and indistinct. This is because when the object is inside the focus, the ray through the optic centre and the ray through the focus *diverge* and never cross, so no focal plane can be formed.

The focal plane is not lost completely, however. Remember that the brain assumes that light always travels in straight lines, so if the rays do not cross on the side of the lens where the screen is, the brain assumes that they cross on the other side of the lens where the object is. Since the rays do not really cross, this image is a figment of the imagination and is thus called a *virtual* image to distinguish it from a *real* image which can be projected on to a screen.

Like the converging lens, the diverging lens has an optical centre and principal axis. But since it bends rays away from the principal axis, its two principal foci are virtual, being the place where all rays parallel to the principal axis would cross if they were drawn back through the lens after refracting.

Correcting eye-sight

The fact that a concave lens forms only virtual images rather limits its value when used by itself. But in combination with other lenses, it has numerous applications, not the least of which is correcting the eye defect *myopia,* or short-sightedness. In this case, the second lens is the convex lens of the eye itself. Short-sightedness is often the result of an eye lens which refracts light rather more than it should, so the focal plane is formed in front of the light-sensitive *retina* which is situated at the back of the eye and the brain receives a fuzzy image. A properly prescribed concave lens can cause the incoming light rays to diverge just enough

1 Defective eyesight is very often due to malformation of the eye. An optician must measure the characteristics of the eye's light system before he can prescribe the necessary corrective lenses.
2 Microscopes are designed to produce an image of objects which are close to the objective lens, such as this shark's jaw.

so that when the lens of the eye over-refracts, the focal plane is formed directly on the retina, where it belongs

In a somewhat similar manner, if light first passes through a convex (converging) lens and then a concave (diverging) lens, a real image can be obtained which is larger than it would have been using a convex lens alone. This is the principle of the telephoto lens of a camera.

Many other optical instruments also depend on a combination of lenses, though not always a convex plus a concave. The compound microscope uses two convex lenses arranged so that the image (focal plane) formed by the first lens falls 'inside the focus' of the second lens. The image of the first lens acts as the 'object' of the second lens, and produces a virtual image which is magnified. Of course, the image of the first lens is not really an 'object' for the second lens; it is only the place where the light rays coming through the first lens cross to form the focal plane. But mathematically and diagrammatically, the virtual image formed by the second lens is precisely where it would be were the image of the first lens a solid chunk of matter.

Really fine optical instruments seldom use just two lenses, because lenses are subject to numerous types of defects. One of the most common is *spherical aberration*. It is almost impossible to grind a single lens which will refract each and every ray passing through it the exact proper amount. In particular, the rays parallel to the principal axis do not all pass through the principal focus, as desired, but cut the principal axis slightly in front or behind the focus.

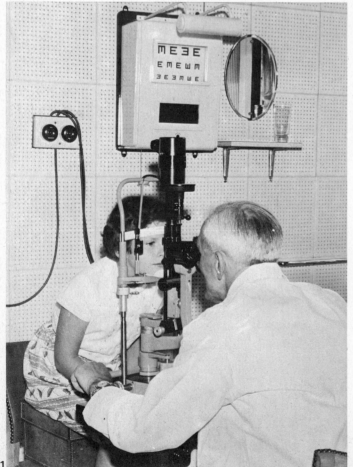

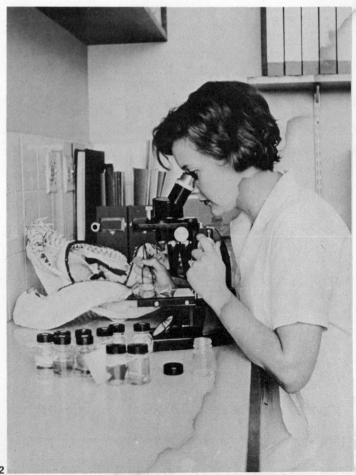

The latent image

A photographer can freeze a moment in time by using the energy of light to bring about photo-chemical reactions. These reactions must be processed before the original light pattern can be produced.

In his darkroom, a photographer of the 1870s develops a plate made of a glass coated with silver salt-gelatine emulsion, on which the light image was recorded.

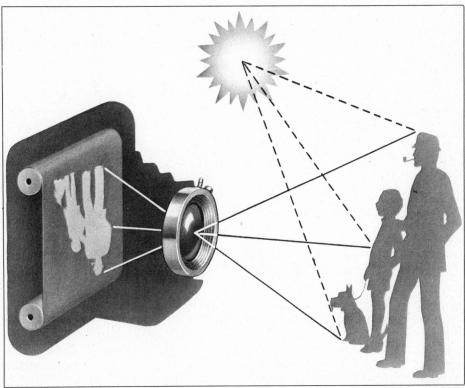

Light striking the man, boy and dog reflects into the lens of the camera. The lens focuses the light and produces an upside-down image of the group on the exposed area of film.

PHOTOGRAPHY AIMS to capture reality, to freeze light into permanence – indeed the word itself means writing with light. To record what he sees, the photographer relies on a thin layer of light-sensitive chemicals that can be processed to make the effects of the light visible and long-lasting. His camera is a light-proof box with a lens which throws an image on to a light-sensitive film. 'Pressing the button' starts a chain of chemical reactions and processes that end with a photograph.

The lens forms the image in the camera by bending the light rays striking it from the outside world. Normally, light rays travel in straight lines, but when they pass through glass they bend. The surfaces of the camera lens are curved so that they concentrate or *focus* all the light rays from the subject to a sharp point in the image. At the centre of the lens, the light passes straight through while rays from the top and bottom of the subject bend and cross over, producing an upside-down image at the back of the camera.

In the simplest cameras, the lenses are made from a single piece of glass and the image is unavoidably fuzzy because light rays near the edge of the lens have to bend so sharply that they cannot come to a clear focus. More expensive lenses contain several components that compensate both

for this defect and for the effects of light of different colours. The lens's components also bear an anti-reflecting coating that stops stray light from *fogging* the film. Because a complex lens can be made wider, without affecting the quality of the image, it gathers more light, and the *exposure,* the time during which light passes through the lens to reach the film, can be made shorter.

F-numbers

To control the amount of light that passes through the lens, the photographer varies the lens's area or *aperture* by opening or closing a circular *iris* or *diaphragm* made of overlapping metal leaves. This changes the brightness of the image. The different apertures, called *f-numbers,* are calculated so that moving from one to the next doubles the aperture and so the brightness.

The photographer can also vary the speed of the *shutter.* This may be a diaphragm within the lens which flashes open when the button is pressed, or it may be a slit in a blind which travels across the camera as near the film as possible. By altering the combination of aperture and shutter speed, the amount of light reaching the film can be controlled. In bright light, the aperture can be reduced and an advantage gained because the lens gives a sharper focus; in dim light the time the shutter is open can be lengthened.

The film that records the image consists of a plastic base that is coated with a light-sensitive layer and backed with a

dye that absorbs stray light. The light-sensitive layer, the *emulsion,* contains tiny crystals of *silver bromide* with some *silver iodide,* embedded in *gelatine.* A modern film contains many thousand million crystals to each square inch of film.

The emulsion is made by adding a solution of silver nitrate to a solution of potassium or sodium bromide in gelatine. This produces grains of silver bromide which cannot settle to the bottom because of the firm-setting gelatine. The warm emulsion is spread over the transparent celluloid base and, as it cools, hardens into a thin layer. The film can then be rolled in light-proof paper or a cassette so that the photographer can put it into the camera in daylight.

When the shutter clicks, light reaches the emulsion for a fraction of a second. The light energy causes free silver atoms in the emulsion to be released from the silver bromide grains. In the brighter parts of the image, enough free silver forms to make minute specks of metallic silver on the surface of the grains. In the dimmer areas, the light energy releases so few silver atoms that they cannot combine into specks. At this point, the film – bearing its *latent image* – must be developed.

To develop or process a film it must be

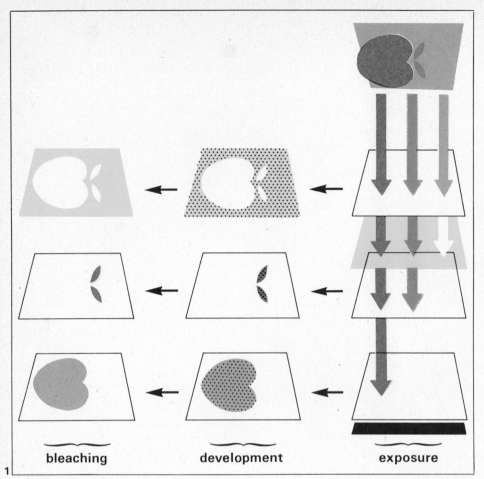

bleaching   development   exposure

1

1 A colour film has three layers of emulsion, the first records blue, a yellow filter then cuts out excess blue light, the second records green and the third, red. Mounted on a plastic base, a backing absorbs excess light.
2 A colour film after processing. When the film is developed, a yellow dye covers the image made by blue light, magenta dye that made by green light and a cyan dye that made by red light. Because each dye holds back light of its complementary colour, the final positive contains the original colours of the subject.

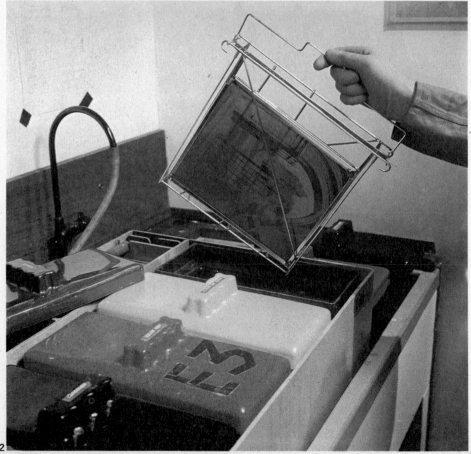

2

submerged in a solution containing a *reducing agent*. All reducing agents convert bromide to metallic silver but some, such as *hydroquinone* and *metol,* act very much more quickly on grains that already contain a small amount of silver: the silver speck speeds up or *catalyses* the reaction. As the reaction continues, the new silver formed increases the effect still further. So the developer converts to silver only those grains in which light energy has already released some metallic specks; the other, unexposed grains are unchanged. The developer solution also contains chemicals to increase and control the rate of the basic reaction.

All or nothing

Development is an all or nothing process which amplifies the minute effects of the light: each grain either turns completely to silver or it remains unaffected. The amount of light energy to trigger off a grain remains the same whether the grain is large or small. If the emulsion contains few but large grains, a smaller amount of light energy can affect a greater proportion of them, although the end result will be coarser.

On the other hand a slow emulsion, containing small grains, needs a long exposure to collect enough light to trigger sufficient numbers of grains to release silver. A fast film – to be used when the light is dim – therefore consists of large grains of crystals, and a slow film – needing more light – contains many more small grains. The slow film gives a finer end result.

To prevent changes when the developed film is taken into the light, the remaining silver bromide must be removed to leave only the metallic silver: in other words, the film must be *fixed*. Silver bromide is insoluble in water. But in a fixing solution of *sodium thiosulphate* (still known as *hypo* from the original name, *sodium hyposulphite*) it forms soluble silver thiosulphates that can be leached from the emulsion. Using an acid fixing solution also neutralizes the alkaline developer and stops further development. Processing the film, which is done in a darkroom, or a light-tight tank, at a temperature around 20 °C., usually takes about ten minutes in the developer, two or three minutes in a fast-acting fixer and up to half an hour washing in water. But by incorporating capsules of the chemicals into the film itself and running the stages into each other, Polaroid Land cameras can deliver a picture within seconds of taking it.

The negative is the half-way point. The finely divided silver formed during development is jet black and where the image was brightest and most silver had been formed, the negative is darkest; where the image was dark, the unchanged silver bromide is washed away leaving the negative transparent. White becomes black and the negative shows the original scene reversed. To produce a photograph, the negative must be printed.

By holding the negative against a sheet of paper coated with a light-sensitive emulsion, and exposing it to light, a *contact print* the same size as the negative

can be made. If the negative is too small to give a reasonably sized print, it can be enlarged. In the enlarger, a strong light is shone through the negative and a lens on to a sheet of printing paper. Because of their fine structure slow films give better enlargements.

For printing, as the exposing light is so bright, the emulsion can be less sensitive than that used in a camera: silver chloride may be used for contact printing and a mixture of chloride and bromide, or bromide alone, for enlarging. If these emulsions were used as film the exposure time would be far too long.

Washing

Exposing the paper produces a latent image in the same way as an image is produced on a film. The development process (reducing agent followed by fixing bath and washing) is the same, too; although the washing must last longer as the paper base soaks up more of the chemicals. Because the paper turns darkest where the negative is transparent and light shines through, the photograph reverses the negative and shows the original scene in black and white.

The black-and-white photograph matches the brightness of the original view; colour pictures, using a more complicated system which still depends on the light-sensitivity of silver bromide, match the colour as well. Virtually any colour

can be made out of a mixture of the three primary colours – red, green and blue. Between them, these wide bands of colour contain nearly all the colours of the visible spectrum. Colour photographs record the red, green and blue constituents of the original light separately and the viewer's eye recombines them.

Colour film contains three separate layers of emulsion, instead of the single layer of black-and-white: each records a different component of the light. The top layer, the layer the light reaches first, is made of ordinary silver bromide emulsion. This is sensitive to blue light and records *blue*. The light then passes through a layer of yellow gelatine which cuts out all the remaining blue light. Below the gelatine filter is an *orthochromatic* emulsion; dyes make the bromide sensitive to green as well as blue light. This layer records green. At the bottom, is a *panchromatic* emulsion, which is especially sensitive to red light and records red. After the picture has been taken, each layer contains a latent image corresponding to the distribution of the colour it records in the original view.

The latent image can be developed to give a colour negative, which can then be printed to give a colour photograph; or a *reversal* process can be used – this first forms a negative then converts the same emulsion to a positive to give a *transparency* or *slide* that can be projected.

To make the transparency, the film is

1 The enlarger enables the photographer to make a black-and-white print that is larger than the original negative. Light projected through the negative throws a magnified image on to light-sensitive printing paper.

2 Rolls of printing paper and developed colour negatives are fed into this machine which carries out the whole printing process automatically.

3 A photographer can vary what the final print looks like by exposing the printing paper to more or less light. As in developing a film he must fix and wash the print.

4 The negative shows everything in reverse – dark areas are light and light dark. During developing a negative is 'fixed' to prevent it reacting further to light when taken out of the darkroom.

5 The negative is the half-way point. To make it a positive it must be printed. This process entails using paper containing a light-sensitive emulsion.

1 One purpose of photography is to make permanent records of an object or event. At a fashion show in Japan photographers use electronic flash units to produce extra light.
2 William Fox Talbot, who took this photograph in 1844, was the first man to invent negative-positive printing. Until then cameras produced positive images and no prints could be made.
3 'Immediate' pictures can now be taken using a Polaroid Land Camera. After the shutter has clicked, developing and printing take place within the camera in about ten seconds.

first developed normally: in the bright parts of the image complete grains of silver bromide are converted to silver. Then a flash of bright white light sensitizes all the remaining silver bromide in each layer – this gives the equivalent of a positive latent image. This image is developed with *paraphenylenediamine* or p.p.d. developer. In each layer, most silver is now formed where little light of the corresponding colour fell. In these areas large quantities of the p.p.d. developer are used, and the resulting chemicals react with *couplers,* compounds already dispersed in the emulsions, to give dyes – in the red layer, a *cyan* dye that absorbs red light and transmits blue and green; in the green layer, a *magenta* dye that absorbs green; and in the blue layer, a *yellow* dye. At this stage the film is completely black and all the silver, and the gelatine yellow-filter layer, must be dissolved away with a solution of *potassium ferricyanide* and hypo. Then all that visibly remains, in the red recording layer for example, is the cyan dye, and most has formed in the areas where the red light of the original image was weakest. When the slide is now projected, little red light is passed by these areas. The final picture on the screen, is made up of the red light, passed by the red layer, green light from the green layer and blue from the blue layer.

To develop a colour negative film, p.p.d. is again used and the products again react with couplers in the emulsion layers. The yellow-filter layer, silver and undeveloped silver bromide are then all removed at once, to leave a dye image which is negative and in complementary colours – a red wall appears green. Most colour negatives have an orange stain all over which comes from unused but coloured couplers. The colour compensates for imperfect dyes – cyan dye absorbs green and blue as well as red light – and after correction in the printing stage gives a better result.

'White light'

The negative is enlarged on to paper coated with a colour emulsion. The layers can be exposed individually through filters which pass red, green and blue light or all at once in the 'white light' method by filtering the enlarger light. The paper can then be developed in the same way as the negative to give a colour print, a full record of the original.

The light spectrum stretches beyond the colours the eye can see and specially treated emulsions detect radiation and record images in both longer and shorter wavelengths than visible light. The silver-bromide link is so delicately balanced and the development process such a strong amplifier of tiny chemical changes that an emulsion can even show the track of a tiny, energetic atomic particle or cosmic ray.

Infra-red 'heat' rays lie beyond the red end of the spectrum. They affect a film in just the same way as visible light – stripping silver from bromine to give a latent image which can be developed. But the long wavelengths are scattered less by dust in the atmosphere and the infra-red photograph shows better detail at greater distances and under conditions of mist and haze. Photographs can be taken in the 'dark', the subject being unaware that he

has been photographed because the eye cannot see infra-red rays. A man hidden in bushes will show up on infra-red film because his warm body gives off heat rays.

Ultraviolet rays are at the other extreme. These rays of short wavelengths are very energetic and all films react to ultraviolet rays. Because of their penetration powers ultraviolet rays are often used in photography to detect forgeries: this they do by revealing traces of writing that are concealed from the naked eye as when cheques have been altered. X-rays are even shorter in wavelength than ultra-violet – and their penetration powers are even greater. X-ray photographs are shadow pictures: a beam of X-rays passes through the object, which absorbs varying amounts depending on its thickness and the material it is made from, to cast a shadow on the film. Developing the film shows the internal structure. Thus in X-rays of human beings, bones absorb more X-rays than flesh, and show up as deeper shadows.

Cosmic rays, with their still higher energy, can also be detected by photographic emulsion. The energetic particles leave a trail of silver behind them in the emulsion.

Photography relies on the effects light has on silver compounds. The silver plate daguerreotypes of the nineteenth century and the modern colour transparencies both depend on the minute change that light produces and development amplifies.

Used to extend and augment visual observations, photography has an enormous range of applications in all the branches of science and technology, including medicine, botany, astronomy, metallurgy, forensic science and aerial surveying. Events and reactions too fast or too slow for the naked eye to see can be permanently recorded. Objects too small or too distant can be photographed through microscopes or telescopes and the detailed results studied.

Putting ink on paper

The purpose of all printing, from colour photographs in fine art books to cheap newspapers, is to put ink on paper. To achieve this, printing has developed into a highly technical industry.

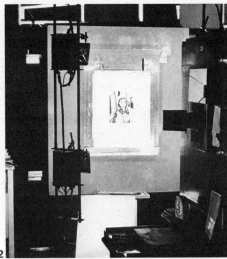

1 Copy typed on a Monotype keyboard is translated into punched tape instructions. These are then fed into a caster which moulds individual letters from molten metal.
2 The contrast of tone in a photograph is captured in printing by making a half-tone photo-engraving. Here a process camera is used to produce relief printing plates.
3 Chemically treated wood pulp is spread on a moving belt and drained of water. Heavy rollers then compress and dry the resulting paper which is wound into large rolls.

AN AUTHOR typing a novel or an artist making a drawing produces a single original, available only to a few, and easily lost or destroyed. Printing multiplies that original. Words, pictures, instructions, information and stories can be reproduced millions of times over.

All printing processes – of which there are three main methods – aim to put ink on to paper. In letterpress or *relief* printing – the first to be invented and still the most widely used – the ink is carried by a raised image; lithography or *planographic* printing uses a flat surface; while in the gravure or *intaglio* process the design is cut into the printing surface.

Letterpress printing uses metal *type* for words and photoengraved blocks for illustrations. The type carries reversed letters standing out from the surrounding metal: when coated with ink and pressed against the paper they print the right way round. Most type is now *set* (put together) by a *Linotype* or *Monotype* machine: only headlines, advertisements and other large letters are still assembled by hand. The operator has a keyboard like a large typewriter on which he types out the text or *copy* and the caster translates it into letters. When he comes to the end of a line, the machine automatically spaces the words so that all lines are the same length: the copy is *justified*. The Linotype machine moulds each line as a single piece of metal, a *slug*, while the Monotype produces lines of individual letters. Once set, the type is *proofed*; ink is rolled on to the type and a trial copy taken by hand. A proof-reader checks it for mistakes and writes instructions for any corrections that need to be made.

Blocks for photoengraving are usually made of zinc topped by a thin layer of copper and a light-sensitive coating. The coating is most acid-resistant in the areas which have received least light – in other words where the printed reproduction will be darkest. When the unprotected areas are etched away with nitric acid, a relief image forms, standing up to receive ink. *Line* blocks are the simplest, used when the drawing is pure black and white; *half-tone* blocks give the gradations of grey needed to print a black-and-white photograph.

The dots of a picture

The vital part in making a half-tone is the *screen*, a transparent plate ruled with two sets of opaque lines at right angles which the engraver places between the original and the plate. More or less light, depending on the brightness of the image, passes through the transparent spots of the screen. When the engraver etches the plate, only pinpoints of black are left in the brightest areas while in dark places almost all the plate bears ink. Thus the tone varies from black to white. A fine screen, used for high-quality work, may have up to 150 lines ruled to the inch; for coarse newsprint, between 55 and 75 lines are usual. By looking closely at a newspaper photograph one can make out the dots that make up a picture.

Blocks and type are then *made-up*; the compositors arrange them in their final positions on the *stone*, a metal-topped table, and lock them into a frame called a *chase*. In letterpress, the made-up type can be used to print directly, which is especially convenient when only a few thousand copies are wanted. But type metal is very soft and machines built for the long runs and high speeds of newspaper and magazine printing use harder duplicate printing plates – *electrotypes* or *stereotypes*.

Electrotypes, the better in quality, are formed by electrically plating with copper a wax mould taken from the type and strengthening the hard copper shell with a backing of type metal. The less expensive stereotypes, which are adequate for newspaper work, are made by casting metal in a papier-mâché mould. Heavy pressure forces the *flong*, a thick paper sheet, into the crevices of the type; when it has been dried by heating, the metal cast can be taken. More modern techniques substitute plastic for both flong and metal cast, but the result is the same: a single plate – flat or curved depending on the machine it is intended for – which bears all the words and pictures in relief.

All letterpress machines work on the same principle: rollers coat the raised type surface with ink and force paper against it to transfer the image. In the *flat-bed* machine, the type itself is flat, paper comes from a pile of sheets and a roller squeezes it against the inked type. Newspapers and magazines use *rotary* or *cylinder* presses which are faster and usually fed by a *web*, a continuous roll of paper. Because setting up the web wastes paper, the process is uneconomical if only a small number of copies are required.

The machine minder locks the *forme*, the complete set of stereotypes, to the curved printing cylinder and *makes-ready* the press by packing thin sheets of paper beneath parts of the forme until all of the type surface touches the printing paper with just the right pressure. When he starts the press, inking rollers cover the type with ink while a pressure roller forces the paper against the cylinder.

By using two printing cylinders, each acting as pressure roller for the other, *perfecting* machines print on both sides of the paper at once. In other cases, the web may travel through several printing units before passing to cutting and folding machines that turn the printed roll into the finished magazine.

Lithography, the second kind of printing process, depends on the fact that grease and water do not mix. The printing plate bears an ink-attracting image while the background is water-holding and, when damped, repels the greasy ink.

The surface of the zinc or aluminium plate is treated to make it attract grease and then given a light-sensitive coating. After exposure to the print matter and development of the image, the plate is etched. Where there has been most light – that is in between the print matter – the plate becomes water-attracting. In modern, two-layer plates the print and non-print areas may even be of different metals – the top layer etches completely away. These plates are very durable and used for large printing runs.

Photographic process

The film used to expose the plate bears both text and pictures. The text can be a photograph of a carefully taken proof of metal type or it may be *film-set*. In the film-setting machine a keyboard produces a punched paper tape which controls the exposure of individual letter negatives on to the final film. Photographs are screened to give half-tones. Because a lithographic

1 The inks used in printing contain varnish to make them glossy and oil to make them flow. The pigment used in common black printing ink is carbon black which is fast and stable.

2 Line blocks are proofed on a small hand machine. Paper is applied under pressure to the inked blocks and the resulting impression checked for accuracy.

3 A letter heading is set by hand. The metal letters are picked out of the cases and placed in the composing stick. Great skill is needed to judge the spacing between the words.

plate results from a photographic process, this method of printing is very suitable for heavily illustrated work: it costs no more to print a page of pictures than a page of text.

Lithographic printing machines are nearly always *offset* (the method is often called *offset litho*). The plate cylinder, which rolls first against a water spreader and then an ink roller which coats only the sensitive image area, prints on to a rubber cylinder. This in turn 'offsets' the ink on to paper pressed against it by a third cylinder. Because of the flexibility of the rubber mat round the second cylinder, less time is needed to adjust the machine and the offset process can easily print on rough materials, cardboard and even plastic. Offset lithography has the advantage that it is less trouble than letterpress (small machines are used in many offices) but it cannot reach the same quality.

In the gravure process, the third main printing technique, the print image is etched into the plate. During printing, the small holes fill with ink which is forced out again by pressure from the paper. The print material is prepared in the same way as for lithography but, in the final stage, all of it, type and pictures, is exposed on to the gravure cylinder through a very fine screen. During etching, the final size of a particular pit depends on the brightness of the image. Because the pit size, and therefore the shading, can be finely controlled, gravure is very suitable for illustrations, but the all-over screen lessens the sharpness of letters.

For special purposes there are other printing techniques which supplement the three main processes. In *silk-screen* printing, a fine fabric stretched across a frame holds a stencil or photographic image. Forcing ink through the fabric gives a heavy printed layer suitable for a poster or carton. *Xerography*, a copying process, electrically shuffles fine powder to form the print image and fuses it in place by heat.

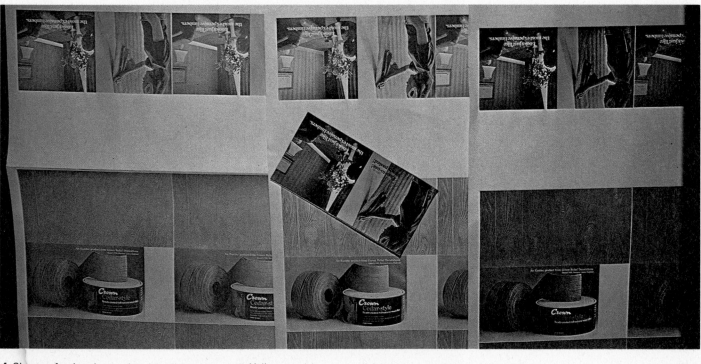

4 Sheets of a brochure printed by lithography. During the three stages, yellow is printed first, then red, followed by blue, which combines to form purple, and finally black is added.

5 Yellow cards on a small letterpress machine are picked up by suction, one at a time, and placed on the platen to be pressed against the inked type.

6 Using the original colour transparency and an enlargement on a light box as guides, an engraver removes excess metal from a half-tone colour block.

6

Any printing process can produce coloured pictures. In the simplest method, *flat-colour,* the printer uses coloured ink in place of black. He can pass the paper through the machine more than once (changing the ink each time) or runs the web through several printing units to give a number of different colours.

'Proper' colour, however, demands *process printing.* The final picture is a mixture of tiny coloured dots which the eye combines into lifelike tints. The first stage is *photographic separation.* The inks used for the final printing are usually three transparent colours – red, yellow and blue – and black. Using filters which pass only the complementary colours, the engraver makes first a photographic negative and then a half-tone corresponding to each of the colours. By holding the screens at different angles for each block, he ensures that the dots that form the picture jumble into an effective pattern.

Once the colours are separated the picture can be printed. In a sheet-fed machine, the paper may pass through the machine four times. On a web machine it will pass through four printing units each giving a different colour. These may vary in order, but usually the yellow is printed first, followed by red, blue and the black impression that completes the picture. For the printed illustration to be sharp, the four half-tones must fall exactly on top of each other: mechanical feelers and electronic eyes are used to keep the four units printing in *register.*

To get the effects he wants, the printer depends on his raw materials: the paper and ink. Some paper is made from cotton, cotton rags, wheat and rice straws, and grasses such as esparto, hemp and jute, but about 85 per cent is produced from wood

1 In a rotary machine, a continuous roll of paper is forced by a pressure cylinder against the impression cylinder which carries 20 inked stereo plates.
2 In this giant rotary press, the paper moves through at the rate of 1,500 feet per minute, is printed on both sides and is delivered folded into pages.
3 A printer prepares the rollers with ink before taking a 'pull' of half-tone blocks. He can then assess the quality before the blocks are put on a machine for mass printing.

pulp obtained from trees. From such pulp, it is possible to make hundreds of different types of paper – greaseproof, transparent, wrapping and high-grade papers with a hard, smooth finish. Cheap paper may also be made from repulped newsprint.

In the major process, the wood is first reduced to chips by machine and then treated with chemicals to produce the pulp. After washing, screening to remove waste material, and bleaching, the pulp is drained of water to form a thick porridge. At this stage, materials such as starch, alum, rosin size and china clay are mixed with the pulp according to the type of paper required. The pulp is then spread on to the first part of a machine which consists of a moving wire cloth belt. Suction boxes drain the water from the pulp and the remaining sheet is squeezed between heavy rollers, dried by heated cylinders and wound into large rolls.

No more need be done for the coarsest of papers – newsprint. But for higher-quality printing, the paper is coated. A mixture of clay and dyes spread over the paper fills small pits between the fibres and gives a smooth printing surface. The printer takes great care that the paper he uses is free from imperfections. He makes sure it stays dry and runs it through his machine at the best angle to prevent stretching: once the paper starts to stretch it is impossible to

keep the separate impressions of the plates in register.

Printing inks are more like paint than watery writing inks: a mixture of ground pigments and dyes for colour, varnish for glossiness and oil to make it flow. There are hundreds of colours but the most common are the three used for process colour – yellow, red and blue – and black. Virtually all black inks are made from carbon particles, the best use carbon formed when natural gas burns in too little air.

As well as being the right colour, the ink must suit both the printing process and the paper being printed. Lithographic ink must repel water, ink for gravure has to be thin so that the paper can suck it from the etch pits. Inks must also dry quickly to prevent smudging as the printed paper passes through other stages. In newsprint, the oil base soaks into the paper; on a higher-quality, coated paper the ink dries as fluid combines with oxygen in the atmosphere or evaporates. Many presses have heaters that speed drying.

Modern presses can print thousands of copies of books, magazines or newspapers in an hour; high-quality litho or gravure produces lifelike coloured pictures. Through such processes are derived the newspaper read by millions or the reference book, with its air of permanence and finely reproduced illustrations.

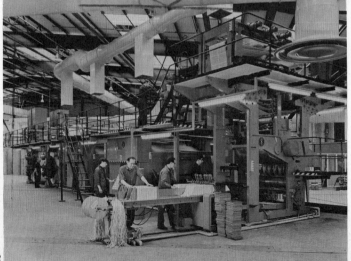

Messages 'on the air'

The pioneers of radio and television – men like Hertz, Marconi and Baird – could scarcely have dreamed that their inventions would transform communications to the extent that they have done.

THE DATE was 12 December 1901. The location, Signal Hill, St John's, Newfoundland. Guglielmo Marconi and two assistants could hardly believe the evidence of their ears. Ever so faintly, but unmistakably, they heard on their primitive receiver *dit-dit-dit* – the letter 'S' of the Morse Code – transmitted at a pre-arranged time from Poldhu in Cornwall, some 1,700 miles to the east. The Atlantic Ocean had been bridged for the first time by wireless telegraphy!

Marconi was jubilant. He was no great scientist but he had faith in wireless communication. The best scientific opinion of the day was that transmission of signals without wires was a novelty suitable only for short ranges. Marconi had shown his critics they were wrong and by a single practical demonstration he accelerated the development of one of the most potent forces for good, and for evil, of the twentieth century.

The Atlantic had been bridged by a submerged telegraph cable as early as 1866. By the time Marconi made his historic experiment most important centres in the world were linked by the electric telegraph. But to be able to transmit information without wires over vast distances – this was really something new. It seemed as if it might prove profitable, too. To lay a transatlantic cable cost a lot of money. The cable itself cost plenty and its annual upkeep even more, spread over the years. Figures of £1 million for first cost and £100,000 a year for maintenance were quoted. In contrast a wireless transmitter would cost, perhaps, £50,000 and its maintenance only £12,000 a year.

Marconi's genius lay not in his inventive capacity but in his ability as a practical innovator. The German physicist Heinrich Hertz is credited with being the first man to demonstrate that electromagnetic waves could be generated at one point and received at another. This was in 1888 and what Hertz did supplied experimental proof of a theory propounded by James Clerk Maxwell some years earlier.

Marconi had heard of Hertz's work. So had the Russian scientist Popov and the British scientist Oliver Lodge. All three had achieved wireless transmission by 1895 but it was Marconi alone who had the vision to see the new science in practical terms.

His family had money and connections in England and in 1896 Marconi sailed from his native Italy armed with letters of introduction and unbounded enthusiasm. He was granted the first patent for telegraphic communication without wires and in the following year formed the Wireless Telegraph and Signal Company. Marconi was then only 23 years old. Three years later the company, based at Chelmsford, changed its name to Marconi's Wireless Telegraph Company.

Wealthy backers of the new company, greedy for the rich dividends that had accompanied the growth of wire telegraphy were in for a shock. Wireless was slow to catch on and no dividend was paid during the years 1897 to 1910. But if there were no dividends there was technical progress. The first wireless station in the world was set up at Alum Bay on the Isle of Wight in 1897. It handled its first paid message in 1898. In that year, too, the new-fangled wireless received royal patronage with Queen Victoria using it to keep in touch with the Prince of Wales who was aboard the royal yacht. In 1899 radio signals from Chelmsford were received in Boulogne – a distance of 85 miles.

Then came the great triumph of 12 December 1901 with the Atlantic bridged for the first time. Marconi achieved this by using a very much longer wavelength than had previously been used. It had been supposed, up to that time, that wireless waves travelled only in straight lines in the same way as light. This would mean that to overcome the curvature of the Earth the transmitting and receiving aerials would need to be immensely high so that they could 'see' each other. Marconi demonstrated that long waves (he used a wavelength of 1,500 metres) must, in some way, be reflected from the sky to get round the bulge of the Earth.

The following year the theory was propounded independently by Oliver Heaviside in England and A. E. Kennelly in the United States that there was, in fact, a layer in the sky which reflected wireless waves of suitable wavelength. In 1925 Appleton was able to demonstrate experimentally that such a layer existed about 60 miles above the Earth's surface. It was also found that other layers existed at

1 Marconi (second left) and his research team outside the tower on Signal Hill, St John's, Newfoundland, where the inventor received the first successful transatlantic radio transmission.
2 Radio for traffic control. The New York policeman at the entrance to the Lincoln Tunnel reports traffic movements to central control using a miniature transmitter-receiver.
3 This tracery of aerials is part of the BBC shortwave transmitting station at Skelton, Cumberland. Its broadcasts span the world.

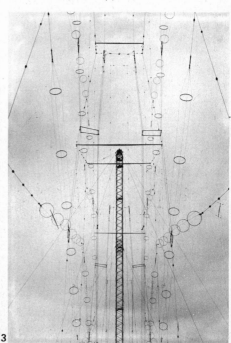

heights varying from 55 to more than 200 miles high in a belt we now call the ionosphere.

The behaviour of the ionosphere is important. It consists of positively charged ions and free electrons and is completely transparent to light and to very short wireless waves. Long waves are heavily reflected and medium waves less so. The layers and their composition vary in a complex manner according to time of day, season and the degree of radiation from the sun. The number of sun spots, for example, has an intense effect on the ionosphere. The ionosphere can be disturbed so fiercely at times by abnormal solar radiation that communication is completely obliterated. At other times changes in the height of the ionized layers give rise to fading and distortion.

Despite Marconi's success with transatlantic trials he was unable to capture commercial traffic between land stations from the cable companies and he turned to the use of wireless for communication with shipping as a profitable alternative. It was here that he succeeded. By the outbreak of the First World War, wireless equipment was becoming a commonplace on ships. Its usefulness was demonstrated dramatically by the sinking of the *Titanic* in 1912. The *Carpathia* picked up the distress signals from the sinking ship and 700 lives were saved. It was shortly after this that most maritime nations passed legislation to oblige all ships over a certain tonnage to fit wireless. From this moment on the commercial success of the Marconi companies was assured.

Spark transmitters

All the early wireless installations used spark transmitters. The signals were generated by starting and stopping spark discharges with a Morse key and messages were universally sent in the dots and dashes of the Morse Code. At the receiving end the detection device was the coherer, a glass tube containing fine particles of metal which had the property of varying in electrical resistance as the spark signals were received and made it possible for them to be heard on headphones.

Ambrose Fleming, a British professor of electrical engineering, had invented the diode valve which was patented in 1904. Fleming was a consultant to Marconi and it was Marconi who held the patents. Another young engineer, Lee de Forest, was also busy experimenting in America and it was he who invented the triode valve. Both valves worked better as detection devices than the coherer. But whereas Fleming's valve was a better solution than the coherer, Lee de Forest's triode valve was superior to both in that it not only detected the weak wireless signals but also amplified them. Lee de Forest demonstrated his triode valve to an American telephone and cable company in 1912 but it was some years before production techniques had developed sufficiently to make the thermionic valve a commercial proposition.

It was the invention and subsequent development of the thermionic valve which made radio broadcasting possible. To

1

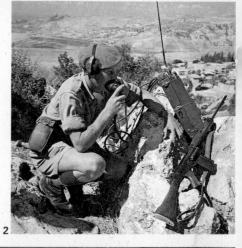

1 This old Gloster Meteor aircraft is about to end its life as a target for naval 'Seacat' anti-aircraft missiles. Radio-controlled pilotless 'drone' aircraft are often used for target practice in the testing and development of new types of anti-aircraft weapons.
2 Radio has obvious military applications. It provides the infantryman with a welcome direct link to his headquarters, so that he can call in air support or report incidents instantaneously. Here, an infantry radio operator on patrol in Cyprus uses a 'back-pack' transmitter.
3 Now a museum-piece, this 1938 combined radio and television receiver incorporated a seven-inch screen and cost 35 guineas. In those days, television was a novelty, almost a toy. Now it is the basis for a massive industry, and a widely used means of communication.

2

3

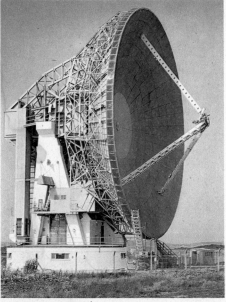

1 For many months of the year, the radio station of the Falkland Islands Dependencies Survey in Antarctica is the only link with the outside world and with the survey's outposts.
2 The reflectors at the Post Office's satellite communications centre at Goonhilly Down, Cornwall, beam vast amounts of information across the Atlantic via artificial satellites.
3 The BBC's television mast at Crystal Palace in south London towers nearly 1,000 feet over the surrounding built-up area, giving good straight-line reception for many miles around.

transmit speech or music demands a continuous wave – not the start-stop type of the spark transmitter. With the new radio valves (we shall use the more modern term 'radio' from now on) it was possible to generate continuous waves at the transmitter and to superimpose on the transmission the modulation of voice or music. At the receiving station the new valves were considerably more sensitive and were used for de-modulation to separate out the sound waves and then to amplify them to operate a loud speaker.

Regular broadcasting started in the United States from the Westinghouse station KDKA at East Pittsburgh on 21 December 1920, and two years later the British Broadcasting Company Ltd (now the British Broadcasting Corporation) was formed and the first programme was transmitted on 14 November 1922. One of the dreams of the early pioneers had been achieved.

The dream of television

But others were dreaming, too. If sounds could be transmitted through space, why not pictures? There was ample reason for believing this to be possible. Picture transmission by cable had already become an accomplished fact. Why not send pictures by radio?

John Logie Baird in Britain and C. F. Jenkins in the United States were both experimenting with television systems by 1923. In 1925, Baird demonstrated his system publicly for the first time. It was based on a principle developed by Paul Nipkow in 1884. Nipkow had evolved a method of sequentially scanning an object, his intention being to transmit pictures by cable. The scanning mechanism was a rotating disc with a series of punched holes in a spiral starting at the outer edge of the disc and progressively getting nearer the centre. If an object is viewed through the holes as the disc is slowly rotated each part of the object is seen in turn. If reflected light from the object passes through the holes and is allowed to fall on a photo-electric sensing device, a series of electric pulses, each proportional to the amount of light, can be generated. These could then be sent down a cable and used to control the brilliance of a light source at the receiving end which is viewed through the spirally set holes of a second Nipkow disc. If the two discs are in perfect synchronism a reproduction of the object can be built up at the receiver. To get a complete instantaneous picture reasonably fast the Nipkow discs must revolve at high speed. This takes advantage of the persistence of vision of the human eye

which does not notice interruptions in vision provided they are of very short duration. All television systems take advantage of this human defect.

Baird was no more a classical scientist than Marconi. He invented television first as Marconi invented radio, but neither discovered the laws of electromagnetism. But he was a keen experimenter and has his place in history as a practical man who made the system work. Nipkow had the idea but was unable to convert the electrical signals back into a picture.

The original Baird system was very crude. His disc had 30 holes in the spiral and so the picture was divided up into 30 lines – a very low standard of definition by modern standards. Nevertheless, it was a start and the British Broadcasting Corporation was first in the world with a regular television service in 1929 using the Baird system. It was transmitted on the medium-wave band on 261 metres for half-hour periods, five days a week.

Meanwhile, other workers had recalled a forecast made by A. A. Campbell Swinton in 1908 that the then newly invented cathode-ray tube might one day become a central component in the transmission of pictures. The mechanical systems involving Nipkow discs, mirror drums or other spinning scanning systems had obvious limitations. It had been mathematically calculated that for a reasonable quality picture the number of individual picture elements to be transmitted should be of the order of 100,000 repeated 20 times every second and no mechanical system could cope happily with this volume of picture information. The next leap forward would have to be an all-electronic system with no moving parts bigger than electrons.

The prime mover in developing modern television was Dr Vladimir Zworykin, a Russian who went to America after the Russian revolution. He joined Westinghouse and worked on new and more sensitive photocells for use in talking films – the talkies – which transformed the cinema industry when introduced in 1926.

By 1928 Zworykin had invented the iconoscope, the first all-electronic television camera tube with no moving parts. In 1930 he continued his work with the Radio Corporation of America which had taken over the radio and television interests of his former employers.

Since those first pioneer days television technology has moved strongly ahead to give the world colour television, and through satellites, the transmission of live pictures over vast distances.

It will be recalled that the development of long-distance radio communication depended very much on the existence of the ionosphere to reflect radio waves from the sky. It should also be recalled that while possessing this valuable property the ionosphere was, by its nature, unreliable. Because of hour to hour variations the quality of signals over long-distance paths was variable and a transmission would often be entirely lost. And because of this unreliability the new science of radio was unsuccessful in ousting the expensive but demonstrably reliable long-distance cable. Moreover, the ionosphere

Television from the moon. The United States' Surveyor VII lunar probe scoops up a sample of the moon's surface and brings it within range of the automatic television camera.

does not reflect short waves which alone can carry the wealth of information (100,000 elements 20 times a second) demanded by television.

This situation has been transformed by the communications satellite and the most promising medium of transmission is now the ultra-short wave directed in an absolutely straight line through the ionosphere to the satellite where the signals are received, amplified and retransmitted back to Earth. The scientists have discovered that very short wavelengths are best after all!

The satellite communication system is now the wonder of the world. On 22 January 1969, Goonhilly 2, Britain's latest and largest space communication station was officially opened by senior representatives of the British Post Office and the Marconi Company. It is located, appropriately, in Cornwall, not far from where Marconi staged his first transatlantic experiments.

But instead of only a letter 'S' of the Morse Code, Goonhilly 2 can handle 400 intercontinental telephone circuits and a television programme simultaneously. Working through the Intelsat III satellite 23,000 miles high over the Atlantic it can handle more traffic alone than all the transatlantic cables and the earlier Goonhilly 1 station capacity added together. It will not only be used for instant com-

munication with the United States and Canada but to Africa and the Middle East as more satellites become available. Moreover, its operational reliability is 99·9 per cent which means that in any one year it will never be out of service for more than a total of nine hours.

Even a visionary like Marconi would be amazed to see a single radio station costing £1·5 million and with an aerial structure weighing about 1,000 tons. Marconi died in Rome on 20 July 1937, but his name as the pioneer broadcaster remains a household word all over the world.

1 Sun spots, associated with intensive magnetic disturbances in the ionosphere, can cause 'fade-out' of radio and television transmission, and interfere with communications.
2 Radio-controlled boats, like this handsome model warship, give pleasure to thousands of amateurs, both children and adults. Many enthusiasts build their own models.

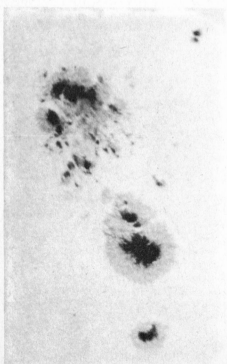

1

2

Science against crime

Many modern scientific developments can be applied to the detection of crime. The modern criminal faces a formidable array of experts backed by computers and sophisticated detection techniques.

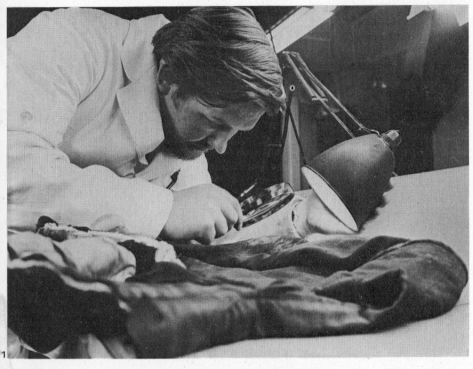

IT IS no accident that the most famous fictional detective of them all, Mr Sherlock Holmes, was provided by his creator, Sir Arthur Conan Doyle, with a knowledge of science which he used in his fight against crime. Conan Doyle had been trained as a doctor of medicine, and as such was aware of the power of science. The closing years of Queen Victoria's reign and the nine years during which Edward VII occupied the throne were notable both for rapid scientific advance on a number of fronts, and a general optimism that science would inevitably produce the answers to the problems which beset mankind, including that of crime.

Yet, when all is said and done, Conan Doyle's work was still only fiction, and Holmes's understanding of science was limited. In real life terms, the situation is very different. The professional police forces of the world have for many years been applying science to their work, and their understanding and techniques are highly sophisticated.

Science in the service of the law is called forensic science. The work of the different experts is complex and may overlap, but in general their methods may be divided into several distinct phases.

In the first phase, the forensic scientists must establish *how* and *when* the offence was committed. Then comes the collection of evidence from the scene of the crime and finally, its evaluation – which may point to the identity of the criminal.

The non-forensic policemen work closely with the experts. At this point in the investigation the former follow up

1 Using the traditional magnifying glass, a laboratory assistant at a police forensic centre begins an examination on the clothes of a man killed by a hit-and-run driver.
2 Further investigation in the same case. Part of the dead man's bicycle is being examined for significant marks. The rest of the bicycle can be seen in the foreground.

any leads provided by the forensic department and by any other sources. From the evidence they narrow the field to one or more suspects.

Once this has been done, the second phase of forensic work begins. The experts turn to the evidence again to see whether or not it is possible to link a suspect or suspects directly to the crime. If the investigation is successful, the police charge the suspect and take him to court. The final phase of forensic work takes place when the forensic scientist appears in court on behalf of the police, as an expert witness.

The chemist's work

The forensic worker may be a specialist in one particular field of science, like chemistry or biology, or he may be an expert in a field which is not truly a science at all, like photography or aspects of weaponry. But most will have this in common. Whatever their basic expertise, they are likely to have a working knowledge of a number of fields outside their own.

Among the truly scientific workers, it is the chemist who plays the widest role. As an example, take the all too common

hit-and-run accident. Very probably paint fragments will have been left behind at the scene of impact, and it falls to the chemist to analyse these, for a good deal of information about the vehicle involved can be gathered in this way.

Some of the analytical work is relatively simple. Only a microscope is necessary to count the number of paint layers that have been applied to the car and to note the colours. This may tell the police something of the history of the vehicle – that it has recently been resprayed, for instance, and that the old colour was bright orange while the new coat was a sober blue or black. Such a fact could help in tracking down the car and, more importantly, its driver.

When it comes to other matters – like identifying the pigments used in the paint, or the constituents of its base – more detailed methods are called for.

The chemist can get a good deal of accurate information about pigments by using a piece of apparatus called a spectrograph. To start with, he takes a small sample from the paint trace and vaporizes it in an electric arc. The vapour glows, emitting radiation consisting of a mixture of wavelengths. The actual wavelengths depend upon the elements present. Within the spectrograph the wavelengths are separated and the operator is provided with a visual indication of the elements involved.

However, the chemist may also wish to know how these elements are combined chemically. In such a case he would probably employ a technique called X-ray crystallography. Here the sample is exposed to X-rays which are then bent or diffracted by the lattice work of atoms which go to make up the various layers of the crystalline pigment. The angle through which the rays are bent depends upon the interatomic spacings within the crystal, spacings which vary from substance to substance in a known way. If the scientist works backwards from the angle of diffraction he can calculate the spacings and arrive at the identity of the compound or compounds concerned.

To discover the bonding agent or base used in the paint, the expert may turn to direct chemical investigation. A paint which is extremely insoluble is likely to be oil-based. The nitrocellulose paints will dissolve readily in amyl acetate or acetone.

It is important for the police to ascertain the chemical nature of paints in this way. Unusual constituents could, for instance, narrow the search down to a handful of spray shops which had taken delivery of such paint and in one of which the offender's car was resprayed. When a suspect's car *is* produced, the chemists will take a sample from it, submit it to the same tests as above and show whether the car was involved in the accident.

Murder

In shootings also there are many ways in which the chemist can lend a hand. Taking a hypothetical murder case by way of example, let us suppose that a bullet fired at the victim passes right through the body and out the other side. The murderer, aware that the firearms people can prove that the bullet came from his gun, prises the bullet from a wall in which it has lodged. Then he disposes of this and the gun separately.

A gun, even a hand gun, is a sizable object, so let us suppose again that the gun is recovered and is traced to the owner, the murderer. At first he will probably be unconcerned. How *can* the police prove that this particular weapon was used during the killings?

The answer could easily come from the forensic chemists. They simply take an outer garment through which the bullet has passed and subject it to an electron beam probe. This detects and analyses the minute traces of lead which have been deposited on the fibres surrounding the bullet hole. Any impurities in this metal are revealed, and if the same metallic mixture can be found inside the gun, its use in the murder is made probable.

The identification of poisons is another chore for the forensic chemist. The proper name for this is toxicology and it is a very wide field indeed.

Nearly all metals and metalloids (substances having some but not all of the properties of metals) are poisonous. Arsenic, one of the latter group, is no exception – in fact it is *the* classic poison. A test for the presence of arsenic in a body, particularly if it is thought that the fatal dose was administered all at once, is the Reinsch method. A piece of clean copper is boiled in a mixture consisting of hydrochloric acid and fragments

1 In this reconstruction of a crime scene, a detective dusts a glass for fingerprints with fine powder. Routine tests like this often give vital clues to the criminal's identity.

2 Forensic scientists test and try to identify samples of materials taken from the scene of the crime. Between the two researchers is a plaster cast of footprints from the area.

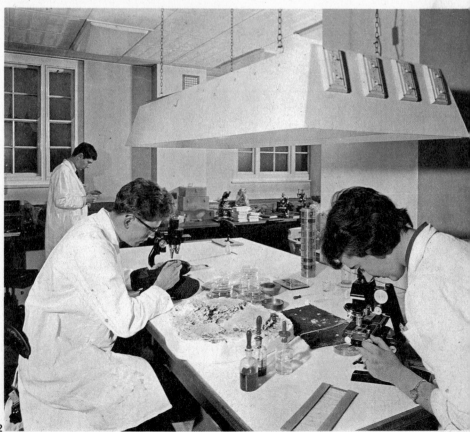

taken from the victim's entrails. If arsenic, or indeed any other poisons of this type, are present, they will be deposited on the copper as a black or grey stain. This can then be analysed spectrographically for final proof of the presence of arsenic.

If the chemist has reason to believe that small quantities of arsenic have been fed to the dead person over a considerable period, he will undoubtedly examine the victim's hair – for arsenic will certainly be deposited there.

Though it may appear otherwise, the chemist is by no means limited to crimes of violence. In short order he may be asked to determine whether forgery has been committed and therefore must investigate both papers and inks; he may be required to show what materials an arsonist used to start his fire; and most frequently of all perhaps, he will have to define with absolute accuracy the amount of alcohol in the blood or urine of a driver accused of drunkenness.

A recurring problem for the forensic biologist is the investigation of stains on objects used in crimes of violence, or on the clothes of the suspected attacker. Such stains may be visible, as on a shirt cuff or knife blade, or they may be invisible, as when blood has spattered on to a shoe and then been wiped away, leaving only the tiniest traces in stitching, cracks and so on. In either case, the biologists have the means of revealing the invisible stains, and showing whether or not these and the visible kind are blood.

A mixture of chemicals

For invisible stains, the peroxidase method is widely used. From experience the biologist will know that there are some areas of clothing or footwear which are more likely to be stained than others. To these areas he will apply a mixture of chemicals which contains among other things a compound which will react with the haemoglobin in the blood (the substance which is responsible for the red coloration) to give a highly coloured product. If benizidine is used along with the other ingredients, the product will be a very strong blue. Phenolphthaline produces a bright pink.

At the same time, the peroxidase test is not absolutely specific. Some plant materials and chemicals will cause a positive reaction so, having rendered the invisible stain visible, the biologist then tests exclusively for the presence of haemoglobin, or the substance into which it may have degenerated with time. A typical approach would be to apply Takayama's test which brings a stain sample into contact with pyridine, a substance present in coal tar and tobacco. Tell-tale pink crystals of pyridine haemochromogen form if the sample contains haem substances. Takayama's test and other similar methods can, of course, be used at once if the stain is visible.

But still the biologist must prove in an assault case that the blood is of the human kind. Most likely he will then turn to the preciptin test.

When the blood of one species of animal is injected into the blood-stream of

3 Frogmen play an increasing part in police investigations. Police divers are often called in to search for bodies, weapons and other objects that may be concealed under water.

4 Most police forces maintain registers of prints from known criminals. Unknown fingerprints can often be identified from the files, though much of this work is now done by computer.

another species the latter's system produces a substance (antibody) to cope with the invading blood proteins, which otherwise would be harmful to it. At such a time, the blood of the recipient is said to be immunized against the invading blood type, the defensive part of the fluid being called the anti-serum.

If a rabbit is injected with human blood, the animal produces a specific anti-serum as protection. The anti-serum can be removed from the rabbit's blood and is then ready for use in the preciptin test. An extract of the blood-stain found on clothing or elsewhere is brought into contact with the rabbit anti-serum. If it is human blood, a film (precipitate) of cloudy material forms where the two liquids meet.

The final step would be to take some blood from the victim and to discover its group. It will then be compared with the grouping of the blood found on the suspected assailant's clothing or perhaps on a weapon owned by him to see if they are the same. If they are, a possible connection has been established.

Similar techniques yield similar kinds of information from other kinds of stain such as saliva on a cigarette butt found at the scene of the crime or sweat on clothing which may have been left behind. The biologist will also seek to identify hair which may be associated with a crime and compare it meaningfully with hair from the head of a suspect.

Again, plant materials may provide vital clues. Clothing will pick up pollen, seeds or even foliage if the wearer brushes past or through vegetation. For such reasons, the biology section of the forensic department will also have experts in botany.

The final group of forensic experts are

1 Microphotograph of the butt of a murder pistol. Particles of hair and blood found in the circled dent on the butt proved that the weapon had been used to beat the victim to death.
2 C.I.D. officers in Yorkshire prepare to take a plaster cast of a footprint found close to the scene of a crime. The footprint is first sprayed to prevent the soil sticking to the wet plaster.

those who practise no particular science but are more concerned with techniques – like photography and gun identification.

The simplest use of the camera is to make a visual record of known criminals, to provide an aid in the tracking down of missing persons, and to make a permanent record of the scene of crime. But cameras of various kinds are invaluable in other more sophisticated ways. Hidden movie and television cameras have been used to record crimes as they actually happen.

Further, the camera brings out details of evidence which may be invisible to the human eye. Infra-red photography can reveal marks on an object which happen to have been obliterated by a medium transparent to infra-red. Powder traces from a close-proximity shooting normally do not show up on a dark cloth, but they, too, can be brought out in this way.

Direction of shot

The firearms expert also has a number of techniques to pinpoint evidence which for the untrained eye would be invisible. From the size and position of bullet holes, the forensic scientist can tell a great deal about the direction and distance from which the shot or shots were fired. From a bullet which is recovered in good condition, he can ascertain the calibre, type and perhaps the make of gun – and even its approximate serial number. This is achieved by making a detailed study of marks on the bullet. Some will be caused by the rifling, the spiral ridges or grooves (lands) on the inside of the barrel. They may vary in number, direction of twist, width and so on, according to the make of gun or year of manufacture.

At the same time, each individual gun has imperfections of machining which are unique to it and will be imprinted on the bullet. Thus, when a gun which generally meets the specification drawn up by the firearms expert is found in the possession of a suspect, test bullets will be fired. One of these is then placed under a comparison microscope along with the clue bullet. If the marks are the same, then clearly both were fired from the same weapon.

Shotguns – so beloved of the Chicago gangsters of the 1920s – are not rifled. Even so, some information can be gained by examination of the shot, gauging its weight and size. This information, added to a count of the pellets which may be found at the scene of a shooting, will sometimes indicate the size of cartridge used and therefore the size of gun.

This then is forensic science, or rather the flavour of it. The examples given here indicate only the tip of the forensic iceberg. Yet plainly, the police scientists have progressed a long way from the celebrated, but shaky methods of Sherlock Holmes. Just as plainly, science is increasingly at the forefront in the fascinating business of crime detection.

A ballistics expert, surrounded by reference weapons, uses a panoramic camera to record bullet marks. By comparing these with marks on the gun, bullet and weapon can be identified.

Detective chemistry

The chemical analyst is chemistry's detective — indeed, chemical analysis plays an important part in present-day police work. The analysts' skills also find wide application in other fields.

ALL OVER THE WORLD chemists with test tubes, Bunsen burners and weighing and recording instruments are at work finding out the composition of solids, liquids and gases, and determining the purity and standards of food and drugs and the materials from which are made the countless things we use every day. These chemists are the analysts. Although analytical chemistry may not be the most glamorous of the sciences, it concerns our well-being very directly. It is chemical analysis that gives us confidence in the branded products we buy, that ensures the purity of the milk left each morning on our doorsteps, prevents us from being poisoned by insecticides and herbicides, gives us an unpolluted water-supply, and even brings the criminal to justice or frees the suspect from suspicion.

Chemical analysis is concerned with identifying substances and establishing their composition. The analytical chemist may be given a liquid, solid, powder or gas sample, and asked to name the substance or substances it contains. At first glance, the sample to be analysed could be almost anything. So the analyst's first step is to make tests that will identify its main constituents. This he does by carrying out a *qualitative analysis*, which is essential both to save time and to prevent some constituent from being undetected.

Qualitative analysis is relatively simple and involves certain routine and simple tests. It merely tells the chemist what is in the substance, and does not tell him the amount of each of its constituents. This has to be established by series of tests called a *quantitative analysis* which measures, sometimes to within extremely fine limits, the quantity of each ingredient by weight.

Organic and inorganic

All chemical substances belong to one or other of two distinct groups. Group one embraces the *organic substance,* which are compounds of carbon and hydrogen; while group two, consists of *inorganic compounds,* which are of mineral origin. Many organic compounds derive from living things.

Organic and inorganic substances require different methods of analysis, but the analyst has one simple rule to distinguish them: most organic substances will burn but inorganic substances generally will not. In many instances, the appearance of a substance gives an indication of its ingredients.

Heating a sample gives much information about its composition, as the vapours given off by some metals impart characteristic colours to a colourless flame. Consequently, the *flame test* can be used to

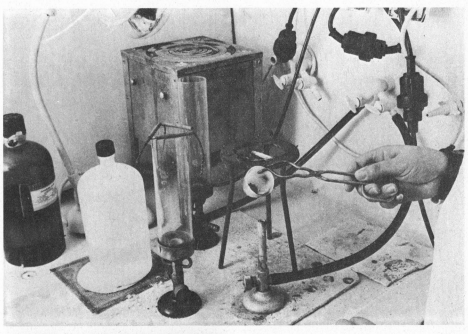

An analyst in the nuclear laboratory at Riisoe, Denmark, uses a Bunsen burner to heat a crucible containing atmospheric dust before testing the sample for radioactive elements.

Testing for poison in blood samples. The analyst is using a machine which automatically carries out standard chemical tests on small samples and reduces total analysis time.

identify metals in compounds.

Another technique of analysing a solid by heating is called the *borax bead test.* A bead of molten borax is placed against the sample, causing a small quantity of the sample to collect on the bead. When the bead and the sample adhering to it are placed in a flame, the bead changes colour according to the constituent of the sample. Nickel gives the flame a brown colour; iron imparts a yellow colour, which turns to yellow-red when the bead has cooled, and so on.

Sometimes a solid can be analysed by heating it with a few drops of concentrated

sulphuric acid and then watching for visible indications of the constituent. A brown gas with oily drops collecting on the sides of the test tube signifies a nitrate, while a milkiness in the test tube suggests a chloride. A similar acidic test can be made by adding dilute hydrochloric acid to the sample in a test tube which is then heated in the flame of a Bunsen burner. This vaporizes the sample, and its constituent can be recognized by the appearance, behaviour, colour or smell of the resultant gas.

Analysing compounds to recognize certain metals can be done by heating them on a charcoal block. A small quantity of the sample to be analysed is put into a shallow hole scooped out of a block of carbon, and anhydrous sodium carbonate added. The sodium carbonate converts the specimen into its appropriate carbonate, while the carbon acts as a reducing agent to separate the metal from its carbonate.

The flame from a Bunsen burner is then directed on to the specimen in the charcoal block. The test gives one of two indications of the metal present in the samples: smell and appearance.

Analysts are frequently concerned to detect the presence of acids and alkalis in materials they test. Acids are often corrosive in action or sour to the taste, while alkalis are soluble hydroxides of a metal, particularly of one of the alkali metals such as caesium, rubidium, sodium or lithium. A simple test to establish acidic or alkaline constituents is that made with an indicator which itself either changes colour or changes the colour of a solution in the presence of an acid or an alkali. Probably the oldest indicator is litmus.

Litmus indicators are derived from lichens which impart red or blue colours and can be in the form of liquids, tablets or the litmus paper so familiar to schoolboys. Litmus paper is made from strips of a kind of blotting paper, soaked in the appropriate dyes to produce blue or red litmus paper.

If a drop of blue litmus solution is added to a strong acid such as nitric, hydrochloric or sulphuric acid it turns red. Weaker acids such as soda water or vinegar give a wine-red colour. In alkalis such as caustic soda or ammonia, red litmus turns blue. One the other hand, if hydrochloric acid is slowly added to caustic soda, which has a drop of litmus in it, a point is reached when the blue colour becomes purple; adding more acid turns the purple to red. When no colour change occurs with a litmus indicator the solution being analysed is said to be neutral because neither acid nor alkali are present.

Testing for sugar and starch

Agricultural scientists often analyse samples of soil to evaluate their acidity, while tests for acidity and alkalinity are vitally important in the work of pathologists and industrial chemists. One very important branch of analysis is concerned with tests to detect the presence of starch and sugar. Tincture of iodine turns starch blue.

There are several kinds of sugar. One of these is the glucose present in many fruits and vegetables, and into which all other sugars are converted by the saliva of the mouth or by the pancreatic juice of the small intestine. Apples and grapes are rich sources of glucose, the presence of which can be established by using Haines solution which turns red if glucose is present. This test is often used by doctors to test people's urine for diabetes.

Precipitation occurs when a substance that does not dissolve is formed in a solution and settles out. Often when chemical substances are mixed together in solution, the precipitates formed have characteristic colours which enable them to be identified. A chemist may be asked to analyse a perfectly clear solution which is thought to contain a silver compound. He will first pour some of the solution into a test tube and add water containing common salt, If silver is present this will at once induce the formation of a precipitate of a white curly substance, which on exposure to a strong light will begin to darken. As compounds of silver darken on exposure to light, the test proves the presence of silver beyond doubt.

With the development of man-made fibres, analysts are frequently required to test fabrics to establish whether, for example, they are made of a mixture of cotton and wool, wool and silk, all wool or all silk, or part silk and part rayon. One

method of distinguishing silk from rayon is to burn a few strands of each separately and note any odour; rayon has no smell, but silk has a distinctive odour. If a piece of fabric is thought to be a mixture of cotton and wool it is put into a beaker of water containing sodium hydroxide and boiled for several minutes. At the end of the test, the piece of fabric will look like a piece of mesh, because the wool has dissolved out, leaving the cotton fibres intact.

An equally simple test reveals the difference between linen and cotton. A sample of each is first soaked in water and then put in a one per cent alcoholic solution of *fuchsin* (a red dye). After the samples have been thoroughly washed they are treated with ammonium hydroxide. This leaves the cotton fibres uncoloured while the linen fibres turn red.

By juggling with chemicals and watching their reactions under conditions of light, heat or cold, or even by odour, analysts can establish beyond doubt the constituents of practically any sample given to them. But this type of analysis consumes a great deal of time and effort, and is being replaced by quicker and, for many types of analysis, more positive methods. The chief of these are *spectroscopic* and *chromatographic analysis,* both of which are now the standard analysis techniques in industrial and other large laboratories.

Spectroscopic analysis is a development of the heat and flame tests already referred

to, and depends on the fact that every element has its own characteristic colour wavelength. This enables a spectrum of the substance to be analysed according to the wavelengths of the light emitted from it and thereby establish its composition.

The heat test for analysing the composition of a sample according to colours is

Biochemists have special pieces of apparatus for analysing the chemistry of living tissue. The Warburg respirometer, shown here, measures the tissues' oxygen uptake.

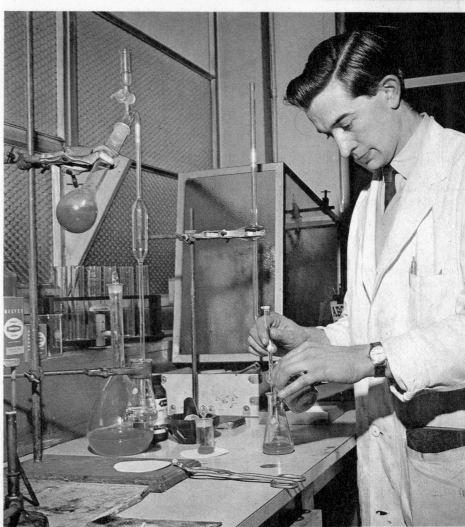

Paint undergoing chemical tests to determine its exact composition. Quality control in many factories involves constant analysis of production samples to check consistency.

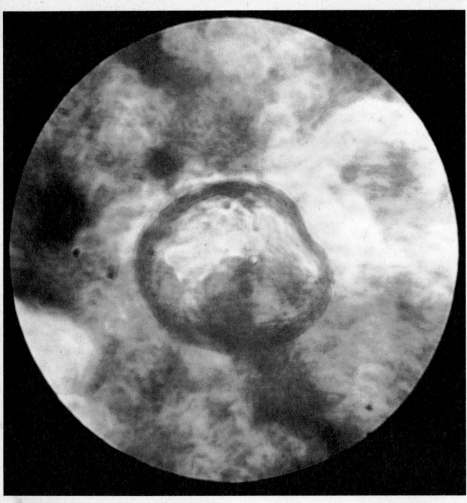

Chemical tests revealed that this speck of matter found in a meteorite had an organic origin. But the carbon compounds may be contaminants introduced as the meteorite landed.

sists of three main parts: a chamber in which the specimen is made to radiate energy; a complex of lens and prism to break up the light into its appropriate wavelengths; and a microscope or other instrument to observe the spectrum and identify the lines or wavelengths. The sample to be analysed is first heated so that it gives out light. The light from the sample is then focused on to the prism, causing it to fan out according to the various wavelengths.

Sodium, for example, gives a single yellow line on the spectrum, but when this line is magnified through the microscope, it is revealed as two yellow lines very close together. The spectrum of any particular element never varies. The only variation is in the intensity of the lines, and the degree of intensity of any particular line indicates the quantity of the element present in the sample.

In spectroscopic analysis, a *photomultiplier* is placed at each line of the spectrum. Each of the photomultipliers is placed behind a slit, through which the appropriate spectrum line passes, to shield it from unwanted light. By means of electronic relays, the current converted by the photomultiplier from the light energy moves a needle across a dial calibrated according to known quantities of the

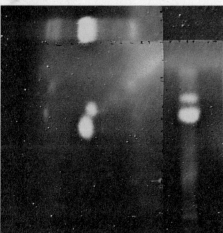

Chromatography makes use of the different rates at which compounds in solution move up wet paper. The various separate compounds here glow in ultra-violet light.

reliable enough when the sample contains only one element. But this kind of analysis is useless when the sample to be analysed contains a mixture of metals. The eye can neither analyse a mixture of colours, nor can it estimate the quantity of any constituent of the sample according to the intensity of the colour. It was to solve that problem that spectroscopic analysis was developed.

Spectroscopic analysing equipment con-

This complex arrangement of tubes and vessels is being used to test artificial fibres to determine their structure. The test sample itself is the brown fluid in the lowest bottle.

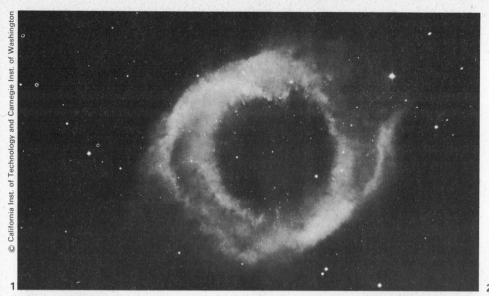

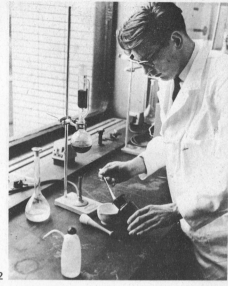

1 Spectroscopic analysis allows astronomers to study the chemistry of the stars. Helium was discovered on a star before chemists knew of its existence on Earth.

2 Using a spatula a scientist doles out chemical before grinding it to a powder with a mortar and pestle. The retort over the Bunsen burner carries a reflex condenser to prevent loss of water.

3 Automatic analysers are now widely used, particularly where large numbers of samples must be tested. This automated chromatograph is being used to analyse lung gases.

various elements. By means of a switch panel, the analyst can tell at a glance the quantity of each element in a sample.

Another form of spectroscopic analysis is *absorption spectroscopy* which, using the infra-red spectrum, is based on the phenomenon that matter absorbs radiation selectively according to source.

Conventional analysis by spectroscopy and absorption spectroscopy usually can be made in a matter of minutes, but a new development now makes possible what is, to all intents, instantaneous analysis. The instrument is called a *time-of-flight mass spectrometer* and is capable of analysing liquids and solids, and giving the precise composition and quantities of constituents in less than ten microseconds.

A time-of-flight mass spectrometer operates by ionizing the gases or vapours present in the sample and accelerating the ions along a field-free drift tube. The ions separate into bunches with velocities relative to the mass of the particular ion. Thus the low mass ions arrive at the end of the drift tube earlier than those of high mass, so producing a spectrum by way of an appropriate particle detector. The resultant ion-currents are amplified by an electron multiplier. One important application of the instrument is to determine instantaneously the exact composition of the anaesthetic gas being administered to and exhaled by a patient undergoing long and complex surgery. It has been used successfully in heart transplant and similar organ operations.

If you examine closely a sheet of used blotting paper, you will noticed that each of the ink blots is not the same colour over its whole surface, and that the edges in particular are of a different colour from the centre. Now get a stick of white chalk of the kind used for writing on blackboards and dip it into a pot of ink. The ink not only rises up the stick of chalk because of what is called *capillary action,* but instead of the chalk being dyed with the colour of the ink, it has several distinct bands of colour.

This is the basis of the analytical technique called *chromatography,* which takes advantage of the phenomenon that certain liquids break up into their chemical constituents when brought into contact with absorbent materials such as chalk (calcium sulphate) or blotting paper. The constituents of the sample being analysed can then be recognized by either their colour or the rate at which they are absorbed. For example, the different colours of the ink blots on the blotting paper and on the stick of chalk prove that ink is made from a number of different substances.

In *paper chromatography,* a drop of the solution to be analysed is placed near one end of a piece of absorbent filter paper. The edge or tip of the paper is then dipped into a suitable solvent. As capillary action raises the solvent up into the paper, the various constituents of the sample move behind the advancing solvent. The speeds of the movements of the various constituents of the sample depend upon their chemical compositions. The paper is then cut up according to the changes on it and the pieces are analysed to establish their exact composition.

With *column chromatography* a solvent and the sample for analysis are mixed together and allowed to flow down a column of powdered limestone enclosed in a glass tube. The constituents of the sample then collect as a coloured band at the top of the tube. The band of colour is then 'developed' by washing in pure solvent, which has the effect of breaking up the single-coloured band into a series of bands, each of which contains one or other of the various constituents of the sample. The column is then sliced according to the colours of the bands and each slice subjected to conventional analysis to establish its exact composition.

Mechanized and automatic analysis techniques have developed rapidly in the past decade and are taking much of the routine drudgery out of analysis, leaving the analyst to interpret the results.

Technology and sport

Developments in technology – photographic timing devices, improved equipment, all-weather arenas, synthetic tracks and mass audiences – have introduced profound changes to the world of sport.

The distances between runners are sometimes so slight as to be hardly discernible to the naked eye. By using a photographic timer the entire finish of the race can be recorded.

SPORT IS essentially an uncomplicated business. It provides the spectacle of men battling against men or against the elements without the trappings of modern civilization. But many people would argue with justification that the existence of modern sport as a mass entertainment for spectators would not have been possible without the technological advances made over the past 100 years.

The origins of many sports can be traced back through the centuries but it was not until the nineteenth century that sport began to be properly organized. And, significantly, this development coincided with technological advances. Newspapers, radio, television and photography are some of the factors responsible for the growth of sport. A hundred years ago it would not have been possible to stage the Olympic Games or the World Cup as truly international events since neither the aeroplane, the modern ship, television nor radio were available. In 1966, 100,000 spectators saw England win the World Cup final at Wembley Stadium near London but the world-wide television audience was an estimated 500 million. Until the twentieth century war seemed Man's great sport and it would not be unrealistic to claim that the sporting hero has taken the place of the war hero.

The development of timing is probably technology's most important single contribution to sport. As Lawrence Wright wrote in his highly entertaining book, *Clockwork Man*: 'Timing could not invade and mechanize sport until watches were accurate.' This applies chiefly to athletics – a sun dial or, later, the town clock were hardly the most satisfactory methods of timing races. But as the science of timing developed, so did athletics. Records began to be published with some regularity from around the 1850s and international records appeared for the first time from around 1880.

It was the stop-watch that provided the means of timing short-distance events such as the 100 metres. There is not much historical documentation about the stop-watch but in the 1830s reference was made to a watch with an independent seconds-hand. Benson's chronograph of 1860 was used to time the Derby horse race in 1866 – when the stop was pressed, the seconds-hand inked dots on a dial, enabling the timing of successive events. Around 1900 there was an electro-chronograph that could be operated by a finishing tape.

Importance of timing

Timing is a vitally important aspect of athletics. When a race is over, the spectators want to know the time. However thrilling a race may be, it loses all significance if the times are sub-standard. Timing has meant that the relative merits of athletes can be judged although they may be thousands of miles apart and may never meet.

Timing has now developed into such a fine art that hand-timing – a human being operating a stop-watch – is fast becoming unacceptable for short-distance events and electronic timing is used at the big meetings like the Olympic Games and the European Championships. When a man presses a stop-watch, he cannot anticipate the start and so the lag in the human nervous system means that there will be a fraction of a delay before he starts his watch. This delay gives the athlete a shorter time than he has actually achieved. The difference between electrical and hand-timing may be as much as a tenth of a second. As electrical timing tends to read

Pole vaulting was transformed with the introduction of the fibreglass pole in place of wood or steel. Because of its flexibility, the pole gives bend and whip to vaulters.

more slowly than hand-timing, records are becoming harder and harder to beat.

For the short-distance races at the Mexico Olympics in 1968, the electronic devices consisted of a synchronized starter's gun linked by cable to the photo-finish camera at the finish line. This type of camera is another example of technology taking over where human judgement is no longer considered accurate enough or sometimes even capable of deciding which runner finished first. The camera does not provide a photograph of six runners in their relative positions when the first athlete reaches the tape. What it does is provide a photograph of each athlete at the moment he reaches the line. This isolated recording of each runner is achieved by the continuous exposure of a film-strip rotating on a spindle exactly opposite the finish line. As well as recording the position of each runner crossing the line, it also records the time in minutes, seconds, tenths and hundredths of seconds that each athlete has taken to run the race.

A timekeeping apparatus used at the Olympic Games in Mexico in 1968 had its own developing tank that provided a negative in 30 seconds. A further half-minute and the camera provides the judges with an enlarged positive copy.

Nevertheless, hand-timing is very much a skilled art. In Britain, there are three grades of timekeeper and they have to pass examinations that include timing between 30 and 40 dummy races. A high standard is also expected of the stop-watches themselves and they are sent in for check-ups every two years. Mechanised devices are not confined to time-keeping in athletics. World records cannot be sent if the wind aiding the athlete exceeds two metres per second. Human judgement was used to decide on the strength of the wind but wind gauges now provide exact measurements.

While timekeeping in its most sophisticated forms revolves around athletics and swimming (at major events each individual swimmer touches a pad which is connected to a master clock), accurate timing is vital for many other sports. This is obvious in the case of show jumping against the clock but even in a game like football, the referee must have a means of adding on injury time to the 90 minutes of the game.

Technology has also played a major part in the development of equipment for sport generally. Rugby is a simple example of how vital high production standards are. When the English firm of James Gilbert Ltd began manufacturing rugby balls in the first half of the nineteenth century, they consisted of pigs' bladders inside a leather case. In 1870, lung power was replaced by a pump for inflation purposes and rubber was substituted for the pig's bladder. All in all, rugby balls have not changed much but by merely feeling a ball, a good rugby player can tell if it is up to standard. When the New Zealand full-back Don Clarke had to contend with the problem of balls being doctored in order to disrupt his kicking accuracy, he solved the problem by kicking inadequate balls over the grandstand.

Skilfully made footballs

Footballs can take more than four months to produce from the first stage of removing the skin from a slaughtered beast. The process is long and complicated and although mechanization plays a large part in the industry, much emphasis is still put on the skills of individual craftsmen. Animal skins are converted into semi-finished leather at a tannery before they arrive at sports factories. *Tanning* is the name given to the age-old discovery that if skins are immersed in water containing the bark of certain trees, they are transformed into very tough and long-wearing material. From the tannery, one British manufacturer uses about a million square feet of leather every year. About 16 per cent of the leather used for sports goods production ends up in the form of footballs. The work can be split into two stages. The first is leather-dressing, known as 'currying', involving, for example, retanning and stretch-removal. The second revolves around the manufacture of the case itself with the insertion of the bladder.

The work involved in producing a good-quality football is highlighted by the fact that the best balls have their panels completely stitched by hand – and a highly skilled stitcher can take as long as two and a half hours each case. One of the few changes in the finished product has been the post-war development of stem bladders instead of having the footballs laced up. The advent of floodlighting football matches has meant that footballs come in a variety of colours instead of the standard tan. Although the finished product has a high degree of toughness, waterproofing is not added during manu-

facture although experts are still working on the problem. Coloured soccer balls, however, are water resistant as the coating applied to them (either white, lemon or orange) is of polyurethane which is an excellent leather finish and which almost totally rejects dirt and moisture.

But technology plays a more dramatic role in the manufacture of golf and tennis balls. The production of tennis balls is a tremendously complicated and technical procedure. The slightest variation and it will fail to pass the necessary weight test. The first stage is the preparation of the rubber compound; a solid mass of rubber is then moulded into a hemisphere and two of these are joined. This assembly stage involves the introduction of gas pressure inside the ball – either air or nitrogen – to give it the correct bounce characteristics. The ball is then covered with Melton Cloth – the woven fabric that provides the furry surface to the ball. But the standards set make this whole process a complex one. The rules lay down that a tennis ball should be more than $2\frac{1}{2}$ in. and less than $2\frac{5}{8}$ in. in diameter and more than 2 oz. but less than $2\frac{1}{16}$ oz. in weight. The manufacturers have to ensure that when dropped from a height of 100 in. on to a concrete base, the ball bounces up again to a height of between 53 and 58 in.

1 The manufacture of footballs for international matches is a long, complicated process involving great skill. After tanning, the leather panels are stitched by hand. Coloured balls are produced for use at floodlit football matches.
2 Golf clubs have to be very finely balanced before use. Here a craftsman hand-finishes wooden heads for the steel shafts.

The greatest development in the tennis world is the steel tennis racket. Extra power, compared to the conventional wooden racket, is the key to its success and the reason why it has had such a big impact on the market, despite the fact that it costs twice as much as the best wooden racket. Steel rackets were first manufactured around 1900 but were dropped as the wire strings proved too tough for the tennis ball.

In the 1960s, the famous French player, René Lacoste, produced his steel racket in France. The unique feature of his racket was the stringing system. Instead of being strung through the frame itself as in the conventional racket, the strings on the Lacoste racket were strung through a number of steel alloy loops on the inside of the frame. This provided the extra power – a type of trampoline effect – when the ball was hit. An American firm then obtained world patent rights from Lacoste to use his unique independent string suspension system. After extensive research, their steel racket was put on the market in 1968. Its impact was tremendous and many other firms attempted to take advantage of its popularity – but without being able to use the patented string suspension system. Other advantages of the patented steel racket included its aerodynamic design which cuts down air resistance and the fact that temperature changes do not affect steel as they do wood – in fact the metal racket does not need a press. Its disadvantages seem to be that it takes a player time to become accustomed to using it and a new stringing technique with a special adapter has to be taught to racket repairers.

Improved equipment

Athletics has seen many equipment changes. The advent of the spiked running shoe in the 1860s is probably the simplest example, while more complicated is the history of the pole vault. The pole used in this event has successively been made of spruce, ash or hickory, bamboo, tubular steel and finally fibreglass. The fibreglass pole provides a contrast to the days when vaulters were occasionally impaled on snapped poles. The great advantage of the fibreglass pole is its flexibility – the bend and whip it gives the vaulter. It has raised vaulting standards dramatically since it was first introduced in the 1950s. American Brian Sternberg thought its advantages were perhaps too great – after setting a new world record clearing a height of 16 ft 8 in. in 1963 with the fibreglass pole, he said: 'I don't attach much value to records made with the fibreglass pole.' Unlike other poles, the fibreglass pole is built with a stress directly related to the vaulter's weight, his take-off position and other factors.

In athletics, racing surfaces underwent a change with the advent of the 'Tartan' track. In good conditions, there is little to choose between a cinder and tartan track. But in bad weather, tartan surfacing has many advantages. It is an all-weather surface – it does not become waterlogged; it can be used in extreme weather conditions – it also requires little

1 The kayak, originally an Eskimo canoe, has become very popular for competitive canoeing. Studies of the angles of the blades of paddles have increased their efficiency.

2 Racing cars have shown fundamental changes in recent years with the quest for a higher and better performance. Some designers have added fins to the cars to act as stabilizers.

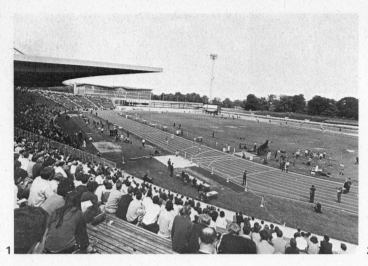

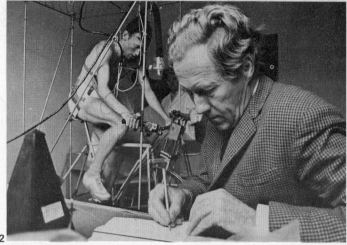

1 A 'tartan' international running track at a sports arena in Britain. Made of compounded synthetic resin, it has a hard-wearing, non-slip surface which can be used in all weathers.
2 To study the effects of high altitude on an athlete's performance preparatory to the Mexican Olympic Games, a doctor checks heart readings during a five-minute 'race'.
3 Starting blocks and spiked shoes are all precision equipment which help world record holders, such as Tommy Smith and John Carlos, to achieve their spectacular speeds on the track.

maintenance. Britain's first tartan track was laid at Crystal Palace in 1968 and it was provided for the Mexico Olympics and also at the new Meadowbank stadium in Edinburgh, the venue of the 1970 Commonwealth Games.

The major tartan surfacing is laid by a 'wet pore' machine, which looks like a macadam road layer. The finished product consists of $\frac{3}{8}$ in. or $\frac{1}{2}$ in. of tartan surfacing (a specially compounded synthetic resin). Underneath this are $2\frac{1}{2}$ in. of dense bituminous macadam in two layers laid at different angles. Underneath again are 8 in. of stabilized base clinker, then 3 in. of ash which is laid on the ground. Smaller surfaces, such as a long-jump run-up, are laid in carpet form with the surface already produced in a factory. The production and laying of all-weather synthetic turfs is increasing. Britain is testing all-weather football pitches and they are in use in America.

Frozen pitches

Underground heating is another scientific aid with increasing impact on the sporting scene. The underground heating system at Murrayfield, the headquarters of the Scottish Rugby Union in Edinburgh, was installed in 1959 to combat rugby's greatest weather hazard – frozen pitches which make it impossible for players to maintain their balance and avoid injuries. The system consists of 39 miles of cable buried about 6 in. below the playing surface. The system is controlled by a thermostat which is switched on when frost is forecast. When the temperature drops, the system operates automatically, ensuring that the ground does not become unplayable. Normally rugby authorities lay down bales of straw all over the field to keep the frost off – an elaborate but not always effective procedure.

Grass itself has been the subject of some extensive research. The Sports Turf Research Institute was started in 1929. It now has 2,000 experimental plots on a 12-acre site at Bingley in Yorkshire. Higher standards have meant that turf is more prone to disease and the centre provides invaluable research and advises the authorities at Britain's major sports grounds. In 1969, the first International Turf Research Conference with more than 70 delegates from all over the world was held in Harrogate, Yorkshire to discuss problems.

Finally a word about the most complex scientific development aiding sport – computers. They are now taking the drudgery out of compiling the most complex fixture list in the world – the English football league with its four divisions and 92 clubs.

Exploding the myths

Man has always been gullible in what he has accepted as true about scientific discoveries and inventions. But increasing knowledge dispels the myths about what has been, and can be achieved.

DURING THE PAST HALF-CENTURY scientific knowledge and techniques have exerted a greater change on our way of life than any form of human endeavour has ever affected it in the past. Every decade of the present century has given us a greater understanding of the processes of nature and a greater ability to control them for better or for worse. It is often said, that the scientist, according to his particular discipline, is within measurable distance of determining what and how much we shall eat; how hard we shall work; what comfort we shall enjoy at work and in leisure; and how long we shall live. Science can provide the means of destroying life on our planet and even the planet itself.

We would seem to have surrendered our destiny to science because the scientist appears to be omnipotent in human society. In other words, there is a growing tendency to consider the scientist infallible and we must accept as right whatever he does or thinks. But this can be a tragic fallacy; many thoughtful people are asking themselves whether scientists should not be curbed in their mounting efforts to let loose on the world little-understood forces; forces that have already involved mankind in problems that may prove to be without solution.

Misused power

Science has put at nations' disposal terrifying means of mass destruction. But it is an all too common fallacy to lay the blame for that at science's door. Nuclear physics began as a planned exercise for the better understanding of matter, but it was governments of non-scientists who realized the military potentialities of nuclear fission and fusion, and encouraged scientists to develop the atom and hydrogen bombs. Many of the scientists who took part in that development believed sincerely that nuclear weapons of mass destruction might deter nations from venturing into wars that could end in the annihilation of both sides. And so far that belief has been justified.

Another common fallacy is that scientists encourage the spending of vast sums of money on such unbelievably costly items as nuclear research when this money could be better used to relieve the conditions of poverty, hunger and disease under which so great a proportion of the

human race suffer. Such is not true; for given the right sort of backing, scientists would look for ways of abolishing hunger and disease; it is the scientists' paymasters who withhold the funds essential to the practical application of scientific means to give every human being a full stomach and a dignified way of life.

America has already spent thousands of millions of dollars and organized an army of scientists and technicians to put men on the moon. Critics of what is certainly one of the greatest achievements of technology say that all that money and effort, if devoted to social progress, would have given the United States the finest health and social security system in the world. What the critics forget is that neither the United States government nor any other government, for that matter, would make

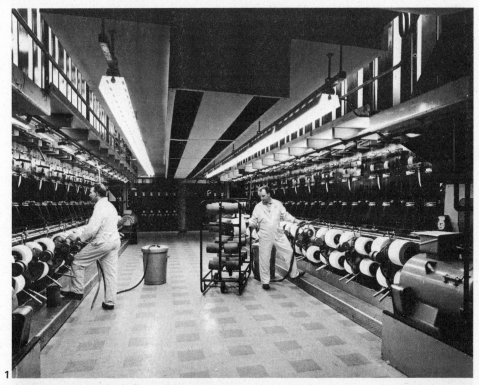

1 Far from making the world a worse place in which to live, modern technology can create excellent working conditions, as seen in this factory where man-made fibre is produced.
2 One of Man's groundless fears has been that industrialization would put many out of work. Yet to keep a few men in space for a few days requires an 'army' of technologists.

1 With radio astronomy Man has been able to probe deeper into space. But the 'red-shift' in the radio waves imposes a definite horizon beyond which Man cannot 'see'.

2 Nuclear power can be used for peaceful purposes as seen in the American nuclear freighter, *Savannah*. In the future Man will have to rely more on such power as a source of energy.

3 Proteins – a most important constituent of life – can be synthesized from petroleum by yeast. Yet, even with all the separate constituents of a living cell, Man cannot create life.

4 When Man first stood on the moon it seemed that the whole of the Universe was open to him for exploration. This is not true; the journeys would far exceed the crew's life spans.

3

1

2

such vast sums available for social services. Even if Congress had suggested it, the electorate would have rebelled. To Americans, space exploration has become a matter of national prestige, as well as one of the pillars of the country's industrial structure.

One very common fallacy is that scientific development of inventions must inevitably mean loss of employment, particularly by the unskilled. When the first motor car slowly chugged along the road, there was a bitter cry that thousands of grooms and coach-builders would be thrown out of work. Yet what happened? The factories making cars and lorries now employ on their production lines countless more men than ever found work as grooms or coach-builders. Not only that, car-factory workers have immeasurably better pay, shorter hours and more comfortable conditions than were ever the lot of the men who looked after horses or built coaches.

The idea that scientific and technological progress are inimical to the worker is as fallacious as the mistaken ideas that inspired the hand-weavers and hand-spinners to wreck Arkwright's spinning and weaving machines at Chorley in the eighteenth century. So far from the cotton workers being put out of work, Arkwright's machinery founded the Lancashire cotton industry which was to clothe the world and provide employment for hundreds of times the number of men and women who had earned a living spinning and weaving by hand.

Scientific research and technical development of machines and processes have merely amplified the abilities of workers; modern machines and processes can exist only as Man employs them to use his skills more effectively. Without such progress, the working week would not have been nearly halved over the past century and women and children still would be labouring long hours for starva-

light a fire terrified their contemporaries with the flames. But in time men learned to control fire and make it work for them. So it is when nuclear energy is under proper control: its benefits can far outweigh its terrors. There is nothing unnatural in the dread that seizes many people when they look ahead to the results that may accrue from the present-day discoveries by physicists. But just as our ancestors did with fire, we must learn to transform the new knowledges of science to our benefit rather than to our destruction.

At the other end of the scale there is the fallacy that there is no limit to what science can achieve. This is a fallacy that scientists themselves are the first to admit.

An outstanding example is the belief, strongly nurtured by writers of space fiction, that there is no limit to the distances that astronauts will be able to travel. Responsible astro-physicists and astronomers are convinced that there is a limit to space travel, and a very definite one. They are agreed that for Man to journey to any other planetary systems except our own is an impossibility.

Lifelong journeys

Stars that are relatively near by astronomical standards, say in the region of tens of light years away, would take several thousands of years to reach at the speeds of spacecraft now available or in the foreseeable future. Even by using powerful nuclear engines, the journeys would far exceed the span of the crew's lifetimes. It has been suggested that it might be possible to design a power plant that would give space vehicles the speed of light. But physicists are unanimous that to to achieve this would involve at the start of the flight a mass almost as great as that of the Earth itself.

Travel to the outer planets of our solar system does not involve solving so many apparently insoluble physical problems as attempts to voyage to the stars. Nevertheless, that does not mean that a manned landing on, for example, Pluto or Saturn is just around the corner. At the present stage of astronautical knowledge and technology, Man's ventures to set foot on the heavenly bodies seem limited to the moon and Mars.

The moon and Mars seem to be the only bodies in the solar system that offer conditions in any way acceptable to Man. Even then, as the landings on the moon have shown, the stay can only be of short duration and the explorers must rely for their lives on lavish and fantastically expensive survival equipment, together with an elaborate communication system to maintain contact with Earth.

That is not to say that Man will not extend his exploration of those bodies in the solar system within his reach, but any permanent settlement of the moon or Mars would seem to be a pipe dream. The best that can be hoped for is the establishment of small-scale stations for the collection of scientific data and its transmission back to Earth.

Development of radio astronomy has given rise to the fallacy that there is no

tion wages at degrading tasks in mines and sweatshops.

Many of the fallacies about the disservices for which science is held responsible stem from the average man's inherent fear of, and resentment against, change. And the knowledge that science cannot but accelerate changes in our way of life is, for many people, grounds for resentment against science, and tends to inspire a yearning for what seems the 'good old days' of a century ago. Such yearnings are hardly consistent when we remember the changes that science has brought to such a relatively prosaic matter as housekeeping. Until science provided the housewife with labour-saving equipment she was little more than a drudge, and unless she could afford servants she spent most of her time in the kitchen, at the washtub and scrubbing floors and beating carpets. Science has done more than anything else to raise the status of the housewife from that of an unpaid servitor to that of a companion to her husband.

It is undoubtedly a fallacy to suggest that Man in general would be better off without science and thereby be able to relive the Golden Age of Classicism. Man must learn to accept and live with the changes science is bringing. He already accepts without question the more obvious benefits that it has brought to him. The problem is, is he going to accept the more dynamic changes which science is bringing about.

Probably the most dynamic change brought about by science was the release of atomic energy. Development of the atom and hydrogen bombs has led many to condemn scientists for inflicting on mankind a mass of problems which we could well do without. But from the atom bomb has developed nuclear power for peaceful purposes and, provided nations retain their sanity, the promise of a fuller life for everyone.

Man's nature is to be fearful of any new form of energy and power. No doubt our distant forebears who first learned to

limit to the depths to which astronomers can probe into the distances of the Universe. There are limits to observation set by fundamental physical barriers.

Thus the progressive reddening of the light received from distant galaxies has convinced physicists and astronomers that hundreds of millions of light years from the Earth, the red-shift must be so great that emissions from super-distant galaxies, whether of light, radio waves or any known source of electromagnetic waves, just could not be detected by any present or probable observatory equipment or technique. Everything supports the belief that a few thousand million of light years away there exists a horizon beyond which Man cannot 'see'.

One of the most fantastic of all the fallacies is the belief that one day babies will be created in test-tubes without the agency of a father or a mother. It is an understandable fallacy when we remember that the body and organs of a human being are no more than a combination of chemical elements: 96 pounds of oxygen, 52 pounds of carbon, 14 pounds of hydrogen, four pounds of calcium, three and a half pounds of nitrogen, one and three quarter pounds of chlorine, one and three quarter pounds of phosphorus, three and a half ounces of sulphur, three and a half ounces of fluorine, two and three quarter ounces of potassium, two and a half ounces of sodium, one and three quarter ounces of magnesium, one and a half ounces of iron, and traces of magnesia, lead, copper, arsenic, silicon, bromine and aluminium, weighing less than one sixteenth of an ounce. These are the materials of which adult Man is made.

Constituents of life

Give these materials to a chemist and he would produce from them five gallons of water, enough carbon to make 10,000 lead pencils, sufficient lime to whitewash a hen coop, fat for six pounds of soap and enough iron to make a large nail. As for the other materials, there is not enough of them to make anything useful.

But a purely chemical analysis of Man is as absurd as to say that a motor-car engine is nothing but so many pounds of cast iron, steel and aluminium. Simply bringing together the analysed constituents of a living cell does not produce a cell in the laboratory.

The infinite complexity of arrangements of atoms that constitute a man is impossibly hard to reproduce except by the fantastically involved methods used in natural growth and reproduction. The idea of a man-made man is acceptable only to authors of science fiction.

When physicists first released nuclear energy it was hailed as a sign that there was no limit to the energy that science could place at Man's disposal. But physicists are quite clear that there is a limit to the quantity of energy that it will ever be possible to produce from a given quantity of matter. Although scientists are learning more and more about our Universe, the benefits their discoveries can bring depend on the use to which mankind puts them.

1 After the moon, the next planet on Man's list is Mars, but then the limits of distance and time begin to impose themselves. It may never be possible to reach the large planet, Saturn.

2 Arkwright's spinning and weaving machines revolutionized the Lancashire cotton industry but met with much opposition from the hand spinners who feared they would be thrown out of work.

NO MACHINES

SWING FOR EVER

LOWER YOUR TITHES

Damned lies and statistics

Statistics play an increasing part in our everyday lives, as well as in specialized studies of science and medicine. What is their history and how much do we need them?

EVERY ONE OF US can be labelled in one classification or another – as a male or female, as employed or unemployed, as above or below the voting age, as a national or alien in the country in which we find ourselves. If we buy life insurance, the premiums are calculated on the statistical probability that we will live for a certain period after the time we take out the insurance policy.

'Figures can prove anything', is a popular but cynical remark. This is true to the extent that by skilfully manipulating and presenting statistics it is certainly possible to give a misleading interpretation of a set of facts. But while statistics can be abused they can equally be put to valuable use in many aspects of life.

Another common cynical saying is that there are 'lies, damned lies, and statistics'. Statisticians often have to battle against the prejudice that their science is a mere painting up of the facts to prove the opposite of the truth. This widespread idea springs from a lack of understanding of the real uses of statistics. A vast number of modern activities require the interpretation of figures – indeed many operations would be impossible without them. Statis-

tics is merely the science of interpreting and using figures to extract the maximum value from them.

The biochemist carrying out an experiment with, say, bacteria, will get his results in the form of tables of figures. He must interpret these figures to discover what conclusions can be drawn from his experiment. Statisticians are frequently called in by scientists to design their experiments so that the maximum information can be derived from them. There is now a considerable body of knowledge about the design of experiments and other applications involving mathematics, much of which has been put forward by statisticians.

Another application to which statistics is widely put is the prediction of chance occurrences. Statisticians employed by the big insurance companies predict the chance of particular groups of people living for particular lengths of time. Like most of the other applications of statistics, this is not concerned with the fate of the individuals who apply for insurance cover, but with the average chances of members of these groups of people.

No modern state can function effectively without a first-class statistical service. In Britain the Central Statistical Office is attached to the Cabinet Office and is an integral part of it. The Statistical Office is charged with collecting statistics relating to the national economy, with analysing them and presenting them to assist the government in formulating its economic and financial policy. In addition

1 An opinion pollster questions a London dustman. Political opinion polls can now predict with great accuracy the voting patterns of the general electorate.

2 An early collection of statistics. The Bills of Mortality for London – this one is for 1664 – were published weekly and included details collected in 130 parishes in and near London.

3 The variations in the prices paid for household goods by these shoppers are gathered together by government statisticians and form the basis for the Index of Retail Prices.

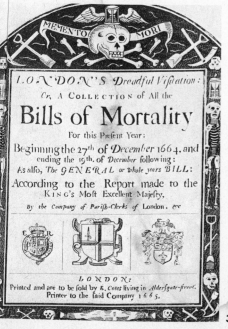

ministries have their own statistical departments. In industry, too, many statisticians are employed in the analysis of past results and in forward planning.

Statistics, as the name implies, were first applied in affairs of state. The first statistical society in England was formed at Manchester in 1833, and the Statistical Society of London (now the Royal Statistical Society) was established on 15 March 1834 for the purpose of procuring, arranging and publishing 'facts calculated to illustrate the conditions and prospects of Society'. Soon the science of statistics spread on to the continent of Europe, and the first International Statistical Congress took place in Brussels in 1853.

A statistic is merely a numerical fact. Statistics are numerical facts arranged and classified. A statistician is a specialist in collecting, analysing and presenting numerical facts in a meaningful way.

Presenting the facts

The way in which facts are presented is important when it comes to understanding their meaning. Dull lists of figures are hard to interpret, and pictorial representation often makes it possible to see the general situation at a glance. Points can be brought out more clearly in diagrammatic form and we are all familiar with graphs, charts and those little stylized men or women, each representing, perhaps, a thousand head of population. Another classical pictorial device is the 'slice of the cake' which might show one pound of the taxpayer's money and how his pound is sliced up into support for defence, education, health services and other sectors of public expenditure.

The statistician's first job, however, is to ensure that the results he collects in the first place are reliable. His second is to marshal his facts because they generally arrive in an untidy form. And one of his problems is numerical indigestion from the sheer mass of figures available to him.

Herman Hollerith was one sufferer from numerical indigestion. He was a statistician in the U.S. Bureau of the Census and under American law a census had to be taken every ten years. The 1880 census was, believe it or not, still being sorted and counted in 1886, and it seemed probable that the job would still not be completed by 1890 when the next census was due.

Herman's solution was to invent the Hollerith punched card on which simple answers of the yes/no type could be indicated by the presence or absence of a hole in set positions on the card. The cards could be put into a machine and the information read off at high speed by electrical detectors. Hollerith's invention was perfected in time for it to be used to process the results of the 1890 census. The census of 1911 was the first British census to use the Hollerith system throughout. Today such mammoth tasks are undertaken by electronic computers, the largest of which are aptly described as 'number crunchers'.

Descriptive statistics often involves processing large quantities of results in order to answer specific questions. Often, the bulk of information available makes it difficult to see the answer without some

form of simplification. In a census return, for example, it is quite unnecessary to take every person's name in order to find out the number of people in the country. But a complete census file provides a source of 'raw' facts from which all sorts of answers to specific questions can be selected and presented in various ways, as required. How many people are householders? Are we really becoming a nation of older people? The latter question can be answered by looking at the numbers of people in various age groups and comparing the figures with previous statistics. We can pin-point trends. By keeping an eye on the birth rate we can estimate the number of school places that will be required in the coming years.

The same results can be expressed in other forms, a simple one being to express

1 A sample taken from each batch of tomatoes at this cannery is tested for quality. Only a small number of tomatoes need be tested for the inspectors to be fairly sure that all are sound.

2 Population censuses originated in Britain. All members of the population are questioned about their job, family composition and home living facilities.

the figures in terms of percentages. This makes it possible to examine this year's trend against former years. In some cases, it may be more helpful to express a trend in percentages rather than in actual figures. It might, for example, be found that the number of unemployed has dropped since the previous year. But if the total labour force had changed since the previous year and was now several thousand less, then the derived percentage figure could indicate that the proportion of unemployed had, in fact, risen.

Index numbers are a way of expressing statistics which affect us all. The two which are of most general interest are the Index of Retail Prices and the Index of Industrial Production. Because the Index of Retail Prices expresses changes that affect all our pockets we shall look at this one carefully.

If we make a list of generally purchased commodities, food items and household goods, and stick to this list year after year we can examine the present cost of each item and compare it with the cost of the same item in previous years and find which goods have gone up in price, which have remained the same and which, possibly, have gone down in price.

Simple calculations might show that our total 'shopping basket' has gone up in price this year by an amount which could be deduced from an average value. This, however, would not be quite fair because we don't buy equal quantities of every commodity on the index. For example, rises in the price of milk and bread which we buy every day are far more significant

1 The raw material of population statistics. Each person in this crowd is an individual, but statisticians can classify individuals into groups with similar characteristics.
2 The SET meter is a means of measuring the number of people watching television at any moment. About 2,500 homes in Britain, a sample of the viewing public, are fitted with these devices.

than rises in other commodities like fish, which we may buy only rarely.

To get a true picture of what retail price changes mean in terms of the cost of living, statisticians use a procedure called 'weighting'. One way of weighting a commodity is to weight it by its importance, in this case by the amount spent on it. If we spend ten times as much on buying bread as on buying fish, bread should have ten times the weight.

It is quite clear that if the Index is to have any meaning the basic facts must be as accurate as possible. There is little point in conducting a survey of what people spend on coal in June or July because this would be quite unrepresentative of what they spend on coal over the whole year. It would equally be misleading to take coal prices only from mining areas where prices are generally lower than in areas remote from the pits.

Index of Retail Prices

Preparation for the Index for 1956 began with a survey over a period of 12 months during 1953 and 1954 in which information was obtained from nearly 13,000

1 Games of chance, like roulette, were the first material for statistical studies of probability or the likelihood of events. In roulette, the odds favour the 'bank'.

2 Throwing dice is one way of arriving at really random numbers. Every face has an equal chance of appearing. Computers are nowadays used to generate tables of random numbers.

households on their expenditure over three consecutive weeks. Individual budgets were collected, spread out over the seasons to eliminate seasonal changes and over a wide area to eliminate regional variations. The very poor and very rich were excluded from the survey. Goods were divided in 91 categories, and once the system had got going the price of each of the categories was re-examined and re-calculated every month. This Index started in 1956 on the basis of the 1953/54 survey and used these prices adjusted to 1956 values.

One of the problems with the Index of Retail Prices is that people's tastes and habits change and that what once might have been considered a luxury may come to be thought a necessity. Consequently, new goods may have to be added to the Index and the pattern of consumption, and therefore the weighting, may change with changing tastes.

These changes are taken into account and weightings revised as necessary. Later surveys have used some 3,000 typical households as the yardstick for the whole country.

The Index is not perfect but it can measure within useful limits the changes in prices of food and other goods and services purchased by most households.

How much information is required to give us the answers we need? In formulating the Index of Retail Prices the statisticians did not require that every household in the country be questioned to provide the facts they wanted. Similarly, when we read that last night eight million people were viewing a popular programme on television the figure was arrived at by questioning a very small sample of the viewing public. Most of us have never been interviewed by a political pollster,

but with some notable exceptions the pollsters have a fair record of successfully predicting how we vote from a remarkably small sample of voters.

In the British Population Census of 1961 all households were asked certain basic questions, but only one in ten was asked for far more detailed information. Because modern government and business needs firm information at more frequent periods than the traditional ten-year census interval, an intermediate census was taken in 1966 and this was achieved on a sample basis. The two elections in the United States which left the pollsters looking silly were in 1936 and 1948. In a sense it was not the statisticians' fault because the samples which were provided were not representative. Analysis afterwards showed that in both cases the selection of people interviewed in the sample had mostly been in the higher income-bracket or were people with higher educations. This mistake shows that sampling must be carried out with care to avoid the sample having an in-built bias.

To overcome this problem it is necessary to ensure that the sample is taken at random. This means that every person must have the same chance of selection as his fellows. The surprising thing about

sampling techniques is that provided the sample is truly random and of reasonable size, its accuracy is maintained over quite wide proportions. A sample of 2,000 in a population of 200,000 need be no less accurate for a population of two million. A striking practical example is that with a voting population of 35 million in Britain a sample of only 2,500 or so – less than one person in 10,000 – gives a fairly accurate prediction of voting intentions.

Random sampling techniques are used extensively in industry in such applications as inspection of products. From a batch of parts or products only a few will be inspected. If none is found faulty then the probability is that the whole batch from which the sample was taken is perfect.

A useful tool

Statistics is an advanced science with a sophisticated vocabulary and a number of important elaborations over and above the simple examples quoted above. In sampling, for example, there are factors such as the standard error, the theory of probability and more advanced or specialized methods such as stratified sampling, multi-stage sampling and quota sampling.

An elementary understanding of statistics is not difficult to attain even without knowledge of higher mathematics, although some skill in arithmetic is necessary. Such an understanding of statistics will reveal the limitation of the science and makes it possible to distinguish the difference between meaningful figures and those which are 'dressed up to deceive'.

Not that statisticians are dishonest. The professional statistician is trained to examine the reliability of his data with some care and to maintain this cautious attitude throughout his calculations. In reality, statistics are only a useful tool for helping us make up or own minds.

Statistics has its limitations as a guide to future action, of course. Predictions based on statistical observations have to make very many assumptions about the way in which the trends being examined are likely to go in the future. This was one of the problems that led the British government to drop its National Plan, a prediction of future trends in the economy that drew heavily on statistical material to work out its conclusions.

In order to predict on the basis of statistical data it is necessary for the statistician to construct a model of the present situation and use it to predict likely trends in the future. Two difficulties arise here. One is that new factors, which could not be foreseen at the time of drawing up the plan, tend to interfere with the working out of the model in practice. In the case of the National Plan, say, it would have been hard to foresee the full scope of such outside eventualities as a dollar crisis. Secondly, the plan must be based on a model which reflects reality. Many would maintain that the National Plan contained elements of wishful thinking.

Problems of waste

Human communities create vast amounts of waste material which can contribute to air and water pollution and to disease. The smooth running of our cities demands a vast waste-disposal industry.

THERE ARE four fundamentals to the creation and maintenance of a hygienic environment in which Man can live with his fellows in reasonable good health. They are: clean surroundings, fresh air, pure water supply and the efficient disposal of domestic and industrial waste. The Greeks and Romans had the right ideas in these respects with their public baths, aqueducts and drainage systems. Unfortunately the fall of the Roman Empire not only ushered in the Dark Ages of learning and culture, it also saw the eclipse of hygienic living.

Matters became worse with the development of towns, when people were herded into verminous and rat-infested buildings where there was neither sanitation nor fresh running water and the very rudiments of hygiene were unknown. As a consequence millions of people fell victim to bubonic plague, smallpox, typhoid, cholera and other epidemic diseases which could have been held in check by the most elementary practice of hygiene. Windows were made small and rooms and beds heavily curtained to keep out fresh air which was thought to carry disease. Drinking water was taken from rivers into which human and household waste was emptied; in fact, the rivers that provided

1 Sewer workers inspect the junction between the main Fleet sewer and one of its tributaries. The junction is just below London's Ludgate Circus. The main sewer was once the Fleet River.
2 Bathers at Hoylake, Cheshire, swim in a pool of sea-water close to the end of a large sewage outfall pipe. Sewage needs careful treatment before it can safely be released.
3 An aerial view of a modern sewage-treatment plant at Colne Valley, Yorkshire. Primary sewage passes first through the settling tanks in the background and is purified in the round tanks.

towns and cities with their water supplies were also noisesome sewers. Personal cleanliness was practically non-existent: many people never had a bath in their lives and seldom troubled even to wash their faces and hands. Bathing was as unpopular with the wealthy as with the poor, and great mansions that boasted rooms hung with rare paintings and elaborate tapestries did not possess a single bathroom. No wonder both men and women drenched themselves in perfumes; they had to conceal the unpleasant smells of their unwashed bodies.

With the Industrial Revolution in the mid-eighteenth century, hygiene reached its nadir. More and more people were attracted away from the relatively hygienic conditions of the countryside to the squalor of the towns, which became more and more overcrowded. Fresh air, sanitation and pure water supplies were practically unknown, so that the general health of industrial nations rapidly deteriorated. Natural hazards from disease were magnified enormously by the concentration within small areas of ever expanding populations and industries drawing their water supplies from sources into which sewage of every description was emptied.

Matters had reached such a sorry pass that in the mid-eighteenth century the average length of life was only 35 years. By 1950 life expectancy had jumped to 67 years, and it is now moving towards the Biblical promise of three score years and ten. This remarkable achievement is due, at least in part, to the phenomenal advance in public hygiene, and to this the chemist has made the major contribution.

Because so many streams and rivers, particularly in thickly populated and highly industrialized areas, perform the dual function of water supply and sewage disposal, the hygiene scientist's first step to create a hygienic environment has been to dispose of sewage in such manner that it cannot pollute water supplies.

False theory

Sewage is mainly water and its most dangerous constituent is the human waste resulting from the chemical changes that food and drink undergo in the body. This represents a constant menace as it is the ideal breeding medium for germs and bacteria. This did not worry the authorities, who believed that the oxygen in stream and river water helped to decompose sewage and that the oxygen absorbed by the sewage during decomposition quickly replenished itself to keep the water clean.

It is quite true that oxygen in open water will induce bacterial action that will decompose sewage and render it relatively harmless, but the oxygen is not replenished at a rate sufficient to decompose constant additions to the sewage intake. In time the river or stream becomes little more than a drain. This is not only harmful to human health, but the lack of oxygen in the water leads to the asphyxiation of fish, plants and other organisms. Ultimately the sewage-laden water releases hydrogen sulphide and other evil-smelling gases.

1 Early detergents were difficult to destroy and caused foaming in rivers even after sewage treatment. Here, a weir near the Stratford Avon has stirred up a quantity of persistent foam.

2 Pure water is a luxury. In many parts of the world, as in this Formosan village, the same river serves the inhabitants for washing and drinking, and may serve other communities downstream.

It was not until the mid-nineteenth century that chemists were able to prove the utter fallacy of the self-purification theory. They proved that not only is domestic sewage dangerous, but certain industrial effluents are as well. Among these are the wastes from collieries, gas, chemical and dye works, food factories, iron and steel works and, more recently, oil refineries. This kind of waste is usually more direct in its action than is ordinary domestic sewage. Coal dust, ash, fine cinders and other solid particles form a blanket that destroys plants and other organisms on river beds, besides killing fish by clogging their gills.

Chemists have shown that sewage containing compounds of zinc, copper, lead and ammonium salts has toxic properties and destroys life by upsetting its biochemistry. Where there is a combination of low oxygen concentration and even a small percentage of toxic chemicals, pollution becomes particularly lethal. Although the oxygen content of a river may be relatively high, chemical pollution will kill practically all organisms living in the river.

The steadily increasing use of detergents in the home and in industry poses a new and serious problem for chemists concerned with sewage disposal. Many detergents contain the suds-producing agent tetrapropylene benzene sulphate. This chemical is structurally very stable so that it is not easily attacked and broken down by bacterial action. Besides lowering the rate at which open water can receive oxygen from the air, the foam created tends to clog sewage-treatment plants. Chemists have now made available substitute foaming-agents that can be broken down by bacterial action. Another serious source of pollution in sewage lies in the herbicides, insecticides and fungicides used in agriculture. These can be washed from the land to which they have been applied and find their way into drainage systems to retain their lethal properties.

Some idea of the major contribution that industry makes to sewage is indicated by the fact that processing a meat carcase at an abattoir produces waste equal to that produced in one day by 30 people. Laundering 100 pounds of soiled clothing deposits into sewage the amount of waste that would be produced in a day by 24 people. Processing 100 pounds of butter produces wastes equal to those from 34 people. Little wonder that in the days before chemists turned their attention to

hygiene, when sewage was dumped straight into the nearest river or stream, every centre of population was subject to periodic epidemics.

Nowadays, sewage is first piped to a disposal plant where chemists analyse its contents. It then has to be rendered harmless and, in some instances, even made useful. There are several methods of treatment, depending on the nature and quantity of the sewage solid content. First, the heavy inorganic material is removed, often by passing the sewage through a machine called a comminutor, which shreds the coarser materials. Sand and other heavy matter falls into a grit chamber from which it is removed by scrapers.

From the grit chamber the sewage is pumped to settling tanks, where some of the finer material is removed. The settling tanks hold the sewage for two or three hours, during which time a substantial portion settles to the bottom as sludge. These treatments remove about 60 per cent of the suspended solids and 35 per cent of the biochemically active material.

Further purification is carried out by adding to the sewage chemical coagulants such as iron salts or aluminium sulphate. This produces a light mass, called floc, which settles and takes with it a large proportion of the offensive material. Chemical coagulants remove between 80 and 90 per cent of suspended solids.

Science's greatest contribution to sewage treatment is probably the biological process which consists of introducing air into the sewage to encourage the growth of bacteria which attack the organic matter to decompose it quickly. Methods whereby this is achieved are: the intermittent sand-filter, the trickling filter, and activated sludge.

Intermittent sand-filtering requires the minimum of mechanical equipment and consists of a bed of sand below which are drains. The sewage flows over the sand and as it soaks into it, slimy jelly alive with bacteria forms on the surface and traps virtually all the harmful constituents of the sewage. An efficiently operated sand-filter will remove as much as 90 per

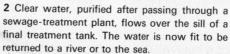

1 Huge volumes of water are needed for industrial and domestic use in large cities. These needs often conflict with local interests, as at the reservoir at Treweryn, North Wales.

2 Clear water, purified after passing through a sewage-treatment plant, flows over the sill of a final treatment tank. The water is now fit to be returned to a river or to the sea.

3 Preparation of activated sludge at a modern sewage-treatment plant. Partially purified sewage is agitated and aerated through compressed-air nozzles along the tank's sides.

cent of suspended solids. This type of plant is expensive to build and to maintain, besides occupying a great deal of ground. At least one acre of sand beds is required to handle a daily intake of 80,000 gallons of sewage – the average amount from 1,000 people.

Trickling filters are cheaper to operate than sand-filters and are just as effective. A trickling filter is a bed of coarse-crushed rock through which the sewage seeps. As it passes through the rock at a faster rate than it would through sand, much less ground area is required. Strictly speaking, the crushed rock does not perform any actual filtering. What it does is to provide a surface on which a bacteria-laden jelly can grow and attack the sewage bacteria. Trickling filters occupying an acre of ground can handle up to 30 million gallons of sewage a day. The continuous flow of sewage through the filter beds washes away excessive amounts of the slime or jelly, so ensuring that air has free access into the bed to encourage growth of the required bacteria. As the effective area of the clinker or crushed stone in the beds is enormous, the plant can handle vast quantities of sewage. Because the organisms need free oxygen to multiply and carry out their action on the sewage, they are said to be *aerobiotic*.

In both the intermittent sand-filter and the trickling filter, the biological slimes or jellies must gather on some collecting medium. With the activated-sludge process, the bacteria-laden slimes form within the sewage itself as air is blown into it. As the slimes float around in the sewage they pick up the dangerous organic matter and decompose it. Sludge then forms and with the sewage goes to a tank where the sludge settles out. Part of the sludge is returned to the sewage entering the aeration tank. In this way, the sewage is constantly seeded with living organisms and the growth of the purifying bacteria is accelerated.

Treating sewage by any of the activated-sludge methods described removes almost all the harmful solids, leaving a clear liquid, which is then sterilized with chlorine and can be pumped as harmless water into a stream or river.

Sludge disposal

Whatever treatment is used, there always remains a large volume of harmful sludge, the disposal of which posed a major problem until it was solved by chemists. The most efficient technique is *anaerobic decomposition*, that is, decomposition by bacteria that grow in the absence of oxygen.

Anaerobic decomposition is carried out in closed tanks which hold the sludge for about three weeks at a temperature of about 33 °C. until it is thoroughly decomposed or, as it is called, digested. At the same time, methane gas is produced and this is used to fire the boilers supplying heat to the digester tanks, and to fuel the motors driving pumps and other equipment.

After sludge has been digested, it contains a high percentage of water which is removed by vacuum drying. Suitably

In Los Angeles, California, air pollution has become such a problem that special patrols are constantly on the alert to check that smog does not exceed acceptable limits.

treated with chemicals, the residue can be sold as fertilizer. Where that is not economically feasible, the sludge residue is burned in incinerators and reduced to an inorganic ash.

The average household needs water for two purposes: drinking and washing, and in each case the requirements differ. Drinking water must be free of harmful bacteria, though its mineral content is not a matter of major concern. On the other hand, water for washing the person and clothes does not have to meet the stringent bacteriological standards of drinking water, but it must be relatively free of dissolved minerals.

Water can be partially purified by a

Water pollution is a serious hazard. In 1969 the accidental release of insecticide into the Rhine killed thousands of the river's fish. It may take years before the stock is fully replenished.

process called coagulation. This involves adding small quantities of calcium hydroxide and aluminium sulphate. These chemicals react to form a colloidal gel which surrounds and traps bacteria and suspended particles. The gel gradually falls through the water and carries the impurities with it to the settling tanks. From the coagulator the water goes to sand-filters to remove the traces of aluminium hydroxide and other suspensions. If necessary, the filtering is supplemented by passing the water through activated-charcoal filters to absorb gaseous impurities that would impart an unpleasant taste.

In most purification plants, the water flows from the filters to a chlorinator, where it is sterilized by dissolving in it chlorine gas. The amount of gas has to be carefully controlled and is determined by careful chemical analysis of the water. Often ammonia gas as well as chlorine are dissolved in the water to combine and form chloramines, which are very efficient sterilizers. In some reservoirs the water is constantly sprayed into the air, so that exposure to oxygen and sunshine will help to destroy harmful bacteria and eliminate unpleasant odours. A somewhat similar result is obtained by running the water in cascades over large surfaces called *aerating tables*.

Clean air is a third fundamental of food hygiene. In populous and industrial areas, the air we breathe can become seriously contaminated by dust, smoke and the carbon monoxide from the exhausts of motor vehicles. In large buildings such as shops and offices where many people congregate, the air becomes stale and very often germ-laden.

Chemistry plays a relatively minor role in ensuring pure air. The problem is either a mechanical one, as in the design of air-conditioning plant, or a legislative one to enforce the burning of smokeless fuels or to limit the emission of carbon monoxide by road transport.

Instruments for death

Since the dawn of time Man has devoted much of his effort and ingenuity to killing his fellow men. Starting with sticks and rocks he has now progressed to devices which threaten the entire planet.

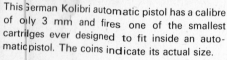

This German Kolibri automatic pistol has a calibre of only 3 mm and fires one of the smallest cartridges ever designed to fit inside an automatic pistol. The coins indicate its actual size.

Built at the Krupp arms factory in Essen, Big Bertha was used to shell Paris from a distance of 40 miles during the First World War. It is one of the largest artillery pieces ever constructed.

THE PROGRESS OF CIVILIZATION runs alongside the sophistication of weaponry – the more civilized we become the better able we are to kill and maim our fellow men. This curious paradox lies at the root of many of the problems of the present day – though science can now bring great benefits to society through its peaceful application it also provides us with vastly improved means of destruction.

Anthropologists speculate about the origins of war and conflict between human beings, but one thing is certain: from very early times weapons have been used not only for hunting and killing game, but for attacking and killing human beings as well.

The frightening array of weaponry that confronts us today – nuclear, chemical and biological weapons, military aircraft, tanks, guns and small arms, together with their sometimes bizarre and ingenious variations – has evolved from small beginnings and become more devastating and sophisticated with the passage of time.

In the process, wars have been transformed from isolated events, in which most people participate only as spectators, to conflicts of world significance which may threaten the future of every one of us.

Present-day weapons can be divided into a number of categories according to the scientific principles which govern their operation. The simplest category involves those weapons that depend for their action on human muscle power. Swords, axes, maces, clubs and their various offspring until quite recent times played a predominant part in warfare. All depend on the delivery of some type of blow with a pointed or cutting edge or with some type of the traditional 'blunt instrument'.

Over the ages, many variations on this theme have been used. The Roman legionaries, for example, favoured short, broad-

The V2 rocket, shown here on its launching pad at Cuxhaven on the Elbe, marked a revolution in rocket warfare. Present-day ballistic missiles owe a great deal to the V2's advanced design.

bladed swords, which were highly effective in hand-to-hand conflict at ground level. Similar considerations dominated the evolution of the short dagger, popular during the battles of the Middle Ages, again for close fighting on the ground.

The horsemen of the Middle Ages, on the other hand, favoured another type of sword: the heavy two-handed variety which could be brought down from above on their victims. Part of the reason for the use of a heavy sword in that period, of course, was the fashion for heavy body armour which prevented lighter weapons from being effective.

Spears, pikes and lances represent another simple type of weapon with a long history. The most sophisticated spears were the halberds, used by foot soldiers in the fourteenth and fifteenth centuries. The halberd was an eight-foot spear which had a combined axe-head, hook and point attached to it. Halberdiers were frequently able to withstand cavalry charges with these weapons.

The projectile has some obvious advantages over the close-combat weapons. It can kill from far off without necessitating close combat. The simplest type of projectile is the sling-shot, which enables missiles to be catapulted further than they can be thrown by hand. The biblical story of David and Goliath indicates the antiquity of this type of weapon.

Much more advanced in principle is the bow, of which there are many thousands of varieties. The bow enables its user to store the energy of his muscles in the tensed bowstring and bow. A bow can store considerable amounts of energy and release it in a very short time, thus sending an arrow or bolt further with greater force than would otherwise be the case.

A later development of the original bow came with the crossbow, in which the

1 The Chieftain tank is one of the latest tanks developed by the British army. Tanks were first used in the First World War, where they marked a turning-point in hostilities.
2 A crossbow, of Spanish design, which once belonged to King Louis XII of France. By cranking the handles the bowman could gradually draw back the bowstring, thus tensing the steel bow. Although the rate of firing was slower than with the conventional bow, bolts could be shot over short distances with greater accuracy.
3 Acheulian hand axes give some idea of how the first weapons may have looked. These sharpened flint-stones were found in gravel sediments near the village of Swanscombe in Kent.
4 A print of 1845 showing soldiers of the Royal Artillery practising with an early version of the bazooka. Because of their unreliability these early rocket weapons were not a great success.
5 An early sixteenth-century painting by the Indian artist Paras shows bullocks dragging siege guns for an attack on the fort of Ranthambh, Rajastan, in 1568.

stored energy was accumulated and held mechanically. Though the crossbow could not fire as many shots in a given time as the longbow, its metal bolts were delivered with more accuracy and greater velocity.

The great revolution in weaponry came, of course, with the invention of gunpowder. This mixture of saltpetre (potassium nitrate), sulphur and charcoal was discovered in China, but its properties were first put to full use in the West. The Italian Wars of 1494–1525 saw the first large-scale use of weapons based on gunpowder – firearms. Gunpowder had been known for a number of years before that date – indeed Roger Bacon, the English scholar, wrote a treatise on 'black powder' in the first half of the thirteenth century. But it took time for weapons to be developed that could exploit the new discovery.

The first use of powder was in cannon, and the first cannon were extremely crude. Indeed, in many cases they were as much a danger to the user as to his intended victim. The original cannon were just iron buckets into which powder and stones were loaded and ignited through a hole at the bottom. Later the tubular form, imparting an accurate trajectory to the missile, developed. These weapons were used mainly in sieges and in defending fortifications. Accuracy was difficult to achieve, as it involved tedious calculations with the aid of the quadrant. Cannons were most useful from high on battlements where their accuracy was improved and their range lengthened.

It was in small arms rather than artillery, however, that the most significant changes were to take place. The bowmen who had dominated the battlefields of Europe since the days of Crécy and Agincourt were pushed off the stage of history by the new breed of musketeers.

The arquebus, the first type of small arm, was really a smaller version of the cannon. Though primitive, cumbersome and fairly dangerous to the user, it could kill at 100 yards. Arquebuses were ignited by applying a fuse to the priming powder. Through the succeeding centuries, the development of firearms was rapid. New

methods of igniting the powder – the wheel-lock and the flint-lock – were superseded by the development of the percussion cap. Finally, the modern breechloading cartridge has now almost entirely overtaken every other type of ignition, except in certain specialized uses. Guns, too, underwent very considerable changes. New methods of loading made possible advances in pistol and gun design, such as the invention of repeating pistols and rifles and machine-guns.

Firing without smoke

One of the most important developments that made possible many new weapons was the self-contained metallic cartridge. Bullet, propellant and primer were now supplied in one unit. The copper cartridge case expanded on firing to fill the breech of the gun and then contracted immediately to make easy extraction possible. This is the type of cartridge used in almost all modern firearms.

Gunpowder itself was superseded by the discovery of the new and more efficient smokeless propellants. Smokeless powder, discovered in 1884, was made of a gelatinized mixture of nitroglycerine and guncotton. Not only did it give off considerably less smoke than black powder, but it was a more stable and powerful mixture.

The usefulness of explosives in warfare

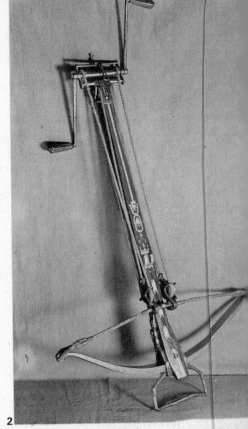

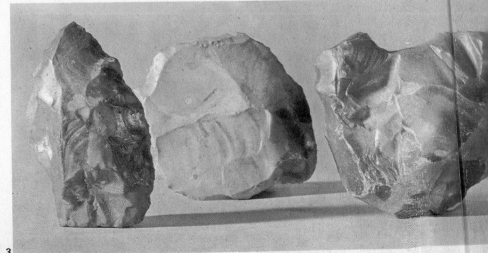

was not, of course, limited to firearms. In the late medieval period, gunpowder was sometimes used to blow up fortifications or to make explosive projectiles. Mines and grenades developed and formed the basis for a new branch of warfare. Grenades, originally crude pots filled with explosive and ignited through a fuse, have advanced enormously – though still in essence very simple. They found particular application in the static trench warfare of the First World War.

The modern grenade really begins with the further development of explosives to produce trinitrotoluene (T.N.T.). Because of its low sensitivity to percussion, its low melting point and its high explosive performance, the T.N.T. grenade was far more reliable than its predecessors. In a scored metal container, the explosive could be relied on to shower an enemy with sharp pieces of metal, thus vastly increasing its killing potential. Other types of grenade were designed to carry noxious gases, like tear gas, to harass the enemy, while others again could be used to lay down smoke-screens.

The mine or bomb – the two were originally almost indistinguishable – contained more explosive than the grenade and was originally used for attacking fortifications (hence 'undermining'). But, particularly in naval warfare, the word mine came to be used to described bombs which, released into the sea, would explode near enemy ships. During the two World Wars, vast areas of sea were mined to prevent enemy ships from venturing into them.

Dropping the bomb

The bomb, on the other hand, really came into its own with the advent of the military aircraft. The early attempts at aerial bombing were not strikingly successful, chiefly because of the difficulty of dropping the missiles sufficiently accurately on target. With the designing of accurate bomb-sights, however, and the building of aircraft capable of carrying larger bombs, air bombing became an extremely effective method of warfare. For the first time, civilians became exposed to the full horrors of war, though they might be hundreds of miles behind the lines. The impersonal character of this method of warfare gave it a potent terrorist value.

Bombs were designed for a wide variety of uses – incendiary, high explosive, armour-piercing, anti-personnel and so on. In some cases, as with the celebrated 'block-busters' used in the raids on the Ruhr Valley dams in 1943, the bombs were specifically tailored to achieve one particular mission.

But the most spectacular bomb of all was only to be developed right at the end of the Second World War. This was the atomic bomb, dropped by American bombers on Hiroshima and Nagasaki. The two cities were razed instantaneously with tens of thousands of deaths. Today, after the invention of the hydrogen bomb, the potential exists to destroy not just cities but whole continents and nations of people.

The hydrogen bomb has since been linked with new forms of rocket to deliver

the weapons at great distances and speeds. The use of rockets to deliver explosive or incendiary weapons is nothing new in warfare: such means of delivery were used by the Chinese in very ancient times. But because of the difficulties of controlling the speed and direction of the primitive rockets of that period it was not until comparatively recently that rockets came to play more than a minor role in warfare. Improvements in propellants, and increased knowledge of the ballistics of rockets, made it possible to design weapons in which a grenade or small explosive charge could be delivered with acceptable accuracy. One weapon of this type, widely used in the Second World War, was the bazooka – a one-man rocket-launcher which delivered a powerful explosive charge for use against tanks. On the eastern front, the Soviet Army made considerable use of rocket-launchers as a substitute for artillery: batteries of rocket-launchers, resembling organ-pipes, were used with devastating effects.

German rocketry was rather more ambitious, and led directly to the design and use of the famous V1 and V2 weapons. The V1 was simply a pilotless plane which was allowed to run in on its target and then glide down when the motor cut out. The V2, its successor, was a far more ambitious project, anticipating in many ways the intercontinental ballistic missiles of today.

Modern rocketry, whether military or civil – and the dividing line between military and civil rocket programmes is often thin – draws on a vast number of sciences to achieve its remarkable feats. The physicist and the engineer, the chemist and the mathematician, are all required to contribute their special skills to the immensely expensive projects which give birth to these monster weapons.

Even the biologists are not left out of the development of modern weapons. Indeed, they may yet produce some of the most devastating weapons of all. Growing public concern has focused attention on the preparations for biological warfare, preparations which have been going ahead in almost all the major countries.

Germs that kill

The principle of biological warfare, of course, is nothing new, but it is only recently that it has been put on a firm scientific basis. In the Middle Ages the poisoning of wells, often by throwing in the bodies of plague victims, was an accepted tactic during siege warfare. Sometimes the bodies of plague victims were lobbed over the walls of a besieged town in an attempt to spread disease.

Such applications were of necessity rather limited in their application, but modern discoveries in biology have completely changed that situation. Now not only can the plague organism, and other organisms causing deadly diseases, be isolated and grown in culture, but their characteristics, their virulence, their power to withstand exposure to air, their temperature tolerance, can be adjusted almost to order by changing their genetic material. Thus microbes can be tailored to

fit particular military requirements.

Apart from the microbes themselves, there is also the possibility of using their poisonous toxins to destroy enemies. Such bacteria as *Clostridia botulina* give rise to poisons so virulent that a pound of botulinum toxin could, in theory, poison every human being on this planet. With weapons like these, polluting wells becomes child's play.

Like the biologist, the chemist is also drawn into the design of new and more bizarre and horrible weapons. During the First World War, large quantities of various disabling gases, like mustard gas,

chlorine and phosgene, were used against enemy troops. These gases killed relatively few of their victims, though many were permanently blinded or maimed. Though similar gases were not used generally in the Second World War, the search has continued for chemical weapons. Among new types developed are the nerve gases, minute quantities of which will paralyse a man completely, and the hallucinogens, with an action similar to the drug LSD.

These frightening new weapons underline the truth of the paradox that the nearer we get to 'civilization' the closer we come to killing the world.

1 An engraving showing naval gunners practising with a 100-pounder Armstrong gun in 1862. This type of gun was one of the first breech-loading artillery pieces introduced into the Navy.

2 An Amazonian indian fishing from his dug-out with bow and arrow. Despite his apparently primitive equipment, he is able to use the bow with remarkable accuracy.

A better life or utter chaos?

Through technology Man hoped to conquer the world but these hopes have not been realized. If he is to have a future, he must clear up the mess he has made and use his knowledge with greater care.

THE TWENTIETH CENTURY opened with glorious prospects. Great steamships were crossing the oceans. Motoring had arrived. Railways had reached an advanced stage of development. The Industrial Revolution had shown the way to cheap consumer goods for everyone. The electric telegraph was well established and the telephone 'was becoming commonplace.

In 1901, the extraordinary young man Guglielmo Marconi demonstrated that it was possible to send messages through space over vast distances without the use of cables. In 1903, Orville Wright made the first hesitant flight in a heavier-than-air flying machine.

It seemed then that nothing was impossible. Scientists, engineers and technologists had the world in their grasp. With patient development of all the new inventions and with parallel advances in the science of medicine to prolong human life, the prospects for mankind looked brighter than at any other time in history. The good life was already on its way.

Looking back from our vantage point we see that the dreamer at the turn of the century had little idea of future developments. Now there are scores of thousands of electronic computers in daily use, millions of cars and television receivers, nuclear power stations, laser beams, electronic microcircuits no bigger than a pinhead, processed foods, pest control, synthetic fibres, and space travel. The good life has arrived.

In November 1965 an area of 80,000 square miles of northeastern United States and Canada was plunged into darkness through a single failure on the electricity power grid system. The result was chaos. No one had realized quite how dependent on the electricity supply Man had become. People were trapped in lifts between floors, radio and television went off the air, traffic signals were out of action, meals were left half-cooked and there was not only chaos, but panic and fear.

The surprising thing about this episode was that the control system of the grid network had been designed to eliminate such a possibility. If one community supply becomes overloaded, then additional electric power is routed in from an area which is lightly loaded. At least, this was the theory. In this instance, a relay on one feeder line at one power station failed and put an unexpected surge of power on to the other feeders from the generating station. The shock wave rippled round the network triggering off safety switches in station after station until several cities, including

New York, had been completely blacked out. The elaborate automatic control system, so carefully designed to take care of every eventuality, had operated in a way quite contrary to the designers' intentions.

This single event raised the question of whether the engineers were being too clever. Had we reached the stage where the man-made machine could, in fact, turn on Man and destroy him? Was this a twentieth-century example of Man creating a monster which he was unable to control?

Danger to health

In 1953 United States scientists believed that radioactive fall-out from nuclear-weapon tests in the atmosphere would be uniform over the globe and that no single area would receive fall-out doses which would be a danger to health. In 1957 it was being said that the fall-out from the stratosphere would be quite slow, allowing plenty of time for the natural decay of radio-isotopes. We now know that fall-out is not evenly distributed and that it descends to the Earth much more quickly than was believed possible.

In 1957, when farmers in the Mississippi Valley started using a pesticide called endrin, a chemical relation of DDT, they could hardly have been expected to realize that a few years later the Mississippi River would be full of dead fish. In Europe a similar mishap came to light when, in June 1969, millions of dead fish were found in the Rhine, which has now been dubbed Europe's sewer.

Not only is the world population increasing at a prodigious rate but each man, woman and child is consuming more of the world's resources. Paul Ehrlich of Stanford University has estimated that in 70 years of life an American citizen uses 26 million gallons of water and 21,000 gallons of petrol. Figures like this remind us that the natural resources of our world are not limitless. Energy reserves in coal and petroleum are being quickly used up. The same applies to other raw materials, both metallic and non-metallic.

In using up our natural resources we are creating new problems. When we burn a ton of coal, wood, petroleum or natural gas we contribute large amounts of carbon dioxide to the atmosphere. In 100 years, from 1860 to 1960, we added 14 per cent to the carbon-dioxide content of the air. Carbon dioxide tends to pass visible light but to absorb infra-red rays, just as glass does in a greenhouse. Scientists are now suggesting that further significant increases in the carbon-dioxide content of the atmosphere may produce a 'greenhouse effect' which could warm up the globe to a level which will melt the Arctic and Antarctic ice-caps and flood our major cities.

A counter-argument claims that the world might get colder. Smog pollution of the atmosphere might effectively act like an increase of low-cloud, shielding off the warming sun's rays and start a return to the Ice Age.

Naturally, there is scientific controversy over a number of points. But there is no controversy over the fact that we are beginning to suffer from ignorance of the long-term effects of our exploitation of

In June 1969, millions of fish in the Rhine were killed after a factory in Germany had accidentally released a poison into the river. Such disasters are on the increase.

nature. It may be arguable whether the world will still be habitable by the year 2000 A D but there is no argument that something should be done now to stop the unconsidered use of chemicals and fuels which are making our world a cess-pit and upsetting the natural balance of nature.

The situation is becoming so serious that even politicians have begun to take notice. President Nixon in his January 1970 State of the Union Message said, 'The great question of the 70s is shall we surrender to our surroundings or shall we make our peace with nature and begin to make reparation for the damage we have done to our air, to our land, and to our water?' The same question has been asked by Prime Minister Wilson in the United Kingdom and by other world leaders.

Unquestionably, the key problem of modern governments is to employ science to check the drift to destruction. Within the main problem the physical scientists have their own subsidiary problems which can help in the solution of the whole. But central to the issue is how far the individual is prepared to go to make the solution possible. At a seminar on 'Man and the Future' staged to celebrate the centennial of the University of Kansas, the question of atmospheric pollution by the motor-car was forcibly raised and the delegates were unanimous in their condemnation of the motor-car as a menace to civilization. And yet, at the conclusion of their deliberations, they left the auditorium and climbed into their cars and drove away in the modern invention they had only a few minutes earlier condemned. The human motivation to use a convenient form of transport had already overcome their convictions.

The problem of carbon-monoxide production in exhaust gases from cars is already receiving attention. New cars emerging from the factories in the United States in 1971 will belch out only 37 per cent as much carbon monoxide as in 1960 but the engine modifications, which will achieve the reduction, will be putting out more nitrogen compounds resulting in a

1 Nuclear power stations provide an answer to the eventual shortage of fossil fuels. Yet disposal of their radioactive waste presents a major problem for the future.

2 The demand for water for domestic and industrial use is increasing rapidly. To meet it, water containing effluent can be re-cycled in special plants and made fit for consumption.

3 In the refinery, oil is transformed into fuel that keeps industries running. But when oil is burnt, large amounts of carbon dioxide are released into the atmosphere which may change the climates.

Autoclaves, 45c–6a
'Automatic pilot', 211b; *212*
Automation, 341a–4c
Averages (arithmetic), 256c
Aviation, civil
radar used in, 134b–5c; *135, 136*
supersonic, 144b–c; *143*
see also **Aircraft**
Avogadro, Amadeo, 4c
his Hypothesis, 4c
Axe, prehistoric, *470*
Axes, rectilinear, *see* **Rectilinear axes**
Axiom (mathematics), 225a, 238a
in the new mathematics, 233b–c
Azoic dyes, 379a–b
Aztecs
calendar of, *275*
observatory of, *273*

B

Baade, W., 290a
Babbage, Charles, 120b–c, 261b–2a
Babylonians, 273b–c
Bach, Johann Sebastian, 268c; *148*
Bain, Alexander, 368a
Baird, John Logie, 443b–c; *137*
Bakelite, 370b, c–1a, 396a
Baking soda, *see* **Sodium bicarbonate**
Balance wheel (in watches), 367b; *367*
Balard, A.-J., 36b
Ball bearing, 303c
Ballistic Missile Early Warning Station (Fylingdales), 134b; *133*
Balloons, 222a, 297a
Bernina, 223
eighteenth-century, *297*
in astronomy, 278a–c
in meteorology, 136c; *76*
Ball-point pen, 269a–71c; *269*
Balmer, J.J., 166b
Band spectrum, 166a
Bardeen, J., 112a
Barium, 62b, 71a,b
compounds of, 72b
in X-ray examinations, 72b–c
Barnard's Star, 288c
Barometer, mercury, 73b–c, 224a
Base (chemistry), 30a–2c
Base ten (decimal) number system, 230a
Base two (binary) number system, 230a–c
computer use of, 230a, 263a
Basic dyes, 378a–b
Bat, echo-sounding used by, *134; 163*
Bathyscaphe *Trieste, 224*
Battery, 362a
for electric vehicles, 362a
torch, 361a–b
Bauxite, 62b, 363c; *351*
Bayeux tapestry, comet in, *275*

Bazooka, 472a; *471*
Beam bridge, 307c–8a
Bearing (engineering), 303c–4a
Beilstein test, 50c–1a
Bell, Alexander Graham, 137a
his telephone, 137a; *140*
Belladonna, 409a
Bell pit (coal-mining), 326a
Benbecula, radio beacon on, *322*
Ben Franklin (research ship), 392c
Benz, Otto, 313a; *313*
Benzaldehyde, 377c
Benzene, 15c, 370a, 377c; *14*
Beriberi, 406a–b
Bernoulli, Daniel, 74a
Bernoulli's Theorem, 224c, 297b
Berthelot, Marcelin, 80b
Berthollet, Claude, 35c–6a
Bertone, Nuccio, *302*
Beryllium, 62b, 71a
alloyed with steel, 68b
Beryllium-oxide ceramics, 383b
Berzelius, Jöns Jacob, *25*
Bessemer, Henry, 354a
Bessemer process, 354a–5c, 356a
Beta rays, 117b, 170b, 174c
Betatron, 174c
Betelgeuse, 288a
Betel nut, 410c
Bicheroux process, 384b
Bicycle pump, 190a
Bifid bow (ship), 386a
Big bang theory, 291c
Big Bertha (gun), *469*
Bile acids, 411c, 412a
Binary comparator, 260c
Binary number system, *see* **Base two number system**
Binoculars, prism, 430a
Biological warfare, 472a–b
Biplane, 298a
Bireme, 386a
Birkland-Eyde process, 86b–c
Bismuth, 349b
Bitumen (asphalt)
in road surfacing, 309a, 310c–11b, 311c
Trinidad asphalt lake, 311b; *310*
Black body (astronomy), 165a, 170a
Blast-furnace, 353b–4a; *160*
Bleaching powder, 36a
Blister steel, 353b
Block (printing), *see* **Photoengraving**
Bloembergen, Nicolaas, 130a
Blood
banks of, 192c
in forensic science, 447c–8a
refrigeration of, 192b–c
Blotting paper, 23c
Body, human
combustion in, 185b
elements found in, 460c
temperature of, 158c–9a
see also **Food**
Bohr, Niels, 10a, 166b–c, 169c; *169*
Boiling, 24b
boiling point of water, 194a–b, 196c
Bolometer, *see* **Germanium bolometer**
Boltzmann, Ludwig, 165a
Bomb, 471c
see also **Atomic bomb; Hydrogen bomb**
Bondi, Hermann, 290a
Bone china, 382a
Boole, George, 257c
Boolean algebra, 257b–60c
Boot, H.A.H., 134a
Borax, *see* **Sodium borate**
Borax bead test, 449b
Borelli, Giovanni, 297a
Boron carbide, 44a
Bosch process, 78b
Bose-Einstein statistics, 172a
Bottle opener, 421c
Boulton, Matthew, 338a
Bow (weapon), 469c–70a
Boyle, Robert, 1c–2b, 73b, c–4a, 185a; *76*
Boyle's Law, 73c–4b
Boys, Sir Charles Vernon, 214c–15a; *216*

Bragg, Sir Lawrence, 14a, 125c–6a, 127a, 128a, 351c–2a; *16*
Bragg, Sir William Henry, 14a, 125b, c–6a, 127a–b; *16*
Bragg's Law, 126a
Brake, hydraulic, *see* **Hydraulic brake**
Brandt, Henning, 38c
Brass, 67c
Brass musical instruments, 147a–8a
brass band, *146*
Braun, Karl, 215a
Braun, Werner von, 300a
Bravais, Auguste, 57b–c
Breathalyser, 50a
Bridge, 306c, 307c–8a
arch, 307c, 308a
beam, 307c–8a
cantilever, 307c, 308a–b; *305*
suspension, 307c, 308a,b
Sydney Harbour bridge, 308a
Tower Bridge, *307*
Britannia (paddle-steamer), *333*
British Broadcasting Corporation, 443b,c
Crystal Palace aerial of, *443*
British Isles
Gulf Stream and climate of, 194b
British thermal unit, 160a
Broadcasting (radio), 442a–3b
Broglie, Louis de, 156c, 164b, 168a, 171b
Bromine, 33a, b, 36c
Brønsted, J.N., 30c
Bronze, 67b–c, 349a
Brown, Robert, 74c
Brownian motion, 74c–5a
Brunel, Marc Isambard, 308c
Bullet, in forensic science, 446a, 448c
Buna S, 372a
Bunt, 403b
Burglar alarm, photo-electric, 168a, 364c
Burning, *see* **Combustion**
Butadiene, 372a
Butane gas, 15a–c

C

Cable, electric, 67c
first transatlantic, 137a, 441a,c
Cadmium, in nuclear reactor, 318a
Caesium, 69a, 349b
atomic clock, 252a, 368c; *249*
Caffeine, 410a, b, 411c
Calcium, 62b, 71a–b
alloying of, 67c
and water, 78a
composition of, 12b
in food, 405c
valence of, 26a
Calcium carbide, 43c, 85c
Calcium carbonate, 44b, c, 71a
chalk, 71a, 81a; *70*
coral, *71*
limestone, 72a
Calcium cyanamide, 85c
Calcium hydride (hydrolith), 78c
Calcium hydroxide (slaked lime) 26a, 71c; *32*

Calcium phosphate, 38a–b
Calcium sulphate, 26a, 86a
hydrated, see Gypsum
Calculating machine, 261a–2a
see also Computer
Calder Hall atomic power station, 320c
Calendar, Aztec, 275
Caliper gauge, 250a
Caloric theory, 181a–c
Calorie, 160a, 178a–b, 183a, 422a
in food, 405c–6a
Calorimeter, 160c; 159
Camera, 433a–b
f-numbers on, 433b
focal length of, 431b
fuzziness, cause of, in simple cameras, 433a–b
lens of, 430a–2a, 433a–b; 433
telephoto, 432c
shutter of, 433b
upside-down image in, 433a; 433
Candle clock, 366b
Canes Venatici, nebula in, 286
Canning (of food), 407c–8a
Cannizzaro, Stanislao, 4c
Cannon, 470a; 469
Can-opener, 423
Canopus, 288a
Cantilever bridge, 307c, 308a–b; 305
Cantor, Georg, 230c–2c, 236c
Canvey Island, desalination plant on, 196
Capacitive reactance, 115a
Capacitor (condenser), 114b–15a
in air-conditioning, 415b
Capella, 288a
Capillary action, capillarity, 23c, 195c–6a
Capstan, 220c; 219
Car, see Motor car
Carbides, 43c–4a
Carbohydrates, 405c–6a
Carbolic acid, see Phenol
Carbon, 41a–4c
and co-valent bonding, 15a–c
atomic weight of, 7a
basis of living things, 41a, 45a, 369a
carbon 10, 42c
carbon 11, 42c
carbon 12, 25b, 41a
carbon 13, 41a
carbon 14, 41a, 324a–c
in coal, 329b–c
in nylon, 370a
in oil, 329c, 345a–b
nucleus of atom of, 7a, 8b
resistivity of, 350b
tetravalent atoms of, 49a
Carbonates, 26a
Carbon dioxide, 25b, 26c–8c, 43c, 44a–b
in soda water, 199c
in the atmosphere, 473c
Carbonic acid, 44b, c
Carboniferous period, coal formed in, 329b
Carbon monoxide, 43c, 44a
Carbon steels, 356c
Carbon tetrachloride, petrol fires fought with 48
Carbonyls, 44a
Carborundum, see Silicon carbide
Cardan shaft, 314a
Cardinality (cardinal number; of a set), 232a–c
Carlisle, A., 97a
Carnallite, 69a
Carnot, Nicolas, 179a
Carotene, 406b
Carothers, Wallace, 369a–c, 375b
Carroll, Lewis (Charles Dodgson), 268c; 257
Cartesian geometry, see Co-ordinate geometry
Cartridge, 470b
Caruso, Enrico, 149a
Carvel construction (ships), 386b
Cascade casting (steel), 356b
Catalan forge, 353a
Catalyst, 80a–b
water as, 196b

Catalytic cracking, 45a, 332b, 348b; 347, 348
Catapult, 220
Catenary, 308b
Cathedral
arch used in building of, 307c
Liverpool, 308
Wells, 307
Cathode, 5b, 95c, 361a
Cathode rays, 5a–c, 125a–b
also called electron beam, 170a
cathode-ray tube, 107c–8a, 118c–19a; 172
Cation, 362a
Caustic potash, see Potassium hydroxide
Caustic soda, 70a
Cavendish, Henry, 77a, 94a, 193a; 80
Caves, 72a
Cayley, Sir George, 297a
Cell (living organisms), 405b
Cell, electric, 198b, 361a–2a
photo-electric cell, 168a, 364b–c
Cellulose, 88c, 373a, 375b
Celsius scale, see Centigrade scale
Cement, 71c
Cementation of iron, 353a
Census, 462a–3a, 464b
Centigrade (Celsius) scale, 158a–b
Central heating, steam, 184a
Central Statistical Office, 461c
Centrepoint building (London), 240
Centrifuge, 205a–6b
astronauts and, 206b; 208
Cepheid variables, 288c, 289c–90a
Ceramics, 381a–3b
bone china, 382a
firing of, 381a–b, 382a; 383
glazing of, 381b
oxides in, 383b
porcelain, 381c–2a
pottery, 100c, 381a–b
refractories, 381b–c
Ceres (asteroid), 284c
Chadwick, James, 8a–b; 319
Chain reaction, nuclear, 317b–18a, 319c
Chairoplanes, 206b–c
Chalk (calcium carbonate), 71a; 70
Challenger, H.M.S., 390b; 389
Champagne, bottling of, 200
Charcoal, 41a, 43c
Charles, Jacques, 75a–b
Charles's Law, 75b,c
Chase (printing), 437b
Château Villandry, formal garden at, 239
Cheddar, Gough's Cave at, 195
Chemistry, 16c, 25a–8c
analytical, 449a–52c
and electricity, see Electro-chemistry
industrial, 393a–6c
in farming, 401a–4c
inorganic, 449a
organic, 44c–9c, 369a, 449a
Chieftain tank, 470
Chile saltpetre, see Sodium nitrate
China, the Chinese
astronomy, 273a
porcelain, 381c–2a
China clay (kaolin), 381c–2a
Chlorates, 36a
Chlorine, 33a,b, 34c–6b
Dumas and, 394c
in dyeing, 377c
in water purification, 468c
valence of, 25c
Chloroform, 34c
Cholesterol, 411c–12a
Chromatography, 49c–50b, 450b, 452b–c; 452
Chrome dyes, 378b
Chrome yellow, 380c
Chromium, 62a
chromium plating, 362a–c
Chronograph, 453c
Chronometer, 367b–c
Cinchona tree ('fever tree'), 410c–11a

Cinchonine, 410c–11a
Circle, 239b–c
circular functions (trigonometry), 244a; 241
circumference of, 239b–c; 237
diameter of, 237
radius of, 239c; 237
similarity of, 239b
Circular motion, 205a–8c, 220c
Circumference (of a circle), 239b–c; 237
Civil (construction) engineering, 301c–2a, 305a–c
Clarinet, 147a
Clausius, Rudolph, 179b
Clay
china clay, 381c–2a
in pottery, 381a–b
Clegg, Samuel, 330a
Clinker construction (ships), 386b
Clock, 366a–8c
astronomical, 292
atomic, 368b–c; 366
ammonia, 130a, 368b
caesium, 252a, 368c; 249
hydrogen, 175b
candle, 366b
electric, 367c–8a
gravitational drawback with, 252a
mechanical, 366b–7c
pendulum in, 366c–7a
spring in, 367a–b; 367
quartz, 252a, 368a–b; 365
shadow, 366a
water, 366a–b; 366
Clock arithmetic, see Modular arithmetic
Cloth, 376b–c
Clothes, see Textile industry
Cloud, cumulus, 194
Cloud chamber, 202b, 294a–b; 5, 172
Coal, 329a–c
carbon content of, 329b–c
gas distilled from, see Coal Gas
hydrogen content of, 329b–c
mining of, 325a–8c; 41, 326, 328
long-wall method, 327c
mechanical, 327c–8c
open-cast, 328a
room and pillar method, 327b–c
upcast and downcast shafts, 326a
origin of, 329b
products of, 331c
food, 331c
Coal gas, 330a–1c
Cobalt, 349c
Cocaine ('snow'), 410a,c
Cockroft, Sir John, 176a
Codeine, 410a,b, 411b–c
Codons, 47c–8b
Coffee, caffeine in, 411c
Cog wheels, 423
Coke, 43c, 328b–c, 331a–b
coke fire, 44a
in smelting, 353c
Cola nuts, 411c
Cold, 189a
See also Absolute zero temperature
Collimator, 429
Colloids, 200a–b
Colour photography, 435b–6c
Colour printing, 440a
Colours of the spectrum, 121a–b, 153c–4a
Column chromatography, 452c
Coma Berenices, nebula in, 285
Combine harvester, 398a–b; 399
Combustion (burning), 185a–8c
spontaneous, 187a
Comet
in Bayeux tapestry, 275
Jurlof-Achmanof, 285
Comminutor, 467b
Commutator, 106a
Compass, magnetic, 103c–4a
deviation in, 212b
variation and, 212b
Composing stick (printing), 438
Compounds, chemical, 25b–8c
Compression (engineering), 305c–6a
in the arch, 306c
Compton, A.H., 168a, 170a,

293a
Compton effect, 168a, 170a
Computer, 120b-c, 261a-4c, 344c; *260, 261, 262, 263, 264*
base two (binary) number system used in, 230a, 263a
  multiplication replaced by addition, 254b
Boolean algebra and, 260a,c
digital, 342a
electronics and, 262b-c
future domestic use of, 428a
in astronomy, 280c
in automation, 341c-2a
integrated circuit in, 262c; *264*
programming of, 262a
superconductivity and, 192a
time-sharing and, 264b-c
transistors in, 262b-c
Concorde, *143, 251*
Concrete, 305c-6b
reinforced, 305c-6a
Condenser, *see* Capacitor
Congo red, 31c
Congruence (geometry), 238c-9a; *237*
Conical pendulum, 206c, 208a; *208*
Coniine, 410c
Conjugate base, 30c
Conservation of angular momentum, 209c-10a
Constant-pressure gas thermometer, 75c
Constant-volume gas thermometer, 75b-c
Construction engineering, *see* Civil engineering
Container ship, 388c
Continuous creation theory, *see* Steady state theory
Contraceptive pill, 412a
Convection, 181a,c-2a
Cooking, infra-red, 425a-b
Coolidge tube, 125c
Co-ordinate (algebraic, analytical, cartesian) geometry, 240a
Co-ordinates (axes), rectilinear, *see* Rectilinear axes
Copernicus, 292b
Copolymers, 56c
Copper, 62a, 349b
as conductor of electricity, 96a, 350b
crystal structure of, 59b
in chromium plating, 362b
mining of, *325, 326, 327, 350*
Copper oxide, 30a
Coral, *71*
Cordite, 88c
Corn binder, *398*
Corona, of the sun, *20*
Coronograph, *280*
Corpus luteum, 412a
Cosecant, 242a
Cosine, 241c
Cosine Rule, 242a, 243a
Cosmic rays, 293a-6c
  photography, 436c
Cosmos, *see* Universe
Cotangent, 241c-2a
Cotton, 373a, 374a, 375c
  Arkwright and, *460*
  damp atmosphere needed for cotton industry, 413b
mechanical harvesting of, *397*
Coulomb, Charles de, 93c-4a
Coulomb's Law (inverse square law), 93c-4a
Counting, *see* Numbers
Couple (forces about an axis), 210a, 220c; *211, 219*
Courtois B., 36c
Co-valent bonding, 10b, 14c-16c, 53a, 58a
Crab nebula, *79, 296*
Cracking (oil refining), 346a
see also Catalytic cracking; Thermal cracking
Creep, 359c
Crete, Minoan ships of, 386a; *385*
Crick, Francis, 47c
Crime, criminals, science in detection of, *see* Forensic science
Critical path analysis, 271c-2a

Critical temperature (of a gas), 24c
Crivelli, Carlo, his *Annunciation*, 267
Crooke's radiometer, *167*
Crookes, Sir William, 90a; *295*
Crop stripper, 398a-b
Crossbow, 469c-70a; *470*
Crowbar, *423*
Cryogenics, 189a-92c
Crystalloids, 200a-b
Crystal Palace
B.B.C. television aerial at, *443*
Tartan running track at, 456a
Crystals, crystallography, 57a-60c
metals, crystalline structure of, 58c, 61a-c, 359a-b
X-rays in crystallography, 59c, 127a-8a; *16*
Crystal wireless set, 138a
Cube
geometry of, 240a
supercube, see Tesseract
Cugnot, Nicolas Joseph, 338b-c
Cullet, 384a
Culross (Fife), coal-mining at, 325c
Cumulus cloud, *194*
Cupro-nickel, 68b
Curare, 409a, 410a
Curie, Madame, 71b
Current, ocean, 392c
Cut and cover method (engineering), 308c
Cutty Sark, 387
Cyclotron, 174c; *318, 323*
Cylinder printing press, *see* Rotary printing press
Cytosine, 47c

D

Dalton, John, 2c-4c; *2, 2-3, 3, 4*
Dam
curvature of retaining wall of, 307c
Hoover Dam, *307*
Damascus, steel swords of, 61a
Darby, Abraham, 353c
Davy, Sir Humphry, 30b, 69a, 71b, 86c, 89a, 193a; *69*
Day, 365a
sidereal, 365c
solar, 365b
Dead-beat escapement, 367a
Decibels, 144a, 150b
Decimal number system, *see* Base ten number system
Dedekind, Richard, 236c
De Forest, Lee, 108c, 118a, 442a
Dehydration of food, 408b
Deimos (moon of Mars), 284b
Democritus, 1a-b; *2*
Dendrites, 61c
Deneb, 288a
Density, 194a, 221c-2a

of water, 194a
Dental anaesthesia, 86c-7a
Derivation (mathematics), 236b
Desalination of sea water, 364a; *32, 196*
Descartes, René, 240a
Desoxy-ribose, 47c
Detergents, 23c, 48c, 417a-18c
biological, 418b
foam from, 466c-7a; *466*
Deuterium (heavy hydrogen), 18a, 77c-8a, 193a
Deuterium oxide (heavy water), 77c-8a, 193a, 319c; *196*
Developing (processing) of photographic film, 433c-6a
Dewdrop, *193*
Dewar flask, *see* Thermos flask
Dewline, *see* Distant Early Warning Line
Di-acid, 46a
Diamagnetic materials, 104c
Diameter (of a circle), *237*
Di-amine, 46a
Diamond, 41a, 42c, 58a-b; *42, 60*
cut by laser beam, *131*
mining of, *327*
Diaphragm (iris; camera), 433b
Diatomic gases, 26b
Dielectric, 114b
Diesel, Rudolf, 335c, 388a
Diesel engine, see Internal combustion engine, diesel
Difference engine (Babbage), 261c, 262a
Diffraction, 170b-1b
of electrons, 16c, 170b-1b
of light, 156a
Diffraction grating, 156a, 279c
Digestion of food, 185b, 196b-c, 197a
Digitalis, 412b
Dihedral, 298c
Dimensions, 240c
fourth, 225c-6a, 240c
Diode valve, 108b-c, 117c, 442a; *117*
Gunn diode, 136c
Direct current, 112a, 113a
Direct dyes, 378b
Dislocation (crystallography), 60a-b
Disproportionation, 54c
Dissociation (electrolysis), 97a-8a
Distant Early Warning Line (Dewline), 134b; *162*
Divers, diving, 224b, 415c-16a; *391, 392, 415*
skin diving, 416a
Division (arithmetic), 254c-6a
Dixon, George, 330a
DNA, 47c-8b
Dodecahedron, *238*
Dodgson, Charles, *see* Carroll, Lewis
Dolomite, 71b
Domain (molecular) theory of magnetism, 102b-c
Door, automatic, 364c
Doppler effect, 135c, 292a
Dorn, Friedrich, 89a, 92c
Double decomposition, 32c
Dounreay nuclear reactor, 320c; *317*
Drag-car racing, 202a; *204*
Drake, Willard, 329c
Drinks
as solutions, 197a
fizzy, 199c
'Drone' aircraft, *442*
Drugs, 409a-12c
alkaloids, 409a-11c, 412c
steroids, 409a, 411c-12c
Drum, 145a-6a
Drum digger, 308c
Dry cell, 361a; *362*
Dry ice, 44b, 408b
Dumas, Jean, 394c-6a
Dunlop, John Boyd, 315b
Duplexing (steel), 356b
De Forest, Lee *(see above)*
Durand, Peter, 407c
Dürer, Albrecht, 268a; *268*
Dust, 413b; *1*
Dyes, 377a-9b
aniline, 396c
fast and fugitive, 378a

first synthetic, 377c
for artificial fibres, 46c–7b
for fabrics, 376b–c, 377a
in the ancient world, 377a–b
Perkin and, 396c
raw materials of, 377c
ten classes of, 378a–9b
Dynamite, 88c; *16*
Dynamo, 105b, 106a–b
Wheatley's 'self-exciting', *108*
Dyne, 202a

E

E (charge on an electron), 5c, 6a–b; *7*
Ear, 149c, 163c
Early Bird (artificial satellite), *114*
Earnshaw, Thomas, 367b
Earth, 283c; *282*
angular momentum of, 220c
a sphere, 275a–b
circular orbit of, 208b
circumference of, 276c
gravity and, 214a–b, 215b–c
magnetism of, 103c–4a, 296a,c
Moon's distance from, 276c, 281a
photographed from the moon, *299*
photographed from space, *283*
procession of, 209b; *209*
radiation belts around, 296c
radius of, 242a
Sun's distance from, 242a, 285a
Earthenware, 381b
Eau de Javelle, 35c–6a
Echo, 150a
Echo-sounding, 389b–90a
Eclipse
Babylonians and, 273b
of the sun, *20, 244, 282–3*
Ecliptic, 281b
Eddington, Sir Arthur, 290a
Edison, Thomas Alva, 106c, 117b, 150c; *149*
Efficiency, mechanical, 422c
eggs, smell of rotten, 40c
Egypt, Egyptians
dyes, 377a–b
glass, 383c
pictograph numerals, 229b–c
pyramids, 302a
shadow clock, 366a
ships, 385a–6a; *387*
water clock, *366*
Ehrlich, Paul, 473c
Eiffel Tower, *358*
Einstein, Albert, *176*
and expansion of the universe, 290a
and relativity, 173a–b, 175c, 176b, 176c
and the photoelectric effect, 170a *172*
his three papers of 1905, 119c
Nobel prize won by, *172*
on the nature of light, 124b, 170a
Elastic limit, 357a–c
Elastic solids, 357a
Elastomers, 371c

El Caracol observatory (Mexico), *273*
Eldeanu process, 346c
Eleatic philosophers, 1a
Electric-arc furnace, *see* **Arc furnace, electric**
Electric cell, *see* **Cell, electric**
Electric clock, 367c–8a
Electricity, 93a–6c
chemical use of, *see* **Electrochemistry**
conductors of, 58c, 95c–6a, 97a 100a–c, 109a–12c, 158a, 194c, 350a–c
impurity semiconductors, 110a–11c
semiconductors, 100c, 109a, 110a–12a
superconductors, 110a
electric current, 5a–b, 58c, 94c–5c, 109a
alternating, 112a, 113a–16c, 244a–b
direct, 112a, 113a
electrons in, 5a–b, 58c, 93a–5c, 100a–b, 109a–12a
field, electric, 94a–b
generator, 17c
atomic, 318a, 340c
see also **Power station, nuclear**
steam, 340c
in steel production, 356a
insulation of, 100a–c, 350b
molecules bound by, 13b
positive and negative, 95c
static, 93a
see also **Electromagnetism; Motor, electric**
Electrochemical series (metals), 80c
Electrochemistry, 361a–4c
see also **Electrolysis**
Electrode, 97a, 361a
Electrodialysis, 364a; *364*
Electroforming, 364a–b
Electrolysis, 97a–9a, 362a; *97*
and ion-bonding, 14a
electroplating, 98a, 99a, 362a–3c
in metallurgy, 64a, 69a, 71b
Electrolyte, 97a, 198b, 361a
Electrolytic cell, 361a
Electro-magnetic radiation, 121a–4c, 153a
quantum theory and, 169a–b
see also **Cosmic rays; Gamma rays; Heat; Light; Radio waves; Sound; Wave mechanics; X-rays**
Electromagnetism, 96a–c, 104b–c, 105a–6a; *95*
electromagnetic induction, 113a
see also **Electro-magnetic radiation**
Electromotive cell, 361a
Electromotive force (e.m.f.), 95b, 113a–16a
Electron, 5a–8c, 9b, 10a–b, 11a–12c, 13b, 16c
and electric current, 58c, 93a–5c, 100a–b, 109a–12a
and magnetism, 104c
diffraction of, 16c, 170b–1b
energy of, 166b–c, 169c–70a, 172a–b
exclusion principle and, 172b
free, 17a
in cathode rays, 5a–c, 108a
mass of, varies with velocity, 174c
relativity theory and, 174c
uncertainty principle and, 170b–c
wave motion of, 164a–b, 170b
Electron beam, *see* **Cathode rays**
'Electronic office', 343a–c
Electronics, 117a–20c
electronic computer, *see* **Computer**
electronic music, 148b–c
in automation, 341a–c
in timing athletic events, 453b–c
Electron microscope, 124c; *50, 52*
Electron-volt, 294a
Electrophoresis, *361*
Electroplating, 98a, 99a, 362a–3c, 437c
Electroscope, gold-leaf, 293a–c; *295*

Electrostatic bond, *see* **Ionic bond**
Electrostatic dipoles, 16b–c
Electrotyping, 362a–3c, 437c
Element (chemistry), 2b, 5a
equivalent weight of, 99a
identified by spectra, 166c; *165*
in human body, 460c
listed, with symbols etc., 27
most abundant on earth, 77a
see also **Four elements, theory of,** *and under individual elements*
Element (group mathematics), 235c–6a
Emetine, *396*
E.m.f., *see* **Electromotive force**
Emissivity (radiation), 165a
Emley Moor (Yorks), television aerials at, *139*
Empedocles, 1b
Employment, threats to, *see* **Unemployment**
Emulsion (photographic film), 433c
in colour film, 435c
Endrin, 473b
Energy, 121a, 165a, 169a
and work, 217a–b, 333a
as quanta, 170a
changes of, in s   s, 198a
conservation of,   422a
heat a form of, 15   a, 177a–80a
heat energy and mechanical energy, 178c–9a
kinetic, 181a, 182c, 217a–18a
light a form of, 153a, 165a
mass equivalent to, 157c–6b
of electrons, 166b–c, 169c–70a, 172a–b
of the stars, 17c–18a, 77a, 176b
of the sun, 17c–18a, 77a, 91b, 176b, 283c
potential, 217a–18c
wave / particle theories of, 161a, 164b
see also **Atomic energy; Electromagnetic radiation**
Engine, Heat (or thermal), 333a
see also **Internal combustion engine; Jet engine; Steam engine; Turbine engine**
Engine, petrol, see **Internal combustion engine**
Engineering, 301a–4c
types of, 301c–4c
civil, 301c–2a, 305a–c
mechanical 302a–4b
other, 304b–c
see also **Bridge; Road,** for applications of engineering
ENIAC (computer), 262b
Entropy, 179c
Enzymes, 405b
Ephedrine, 410a
Epicurus, 1b; *3*
Epoxy resins, 360a–c
Epsom salts, 71b
Equation, chemical, 26b–8c
Equator, Babylonian concept of, 273b
Equilateral triangle, 238b, 239a; *237*
Equilibrium (thermodynamics), 180c
Equivalence (relativity theory), 176b–c
Equivalent weight of an element, 99a
Eratosthenes, 276c
Erg, 217b
Ergometrine, 410a
Escapement (clock), 366c–7b
anchor, 366c–7a
dead-beat, 367a
verge, 366c
Eskimos, *182*
drinking water obtained by, 200c
Etching, 88c
Ether (distillate), 45a
Ether (space theory), 173a,b,c
Ethylene glycol, 46c
Euclid, Euclidean geometry, 226b–c, 237a–8b, 239c–40b
fifth postulate, 226b–c, 238b
line defined by, 233a–b, 237b, 238a
parallel lines and, 238a–b
plane in, 237b–8a

point defined by, 237b–8a
Eudoxus of Cnidus, 275c
Eutectic, 65c
Evaporation, 24a–b, 157b
Exclusion principle (Pauli), 172b–c
Expansion, heat as cause of, 22a, 160a, 179a, 182a
Expansion of the universe, 290a, 292a
Experiment (paddle-steamer), 388a–b
Explorer I, 296c
Explosives, 88b–c
ammonium nitrate used in, 86a
Exposure (photography), 433b
exposure meter (light meter), 168a, 364c
Extractive distillation (oil refining), 347c
Extrusion (plastics), *see* **Injection moulding**

F

Fabrics
colours for, *see* **Dyes**
in analytical chemistry, 450a–b
manufacture of, *see* **Textile industry**
materials for, *see* **Fibres**
Fahrenheit scale, 158a–c
Fair-grounds, examples of circular motion in, 205c, 206b–c
Fan, electric, 184c
Faraday (unit of measurement), 99a
Faraday, Michael, 97a, 98a–9a, 105b–6a, 106b; *98*
Farming, 397a–404c
chemistry in, 401a–4c
hydroponic, 404b–c
mechanized, 397a–400c
Fatigue, 64a, 359c
Fats, 405c–6a
Feed-back principle, 341a–c
Feldspar, 69a
Fermat, Piemede, 240a
Fermi, Enrico, 317a,c, 318a
Fermi-Dirac statistics, 172a
Ferromagnetic materials, 104c
Fertilizers, 402a–3b
ammonia in, 80a, 86a
dangers of, 404a–b
manure as, 402a
phosphorus in, 38b, 39c
potassium compounds as, 71a
sulphuric acid in manufacture of, 40b
synthetic, 402c–3b
Fever tree, *see* **Cinchona tree**
Fibonacci, *see* **Leonardo of Pisa**
Fibres
artificial, 45c–7b, 373a, 375b–c, 376a
nylon, 45c, 46a–c, 369a–70b; *45, 53*
rayon, 375b; *373*
natural, 373a

see also **Cotton; Wool**
Field (mathematics), 236a
Field, electric, 94a–b
Field, magnetic, 101a; *101, 103*
and discovery of the elctron, 5b–c; *6*
Earth's, and cosmic rays, 296a
Fifteen puzzle, *see* **Jeu de Taquin**
Film, photographic, 433b–4c
colour, 435c–6b
developing of, 433c–4a
fixing of, 434c
grains in, 434c
Film-setting (printing), 438a
Fire, 185a
as element, *see* **Four elements, theory of**
Fire, electric, elements of, 68b, 96a
Firearms, 470a–b
in forensic science, 446a, 448c; *448*
recoil of, 203b–c
Fireclay, 381c
Fire-eater, *187*
Fire extinguishers, 44b-c, 70a–la; *185*
Fireworks, 72b, c; *70, 186*
Firsoff, V.A., 286b–c
Fish, fishing, 391a–c; *390*
fish farming, 391c, 476b–c
Fission, nuclear, *see* **Nuclear fission**
Flame test, 449a–b
Flashlight (photography), *see* **Photoflash lamp**
Flash point (kindling temperature), 186a, 188a
Flat-bed printing press, 437c
Flax, 373a
Fleming, Sir John Ambrose, 108b, 117c, 138a, 442a
Flight, 297a–300c
Flint axes, prehistoric, *470*
Float glass system, 384c
Floc, 467c
Fluids, 221a–4c
fluid dynamics, 224c
fluid statics, 221a
Fluorine, 10a, 33a, 33b, 33b–4a
fluoridation of drinking water, 34a
Flute, 147a, 148a
Flying bomb, *see* **V1 flying bomb**
Flying Scotsman, 338
F-numbers (photography), 433b
Foam, detergent, 466c–7a; *466*
Focal length, 431b
Focal plane, 430c, 431c, 432a
Foliot (clock), 366c; *367*
Follicular hormones, *see* **Oestrogens**
Food, 405a–8c
digestion of, 185b, 196b–c, 197a
nutrients of, classified, 405c
preservation of, 407b–8c
canning, 407c–8a
dehydration, 408b–c
refrigeration, 184a–b, 192b–c, 408a–b
ultrasonic, 408c
synthetic, 331c
Foot (measurement), British and US compared, 248b
Footballs, 454a; *454*
Force, 202a,b–3a
centrifugal, 205a–c, 208a–b
centripetal, 205a–b
units of, 202a, 422a
Ford, Henry, 313c
Forensic science, 445a–8c
Forme (printing), 437c
Formulae, chemical, 25a,b–8c
Forth Road Bridge, *270–1, 301*
Foucault, Jean Bernard Léon, 156b
Four elements, theory of, 1b–c, 9a, 185a
Fourth dimension, 225c–6a, 240c
Fourth state of matter (plasma), 17a
Foxglove, 412b; *411*
Fraction (arithmetic), 256c
Fractional distillation, 45a–b
in metallurgy, 64a
in oil refining, 45a–b, 331c–2a, 346a–b

Francium, 69a
Frasch, Herman, 40a, 396a
Fraunhofer, Joseph von, 156a
Free electron, 17a
Free radicals, 53a–6c
Free will, uncertainty principle and, 172c
Freezing point
of aqueous solutions, 196b
of water, 194a,b
French horn, 148a
Freons, 34a
Frequency (of waves), 161c, 162a
of light waves, 153c
of sound waves, 144a, 149a–c, 162a
Frequency modulation, 118a, 138b, 140c
Freud, Sigmund, 410c
Friedmann, Willem de Sitter, 290a
Fulham power station, turbine at, *304*
Fuller, Buckminster, 268c; *238*
Fuller, Jesse, *145*
Functional groups (molecular structure), 49a
Functions, trigonometric, 241b–4c
Fundamental Law of Refraction, 429b
Fungicides, 403b
dangers of, 467a
Funk, Casimir, 406a–b
'Fur' (in kettles, etc.), 72a
Fuse, electric, 106c
Fusee, 367a; *368*
Fusion, nuclear, *see* **Thermonuclear fusion**

G

G (gravitational acceleration), 202b
Galaxy (nebula), 281a, 289a–c, 292a–c
Crab, *79, 296*
distance of, 289a
first discovery of, 289b
Horsehead, *73*
in Andromeda, 289b, 292b; *287, 288*
in Canes Venatici, *286*
in Coma Berenices, *285*
in the Swan, *288*
number of, 285a, 289a
recession of, 292a
Trifid mist in Sagittarius, *290*
visible with the naked eye, 292b–c
Galilei, Galileo, *213*
and gravity, 213a–14a, 218b; *213, 215*
and pendulum clock, 366c
and telescope, 277a–b
and water pump, 73a
Gallium, 10c, 12b–c
Gallium arsenide, 111c
Gall-stones, 412a
Galvanic cell, 361a
Galvanometer, 105a; *96*
Gamma-radiograph, *321*

Gamma rays, 121a, 124b, 128c
Gangue, 63c
Garden, formal, *239*
Gas, gases, 73a–6c
as weapon, 472b–c; *33*
classed with liquids as fluids, 221a
critical temperature of, 24c
Dalton and, 2c, 4b–c
expands when heated, 179b
gas-lighting, *see* Lighting, gas
Gay-Lussac and, 4b–c
heated by compression, 179b
in heat engines, 333a
   see also Internal combustion engine; Jet engine; Steam engine; Turbine engine
ionized, 17a
kinetic theory of, 74b–5c
liquefaction of, 190a, 191c, 192b–c
molecules of, 74b–5b, 76a–c
natural, 390a; *80, 179, 330*
'North Sea', *80, 179, 330*
vapour and, 23c
viscosity of, 76c
see also Inert gases *and under individual gases, e.g.* Oxygen
Gas bearing (engineering), 303c
Gas chromatography, 50a
Gassendi, Pierre, 2b
Gas-turbine engine, *see* Turbine engine
Gay-Lussac, Joseph Louis, 4b–c
Geiger counter, 321b,c, 322c, 323a,b,c; *170*
Geiger-Müller tube, 294a
Generator, electrical, 17c
'Genetic code', 47c–8b
Geometry, 237a–40c
Euclidean, 226b–c, 237a–8b, 239c–40b
projective, 268a
Riemannian, 226c–7a, 272a–c
Germanium, 10c, 349b
as conductor of electricity, 110a
Germanium bolometer, 280b
Giesel, Friedrich, 293a
Gilbert, William, 93c, 103c
Gilchrist, Percy, 354b
Gillespie, Dizzy, *147*
Gimbal, 211a; *210*
Glass, 71c, 360a, 383b–4c; *72, 381, 382, 383, 384*
as electrical insulator, 100c
coloured, 384a
Egyptian, 383c
photochromism and, 425c–6a
plate, 384b–c
viscosity of, 383c
Glass-harp, *145*
Glasshouse, 400a
Glazes, in pottery, 381b
Glider, 297a–c
Glucose, 47c, 48b, 450a
Glycogen, 48b–c
Goitre, *36*
Gold, 62a, 349b; *350*
alloying of, 68c
as conductor of electricity, 350b
crystal structure of, 59b
mining of, 325c; *325, 326, 328*
Gold, Thomas, 290a
Goldbach's Theorem, 226a
Golden Section, 268b–c; *265*
Goonhilly Down (Cornwall), communication station at, 444a; *443*
Gough's Cave (Cheddar), *195*
Governor, mechanical, 206c, 341a, 366c; *206*
Graham, George, 367a
Graham, Thomas, 200a
Gramophone, early example of, *149*
Graphite, 41a, 42a–3c, 329c
in nuclear reactor, 317c–18a, 319c
Graphitic acids, 42c
Grass, research on, for sports grounds, 456b–c
Gravity, gravitation, 21c, 202b, 213a–16a
clocks and, 252a
Galileo and, 213a–14a, 218b; *213, 215*
Newton and, 208c, 213a, 214a–c, 215c, 216a
relativity and, 176b–c
spring balance and, 251a–b
supernovae and, 286b

Gravure (intaglio) printing, 437a, 439b–c
Great circle, 226c; *225*
Great Eastern (ship), *385*
Great Western (ship), 388b
Greeks, ancient, 1a–b, 275a–6c
Greenhouse, 168c
Greenwich observatory, *276*
Grenade, 471c
Group (mathematics), 235c–6a
Klein group, 236a
Guanine, 47c
Guericke, Otto von, 73b–c; *76*
Guitar, 146a–7a
Gulf Stream, 194b, 392c
Gun cotton (nitrocellulose), 88c
Gunmetal, 67c; *67*
Gunn, John, 136c
Gunpowder, 82a, 88c, 470a–b, 471c
Gypsum (hydrated calcium sulphate), 71b, 72a
Gyrocompass, 212a–c; *210*
Gyroscope, 209a, 210a–12c
gyroscopic inertia, 209a, 211b
gyroscopic reaction moment, 210a
Gyrostabilizer, 211b–c

H

Haber, Fritz, 80a
Haber Process, 85a
Hahn, Otto, 317b
Haines solution, 450a
Hairspring, in watches, 367a–b; *367*
Halberd, 469c
Half-tone (printing), 437b
colour, 440a
screen for, 437b
Halides, 33b
Halogens, 33a–6c
and hydrogen, 78c, 79a–80a
see also Bromine; Chlorine; Fluorine; Iodine
Hand lotion, 418c
Hardcore, 310c, 312a
Harp, 147a
Harrison, John, and the chronometer, 367b
Harwell, 320c
ZETA experiment at, 20a; *18*
Hawaii, volcanoes in, *153*
Heat, 157a–60c, 177a–80a, 181a, 189b–c
a form of energy, 157a, 165a, 170a, 177a–80a
as quanta, 168c
conductors of, 158a
effects of, on metals, 352c
expansion caused by, 22a, 160a, 179a, 182a
in forming solutions, 198a
insulators, insulation, 158a, 182b–c
latent, 24a
mechanical equivalent of, 178a
mechanical work and, 177c–8a,

333a
   see also Internal combustion engine; Jet engine; Steam engine; Turbine engine
of condensation, 183c
of fusion, 183c
of solidification, 183c
of vaporization, 183c
retained by water, 194b
specific, 160a–c, 183b
thermodynamics, 177a–80c, 181a–2a
conduction, 181a–c
convection, 181a, c–2a
radiation, 165a–6a, 168c, 170a, 181a, 182a
units of measurement of, 160a, 178a–b, 183a
wave theory of, 121c
Heaviside, Oliver, 441c
Heaviside Layer, 138c–9a
Heavy hydrogen, *see* Deuterium
Heavy metals, 62a
Heavy water, *see* Deuterium oxide
Heisenberg, Werner, 171b–c
Helicopter, 297a, 298b–300a
Helium, 89a–91b
atomic structure of, *11*
in thermonuclear fusion, 18a, 90c
liquid, 190a, 191c, 192a
Hemlock, 410c
Henry (unit of inductance), 113b
Henry, Joseph, 96c, 104b, c, 105a, 113b
Heracleitus of Pontus, 276a
Herbicides (weed-killers), 403c
dangers of, 404b, 467a
Heroin, 411b
Hero of Alexandria, 237a, 239c, 340a
Heroult, Paul, 356a
Herschel, Sir William, 121b–c
Hertz, Heinrich, 122a, 441b; *121*
Hertzsprung, E., 285c
Hertzsprung-Russell diagram, 285c
Hess, Victor, 293a
Heterolytic fission, 53a
Hevesy, Georg von, 321a
Hexa-methylene diamine, 46a, 370a
Hexogen (RDX), 88c
High-frequency (induction) furnace, 356a
High-speed steels, *see* Tool steels
Hillebrand, William, 90a
Hindu-Arabic numerals, 230a
Hipp, Mathias, 368a
Hipparchus, 276b–c
Hittites, steel made by, 61a
Hoffmann, August von, 396c
Hoffmann, Bruno, *145*
Hollerith, Herman, 462a
Homolytic fission, 53a
Honeycomb, *238*
Hooke, Robert, 156b, 357a, 366c, 367a
Hooke's Law, 357a
Hoover Dam, *307*
Hormones
and sex, 409a, 411c–12b
in agriculture, 404a
Horsehead nebula, *73*
Horsepower, 219a, 424a–c
Hovercraft, 388c; *215*
Hoyle, Fred, 290a
Hubble, Edwin, 289c, 292a; *288*
Hunstman, Benjamin, 354a
Huygens, Christiaan, 121a, 156b, 366c, 367a
Hydraulic brake, 224c, 316b
Hydraulic lift, 224c
Hydrazine, 86a
Hydrocarbons, 80b–c, 345a
Hydrochloric acid (spirits of salt), 15c, 29b, 36a
Dumas and, 394c
Hydrofluoric acid, 34a
Hydrofoil, 388b; *270*
Hydrogen, 77a–80c
and oxygen, 78c–9a
as rocket fuel, 300b
atomic clock, and relativity, 175b
atomic structure of, 10a; *10*
atomic weight of, 25a
compounds of, 77a, 80c
halogens and, 78c, 79a–80a

heavy, *see* **Deuterium**
in coal, 329b–c
in earth's atmosphere, 76b–c
in nylon, 370a
in oil, 329c, 345a–b
in organic chemistry, 49a
in stars, 77a, 286b–c
in thermonuclear fusion, 17c–18a
in the sun, 77a, 91b
isotopes of, 77c–8a
liquefaction of, 191c, 192a
molecular mass of, 76b
nucleus of, 7a, 8b
spectrum of, 166b
valence of, 25c
Hydrogen bomb, 471c–2a; *78*
energy source of, 18a, 176b
Hydrogen bond, 16c, 47a
Hydrogen chloride, 15c–16a, 25c, 36a
Hydrogen fluoride, 33c–4a
Hydrogen ions, 29a, 30b–1c
Hydrogen peroxide, 84a–b, 188b
Hydrogen sulphide, 40c
Hydrolith, *see* **Calcium hydride**
Hydrolysis, 196b
Hydroponic cultivation, 404b–c
Hydroquinone, 434c
Hydroxides, 26a
Hydroxyl ions, 29a, 30c–1c
Hygiene, public, 465a–8c
Hyoscine, *see* **Scopolamine**
Hyperon, 294c
Hypo (sodium thiosulphate), 71a, 434c
crystals of, *57*
Hypochlorites, 35c
Hypochlorous acid, 35c
Hypotenuse (of a triangle), in trigonometry, 241c

I

Ice, 196c, 222a
drinking water from, 200c
melted with salt, 200c
Iceberg, 194c, 222a; *195, 197, 222*
Iconoscope, 443c
Imaginary numbers, 227c–8a
Impedance (electric circuit), 115a
Inclined plane, 421a
Galileo and, 214a; *213*
Index of refraction (light), 154b, 429c–30a
India, astronomy in, *274*
Indicator (chemistry), 31c–2b, 450a
Inductance, unit of, *see* **Henry**
Induction furnace, *see* **High-frequency furnace**
Inductive reactance, 115a
Industry
effluents from, 466b–7a
mathematics in, 269a–72c
Inert gases (inert elements), 12a, 89a–92c
Inertia, 201c
gyroscopic, 209a. 211b

Infinite numbers, 231c–2c
Infra-red radiation, 121a, 122b–3c, 153a, 157a, 165a; *153*
discovery of, 121c
domestic applications of, 425a–c
in photography, 165a, 436a–b; *158–9*
Inherited characteristics, DNA and, 47c
Injection moulding (extrusion), 270a
Ink, printer's, 440c; *331, 438*
Inorganic chemistry, 449a
Insecticides, 403c–4b
dangers of, 404b, 467a
Insulation, 158a, 183b–c
Intaglio printing, *see* **Gravure printing**
Integrated circuit (computer), 262c; *264*
Intelsat III (satellite), 444a
Interference
in light waves, 154c–6a, 163c–4a
in sound waves, 164a
Intermittent sand-filter, 467c–8a
Internal combustion (petrol) engine, 178b–9a, 179a–b, 185c–6a, 331c, 333a, 334a–5c
diesel, 334b, 335c, 388a
four stroke, 334a–b
in aircraft, 298a
in cars, 313a–b, 314a–b
thermal efficiency of, 334a–b
two stroke, 334b–5a; *335*
International Bureau of Weights and Measures, 245a
Invar, 68b
Inverse square law (Coulomb's law), 93c–4a
Iodine, 11c, 33a, b, 36c
Ionic (electrostatic, polar) bond, 10b, 13b–14b, 15c–16a, 57c
Ionium, 7a
Ionization chamber, 294a
Ionized gas, 17a
Ionosphere, 442a
radio waves reflected by, 122a, 442a, 443c–4a
Ions, 10b, 13c, 17a–b, 30b–1c, 361a
anions and cations, 362a
Iris (camera), *see* **Diaphragm**
Iron, 349a, b, 353a; *351*
alloying of, 68b
cementation of, 353a
first ship made of, 388a
in engineering, 302a
in food, 405c
in production of hydrogen, 78b
smelting of, 65a, 185c, 349a
Iron oxide (rust), 82c–3c, 186a, 186a–7a
in preparation of hydrogen, 78b
Isomorphism (mathematics), 233a, 234a–5c
Isoprene, 372a
Isosceles triangle, 238b; *237*
Isotopes, 7a–8c, 9b–10a, 11c; *7*
of carbon, 41a
of hydrogen, 77c–8a
of lead, 92c
of radon, 92c
of uranium, 318a–19c
radioactive (trace elements), 321a–4c, 401a; *12*

J

Jacob the Czech, 367a
Javan, Ali, 132a
Jet engine, jet propulsion, 298a-b, 300a, 333a, 336c
fuel for, 345c
turbo-jet, 336c; *335*
Jenkins, C. F., 443b
Jeu de Taquin (15 puzzle), 228c
Jodrell Bank radio telescope, 122b, 280c, 292.; *163, 278*
John Hancock Building (Chicago), *305*
Joule (unit of measurement), 178a, 422a
Joule, James Prescott, 177c–8a, 422a; *177*
his electromagnet, *95*
Jupiter (planet), 283c, 284b, c; *282, 283*
Jurlof-Achmanof (comet), *285*
Justification (printing), 437a

K

Kalkstickstoff Process, 85c
Kamerlingh Onnes, Heike, 190a, 191c
Kant, Immanuel, 285b
Kaolin, *see* **China clay**
Kelly, William, 354a
Kelvin, Lord (William Thomson), 75b, 159c, 179b,c–80a, 182b–c; *2, 3*
Kelvin scale, *see* **Absolute scale**
Kennelly, A. E., 441c
Kepler, Johannes, 215c–16a
Kerosene, *see* **Paraffin**
Kettle
'fur' in, 72a
'steam' from, 196c
Kew Gardens, *415*
Kilburn, T., 262b
Killed spirit of salt, 36a
Kilogram, 245a
Kindling temperature, *see* **Flash point**
Kinetic energy, 181a, 182c, 217a–18b
Kinetic theory of gases, 74a–5c
Kingston by-pass, *310*
Kippers, *406*
Kitchen stove, 425a
infra-red, 425a–c
oven-cleaning, 428c
Klein group, 236a
Knitting, 376b
Koller, Karl, 410c
Krypton, 89a, 92a–b
krypton, 86, 246a
krypton interferometer, *246*

L

Lacoste, René, 455c
Lacquer, 380c
Lalande 21185 (star), 288b, c
Lampblack, 43c
Lanthanide series, see Rare earth elements
Laplace, Marquis de, 285b
Laser, 129a, b, 131c-2c, 251a; 90, 155
gas, 132a; 129
in communications, 132b, 140b-c, 156c
injection, 132a
in surgery, 132c; 129
military use of, 132b-c
ruby, 131c-2a
Latent heat, 24a
Lattice (crystallography), 57a-8b, 359a
Laue, Max von, 59c, 127a; 16
Laughing gas, see Nitrous oxide
Lavoisier, Antoine, 2b, 81c-2a, 188c; 81, 188
Law, law enforcement, science in, see Forensic science
Lawhill (ship), 388
Law of conservation of energy, 217c, 422a
Law of conservation of mass, 2c
Law of definite proportions, 2c
Law of magnetic attraction and repulsion, 102a-c
Law of multiple proportions, 4a
Laws of motion, Newton's, 202a-4a
First, 202a-c
Second, 202c-3a
Third, 203a-b
Lawton, W. E., 94a
Lead, 62a, 349b
in paint, 380a
isotopes of, 92c
Leap Year, 365c
Leather, 454a
Leblanc, Nicolas, 394b-c
Leclanché, Georges, 362
Le Corbusier, 268c
Leibniz, Gottfried Wilhelm von, 261a
Lemaitre, Georges, 291c
Length
measurement of, 245c, 249a-b, 250a-b
international standard of, 245c
reduced by acceleration (relativity theory), 174a-b
Lens, 154b-c, 430b-2c; 156, 430
in photography, 433a-b; 433
aperture of, 433b
iris (diaphragm) and, 433b
Leonardo da Vinci, 268a, b-c, 297a, 313a; 421
his St Jerome, 268c; 266
Leonardo of Pisa (Fibonacci), 268a-b
Letterpress (relief) printing, 437a-8a; 439
Leucippus of Miletus, 1a
Lever, 422a; 421, 424
Lewis, G. N., 14c
Life, living things
carbon the basis of, 41a, 45a
elsewhere in the universe, 283b,
285a 286c-8a, 288b-c
on Mercury, 284a
Lifeboat, 222
Life expectancy, 466a
Lift, hydraulic, see Hydraulic lift
Light, 153a-6c
a form of energy, 153a, 165a, 170a
colours of spectrum, 121a-b, 153c-4a, 166a-c
corpuscle (particle) theory of, 124b, 156a-c, 166c, 168a, 170a
deflected by gravitation, 176c
diffraction of, 156a
ether and, 173a
in photography, see Photography
interference and, 154c-6a, 163c-4a
refraction of, 154a-c, 156a-b, 429a-30a
speed of, 170a, 173a-c, 174b-c, 279c
in water, 430a
tired light theory, 292a
wave theory of, 121a, 123c, 124b, 156b-c, 168a
amplitude of light waves, 153, 163c
wavelengths of, 153b-c, 163c
X-rays and, 125b-c
see also Laser; Maser
Lighting, electric, 92a, 106c, 426a-7a
Lighting, gas, 330a
Light meter (exposure meter; photography), 168a, 364c
Lighting, 17a
lighting conductor, 100b-c
Light year, 279c
Lignite, 329c
Lime, 71c
slaked, see Calcium hydroxide
Limestone
industrial use of, 72a
in glass, 383c
Line
Euclid's definition of, 233a-b, 237b, 238a
parallel lines, 226c-7a, 238a-b
Line block (printing), 437b
Linen, 373a
Lines of force (magnetism), 101a; 101, 103
Line spectrum (atomic spectrum), 166a-c
Linotype, 437a
Linseed oil, 380a
Lippershey, Hans, 277a
Liquids, 23a-4c, 360a
classed with gases as fluids, 221a
gases liquefied, 190a, 191c, 192b-c
solids melt to form, 23a
solutions and, 197a-c
Lithium, 11b, 69a
atomic structure of, 11
isotopes of, 9c-10a
Lithium aluminium hydride, 71a
Lithography (planographic printing), 437a, 438a-9b
offset, 439a-b
Litmus, litmus paper, 31c, 450a; 30
Liverpool cathedral, 308
Lloyd, Sam, 228c
Lockyer, Norman, 90a
Locusts, radar used against, 133a
Lodge, Sir Oliver, 441b
Logarithm, 261a
Logic, 257a-b, 259a
syllogism, 259a
Longitude, chronometer used to find, 367c
Lorentz, H.A., 174a
Lovelace, Lady, 262a
Low, Dr, germanium bolometer invented by, 280b
Lowry, T.M., 30c
Lucretius, 2, 3
Lunin, Nikolai, 406a
Lurgi process, 331b
Lye, 417b
Lyons, Harold, 368b
Lysergic acid, 410a

M

McAdam, John Loudon, 310b
Machine, 421a-4c
see also Engine, heat
Machine-gun, recoil of, 203c
Mach numbers, 144c, 300a
Mackintosh waterproof coat, 331c
McNary Dam, hydroelectric power terminal at, 113
McReynolds, A.W., 174c
Macroscopic phenomena, defined, 21a
Madder, 377b
Magdeburg hemispheres, 73c; 76
Magellanic Clouds, 292b,c
Magic, 265a-c
Magic square, 228b
Magnesium, 62b, 71a,b, 78b-c
crystal structure of, 59b
Magnesium hydroxide, 71c
Magnetic field, see Field, magnetic
Magnetic mirror, 20b-c
Magnetic recording tape, 53
Magnetic well, 20c
Magnetism, magnetic force, 96b-c, 101a-4c
attraction and repulsion, 102a-c
electrons in, 104c
induced, 103c
lines of force, 101a; 101, 103
magnetic field, 101a; 101, 103
magnetic flux, 101a
see also Electromagnetism
Magneto-hydrodynamics, see M.H.D.
Magnetosphere, 296c
Maiman, Theodore H., 131c
Mamhilad (Monmouthshire), Roman road at, 309
Manganese, 349b, 390b-c
Manhattan Project, 317a
Man-made fibres, see Fibres, artificial
Manure, as fertilizer, 402a
Marble, 42, 423
Marconi Guglielmo, 134a, 138a, 441a-c, 442a; 441
Market research, 269c
Mars (planet), 283c, 284b, 459c; 282, 283
moons of, 284b
Marsh gas, see Methane
Martin brothers, 355c
Maser, 129a-31c; 89
Mass, 2c, 201c-2a, 215c
energy equivalent to, 175c-6b
gravity and, 214c
measurement of, 245a, 249a-b
international standard of, 245a
relativity theory and, 174b-c, 175c-6b
weight distinguished from, 215c
Mass number, 9b
Mass production, of cars, 313c-14a
Mass spectrometry, 52a
Matches, 37a, 82a-b, 188a-b

Maté (Paraguay tea), 411c
Mathematics, 225a–44c
and art, 265a–8c
arithmetic, 253a–6c
axioms in, 225a, 233b–c, 238a
geometry, 226b–7a, 237a–40c
in industry, 269a–72c
Le Corbusier's definition of, 268c
new mathematics, 233a–6c
numbers, 226a–b, 227a–8a, 228c, 229a–32c
numerals, 229b–30a, 232c
operator, 228a, 233c–4a
pure and applied, 272c
reductio ad absurdum, 228a–b
set, 232a–c, 236c
topology, 225a, 240b–c
trigonometry, 241a–4c
Matter
fourth state of (plasma), 17a
three states of, 221a
Maxwell, James Clerk, 94a, 441b
Maxwell-Boltzmann distribution curve (hydrogen), 76b
Maxwell-Boltzmann statistics, 172a
Mean free path (of a molecule), 75a
Mean solar day, mean time, 365b
Measurement, 245a–52c
Mechanical engineering, 302a–4b
Medicine
radioactive isotopes used in, 321c–2c
sodium compounds used in, 70a
X-rays used in, 72b–c, 128a–b, 128c; 72, 125
see also Drugs; Surgery
Medium steel, 352c
Medway bridge, 305
Melting, 23a, 157b
Mendeleeff, Dmitri, 9a, 10b–c, 11c; 9
Mendelevium, 9
Meniscus, 23c; 23
Mercaptans, 346b, 348c
Mercury (element), 349b; 22
barometer, 73b
meniscus of, 23c; 23
thermometer, 159c
Mercury (planet), 281b, 283c, 284a; 282
Meson, 294c
Messier 31, see Andromeda, nebula in
Metalloids, 111c
Metallurgy
alloying, 65a–8c
modern science of, 61a, 63c–4c, 65a
Metals, 61a–4c, 65a, 349–52c
alloys of, 64a
as conductors of electricity, 58c, 109a, 350a–c
classification of, 62a, 352a
crystalline structure of, 58c, 61a–c, 359a–b
definition/characteristics of, 62a, 349b–52a
effects of heat on, 352c
electrochemistry and, 80c, 363c–4a
fabrication of, 64a–b
fatigue in, 64a, 359c
joining of, 64b–c
plastic deformation of, 359c
strength of, 64a
work-hardening of, 352b
Meteorites, 62, 351, 451
Meteorology
balloons in, 136c; 76
radar in, 136c
Methane (marsh gas), 14c, 49a
Dalton and, 2–3
in coal mines, 326a, 330a
Methyl orange, 31c–2a
Metol, 434c
Metre, 245c, 246a
Metric system, 248c
Metrology, 250a
Meyer, Julius Lothar, 10b
M.H.D. (magneto-hydrodynamics), 17b
M.H.D. generator, 17b–c
Michelangelo, his Pietà, 125

Michelson-Morley experiment, 173c; 175
Micrometer screw gauge, 250a; 249
Microphone, 163c
Microscope, 432
compound, 432c
traversing, 250b
Microscopic phenomena, defined, 21a
Mild steel, 352c, 354a–b
Milk, evaporating of, 194b
Milk of magnesia, 71c
Milky Way, 281a, 288a–b, 289a, 292b–c
number of stars in, 285a, 287c
radio source in, 280c
Millikan, Robert A., 6a–b, 293c; 7
Millimicron, 153b–c
Mine, explosive, 471c
Minerals
as nutrients, 405c
definition of, 63c
Mini-climate (engineering), 308c
Mining, 325a–8c
coal, 325a–8c; 41, 326, 328
copper, 325, 326, 327, 350
diamonds, 327
gold, 325c; 325, 326, 328
tungsten, 328
Minoans, see Crete, Minoan
Miscibility, 200a
Mississippi river
pollution of, 475
riverboats on, 388b; 339
Mobius strip, 225a; 227
Moderator (nuclear reactor), 319c
Modular arithmetic (clock arithmetic), 234a
Modulus, 357a
Moissan, Henri, 33c, 42c
Molecular spectroscopy, 16c
Molecular theory of magnetism, see Domain theory of magnetism
Molecules, 4b, 5a, 13a–16c, 21b–24c; 4
electricity as binding force between, 13b
long-chain, see Polymers
of gases, 74b–5b, 76a–c
Momentum, 202a, 219b–c
angular, 209c–10a, 220c
conservation of, 219c–20a
Monads, 3
Monastral Blue, 47a
Monel, 68b
Mongolfier brothers, 297
Monomers, 369c, 373a
Monotype, 437a; 437
Month, lunar, 365a
Moon
angular momentum of, 220c
astronauts on, 129a, 459c; 415, 459
Apollo lunar module, 303
laser reflector left on moon, 129a; 131
television from, 444
Earth's distance from, 276c, 281a
gravity and, 214a–b, 215b–c
tides raised on Earth by, 220c
Mordant (dyeing), 377a
Morphine, 410a, b, 411b
Morrison, W.A., 368a
Morse, Samuel, 137a
Morton, William, 87a
Motion, 201a–4c
circular, 205a–8c, 220c
Newton's Laws of, 202a–4a
First, 202a–c
Second, 202c–3a, 206a
Third, 203a–b
of fluids, see Fluids, fluid dynamics
periodic, see Simple harmonic motion
planetary, 215c–16a
rotational, 209a
Motor, electric, 105b–6a; 105
superconducting, 192a; 189
Motor car, 313a–16c, 474c–5a
Benz and, 313a; 313
braking system of, 224c, 316a–c
cornering in, 205a–c
electrically powered, 313b, 316c,

362a, 475a; 362
gas-turbine engine in, 314c–15a; 313
internal combustion engine in, 313a–b, 314a–b
Pirana, 302
position of engine in, 314a
roads for, 310c
rotary piston engine in, 314b–c
steam-powered, 313a–b, 339c; 337
suspension and springing in, 315a–16a
tyre, pneumatic, in, 315b
Motor oil, 45a
Motorway, 312b–c; 309
Mount Palomar telescope, 277c, 360a; 279
Mount Wilson observatory, 288
Mozart, W.A., 268c
Multi-cavity magnetron, 134a
Multiplication (arithmetic), 254b–c
Muon, 294c
Murdoch, William, 338c
Murdock, William, 330a
Music, 145a–8c
electronic, 148b–c
frequency, and musical notes, 144a, 149c
instruments, 145a–8a
frequencies of, 149c
tuning of, 164a
mathematics and, 268c
recording of, 151a–2c
Musical box, 149
Mussels, 391
Myopia (short-sightedness), 432b

N

Naphtha, 331c
Naphthalene, 377c; 332
Naphthenes (crude oil), 345a
Napier, John, 261a
National Grid, British, 116b
Navigation
longitude found by chronometer 367c
Nebula, see Galaxy
Nebular hypothesis, 285b
Negative, photographic, 434c–5b; 435
Negative numbers, 227c
Neon, 89a, 91b–c
atomic structure of, 10
isotopes of, 8a,c
Neoprene, 372a
Neptune (planet), 283c, 284c; 282
Neutralization reactions, 32a–b
Neutrino, 294c
Neutron, 8b–c, 9b, 294c
Chadwick and, 8a–b; 319
in nuclear fission, 317b–20a
Newlands, John, 10b
New mathematics, 233a–6c
axiomatic approach in, 233c
Newton (unit of force), 422a

Newton, Sir Isaac, 1c–2b; *2, 3*
and gravitation, 208c, 213a, 214a–c, 215c, 216a
and the corpuscular theory of light, 156a–b
and the spectrum, 121a–b, 153c
his Laws of Motion, 202a–4a, 206a
replica of his telescope, *277*
Newton's rings, 155c
New York, pollution of, *475*
Nicholson, W., 97a
Nichrome, 68b
Nickel, 62a, 349b
alloyed with steel, 68b, 356c
crystal structure of, 59b
in chromium plating, 362b
Nicotine, 410c
Nightshade, 409a–10a
deadly, 409a, 410a; *410*
Nipkow, Paul, 443b–c
Nitrates, 88b
Nitration, 88b–c
Nitre, *see* **Sodium nitrate**
Nitric acid *(aqua fortis),* 29a,c
and nitrates, 88b
in etching, 88c
in liquid propellant rockets, 88b
manufacture of, 87a, 88a–b
Nitric oxide, 87a
Nitrocellulose, *see* **Gun cotton**
Nitrogen, 85a–8c
hydrogen and, 80a–b
in agriculture, 401a
in nylon, 370a
in organic chemistry, 49a
liquefaction of, 192b–c; *191*
oxygen and, 86a–8a
plants and, 85c
Nitrogen dioxide, 87a–8a
Nitroglycerine, 88c
Nitron (radon), 92c
Nitrous oxide (laughing gas), 86c–7a
Nixon, President, 473a
Nobel, Alfred, 88c, 396a; *85*
Nobel prizes, 88c
chemistry
Rutherford (1908), *8*
physics
the Braggs (1915), 126a; *16*
Broglie (1929), 168a
Einstein (1921), *172*
Pauli (1945), 172c
J. J. Thomson (1906), *8*
Nodes (music), 149c–50a
'Non-stick' frying pans, 34a, 419b–c
Norsemen, *see* **Vikings**
'North Sea' gas, *80, 179, 330*
Nuclear fission, 18a, 176a
see also **Atomic bomb; Nuclear reactor**
Nuclear fusion, *see* **Thermonuclear fusion**
Nuclear power station, *see* **Power station, nuclear**
Nuclear reactor, 317a–20c, 340c; *338*
as future domestic power source, 428a–c
breeder, 320b–c
coolant for, 320a
critical size of, 319c–20a
radioactive isotopes produced in, 321a–b
reflector in, 320a
Nuclear ship, *see* **Ships, nuclear-powered**
Nuclear weapons, 457a
see also **Atomic bomb; Hydrogen bomb**
Nucleic acids, 47b,c–8b
Nucleus of the atom, 6c–8c, 9b
Numbers, 226a–b, 227a–8a, 229a–32c
imaginary, 227c–8a
in arithmetic, 253a–b
infinite, 231c–2c
negative, 227c
numerals representing, 229b–30a, 232c
perfect, 228c
prime, 226a
Numerals, 232c
Egyptian, 229b–c
Hindu-Arabic, 230a
Roman, 229c–30a
Nutcracker, 421c–2a
Nylon, 45c, 46a–c, 369a–70b, 375b–c; *43, 53*
elements composing, 370a

O

Oboe, 147a
Obry, Ludwig, 211b
Observatory
at Greenwich, *276*
at Samarkand, 275a
Aztec, *273*
orbiting satellite as, 278c–9a; *278*
Royal (Hurstmonceux), *431*
Ocean, *see* **Sea**
Octamethyl pyrophosphoramide, 404a
Octane rating, 348a, c
Oersted, Hans Christian, 96a, 104b; *96*
Oestradiol, 412a
Oestrogens (follicular hormones), 412a
Office work, automation and, 343a–c
Offset lithography, 439a–b
Ohm (unit of resistance), 96a
Ohm, Georg, 96a; *96*
Ohm's Law, 96a
Oil, 329a,c–30a, 331c
carbon and hydrogen content of, 329c, 345a–b
classes of crude, 345a–b
first oil well, 329c
from the sea bed, 390a
refining of, *see* **Oil refining**
synthetic food from, 331c
synthetic rubber from, 332c
Oil of vitriol, *see* **Sulphuric acid**
Oil refining, 45a–b, 332a–b, 345a–8c; *45, 394-5, 476*
radioactive isotopes used in, 322c–3a
siting of refinery, 345c–6a
Oil tanker, 388c; *388*
Olefins, 348a,c
Omega-minus particle, 236a
One-to-one correspondences, 231c–2c
Operator (mathematics), 228a, 233c–4a
Opium, 409a, 411b
smoking of, 411b; *409*
Opposite side (trigonometry), 241c
Optical instruments, 430a
camera, 430a–2a, 432c
microscope, 250b, 432c; *432*
periscope, 430a
prism binoculars, 430a
Orbit
of artificial satellites, 216a
of planets, 215c–16a
Orbitals (of electrons), 10a, 15c, 172b
Ore, definition of, 63c
Organic chemistry, 44c–9c, 369a,

449a
Orrery, *276*
Orthochromatic emulsion (photography), 435c
'Oscillating' theory of the universe, 291c
Oscillator, 164a
Oughtred, William, 261a
Oven-cleaning, 428c
Overtones (music), 149c
Oxidation, 82a, 185a–b, 186a
Oxides, 82b–4a
of nitrogen, 86a–8a
Oxidized dyes, 379b
Oxidizing agent, 82a, 188a
Oxy-acetylene torch, 186a; *183, 188*
Oxygen, 10b, 81a–4c
atomic weight of, 9c, 25b
compounds of, 81a
in combustion, 185a–8c
in nylon, 370a
in organic chemistry, 49a
liquefaction of, 192b
nitrogen and, 86a–8a
sewage decomposed by, 466a–c
valence, 25c
Ozone, 4b–c, 415b

P

Paddle-steamer, 388a–b
Bell's *Comet, 340*
Britannia, 333
Fitch's *Experiment,* 388a–b
Great Eastern, 385
Great Western, 388b
Mississippi riverboat, 388b; *339*
Paint, 379b–80c
driers in, 380a
emulsion, 380b–c
in forensic science, 445c–6a
pigments in, 379c–80a
polymerization of, 380a
resins in, 380a
silicones in, 419c
vehicle of, 380a
Paint spray, 224c
Panchromatic emulsion (photography), 435c
Paper, for printing, 440a–c; *437*
Paper chromatography, 452c
Papin, Denis, 337c–8a
Parachute, 297a
Paraffin (kerosene), 345b–c
Paraffins (crude oil), 345a
Paraguay tea, *see* **Maté**
Parallax, 279a–c
solar, 241a
stellar, 241a, 279a–c
Parallel lines, 226c–7a, 238a–b
Parallelogram, 238c; *237*
Paramagnetic materials, 104c
Parsec, 242a, 288c
Parsons, Sir Charles, 340a, 388a
Parthenon (Athens), *265*
Pascal, Blaise, *224*
and fluids, 223a, 224b
his mechanical calculators, 261a
his Principle, 224b–c
Pauli, Wolfgang, 172b–c

Payne, John, 355c
Peat, 329c
Pellagra, 406c
Pelletierine, 410c
Pendulum, 244b
conical, 206c, 208a; *208*
Galileo and, 213c, 366c; *213*
in clocks, 366c-7a
Pentagon, *238*
Pentode valve, 118a
Percussion musical instruments, 145a-6a
Perfecting (printing), 438a
Perfect numbers, 228c
Periodic table of the elements, 9b, 10b-12c; *12*
inert gases in, 89a
Periscope, 430a
Perkin, William, 377c, 396a-c
Permanent set, 357b
Peroxidase method, 447c
Perpetual motion, 422c
Perspex, 56c, 370b,c-1a
Perspiration, *see* Sweating
Pest-control, in agriculture, 403b
PETN (pentaerythritol tetranitrate), 88c
Petrol, 45a, 345c
a co-valent compound, 15a
'anti-knock' ingredients of, 36b, 348a
artificial fibres made from petroleum products, 45c
Petrol engine, *see* Internal combustion engine
Petunce, 381c
Pewter, 67c
*p*H, 31c
Phase (of waves), 161c-2a
in light waves, 163c-4a
Phenanthrene, 411a, c
Phenol (carbolic acid), 46b
Phenolphthalein, 31c-2a
Philosophy, uncertainty principle and, 172c
Phlogiston, 82a, 188c
Phobos (moon of Mars), 284b
Phoenicians, 386a
Phonograph, 150c; *149*
Phosgene, 377c
Phosphor bronze, 67c
Phosphorite, 390b
Phosphorus, 37a-9c
black, 39c
in agriculture, 401a-c
red, 38c-9c
yellow, 38c-9c
Photochromism, 425c-6a
Photo-elesticity, 358a-b
Photo-electric effect, 119b, 168a, 170a; *172*
photo-electric cell, 168a, 364b-c, 427b
Photoengraving, 437a-b
half-tone, 437b
line, 437b
Photoflash lamp, 186a
Photography, 433a-6c
colour, 435b-6b
cosmic rays and, 294a, b, 436c
in darkness, 436b-c
infra-red, 165a, 436a-b; *158-9*
ultraviolet, 436c
X-rays and, 436c
Photomultiplier, 451c
Photon (quantum of energy), 124b, 156c, 166c, 170a
Phthalocyanines, 47a
Pi (mathematics), 239c
Piano, 147a; *147*
Piccolo, 147a
Picric acid, 377c
Pictographs, Egyptian, 229b-c
Piero della Francesca, his *St Michael, 127*
Pietà (Michelangelo), *125*
Piezo-electric crystal, piezo-electric effect, 252a, 368a
Pigments (paint), 379c-80a
extenders, 380a
prime, 380a
Pile, nuclear, 317a, 318a
Pinch effect (electric current), 19c-20a
Pion, 294c
Pi orbital, 15c

Piperine, crystal of, *59*
Pirana sports car, *302*
Pirelli buidling (Milan), *240*
Pisa
Baptisterio at, *265*
Leaning Tower of, *215*
Placenta, 412a
Planck, Max, 124b, 156b, 168a, 170a; *169*
Plane, in Euclidean geometry, 237b-8a
Planetarium, *279*
Planets, 281a-4c
in astrology, 274a
orbits of, 215c-16a
origin of, 281c-3b, 285b
outside the solar system, 288b-c
relative sizes of *282*
velocity of, 216a
Planographic printing, *see* Lithography
Plan Position Indicator (radar), 134b
Plants
nitrogen and, 85c
poisons from, 409a, 412b-c
Plasma, 17a
plasma jet torch, *18*
plasma physics, 17a-20c
plasma space engine, *17*
Plaster of Paris, 72a
Plastic bronze, 67c
Plastics, 53a-4c, 56c, 359c, 369a; *54, 55*
definition of, 369a
in car manufacture, *56*
injection moulding of, 270a
Plate glass, 384b-c
Plat-forming (oil refining), 45b
Platinum, 349b
Platinum resistance thermometer, 158a, 160a
Plato, on Euclidean geometry, 226b
Pleiades, *286-7*
Plimpton, S.J., 94a
Pliny, 415c
Ploughing, mechanical, 398b
Pluto (planet), 281b, 283c-4a; *282*
Plutonium, 320b
Point, Euclid's definition of, 237b-8a
Poison
forensic science and, 446c-7c
from plants, 409a, 412b-c
Polar bond, *see* Ionic bond
Poles (of the Earth), 104a
Pole vaulting, 455c; *453*
Pollux (star), 288a
Polyamide fibre, 46a
Polyethylene, *see* Polythene
Polymers, polymerization, 45c-8c, 53b-4c, 56c, 369b-70a, 373a
in oil refining, 346a
of paint, 380a
Polystyrene, 54c
Polythene (polyethylene), 370c, 371a-b, 372a; *371*
Polyvinylchloride, *see* PVC
Pond-skater (insect), 195c
Pont du Gard (aqueduct; Nimes), 307c; *306*
Poppy, drugs derived from, 411b
Porcelain, 381c-2a
as electrical insulator, 100c
Chinese, 381c-2a
Positional notation systems, 230a
Post-tensioning (engineering), 306a-b
Potash, *see* Potassium carbonate
Potassium, 62b, 69a, 71a
and water, 78a
composition of, 12a-b
in agriculture, 401a-c
Potassium carbonate (potash), 29a
Potassium chloride, 71a
Potassium ferricyanide, 436a
Potassium hydroxide (caustic potash), 29a
Potassium hypochlorite, 35c-6a
Potassium nitrate (saltpetre), 71a
Potato, mechanical harvesting of, 400a; *400*
Potential difference (electricity), 94c

Potential energy, 217a-18c
Pottery, 381a-b
Pound (weight), British and US compared, 248b
Poundal, 202a
Powder metallurgy, 64b
Power
mechanical, 218c, 423a-4c
nuclear, *see* Nuclear reactor; Power station, nuclear
Power station, nuclear, 18a, 320a-c, 340c, 475a-6c
and fish-farming, 476b-c
Calder Hall, 320c
Dounreay, 320c; *317*
Poynting, John Henry, 215b; *216*
Precession, 209b-c, 210a
of the Earth, 209b; *209*
Precipitation reactions, 32c
in analytical chemistry, 450a
Preciptin test, 447c-8a
Pressure, 223a-b
in fluids, 223b-4c
Pressure cooker, 24b
Prestressing (engineering), 306a
Priestley, Joseph, 81a, 188c
Primary cell, 361a
voltage of, 362a
Prime numbers, 226a
Printing, 437a-40c
electrotyping, 326c, 437c
gravure, 437a, 439b-c
in colour, 440a
ink for, 440c; *331, 438*
letterpress, 437a-8a; *439*
lithography, 437a, 438a-9b
on fabrics, 376c
paper for, 440a-c; *437*
photoengraving, 437a-b
press, 437c-6a; *440*
proofing, 437a
setting of type, 437a, 438a; *438*
silk-screen, 439c
stereotyping, 437c
xerography, 439c
Prism, spectrum formed by, 153c-4a, 154c; *155*
Prism binoculars, *see* Binoculars, prism
Probability, in atomic theory, 171c
Processing of photographic film, *see* Developing of photographic film
Progesterone, 412a
Progestins, 412a
Projective geometry, 268a
Proofing (printing), 437a
Propane gase, *329*
Propeller
on aircraft (airscrew), 298a
driven by turbine engine (turbo-prop), 336b
on ships, 388b
Proteins, 47b-c, 405c
Proton, 7a, 8b-c, 9b-10a
Proxima Centauri, 285a, 288b
Prussian blue, 380a
Ptolemy, 276c; *273*
and the solar system, *291*
Pulley, 421a
Pulsar, 288c
Pulse modulation, 140c
Pump, water, 338a
Punched cards, 462a
PVC (polyvinylchloride), 36a, 53c, 370c; *34, 36*
Pyramid
Egyptian, 302a
Mexican, *307*
Pyridine, 410c
Pyrometer, 160a
Pyrrole, 410c
Pythagoras, 144a, 275a; *232*
Pythagoreans, *3*

Q

Quadrilateral, 238b; *237*
Quantum statistics, *see* **Wave mechanics**
Quantum theory, 10a, 13b–c,, 124b, 156b–c, 166c–8a, 169a–72c
Quartz clock, 252a, 368a–b; *365*
Quasar, 286c, 288c, 292c
Quats (quaternary ammonium compounds), 418c
Queen Elizabeth 2 (ship), *386*
propeller of, *271*
Quinine, 409a, 410a,c–11a
Quinoline, 411a
Quinquereme, 386a

R

Racon beacon, 136a–b
Radar, 133a–6c, 250c–1a
Doppler, 135b
in civil aviation, 134b–5c; *135*
in meteorology, 136c
in shipping, 135c–6b; *134, 136*
originally called radiolocation, 134a
origin of name, 134a
radar altimeter, 135b
underwater (sonar), 136b–c
Radiation, nuclear, plant growth affected by, *169*
Radiation, of energy, 121a, 165a
see also **Electro-magnetic radiation**
Radiation belts around the Earth, 296c
Radicals (chemistry), 26a–b
free radicals, 53a–6c
Radio (wireless), 117c–18a, 441a–3b
and radar, 133c–4a
broadcasting, 442a–3b
first wireless station, 441b
Marconi and, 441a–c, 442a
on ships, 442a
pictures sent by, 139a
spark transmitter, 442a
superhet receiver, 164a
see also **Radio waves; Television; Valve, radio**
Radioactivity, 92c
dating by, 41a, 324a–c
fall-out from, 473b
of carbon, 41a–2c
see also **Atomic energy** and radioactive elements, e.g. **Radium**
Radio astronomy, 280b–c, 290a, 292c, 459c–60c
see also **Radio telescopes**
Radiometer, Crooke's, *167*
Radio telephony, 138a
Radio telescopes, 122b, 280b–c; *123*
at Arecibo, *277*
at Jodrell Bank, 122b, 280c, 292c; *163, 278*
maser used with, 129b, 130c
Radio waves, 121a, 122a–b, 137c–9a, 441c
carrier wave, 138a–b
micro-waves, 122a–b
see also **Maser**
reflected off plasma, 17a
Radium, 62b, 71a, 72c, 92c
Radium D, 321a
rarity of, 71b
'Radium emanation', *see* **Radon**
Radius (of a circle), 239c; *237*
Radon ('radium emanation'), 89a, 92b–c; *89*
Railways
automatic controls used in, *341*
steam locomotives and, 333a, 338c–9b; *337, 338*
Rainbow, 123c; *154*
Rain-making experiments, 44b
Ram jet, 298b, 336c
Ramsay, William, 89a, 90a, 91b, 91c–2a, 92c; *89*
Randall, J. T., 134a
Random sampling (statistics), 269c
Rare earth elements (Lanthanide series), 11a, 12a, c
Rattle-snakes, and infra-red radiation, 153a
Rayleigh, Lord (Robert Strutt), 89a, 91c, 170a
Rayon (artificial silk), 88c, 375b; *86, 373*
RDX, *see* **Hexogen**
Reactions, chemical, 28c
Réaumur, René de, 355c
Reaumur scale, 158a–b
Recoil (of firearms), 203b–c
Record, gramophone, 151a–2b, 152c; *151, 152*
Rectangle, 238c; *237*
Rectifier (electricity), 11c–12a
Rectilinear axes (co-ordinates), 201a
Red giant stars, 286b
Red lead, 380a
Redox (reduction-oxydation), 26c
Red-shift, 290a, 292a, 460c
Reducing agent (photography), 434c
Reductio ad absurdum (mathematics), 228a–b
Reduction-oxydation, *see* **Redox**
Refining, 345a
metals, 363c–4a
oil, *see* **Oil refining**
sugar, *see* **Sugar**, refining of
Reflection grating, 156a
Reforming (oil refining), 346a
thermal, 348a
Refraction of light, 154a–c, 156a–b, 429a–30a
angle of, 429c
Fundamental Law of, 429b
index of, 154b, 429c–30a
Refractories (ceramics), 381b–c
Refrigerator, refrigeration, 184a–b, 408a–b
deep-freezing, 408b
nitrogen as refrigerant, 192b–c
Regenerative gas furnace, 355c
Reinsch method, 446c–7c
Relativity, 173a–6c
General Theory of, 176b–c
gravitation and, 176b–c
Special Theory of, 173b–6b
Relief printing, *see* **Letterpress printing**
Republic, sinking of the (1909), 138
Reservoir, *467*
Resistance, electrical, 95c–6a
Resistivity (electricity), 350a–b
Resnier, General, *297*
Resonance (electric current), 115a
Retail Prices, Index of, 463a–4a
Rheology, 360a
Rhodium, 428c
Riboflavin, *see* **Vitamins**, Vitamin B_2
Ribose, 47c
Ribosomes, 47c–8a
Riemann, Georg Friedrich Bernhard, Riemannian geometry, 226b–7a, 240b
in space research, 272a–c
Rigel, 288a
Right-angled (right) triangle, 238b–c; *237*
Right-hand grip rule, 96b
Rivers
Mississippi, *475*
pollution of, 466a–7a, 476b
RMS value, *see* **Root mean square value**
RNA, 48a
Road, 309a–12c
design and planning of, 312c
foundations for, 310b–c, 311c–12b
motorway, 312b–c; *309*
Roman, 309a–b; *309*
surface for
bituminous, 309a, 310c–11b, 311c
sett paving, 311c
wood-block, 311b
turnpike, 310a
water-bound, 310b
Rocket, 203c, 300a–c; *203*
as weapon, 472a
V2, 84a, 300a, 472a; *300*
gyroscope and, 212a
liquid propellant in, 84c
hydrazine, 86a
hydrogen, 300b
nitric acid and, 88b
nose cone of, *17*
radio control of, 139a–40a
relativity and, 272c
Riemannian geometry and, 272a–c
Saturn-Apollo IV, *299*
stabilization of, 212a
Rocket (locomotive), 339b
Rocks, 63c, 81a
Rogers, F.T., 174c
Rogers, M.M., 174c
Roman numerals, 229c–30a
Romans
aqueducts of, 307c; *193, 306*
concrete invented by, 305c
roads of, 309a–b; *309*
Romney Marsh, sound amplifier on, 133c
Röntgen, Wilhelm Konrad, 124a, 125a–b; *125*
Röntgen rays, *see* **X-rays**
Root mean square (RMS) value, 114a–b
Rotary piston engine, in cars, 314b–c
Rotary (cylinder) printing press, 437c; *440*
Rotation, 209a, 220c
Rowland, Henry, 156a
Royal Festival Hall (London), *150*
Royal Observatory (Hurstmonceux), telescope at, *431*
Royal Statistical Society, 462a
Rubber, 372a
as insulator, 350b
carbon black added to, *44*
replaced by plastics, 369a
synthetic, 56c, 332c, 371c, 372a; *56*
vulcanization of, *40*
Rubidium, 69a
composition of, 12c
Rugby
manufacture of balls, 454a
underground heating of pitch, 456a

Rule of greatest simplicity (Dalton), 4b
Rumford, Count (Benjamin Thompson), 177b, 181a; *181*
Running shoe, spiked, 455c
Russell, H.N., 285c
Rust (fungoid disease), 403b
Rust (on iron), *see* **Iron oxide**
Rutherford, Daniel, 85a
Rutherford, Ernest, Lord, 6c–7a, 90c–1a, 92c, 321a; *1, 2, 3, 5, 7, 8*

S

Sails (shipping), 386c–8a
fore-and-aft, 386c–7c
square, 386a
St Jerome (Leonardo), 268c; *266*
St Michael (Piero della Francesca), *127*
St Paul's Cathedral (London), *151*
St. Venant, B. de, 359c
St. Venant solid, 359c
Salt, common (sodium chloride), 13a, 14a, 57c
extracted from sea water, 364a; *32, 196*
ice melted with, 200c
mining of, *69*
Salt End (Hull) chemical plant, *330*
Saltpetre, *see* **Potassium nitrate**
Salts, 30a–2c
defined, 30a
Samarkand, observatory at, 275a
Sampling (statistical procedure), 464a–c
Sand
in glass, 383c
in sewage treatment, 467c–8a
Sandage, Allan, 291c
Sand-glass, 366b
Saponins, 412b–c
Sardines, *406*
Satellite, artificial
astronomy and, 278c–9a; *278*
Early Bird, *114*
Explorer I, 296c
in communications, 444a–c
Intelsat III, 444a
orbit of, 208b, 216a
plasma space engine for, *17*
radar used at Woomera tracking station, *135*
Saturated vapour pressure, 24a
Saturn (planet), 283c, 284c; *282, 284*
Saturn-Apollo IV rocket, *299*
Savannah (nuclear freighter), *458*
Savery Thomas, 338a
Saxophone, 147a
Scandium, 12b
Schaefer, Dr Glen, 133a
Schawlow, Arthur L., 131c
Scheele, Karl Wilhelm, 34c, 81a
Schlick, Otto, 211b

Schroder, Ernst 257c
Schrödinger, Erwin, 168a, 171b; *169*
Schweickart, Russell, *139*
Science, social implications of, 457a–60c, 473a–6c
Scintillator, 294a,b
Scissors, *423*
Scopolamine (hyoscine), 410c
Screw measurement of length, 250a–b
Sea, ocean, 389a–92c
bed of, 389a–90a; *392*
echo-sounding, 389b–90a
seismic sounding, 390a; *389, 392*
currents of, 392c
fish in, 391a–c
see also **Divers; Sea water**
Sea water, 197a, 389a
desalination of, 364a; *32, 196*
elements found in, 389a; *198*
Secant, 242a
Secondary cell, *see* **Accumulator**
Seeding, mechanical, 399a–400a
Seismic sounding, 390a; *389, 392*
Selenium, 352a
Semiconductor (electricity), 100c, 109a, 110a–12a, 138b–c
Servo-mechanisms, 341a–c
Set (mathematics), 232a–c, 236c
group, 235c–6a
SET meter, *463*
Settling tank, 467b
Sett paving, 311c
Sex, hormones and, 409a, 411c–12b
Sewage, 466a–8b
disposal plants, 467b–8b; *465, 466*
Shadow clock, Egyptian, 366a
Shampoo, 418c
Shear steel, 353b
Sherbet, 70a
Ships, shipping, 385a–8c
carvel-built, 386b
clinker-built, 386b
container, 388c
Cretan, 386a; *385*
Egyptian, 385a–6a; *387*
gyrocompass used in, *210*
gyrostabilizer used in, 211b–c
iron, first, 388a
metal, why they float, 222a
nuclear-powered, 340c, 388a; *339, 458*
radar used in, 135c–6b; *134, 136*
sails and, 386a,c–8a
steamship, 339c–40b, 388a–b; *333, 339, 340*
wireless and, 442a
Shock-absorbers (motor car), 315c–16a
Shockley, W., 112a
Short-sightedness, *see* **Myopia**
Shortt, W.H., 368a
Shrink resistance, 376c
Sidereal day, 365c
Siebe, Augustus, 415c
Siemens, Sir William, 355c
Sigma (operator), 228a
Sigma orbital, 15c
Silicon
as conductor of electricity, 110a
as possible basis of life, 45a
Silicon carbide (carborundum), 44a
Silicones, 418c–20c
Silk, 376a
artificial, *see* **Rayon**
silkworm cocoons, 376a; *375*
Silk-screen printing, 439c
Silver, 349b
as conductor of electricity, 350b
crystal structure of, 59b
Silver bromide, in photography, 433c, 435c–6c
Silver iodide, in photography, 433c
Silverware, rhodium-plating of, 428c
Similarity (geometry), 238c, 239a–c, 241a–b; *237*
Simple harmonic motion, 244b
Sine, 241c

sine curve, 244a–b
sine rule, 242a–3a
Sirius, 288a
Skin-diving, 416a
Slag, 353c–4a
basic, 354b
Slaked lime, *see* **Calcium hydroxide**
Slide (colour photography), *see* **Transparency**
Slide rule, 261a
Slipher, V.M., 292a
Smelling salts, 44c, 86a
Smelting, 64a, 185c, 349a
coke used in, 353c
electrochemistry in, 363c
Smokeless powder, 470b
Smut (fungoid disease), 403b
SNAP (System for Auxiliary Nuclear Power), 428a–c
Snare drum, 145c
Snell's Law, 429c–30a
'Snow' (drug), *see* **Cocaine**
Snowflakes, 196c; *57*
Soap, 48c, 70a, 417a–c
Socrates, 410c; *412*
Soda ash, *see* **Sodium carbonate**
Soda water, 44b, 199c
Soddy, Frederick, 7a
Sodium, 62b, 69a–71a
and water, 78a
liquid, 69b
sodium lamps, 69c; *70*
Sodium bicarbonate (baking soda), 44c
Sodium borate (borax), 71a
Sodium carbonate (washing soda; soda ash), 44b, c, 70a
in glass, 383c
Leblanc and, 394b–c
Sodium chlorate, 71a
Sodium chloride (salt), 13a, 14a, 57c, 389a
Sodium cyanide, 71a
Sodium (window) glass, 383c
Sodium hydroxide, 26c, 69c–70a
Sodium nitrate (Chile saltpetre; nitre), 71a, 88b
Sodium platino-cyanide, *59*
Sodium thiosulphate, *see* **Hypo**
Solar day, 365b
mean, 365b
Solar system, 281a–4c
exploration of, 459c
Ptolemy's view of, *291*
theories of origin of, 281c
see also **Earth; Sun**
Solder, 67c
Solenoid, 105a
Solids, solid bodies, expansion of, when heated, 22a–3a
Solubility, 198b
Solubilized vat dyes, 379b
Solute, 197b–c
Solution (chemistry), 197a–200c
energy change in, 198a
heat in forming, 198a
homogeneous, 197a
in water, *see* **Aqueous solution**
organic, 199c–200a
point of saturation of, 198a
pressure and, 199c
saturated, 198a
supersaturated, 200b
temperature and, 198c
Solvay, Ernest, 70a
Solvay (ammonia-soda) process, 44b, 70a
Solvent, 197b–c
Sonar (underwater radar), 136b–c, 142c
Sonic boom, 144c; *143*
Sonic brain gauge, *144*
Soot, 41a, 43c
Sorby, Professor Henry, 61a
Sørenson, S.P., 31c
Sound, 141a–4c, 149a
definition of, 141a
infra-sonic, 144b
in music, 144a, 145a
loudness of, 143a–4a, 150a–b
intensity levels, 144a
sonic boom, 144c; *143*
pitch of, 144a
recording of, 150b–2c
speeds of, 142b–c, 144c, 195b

ultrasonic, 144b
water as conductor of, 194c–5b
waves of, 142a–b, 162a–3c
  amplitude of, 142a
  frequency of, 144a, 149a–c,
    162a
  interference in, 164a
Space research
limits to, 460c
Riemannian geometry in, 272a–c
see also **Astronauts; Space
  vehicles**
Space travel, limits to, 459b
Space vehicles, 139a–40a, 416a
see also **Rocket**
Space walk, 203c–4a; *139, 298*
Spark transmitter, 442a
Specific gravity, 221c–2a
Specific heat, 160a–c, 183b,
  194a
Spectrograph, 154c, 445c
Spectrometer, 156a, 452a
Spectroscopy, 51a–c, 450b–2b
spectroscope, 154c, 166a; *165,
  321*
Spectrum, 121b, 123c, 153c–4a,
  154c, 166a–c, 450c; *155, 165*
Speed, and velocity, 201a
Sperry, E.A., 211b
**Sperry Gyrosyn Compass Sys-
  tems,** *210*
Sphere, geometry of, 240a
Riemannian, 226c–7a
Spheres, heavenly, 275b–c
Spherical aberration, 432c
Spin-drier, 205a, 206b
Spinning (motion), see **Rotation**
Spirits of salt, see **Hydrochloric
  acid**
Spontaneous combustion, 187a
Sport, technology and, 453a–6c
Spring, in clocks and watches,
  367a–b; *367*
Spring balance, 251a–b
Sputnik
model of, *278*
Sputnik I, *298*
Square, 238c
Square root of a negative number,
  227c
Stahl, George, 188b–c
Stains, in forensic science,
  447c–8a
Stalactites, 72a; *71, 195*
Stalagmites, 72a; *71, 195*
Stars, 273a, 285a–8c
birth of, nebular hypothesis of, 285b
brightness of, 279c
  brightest, 288a
composition of, 279c
distance of, 242a, 279a–c
  nearest, 281a, 285a
energy of, 17c–18a, 77a, 176b
hydrogen in, 77a
main sequence, 285c–8a
number of, in our galaxy, 285a
planets attached to, 288b–c
red giant, 286b
speed of movement of, 280a
supernovae, 286b
temperature of, 280a
white dwarf, 286a
yellow dwarf, 286a
see also **Astronomy**
State (mathematics), 233c–5b
Static electricity, 93a
Statistical mechanics, 172a
Statistics, 461a–4c
in censuses, 462a–3a, 464b
in market research, 269c
sampling technique in, 464a–c
weighting of, 463c
**Steady state (continuous crea-
  tion) theory,** 290a–1c
Steam, 196c
Steam engine, 179a, 185c, 196c,
  333a, 337a–40c
efficiency of, 422c
in railway trains, 333a, 338c–9b;
  337, 338
in road transport, 313a–b,
  339b–c; *337*
in ships, see **Steamship**
mechanical governor in, 206c,
  341a; *206*
reciprocating, 333b–4a, 339c–40a

turbine, see **Turbine engine,** steam
  Watt and, 218c–19a, 313a,
  338a–b, 424a–c; *337*
Steamship, 339c–40b, 388a–b
paddle-steamer, 388a–b; *333, 339,
  340, 385*
Steel, 352c, 353b–6c
alloy, 68b, 356a,c
basis of strength of, 60b
blister, 353b
carbon, 356c
density of, 221c
in engineering, 305c–6b
in the ancient world, 61a
medium, 352c
mild, 352c
shear, 353b
specific gravity of, 222a
stainless, 68b, 352c
tennis racket made of, 455c
tool (high-speed), 356c
ultimate strength of, 357c
Steel band (music), *145*
Stefan, Josef, 165a
Stellarator, 20b; *20*
Stensen, Niels, 57a
Stephenson, George, 339a–b
Stereotype (printing), 437c
Steroids (drugs), 409a, 411c–12c
Stockhausen, Karlheinz, 148b–c
Stokes' Law, 6b
Stonehenge, *306*
Stop-watch, 453b–c
Storage cell, see **Accumulator**
Stovepipe jet, 298b
Strain, 357a–60c
stress distinguished from, 357a
Stratoscope, 278b–c
Streamlining, 76c; *74*
Strength, ultimate, 357c
of steel, 357c
Stress, 357a–60c
creep, 359c
elastic limit, 357a–b
experimental stress analysis, 358a–b
fatigue, 64a, 359c
modulus, 357a
permanent set, 357b
plasticity, 359c
strain distinguished from, 357a
ultimate strength, 357c
yield point, 357b
Stringed musical instruments,
  146a–7a
Strontium, 62b, 71a,b
composition of, 12c
compounds of, 72a–b
Strontium-90, 72b
Strutt, Robert, see **Rayleigh, Lord**
Strychnine, 410a,b
Stückhofen, 353b
Sturgeon, William, 96c, 104b,
  105a
Styrene, 372a
Submarine, 388c; *414*
nuclear, 340c; *339*
Substitution reacting, 394c–6a
Subtraction (arithmetic), 254a–b
Sufi, Al-, 289b
Sugar
in analytical chemistry, 450a
in aqueous solution, 197c–8a,
  198b–9c
refining of, 194b, 345a; *193, 346*
Sulphates (vitriols), 26a, 29c
Sulphur, 37a–8a, 39c–40c; *40*
Frasch and, 396a
monoclinic, 40a
rhombic, 40a
Sulphur dyes, 378b
Sulphuric acid (oil of vitriol), 29c
in analytical chemistry, 449c
in manufacture of fertilizers, 40b
manufacture of, 40b–c
Sun, 283b–c, 285a, 286a
age of, 287c
corona of, *20*
coronograph, *280*
Earth's distance from, 242a, 285a
eclipse of, *20, 244, 282–3*
energy of, 17c–18a, 77a, 91b,
  176b, 283c
heat from, 122c
helium in, 91b
hydrogen in, 77a, 91b
refraction of light from, 429a

solar flare, *281*
Sundial, 366a; *230, 237*
Sunset, red colour of, 123c
Sunspots, *121, 444*
Superconductivity, 157c, 191c–2a
Supercube, see **Tesseract**
Superfluidity, 191c
Superheterodyne radio receiver,
  164a
Supernova, 286b
Supersaturation, 200b
Supersonic aircraft, 144b–c; *143*
Surface tension (in liquids), 23b,
  195c; *22, 23, 193*
Surgery
cryogenics in, 192c
laser used in, 132c; *129*
Surveying, Hero of Alexandria and,
  237a
Surveyor VII lunar probe, *444*
Suspension (chemistry), solution
  contrasted with, 198b
Suspension bridge, 307c, 308a,b
Swakopmund (South Africa), salt
  pans at, *198*
Swan (constellation), nebula in,
  288
Swan, Joseph, 106c
Swastika 265c, 267c
Sweating, 24a, 184c
Swedenborg, Emmanuel, riding on
  compressed air suggested by,
  215
Swinton, A. A. Campbell, 443c
Switch, switching, 260a–c
parallel, 260b
series, 260b
Sydney Harbour bridge, 308a
Sydney Opera House, *266-7*
Syllogism, 259a
Sylvite, 69a
Symbols, of elements, listed, 27
Symmetry, in art, 265c–7c
Synthesis, chemical, 52b–c
Synthetic fibres, see **Fibres,
  artificial**
Systems analysis, 343c

T

Takayama's test, 447c
Takemitsu, Toru, *148*
Talbot, William Fox, *436*
Tangent (trigonometry), 241c
Tank (weapon), *470*
Tanning, 454a
Tape-planter, 399c–400a
Tape recorder, 152b–c
Tar, 45a, 331c, 360a
Tartan athletics track, 455c–6a;
  456
Tea
caffeine in, 411c
mechanical harvesting of, *397*
Telegraph, 137a, 441a,c
Telephone, 137a–c
Bell's, 137a; *140*
Croydon exchange (1884), *137*

Edwardian, *139*
future applications of, 427b–8a
Telephoto lens, 432c
Telescope, 277a–9a
at Mount Palomar, 277c; *279*
at Royal Observatory (Hurstmonceux), *431*
invention of, 277a
Newton's, replica of, *277*
radio, *see* **Radio telescopes**
Teletypewriter, 137a
Television, 139a, 443b–4c
Baird and, 443b–c; *137*
camera, 119b
from the moon, *444*
future developments in, 427a–b
receiver, 119a,c; *111, 138*
satellites and, 444a–c
SET meter, *463*
Zworykin and, 443c
Telford, Thomas, 310a–c
Tellurium, 11c
weakness of crystals of, 60a
Telstar, *89*
Temperature, 158a–60a
and solubility, 199c
of stars, 280a
Tennant, Charles, 36a
Tennis balls, 454b
Tennis racket, 455c
Tension (engineering), 305c–6b
Terephthalic acid, 46c
Terylene, 45c, 46c, 47a; *49*
Tesseract (supercube), 226a; *225*
Testosterone, 412b
Test-tube babies, 460c
Tetra-ethyl lead, 348c
Tetrahedron, 240a
Tetrapropylene benzene sulphate, 466c–7a
Textile industry, 373a–6c
see also **Fibres**
Thallium, absorption spectra of, *121*
Thebaine, 410b, 411b
Thermal capacity, 160b
Thermal cracking, 347c–8a
Thermal efficiency, 333a
brake, 334b
Thermionic emission, 108a–c
see also **Valve,** radio
Thermocouple, 280a
Thermodynamics, 177a–80c, 181a
First Law of, 177c–9a
in chemical reactions, 180a–c
Second Law of, 179b–c, 184c
Thermometer, 158a, 159c–60a
Thermonuclear fusion, 17c, 20c, 176b
in stars, 286b
Thermos flask (vacuum flask; Dewar flask), 168c; *168*
Thermostat, 182a
Thetatron experiment, *18*
Thin-layer chromatography, 50a–b
Thomas, Charles, 261a
Thomas, Sidney, 354b
Thompson, Benjamin, *see* **Rumford, Count**
Thomson, G. P., 124c, 170b
Thomson, Sir Joseph John, 5a–c, 7a–8a, 108a; *3, 6, 7, 8*
Thomson, William, *see* **Kelvin, Lord**
Thorium, 7a, 8c
Thoron (radon), 92c
Thundercloud, source of energy of, 24a
Tides, 220c
Babylonians and, 273c
Time, 365a
measurement of, 249a–b, 252a–c, 365a–c
see also **Clock**
relativity theory and, 174c–5b
time-dilation, 174c–5b
Time-of-flight mass spectrometer, 452a
Timing, in sport, 453a–4a
Tin, 62a, 349b
Tin oxide, 2b
Tired light theory, 292a
Titanic (ship), 442a
Titanium, 349b
Titusville (Pennsylvania), 329c

T.N.T. (trinitrotoluene), 88c, 471c
Todd, Sir Alexander (Lord Todd), 47c
TOKAMAK experiment, 18c–19c
Tolerance (measurement), 247a–8a
Toluene, 377c
Toluene sulphonic acid, 377c
Tompion (clockmaker), *368*
Tool (high-speed) **steels,** 356c
Top (spinning top), motion of, 209a, 210a; *209, 211*
Topology (mathematics), 225a, 240b–c
Torch battery, 361a–b
Toroidal pinch, 20a
Torpedo, gyroscopic control of, 211c–12a
Torque, 210a, 220c; *211*
Torricelli, Evangelista, 73a–b; *76*
Torsion suspension, 215a
Total internal reflection, 430a
Tourmaline crystals, *58*
Tower Bridge, *307*
Townes, C. H., 129a–b, 129c–30a, 131c
Toxicology, 446a–7c
Trace elements, *see* **Isotopes,** radioactive
Traction engine, *339*
Tractor, 398b–9a
Transformer, 115b–16a
Transistor, 100c, 112a–c, 118a–c
in computers, 262b–c
in television receiver, *111*
Transition elements, 11a, 12a–c
Transparency (slide; colour photography), 435c–6b
Trapezium, 238c
Travers, Morris, 91b
Traversing microscope, 250b
Treaty of the Metre (1875), 245a, 248a
Tree, triangle used to measure height of, 241a; *241*
Trevithick, Richard, 338c; *337*
Treweryn (North Wales), reservoir at, *467*
Triangle, 238b–9b
congruent, 239a
equilateral, 238b, 239a; *237*
in Riemannian geometry, 227a
in trigonometry, 241a–3c
isosceles, 238b; *237*
right-angled, 238b–c; *237*
similar, 239b, 241a–b; *237*
Trickling filter, 467c, 468a
Trieste (bathyscaphe), *224*
Trifid mist (in Sagittarius), *290*
Trigonometry, 239c, 241a–4c
trigonometric functions, 241b–4c
circular, 244a; *241*
Trinitrotoluene, *see* **T.N.T.**
Triode valve, 108c, 112b–c, 118a, 442a
Triquetum, 265c, 267a
Trireme, 386a
Tritium, 18a, 78a
Trombone, 147a, 148a
Trumpet, 147a–8a
Truth table, 260c
Tuba, 147a, 148a
Tull, Jethro, 399a
Tungsten, 62a, 349b
mining of, *328*
Tungsten carbide, 44a
Tuning fork, and time-measurement, 252c
Tunnelling, 308c; *305*
Turbine, 336b
Turbine engine, 333a, 335c–6c
in cars, 314c–15a; *313*
steam, 340a–c, 388a
turbo-jet, 336c; *335*
turbo-prop, 336b
Turnpike, 310a
Tylorstown (Rhondda Valley), coal mine at, *326*
Tympani (drums), 146a
Type, printer's, 437a
Tyre, pneumatic, 315b
Tyrian purple, 377b

U

Ultrasonics, in food preservation, 408c
Ultra-violet radiation, 121a, 123c–4a, 153a–b
future domestic applications of, 425c
in photography, 436c
Uncertainty principle, 171b–c
free will and, 172c
Undefined terms, as axioms in the new mathematics, 233b–c
Unemployment
automation and, 344c
science and, 458c
Universe (cosmos), 285a–92c
life elsewhere in, 283b, 285a, 286c–8a, 288b–c
theories of, 289a, 290a–2c
expansion of, 290a, 292a
'heat-death' of, 184c
running down of, 179c–80a, 184c
Upwellings (ocean currents), 392c
Uracil, 47c
Uranium
in nuclear reactor, 317b–19c
in the sea, *198*
isotopes of, 318a–19c
Uranus (planet), 281b, 283c, 284c; *282*
Urea, 45a
Uxmal, pyramid at, *307*

V

V1 flying bomb, 472a; *336*
V2 rocket, 84a, 300a, 472a; *300, 469*
Vacuum
Nature's supposed abhorrence of, 73a
sound does not travel in, 144c
Vacuum distillation, 64a
Vacuum flask, *see* **Thermos flask**

Valence number, 10b, 25c–6b
Valve, radio, 108a–c, 442a–3b; *108*
see also **Diode valve; Pentode valve; Triode valve**
Van Allen, James, 296c
Van Allen Belts, 296c
Vapour, 23c–4c
heat of vaporisation, 183c
Varnish, 380c
Vat dyes, 378b–9a
Vector, 201a, 202a, 204a–b, 206a
Vegetius, 415c
Velocity, 201a–b, 206a
Venn, John, 257c
Venn diagrams, 259b–60a; *259*
Venus (planet), 281b–c, 283c, 284a–b; *282*
Verge escapement, 366c
Vernier scale, 250a
Vertical take-off aircraft, *see* **VTOL craft**
Vibration
of atoms, with heat, 157b–c
of sound waves, 141a–b, 149a–c
Victoria, Queen, wireless used by, 441b
Victory, H.M.S., *422*
Vikings, ships of, 386b,c
Vinegar, 198b
Vinyl, records made of, 151a
Violin, 147a
Viper, H.M.S., 340a; *340*
Viscosity
of a gas, 76c
of glass, 383c
of ink, 270a
Vitamins, 406a–7b
A, 406b
B_1, 406b–c
B_2 (Vitamin G; riboflavin), 406c
B_{12}, 406c
C (ascorbic acid), 406c–7a
D, 407a
discovery of, 406a–b
E, 407a
K, 407a–b
Vitriols, *see* **Sulphates**
Volcanoes, in Hawaii, infra-red radiation from, *153*
Volt, 94c–5b
electron volt, 294a
voltages of primary and secondary cells, 362a
Voltaic cell, 361a
Volumetric analysis, 32b
Von Neumann, John, 120c, 344c
VTOL (vertical take-off and landing) craft, 300a

W

Wall of Death, 205c
Walton, Ernest, 176a
Wankel, Felix, 314c
War, warfare, 469a–72c
Warburg respirometer, *450*
Warp (cloth), 376b
Washing soda, *see* **Sodium carbonate**

Watch (timepiece), 367b; *367*
stop-watch, 453b–c
Water, 81a, 193a–6c
a co-valent compound, 15a
as catalyst, 196b
as conductor of electricity, 97a, 194c
as conductor of sound, 194c–5b
as lubricant, 195b–c
boiling point of, 194a–b, 196c
calcium and, 78a
composition of, 10b, 25c–6a; *11*
density of, 194a
expands on freezing, 222a
freezing point of, 194a,b
hard, 418a
heat retained by, 194b
hydrolysis, 196b
meniscus of, 23c; *23*
potassium and, 78a
public supplies of, 466a–7a, 468b–c, 476b
shape of drops of, 23b–c
sodium and, 78a
solutions of, *see* **Aqueous solution**
speed of light in, 430a
surface tension in, 195c
see also **Sea; Sea water**
Water clock, 366a–b; *366*
Water gas, 331a–b
Waterproofing, 23c, 419c–20a; *420*
Mackintosh, 331c
Water-wheel, 220c; *218*
Watson, James, 47c
Watson-Watt, Robert, 133c–4a
Watt (unit of measurement), 424a
Watt, James, 218c–19a, 313a, 338a–b, 424a–c; *337*
Wave mechanics (quantum statistics), 124c, 168a, 169b, 171b, 172c
Wave motion, 161a–4c
frequency, 161c, 162a
period, 161b
velocity, 161b
wavelength, 161b, 162a
see also **Electro-magnetic radiation**
Weapons, 469a–72c
see also **Firearms**
Weaving, 376b; *374*
Weed-killer, *see* **Herbicides**
Weft (cloth), 376b
Weight
density and, 221c
lost by immersion in fluids, 221a–c
mass and, 2c, 215c
Weights and measures, 245a–8c
Welding, *63, 160*
argon in, *90*
electron beam in, *119, 235*
oxy-acetylene torch in, *183*
Wells, Horace, 87a
Wells Cathedral, *307*
Weyl, Hermann, 265c
Wheat
diseases of, 403b
harvesting of, 398a–b; *398, 399*
Wheatstone, Sir Charles, his 'self-exciting' dynamo, *108*
Whisky, *47*
White dwarf stars, 286b
Sirius, 288a
White gold, 68c
White lead, 380c
Whittington, Dick, 325a
Whittle, Frank, 298a
Wiener, Norbert, 343c–4c
Wilkinson, John, 338a
Williams, F.C., 262b
Wilson, Charles T.R., 293a
Wilson cloud chamber, *172*
Wimshurst machine, *93*
Windmill, 220c; *219*
Wind musical instruments, 147a–8a
Window glass, *see* **Sodium glass**
Wind tunnel, car tested in, *269*
Winkler, Clemens, 10c
Wireless, *see* **Radio**
Wohler, Friedrich, 45a
Wood-ash, as fertilizer, 402a
Wood's metal, 349c, 352a
Woodwind musical instruments, 147a, 148a

Wool, 374a, 375c–6a; *373*
Woomera desert, satellite tracking station in, *135*
Work, mechanical, 217a–b, 218c–19a, 421a–2c
energy and, 217a–b, 333a
heat and, 177c–8a, 333a
Work-hardening of metals, 352b
Worsted, 376a
Wright, Lawrence, 453a
Wright, Orville and Wilbur, 297c–8a; *300*

Xenon, 89a, 92a–b
Xerography, 439c
X-ray diffraction, 14a
X-rays (Röntgen rays), 121a, 124a–b,c, 125a–8c
and cosmic rays, 293a
and light, 125b–c
as quanta, 168a
characteristic, 126a–7a
Compton effect and, 168a, 170a
dangers of, 128b–c
in crystallography, 59c, 127a–8a, 445c–6a; *16*
in industry, 128b
in medicine, 72b–c, 128a–b,c; *72, 125*
in photography, 436c
X-ray spectrometer, 125c–6a

Year, 365a,c
leap, 365c
Yellow dwarf stars, 286a
Yellow gold, 68c
Yield point (strain), 357b
Young, Thomas, 357a
Young's modulus, 357a
Yttrium, 14c

Zeno of Elea, 1a
Zeolite crystals, *58*
ZETA experiment (Harwell), 20a; *18*
Zinc, 62a, 349b
crystal structure of, 59b
oxidation of, 78b
Zinc oxide, 78b
Zinc sulphide, *350*
Zirconium-oxide ceramics, 383b
Zworykin, Vladimir, 443c